Principles of
PHYSICAL CHEMISTRY

Samuel H. Maron

PROFESSOR OF PHYSICAL CHEMISTRY
CASE INSTITUTE OF TECHNOLOGY

Carl F. Prutton

VICE PRESIDENT, THE FOOD MACHINERY AND
CHEMICAL CORPORATION
FORMERLY PROFESSOR OF CHEMISTRY AND CHEMICAL
ENGINEERING, CASE INSTITUTE OF TECHNOLOGY

THIRD EDITION OF
Fundamental Principles of Physical Chemistry

THE MACMILLAN COMPANY · NEW YORK

Printed in the United States of America

Second Printing 1959

Previous editions under the title FUNDAMENTAL PRINCIPLES OF PHYSICAL CHEMISTRY *copyright 1944 and 1951 by The Macmillan Company*

Library of Congress catalog card number: 58-5133

Preface

In the preface to the first edition the authors stated that their "aim in writing this text on elementary physical chemistry is to place in the hands of teachers and students a book which covers the fundamental principles of the subject in a thorough, sound, up-to-date, and clear manner.

"In deciding what constitutes the fundamental principles the authors were continually guided by the needs of the chemist and chemical engineer for a sound grounding in physical chemistry. Although physical chemistry is offered to various students with various purposes in mind, the fact remains that those who expect to be engaged in any branch of chemical or related work must be conversant with the principles of this subject, and they must be able to use and apply these principles effectively and correctly. In order to do this they must be exposed to a basic training sufficiently complete to permit them to understand the subject, not only in a general and qualitative way, but also in its more intimate experimental and quantitative aspects. To achieve such mastery the authors feel that use of mathematics and some thermodynamics is absolutely essential. For this reason the necessary calculus is employed here without any apology, and the elements of thermodynamics are introduced early and are used throughout the book as an integral part of the subject. . . .

"Throughout the book considerable attention is devoted to the experimental aspects of physical chemistry. This is done expressly, because it is felt that a student can better understand what he is dealing with when he has some idea how the quantities involved are obtained. At the end of each chapter are given bibliographies, to which the student may turn for further details, and extended lists of exercises to test his familiarity with the subject matter and to develop in him facility in handling equations and data.

"The book as a whole is intended primarily for a full year course in physical chemistry for students of chemistry and chemical engineering. By judicious selection of various portions of the contents, this book should be readily adaptable to any one-semester course for students in other branches of science, such as physics, metallurgy, biology, and biochemistry. What is to be omitted and what is not is largely a matter of circumstances and needs, and can be left safely to the discretion and decision of each individual teacher."

The above aims and philosophy have been followed in preparing the present edition. Although the general order of presentation is the same as used before, extensive changes have been made in the organization of the subject matter and in the discussion of some topics. Thus, Chapter 2 is now devoted exclusively to the first law of thermodynamics and its application to gases, while Chapter 10 deals with both the second and third laws. Again, discussion of nonelectrolytes and electrolytes has been combined under the head of "Colligative Properties of Solutions," and the exposition of molecular structure and properties has been consolidated into a single chapter titled "Molecular Structure." On the other hand, the chapter on surface phenomena and colloids has been divided into separate chapters dealing with these topics, and each of these subjects has been considerably expanded and brought up to date.

To avoid increasing the size of the book, all changes and additions have been made at the expense of less significant subject matter. At the same time the number of problems has been increased to 634, the largest number in any book of this type.

In conclusion the authors wish to express their appreciation to colleagues, friends, and teachers who have been kind enough to offer us their suggestions and criticisms for improvement of the text, and who have called to our attention the inevitable errors which, despite all efforts, still manage to escape attention. Particular thanks are due to Professor Walter Kauzmann of Princeton University for the trouble he has taken to send us extensive comments and suggestions for improvement, and to Professor Irvin M. Krieger of Case Institute for his continual interest and willingness to read and criticize the entire manuscript. Finally, we also wish to acknowledge our deep gratitude to the publishers, The Macmillan Company, and their staff for their ever-present cooperation, courtesy, and desire to go to any length to produce a book satisfactory to the authors.

Contents

Contents

Principles of
Physical Chemistry

Principles of
Physical Chemistry

THE MACMILLAN COMPANY
NEW YORK · CHICAGO
DALLAS · ATLANTA · SAN FRANCISCO
LONDON · MANILA
IN CANADA
BRETT-MACMILLAN LTD.
GALT, ONTARIO

Introduction

SCIENCE AND THE SCIENTIFIC METHOD

Science is organized and systematized knowledge relating to our physical world. This knowledge did not spring into being full blown, but has been accumulated painstakingly through the efforts of many researchers and observers. In its inception this cumulative process was quite simple. It involved merely the observation of phenomena as they occur in nature and their faithful recording. As the facts and observations multiplied, regularities were sought and discovered in them which were then formulated into *laws*. Each law was capable of embracing a number of facts and of summarizing them in succinct form.

However, natural laws do not constitute an interpretation of nature, but rather a description. To supply the reason for the operation of a law scientists began to propose purely suggestive explanations, or *hypotheses*, in terms of which the operation of the law could be accounted. From these hypotheses logical predictions were then derived and compared with the observed phenomena. If the two tallied fairly well, the hypothesis was accepted, provisionally at least, and became a *theory*. On the other hand, if the logical deductions of a hypothesis did not agree with experimental facts, the hypothesis was discarded to await a more satisfactory explanation.

At present we do not rely on purely fortuitous observation for our information. With the state of scientific knowledge as advanced as it is, experiments are carefully planned and conducted to yield the specific data sought. It is thus possible to arrive at desired facts more rapidly and efficiently. Again, with planned research hypotheses and theories may be subjected to deliberate test by arranging experiments designed to answer directly the specific point in question. By such means faulty concepts can be eliminated, incomplete theories refined, and new principles discovered.

This modus operandi of science is called the *scientific method*. It will be noticed that in its operation the scientific method involves essentially four stages, namely: (a) the accumulation of facts; (b) the organization of facts into laws; (c) the postulation of hypotheses to account for the facts and the laws; and (d) the comparison of the hypothetical deductions with the experimental results. Whenever possible, facts and their correlations, as well as their explanations, are expressed in mathematical terms. It is this precision of language more than any other single factor which differentiates the physical sciences from more purely descriptive sciences such as biology or medicine.

The intimate combination of experiment and theory embodied in the scientific method has proved very fruitful, and has led to the development of our present highly advanced state of science and technology. It must be emphasized, however, that the function of theory and hypothesis in this advance has not been merely to explain what is already known. Were this the only contribution of theory, speculation would have been more of interest than value. The real function of theory and speculation lies much more intrinsically in its ability to define the experimental variables, and in its ability to foretell phenomena and effects that are as yet unknown. When thus used, theory and hypothesis may serve not only as powerful guides in the interpretation of phenomena, but also as effective tools for the advancement of our knowledge of the physical world and its control for our benefit.

PHYSICAL CHEMISTRY

The branch of chemistry which concerns itself with the study of the physical properties and structure of matter, with the laws of chemical interaction, and with the theories governing these is called *physical chemistry*. The purpose of physical chemistry is, first, to collect the appropriate data required to define the properties of gases, liquids, solids, solutions, and colloidal dispersions, to systematize them into laws, and to give them a theoretical foundation. Next, physical chemistry is interested in establishing the energy relations obtaining in physical and chemical transformations, in ascertaining the extent and speed with which they take place, and in defining quantitatively the controlling factors. In this connection must be considered not only the more common variables of temperature, pressure, and concentration, but also the effects of the intimate interaction of matter with electricity and light. Finally, matter itself must be examined to determine its nature and structure. This is necessary in order that we may be able to arrive at a basic understanding of physical and chemical behavior in terms of the properties of the fundamental constituents of matter.

To accomplish its purposes physical chemistry must rely to a large degree on experiment. Experimental methods and techniques play thus a very important role. The subject also draws generously on the laws and methods of physics and mathematics. In fact, physical chemistry may be looked upon as the field where physics and mathematics are applied extensively to the study and solution of problems of prime chemical interest. With the appropriate data at hand, physical chemistry then proceeds to its correlational and theoretical goal through two general modes of attack, namely, the *thermodynamic* and the *kinetic*. In the thermodynamic approach the fundamental laws of thermodynamics are utilized to yield deductions based on the energy relations connecting the initial and final stages of a process. By circumventing the steps intervening between the start and end of a process, thermodynamics enables us to arrive at many valuable deductions without our knowing all the intimate details of the intermediate stages. Consequently, although this approach is able to tell us what can happen, and to what extent, it is unable, by its very nature, to give us information on *how*, or *how rapidly*, a change will actually occur. On the other hand, the kinetic approach requires for its operation an intimate and detailed "picture" of the process. From the mechanism postulated may be deduced then the law for the over-all process and its various stages. Evidently the kinetic approach to a problem is more explanatory in character, but unfortunately it is generally more complicated and difficult to apply. These two modes of attack will be illustrated at various stages in the text. From the examples given there the student will be able to differentiate more clearly between them and come to appreciate their respective powers and utilities.

HISTORY OF PHYSICAL CHEMISTRY

The roots of physical chemistry lie in the fields of both chemistry and physics. At first these two branches of science developed more or less independently. However, in the nineteenth century it was found that the discoveries in physics had important bearing on and application to chemistry, and hence need arose for a distinct field dealing primarily with the application of physical laws to chemical phenomena. This need finally impelled Wilhelm Ostwald, van't Hoff, and Arrhenius to organize and systematize the subject matter generally included now under the head of physical chemistry, and led them in 1881 to found the *Zeitschrift für physikalische Chemie.* The inception of physical chemistry as a formal branch of chemical science may be dated from the appearance of this journal.

Stimulated by this publication, and fostered by the contributions of the men mentioned, physical chemistry entered a period of very rapid growth. Aiding this progress were not only advances in chemistry, but also the remarkable series of discoveries in physics which started with the discovery of the electron, and which include the discovery of x rays and radioactivity, the establishment of the quantum theory, and the unfolding of our understanding of subatomic phenomena. Thanks to these contributions, physical chemistry has developed in the past 80 years or so to a position of importance and utility not only to chemistry but to other sciences as well.

IMPORTANCE OF PHYSICAL CHEMISTRY

Since physical chemistry deals with the principles and theories of chemistry, it goes without saying that any student or practitioner of this science must be familiar with physical chemistry in order to understand his own subject. The same applies also to the chemical engineer. The essential difference between a chemist and a chemical engineer is that whereas the former conducts his reactions and operations on a small scale, the chemical engineer carries them out in large commercial units. To transfer an operation from the laboratory to a plant the chemical engineer must of course be able to apply engineering and economic principles. However, at the same time he must understand also the fundamentally chemical nature of the processes he is dealing with, and for that he needs physical chemistry. As a matter of fact, chemical engineering has frequently been described as applied physical chemistry. Viewed in this light, many of the aspects of chemical engineering fall within the realm of physical chemistry and can be handled in terms of well-established and familiar physicochemical laws. On the other hand, any attempt to consider chemical engineering as a purely empirical pursuit robs it of the attributes of a science and translates it into an art.

What has been said about the importance of physical chemistry to the chemist and chemical engineer applies equally well to the metallurgist and metallurgical engineer. The latter two perform essentially the same functions as the two former, except that their attention is confined primarily to metals. From this point of view the prominent position of physical chemistry, whether under this or other titles, in these subjects becomes clear, and accounts for the valuable contributions made to these fields by the application of physicochemical principles.

Finally, physical chemistry finds application also in physics, geology, and in the various ramifications of the biological sciences. To appreciate the extent of its utility it is only necessary to compare a book on chemical physics, geology, or biochemistry with one on physical chemistry. From such a comparison it becomes quite evident why physical chemistry is often included in curricula in these subjects, and why it can be applied with effect in these sciences.

1

Gases

All matter exists in one of three states of aggregation, solid, liquid, or gaseous. A solid may be defined as a body possessing both definite volume and definite shape at a given temperature and pressure. A liquid in bulk, on the other hand, has a definite volume but no definite shape, while a gas has neither definite shape nor volume. Liquids and gases are both termed *fluids*. A liquid, insofar as it fills the container, will always adopt the shape of the container in which it is placed, but will retain its definite volume, while a gas will always fill completely any container in which it may be confined.

The distinctions among the three states of matter are not always as clear cut as the above definitions would imply. For example, a liquid at the critical point is indistinguishable from its vapor. Again, such substances as glass or asphalt, although exhibiting many of the properties of a solid, will, under certain conditions of temperature, become plastic and exhibit properties not ascribed to pure solids. For this reason such substances are usually considered to be supercooled liquids with very high viscosity.

The particular state of aggregation of a substance is determined by the temperature and pressure under which it exists. However, within certain limits of temperature and pressure a substance may exist in more than one state at the same time. In fact, under special conditions a substance may exist in all three states simultaneously. Thus at 4.57 mm Hg pressure and at 0.0099°C, ice, water, and water vapor may all be present simultaneously, and all be stable. This subject of simultaneous existence in more than one state will be discussed more completely in subsequent chapters.

NATURE OF GASES

A gas may be regarded as consisting of molecules traveling in straight lines at random and at high rates of speed within the containing space, and colliding frequently with other molecules or the walls of the container. The force exerted per unit area on the walls of the container by the colliding molecules is known as the *pressure*—a force present at all times and distributed uniformly over the entire surface. The fact that small molecules produce a considerable bombarding force upon container walls suggests that the number of collisions with the walls must be large and that the molecules must be moving with high velocities.

The space occupied by the molecules themselves within a gaseous volume is a small fraction of the total volume of the gas under ordinary conditions of temperature and pressure. Thus, if all the air in a room 20 by 10 by 10 ft were liquefied, the volume of the liquid would be approximately 2.4 cu ft, or about 0.1 per cent of the volume of the room, and yet the molecules would not be touching each other. Hence we may conclude that molecules generally are separated from each other by distances which are large compared to molecular diameters, and that within a gas the space actually occupied by molecules is very small, most of the volume being "free" space. This accounts for the much lower densities of gases as compared to liquids and solids.

Also, this large amount of "free" space within a gas makes compression of the gas fairly easy. The compression process merely reduces the large "free" space and, by reducing the average distance between the molecules, brings them closer together. When there is no attraction between the molecules, the decrease in "free" space on compression is equal to the observed decrease in the total volume of the gas. Similarly, on expansion the average distance between molecules is increased, and thereby also the "free" space of the gas. In any case the random motion of the molecules will give the effect of completely filling any containing vessel in which the gas is placed.

In terms of the structure of a gas outlined above it is easy to understand why gases interdiffuse or mix. Two different gases such as nitrogen and oxygen, or any number of nonreactive gases, when placed in a container will by their motion mix with one another very quickly regardless of density. This mixture of gases will in many respects behave like a single gas, and the molecules of the various gases will collide with each other regardless of similarity or dissimilarity. Further, the total pressure exerted by the mixture will be determined by the total number of collisions between the molecules of all kinds and the walls of the container, a pressure to which each particular kind of molecule contributes its share.

IDEAL AND REAL GASES

For purposes of discussion, it is convenient to classify all gases into two types, namely, (a) *ideal* gases, and (b) *nonideal* or *real* gases. An ideal gas is one that obeys certain laws which will be presented shortly, while a real gas is one that obeys these laws only at low pressures. The deviations from the ideal laws are due in general to two factors of which the ideal laws take no account, namely, the volume actually occupied by the molecules themselves, and the attractive forces existing between the molecules.

An ideal gas is one in which the volume occupied by the molecules themselves is negligible compared to the total volume at all pressures and temperatures, and one in which the intermolecular attraction is extremely small under all conditions. In a nonideal or real gas both of these quantities are appreciable, the magnitude of each depending on the nature, the temperature, and the pressure of the gas. We can easily see that an ideal gas must be a hypothetical gas, as all actual gases must contain molecules which occupy a definite volume and exert attractions between each other. However, very often the influence of these factors becomes negligible, and the gas then may be considered to be ideal. We shall find that the latter condition will obtain in particular at low pressures and relatively high temperatures, conditions under which the "free" space within the gas is large and the attractive forces between molecules small.

EMPIRICAL GENERALIZATIONS OF IDEAL GAS BEHAVIOR

Through the study of gases there have been evolved certain laws or generalizations which are always the starting point in any discussion of gas behavior. These are: (a) Boyle's law, (b) Charles's or Gay-Lussac's law, (c) Dalton's law of partial pressures, and (d) Graham's law of diffusion. Another generalization is Avogadro's principle, but this will be considered later.

BOYLE'S LAW

In 1662 Robert Boyle reported that the volume of a gas at constant temperature decreased with increasing pressure, and that, within the limits of his experimental accuracy, *the volume of any definite quantity of gas at constant temperature varied inversely as the pressure on the gas.* This highly important generalization is known as *Boyle's law.* Expressed mathematically, this law states that at *constant temperature* $V \propto 1/P$

or that
$$V = \frac{K_1}{P}$$

where V is the volume and P the pressure of the gas, while K_1 is a proportionality factor whose value is dependent on the temperature, weight of gas, its nature, and the units in which P and V are expressed. On rearrangement this equation becomes

$$PV = K_1 \tag{1}$$

from which it follows that if in a certain state the pressure and volume of the gas are P_1 and V_1, while in another state they are P_2 and V_2, then at constant temperature

$$P_1V_1 = K_1 = P_2V_2$$

and
$$\frac{P_1}{P_2} = \frac{V_2}{V_1} \tag{2}$$

If the pressure of a gas is plotted against the volume in accordance with equation (1), we obtain a family of curves such as that shown in

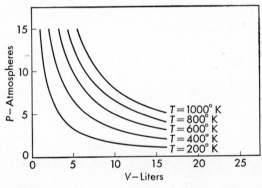

Fig. 1.   Isothermal Plot of P vs. V According to Boyle's Law (1 Mole of Gas).

Fig. 1. Each curve is a hyperbola with a different value of K_1. Since for a given weight of gas K_1 varies only with temperature, each curve corresponds to a different fixed temperature and is known as an *isotherm* (constant temperature plot). The higher curves correspond to the higher temperatures.

THE CHARLES OR GAY-LUSSAC LAW

Charles in 1787 observed that the gases hydrogen, air, carbon dioxide, and oxygen expanded an equal amount upon being heated from 0° to 80° C at constant pressure. However, it was Gay-Lussac in 1802 who first found that for *all* gases the increase in volume for each degree centigrade rise in temperature was equal approximately to $\frac{1}{273}$ of the volume of the gas at 0° C. A more precise value of this fraction is $\frac{1}{273.15}$. If we designate by V_0 the volume of a gas at 0° C and by V its volume at any temperature $t°$ C, then in terms of Gay-Lussac's finding V may be written as

$$V = V_0 + \frac{t}{273.15} \, V_0$$

$$= V_0 \left(1 + \frac{t}{273.15} \right)$$

$$= V_0 \left(\frac{273.15 + t}{273.15} \right) \tag{3}$$

We may define now a new temperature scale such that any temperature t

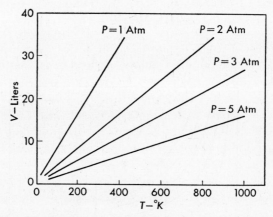

Fig. 2.   Isobaric Plot of V vs. T According to Charles's Law (1 Mole of Gas).

on it will be given by $T = 273.15 + t$, and 0° C by $T_0 = 273.15$. Then equation (3) becomes simply,

$$\frac{V}{V_0} = \frac{T}{T_0}$$

or generally
$$\frac{V_2}{V_1} = \frac{T_2}{T_1} \tag{4}$$

This new temperature scale, designated as the absolute or Kelvin scale of temperature, is of fundamental importance in all science. In terms of this temperature scale, equation (4) tells us that *the volume of a definite quantity of gas at constant pressure is directly proportional to the absolute temperature*, or that

$$V = K_2 T \tag{5}$$

where K_2 is a proportionality factor determined by the pressure, the nature and amount of gas, and the units of V. The above statement and equation (5) are expressions of *Charles's or Gay-Lussac's law of volumes*.

According to equation (5) the volume of a gas should be a straight line function of the absolute temperature at any constant pressure. Such a plot of V vs. T at selected pressures is shown in Fig. 2. Since for a given amount of gas K_2 will have different values at different pressures, we obtain a series of straight lines, one for each constant pressure. Each constant pressure line is called an *isobar*. For every isobar the slope is the greater the lower the pressure.

Equation (5) suggests also that if we were to cool a gas to $0°$ K ($-273°$ C), its volume would become zero. However, no such phenomenon is ever encountered, for usually long before $0°$ K is approached a gas liquefies or solidifies. Again, as will be shown below, under such drastic conditions the equation itself cannot be considered to hold.

THE COMBINED GAS LAW

The two laws discussed give the separate variation of the volume of a gas with pressure and with temperature. To obtain the simultaneous variation of the volume with temperature and pressure, we proceed as follows. Consider a quantity of gas at P_1, V_1, and T_1, and suppose that it is desired to obtain the volume of the gas, V_2, at P_2 and T_2. First of all let us compress (or expand) the gas from P_1 to P_2 at constant temperature T_1. The resulting volume V_x then will be, according to Boyle's law,

$$\frac{V_x}{V_1} = \frac{P_1}{P_2}$$
$$V_x = \frac{V_1 P_1}{P_2} \tag{6}$$

If the gas at V_x, P_2, and T_1 is heated now at constant pressure P_2 from T_1 to T_2, the final state at P_2 and T_2 will have the volume V_2 given by Charles's law, namely,

$$\frac{V_2}{V_x} = \frac{T_2}{T_1}$$
$$V_2 = \frac{V_x T_2}{T_1}$$

Substituting into this relation the value of V_x from equation (6), V_2 becomes

$$V_2 = \frac{V_x T_2}{T_1} = \frac{P_1 V_1 T_2}{P_2 T_1}$$

and on rearranging terms we see that

$$\frac{P_1 V_1}{T_1} = \frac{P_2 V_2}{T_2} = \text{constant} = K \tag{7}$$

i.e., the ratio PV/T for any given state of a gas is a constant. Consequently we may drop the subscripts and write for any gas which obeys Boyle's and Charles's laws

$$PV = KT \tag{8}$$

Equation (8) is known as the *combined gas law*, because it represents a combination of Boyle's and Charles's laws. It gives the complete relationship between the pressure, volume, and temperature of any gas as soon as the constant K is evaluated. That Boyle's and Charles's laws are merely special cases of equation (8) is easily shown. When T is constant, equation (8) reduces to $PV =$ constant, or Boyle's law. Again, when P is constant, equation (8) becomes

$$V = \frac{K}{P} T = K_2 T$$

or Charles's law.

THE GAS CONSTANT

The numerical value of the constant K in equation (8) is determined by the number of moles[1] of gas involved and the units in which P and V are expressed; but it is *totally independent of the nature of the gas.* Equation (8) shows that for any given pressure and temperature an increase in the quantity of gas increases the volume, and thereby also correspondingly the magnitude of K. In other words, K is directly proportional to the number of moles of gas involved. For convenience this constant may be replaced, therefore, by the expression $K = nR$, where n is the number of moles of gas occupying volume V at P and T, while R is the *gas constant per mole.* Thus expressed R becomes a *universal constant for all gases* and equation (8) takes the final form

$$PV = nRT \tag{9}$$

Equation (9) is the *ideal gas equation*, one of the most important relations in physical chemistry. It connects directly the volume, temperature, pressure, and number of moles of a gas, and permits all types of gas calculations as soon as the constant R is known. R may be found from the fact that 1 mole of *any* ideal gas at standard conditions, i.e., at $0°$ C and 1 atm pressure, occupies a volume of 22.415 liters. If we express then the *volume in liters* and the *pressure in atmospheres*, R follows from equation (9) as

$$R = \frac{PV}{nT} = \frac{1 \times 22.415}{1 \times 273.15} = 0.08206 \text{ liter-atm degree}^{-1} \text{ mole}^{-1}$$

[1] A *mole* is the mass of a substance in grams equal numerically to its molecular weight.

This value of R can be used only when volume is taken in liters and pressure in atmospheres. For other combinations of units R will have other values. Thus, if the pressure be expressed in atmospheres while the volume in cubic centimeters, R becomes

$$R = \frac{1 \times 22{,}415}{1 \times 273.15} = 82.06 \text{ cc-atm degree}^{-1} \text{ mole}^{-1}$$

Since pressure is force per unit area and volume is area times length, it immediately follows that the units of PV/nT and hence of R are:

$$\frac{PV}{nT} = R = \frac{\dfrac{\text{force}}{\text{area}} \times \text{area} \times \text{length}}{\text{moles} \times \text{degrees}} = \frac{\text{force} \times \text{length}}{\text{moles} \times \text{degrees}} = \frac{\text{work degree}^{-1}}{\text{mole}^{-1}}$$

Consequently R may be expressed in any set of units representing work or energy. Although in gas calculations in the metric system the units given above are the most useful, there is necessity in other types of calculations to employ R in some alternate energy units. These are usually ergs, joules, and calories.

To obtain R in ergs the pressure must be expressed in dynes per square centimeter and the volume in cubic centimeters. For the volume at standard conditions we have $V = 22{,}415$ cc. Again, a pressure of 1 atm is the pressure of a column of mercury 76 cm high and 1 cm^2 in cross section at 0° C. The total volume of such a column is thus 76 cc, and the mass 76×13.595, where the latter quantity is the density of mercury at 0° C. The pressure in dynes per square centimeter will be then this mass multiplied by the acceleration of gravity, 980.66 cm sec^{-2}, or $P = 76 \times 13.595 \times 980.66$ dynes per square centimeter. Inserting these values of V and P into the expression for R, we find that

$$R = \frac{(76 \times 13.595 \times 980.66)(22{,}415)}{1 \times 273.15} = \underline{8.315 \times 10^7 \text{ ergs degree}^{-1} \text{ mole}^{-1}}$$

Further, since 1 joule $= 10^7$ ergs, and 1 calorie $= 4.184$ joules, we arrive also at

$$R = \underline{8.315 \text{ joules degree}^{-1} \text{ mole}^{-1}}$$
$$= \frac{8.315}{4.184} = \underline{1.987 \text{ cal degree}^{-1} \text{ mole}^{-1}}$$

It should be clearly understood that, although R may be expressed in various units, for pressure-volume calculations involving gases R *must always be taken in the same units as those used for pressure and volume.* In other words, for pressure in atmospheres and volume in liters $R = 0.08206$ liter-atm, while for pressure in atmospheres and volume in cubic centimeters, $R = 82.06$ cc-atm. When other units are encountered it is generally simpler to convert them to those given above than to find the corresponding values of R.

In chemical engineering calculations are frequently made employing English instead of metric units, and using the pound-mole, i.e., the weight in pounds corresponding to the molecular weight, rather than the gram-mole. Further, the temperature may be in degrees Fahrenheit, ° F, in which case the absolute temperature is expressed in degrees Rankine, ° R = 459.7 + ° F. To facilitate such calculations a summary of the values of R in various units is given in Table 1.

TABLE 1

VALUES OF R IN VARIOUS UNITS

Units of Pressure	Units of Volume	Tem-pera-ture	n	R
Atmospheres	liters	° K	gram-moles	0.08206 liter-atm (° K)$^{-1}$ (g-mole)$^{-1}$
Atmospheres	cc	° K	gram-moles	82.06 cc-atm (° K)$^{-1}$ (g-mole)$^{-1}$
Dynes/cm^2	cc	° K	gram-moles	8.315 × 10^7 ergs (° K)$^{-1}$ (g-mole)$^{-1}$
mm Hg	cc	° K	gram-moles	62,360 cc-mm Hg (° K)$^{-1}$ (g-mole)$^{-1}$
Atmospheres	cu ft	° R	pound-moles	0.730 cu ft-atm (° R)$^{-1}$ (lb-mole)$^{-1}$
Pounds/sq in.	cu ft	° R	pound-moles	10.73 cu ft-(lb/in.^{2}) (° R)$^{-1}$ (lb-mole)$^{-1}$
Pounds/sq in.	cu in.	° R	pound-moles	18,540 cu in.-(lb/in.^{2}) (° R)$^{-1}$ (lb-mole)$^{-1}$
R in joules		° K	gram-moles	8.315 joules (° K)$^{-1}$ (g-mole)$^{-1}$
R in calories		° K	gram-moles	1.987 cal (° K)$^{-1}$ (g-mole)$^{-1}$

CALCULATIONS INVOLVING IDEAL GAS LAW

The ideal gas law may be employed to find any one of the variables P, V, T, or n from any specified set of three of these. As an illustration, suppose that we want to know what will be the volume occupied by 10 g of oxygen at 25° C and 650 mm Hg pressure. From the data we have that:

$$n = \frac{10}{32} = 0.312 \text{ mole}$$

$$T = 273.2 + 25 = 298.2° \text{ K}$$

$$P = \frac{650}{760} = 0.855 \text{ atm}$$

$$R = 0.0821 \text{ liter-atm}$$

Insertion of these into equation (9) yields for the volume:

$$V = \frac{nRT}{P} = \frac{0.312 \times 0.0821 \times 298.2}{0.855}$$

$$= 8.94 \text{ liters}$$

Similarly, from appropriately specified data the other quantities involved in the ideal gas equation may be found.

DALTON'S LAW OF PARTIAL PRESSURES

It has already been pointed out that different gases introduced into the same container interdiffuse or mix rapidly. Dalton's *law of partial pressures* states that *at constant temperature the total pressure exerted by a mixture of gases in a definite volume is equal to the sum of the individual pressures which each gas would exert if it occupied the same total volume alone.* In other words,

$$P_{total} = P_1 + P_2 + P_3 + \cdots \tag{10}$$

where the individual pressures, P_1, P_2, P_3 etc., are termed the *partial pressures* of the respective gases. The partial pressure of each constituent may be thought of as the pressure which that constituent would exert if it where isolated in the same volume and at the same temperature as that of the mixture. In terms of the partial pressures, Dalton's law may be restated as follows: *The total pressure of a mixture of gases is equal to the sum of the partial pressures of the individual components of the mixture.*

The significance of Dalton's law and of the concept of partial pressures is best brought out by the following example. If we were to take three *1-liter* flasks filled respectively with hydrogen at 70 mm Hg pressure, carbon monoxide at 500 mm, and nitrogen at 1000 mm, all at the same temperature, and were to force all these gases into a fourth *1-liter* flask, the total pressure within the fourth flask would be

$$\begin{aligned} P &= P_{H_2} + P_{CO} + P_{N_2} \\ &= 70 + 500 + 1000 \\ &= 1570 \text{ mm Hg} \end{aligned}$$

and the pressures of the individual gases within their 1-liter flasks would be the partial pressures of these gases in the mixture.

Consider now a gaseous mixture composed of n_1 moles of one gas, n_2 moles of another gas, and n_3 moles of still a third. Let the total volume be V and the temperature T. If the conditions of pressure and temperature are not too extreme, the ideal gas laws would be valid for each gas in the mixture, and we obtain for the respective partial pressures:

$$P_1 = \frac{n_1 RT}{V} \tag{11a}$$

$$P_2 = \frac{n_2 RT}{V} \tag{11b}$$

$$P_3 = \frac{n_3 RT}{V} \tag{11c}$$

According to Dalton's law the total pressure P thus becomes

$$P = \frac{n_1 RT}{V} + \frac{n_2 RT}{V} + \frac{n_3 RT}{V}$$
$$= \frac{(n_1 + n_2 + n_3) RT}{V}$$
$$= \frac{n_t RT}{V} \tag{12}$$

where $n_t = (n_1 + n_2 + n_3) = $ total number of moles of gas in the mixture. We see from equation (12), therefore, that the gas laws may be applied to mixtures as well as to pure gases, and in exactly the same way.

On division of equations (11a)–(11c) by equation (12) is is found that

$$P_1 = \frac{n_1}{n_t} P \tag{13a}$$

$$P_2 = \frac{n_2}{n_t} P \tag{13b}$$

and $\qquad\qquad\qquad P_3 = \frac{n_3}{n_t} P \tag{13c}$

Equations such as (13) are very important in chemical and chemical engineering calculations, for they relate the partial pressure of a gas to the total pressure of the mixture. Since the fractions n_1/n_t, n_2/n_t, and n_3/n_t represent the moles of a particular constituent present in the mixture divided by the total number of moles of all gases present, these quantities are called *mol fractions*[1] and are designated by the respective symbols N_1, N_2, N_3, etc. Of necessity the sum of all the mol fractions for a system will have to be unity, namely,

$$N_1 + N_2 + N_3 + \cdots = 1 \tag{14}$$

In terms of these definitions *the partial pressure of any component in a gas mixture is equal to the mol fraction of that component multiplied by the total pressure.* This is true only when the ideal gas law applies to each constituent of the gas mixture.

AMAGAT'S LAW OF PARTIAL VOLUMES

A law similar to Dalton's is *Amagat's law of partial volumes.* This law states that *in any gas mixture the total volume may be considered to be the sum of the partial volumes of the constituents of the mixture,* i.e.,

$$V = V_1 + V_2 + V_3 + \cdots \tag{15}$$

[1] Also referred to occasionally as *pressure* or *volume fractions.*

where V is the total volume while V_1, V_2, etc., are the partial volumes. By the partial volume of a constituent is meant the volume which that constituent would occupy if present alone at the given temperature and at the *total pressure* of the mixture. By an argument similar to the one employed for partial pressures it is readily shown that, if the ideal gas laws are again applicable, then,

$$V_1 = N_1V, \qquad V_2 = N_2V, \text{ etc.} \tag{16}$$

where V_1, V_2, etc., are the partial volumes, N_1, N_2, etc., the mol fractions, and V the total volume at any pressure and temperature.

Dalton's and Amagat's laws are equivalent and hold equally well with gases that approximate ideal behavior, i.e., with gases that are not too close to their condensation temperatures or at too elevated pressures. At high pressures and near their condensation temperatures gases begin to exhibit considerable intermolecular attractions and effects which are no longer general but are specific to the composition and nature of the substances. Under such conditions deviations appear not only from equations (13) and (16), but also from equations (10) and (15). In general the law of partial volumes holds somewhat better than the law of partial pressures at high pressures and low temperatures.

GRAHAM'S LAW OF DIFFUSION

It has long been known that different gases can diffuse through a tube or escape from a container having a fine opening at different rates dependent on the densities or molecular weights of the gases. The law governing such diffusions was first enunciated by Graham in 1829 and bears his name. This law states that *at constant temperature and pressure the rates of diffusion of various gases vary inversely as the square roots of their densities or molecular weights.* Thus, if we let v_1 and v_2 be the rates of diffusion of two gases, and d_1 and d_2 be their respective densities, then

$$\frac{v_1}{v_2} = \frac{\sqrt{d_2}}{\sqrt{d_1}} \tag{17}$$

Again, since at the same pressure and temperature both gases must have the same molar volume, we have also that

$$\frac{v_1}{v_2} = \frac{\sqrt{d_2 V_m}}{\sqrt{d_1 V_m}} = \frac{\sqrt{M_2}}{\sqrt{M_1}} \tag{18}$$

where M_1 and M_2 are the molecular weights of the two gases.

THE KINETIC THEORY OF GASES

All the principles of gas behavior which have been discussed so far have been arrived at by experiment. The *kinetic theory of gases*, on the other hand, attempts to elucidate the behavior of gases by theoretical means in terms of a postulated "picture" of a gas and certain assumptions regarding its behavior. The theory was first proposed by Bernoulli in 1738, and was considerably elaborated and extended by Clausius, Maxwell, Boltzmann, van der Waals, and Jeans.

The kinetic theory is based on the following fundamental postulates:

1. Gases are considered to be composed of minute discrete particles called *molecules*. For any one gas all molecules are thought to be of the same mass and size but to differ in these from gas to gas.
2. The molecules within a container are not stationary but are believed to be in ceaseless chaotic motion during which they collide with each other and with the walls of the container.
3. The bombardment of the container walls by the molecules gives rise to the phenomenon we call *pressure*, i.e., the force exerted on the walls per unit area is the average force per unit area which the molecules exert in their collisions with the walls.
4. Inasmuch as the pressure of a gas within a container does not vary with time at any given pressure and temperature, the molecular collisions must involve no energy loss due to friction. In other words, all molecular collisions are elastic.
5. At relatively low pressures the average distances between molecules are large compared to molecular diameters, and hence the attractive forces between molecules, which depend on the distance of molecular separation, may be considered negligible.
6. Again, since the molecules are small compared to the distance between them, they may be considered to a first approximation to be point masses.
7. Finally, the absolute temperature is a quantity proportional to the *average* kinetic energy of all the molecules in a system.

A mathematical treatment of this concept of a gas leads to fundamental conclusions that are directly verifiable by experiment. Consider a cubical container filled with n' molecules of gas, all the same, and all with molecular mass m and velocity u. This velocity u may be resolved into its three components along the x, y, and z axes, as is shown in Fig. 3. If we call these velocity components u_x, u_y, u_z, then

$$u^2 = u_x^2 + u_y^2 + u_z^2 \tag{19}$$

where u is called the *root-mean-square velocity*. Each of these components may now be treated as though a single molecule of mass m were to move independently with each of the component velocities in the appropriate directions x, y, or z. The total effect of these independent motions is obtained by combining the velocities according to equation (19).

Suppose now that the molecule of mass m is moving in the x direction to the right with velocity u_x. It will strike the yz plane with a momentum mu_x, and, since the collision is elastic, it will rebound with velocity $-u_x$ and momentum $-mu_x$. Consequently the *change in momentum* per molecule per single collision in the x direction is $mu_x - (-mu_x) = 2\,mu_x$. Before the molecule can strike the same wall again it must travel to the opposite wall, collide with it, rebound, and return. To do this it must cover the distance $2\,l$, where l is the length of the cube edge. Hence the number of collisions with the right-hand wall which the molecule will experience per second will be $u_x/2\,l$, and thereby the change in momentum per second for the one molecule on the given wall will be

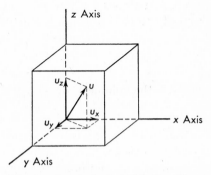

$$(2\,mu_x)\,\frac{u_x}{2\,l} = \frac{mu_x^2}{l} \quad (20)$$

Fig. 3. Resolution of Velocity Along x, y, and z Axes.

But the same change in momentum will be experienced also by the same molecule at the other yz plane, so that the total change in momentum per molecule per second in the x direction is twice the quantity in equation (20), or

$$\text{Change in momentum/second/molecule in } x \text{ direction} = \frac{2\,mu_x^2}{l} \quad (21)$$

A moment's reflection will show that analogous changes in momentum take place in the y and z directions, and that these are given by $2\,mu_y^2/l$ and $2\,mu_z^2/l$ per molecule per second. From these the

$$\text{Total change in momentum/molecule/second} = \frac{2\,mu_x^2}{l} + \frac{2\,mu_y^2}{l} + \frac{2\,mu_z^2}{l}$$

$$= \frac{2\,m}{l}\,(u_x^2 + u_y^2 + u_z^2)$$

$$= \frac{2\,m}{l}\,u^2 \quad (22)$$

by equation (19). As there are n' molecules in the cube, the change in momentum per second for all of them will be equation (22) multiplied by n', or

$$\text{Total change in momentum per second} = \frac{2\,n'mu^2}{l} \tag{23}$$

However, the rate of change of momentum is the acting force, f. Again, pressure is the force per unit area. Consequently,

$$P = \frac{f}{A} = \frac{2\,mn'u^2}{lA} \tag{24}$$

where P is the pressure while A is the total area over which the force is applied. For the cube in question $A = 6\,l^2$, and hence,

$$P = \frac{mn'u^2}{3\,l^3} \tag{25}$$

But l^3 is the volume V of the cube, and so

$$P = \frac{mn'u^2}{3\,V}$$

or
$$PV = \frac{1}{3}\,mn'u^2 \tag{26}$$

According to equation (26) the product PV for any gas should equal one-third the mass of all the molecules (mn') multiplied by the square of the root-mean-square velocity. Although this equation was derived on the assumption of a cubical vessel, it can be shown that the same result is obtained no matter what shape of vessel is considered, and consequently the above deduction must be perfectly general. Equation (26) is the fundamental relation of the kinetic theory of gases.

DEDUCTIONS FROM KINETIC THEORY OF GASES

Boyle's Law. We have seen that one of the fundamental postulates of the kinetic theory is the direct proportionality between kinetic energy of the molecules, i.e., $\frac{1}{2}\,mn'u^2$, and the absolute temperature, namely, that

$$\frac{1}{2}\,mn'u^2 = k_1T \tag{27}$$

where k_1 is a proportionality constant. If now equation (26) is multiplied and divided by 2, we have

$$PV = \frac{2}{3}\left(\frac{1}{2}\,mn'u^2\right)$$

and hence, on insertion of equation (27),

$$PV = \frac{2}{3} k_1 T \qquad (28)$$

At constant temperature equation (28) becomes thus $PV = \text{constant}$, which is Boyle's law.

Charles's Law. This law holds at constant pressure. If this condition is imposed on equation (28), we get

$$V = \left(\frac{2 \, k_1}{3 \, P}\right)T$$
$$= K_2 T \qquad (29)$$

which is a statement of Charles's law.

Avogadro's Principle. In 1811 Avogadro enunciated the principle that *equal volumes of all gases at the same pressure and temperature contain equal numbers of molecules.* This principle is readily deducible from the kinetic theory of gases. Since the volumes and pressures are equal, $P_1 V_1 = P_2 V_2$ for two different gases, and hence it follows from equation (26) that

$$\frac{1}{3} n_1' m_1 u_1^2 = \frac{1}{3} n_2' m_2 u_2^2$$

Again, as the temperature is also constant, the average kinetic energy per molecule must be the same, or

$$\frac{1}{2} m_1 u_1^2 = \frac{1}{2} m_2 u_2^2$$

Inserting the latter relation into the preceding, we see that

$$n_1' = n_2' \qquad (30)$$

which is a statement of Avogadro's principle.

The actual number of molecules in a gram-mole of any gas is an important physical constant known as *Avogadro's number*, symbol N. This constant may be arrived at by a number of methods. The best present value for this quantity is 6.0232×10^{23} molecules per gram-mole. Once this constant is available, the mass of any particular molecule can readily be computed by merely dividing the molecular weight of the substance by Avogadro's number. Thus, since the molecular weight of oxygen is 32, the mass of an individual molecule must be

$$m_{O_2} = \frac{32}{6.023 \times 10^{23}} = 5.31 \times 10^{-23} \text{ g/molecule}$$

Graham's Law of Diffusion. Graham's law also follows readily from the kinetic theory of gases. Since at constant volume and pressure for two different gases

$$\frac{1}{3} n_1' m_1 u_1^2 = \frac{1}{3} n_2' m_2 u_2^2$$

then,

$$\frac{u_1^2}{u_2^2} = \frac{m_2 n_2'}{m_1 n_1'}$$

and

$$\frac{u_1}{u_2} = \sqrt{\frac{m_2 n_2'}{m_1 n_1'}} \qquad (31)$$

Further, if $n_2' = n_1' = N$, then

$$\frac{u_1}{u_2} = \sqrt{\frac{m_2 N}{m_1 N}} = \sqrt{\frac{M_2}{M_1}} \qquad (32)$$

Again, since at constant temperature and pressure the molar volumes are identical, we have also

$$\frac{u_1}{u_2} = \sqrt{\frac{d_2}{d_1}} \qquad (33)$$

where d_2 and d_1 are the densities of the two gases. Equations (32) and (33) are identical with (17) and (18), and are, of course, statements of Graham's law.

All these deductions point to the fact that the theoretical relation $PV = \frac{1}{3} n'mu^2$ is in agreement with the empirical ideal gas law $PV = nRT$. Consequently we may write without further hesitation that

$$PV = \frac{1}{3} n'mu^2 = nRT$$

and, since $n' = nN$,

$$PV = \frac{1}{3} n(Nm)u^2 = nRT$$

$$= \frac{nMu^2}{3} = nRT \qquad (34)$$

where $M = Nm$ is the molecular weight of the gas in question, and n is the number of *moles* of gas in the volume V at pressure P and temperature T.

FURTHER DEDUCTIONS FROM THE KINETIC THEORY

The value of any theory lies not only in its ability to account for known experimental facts but also in its suggestiveness of new modes of attack. In this respect the kinetic theory of gases has been very fruitful. We have seen that equation (26), a direct consequence and expression of the theory, gives all the laws of ideal gas behavior. At the same time, however, many other highly important relations can be deduced from it, some of which are outlined below.

The Velocity of Gas Molecules. According to the kinetic theory all molecules at the same temperature must have the same average kinetic energy, i.e.,

$$\frac{1}{2} m_1 u_1^2 = \frac{1}{2} m_2 u_2^2 = \frac{1}{2} m_3 u_3^2, \text{ etc.}$$

It follows, therefore, that the higher the mass of a molecule, the more slowly must it be moving. It is of considerable interest to ascertain the actual velocity with which various molecules move. From equation (34) we have that

$$\frac{1}{3} n M u^2 = n R T$$

and hence, $$u = \sqrt{\frac{3 \, RT}{M}} \tag{35a}$$

Again, since $RT = PV/n$, and $nM/V = d$, the density of the gas in question at temperature T and pressure P, equation (35a) may be written also as

$$u = \sqrt{\frac{3 \, P}{d}} \tag{35b}$$

By either of these equations the root-mean-square velocity of a gas may be calculated from directly measurable quantities. In doing this R must be expressed in ergs per degree per mole, P in dynes per square centimeter, and the density in grams per cubic centimeter. With these units u will be given in centimeters per second.

To calculate the velocity of hydrogen molecules at 0° C we know that $R = 8.315 \times 10^7$ ergs per mole per degree, $T = 273.15$, and $M = 2.016$. Hence equation (35a) yields for u

$$\begin{aligned} u &= \sqrt{\frac{3 \, RT}{M}} \\ &= \sqrt{\frac{3 \times 8.315 \times 10^7 \times 273.15}{2.016}} \\ &= 184{,}000 \text{ cm/sec} \\ &= 68 \text{ miles/min} \end{aligned}$$

Since hydrogen is the lightest of all elements, this tremendously high velocity represents an upper limit for rates of molecular motion. For all other molecules the speeds will be lower in accordance with Graham's law. Thus for sulfur dioxide, with $M = 64$, the velocity of 0° C would be

$$\frac{u_{SO_2}}{68} = \sqrt{\frac{2}{64}}$$

$$u_{SO_2} = 12 \text{ miles/min}$$

The Kinetic Energy of Translation. The only type of energy we have ascribed thus far to gas molecules is that due to molecular motion along three coordinate axes, i.e., *kinetic energy of translation*. The amount of this energy is again deducible from equation (34). Since from this equation

$$\frac{1}{3} nMu^2 = nRT$$

and since the kinetic energy, E_k, is given by

$$E_k = \frac{1}{2} nMu^2$$

then
$$E_k = \frac{3}{2} \left(\frac{1}{3} nMu^2 \right)$$

$$= \frac{3}{2} nRT \qquad\qquad\qquad (36a)$$

for n moles, or
$$E_k = \frac{3}{2} RT \qquad\qquad\qquad (36b)$$

per mole. Consequently the translational energy of an ideal gas is completely independent of the nature or pressure of the gas, and depends only on the absolute temperature. At, say, 300° K all ideal gases will thus contain per mole

$$E_k = \frac{3}{2} R(300)$$

$$= 450 \, R$$

$$= 895 \text{ cal}$$

or approximately 900 cal of translational kinetic energy.

Distribution of Molecular Velocities. For convenience of treatment all molecules in a given gas and at a given temperature were considered to be composed of molecules moving with a constant root-mean-square velocity u. Actually, however, all molecules do not possess the same velocity, for as a result of collisions a redistribution of both energy and velocity takes place. Maxwell, utilizing probability considerations, has in fact shown that the actual distribution of molecular velocities in a gas depends both on the temperature and molecular weight of a gas and follows in general the course shown in Fig. 4.

In this figure the ordinate represents schematically the fraction of molecules out of a total aggregation which will have a velocity between

c and $c + dc$, while the abscissa has the velocity c. The various plots indicate different temperatures which increase in the order T_1, T_2, T_3. From these plots it may be seen that the probability of a molecule being motionless at any instant is very small. Further, for incidence of velocities greater than zero the probability increases with c, passes through a maximum, and then falls away more or less rapidly toward zero again for very high rates of motion. It is evident, therefore, that both very low and very high speeds are highly improbable, and that most of the molecules in a gas have velocities grouped about the *most probable velocity* corresponding to the peak of the curve at each temperature. The most probable velocity is in any gas not a constant, but shifts toward higher values of c with

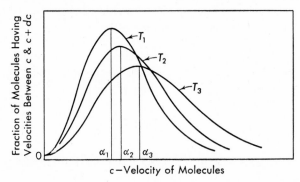

Fig. 4.   Distribution of Molecular Velocities in a Gas.

increase in temperature; i.e., at higher temperatures higher velocities are more probable than at low.

Mathematical analysis shows that the most probable velocity, α, is not equal either to the root-mean-square velocity u or the average velocity of all the molecules v. If we designate by c_1, c_2, c_3 $\cdots$ c_n the individual velocities of n' molecules in a gas, then the average velocity v is defined as

$$v = \frac{c_1 + c_2 + c_3 + \cdots c_n}{n'}$$

and the root-mean-square velocity as

$$u = \sqrt{\frac{c_1^2 + c_2^2 + c_3^2 \cdots c_n^2}{n'}}$$

Kinetic theory arguments reveal that these various velocities are related by the equations

$$v = 0.921\ u$$

$$\alpha = \sqrt{\frac{2}{3}}\ u$$

and hence, on substitution of the value of u from equation (35a), we have

$$u = \sqrt{\frac{3\,RT}{M}} \tag{35a}$$

$$v = 0.921\sqrt{\frac{3\,RT}{M}} \tag{37}$$

$$\alpha = \sqrt{\frac{2\,RT}{M}} \tag{38}$$

or $\qquad \alpha : v : u = 1 : 1.128 : 1.224$

Frequency of Collisions and Mean Free Path. It can be shown that in a gas containing n^* identical molecules per cubic centimeter, the number of molecules with which a *single* gas molecule will collide per second is

$$\sqrt{2}\,\pi v\sigma^2 n^*$$

where v is the average molecular velocity in centimeters per second and σ the molecular diameter in centimeters. Hence the total number of colliding molecules per cubic centimeter per second, Z, must be n^* times this quantity, or

$$Z = \sqrt{2}\,\pi v\sigma^2 (n^*)^2 \tag{39}$$

Further, since each collision involves two molecules, the number of molecular collisions occurring in each cubic centimeter per second, N_c, will be one-half this number, namely,

$$N_c = \frac{Z}{2} = \frac{1}{\sqrt{2}}\,\pi v\sigma^2 (n^*)^2 \tag{40}$$

Another important quantity in kinetic theory considerations is the average distance a molecule traverses before colliding, or the *mean free path*, l, as it is commonly referred to. If a molecule has an average velocity v cm per sec, and if within this period it experiences, as we have seen, $\sqrt{2}\,\pi v\sigma^2 n^*$ collisions, then the average distance between collisions, or mean free path, must be

$$l = \frac{v}{\sqrt{2}\,\pi v\sigma^2 n^*}$$

$$= \frac{1}{\sqrt{2}\,\pi\sigma^2 n^*} \tag{41}$$

The quantities N_c, Z, and l are readily calculable as soon as the molecular diameters σ are available. These are usually obtained from gas viscosity measurements, for according to kinetic theory the viscosity coefficient η is given approximately by the relation

$$\eta = \frac{1}{3}vld \tag{42}$$

where d is the density in grams per cubic centimer and the other symbols have the significance given above. Knowing the mean free path l, σ may be calculated by equation (41). The question of gas visocisty will be discussed more fully toward the end of this chapter.

APPLICABILITY OF THE IDEAL GAS LAWS

The concordance between the empirical generalizations embodied in the expression $PV = nRT$ and the deductions of the kinetic theory of gases lends considerable credence to our conception of the nature of gases and their behavior. However, there still remains the question of how completely and accurately can the expression $PV = nRT$ reproduce the

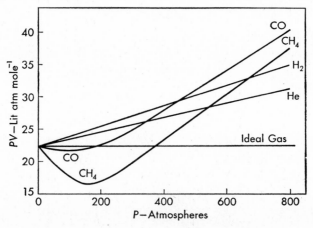

Fig. 5.   *PV* vs. *P* Plot for Several Gases at 0° C.

actual P-V-T relations of all gases. To test this point we may resort to the fact that at constant temperature the combined gas law reduces to $PV = nRT =$ constant. Hence, as long as T does not vary, the product PV for a given quantity of gas should remain the same at all pressures. A plot of PV vs. P at constant T should yield, therefore, a straight line parallel to the abscissa.

Such a plot of PV vs. P constructed from actual data for several gases at 0° C is shown in Fig. 5. The fact immediately apparent is that PV is not constant over most of the pressure range shown. The curves are in general of two types. One, including only hydrogen and helium here, starts at the value of PV demanded by $PV = nRT$ for the temperature in question and increases continually with pressure. In every case the product PV is greater than demanded by theory. On the other hand, in the second type the plot starts again at the same point as before, but now the product PV decreases at first with pressure, passes through a minimum characteristic of each gas and the temperature, and then increases to values which may rise appreciably above the theoretical.

Actually, both types of curves are part of a single pattern of behavior exhibited by all gases. To show this, it is convenient to employ a quantity z, called the *compressibility factor*, which is defined as

$$z = \frac{PV}{nRT} \tag{43}$$

For an ideal gas $z = 1$ at all temperatures and pressures. In the case of actual gases the compressibility factor may vary with both of these

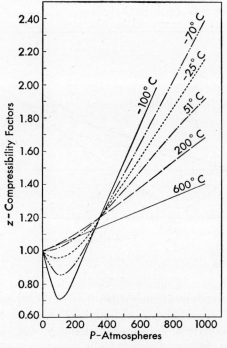

Fig. 6. Compressibility Factors for Nitrogen.

variables, and hence its deviation from a value of unity is an index of deviation from ideal behavior.

From the experimental $P–V–T$ data for a gas z may be calculated by means of equation (43), and its variation with temperature and pressure observed. Figure 6 shows a plot of z vs. P for nitrogen at various constant temperatures. Inspection of this plot reveals that all the isotherms start with $z = 1$ at $P = 0$, and change with pressure in a manner dependent on the temperature. However, there is one temperature, in this case 51° C, at which z remains close to unity over an appreciable pressure range. In fact, between $P = 0$ and $P = 100$ atm z changes only from 1.00 to 1.02. Beyond 100 atm z rises quite rapidly with increasing pressure and attains values considerably above $z = 1$. This temperature at which a real gas obeys the ideal gas law over an appreciable pressure range is called the *Boyle temperature or Boyle point*. The Boyle temperature is also a dividing line in the types of isotherms exhibited by the gas. Above the Boyle point the gas shows only positive deviations from ideality, and hence all values of z are greater than unity. Below the Boyle temperature, however, the values of z first decrease with increasing pressure, go through a minimum, and then increase to values which may climb appreciably above $z = 1$. It should also be observed that the lower the temperature, the lower the minima and that they occur at pressures which vary with the temperature.

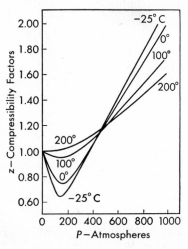

Fig. 7.   Compressibility   Factors for Methane.

The plots shown in Fig. 6 are typical of the P–V–T behavior of *all* gases when data covering wide ranges of pressure and temperature are considered. The only differences observed are in the Boyle temperatures and in the positions of the isotherms on the plots, since these are dependent in each instance on the gas in question. Nevertheless, it is always found that above the Boyle temperature only positive deviations from ideality are observed. Below the Boyle temperature, on the other hand, increase of pressure causes the z values first to decrease below $z = 1$ to go through a minimum and then to increase to values which eventually go appreciably above $z = 1$.

In terms of the above discussion a glance at Fig. 5 should suffice to indicate that at 0° C hydrogen and helium are already above their Boyle temperatures, whereas carbon monoxide and methane are still below theirs. It is also to be expected that at sufficiently low temperatures, hydrogen and helium should exhibit minima in their z vs. P plots, while at higher temperatures carbon monoxide and methane should show plots similar to those of hydrogen and helium at 0° C. Such is actually the case, as may be seen from the compressibility factor plot for methane given in Fig. 7.

The highly individualistic behavior exhibited by various gases indicates that in order to represent their P–V–T relations equations of state, i.e., equations involving P, V, and T, would be required which would contain not only these variables but also terms making allowance for the specific forces operative in each gas. However, $P-V-T$ studies on gases at low pressures do show that when the pressures are lowered gases begin to approximate more closely the ideal gas law, and, furthermore, the lower the pressure the better is the agreement between the observed PV product and that calculated from the combined gas law. At these low pressures all gases lose their individualistic behavior and merge to obey the simple and general expression obtained from the kinetic theory of gases. For this reason the expression $PV = nRT$ is considered to be a *limiting law* only, a law which gases obey strictly only when they are diluted highly enough so that the volume of the molecules themselves is negligible compared to the total volume, and the intermolecular attractive forces are too feeble to exercise any influence on the pressure of the gas. It may be concluded, therefore, that a gas becomes more ideal as the pressure is lowered and will become completely ideal as the pressure approaches zero. This conclusion is confirmed by the fact that, as P approaches zero, the compressibility factors at all temperatures go to $z = 1$.

How far this concordance between the ideal gas law and observation will extend into the range of higher pressures depends on the nature of the gas and the temperature. For gases which are permanent at ordinary temperatures, i.e., which are above their critical temperatures,[1] such as hydrogen, nitrogen, oxygen, and helium, this concordance may extend within 5 per cent or so up to pressures as high as 50 atm. On the other hand, with easily condensible gases, such as carbon dioxide, sulfur dioxide, chlorine, and methyl chloride, discrepancies as large as 2 or 3 per cent may appear at 1 atm pressure. The use of the ideal gas law for such gases is considerably limited, therefore, when fairly precise calculations are required. In any case, before using the ideal gas law at any appreciable pressure it is always advisable to consider the nature of the gas in question and how far it is above its critical temperature. The greater this distance, the wider in general will be the pressure range over which calculations can be made within a given accuracy.

USE OF COMPRESSIBILITY FACTORS

When the compressibility factors of a gas are known under various conditions, they may be employed quite readily for making exact gas calculations. For instance, suppose that the volume of 10 moles of methane is required at 100 atm pressure and 0° C. At this pressure and temperature $z = 0.783$, and hence, according to equation (43),

---

[1] The critical temperature is the highest temperature at which a gas may be liquefied.

$$V = \frac{znRT}{P}$$

$$= \frac{0.783 \times 10 \times 0.0821 \times 273.2}{100}$$

$$= 1.754 \text{ liters}$$

The experimentally observed volume is 1,756 liters. Again, suppose that a certain quantity of methane occupies a volume of 0.138 liter under a pressure of 300 atm at 200° C, and the volume is required at 600 atm at 0° C. For 300 atm at 200° C, $z_2 = 1.067$, while for 600 atm at 0° C, $z_1 = 1.367$. Since for the lower temperature we have $P_1V_1 = z_1nRT_1$ while for the higher one $P_2V_2 = z_2nRT_2$, then

$$\frac{P_1V_1}{P_2V_2} = \frac{z_1nRT_1}{z_2nRT_2} = \frac{z_1T_1}{z_2T_2} \tag{44}$$

and hence on substitution of the given values we get,

$$V_1 = \left(\frac{z_1T_1}{z_2T_2}\right)\left(\frac{P_2V_2}{P_1}\right)$$

$$= \left(\frac{1.367 \times 273.2}{1.067 \times 473.2}\right)\left(\frac{300 \times 0.138}{600}\right)$$

$$= 0.051 \text{ liter}$$

THE VAN DER WAALS EQUATION OF STATE

Because of the deviation of real gases from the behavior demanded by the ideal gas law, many attempts have been made to set up equations of state which will reproduce more satisfactorily the P–V–T relations of gases. Of these equations one of the earliest and best known is that of van der Waals.

The van der Waals equation differs from the ideal gas law in that it makes allowance both for the volume occupied by the molecules themselves and for the attractive forces between them. Simple kinetic theory, upon which the ideal gas laws are predicated, considers the molecules to be point masses occupying zero volume. Although such an assumption is not serious when the molecules are far apart, i.e., at low pressures, at high pressures, when the molecules are close together, the volume of the molecules themselves may become a sizable fraction of the total volume. Under such conditions the "free space" available for compression becomes considerably less than the total volume, and the latter cannot be taken as the space through which a gas may be compressed.

To make this correction necessitated by the finite dimensions of the molecules, let b be the effective volume of the molecules in *one* mole of gas and V the volume of n moles of gas. In this total volume that occupied by the molecules themselves will be thus nb, and hence the volume available for compression will be not V but $(V - nb)$. Since the latter is the "free space," it should be substituted for V in the ideal gas law. It may be anticipated that b will be characteristic and different for each gas.

The second factor of which van der Waals took cognizance is the attractive force operative between molecules. Consider the wall of a container which is being bombarded by gaseous molecules. The force per unit area due to this bombardment is the observed pressure. When the gas molecules are not constrained by attractions for each other, they will bombard the wall with the full force due to their outward motion. If, however, under the same conditions a molecule moving outward is subjected by molecular attraction to an inward "pull," some of the energy of its outward motion will have to be employed to overcome the inward attraction. Such a molecule will not strike the wall with as high a force as if it were not "dragged back" by the other molecules within the gas, and consequently the pressure resulting from the bombardment will be lessened by an amount P'. The observed pressure, P, will thus be less than the ideal pressure, P_i, by the amount P', or

$$P = P_i - P'$$

Since in the expression $P_iV = nRT$ the pressure P_i refers to the ideal pressure, we must substitute for it its value from the expression given above, or $P_i = (P + P')$. If we combine this corrected pressure with the expression for the corrected volume we obtain, unstead of $PV = nRT$, the equation

$$(P + P')(V - nb) = nRT \tag{45}$$

van der Waals indicated that the magnitude of the pressure correction P' for n moles of gas present in volume V is given by

$$P' = \frac{n^2a}{V^2}$$

where a is a constant characteristic of each gas and independent of pressure and temperature. It is for each gas a measure of the magnitude of the intermolecular attractive forces within the gas. If this expression for P' is substituted in equation (45), we get

$$\left(P + \frac{n^2a}{V^2}\right)\left(V - nb\right) = nRT \tag{46}$$

This is the celebrated equation of state which was first developed by van der Waals in 1873 and which bears his name.

USE OF VAN DER WAALS' EQUATION

In applying van der Waals' equation care must be exercised in the choice of appropriate units, particularly for the constants a and b. Since n^2a/V^2 must represent a pressure, the units of a must be pressure $\times$ (volume)^2/(mole)^2, i.e., atm-liter^2 mole^{-2}, or atm-cc^2 mole^{-2}. In any event, the units used must be the same as those of P and V, and this applies also to R. In turn, b is a volume and must correspond to the units of V.

TABLE 2

van der Waals Constants for Various Gases
(a in atm-liter^2 mole^{-2}; b in liter mole^{-1})

Gas	Formula	a	b
Acetylene	C_2H_2	4.39	0.0514
Ammonia	NH_3	4.17	0.0371
Argon	A	1.35	0.0322
Carbon dioxide	CO_2	3.59	0.0427
Carbon disulfide	CS_2	11.62	0.0769
Carbon monoxide	CO	1.49	0.0399
Carbon tetrachloride	CCl_4	20.39	0.1383
Chlorine	Cl_2	6.49	0.0562
Chloroform	$CHCl_3$	15.17	0.1022
Ethane	C_2H_6	5.49	0.0638
Ethyl ether	$(C_2H_5)_2O$	17.38	0.1344
Ethylene	C_2H_4	4.47	0.0571
Helium	He	0.034	0.0237
Hydrogen	H_2	0.244	0.0266
Hydrogen bromide	HBr	4.45	0.0443
Hydrogen chloride	HCl	3.67	0.0408
Methane	CH_4	2.25	0.0428
Neon	Ne	0.211	0.0171
Nitric oxide	NO	1.34	0.0279
Nitrogen	N_2	1.39	0.0391
Nitrogen dioxide	NO_2	5.28	0.0442
Nitrous oxide	N_2O	3.78	0.0442
Oxygen	O_2	1.36	0.0318
Sulfur dioxide	SO_2	6.71	0.0564
Water	H_2O	5.46	0.0305

The use of the equation can be illustrated with an example. Suppose it is desired to calculate by van der Waals' equation the pressure at which 2 moles of ammonia will occupy a volume of 5 liters at 27° C. For ammonia, $a = 4.17$ atm-liter^2 mole^{-2}, while $b = 0.0371$ liter per mole. Hence,

$$P = \frac{nRT}{V - nb} - \frac{n^2a}{V^2}$$
$$= \frac{2(0.0821)300.2}{5 - 2(0.0371)} - \frac{(2)^2 \times 4.17}{(5)^2}$$
$$= 9.33 \text{ atm}$$

The corresponding pressure calculated from the ideal gas law is 9.86 atm.

Table 2 lists the van der Waals constants a and b for a number of gases. Such gases as carbon disulfide, ammonia, sulfur dioxide, chloroform, etc., which are easily condensible, have relatively high values of a, indicating strong intermolecular attractions. On the other hand, for the permanent gases such as argon, carbon monoxide, helium, and hydrogen, the a values are considerably lower, and hence in these the intermolecular forces are considerably weaker.

The van der Waals equation is much more accurate than the simple ideal gas law and is valid over a much wider pressure range, as may be seen from Table 3. However, under extreme conditions, such as temperatures near the critical and at very high pressures, its predictions deviate

TABLE 3

COMPARISON OF IDEAL GAS LAW AND VAN DER WAALS' EQUATION AT 100° C

Observed P (atm)	Hydrogen				Carbon Dioxide			
	P Calc. Ideal	% Devia- tion	P Calc. van der Waals	% Devia- tion	P Calc. Ideal	% Devia- tion	P Calc. van der Waals	% Devia- tion
50	48.7	−2.6	50.2	+0.4	57.0	+14.0	49.5	−1.0
75	72.3	−3.6	75.7	+0.9	92.3	+17.3	73.3	−2.3
100	95.0	−5.0	100.8	+0.8	133.5	+33.5	95.8	−4.2

considerably in many instances from experimentally observed values. It is very doubtful whether it is justifiable to consider a and b as constants independent of pressure and temperature. In fact, in order to fit the equation to experimental data with a relatively high order of fidelity it is necessary to choose different values of a and b over different ranges of pressure and temperature.

OTHER EQUATIONS OF STATE

A large number of other equations of state have been proposed to represent the P-V-T relations of gases. Some of these are based to some extent on theoretical considerations, while other are entirely empirical. We shall consider now several of the more important of these equations.

The Kamerlingh Onnes Equation of State. This empirical equation expresses PV as a power series of the pressure at any given temperature, namely,

$$PV = A + BP + CP^2 + DP^3 + \cdots \qquad (47)$$

P is the pressure, generally in atmospheres, and V is the *molar* volume in liters or cubic centimeters. The coefficients A, B, C, etc., are known respectively as the first, second, third, etc., *virial coefficients*. At very low pressures only the first of these coefficients is significant, and it is equal to RT. At higher pressures, however, the others as well are important and must be considered. In general the order of significance of the coefficients is their order in the equation. These coefficients, although constant at any given temperature, change in value as the temperature is changed. Of necessity the first virial coefficient A is always positive and increases with temperature. The second coefficient, on the other hand, is negative at low temperatures, passes through zero, and becomes increasingly positive as the temperature is raised. The temperature at which

TABLE 4

VIRIAL COEFFICIENTS OF SOME GASES

(P in atm, V in liters mole^{-1})

$t°$ C	A	$B \times 10^2$	$C \times 10^5$	$D \times 10^8$	$E \times 10^{11}$
			Nitrogen		
-50	18.312	-2.8790	14.980	-14.470	4.657
0	22.414	-1.0512	8.626	-6.910	1.704
100	30.619	0.6662	4.411	-3.534	0.9687
200	38.824	1.4763	2.775	-2.379	0.7600
			Carbon Monoxide		
-50	18.312	-3.6878	17.900	-17.911	6.225
0	22.414	-1.4825	9.823	-7.721	1.947
100	30.619	0.4036	4.874	-3.618	0.9235
200	38.824	1.3163	3.052	-2.449	0.7266
			Hydrogen		
-50	18.312	1.2027	1.164	-1.741	1.022
0	22.414	1.3638	0.7851	-1.206	0.7354
500	63.447	1.7974	0.1003	-0.1619	0.1050

$B = 0$ is the *Boyle temperature*, for at this temperature Boyle's law is valid over a fairly wide pressure range.

By using a sufficient number of terms this equation can be fitted to experimental data with a high order of accuracy. The virial coefficients for several gases are shown in Table 4. With these it is possible to calculate PV up to 1000 atm.

The Berthelot Equation. The high-pressure form of this equation is rather difficult to handle. For low pressures the equation reduces to

$$ PV = nRT \left[1 + \frac{9\,PT_c}{128 P_c T} \left(1 - \frac{6\,T_c^2}{T^2} \right) \right] \tag{48} $$

where P, V, R, T, and n have the same meaning as in the ideal gas law, while P_c and T_c are the critical pressure and critical temperature respectively. The meaning of the latter quantities will be discussed more fully in Chapter 3. For pressures of about an atmosphere and below this equation is very accurate, and it is consequently very useful in calculating the molecular weights of gases from their densities. Its use will be illustrated in that connection.

The Beattie-Bridgeman Equation of State. This semitheoretical equation of state involving five constants is one of the most accurate equations of state available at present. It may be stated in two forms, one explicit in pressure, the other in molar volume V_m, namely,

$$ P = \frac{RT}{V_m} + \frac{\beta}{V_m^2} + \frac{\gamma}{V_m^3} + \frac{\delta}{V_m^4} \tag{49} $$

$$ V_m = \frac{RT}{P} + \frac{\beta}{RT} + \frac{\gamma P}{(RT)^2} + \frac{\delta P^2}{(RT)^3} \tag{50} $$

where

$$ \beta = RTB_0 - A_0 - \frac{Rc}{T^2} \tag{51a} $$

$$ \gamma = -RTB_0 b + A_0 a - \frac{RcB_0}{T^2} \tag{51b} $$

$$ \delta = \frac{RB_0 bc}{T^2} \tag{51c} $$

In these relations T is again the absolute temperature and R the gas constant, while A_0, B_0, a, b, and c are constants characteristic of each gas. Of the two forms (49) and (50) the first is the more accurate, for the second was deduced from it with certain approximations.

This equation is applicable over wide ranges of temperature and pressure with excellent accuracy. Volumes and pressures calculated by it agree with experiment to 0.3 per cent or less up to pressures of 100 atm and temperatures as low as $-150°$ C. With lower accuracy the equation may be extended to considerably higher pressures.

TABLE 5

BEATTIE-BRIDGMAN CONSTANTS FOR SOME GASES*

(For P in atm, V in liters mole^{-1})

Gas	A_0	a	B_0	b	c
He	0.0216	0.05984	0.01400	0.0	0.004×10^4
Ne	0.2125	0.2196	0.02060	0.0	0.101×10^4
A	1.2907	0.02328	0.03931	0.0	5.99×10^4
H_2	0.1975	−0.00506	0.02096	−0.04359	0.0504×10^4
N_2	1.3445	0.02617	0.05046	−0.00691	4.20×10^4
O_2	1.4911	0.02562	0.04624	0.004208	4.80×10^4
Air	1.3012	0.01931	0.04611	−0.01101	4.34×10^4
CO_2	5.0065	0.07132	0.10476	0.07235	66.00×10^4
CH_4	2.2769	0.01855	0.05587	−0.01587	12.83×10^4
$(C_2H_5)_2O$	31.278	0.12426	0.45446	0.11954	33.33×10^4

* *J. Am. Chem. Soc.*, **50**, 3136 (1928). See also Maron and Turnbull, *Ind. Eng. Chem.*, **33**, 408 (1941).

Constants for various gases to be used with the Beattie-Bridgeman equation are given in Table 5. Further details on and applications of the equation may be found in the original literature.[1]

MOLECULAR WEIGHTS OF GASES

The molecular weight of a gas is an important quantity, and its numerical value is highly essential for all types of calculations. Consequently we turn our attention to the significance of the molecular weight and to a description of various methods for determining the molecular weights of gases.

It should be clearly realized that chemical analysis alone is insufficient to establish the molecular weight of a substance. Chemical analysis merely establishes the elements entering into the composition of a molecule and their proportions, but it does not tell us how many atoms of each substance are involved. For instance, chemical analysis of ethane shows that it is composed of carbon and hydrogen in the proportion of three atoms of hydrogen for each atom of carbon. From this alone we should be tempted to write the formula as CH_3. Actually, however, density measurements on the gas show that the formula is not CH_3 but a multiple of it, $(CH_3)_2$ or C_2H_6; i.e., the molecule is composed of two atoms of carbon and six atoms of hydrogen. In brief, chemical analysis can yield only the composition and empirical formula of a substance. Physicochemical measurements, on the other hand, can establish the

[1] See *J. Am. Chem. Soc.*, **49**, 1665 (1927); *ibid.*, **50**, 3133 (1928); *ibid.*, **52**, 1382 (1930); *ibid.*, **53**, 843, 860 (1931); *Proc. Am. Acad. Arts and Sci.*, **63**, 229 (1928).

molecular weight, and they can give us then the multiple by which the empirical formula weight must be multiplied in order to arrive at the actual molecular weight of the substance.

All molecular weights are based on the arbitrarily assumed standard of 16.0000 for the chemical atomic weight of oxygen. Since it has been proved that the oxygen molecule contains two atoms in each molecule, it follows immediately that the molecular weight of oxygen is 32.0000. Knowing the molecular weight of oxygen, the molecular weights of all other gases may be determined by physicochemical methods through application of the Avogadro hypothesis.

The Avogadro hypothesis states that under the same conditions of temperature and pressure equal volumes of all gases contain the same number of molecules. If we were to determine, then, the volume that a mole of oxygen occupies under a specified set of conditions, this would be also the volume that a mole of any other gas would occupy under the same conditions; and the weight of this volume would yield directly the molecular weight of the gas. Since by Avogadro's hypothesis the two volumes would contain the same number of molecules, the molecular weights, defined on the basis of $O_2 = 32.0000$, would be in the same proportion as the actual masses of the individual molecules.

In physical chemistry the unit of mass commonly employed is the gram, and the gram-mole is the weight of a substance in grams corresponding to the molecular weight. For oxygen the gram-mole is 32.0000 grams by definition.[1] Further, by direct measurement it has been found that the density of oxygen at standard conditions, i.e., 1 atm pressure and 273.15° K, is 1.4290 g per liter. Since density is the weight per unit volume, it follows that the molar volume of oxygen is

$$\frac{32.0000}{1.4290} = 22.39 \text{ liters}$$

at standard conditions. As this is also the molar volume of any other gas at standard conditions, the problem of determining the molecular weight of any gas reduces essentially to determining the weight of 22.39 liters of the gas at 1 atm pressure and 273.15° K.

Actually, it is not necessary or convenient to make measurements under the specified conditions. Measurements may be made under any desired conditions, and the molecular weight may be calculated conveniently from the ideal gas law. If W be the weight of gas under consideration and M its molecular weight, then $n = W/M$, and

$$PV = nRT = \frac{W}{M} RT \tag{52}$$

---

[1] Similarly, a pound-mole is the weight of a substance in pounds corresponding to the molecular weight.

To obtain the molecular weight of any gas we need only determine the temperature and pressure at which a weight of gas W occupies the volume V, substitute these quantities in equation (52), and solve for M

$$M = \frac{WRT}{PV} \qquad (53)$$

Equation (53) may be expressed also in terms of the density of the gas d. Since $d = W/V$,

$$M = \frac{dRT}{P} \qquad (54)$$

and the molecular weight follows from the density of the gas at any given temperature and pressure. Most methods for determining the molecular weights of gases are based on these equations.

REGNAULT'S METHOD FOR DETERMINATION OF MOLECULAR WEIGHTS

This method is employed to determine the molecular weights of substances which are gaseous at room temperature. The procedure in outline is as follows: A dry glass bulb of 300- to 500-cc capacity fitted with a stopcock is evacuated and weighed. It is then filled at a definite temperature and pressure with the gas whose molecular weight is to be determined and weighed again. The difference in weights represents the weight of gas W in the flask. The volume of the flask is determined by filling it with water or mercury, whose densities are known, and again weighing. From the data thus obtained the molecular weight may be calculated by equation (53).

For more precise work a larger bulb is used to increase the mass of gas and a similar bulb is employed as a counterpoise. The observed weights are also reduced to vacuo.

DUMAS' METHOD FOR DETERMINATION OF VAPOR DENSITIES

This method is used to determine the molecular weights in the vapor phase of readily volatile liquids. A retort-shaped bulb, having a small opening drawn to a capillary, is first weighed full of air. A sample of several cubic centimeters of the liquid in question is drawn into the bulb by cooling it with the tip below the surface of the liquid, and the bulb is then immersed in a bath whose temperature is above the boiling point of the liquid. The boiling is permitted to proceed until the vapors of boiling liquid have expelled all the air from the bulb, and the liquid in the flask has completely vaporized. The flask is then sealed, cooled to room temperature, and weighed. The volume of the bulb is determined as in

Regnault's method. The pressure of the vapor when the bulb is sealed is the same as atmospheric, while the temperature is that of the bath. The weight of vapor, after corrections for buoyancy, is obtained from the following equation:

$$W_{\text{vapor}} = W_{\text{(bulb+vapor)}} - W_{\text{(bulb+air)}} + W_{\text{air}} \qquad (55)$$

W_{air} is obtained by multiplying the volume of the flask by the density of the air. Knowing P, V, T, and W_{vapor}, the molecular weight of the liquid in the vapor phase may be calculated as before.

THE VICTOR MEYER METHOD FOR VAPOR DENSITIES

This method serves the same purpose as the Dumas method for the determination of vapor densities but is considerably simpler and more flexible. A sketch of the apparatus is shown in Fig. 8. It consists of an inner tube B, approximately 50 cm long, which is surrounded by a jacket A, partly filled as indicated with a liquid whose boiling point is at least 30° higher than that of the substance to be studied. The function of the outer jacket is to keep the temperature of the inner tube constant by boiling the liquid in A throughout a run. Inside the inner tube, in turn, is another tube C, open at the bottom, down which passes a metal or glass rod, anchored with rubber tubing at the top in the manner shown and fitted with a hook at the bottom. The outlet from B communicates with a gas burette G, filled either with water, in which case correction for the aqueous pressure must be applied, or preferably mercury.

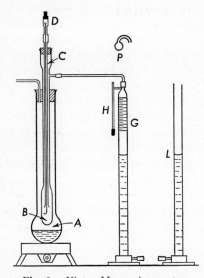

Fig. 8.   Victor Meyer Apparatus.

L is a leveling bulb to permit adjustment of gas pressure in G to that of the atmosphere.

The liquid whose molecular weight is to be determined is enclosed in a small glass ampoule with finely drawn tip, P. This ampoule is first weighed empty. Next, enough of the liquid is drawn in to yield 40 to 60 cc of vapor, and the bulb is sealed carefully in a flame and weighed again. The difference between the first and second weighings gives the weight of the liquid W to be vaporized. This ampoule is hung then on the hook projecting from C, and the entire apparatus assembled as shown in the figure.

To make a measurement, the liquid in A is brought to boiling and kept
there for the entire run. When thermal equilibrium has been established,
the levels in G and L are equalized and the burette reading is taken.
Next the ampoule is smashed by pulling upward on the rod at D so as to
bring the neck of the ampoule up against the bottom of C. With the bulb
broken the liquid vaporizes, and the vapors generated displace air from
the bottom of B into the gas burette G. The volume of air thus displaced
is equal to the volume of the vapors formed at the temperature of the
inner tube. Once in the gas burette the air cools to room temperature,
and its volume can be measured by again reading the burette. Provided
the levels in G and L are equalized, the pressure of this air is the same
as that of the atmosphere outside the burette, while the temperature is
that read on the thermometer H. The volume of displaced air thus
obtained, i.e., final minus initial burette readings, is equal to the volume
which the vapors of the liquid would occupy if they could be cooled to the
temperature of the room and atmospheric pressure. Having measured
in this manner the weight of liquid W, and its volume as a *vapor* at room
temperature T and barometric pressure P, the density of the vapor and
its molecular weight may readily be calculated from the observed data.

To illustrate the method of calculation, consider the following example.
In determining the molecular weight of ethyl alcohol the data obtained
were:

> Weight of liquid taken = 0.1211 g
> Volume of air measured over water = 67.30 cc
> Temperature = 28.0° C
> Atmospheric pressure = 755.2 mm Hg (corrected)
> Vapor pressure of water at 28° C (from tables) = 28.3 mm Hg

Since the total pressure in the burette is the sum of the pressures of vapor
P and that of water P_{H_2O}, and since this total is equal to atmospheric
pressure, then

$$P = P_{atm} - P_{H_2O}$$
$$= 755.2 - 28.3$$
$$= 726.9 \text{ mm Hg}$$

Inserting this value of P along with those of W, T, and V into equation (53), the molecular weight of ethyl alcohol follows as

$$M = \frac{WRT}{PV}$$
$$= \frac{0.1211 \times 82.06 \times 301.2}{(726.9/760)67.30}$$
$$= 46.5 \text{ g mole}^{-1}$$

The molecular weight obtained from atomic weights is 46.07.

EXACT DETERMINATION OF VAPOR DENSITIES AND MOLECULAR WEIGHTS

The molecular weights calculated from the ideal gas law are, even with good data, only approximate. The reason is that already at atmospheric pressure the ideal gas law fails to represent accurately the behavior of the vapors. For most purposes an approximate molecular weight when used in conjunction with an empirical chemical formula will suffice to establish the exact molecular weight of a substance in the gas phase. Occasionally, however, as in atomic weight determinations, an exact molecular weight is desired, and this must be obtained from either a more precise gas equation or by special treatment of the ideal gas law.

When the constants a and b of a substance are known, use of van der Waals' equation will give better concordance between observed and calculated values of the molecular weight. For the purpose at hand, however, the Berthelot equation is more convenient and gives good results. It can be used, of course, only when the critical temperature and pressure of the substance are available. Since $n = W/M$, equation (48) gives for M

$$M = \left(\frac{W}{V}\right)\left(\frac{RT}{P}\right)\left[1 + \frac{9\,PT_c}{128\,P_cT}\left(1 - \frac{6\,T_c^2}{T^2}\right)\right] \qquad (56)$$

Further, since $W/V = d$, equation (56) may also be written as

$$M = \frac{dRT}{P}\left[1 + \frac{9\,PT_c}{128\,P_cT}\left(1 - \frac{6\,T_c^2}{T^2}\right)\right] \qquad (57)$$

from which the density follows when M is known or vice versa.

The higher accuracy of the Berthelot equation can be illustrated with the following data on methyl chloride. For methyl chloride, T_c = 416.2° K, P_c = 65.8 atm, while the density at standard conditions is 2.3076 g per liter. Hence, by equation (57),

$$M = \frac{2.3076\times0.08206\times273.2}{1}\left[1 + \frac{9\times1\times416.2}{128\times65.8\times273.2}\left(1 - 6\,\frac{(416.2)^2}{(273.2)^2}\right)\right]$$
$$= 50.62 \text{ g mole}^{-1}$$

as against the theoretically calculated 50.48. Using the same data and the ideal gas law, the molecular weight obtained is 51.71.

A means of obtaining exact molecular weights is the method of *limiting densities*. This method, which gives excellent results, is based upon the fact that as zero pressure is approached the ideal gas laws become exact for all gases. The densities of a gas or vapor are determined at a given temperature at atmospheric pressure and at several other pressures below one atmosphere. The ratio d/P is then plotted against P. If the vapor or gas were ideal, this ratio would be the same at all pressures, for

$$P = \frac{d}{M} RT$$

and $\qquad\qquad \frac{d}{P} = \frac{M}{RT} = \text{constant} \qquad\qquad (58)$

However, since this is not true for real gases, the ratio d/P changes with decreasing pressure. Fortunately the plot is practically linear and can be

TABLE 6

DENSITIES OF HBr AT VARIOUS PRESSURES (0° C)

P (atm)	d (g/liter)	d/P
1	3.6444	3.6444
⅔	2.4220	3.6330
⅓	1.2074	3.6222
0	—	3.6108 (extp'd)

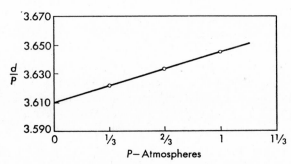

Fig. 9.   Plot of d/P vs. P for HBr at 0° C.

extrapolated to zero pressure without any difficulty. At zero pressure the limiting ratio d/P is that for the ideal gas, and so

$$\left(\frac{d}{P}\right)_{P=0} = \frac{M}{RT}$$

and $\qquad\qquad M = RT \left(\frac{d}{P}\right)_{P=0} \qquad\qquad (59)$

This method can be illustrated with the data on hydrogen bromide shown in Table 6, while the plot of d/P vs. P is shown in Fig. 9. The extrapolated value of d/P is 3.6108 g per liter per atm at 0° C. Hence the molecular weight of hydrogen bromide is

$$M = 3.6108 \times 0.08206 \times 273.15 = 80.93 \text{ g mole}^{-1}$$

The value calculated from atomic weights is 80.92.

RESULTS OF VAPOR DENSITY MEASUREMENTS

The measurement of the vapor densities of a large number of substances shows that the molecular weight of these substances in the gas phase over a certain temperature interval is what would be expected from their simple formula. Among these may be mentioned ammonia, carbon dioxide, hydrogen, nitrogen, carbon monoxide, methyl chloride, methyl fluoride, ethyl ether, methyl ether, carbon tetrachloride, chloroform, carbon disulfide, acetone. There are other substances, however, which exhibit a highly anomalous behavior. These may be segregated into two groups: (a) those which exhibit vapor densities, and consequently molecular weights, very much higher than would be expected on the basis of their simple formulas, and (b) those which exhibit vapor densities much lower than expected from their simple formulas. All these abnormalities are very much greater than can be accounted for by either experimental uncertainty or deviation from ideal behavior.

The substances exhibiting abnormally high vapor densities are considered to be associated in the vapor phase, i.e., the molecules are considered to be composed of more than a single structural unit. In line with this view is the fact that the calculated molecular weight is usually a whole-number multiple of the simple formula. Thus aluminum chloride is shown in the vapor phase to be $(AlCl_3)_2$ or Al_2Cl_6, ferric chloride Fe_2Cl_6, beryllium chloride Be_2Cl_4, and gallium chloride Ga_2Cl_6. Sulfur is another substance which shows different stages of association in the gas phase at different temperatures.

Substances exhibiting abnormally low vapor densities break down or dissociate in the vapor phase under the influence of heat into simpler molecules, leading thus to a greater number of particles and a lower density for any given pressure. Deville in 1857 and Kopp in 1864 actually showed that the vapor of ammonium chloride, which exhibits an abnormally low density, contained ammonia and hydrogen chloride as a result of the reaction

$$NH_4Cl = NH_3 + HCl$$

Similarly, phosphorus pentachloride dissociates in the vapor phase as follows,

$$PCl_5 = PCl_3 + Cl_2$$

while nitrogen tetroxide dissociates according to

$$N_2O_4 = 2\,NO_2$$

In any instance of abnormally low vapor densities the extent of dissociation is a function of the temperature and pressure. At sufficiently high temperatures these substances may be completely dissociated, while at sufficiently low temperatures they may behave almost normally. In fact, practically all substances can be shown to be abnormal if the temperature is made high enough. Even such a stable compound as carbon dioxide dissociates above 2000° C to some extent into carbon monoxide and oxygen. Similarly, aluminum chloride at 400° C is Al_2Cl_6, at 500° it is a mixture of Al_2Cl_6 and $AlCl_3$, while at 1100° it is all $AlCl_3$. If heated further, $AlCl_3$ will actually dissociate into aluminum and chlorine. Hence when we speak of the molecular weight of a substance in the gas phase, it is very important to keep in mind the temperature to which reference is made.

SPECIFIC HEAT AND HEAT CAPACITY

The specific heat of any substance is defined as the quantity of heat required to raise the temperature of unit weight of the substance 1 degree of temperature. In terms of calories and degrees centigrade, the specific heat is the number of calories of heat required to raise the temperature of 1 g of a substance 1 degree centigrade.

Chemical calculations are most frequently made on a molar basis, and for that reason it is very convenient to deal with the *heat capacity* per mole. The heat capacity per mole is the amount of heat required to raise the temperature of 1 mole of a substance 1 degree centigrade. It is equal, of necessity, to the specific heat per gram multiplied by the molecular weight of the substance.

Two types of specific heats are recognized, depending on whether the substance is heated at constant volume or at constant pressure. When a substance is heated at constant volume, all of the energy supplied goes to increase the internal energy of the substance, and we speak then of the *specific heat* or *heat capacity at constant volume*, C_v. On the other hand, when a substance is heated at constant pressure, energy must be supplied not only to increase its internal energy, but also to make possible expansion of the substance against the confining atmospheric pressure. *The specific heat* or *heat capacity at constant pressure*, C_p, must therefore be larger than that at constant volume by the amount of work which must be performed in the expansion accompanying 1 degree rise in temperature. In liquids and solids, where volume changes on heating are small, this difference between C_p and C_v is usually very slight. With gases, however, where the volume changes with temperature are always large, the difference $C_p - C_v$ is always significant and cannot be disregarded.

SPECIFIC HEATS OF GASES AND KINETIC THEORY

Some important deductions concerning the specific heats of gases can be made from the kinetic theory of gas behavior. According to equation (36b) the kinetic energy of translation of an ideal gas per mole is

$$E_k = \frac{3}{2} RT$$

If this is the only type of energy the gas possesses (monatomic gas), the energy difference of the gas $(E_{k_2} - E_{k_1})$ between two temperatures T_2 and T_1 is

$$\Delta E = E_{k_2} - E_{k_1} = \frac{3}{2} R(T_2 - T_1) \text{ per mole}$$

When the temperature difference $T_2 - T_1 = 1$, ΔE becomes the energy required to raise the translational energy of 1 mole of gas 1 degree without involving any external work, or, in other words, the heat capacity per mole at constant volume C_v. Hence we may write

$$C_v = \frac{3}{2} R = \frac{3}{2} \times 1.987$$
$$= 2.98 \text{ cal degree}^{-1} \text{ mole}^{-1} \tag{60}$$

The kinetic theory predicts, therefore, that C_v for any ideal gas *containing only translational energy* should be approximately 3 cal per mole, and, further, that this heat capacity should be constant and independent of temperature.

A similar prediction can be arrived at with respect to the heat capacity at constant pressure, C_p. In view of the preceding considerations it follows that

$$C_p = C_v + w \quad \text{degree}^{-1} \text{ mole}^{-1} \tag{61}$$

where w is the work which must be performed against a confining pressure P when 1 mole of an ideal gas is expanded from a volume V_1 at T_1 to a volume V_2 at $T_2 = T_1 + 1$. The value of w can be obtained readily from the relation

$$w = \int_{V_1}^{V_2} P dV \tag{62}$$

which will be discussed in greater detail in the next chapter. If we differentiate now $PV = RT$ per mole at constant pressure, we have

$$PdV = RdT$$

and on substitution of RdT for PdV in equation (62), we see that

$$w = \int_{V_1}^{V_2} PdV = \int_{T_1}^{T_2} RdT$$
$$= R(T_2 - T_1) \quad \text{mole}^{-1}$$

For $T_2 - T_1 = 1$ this reduces to $w = R$ per mole, and hence for an ideal gas

$$C_p = C_v + R \quad \text{cal degree}^{-1} \text{mole}^{-1} \tag{63}$$

This important conclusion that $C_p - C_v = R$ is valid for all ideal gases, and permits the simple conversion of C_p to C_v or vice versa. Inserting the values of C_v from equation (60) and of R, we see that for any ideal gas *involving only translational energy* C_p should be

$$C_p = \frac{5}{2} R$$
$$= 4.97 \text{ cal degree}^{-1} \text{mole}^{-1} \tag{64}$$

Consequently, like C_v, C_p should be constant and independent of temperature for all gases. Again, the ratio C_p/C_v, commonly designated by γ, should also be a constant equal to

$$\gamma = \frac{C_p}{C_v} = \frac{5/2\ R}{3/2\ R}$$
$$= 1.67 \tag{65}$$

In Table 7 are listed values of C_p, C_v, $C_p - C_v$, and γ for various gases at 15° C. It will be observed, first of all, that the requirement $C_p - C_v = R = 1.99$ cal per mole is met fairly well by practically all the gases in the table. Second, the predictions of the kinetic theory that $C_p = 4.97$ and $C_v = 2.98$ cal per mole are borne out by the specific heats of a group of gases which includes besides argon and helium also krypton, xenon, and a number of metallic vapors. However, for all the other gases in the table the prediction is not valid. Inspection of the table reveals that the various gases can be divided into classes based upon their values of γ. The first group, comprising gases that obey the kinetic theory, has the expected $\gamma = 1.67$. The others, in turn, may be grouped as those with γ equal approximately to 1.4, 1.3, and lower. In no case does γ fall below unity, although this value may be approached. Further, the decrease in the value of γ is always associated with an increase in the complexity of the molecules involved. Thus argon and helium with $\gamma = 1.67$ are monatomic, i.e., the molecules are composed only of a single atom of the

TABLE 7

HEAT CAPACITIES OF GASES AT 15° C*

(Cal mole^{-1} degree^{-1})

Gas	Formula	C_p	C_v	$C_p - C_v$	γ
Argon	A	5.00	3.01	1.99	1.66
Helium	He	4.99	3.00	1.99	1.66
Carbon monoxide	CO	6.93	4.93	2.00	1.40
Chlorine	Cl_2	8.14	6.00	2.14	1.36
Hydrogen	H_2	6.82	4.83	1.99	1.41
Hydrogen chloride	HCl	7.07	5.01	2.06	1.41
Nitrogen	N_2	6.93	4.94	1.99	1.40
Oxygen	O_2	6.95	4.96	1.99	1.40
Carbon dioxide	CO_2	8.75	6.71	2.04	1.30
Hydrogen sulfide	H_2S	8.62	6.53	2.09	1.32
Nitrous oxide	N_2O	8.81	6.76	2.05	1.30
Sulfur dioxide	SO_2	9.70	7.52	2.18	1.29
Acetylene	C_2H_2	9.96	7.91	2.05	1.26
Ethylene	C_2H_4	10.05	7.99	2.06	1.25
Ethane	C_2H_6	11.59	9.51	2.08	1.22
Benzene	C_6H_6	25.4	23.1	2.3	1.10
n-Hexane	C_6H_{14}	31.4	29.1	2.3	1.08

* *International Critical Tables*, McGraw-Hill Book Company, Inc., New York, 1926, Vol. V.

element. Again, the substances with γ equal to about 1.4, such as oxygen, nitrogen, and chlorine, are diatomic, those with γ equal to about 1.3 triatomic, while all others with γ still lower are more complex. Finally, all substances exhibiting γ values lower than 1.67 also have values of C_p and C_v considerably greater than the predicted $C_p = \frac{5}{2} R$ and $C_v = \frac{3}{2} R$.

THE HEAT CAPACITY OF POLYATOMIC GASES

These high heat capacities suggest that the fundamental assumption made, that the only energy involved in a gas is kinetic energy of translation, is not always correct. A monatomic molecule can execute only translational motion along the coordinate axes, and for such a gas the deductions of the kinetic theory should be valid, as is actually the case. A more complex molecule, however, may be subject not only to translational motion as a unit, but to rotation and vibration as well. If we think simply of a diatomic molecule as a "dumbbell" held together along its line of centers by an elastic spring, then the two atoms may execute vibrations with respect to each other along their line of centers. Further, the molecule as a whole may undergo rotation about axes perpendicular to the line joining the centers of mass of these molecules. These extra motions involve additional terms for the energy of the gas; and if these motions are subject to temperature variation, as they are, additional terms will appear in the heat capacity equation for the gas.

VISCOSITY OF GASES

Gases and liquids possess a property known as the *viscosity*, which may be defined as the resistance that one part of a fluid offers to the flow of another part of the fluid. Viscosity is produced by the shearing effect of moving one layer of the fluid past another and is quite distinct from inter-molecular attraction. It may be thought of as caused by the internal friction of the molecules themselves and is present in ideal gases as well as in real gases and liquids.

If we visualize a fluid as being stratified in layers, then the force f required to move a layer of fluid of area A with a velocity v^1 past another layer a distance ∂ cm away has been shown to be

$$f = \frac{\eta A v^1}{\partial} \tag{66}$$

Here η is a proportionality constant known as the *viscosity coefficient* of the fluid. The viscosity coefficient may be thought of as the force per unit area required to move a layer of fluid with a velocity of 1 cm per second past another parallel layer 1 cm away. Although the force f may vary with experimental conditions, the viscosity coefficient η is a physical quantity characteristic of each fluid. For gases η is small in magnitude, but in liquids η is fairly large and is of considerable importance in characterizing liquids and their behavior.

It has already been pointed out that according to the kinetic theory of gases the viscosity coefficient of a gas is related to the density d, the mean free path l, and the average velocity v by the relation

$$\eta = \frac{1}{3} v l d \tag{42}$$

Since the mean free path varies inversely as the density of the gas, it may be concluded that the viscosity of an ideal gas should be independent of density, and hence also the pressure. This deduction has been confirmed at relatively low pressures.

Equation (42) may be employed to calculate the mean free path directly from the viscosity coefficients. To do this we need only substitute the value of v from equation (37), in which case l becomes

$$l = \frac{3\,\eta}{vd} = \frac{3\,\eta}{0.921\,d\,\sqrt{3\,RT/M}}$$
$$= \frac{1.88\,\eta}{d\,\sqrt{RT/M}} \tag{67}$$

Once *l* is thus found it may be inserted into equation (41), and the molecular diameter of the gas molecule σ may be evaluated.

In the cgs (centimeter-gram-second) system of units, the viscosity coefficient of a fluid is expressed in *poises*, a poise being the viscosity coefficient requiring a force of 1 dyne when *A*, *v*, and ∂ are all unity in equation (66). Since this unit is rather large, the viscosities of gases are usually given in *micropoises*, or 10^{-6} poise.

The viscosity of gases generally *increases* with increase in temperature. Thus, $\eta = 5.7$ micropoises for hydrogen at $-258°$ C, while at $300°$ C it is $\eta = 139.2$. Again, whereas the kinetic theory predicts that the viscosity of ideal gases should be pressure independent, actually gases may exhibit considerable variation in viscosity with pressure. For instance, at $35°$ C and atmospheric pressure $\eta = 156$ micropoises for carbon dioxide, but at 80 atm and the same temperature $\eta = 361$ micropoises.

REFERENCES FOR FURTHER READING

1. S. Glasstone, *Textbook of Physical Chemistry*, D. Van Nostrand Company, Inc., New York, 1946, Chap. IV.
2. E. Kennard, *Kinetic Theory of Gases*, McGraw-Hill Book Company, Inc., New York, 1938.
3. L. Loeb, *Kinetic Theory of Gases*, McGraw-Hill Book Company, Inc., New York, 1936.
4. D. M. Newitt, *High Pressure Plant and the Properties of Fluids at High Pressures*, Oxford University Press, London, 1940.
5. S. F. Pickering, "Relations between Temperatures, Pressures, and Densities of Gases," *Circular No. 279*, U.S. Bureau of Standards, Washington, D. C., 1925.
6. H. S. Taylor and S. Glasstone, *A Treatise on Physical Chemistry*, D. Van Nostrand Company, Inc., New York, 1951, Vol. II, Chaps. I and II.

PROBLEMS

1. At $0°$ C and under a pressure of 1 m Hg, a given weight of N_2 occupies a volume of 1 liter. At $-100°$ C the same weight of gas under the same pressure occupies a volume of 0.6313 liter. Calculate the absolute zero in degrees centigrade, and give reasons for the observed difference from the accepted value.

2. A gas occupies a volume of 2 liters under a pressure of 720 mm Hg at $25°$ C. What volume will the gas occupy under standard conditions of temperature and pressure?   *Ans.* 1.736 liters.

3. Calculate the density in grams per liter of ammonia at $100°$ C under a pressure of 800 mm Hg.   *Ans.* 0.585 g/liter.

4. Using the ideal gas law, find what volume 4 g of CH_4 would occupy at $27°$ C at a pressure of 2.5 atm.

5. Calculate the pressure exerted by 2 g of O_2 confined in a 2-liter container at $200°$ C.

6. (a) Find the weight of helium gas necessary to fill a balloon whose capacity is 1,000,000 cu ft at 1 atm pressure and 27° C. (b) What will be the lifting power of the balloon in pounds per cubic foot under these conditions?

Ans. (a) 10,143 lb; (b) 0.0631 lb/cu ft.

7. The composition of a mixture of gases in percentage by volume is 30% N_2, 50% CO, 15% H_2, and 5% O_2. Calculate the percentage by weight of each gas in the mixture.

8. Assuming that dry air contains 79% N_2 and 21% O_2 by volume, calculate the density of moist air at 25° C and 1 atm pressure when the relative humidity is 60%. The vapor pressure of water at 25° C is 23.76 mm. *Ans.* 1.171 g/liter.

9. Find the total pressure exerted by 2 g of ethane and 3 g of CO_2 contained in a 5-liter vessel at 50° C.

10. At 27° C, 500 cc of H_2, measured under a pressure 400 mm Hg, and 1000 cc of N_2, measured under a pressure of 600 mm Hg, are introduced into an evacuated 2-liter flask. Calculate the resulting pressure.

11. Compare the times of diffusion through a given orifice, and under the same conditions of temperature and pressure, of the gases H_2, NH_3, and CO_2 relative to that of N_2.

12. The time required for a given volume of N_2 to diffuse through an orifice is 35 sec. Calculate the molecular weight of a gas which requires 50 sec to diffuse through the same orifice under identical conditions. *Ans.* 57.15 g/mole.

13. What is the total kinetic energy of translation in ergs of 1 mole of a perfect gas at 27° C? In calories?

14. Calculate the root-mean-square velocity in centimeters per second of N_2 molecules at 27° C. Repeat the calculation at 127° C.

15. By means of a mercury vapor pump a vacuum of 10^{-7} mm Hg is obtained within a certain apparatus. Calculate the number of molecules which still remain in 1 cc of the apparatus at 27° C. *Ans.* 3.24×10^9.

16. Calculate the root-mean-square, average, and most probable velocities in centimeters per second of H_2 molecules at 0° C.

17. The molecular diameter of CO is 3.19×10^{-8} cm. At 300° K and a pressure of 100 mm Hg what will be (a) the number of molecules colliding per cubic centimeter per second; (b) the number of bimolecular collisions; and (c) the mean free path of the gas?

18. Repeat the calculations called for in problem 17 for the same temperature but a pressure of 200 mm Hg. How pronounced is the effect of pressure on the quantities sought?

19. Repeat the calculations called for in problem 17 for a pressure of 100 mm Hg and a temperature of 600° K. How pronounced is the effect of temperature on the quantities calculated?

20. (a) Using the van der Waals equation, calculate the pressure developed by 100 g of CO_2 contained in a volume of 5 liters at 40° C. (b) Compare this value with that calculated using the simple gas law.

Ans. (a) 11.17 atm; (b) 11.67 atm.

21. By use of the van der Waals equation, find the temperature at which 3 moles of SO_2 will occupy a volume of 10 liters at a pressure of 15 atm.

22. Using the Beattie-Bridgeman equation explicit in volume, calculate the density in grams per cubic centimeter of N_2 at 0° C and 100 atm pressure.

23. At 0° C and under a pressure of 100 atm the compressibility factor of O_2 is 0.927. Calculate the weight of O_2 necessary to fill a gas cylinder of 2 cu ft capacity under the given conditions.

24. Employing the Kamerlingh Onnes equation of state, find the compressibility factors of CO at $-50°$ C and pressures of (a) 10, (b) 100, and (c) 1000 atm pressure. *Ans.* (a) $z = 0.981$.

25. Utilizing the virial coefficients listed in Table 4, determine analytically the pressure at which the PV vs. P plot for N_2 at $-50°$ C exhibits a minimum.

26. The following data were taken in measuring the molecular weight of a certain gas by the Regnault method:

    Wt. of evacuated bulb = 42.5050 g
    Wt. of bulb + gas   = 43.3412 g
    Wt. of bulb + H₂O   = 365.31 g
    Temperature   = 25° C
    Pressure (corrected) = 745 mm

    Find the molecular weight of the gas.

27. The elementary analysis of a compound yielded the following results: C, 39.98%; H, 6.72%; and O, 53.30%. In a Victor Meyer determination 0.1510 g of the vaporized compound displaced 33.8 cc of air measured at 25° C over H_2O and at a barometric pressure of 745 mm. Calculate (a) the empirical formula, (b) the approximate molecular weight, and (c) the molecular formula of the compound. *Ans.* CH_2O; 115.2 g/mole.

28. A sample of vapor weighing 0.180 g occupies a volume of 53.1 cc at 27° C and 760 mm pressure (corrected). The critical pressure of the vapor is 47.7 atm, while the critical temperature is 288.5° C. By use of the Berthelot equation calculate the molecular weight of the vapor, and compare the result with that calculated by the ideal gas law.

29. The densities of CH_4 at 0° C were measured at several pressures with the following results:

Pressure (atm)	Density (g/liter)
¼	0.17893
½	0.35808
¾	0.53745
1	0.71707

    Find the exact molecular weight of CH_4.

30. How much heat will be required to raise the temperature of 10 g of N_2 from 0° C to 100° C at a pressure of 1 atm? At constant volume?

31. The viscosity coefficient of gaseous Cl_2 at 1 atm pressure and 20° C is 147.0 micropoises. Find the molecular diameter of the chlorine molecule.

32. Consider two parallel layers of NH_3 gas, one of large area and stationary, while the other 10 cm² in area and moving at a fixed distance of 1×10^{-6} cm above the first. What force in dynes will be required to keep the upper layer moving with a velocity of 5 cm per second when the pressure of the gas is 10 mm Hg and the temperature is 300° K? The molecular diameter of the NH_3 molecule is 3.0×10^{-8} cm.

2

The First Law of Thermodynamics
and Its Application to Gases

One of the most fundamental manifestations in nature is the energy that accompanies all changes and transformations. Such diversified phenomena as the drop of a stone, the motion of a billiard ball, the impinging of light, the burning of coal, and the growth and reactions of the complex mechanism known as a living being all involve absorption, emission, and redistribution of energy. The most common form in which this energy appears, and the form to which all others tend, is heat. Besides this, there is mechanical energy involved in the motion of all machinery; electrical energy, exhibited by a current in heating a conductor and in doing chemical and mechanical work; radiant energy, inherent in visible light and in radiation in general; and finally, chemical energy, the energy stored in all substances, and which appears when the substances undergo transformation. As diversified and distinct as these various forms may at first glance appear, they are, nevertheless, related to one another, and under certain conditions may be transformed from one into the other. A study of this interrelation of the various forms of energy in a system constitutes the subject of *thermodynamics*.

Since thermodynamic laws deal with energy, they are applicable in general to all phenomena in nature. They hold quite rigidly because they are based on the behavior of macroscopic systems, i.e., systems comparatively large and involving many molecules, rather than on the behavior of microscopic systems in which comparatively few molecules are involved. Moreover, thermodynamics does not consider the time element in transformations; it is interested merely in the initial and final states of a system without any curiosity as to speed with which the change has been accomplished.

Within any system the energy may be kinetic or potential in nature, or both. Kinetic energy is the energy a system possesses by virtue of its motion, be it molecular or motion of the body as a whole. Potential energy, on the other hand, is the energy a system possesses by virtue of its position, i.e., energy due to the structure of the body or due to its configuration with respect to other bodies. The total energy content of any system is the sum of the potential and kinetic energies.

Although the absolute value of the total energy contained in a system can be calculated from the famous Einstein relation $E = mc^2$, where E is the energy, m the mass, and c the velocity of light, this fact is of little help in ordinary thermodynamic considerations. The reason is that the energies involved are so large that any changes in them as a result of the usual chemical or physical processes would be negligible compared to the totals. Further, the changes in the masses resulting from the energy transfers would be so small as to be beyond detection by our available means of weighing. Consequently thermodynamics prefers to deal with the energy differences which accompany changes in systems since these can be measured. These differences are expressed in the ordinary work units used in connection with the various forms of energy. Thus the cgs unit of mechanical energy is the *erg;* of electrical energy, the *joule;* of thermal energy, the calorie. The relation of the unit of mechanical work to the thermal unit is known as the *mechanical equivalent of heat.* The first determinations of this equivalent by Joule laid one of the foundation stones upon which the first law of thermodynamics was reared.

THE FIRST LAW OF THERMODYNAMICS

The first law of thermodynamics is the law of conservation of energy, namely, that *energy can be neither created nor destroyed.* Worded differently, the law says that for any quantity of a form of energy that disappears, another or other forms of energy will appear in total quantity exactly equal to the amount that disappeared. To be more specific, consider the fate of a quantity of heat q added to a system. This heat will go to raise the internal energy of the system and also to do any outside work the system may perform as a result of the absorption of heat. If we let ΔE be the increase in the internal energy of the system and w be the work done by the system on its surroundings, then by the first law

$$\Delta E + w = q$$

and
$$\Delta E = q - w \tag{1}$$

Equation (1) is the first law of thermodynamics expressed mathematically. The increase in the internal energy of the system is defined as the difference between the internal energy of the system in its final state, E_2, and the internal energy of the system in its initial state, E_1. Obviously, therefore, ΔE is given by

$$\Delta E = E_2 - E_1 \qquad (2)$$

and *depends only on the initial and final states of the system*. The values of q, the heat is absorbed, and w, the work done by the system, depend, however, on the manner in which the process is conducted. The quantities q, w, and ΔE are measurable, but the absolute magnitudes of E_1 and E_2 are not.

The symbol w represents the total work performed by a system against its surroundings. In a galvanic cell, for instance, w may represent the electrical energy supplied plus, if there is a change in volume, any energy utilized to effect the expansion or contraction against a pressure P. The magnitude of the pressure-volume or mechanical work term is easily derivable as follows.

Consider a cylinder, Fig. 1, of cross-sectional area A, fitted with a frictionless piston. Let the pressure on the piston be P. Then, since pressure is force per unit of area, the total force acting on the piston is $f = P \times A$. If the piston is moved now through a distance dl, the work dw done is

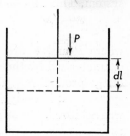

Fig. 1. Pressure-Volume Work.

$$dw = fdl = P \times A \times dl$$

But $A \times dl$ is the element of volume dV, swept out by the piston in its motion. Hence,

$$dw = fdl = PdV \qquad (3)$$

and, on integration between the limits V_1 and V_2,

$$w = \int_{V_1}^{V_2} PdV \qquad (4)$$

Equation (4) is perfectly general and applies to the calculation of the P-V work done in any expansion or contraction.

If the only work done by a system is of this type, the expression for the first law becomes

$$\Delta E = q - w$$

$$= q - \int_{V_1}^{V_2} PdV \qquad (5)$$

From equation (5) we see that when any process is conducted at constant volume, dV is zero, and the equation reduces to

$$\Delta E = q \qquad (6)$$

i.e., when a system does only pressure-volume work, all the heat absorbed at constant volume goes to increase the internal energy of the system.

Again, if P is constant, then $\int_{V_1}^{V_2} PdV = P(V_2 - V_1)$, and equation (5) becomes

$$\Delta E = q - P(V_2 - V_1)$$

or $$q = \Delta E + P(V_2 - V_1) \qquad (7)$$

THE ENTHALPY (HEAT CONTENT) OF A SYSTEM

Thermal changes at constant pressure are most conveniently expressed in terms of another function, H, called the *enthalpy or heat content* of a system. This function is defined by the relation

$$H = E + PV \qquad (8)$$

where P and V are the pressure and volume *of the system*. Since E is characterized by the state of the system only, and since the same is true of the product PV, H, like E, is also a function only of the state of the system and is completely independent of the manner in which the state was achieved. Consequently the change in enthalpy, ΔH, may be written as

$$\Delta H = H_2 - H_1 \qquad (9)$$

where H_2 is the enthalpy of the system in the final state and H_1 the enthalpy in the initial state. Substituting for H_2 and H_1 their equivalents from equation (8), with the appropriate subscripts, we obtain for ΔH

$$\begin{aligned}
\Delta H &= H_2 - H_1 \\
&= (E_2 + P_2V_2) - (E_1 + P_1V_1) \\
&= (E_2 - E_1) + (P_2V_2 - P_1V_1) \\
&= \Delta E + (P_2V_2 - P_1V_1)
\end{aligned} \qquad (10)$$

When the pressure P is constant throughout the process, then

$$\begin{aligned}
\Delta H &= \Delta E + P(V_2 - V_1) \\
&= \Delta E + P\Delta V
\end{aligned} \qquad (11)$$

i.e., the change in enthalpy at constant pressure is equal to the increase in internal energy plus any pressure-volume work done. Hence at constant pressure ΔH represents the heat absorbed by a system in going from an initial to a final state, *provided the only work done is P-V work*. When the initial and final pressures are not the same, ΔH is calculated not by equation (11) but by equation (10).

In this book we shall employ the convention of Lewis and Randall,[1]

---

[1] *Thermodynamics and the Free Energy of Chemical Substances*, McGraw-Hill Book Company, Inc., New York, 1923.

according to which any gain in a quantity on the part of a system is considered to be positive and any loss negative. On this basis values of q, ΔE, and ΔH which are greater than zero correspond to absorption of heat by the system and to increases in E and H of the system. Conversely, when these quantities are less than zero, they denote loss of heat by the system and decreases in E and H of the system. Finally, when $w > 0$ work is done *by* the system, while when $w < 0$ work is done *on* the system.

HEAT CAPACITY

Consider a very small quantity of heat dq added to a system, and suppose that as a result of the heat absorption the temperature rise produced is dT. Then the amount of heat required to raise the temperature of the system 1 degree is

$$C = \frac{dq}{dT}$$

and C is thus the heat capacity of the system. Now, from equation (5) we get $dq = dE + PdV$, and hence

$$C = \frac{dE + PdV}{dT} \tag{12}$$

When the volume is held constant $dV = 0$, and equation (12) reduces to

$$C_v = \left(\frac{\partial E}{\partial T}\right)_V \tag{13}$$

This equation is the thermodynamic relation defining C_v and tells us that C_v is the rate of change of the internal energy with temperature at constant volume.

However, when the heat absorption occurs at constant pressure equation (12) becomes

$$C_p = \left(\frac{\partial E}{\partial T}\right)_P + P\left(\frac{\partial V}{\partial T}\right)_P$$

But, if equation (8) be differentiated with respect to T at constant P we get

$$\left(\frac{\partial H}{\partial T}\right)_P = \left(\frac{\partial E}{\partial T}\right)_P + P\left(\frac{\partial V}{\partial T}\right)_P$$

Consequently,

$$C_p = \left(\frac{\partial H}{\partial T}\right)_P \tag{14}$$

which is the thermodynamic definition of C_p, i.e., C_p is the rate of change of the enthalpy with temperature at constant pressure.

THE DIFFERENCE BETWEEN C_p AND C_v

The difference between the two heat capacities is readily deducible by a thermodynamic argument. The methods employed in this derivation are quite typical of thermodynamics and illustrate a mode of attack frequently employed. From equations (13) and (14) we have

$$C_p - C_v = \left(\frac{\partial H}{\partial T}\right)_P - \left(\frac{\partial E}{\partial T}\right)_V \tag{15}$$

But, $H = E + PV$. Differentiating this quantity with respect to temperature at constant pressure we obtain

$$\left(\frac{\partial H}{\partial T}\right)_P = \left(\frac{\partial E}{\partial T}\right)_P + P\left(\frac{\partial V}{\partial T}\right)_P \tag{16}$$

Substituting the value for $(\partial H/\partial T)_P$ from equation (16) into equation (15), the latter becomes

$$C_p - C_v = \left(\frac{\partial E}{\partial T}\right)_P + P\left(\frac{\partial V}{\partial T}\right)_P - \left(\frac{\partial E}{\partial T}\right)_V \tag{17}$$

The problem now is to relate the first and third terms on the right of equation (17). To do this we proceed as follows. The internal energy E will be, in general, a function of any two of the three variables P, V, T. If we take as our independent variables V and T, then

$$E = f(T, V)$$

and
$$dE = \left(\frac{\partial E}{\partial T}\right)_V dT + \left(\frac{\partial E}{\partial V}\right)_T dV \tag{18}$$

Dividing both sides of the equation by dT and imposing the condition of constant pressure, we get

$$\left(\frac{\partial E}{\partial T}\right)_P = \left(\frac{\partial E}{\partial T}\right)_V + \left(\frac{\partial E}{\partial V}\right)_T \left(\frac{\partial V}{\partial T}\right)_P \tag{19}$$

Equation (19) substituted in equation (17) yields finally

$$\begin{aligned}
C_p - C_v &= \left(\frac{\partial E}{\partial T}\right)_V + \left(\frac{\partial E}{\partial V}\right)_T \left(\frac{\partial V}{\partial T}\right)_P + P\left(\frac{\partial V}{\partial T}\right)_P - \left(\frac{\partial E}{\partial T}\right)_V \\
&= \left(\frac{\partial E}{\partial V}\right)_T \left(\frac{\partial V}{\partial T}\right)_P + P\left(\frac{\partial V}{\partial T}\right)_P \tag{20}
\end{aligned}$$

Equation (20) is perfectly general. However, for an ideal gas considerable simplification is possible. First, it will be shown below that for an ideal gas $(\partial E/\partial V)_T = 0$, and hence the first term on the right is zero. Second, since for a mole of ideal gas $PV = RT$, differentiation of the ideal gas law with respect to T at constant P yields

$$P\left(\frac{\partial V}{\partial T}\right)_P = R$$

and consequently equation (20) becomes

$$C_p - C_v = P\left(\frac{\partial V}{\partial T}\right)_P = R \tag{21}$$

This is the result obtained previously through the kinetic theory of gases.

THE WORK OF EXPANSION OF GASES

As the work performed in the expansion and contraction of gases is of extreme importance in thermodynamics and physical chemistry, it deserves careful attention. There are many conditions under which pressure-volume changes may take place; but for all of these the work performed is given in general by the expression

$$w = \int_{V_1}^{V_2} P\,dV \tag{4}$$

However, the manner in which the integration is performed is dependent on the manner in which the volume change is accomplished. For a clear understanding of what follows the student should realize that *the P in the work expression is not necessarily the pressure of the working gas but the pressure against which the gas is working*, i.e., P is the pressure opposing the gas expansion. Once this is realized, no difficulty will be encountered.

According to equation (4), the work done by a gas will be zero when either dV or P is zero. When $dV = 0$, the volume of the system is constant, no expansion takes place, and no work is done. Again, when $P = 0$ the gas in expanding encounters no opposition and hence does no work. The latter process, involving expanding into a vacuum, is called *free expansion*. In both these cases, since $w = 0$, the first law takes the simple form $\Delta E = q$; i.e., any absorbed heat goes merely to increase the internal energy of the gas, or, in other words, to increase its temperature.

When a gas expands against a *constant pressure* from a volume V_1 to a volume V_2, equation (4) integrates simply to

$$w = \int_{V_1}^{V_2} P\,dV$$
$$= P(V_2 - V_1) \tag{22}$$

For $V_2 > V_1$ the process is an expansion and work is done by the gas;

when, however, $V_1 > V_2$, the process is a contraction (negative expansion), $V_2 - V_1$ and also w are negative, and work must be done on the gas to perform the volume change.

If the pressure against which a gas expands is not constant throughout the process, P must be substituted as a function of V in equation (4) before the expression may be integrated. If the function $P = f(V)$ is not known, but experimental data are available on the variation of the pressure with volume during the process, the integration may be performed graphically by plotting P against V and determining the area under the curve between the volumes V_1 and V_2.

ISOTHERMAL AND ADIABATIC EXPANSION OF IDEAL GASES

The energy relations and the state of any gaseous system during the performance of work depend not only on the manner in which work is performed, but also on certain experimental conditions imposed upon the system as a whole. Two such constraints of especial importance are the performance of work under (a) isothermal and (b) adiabatic conditions.

Isothermal Expansion of an Ideal Gas. Any expansion conducted in a system in a manner such that the temperature remains constant during the entire operation is referred to as an *isothermal* expansion. In general a quantity of heat q added to a gaseous system will contribute both to the performance of work and to an increase in the internal energy of the gas. Since the internal energy of an *ideal* gas is a function of temperature only, an increase therein must result in an increase of the temperature of the gas. However, if the temperature of the gas is held constant, the internal energy cannot change, and any external work performed by the gas can be accomplished only at the expense of absorbed heat. This conclusion follows directly from the first law of thermodynamics, for, when E is constant, $\Delta E = 0$, and hence equation (1) becomes

$$q = w \tag{23}$$

We see, therefore, that the criterion for an isothermal process in an ideal gas is that $\Delta E = 0$, and consequently we may write for such a process

$$q = w = \int_{V_1}^{V_2} P\,dV \tag{24}$$

The magnitude of q obviously will depend on the manner in which the work is performed. If the pressure P against which the ideal gas expands is constant, the work performed, and q, are both given by equation (22), namely,

$$q = w = P(V_2 - V_1) \tag{25}$$

When the pressure is variable, however, the work done, and q, may vary over a wide range up to a maximum value. The conditions for obtaining this maximum work as well as the calculation of it for the case of an ideal gas will be given below.

Adiabatic Expansion of an Ideal Gas. Any change in a system taking place under such conditions that heat is neither absorbed nor evolved by the system is said to take place *adiabatically*. The criterion for such a process is that $q = 0$. Making this substitution in equation (1) we get

$$w = -\Delta E \tag{26}$$

From equation (26) it follows that any work in an adiabatic process is done at the expense of the internal energy. As work is performed, the internal energy of the system decreases, and consequently the temperature drops.

An equation that every ideal gas must obey at every stage of an adiabatic expansion can be derived readily from equation (26). Consider n moles of an ideal gas at a pressure P and a volume V. For an infinitesimal increase in volume dV at the pressure P, the work done by the gas is PdV. Since this work is accomplished at the expense of the internal energy of the gas, the internal energy must *decrease* by an amount dE. According to equation (26), therefore,

$$PdV = -dE$$

However, from equation (13) $dE = nC_v dT$. Consequently

$$PdV = -dE = -nC_v dT \tag{27}$$

If the expansion is so controlled that at every stage the external pressure differs from the internal only by an infinitesimal amount, then for P may be substituted $P = nRT/V$ from the equation of an ideal gas. Equation (27) becomes thus

$$-nC_v dT = \frac{nRTdV}{V}$$

$$\frac{C_v}{R}\left(\frac{dT}{T}\right) = -\frac{dV}{V}$$

Considering C_v to be constant and integrating between the limits V_1 at T_1 and V_2 at T_2, we have

$$\frac{C_v}{R}\int_{T_1}^{T_2}\frac{dT}{T} = -\int_{V_1}^{V_2}\frac{dV}{V}$$

$$\frac{C_v}{R}\ln\left(\frac{T_2}{T_1}\right) = -\ln\left(\frac{V_2}{V_1}\right)$$

On rearranging and taking antilogarithms we obtain

$$V_1 T_1^{C_v/R} = V_2 T_2^{C_v/R} = C_1 \tag{28}$$

where C_1 is a constant.

Other forms of equation (28) may be easily derived by eliminating dT or dV instead of P from equation (27). A very common form is one involving P and V, namely,

$$P_1 V_1^{\gamma} = P_2 V_2^{\gamma} = C_2 \tag{29}$$

where C_2 is a constant and $\gamma = C_p/C_v$, the ratio of specific heats. It should be realized that equations (28) and (29) do not displace the ideal gas law $PV = nRT$ but merely *supplement* it. The ideal gas law is applicable under *all* conditions of an ideal gas, while equations (28) and (29) apply only under adiabatic conditions.

The constants C_1 and C_2 depend on the amounts of gas present and differ from each other numerically. The constants may be eliminated in calculations by taking the ratio of initial to final conditions. Thus from equation (29)

$$P_1 V_1^{\gamma} = P_2 V_2^{\gamma}$$

and
$$\frac{P_1}{P_2} = \left(\frac{V_2}{V_1}\right)^{\gamma} \tag{30}$$

Equation (30), like Boyle's law, permits a recalculation of volumes from pressures alone or vice versa. During the adiabatic expansion, however, the temperature of the gas does not remain constant. The initial and final temperatures may be obtained in any instance by substituting the initial and final values of P and V, along with n, in the expression $PV = nRT$.

The use of these equations can be illustrated by an example. Two moles of hydrogen at standard conditions are compressed adiabatically to a volume of 10 liters. For hydrogen, $\gamma = 1.41$. From these data it is desired to find the final pressure and temperature of the gas. The known and unknown quantities are

Initial	Final
$P_1 = 1$ atm	$P_2 = ?$
$V_1 = 2(22.4) = 44.8$ liters	$V_2 = 10$ liters
$T_1 = 273.2°$ K	$T_2 = ?$
$n = 2$	$n = 2$
$\gamma = 1.41$	$\gamma = 1.41$

Applying equation (30), we have for P_2,

$$P_2 = P_1 \left(\frac{V_1}{V_2}\right)^{\gamma} = 1 \left(\frac{44.8}{10}\right)^{1.41}$$
$$= 8.3 \text{ atm}$$

Had the expansion taken place *isothermally*, the new pressure would have been 4.5 atm. Knowing now P_2 and V_2, T_2 follows as

$$T_2 = \frac{P_2 V_2}{nR} = \frac{8.3 \times 10}{2 \times 0.0821}$$
$$= 505.5° \text{ K} \quad \text{or} \quad 232.3° \text{ C}$$

THE CONCEPT OF REVERSIBILITY

Unlike the internal energy and heat content, the work obtainable when a system undergoes change depends not only on the initial and final states but also on how the change takes place. Conditions can be so arranged that the work performed by the system can vary all the way from zero, in case of expansion into a vacuum, up to the maximum realizable work for a specified transformation when the process is conducted as is to be described now. These facts indicate the great theoretical as well as practical importance of knowing the manner in which the change is accomplished.

Consider a cylinder containing water at its boiling point in equilibrium with its vapor. The cylinder is fitted with a weightless, frictionless piston and is immersed in a reservoir kept at the same temperature as the water. If the piston is confined by a pressure of 1 atm, this temperature is 100°, and the pressure of the vapor is also 1 atm. Suppose now that the pressure on the piston is diminished by an infinitesimal amount. The piston immediately moves upward, increasing the volume. This change in volume results in a corresponding drop in the vapor pressure of the water. To bring this pressure back to the vapor pressure at the temperature in question, some water evaporates. As this operation is conducted strictly isothermally, the heat necessary for the vaporization of the water is abstracted from the reservoir.

The changes just described, which will proceed as long as the internal pressure of the gas is greater by an infinitesimal amount than the pressure on the piston, will finally result in the complete evaporation of all the water in the cylinder. To stop this evaporation it is necessary merely to increase the confining pressure infinitesimally. This makes the internal and external pressures equal, and neither evaporation of the water nor condensation of the vapor will take place as long as the temperature of the system remains constant.

Consider now, again, what happens when the pressure on the cylinder is increased by an infinitesimal amount. The piston immediately moves downward and compresses the vapor to a pressure above the equilibrium value for the given temperature. To reestablish equilibrium, some of the water condenses. The heat given off by this condensation is taken up by the reservoir, so the isothermal condition of the system is not disturbed.

The essential point about the process described is that *the driving force is at all times only infinitesimally greater than the opposing force* and that by an infinitesimal increase of the opposing force the whole process can be reversed and made to retrace all the stages it has previously occupied. Whenever a process meets these conditions it is said to be *reversible*. Strictly speaking, all naturally occurring processes are *irreversible*. Reversibility can be approached, however. In the potentiometric method for measuring the potentials of galvanic cells, the voltage of the cell is opposed by another voltage until practically no current flows. By making the opposing voltage only slightly smaller than the voltage of the cell, the cell can be made to discharge while, if the opposing voltage is increased slightly above that of the cell, the cell can be made to charge. In this manner, any current flowing through the circuit has to do work against a potential which is at all times only slightly less than its own. This arrangement is the closest approximation which can at present be made to a truly reversible process.

Although the idea of reversibility has been developed here for two specific cases, it can be extended to all processes, irrespective of their nature. *Any process*, no matter what it be, *in which the driving force is only infinitesimally greater than the opposing force, and which can be reversed by increasing the opposing force by an infinitesimal amount, constitutes a reversible process.* On the other hand, any change which does *not* meet these requirements is said to be *irreversible*.

REVERSIBILITY AND MAXIMUM WORK

The amount of work a system has to perform to bring about a certain change depends on the opposition the system experiences to the change. The greater that resistance is, the more work must be done by the system to overcome it. To be specific, let us consider the expansion of an ideal gas against a pressure P through an infinitesimal volume change dV. The work done is evidently PdV. When P is zero, i.e., when the system expands into a vacuum, the piston confining the gas experiences no restraining force, and if it is frictionless and weightless, no work is involved, and $PdV = 0$. However, as P is increased from zero, more and more work has to be done as the pressure approaches that of the gas itself. When the latter point is reached, the two forces become balanced and no further change in volume is possible. If we continue to increase the pressure, the pressure on the gas becomes greater than the pressure of the gas, the volume begins to decrease, and work is done *on* rather than *by* the system. From this description it is evident that the work which may be performed by a system is a maximum when the opposing pressure P differs only infinitesimally in magnitude from the internal pressure of the gas itself. But these are exactly the conditions defined for the reversibility of a process. Hence it may be concluded that *maximum work is obtainable from a system when any change taking place in it is entirely reversible.*

The expression for the maximum work performed, w_m, when an *ideal gas* expands *isothermally and reversibly* may be derived as follows. We have seen that the work resulting from a volume change V_1 to V_2 against a pressure P is given by equation (4), where the indicated integration requires a relation for P in terms of V. Since for a reversible process the external pressure is at all times only infinitesimally lower than the pressure of the gas itself, we may substitute for P in equation (4) the ideal gas pressure $P = nRT/V$. Equation (4) becomes then,

$$w_m = \int_{V_1}^{V_2} \frac{nRTdV}{V}$$
$$= nRT \int_{V_1}^{V_2} \frac{dV}{V}$$

as the process is also isothermal and T is thus constant. Integrating, we find that

$$w_m = nRT \ln \frac{V_2}{V_1} \qquad (31)$$

which is the expression sought for the *maximum work* obtainable from an isothermal reversible expansion of n moles of an ideal gas from volume V_1 to V_2 at temperature T. Again, since the temperature is constant, $V_2/V_1 = P_1/P_2$ by Boyle's law, and hence equation (31) may also be written in the alternate and equivalent form

$$w_m = nRT \ln \frac{P_1}{P_2} \qquad (32)$$

The application of equation (31), and the distinction between isothermal reversible work and isothermal work against a constant pressure, may best be understood from the following examples.

Example (a): Find the work done when 2 moles of hydrogen expand isothermally from 15 to 50 liters against a *constant pressure* of 1 atm at 25° C. By equation (22),

$$w = P(V_2 - V_1) = 1(50 - 15) = 35 \text{ liter-atm}$$
$$= 847.5 \text{ cal}$$

Example (b): Calculate the work performed when 2 moles of hydrogen expand *isothermally* and *reversibly* at 25° C from 15 to 50 liters. Using equation (31),

$$w_m = nRT \ln \frac{V_2}{V_1} = 2.3 \; nRT \log \frac{V_2}{V_1}$$

$$= (2.3 \times 2 \times 1.99 \times 298) \log \frac{50}{15}$$

$$= 1428 \text{ cal}$$

The heats absorbed during the expansions are equal to w in both cases and are therefore $q = 847.5$ cal in (a), and $q = 1428$ cal in (b). The internal energy change is zero in both instances, since there is no change in temperature.

THE MAXIMUM WORK FUNCTION *A*

We have seen that the amount of work obtained from a process depends on the manner in which the work has been performed. In performing the work reversibly, however, we establish under *isothermal conditions* a definite path of passing from the initial to the final state along which the maximum work done is definite and dependent only on the two states of the system in question. At *constant temperature*, then, the maximum work, being a function of the states of the system only, takes on the attributes of such functions as the internal energy E and the heat content H. We may think of a system, therefore, as possessing in each state a certain amount of *maximum work content A*, also called the *Helmholtz free energy*, such that when the system passes from one state to another, the change in A, ΔA, is given by

$$\Delta A = A_2 - A_1 \tag{33}$$

A_2 and A_1 are the maximum work contents of the system in the final and initial states respectively. A value of $\Delta A > 0$ corresponds to an increase in the work content of the system, while $\Delta A < 0$ indicates a loss of maximum work content by the system. When all the work in a particular process is performed *isothermally and reversibly*, then the work, w_m, is done at the expense of the maximum work content of the system, and therefore

$$w_m = -\Delta A \tag{34}$$

Equation (34) is valid only under the conditions specified, and it does not apply to nonisothermal processes even when they are reversible. In terms of equation (34) the first law of thermodynamics applied to an *isothermal and reversible* process may also be written in the form

$$\Delta E = q_r - w_m = q_r + \Delta A \tag{35}$$

where the subscript on q indicates that the process is reversible.

MAXIMUM WORK OF ADIABATIC EXPANSION OF AN IDEAL GAS

As an instance of maximum work obtainable under nonisothermal conditions may be given the work performed in the *adiabatic reversible* expansion of an ideal gas. The expression in question is arrived at as follows. Differentiation of the expression $PV^\gamma = $ constant yields

$$\gamma PV^{\gamma-1}dV + V^\gamma dP = 0$$
$$\gamma PdV + VdP = 0$$

or

$$VdP = -\gamma PdV$$

Again, complete differentiation of $PV = nRT$ gives

$$PdV + VdP = nRdT$$

which on substitution of the expression for VdP becomes

$$PdV - \gamma PdV = nRdT$$

and

$$PdV = \frac{nRdT}{(1 - \gamma)}$$

On inserting this identity for PdV into equation (4) and changing the limits to the temperatures corresponding to the volumes, we obtain

$$w_m = \int_{V_1}^{V_2} PdV = \int_{T_1}^{T_2} \frac{nRdT}{(1 - \gamma)}$$
$$= \frac{nR(T_2 - T_1)}{(1 - \gamma)} \tag{36}$$

In equation (36) T_1 is the initial temperature of n moles of gas, T_2 is the final temperature resulting from the *reversible* expansion, while γ is the ratio C_p/C_v for the gas. Whenever $T_2 > T_1$, w_m is negative and work is done on the gas. On the other hand, when work is done by the gas $T_2 < T_1$, and w_m is positive.

THE JOULE-THOMSON EFFECT

An ideal gas exhibits no intermolecular attraction, and for it the product PV is a constant at any given temperature at all pressures. Hence when such a gas expands under adiabatic conditions into a vacuum, no heat is absorbed or evolved, no external work or work to separate the molecules has to be performed, and so

$$q = 0, \quad w = 0, \quad \text{and} \quad \Delta E = 0$$

Thus the internal energy of the gas remains constant as well as PV, and consequently the temperature is the same before and after expansion. This is equivalent to saying that at constant temperature the internal energy of an ideal gas is independent of the volume the gas occupies, or, mathematically,

$$\left(\frac{\partial E}{\partial V}\right)_T = 0 \tag{37}$$

The adiabatic condition was imposed for our purpose merely to prevent any interchange of energy between the surroundings and the gas, and thus to avoid an increase or decrease in the internal energy by heat absorption or evolution.

The situation with *real* gases is different and was first investigated by Joule and Thomson (Lord Kelvin). Their experimental setup is illustrated schematically in Fig. 2. A tube, thoroughly insulated to

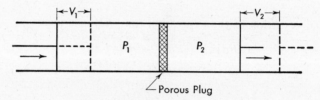

Fig. 2.   Joule-Thomson Experiment.

approximate adiabatic conditions, was fitted with a porous plug, as indicated, to allow gas to be kept on either side of it at the different pressures P_1 and P_2 ($P_1 > P_2$). By applying pressure on the piston on the left slowly enough so as not to change the pressure P_1, a volume of gas V_1 was forced slowly through the porous plug and allowed then to expand to the pressure P_2 and volume V_2 by moving the piston on the right outward. While the expansion was taking place, accurate temperature readings were taken on the gas in the two chambers to ascertain whether the expansion was accompanied by a temperature change.

The work done *on* the system at the left piston is $-P_1V_1$, the work done *by* the system at the right piston is P_2V_2, and hence the net work done *by* the system is

$$w = P_2V_2 - P_1V_1$$

Since the process was conducted adiabatically, $q = 0$, and, therefore,

$$\Delta E = E_2 - E_1 = -w = -(P_2V_2 - P_1V_1)$$
$$E_2 + P_2V_2 = E_1 + P_1V_1$$
$$H_2 = H_1$$
$$\Delta H = 0$$

The process was conducted, then, at *constant enthalpy*. Under these conditions Joule and Thomson observed near room temperatures that all gases, with the exception of hydrogen, experienced a cooling on expansion, while hydrogen actually became warmer. The extent of the temperature change was found to depend on the initial temperature and pressure of the gas. Later, when helium was discovered, it was shown that this gas as well undergoes a heating effect on expansion. The magnitude of the observed effects may be judged from Table 1, where μ, the *Joule-Thomson coefficient*, is defined as

$$\mu = \left(\frac{\partial T}{\partial P}\right)_H \tag{38}$$

It may be thought of as the number of degrees temperature change produced per atmosphere drop in pressure under conditions of constant enthalpy. For a cooling μ is positive, while for an observed heating μ is negative.

TABLE 1

JOULE-THOMSON COEFFICIENTS FOR SEVERAL GASES*

Gas	$t°$ C	μ at Pressures (atm)				
		0–6	2	10	15	40
Hydrogen	6.8	−0.030				
	90.1	−0.044				
Carbon dioxide	0.0	1.35				1.46
	20.0	1.14	1.21	1.31	1.37	1.20
	40.0	0.96				1.04
	100.0	0.62				
		$P = 0$	25	50	100	150
Air	−55	0.44	0.40	0.3	0.28	0.18
	0.6	0.27	0.25	0.24	0.19	0.16
	49	0.20	0.18	0.17	0.15	0.12
	150	0.09	0.09	0.07	0.06	0.05
	250	0.02	0.02	0.02	0.01	0.01

* Taylor and Glasstone, *Treatise on Physical Chemistry*, D. Van Nostrand Company, Inc., New York, 1942, Vol. I, p. 457.

THE INVERSION TEMPERATURE

Hydrogen and helium can be cooled by adiabatic expansion if they are first brought to a sufficiently low temperature. Each gas, before it will cool on expansion, must be below a temperature known as the *inversion temperature,* namely, *the temperature at which the gas exhibits neither cooling nor heating on expansion at constant enthalpy.* At the inversion temperature $\mu = 0$. Above the inversion temperature gases exhibit a heating effect, while below the inversion temperature cooling is observed. As it happens, all gases except hydrogen and helium are considerably below their inversion points at room temperatures and thus exhibit positive Joule-Thomson coefficients. For hydrogen, however, the inversion temperature is at about $-80°$ C, while for helium the temperature is still lower. Once cooled below their inversion temperatures, hydrogen and helium behave like other gases and cool on adiabatic expansion.

The Joule-Thomson effect is of great practical importance in the liquefaction of gases. The manner in which it is utilized will be explained in the next chapter.

THE CARNOT CYCLE

A question of great significance in any consideration of energy transformation concerns the extent to which heat is convertible to other forms of energy which may be utilized to do work. Experience has shown that periodically operating heat engines which absorb a quantity of heat at some temperature T_2 and reject the waste heat at a lower temperature T_1 can convert only a fraction of the absorbed heat into work. Offhand it may be thought that this limited convertibility of heat into work lies in the inefficiency of the engines. However, it can be deduced by theoretical considerations that even an ideal engine, operating under ideal conditions, would be able to convert only a certain fraction of the absorbed heat into work and that this fraction would be determined only by the operating temperatures T_2 and T_1 and would be totally independent of the nature of the engine. In other words, there is a natural limitation to the convertibility of heat to work above and beyond any imperfections which may be present in any contrivances employed.

To establish the above deductions and to arrive at the maximum possible convertibility of heat into work, let us consider the sequence of operations called a *Carnot cycle.* A cycle is any series of operations so carried out that at the end the system is back to its initial state. Any process so conducted is referred to as a complete cyclic process. The one we are at present interested in consists of four distinct steps, two isothermal and two adiabatic, and is so conducted that the net work obtained represents the maximum work that can be derived from a quantity of heat absorbed at one temperature and given out at another, lower, temperature.

Isothermal Expansion at T_2. Imagine a cylinder fitted with a weightless, frictionless piston and containing n moles of an ideal gas. Let the pressure, volume, and temperature of this gas be P_2, V_2, and T_2 respectively. Allow this gas now to expand *isothermally* and *reversibly* to pressure P_1 and volume V_1. In doing so, the gas absorbs a quantity of heat q_2 equal to the work done. This expansion is represented on the diagram in Fig. 3 by the line $P_2V_2P_1V_1$, and involves the work w_1, given by

$$w_1 = nRT_2 \ln \frac{V_1}{V_2} = q_2 \tag{a}$$

Adiabatic Expansion. Now expand this gas reversibly under adiabatic conditions to a new state P_3, V_3. Since the change is adiabatic, all the

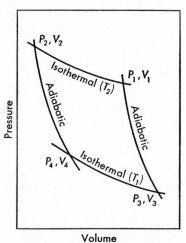

Fig. 3.   The Carnot Cycle.

work done is at the expense of the internal energy, and involves a drop in temperature from T_2 to T_1. We thus have

$$w_2 = -\Delta E = -nC_v(T_1 - T_2) \tag{b}$$

Isothermal Compression at T_1. In the third stage of the cycle the gas is compressed isothermally and reversibly from P_3, V_3, to P_4, V_4 at temperature T_1. During this step a quantity of heat q_1 is given up to the surroundings, and the work performed, w_3, is

$$w_3 = nRT_1 \ln \frac{V_4}{V_3} = -q_1 \tag{c}$$

Adiabatic Compression. Finally, the gas is returned to its initial state P_2, V_2, and temperature T_2 by compressing it adiabatically and reversibly. During this stage there is an increase in internal energy equal to the work of compression w_4, or

$$w_4 = -\Delta E = -nC_v(T_2 - T_1) = nC_v(T_1 - T_2) \tag{d}$$

The total work performed during this complete cycle is obviously the sum of the work terms involved in the four steps, namely,

$$w_m = w_1 + w_2 + w_3 + w_4$$

$$= nRT_2 \ln \frac{V_1}{V_2} - nC_v(T_1 - T_2) + nRT_1 \ln \frac{V_4}{V_3} + nC_v(T_1 - T_2)$$

$$= nRT_2 \ln \frac{V_1}{V_2} + nRT_1 \ln \frac{V_4}{V_3}$$

Consequently,

$$w_m = nRT_2 \ln \frac{V_1}{V_2} + nRT_1 \ln \frac{V_4}{V_3} = q_2 - q_1 \qquad \text{(A)}$$

Again, since from step (1) $q_2 = nRT_2 \ln V_1/V_2$, division of equation (A) by q_2 yields

$$\frac{w_m}{q_2} = \frac{(q_2 - q_1)}{q_2} = \frac{RT_2 \ln (V_1/V_2) + RT_1 \ln (V_4/V_3)}{RT_2 \ln (V_1/V_2)} \qquad \text{(B)}$$

Equation (B) can be simplified considerably. Since the points (P_1, V_1) and (P_3, V_3) lie on the same adiabatic, then by equation (28),

$$T_2^{C_v/R} V_1 = T_1^{C_v/R} V_3$$

Similarly, we have for the points (P_2, V_2) and (P_4, V_4), which lie on the same adiabatic,

$$T_2^{C_v/R} V_2 = T_1^{C_v/R} V_4$$

On dividing the first of these equations by the second, we obtain

$$\frac{V_1}{V_2} = \frac{V_3}{V_4}$$

and consequently,

$$\ln \frac{V_4}{V_3} = -\ln \frac{V_1}{V_2}$$

Substituting this value for $\ln V_4/V_3$ in equation (B) we get, finally,

$$\frac{w_m}{q_2} = \frac{RT_2 \ln (V_1/V_2) - RT_1 \ln (V_1/V_2)}{RT_2 \ln (V_1/V_2)}$$

$$= \frac{T_2 - T_1}{T_2} \qquad \text{(39)}$$

and $\qquad\qquad w_m = q_2 \left(\frac{T_2 - T_1}{T_2} \right) \qquad\qquad$ (40)

In essence, equation (40) states that when a system during a reversible cyclical process absorbs a quantity of heat q_2 at temperature T_2 and then undergoes a temperature drop $(T_2 - T_1)$, the external work that may be recovered from the process is equal to the heat absorbed at T_2

multiplied by the ratio $(T_2 - T_1)/T_2$. It is important to observe that the absorption takes place at the higher temperature and that the heat passes from the higher temperature to the lower. Since during this cyclical process all the stages are in every way reversible, *the work done is the maximum possible* under the given temperature conditions. Its magnitude is that indicated by the enclosed area in Fig. 3.

Although equation (40) was derived by using an ideal gas in the cycle described, it is possible to show that the same result can be obtained through the use of any medium, whether ideal or not. Consequently equation (40) is a relation of general validity for the maximum work recoverable from q_2 in any cyclical process operating between the two temperatures T_2 and T_1. This equation may be taken, therefore, as a statement of the optimum, but nevertheless limited, convertibility of heat into work by an engine operating in a cycle between the two temperatures.

THE THERMODYNAMIC EFFICIENCY

The ratio w_m/q_2 in equation (39) is designated the *thermodynamic efficiency* of the process and represents the maximum fraction of the heat absorbed which is recoverable as work between the temperatures T_2 and T_1. The right-hand side of this equation points to the startling conclusion that this fraction depends only on the two temperatures between which the cycle is operated and is independent of all other factors as long as the process is cyclical and reversible. Furthermore, *the thermodynamic efficiency must be the same for all such processes operating under the given temperature conditions.* The necessity for this deduction was pointed out by Carnot, who argued that if any machine were more efficient than one executing a Carnot cycle, the two could be so coupled together as to obtain during a complete cycle a net quantity of work at the higher temperature at the expense of the heat at the lower temperature. But such a situation is contrary to our experience with the convertibility of heat into work, and hence there can be no engine more efficient than a Carnot engine.

No processes in nature approach in efficiency a cylical reversible operation. Nevertheless, the thermodynamic efficiency, by setting an upper limit, provides a goal toward which improvements in machinery and modes of operation may strive.

THE CLAPEYRON EQUATION

We shall use now the Carnot cycle to derive a very important relation known as the Clapeyron equation. For this purpose consider a system composed of two phases of a substance in equilibrium at a temperature T, pressure P, and volume V_1. Such a system may be ice in equilibrium with liquid water, or water in equilibrium with its vapor. This system is to be subjected now to the Carnot cycle shown in Fig. 4. The first stage involves the absorption of a quantity of heat q, as a result of which a mass m of phase A is transformed to phase B isothermally and reversibly at constant pressure P and with the volume change from V_1 to V_2. In the second step of the cycle the system is expanded adiabatically and reversibly from point (V_2, P, T) to point (V_2', P', T'), with a drop in pressure from P to P' and in temperature from T to T'. In the third stage the system is compressed isothermally and reversibly at constant pressure P' from

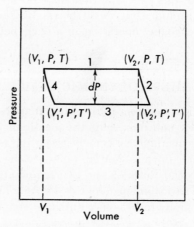

Fig. 4.   Carnot Cycle for Derivation of Clapeyron Equation.

point (V_2', P', T') to point (V_1', P', T'). During this stage phase B changes to phase A, and a quantity of heat q' is rejected. Finally, the system is returned to its initial state by a reversible adiabatic compression.

Since this entire series of operations is conducted reversibly, the work performed in the cycle is given by equation (40), or

$$w_m = q \frac{(T - T')}{T} \tag{40a}$$

If we consider the temperature difference to be infinitesimally small, then we may write $(T - T') = dT$, and $(P - P') = dP$. Again, since the heat at temperature T was absorbed at constant pressure, $q = \Delta E + P(V_2 - V_1) = \Delta H$. Finally, since the two temperatures are very close together, the diagram in Fig. 4 can be considered to be a parallelogram, whose area is then $(V_2 - V_1)dP$. But, this area is the work performed during the cycle, and hence $w_m = (V_2 - V_1)dP$. Inserting these values of

$(T - T')$, q, and w_m into equation (40a) we obtain

$$(V_2 - V_1)dP = \Delta H \frac{dT}{T}$$

or
$$\frac{dP}{dT} = \frac{\Delta H}{T(V_2 - V_1)} = \frac{\Delta H}{T\Delta V} \tag{41}$$

This is the *Clapeyron equation*. It is applicable to all types of transitions in form or state of a substance. We may designate in general ΔH the heat of transition, T the temperature of transition, V_2 the volume of a definite weight of final form, and V_1 the volume of the same weight of the initial form of the substance. dP/dT is the variation of the pressure of the system with temperature. Applications of this equation to various transitions will be given in subsequent chapters.

REFERENCES FOR FURTHER READING

1. S. Glasstone, *Thermodynamics for Chemists*, D. Van Nostrand Company, Inc., New York, 1947.
2. I. M. Klotz, *Chemical Thermodynamics*, Prentice-Hall, Inc., New York, 1950.
3. G. N. Lewis and M. Randall, *Thermodynamics and the Free Energy of Chemical Substances*, McGraw-Hill Book Company, Inc., New York, 1923.
4. F. D. Rossini, *Chemical Thermodynamics*, John Wiley & Sons, Inc., New York, 1950.
5. L. Steiner, *Introduction to Chemical Thermodynamics*, McGraw-Hill Book Company, Inc., New York, 1948.

PROBLEMS

1. A weight of 1 kg falls freely to a platform from a height of 10 m. What amount of heat in calories will be evolved when the weight strikes the platform?
2. A piston whose area is 6 sq in. moves through a distance of 8 in. against a constant pressure of 3 atm. Calculate the work done (a) in joules and (b) in calories.
3. A gas in expanding against a constant pressure of 1 atm from 10 to 16 liters absorbs 30 cal of heat. What is the change in internal energy of the gas?
4. Two liters of N_2 at 0° C and 5 atm pressure are expanded isothermally against a constant pressure of 1 atm until the pressure of the gas is also 1 atm. Assuming the gas to be ideal, what are the values of w, ΔE, ΔH, and q for the process?
   Ans. $w = q = 193.7$ cal; $\Delta E = \Delta H = 0$.
5. For a certain ideal gas $C_v = 6.76$ cal mole^{-1} degree^{-1}. If 10 moles of the gas are heated from 0° C to 100° C, what will be ΔE and ΔH for the process?
   Ans. $\Delta E = 6760$ cal; $\Delta H = 8750$ cal.
6. Three moles of an ideal gas at 1 atm pressure and 20° C are heated at constant pressure until the final temperature is 80° C. For the gas $C_v = 7.50 + 3.2 \times 10^{-3} T$ cal mole^{-1} degree^{-1}. Calculate w, ΔE, ΔH, and q for the process.
7. Calculate the work done by 5 moles of an ideal gas during expansion from 5 atm at 25° C to 2 atm at 50° C against a constant pressure of 0.5 atm. If

for the gas $C_p = 5.0$ cal mole^{-1} degree^{-1}, find also ΔE, ΔH, and q for the process.

8. Assuming CO_2 to be an ideal gas, calculate the work done by 10 g of CO_2 in expanding isothermally and reversibly from a volume of 5 liters to 10 liters at 27° C. What are q, ΔE, and ΔH for the process?
   Ans. $w = q = 93.9$ cal; $\Delta E = \Delta H = 0$.

9. Two liters of N_2 at 0° C and 5 atm pressure are expanded isothermally and reversibly until the confining pressure is 1 atm. Assuming the gas to be ideal, calculate w, q, ΔE, and ΔH for the expansion.
   Ans. $w = q = 389.7$ cal; $\Delta E = \Delta H = 0$.

10. Calculate the minimum work necessary to compress 20 g of O_2 from 10 to 5 liters at 0° C. How much heat is evolved in the process?

11. Using the van der Waals equation, find the minimum work necessary to compress 1 mole of CO_2 from a volume of 10 liters to 1 liter at 27° C.
    Ans. $w = -1318$ cal.

12. Employing the Beattie-Bridgeman equation of state explicit in volume, equation (50) of Chapter 1, deduce the **expression** for the maximum work performed in the isothermal expansion of n moles of a gas from pressure P_1 to P_2 at temperature T.

13. Eight grams of O_2 at 27° C and under a pressure of 10 atm are permitted to expand adiabatically and reversibly until the final pressure is 1 atm. Find the final temperature and the work done in the process. Assume that $C_p = \frac{7}{2} R$ for O_2.
    Ans. $t = -117.7°$ C; $w = 179.6$ cal.

14. Ten grams of N_2 at 17° C are compressed adiabatically and reversibly from 8 to 5 liters. Calculate the final temperature and the work done on the gas. What are ΔE and ΔH for the process? Assume $C_p = \frac{7}{2} R$.

15. For a certain ideal gas $C_p = 8.58$ cal mole^{-1} degree^{-1}. What will be the final volume and temperature when 2 moles of the gas at 20° C and 15 atm are allowed to expand adiabatically and reversibly to 5 atm pressure?
    Ans. $V = 7.45$ liters; $t = -46°$ C.

16. Find w, q, ΔE, and ΔH for the process given in problem 15.

17. Consider again the gas in problem 15, but suppose now that the expansion takes place adiabatically against a constant pressure of 5 atm. What will be the final volume and temperature of the gas?
    Ans. $V = 8.15$ liters; $t = -25.0°$ C.

18. Find w, q, ΔE, and ΔH for the process in problem 17.

19. A certain fuel furnishes 7000 cal/gram. Calculate the maximum work obtainable per gram in a heat engine in which (a) Hg at its normal boiling point and (b) H_2O at its normal boiling point are used in the boiler. Assume in each case that the condenser is at 40° C. *Ans.* (a) 3522 cal; (b) 1126 cal.

20. What are the thermodynamic efficiencies of the processes given in problem 19?

21. If a Carnot engine operates between an upper temperature T_2 and a lower temperature T_1, what will have to be the value of the latter in order to obtain a thermodynamic efficiency of 100%?

22. How much work is done in condensing 1 lb of steam at its boiling point under a constant pressure of 1 atm? What are the values of q, ΔH, and ΔE for the process?
    Ans. $w = -18,660$ cal; $q = \Delta H = -244,660$ cal; $\Delta E = -226,240$ cal.

3

Liquids

Liquids, unlike gases, are characterized by a definite volume which is independent of their container; and, compared with gases, they are only slightly compressible. The densities and viscosities of liquids are greater than those of gases. Gases will mix in all proportions, but certain liquids are partially and sometimes completely immiscible. Thus, alcohol and water mix in all proportions, ether and water only in certain limited proportions, and mercury and water not at all.

From the standpoint of kinetic theory, a liquid may be considered as a continuation of the gas phase into the region of small volumes and very high molecular attractions. The cohesive forces in a liquid must be stronger than those in a gas at even high pressures, for they are high enough to keep the molecules confined to a definite volume. Still, the molecules within the liquid must not be thought of as rigidly fixed. They have some freedom of motion, but this motion is considerably restricted, and hence the mean free path is much shorter than in the gas phase.

At best, our knowledge of the nature of the liquid state is still very incomplete. Because of the proximity of molecules to each other within the liquid, effects frequently manifest themselves in liquids which, if present, are of only secondary significance in gases. Thus, because of purely molecular (van der Waals) forces, and in certain cases electrical (dipole) forces, many liquids exhibit a tendency to cluster or associate, and also to orient themselves in some definite manner. The situation within a liquid is very complex, and the progress made in unraveling the multitudinous effects has been rather slow.

CRITICAL PHENOMENA IN LIQUIDS

If a liquid, such as water, is sealed in an evacuated tube, a certain amount will evaporate to form vapor. This vapor will exert a pressure just as any gas does, and, provided the temperature is maintained constant, an equilibrium will be established between the liquid and vapor phases. The vapor pressure established is characteristic for each liquid and is a constant at any given temperature; it is known as the *saturated vapor pressure* of the liquid. The saturated vapor pressure increases continuously with temperature. Thus, at 25° C the vapor pressure of water is 23.76 mm Hg, while at 100° C it is 760 mm Hg. As the water in the sealed tube is heated further, more and more water evaporates and the pressure continues to increase. At all times there is a definite line of demarcation, or meniscus, between the liquid and vapor phases. When we reach the temperature of 374° C, however, the meniscus becomes indefinite, fades into the vapor, and disappears. At this temperature the physical properties of liquid and vapor become identical, and no distinction can be observed between the two. A liquid in this condition is said to be at the *critical point*. The temperature, saturated vapor pressure, and molar volume corresponding to this point are designated the *critical temperature, critical pressure*, and *critical volume* respectively. Their values, which are constant and characteristic for each substance, are known as the *critical constants*. For water the critical constants are: $t_c = 374.4°$ C, $P_c = 219.5$ atm, and $V_c = 58.7$ cc per mole.

On heating the sealed tube even slightly above the critical temperature, no evidence can be found of the presence of liquid. The whole mass is gaseous and remains in that state no matter how high it is heated, or how large an external pressure is applied. Since the phenomena described for water are exhibited by all liquids, it must be concluded that *no liquid can exist as such at temperatures above the critical under any applied pressure*.

The critical phenomena are reversible. When the gas in the sealed tube is cooled below the critical temperature, if the pressure is sufficiently high the meniscus reappears, and again we have the two phases, liquid and vapor.

THE *P–V–T* RELATIONS OF GASES AND LIQUIDS

The first complete data on the $P-V-T$ relations of a substance in both gaseous and liquid states were obtained by Andrews[1] on carbon dioxide. Andrews measured the variation of the volume of carbon dioxide with pressure at various constant temperatures, and he was able to show that

[1] Andrews, *Trans. Roy. Soc.*, **159**, 583 (1869).

the critical temperature of carbon dioxide is 31° C at a critical pressure of 73 atm.

Figure 1 shows the plot of pressure vs. volume for carbon dioxide at various constant temperatures. Each *P–V* plot is called an *isothermal*. The data on which the plot is based are not due to Andrews but are the

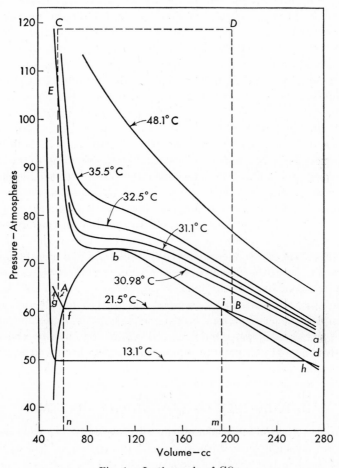

Fig. 1.   Isothermals of CO_2.

composite results of several subsequent investigators. The 48.1° C isothermal is very similar to the hyperbolic plot demanded by Boyle's law and shows no presence of liquid carbon dioxide even at the highest pressures attained. The same conditions obtain at 35.5° C, 32.5° C, and 31.10° C, except that now the data indicate that Boyle's law when applied to carbon dioxide is considerably in error, since the gas does not behave ideally. At 30.98° C, however, the carbon dioxide remains gaseous only up to a pressure of 73 atm (line *ab*). At 73 atm (point *b*) liquid first appears, and since this is the highest temperature at which liquid is observed, 30.98° C must be the critical temperature of carbon dioxide. Further increase in pressure at this temperature (line *bE*) shows only the presence of liquid, and consequently this line must represent the compressibility of liquid carbon dioxide at this temperature. Below 30.98° C, the behavior of the gas on compression is quite different, as may be judged from the 21.5° C and 13.1° C isotherms. At 21.5° C, for instance, only gas exists on compression along line *di*. At *i* liquid, of specific volume *n*, first appears, and the pressure of the system remains constant thereafter as long as both gas and liquid are present. At this stage further application of pressure results merely in further condensation of gas until point *f* is reached. At *f* all the gas has been condensed, and further application of pressure results merely in compression of the liquid, as is shown by the steep line *fg*. At lower temperatures the behavior is similar to that at 21.5° C, except that the horizontal portions, corresponding to the range of coexistence of liquid and vapor, become longer the lower the temperature.

It may be concluded from this explanation that, in the area to the left of the dome-shaped area and below the line *bE*, only liquid carbon dioxide will exist; to the right of the line *bE* and to the right of the dome-shaped area, only gaseous carbon dioxide will exist; while within the dome-shaped area is the range of coexistence of liquid and vapor carbon dicxide.

All gases upon isothermal compression behave similarly to carbon dioxide. For each, of course, the curves will be displaced in line with the characteristics and critical temperature of the gas in question. Thus, for example, the critical temperature of helium is −268° C and the dome-shaped area is moved downward, while for chlorine the critical temperature is 144° C and the dome-shaped area is moved above that for carbon dioxide.

THE PRINCIPLE OF CONTINUITY OF STATES

For further theoretical considerations it is essential to show that the liquid state does not represent a sharp and discontinuous transition from the gaseous state but is rather a continuation of the gaseous phase into the region of very strong intermolecular attractions and small volumes. This can be shown from the following considerations. Suppose we wish to convert liquid carbon dioxide at 21.5° C and the pressure given by point *A* in Fig. 1 to gaseous carbon dioxide at the same temperature and the pressure given by point *B*. The most obvious way to accomplish this transformation is to follow the 21.5° C isotherm and reduce the pressure along *AfiB*. In doing this gas appears suddenly and discontinuously, and coexists with liquid along *fi* until finally all liquid disppears at *i*. The same transformation may, however, be accomplished in another way. If the liquid at A is heated at constant volume, increase of temperature will lead to increased pressure, and the mass will move along the line AEC. As long as the carbon dioxide is below the critical isotherm, point E, the carbon dioxide is liquid; as soon as the carbon dioxide passes the critical isotherm, however, it becomes gaseous. At the critical temperature, as we have seen, the liquid passes to gas imperceptibly and continuously, and hence in heating the liquid from A to C we convert it without discontinuity to gas. The gas at C may now be expanded to D at constant pressure by heating, and then cooled at constant volume from D to B. By this series of operations we can convert liquid to gaseous carbon dioxide at 21.5° C without introducing any discontinuity between the phases.

The implication involved in this principle of the continuity of the gaseous and liquid states is highly important. It suggests that if we have an equation of state which is satisfactory in the region of high pressures and low temperatures that equation should be applicable also to the conditions prevailing at the critical point and to the liquid itself. We shall see now how the van der Waals equation meets these requirements.

APPLICATION OF VAN DER WAALS' EQUATION TO THE ISOTHERMALS OF CARBON DIOXIDE

By substituting $n = 1$ and the values of the constants a and b for carbon dioxide in van der Waals' equation, namely,

$$\left(P + \frac{a}{V^2}\right)(V - b) = RT$$

we can calculate for any given temperature the P–V relationships above, at, and below the critical temperature. The results of such a calculation are summarized in Fig. 2. The plot is, in general, similar to the one obtained experimentally. At t_1, for instance, which is above the critical temperature, the P–V relationship corresponds closely to that of the 48.1° C isotherm in Fig. 1. At t_c, which is the critical temperature, a slight break is observed at a, the critical point, which is again in accord with observation. However, below the critical temperature, the range determining the coexistence of liquid and gas is indicated by a continuous S-shaped portion as bcd at t_3, rather than by the horizontal constant pressure range actually observed. In this respect, therefore, and in point of strict quantitative agreement with observed data, the van der Waals equation leaves something to be desired. Nevertheless, some investigators have found that by compressing the gas very carefully part of the curve bc may be realized, though only in an unstable condition. Similarly,

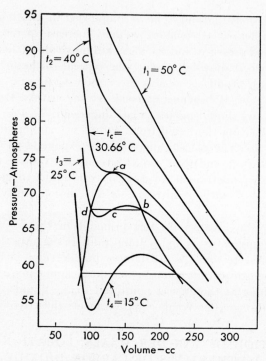

Fig. 2.　Isothermals of CO_2 According to van der Waals' Equation.

if the pressure on a liquid be released slowly, part of curve cd can be obtained, but again the condition is unstable.

DETERMINATION OF VAN DER WAALS CONSTANTS

If it be assumed that van der Waals' equation is applicable at the critical point, then the van der Waals constant for any gas can be calculated from the critical constants of the gas in the following manner. On expanding and rearranging the equation we have

$$\left(P + \frac{a}{V^2}\right)(V - b) = RT$$

$$PV^3 - V^2(RT + Pb) + aV - ab = 0$$

and

$$V^3 - \left(\frac{RT + Pb}{P}\right)V^2 + \left(\frac{a}{P}\right)V - \left(\frac{ab}{P}\right) = 0 \qquad (1)$$

This is a cubic equation in V and for any given value of P and T will yield three separate solutions for V. The three roots of this equation may all be real, or one may be real and positive and the other two imaginary. Thus in Fig. 2 the equation yields the three roots d, c, and b at t_3, while at t_1 it yields only one real root. However, at the critical point the three roots are not only real and positive but also identical and equal to V_c. Hence the difference $(V - V_c) = 0$, and consequently,

$$(V - V_c)^3 = 0 \tag{2}$$

On expansion by the binomial theorem equation (2) becomes

$$V^3 - (3 V_c) V^2 + (3 V_c^2) V - V_c^3 = 0 \tag{3}$$

At the critical point equations (3) and (1) must be identical. On comparing and equating coefficients we get

$$3 V_c = \frac{RT_c + bP_c}{P_c} \tag{4}$$

$$3 V_c^2 = \frac{a}{P_c} \tag{5}$$

$$V_c^3 = \frac{ab}{P_c} \tag{6}$$

From equation (5) a follows as

$$a = 3 V_c^2 P_c \tag{7}$$

while from equations (5) and (6) b is given by

$$b = \frac{V_c}{3} \tag{8}$$

Thus a and b may be calculated from known values of P_c and V_c, or vice versa.

Usually V_c is the critical constant known least accurately, and it is therefore preferable to calculate a and b from T_c and P_c only. This can readily be done. On eliminating V_c between equations (4) and (8) we get

$$b = \frac{RT_c}{8 P_c} \tag{9}$$

Again, on combining equations (4), (8), and (5) a follows as

$$a = \frac{27}{64} \frac{R^2 T_c^2}{P_c} \tag{10}$$

Combination of equations (4) and (8) leads also to the value of R in terms of the critical constants, namely,

$$R = \frac{8}{3} \frac{P_c V_c}{T_c} = 2.67 \frac{P_c V_c}{T_c} \tag{11}$$

Although the van der Waals equation predicts the coefficient in equation (11) to be 2.67, the values for it calculated from experimental data are generally higher and differ for various gases. Thus for helium this constant comes out to be 3.18, while for water it is 4.97. These differences are due to inaccuracies inherent in the van der Waals equation.

THE CRITICAL CONSTANTS OF GASES

Table 1 gives the critical constants of a number of gases. Instead of the critical volume is given the critical density, which is the weight of substance at the critical point per cubic centimeter. The critical volume is obtained by dividing the molecular weight of the substance by the critical density.

TABLE 1

CRITICAL CONSTANTS OF GASES

Gas	t_c (° C)	P_c (atm)	d_c (g/cc)
Ammonia	132.4	111.5	0.235
Argon	−122	48	0.531
Carbon dioxide	30.98	73.0	0.460
Carbon monoxide	−139	35	0.311
Chlorine	144.0	76.1	0.573
Ethane	32.1	48.8	0.21
Ethyl alcohol	243.1	63.1	0.2755
Ethylene	9.7	50.9	0.22
Helium	−267.9	2.26	0.0693
Hydrogen	−239.9	12.8	0.0310
Neon	−228.7	25.9	0.484
Nitric oxide	−94	65	0.52
Nitrogen	−147.1	33.5	0.3110
Oxygen	−118.8	49.7	0.430
Propane	96.81	42.01	0.226
Toluene	320.6	41.6	0.292
Water	374.4	219.5	0.307

Cailletet and Mathias found that when the mean values of the sum of the densities of liquid and saturated vapor of a substance are plotted against the temperature, the plot is a straight line. This is shown in Fig. 3. The equation of the line is

$$t = A + B\left(\frac{d_l + d_v}{2}\right) \tag{12}$$

where d_l is the density of the liquid at any temperature t, d_v the density of the saturated vapor at the same temperature, and A and B constants evaluated from the plot. Once the equation is determined, the critical density may be calculated with ease, for at t_c the critical temperature,

$d_v = d_l = d_c$, and the equation reduces to

$$t_c = A + B\left(\frac{2\,d_c}{2}\right) = A + Bd_c \tag{13}$$

Substitution of t_c yields then the critical density. Critical densities can usually be obtained more accurately in this manner than by direct measurement at the critical point.

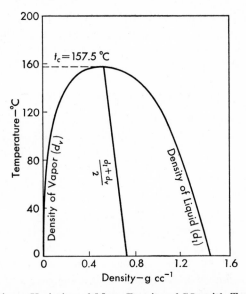

Fig. 3. Linear Variation of Mean Density of SO_2 with Temperature.

THE PRINCIPLE OF CORRESPONDING STATES

If we substitute in the van der Waals equation the values of a, b, and R as given by equations (9), (10), and (11), we obtain

$$\left(P + \frac{3\,V_c^2 P_c}{V^2}\right)\left(V - \frac{V_c}{3}\right) = \frac{8}{3}\frac{P_c V_c T}{T_c} \tag{14}$$

Dividing both sides of equation (14) by $P_c V_c$, we get

$$\left(\frac{P}{P_c} + \frac{3\,V_c^2}{V^2}\right)\left(\frac{V}{V_c} - \frac{1}{3}\right) = \frac{8}{3}\frac{T}{T_c}$$

or

$$\left(P_r + \frac{3}{V_r^2}\right)(3\,V_r - 1) = 8\,T_r \tag{15}$$

where $P_r = P/P_c$, $V_r = V/V_c$, and $T_r = T/T_c$. P_r is termed the *reduced pressure*, V_r the *reduced volume*, and T_r the *reduced temperature*. Expressed in terms of P_r, V_r, and T_r, equation (15) involves no constants characterizing the individuality of various substances and should therefore be generally applicable to all liquids and gases. It is known as a *reduced equation of state*. Its physical meaning is that at any given value of T_r and P_r, all liquids and gases should have the same corresponding volumes, V_r.

The principle of corresponding states is only approximately correct, but it does suggest that frequently better correlation of experimental data may be obtained when the various substances are in corresponding states, i.e., at equal values of T_r, V_r, or P_r. The principle finds frequent and useful application in thermodynamic and chemical engineering calculations, especially at elevated pressures. For examples see Maron and Turnbull,[1] Watson and Smith,[2] and Newton.[3]

LIQUEFACTION OF GASES

The particular method employed in the liquefaction of a gas depends on the nature of the gas. Vapors of substances which are liquid at or near room temperature and atmospheric pressure are condensed simply by cooling. Other substances which are liquid at lower temperatures may be condensed either by pressure or by a combination of cooling and compression. Such gases as chlorine, sulfur dioxide, hydrogen sulfide, ammonia, methyl chloride, and "freon" (CF_2Cl_2) may be liquefied readily by compression alone. Cooling reduces considerably the pressure required for liquefaction, as may be seen from Fig. 1. With the "permanent" gases, however, such as oxygen, nitrogen, hydrogen, and helium, application of pressure alone will not produce liquefaction, and more involved methods of cooling, compression, and even expansion are required before the gases will liquefy.

Any gas, before liquefaction is possible, must be cooled below its critical temperature. Since their critical temperatures are very low, as may be seen from Table 1, liquefaction of the "permanent" gases requires intense cooling as well as considerable compression. To attain these low temperatures, two general principles, or a combination of the two, are employed, namely, (a) adiabatic expansion, in which advantage is taken of the Joule-Thomson effect to attain cooling; and (b) allowing the gas to cool itself by performing work in an adiabatic expansion against a piston. These two methods are exemplified in the Linde and Claude processes for the liquefaction of air.

The basic principle of the Linde process is the adiabatic Joule-Thomson expansion and consequent cooling of the air. The steps in the process are in outline as shown in Fig. 4. Air is first compressed to approximately

---

[1] Maron and Turnbull, *Ind. Eng. Chem.*, **34**, 544 (1942).
[2] Watson and Smith, *National Petroleum News*, July 1, 1936.
[3] Newton, *Ind. Eng. Chem.*, **27**, 302 (1935).

100 atm. During the compression most of the water in the air condenses and is removed. The heat generated in compression is removed by passing the gas through coils C, refrigerated by water or ammonia. The dry gas is passed, then, through a copper spiral coil S, from which it is expanded to almost atmospheric pressure through a controlled valve V. The issuing gas, cooled now due to the Joule-Thomson effect, passes over the copper coil and cools further the incoming compressed gas. On repeating the cycle several times, the temperature of the expanding gas finally drops far enough to condense part of the air to liquid, which collects in the bottom of the chamber L and can be drawn off. Any uncondensed air is recirculated.

In the Claude process the gas, instead of being permitted to expand freely, is forced to do work against a confining piston. Since the gas is

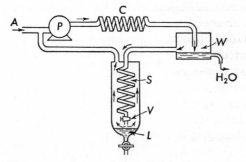

Fig. 4.   Linde Process for Liquefaction of Air.

adiabatically insulated, work is achieved at the expense of the internal energy of the gas, and a cooling results. The Claude process is more economical than the Linde process in that it permits the recovery of part of the work expended in compression, work which is lost completely in the free expansion of the Linde process. The work thus gained may be utilized to operate the compressors.

Easily liquefiable gases, such as sulfur dioxide, ammonia, methyl chloride, and dichloro-difluoromethane or "freon," are used in refrigeration and air conditioning. In the laboratory other refrigerants frequently employed are ice, liquid air, and a mixture of "dry ice" (solid carbon dioxide) and alcohol, ether, or acetone. With one of the last named mixtures temperatures of -80 to $-90°$ C can be obtained. Liquid air will give a temperature of $-180°$ C, while, if needed, liquid hydrogen can give a temperature of $-250°$ C.

THE VAPOR PRESSURE OF LIQUIDS

Attention has already been called to the fact that a liquid when placed in a container will partially evaporate to establish a pressure of vapor above the liquid. The pressure established will depend on the temperature of the liquid and will be a constant at any given temperature. The phenomenon is easily explainable in terms of the kinetic theory. The molecules within the liquid, like those in a gas, do not all have the same velocity at a given temperature, but range in velocities from zero for some to very high velocities for others. Most of them, however, are grouped about a mean velocity which is determined by the temperature. When certain molecules within the liquid move in the direction of the surface, and possess sufficient kinetic energy to overcome the large attractive forces of the rest of the molecules, they will excape from the surface into the space above and establish there a vapor pressure. The process does not proceed indefinitely, for some molecules in the gas phase will collide with the surface and will be recaptured by the liquid. When the rate of escape from the liquid becomes equal to the rate of return of molecules to the liquid, an equilibrium is established, and the pressure then remains constant as long as the temperature remains unchanged. This constant vapor pressure is referred to as the *saturated vapor pressure* of the liquid at the particular temperature. As long as this vapor pressure is maintained, the liquid exhibits no further tendency to evaporate. At any lower pressure the liquid will evaporate into the gas phase, while at any higher pressure vapor will tend to condense until the equilibrium pressure is reestablished.

Inasmuch as the evaporation involves the escape of molecules of high kinetic energy, the average kinetic energy of the molecules within the liquid must decrease, and hence the temperature of the liquid tends to drop. To preserve isothermal conditions, heat must be supplied. The quantity of heat required depends on the liquid in question, the amount evaporated, and the temperature. For any liquid at a given temperature the amount of heat required per unit weight of liquid is a definite quantity known as the *heat of vaporization* of the liquid. It is the difference in the enthalpies or heat contents of vapor and liquid respectively, namely,

$$\Delta H_v = H_v - H_l \tag{16}$$

where ΔH_v is the heat of vaporization, H_v the heat content of vapor, and H_l the heat content of liquid. For an evaporation ΔH_v is always positive, i.e., heat is always absorbed, while for a condensation ΔH_v is always negative and equal numerically to the heat absorbed in the vaporization. As may be expected from the definition of the heat content, ΔH_v represents the sum of the difference in the internal energy of vapor and liquid, $\Delta E_v = E_v - E_l$, and the work involved in the expansion from liquid to vapor; i.e.,

$$\Delta H_v = \Delta E_v + P\Delta V \tag{17}$$

where P is the vapor pressure and $\Delta V = V_v - V_l$.

MEASUREMENT OF VAPOR PRESSURE

The various methods available for measuring the vapor pressure of a liquid may be classified generally into static and dynamic methods. In the static methods the liquid is permitted to establish its vapor pressure without being disturbed in any way, while in the dynamic methods the liquid either is boiled or has a stream of inert gas passing through it. The line of demarcation between these two classifications is not always sharp, and a particular procedure may actually be a combination of the two.

The isoteniscope method of Menzies and Smith is precise, flexible, and convenient for the measurement of the vapor pressures of a substance over a range of temperatures. A simple laboratory setup is illustrated

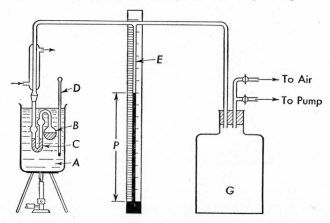

Fig. 5.   Isoteniscope Assembly for Determination of Vapor Pressure.

in Fig. 5. The isoteniscope bulb B is filled one-half to three-quarters full with the liquid to be studied, and the U-shaped portion of the tube, C, is filled to a depth of 2 or 3 cm with the same liquid. The isoteniscope is then attached to the rest of the apparatus and surrounded by a water bath A, whose temperature is measured by thermometer D. E is a barometric leg for measuring the pressure in the apparatus, while G is a large bottle to smooth out pressure fluctuations in the system. This bottle can be connected alternately to a suction pump or the air. In operation the system is evacuated until the liquid boils vigorously at B to expel all air from BC. The bath A is then adjusted to the desired temperature, and air is slowly admitted to the system until the liquid levels in the U-tube C are exactly equal. Under these conditions the pressure on either side of the U-tube must be the same. Hence, the vapor pressure in B must be the same as the pressure in the rest of the apparatus and can be obtained from the reading of the barometer and the mercury column at E. The difference between the barometric pressure and that at E is the vapor pressure of the liquid in B at the temperature of the bath. Readings at different temperatures can be obtained by merely changing the temperature of bath A and repeating the operation.

A simple dynamic method is shown in Fig. 6. The liquid in question, B, is boiled, after deaeration, under a measured external pressure, and the temperature of the condensing vapor is read from thermometer T. The barometric pressure minus the pressure P is the pressure at which the liquid boils, and this is the vapor pressure of the liquid at the temperature T. By changing the pressure P, the liquid may be boiled at different temperatures, and the vapor pressures at these temperatures thus obtained. The function of bottle C is to condense any escaping

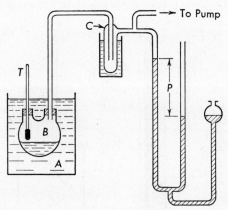

Fig. 6. Boiling Point Method for Determination of Vapor Pressure.

vapor and thus prevent the distillation of liquid into the mercury manometer.

A more elaborate dynamic method proposed by Walker involves the saturation of some inert gas, such as nitrogen, with vapor by bubbling a measured quantity of the gas through the liquid at constant temperature and subsequently condensing out, or absorbing, and weighing the vapor of the liquid in question. If P_T is the total pressure in the apparatus at saturation, n_g the moles of gas passed through, and $n_v = W_v/M_v$ the number of moles of vapor collected, then the partial pressure of the vapor P, which is the same as the vapor pressure of the liquid at saturation, is

$$P = \left(\frac{n_v}{n_g + n_v}\right)P_T \tag{18}$$

This method is as a rule much more tedious than the others mentioned, but with care can be made to yield excellent results. It is especially useful in determinations of partial vapor pressures of mixtures of liquids.

VARIATION OF VAPOR PRESSURE WITH TEMPERATURE

The vapor pressure of a liquid, though constant at a given temperature, increases continuously with increase in temperature up to the critical point of the liquid. Above the critical temperature the liquid no longer exists, and consequently the concept of a saturated vapor pressure is no longer valid. In terms of kinetic theory the increase in vapor pressure with temperature is easily understandable. As the temperature increases, a greater proportion of the molecules acquire sufficient energy to escape from the liquid, and consequently a higher pressure is necessary to establish equilibrium between vapor and liquid. Above the critical temperature the escaping tendency of the molecules is so high that no applied pressure is sufficient to keep any of them in the liquid state, and the whole mass persists as a gas.

TABLE 2

VAPOR PRESSURES OF LIQUIDS AT VARIOUS TEMPERATURES
(mm Hg)

Temperature (°C)	CCl_4	C_2H_5OH	CH_3COOH	C_6H_6	H_2O
0	32.9	12.7	3.5	25.3	4.6
10	56.0	24.2	6.4	45.2	9.2
20	91.0	44.5	11.8	75.6	17.5
30	142.3	78.5	20.1	120.2	31.8
40	214.8	133.7	34.2	183.6	55.3
50	314.4	219.9	56.3	271.4	92.5
60	447.4	350.2	88.3	390.1	149.4
70	621.1	541.1	137.9	547.4	233.7
80	843.3	812.9	202.3	753.6	355.1
90	1122.0	1187.0	292.7	1016.1	525.8
100	1463.0	1693.0	417.	1344.3	760.0

The manner in which the vapor pressure varies with temperature is shown in Table 2, and graphically in Fig. 7. The vapor pressure increases slowly at the lower temperatures, and then quite rapidly, as is shown by the steep rise in the curves. This variation of vapor pressure with temperature can be expressed mathematically by means of the Clausius-Clapeyron equation.

We have seen in the last chapter that for a change of phase the Clapeyron equation (41) gives

$$\frac{dP}{dT} = \frac{\Delta H}{T(V_2 - V_1)}$$

For the transition of liquid to vapor under consideration here, P is the vapor pressure at temperature T, $\Delta H = \Delta H_v$ the heat of vaporization of a given weight of liquid, $V_1 = V_l$ its volume, while $V_2 = V_g$ the volume of the same weight of vapor. Consequently, for a vaporization the Clapeyron equation can be written as

$$\frac{dP}{dT} = \frac{\Delta H_v}{T(V_g - V_l)} \qquad (19)$$

At temperatures considerably removed from the critical, V_l is quite small compared to V_g and may be neglected. Thus, at 100° C, V_g for

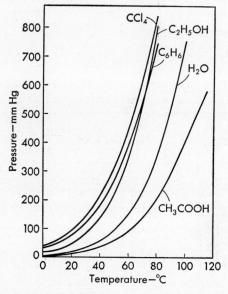

Fig. 7.   Variation of Vapor Pressure with Temperature.

water is 1671 cc per gram, while V_l is only 1.04 cc per gram. Further, if we assume that the vapor behaves essentially as an ideal gas, then V_g per mole is given by $V_g = RT/P$, and equation (19) becomes

$$\frac{dP}{dT} = \frac{\Delta H_v}{TV_g} = \frac{\Delta H_v P}{RT^2} \qquad (20)$$

$$\frac{d \ln P}{dT} = \frac{1}{dT}\left(\frac{dP}{P}\right) = \frac{\Delta H_v}{RT^2} \qquad (21)$$

Before this equation can be integrated, ΔH_v, which is now the heat of vaporization per mole, must be known as a function of temperature. If we assume as an approximation, however, that over the interval in question ΔH_v remains essentially constant, integration yields

$$\ln P = \frac{\Delta H_v}{R} \int \frac{dT}{T^2} + C'$$

$$= -\frac{\Delta H_v}{R}\left(\frac{1}{T}\right) + C'$$

and
$$\log_{10} P = -\frac{\Delta H_v}{2.303\,R}\left(\frac{1}{T}\right) + C \qquad (22)$$

where C' and C are constants of integration.

Equations (21) and (22) are forms of the celebrated *Clausius-Clapeyron equation*. The latter predicts that the logarithm of the vapor pressure

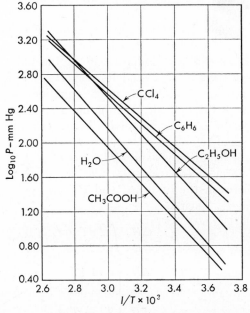

Fig. 8.   Plot of $\log_{10} P$ vs. $1/T$ for Several Liquids.

should be a function of the reciprocal of the absolute temperature. Further, comparison of the equation with the equation of a straight line, namely, $y = mx + b$, suggests that if $\log_{10} P$ for any liquid is plotted against $1/T$, the plot should be a straight line with slope $m = (-\Delta H_v/2.303\,R)$, and y − intercept $b = C$. That this is in accord with the facts may be seen from Fig. 8, where the same data as were shown in Fig. 7 are now plotted as $\log_{10} P$ vs. $1/T$. From the slopes of the lines the heats of vaporization of the various liquids may be calculated, for

$$\text{slope} = m = \frac{-\Delta H_v}{2.303\,R} \qquad (23)$$

and consequently,

$$\Delta H_v = -2.303 \ Rm = -4.576 \ m \ \text{cal mole}^{-1} \tag{24}$$

The heat of vaporization is obtained in calories per mole when the value of R used is in calories per mole per degree, namely, $R = 1.987$. The heat of vaporization of a liquid thus calculated will be the mean value of the heat of vaporization over the temperature interval considered.

To obtain C in equation (22) it is best to substitute in the equation the calculated value of ΔH_v and a value of $\log_{10} P$ and $1/T$ corresponding to a point on the line, and solve for C. Once ΔH_v and C for a given liquid are known, the vapor pressure of the liquid at any temperature over the range of the equation can easily be calculated by merely substituting the desired value of T.

A word about the units of the various terms in equation (22) is in order. Since ΔH_v and R are both in calories, the first term on the right-hand side of the equation is independent of the units in which P is expressed. C, however, is not, and its magnitude will depend on the units of P. Consequently, in setting up an equation for the vapor pressure, it is essential to state clearly whether P is expressed in atmospheres, millimeters of mercury, or some other unit. Similarly, in using an equation from some reference source, attention should be paid to the units in which the equation is expressed.

An alternate form of equation (22) may be obtained by integrating equation (21) between the limits P_1 and P_2 corresponding to the temperatures T_1 and T_2. Then,

$$\int_{P_1}^{P_2} d \ln P = \frac{\Delta H_v}{R} \int_{T_1}^{T_2} \frac{dT}{T^2}$$

$$\ln \frac{P_2}{P_1} = \frac{\Delta H_v}{R} \left[-\frac{1}{T} \right]_{T_1}^{T_2}$$

$$= \frac{\Delta H_v}{R} \left[\frac{T_2 - T_1}{T_1 T_2} \right]$$

or

$$\log_{10} \frac{P_2}{P_1} = \frac{\Delta H_v}{2.303 \ R} \left[\frac{T_2 - T_1}{T_1 T_2} \right] \tag{25}$$

Equation (25) permits the calculation of ΔH_v from the values of the vapor pressure at two temperatures; or, when ΔH_v is known, P at some desired temperature may be calculated from a single available vapor pressure at a given temperature.

Example: At 373.6° K and 372.6° K the vapor pressures of H_2O are 1.018 and 0.982 atm respectively. What is the heat of vaporization of water? Employing equation 25, we have

$$\log_{10} \frac{P_2}{P_1} = \frac{\Delta H_v}{2.303\ R} \left[\frac{T_2 - T_1}{T_1 T_2} \right]$$

$$\log \frac{1.018}{0.982} = \frac{\Delta H_v}{2.303 \times 1.987} \left[\frac{373.6 - 372.6}{373.6 \times 372.6} \right]$$

$$\Delta H_v = 9790\ \text{cal/mole}$$
$$= 540\ \text{cal/g}$$

The experimentally observed value at 373.21° K is 538.7 cal per gram.

Equation (22) will not be strictly valid over wide temperature ranges, particularly because of the assumption of constancy of ΔH_v. When data are available on the variation of ΔH_v with temperature, equation (21) may be integrated to give better agreement with experiment and over a much wider temperature range. When such data are not available, vapor pressure-temperature data are usually correlated by empirical equations of the form

$$\log P = A - \frac{B}{T} + C \log T + DT + \cdots \tag{26}$$

where A, B, C, and D are fitted constants.

THE HEAT OF VAPORIZATION OF LIQUIDS

The heats of vaporization of liquids may also be measured directly in a calorimeter by condensing a definite weight of vapor and observing the temperature rise of the calorimeter, or by supplying to a liquid a definite

TABLE 3

HEATS OF VAPORIZATION OF LIQUIDS*

(Cal/g)

Temperature (° C)	H_2O	CH_3OH	CH_3COOH	C_2H_5OH	Ethyl Ether	CCl_4
0	595	285	—	220	93	52
20	585	280	87.3	218	88	—
40	574	273	—	215	83	—
60	563	265	93.3	210	78	—
80	552	253	—	203	72	46
100	539	241	95.6	194	67	44
120	526	227	—	182	61	42
140	512	213	94.5	170	54	40
160	496	194	—	156	44	38
180	478	175	88.5	136	30	35

* *International Critical Tables*, McGraw-Hill Book Company, Inc., New York, 1929, Vol. V.

amount of electrical energy and measuring the weight of liquid vaporized thereby. The heats of vaporization of several liquids thus obtained at various temperatures are shown in Table 3. The heat of vaporization of a liquid decreases in general with increase in temperature and becomes zero at the critical temperature. For acetic acid, however, ΔH_v increases at first, goes through a maximum at about 120° C, and then decreases with increase in temperature. In magnitude the heats of vaporization of various liquids differ widely. Especially is the heat of vaporization of water abnormally high, a fact which speaks for the complexity of the liquid.

THE BOILING POINT OF A LIQUID

The *normal* boiling point of a liquid is the temperature at which the vapor pressure of the liquid equals 760 mm Hg pressure, or 1 atm. However, a liquid can be made to boil at any temperature between its freezing point and the critical temperature by merely raising or lowering, as the case may be, the external pressure on the liquid. Therefore, it may be

TABLE 4

TROUTON'S CONSTANTS FOR LIQUIDS

Liquid	ΔH_v at Boiling Point (cal mole^{-1})	Normal Boiling Point (°K)	Trouton Constant
Nitrogen	1,338	77.4	17.3
Oxygen	1,636	90.2	18.1
Ammonia	5,570	239.8	23.2
Ethyl ether	6,220	307.8	20.2
Acetone	7,230	329.4	21.9
Methyl acetate	7,270	330.5	22.0
Chloroform	7,040	334.4	21.0
n-Hexane	6,850	341.9	20.0
Carbon tetrachloride	7,140	350.0	20.4
Benzene	7,350	353.3	20.8
Nitrobenzene	9,660	484.1	20.0
Mercury	14,200	629.8	22.5
Zinc	23,700	1,180	20.1
Hydrogen	216	20.5	10.5
Formic acid	5,520	374.0	14.8
Acetic acid	5,810	391.3	14.8
Water	9,710	373.2	26.0
n-Propyl alcohol	9,880	370.4	26.7
Ethyl alcohol	9,410	351.6	26.8
Bismuth	46,100	1,723	26.8
Tin	77,700	2,533	30.7

stated in general that the boiling point of a liquid is the temperature at which the vapor pressure of a liquid becomes equal to the external pressure acting upon the surface of the liquid. Boiling is characterized by the formation within the liquid of bubbles of vapor which rise and escape into the vapor phase.

The change in boiling point produced by a change in pressure may be calculated with the aid of the Clausius-Clapeyron equation. If ΔH_v for the liquid is known, and if T_1 is the boiling point at pressure P_1, the boiling point T_2 at pressure P_2 follows from equation (25). When however, ΔH_v is not known, then its value may be estimated from *Trouton's rule*. This rule states that

$$\frac{\Delta H_v}{T_b} = \text{constant} \tag{27}$$

i.e., *that the ratio of the molar heat of vaporization of a liquid to its normal boiling point on the absolute scale is a constant the same for all liquids.* For ΔH_v in calories per mole and T in ° K the value of the constant is usually taken as about 21. That this rule is only approximate may be seen from Table 4. It holds fairly well for the liquids shown in the first section of the table, but the constants are low for hydrogen and the acids, and high for water, alcohols, and some of the metals.

SURFACE TENSION OF LIQUIDS

Within the body of the liquid a molecule is acted upon by molecular attractions which are distributed more or less symmetrically about the molecule. At the surface, however, a molecule is only partially surrounded by other molecules, and as a consequence it experiences only an attraction toward the body of the liquid. This latter attraction tends to draw the surface molecules inward, and in doing so makes the liquid behave as if it were surrounded by an invisible membrane. This behavior of the surface, called *surface tension*, is the effect responsible for the resistance a liquid exhibits to surface penetration, the nearly spherical shape of falling water droplets, the spherical shape of mercury particles on a flat surface, the rise of liquids in capillary tubes, and the flotation of metal foils on liquid surfaces. From a purely thermodynamic point of view surface tension may be thought of as due to the tendency of a liquid to reduce its surface to a point of minimum potential surface energy, a condition requisite for stable surface equilibrium. Since a sphere has the smallest area for a given volume, the tendency of a liquid particle should be to draw itself into a sphere due to the action of surface tension, as is actually the case.

Since the natural tendency of a liquid is to decrease its surface, any

increase in surface can only be accomplished with the expenditure of
work. Consider a liquid film contained within a rectangular wire frame,
$ABCD$, as shown in Fig. 9. The side $CD = l$ is movable. If a force F
is required to move the wire CD against the force of surface tension acting
in the film along CD, the work done, w, in moving the wire from CD to
EG is

$$w = Fx \qquad (28)$$

The force acting, F, must, of course, be balanced by the force of surface
tension along CD. If we designate
by γ the force *per centimeter* along
CD, and since there are two surfaces to the film,

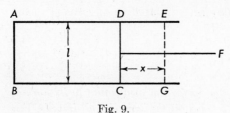

Fig. 9.

$$F = 2\,\gamma l \qquad (29)$$

and $\qquad w = Fx = 2\,\gamma lx \qquad (30)$

From equation (29) γ may be de-
fined as $\gamma = F/2\ l$, or the *force in dynes acting along 1 cm length of surface.*
However, $2\ lx$ is the area of new surface of liquid generated by CD, ΔA,
and hence equation (30) becomes also

$$w = \gamma(2\ lx) = \gamma\Delta A$$

and $$\gamma = \frac{w}{\Delta A} \qquad (31)$$

Consequently, γ may be considered also as the *work in ergs necessary to
generate a square centimeter of surface area,* and is, therefore, referred to
frequently as the free surface energy of a liquid per square centimeter of
area.

MEASUREMENT OF SURFACE TENSION

The surface tension is a characteristic property of each liquid and differs
greatly in magnitude for different liquids. Of the various methods available for measuring surface tension, such as the tensiometer, drop weight,
bubble pressure, or capillary rise methods, the last is by far the most
important and is considered the standard. The capillary rise method for
the estimation of surface tension is based on the fact that most liquids
when brought into contact with a fine glass capillary tube will rise in the
tube to a level above that of the liquid outside the tube. This will occur
only when the liquid "wets" glass, i.e., adheres to it. If the liquid does not
"wet" glass, as mercury for instance, the level inside the capillary will
fall below that outside, and the mercury will exhibit a convex surface, as
against the concave surface in the first instance.

To understand the theory of the capillary rise method, consider a fine capillary tube of uniform radius r immersed in a vessel containing a liquid that wets glass (Fig. 10). By wetting the inner wall of the capillary the surface of the liquid is increased. To decrease its free surface the liquid must rise within the capillary. As soon as this happens, however, the glass is again wet, and again the liquid draws itself upward. This process does not continue indefinitely, but stops when the force of surface tension acting upward becomes equal to the force due to the column of liquid acting downward. If we call γ the surface tension in dynes per centimeter of inner circumference, and consider the force to be acting at an angle θ, called the *contact angle*, with the vertical, then the force due to surface tension is

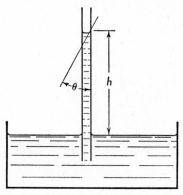

$$F_1 = 2\,\pi r \gamma \cos \theta$$

This force is balanced by that due to the column of liquid of height h, or

$$F_2 = \pi r^2 h d g$$

Fig. 10.   Capillary Rise Method for Determination of Surface Tension.

where d is the density of the liquid and g is the acceleration of gravity in centimeters per second per second. Therefore, since at equilibrium $F_2 = F_1$,

$$2\,\pi r \gamma \cos \theta = \pi r^2 h d g$$

and

$$\gamma = \frac{\pi r^2 h d g}{2\,\pi r \cos \theta} = \frac{r h d g}{2 \cos \theta} \tag{32}$$

For most liquids which wet glass θ is essentially zero, and $\cos \theta = 1$. Then

$$\gamma = \frac{r h d g}{2} \tag{33}$$

and γ may be calculated provided we know the radius of the capillary, the density of the liquid, and the height to which the liquid will rise in the capillary.

For precise work two corrections must be applied, one for the volume of the meniscus and another for the density of the gas above the liquid. Under these conditions equation (33) becomes

$$\gamma = \frac{(h + r/3)(d_l - d_v) r g}{2} \tag{34}$$

where d_l is the density of the liquid and d_v the density of the gas above the liquid.

In the tensiometer method a platinum fork or ring is immersed in the liquid to be tested, and the force necessary to separate the fork or ring from the liquid surface is then measured. The force required for this operation can be related to the surface tension of the liquid. In the drop weight method, on the other hand, the liquid whose surface tension is to be determined is allowed to pass very slowly through a calibrated capillary tip so as to form an approximately spherical drop. When the drop has attained a definite weight, depending on the size of the capillary tip and the surface tension of the liquid, a portion of it will detach itself and fall. Harkins and Brown[1] have shown that the surface tension of the liquid may be determined from the weight of the falling drop W, and the radius of the capillary tip by the relation

$$\gamma = \frac{Wg}{2\,\pi r f} \tag{35}$$

where f is a complicated function of $(r/V^{1/3})$, V being the volume of the drop. For the nature of the function f and details of the method the student is referred to Harkins's papers on the subject.

VARIATION OF SURFACE TENSION WITH TEMPERATURE

As may be seen from Table 5, the surface tension of liquids decreases as the temperature is increased, and becomes zero at the critical temperature. The variation of surface tension with temperature may be represented by the Ramsay-Shields equation,

$$\gamma \left(\frac{M}{d_l}\right)^{2/3} = k(t_c - t - 6) \tag{36}$$

where γ is the surface tension at temperature t, and M, d_l, and t_c are the molecular weight, density, and critical temperature of the liquid, respectively. Since M/d_l is the molar volume of the liquid, $(M/d_l)^{2/3}$ is a quantity proportional to the molar surface of the liquid, and hence the product on the left of equation (36) is frequently referred to as the *molar surface energy*. k is a constant which is supposed to be independent of temperature.

The Ramsay-Shields equation has been found to be valid for many liquids up to within 30° to 50° of the critical temperature. However, the equation predicts that γ will be zero at $t = (t_c - 6)$ and that it will become negative at the critical temperature. To obviate this difficulty Katayama suggested the modified equation

$$\gamma \left(\frac{M}{d_l - d_v}\right)^{2/3} = k'(t_c - t) \tag{37}$$

[1] Harkins and Brown, *J. Am. Chem. Soc.*, **41**, 499 (1919).

TABLE 5

SURFACE TENSION OF LIQUIDS AT VARIOUS TEMPERATURES*

(Dynes cm^{-1})

Liquid	0° C	20° C	40° C	60° C	80° C	100° C
Water	75.64	72.75	69.56	66.18	62.61	58.85
C_2H_5OH	24.05	22.27	20.60	19.01	—	—
CH_3OH	24.5	22.6	20.9	—	—	15.7
CCl_4	—	26.8	24.3	21.9	—	—
Ethyl ether	—	17.0	—	—	—	7.97
Acetone	26.2	23.7	21.2	18.6	16.2	—
Toluene	30.74	28.43	26.13	23.81	21.53	19.39
Benzene	31.6	28.9	26.3	23.7	21.3	—

* *International Critical Tables*, McGraw-Hill Book Company, Inc., New York, 1928, Vol. IV.

where d_v is the density of the vapor at temperature t. In this equation $\gamma = 0$ when $t = t_c$.

THE VISCOSITY OF LIQUIDS

Liquids exhibit much greater resistance to flow than gases, and consequently they have much higher viscosity coefficients. The viscosity coefficients of gases increase with temperature, while those of most liquids decrease with rising temperature. Again, we have seen that the viscosity coefficients for gases at moderate pressures are essentially independent of pressure, whereas with liquids increase of pressure leads to an increase in viscosity.

Most methods employed for the measurement of the viscosity of liquids are based on either the Poiseuille or Stokes equations. The Poiseuille equation for the coefficient of viscosity of a fluid is

$$\eta = \frac{\pi P r^4 t}{8\, lV} \tag{38}$$

where V is the volume of liquid of viscosity η which flows in time t through a capillary tube of radius r and length l under a pressure head of P dynes per square centimeter. This equation has been verified repeatedly. To determine the viscosity of a liquid by this equation it is not always necessary to measure all the quantities indicated when once the viscosity of some reference liquid, usually water, is known with accuracy. If we measure the time of flow of the same volume of two different liquids through the same capillary, then according to the Poiseuille equation the ratio of the viscosity coefficients of the two liquids is given by

$$\frac{\eta_1}{\eta_2} = \frac{\pi P_1 r^4 t_1}{8\,lV} \cdot \frac{8\,lV}{\pi P_2 r^4 t_2} = \frac{P_1 t_1}{P_2 t_2}$$

Since the pressures P_1 and P_2 are proportional to the densities of the two liquids d_1 and d_2, we may write also

$$\frac{\eta_1}{\eta_2} = \frac{P_1 t_1}{P_2 t_2} = \frac{d_1 t_1}{d_2 t_2} \tag{39}$$

Consequently, once d_1, d_2, and η_2 are known, determination of t_1 and t_2 permits the calculation of η_1, the viscosity coefficient of the liquid under consideration.

The quantities t_1 and t_2 in equation (39) are most conveniently measured with an Ostwald viscometer (Fig. 11). A definite quantity of liquid is introduced into the viscometer immersed in a thermostat and is then drawn up by suction into bulb B until the liquid level is above the mark a. The liquid is then allowed to drain, and the time necessary for the liquid level to fall from a to b is measured with a stopwatch. The viscometer is now cleaned, the reference liquid added, and the whole operation repeated. In this simple manner t_1 and t_2 are obtained, and the viscosity of the liquid is calculated by equation (39).

Stokes's law is concerned with the fall of bodies through fluid media. A *spherical* body of radius r and density d, falling under gravity through a fluid of density d_m, is acted on by the gravitational force f_1,

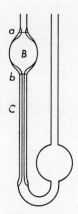

Fig. 11. Ostwald Viscometer.

$$f_1 = \frac{4}{3}\pi r^3 (d - d_m)g \tag{40}$$

where g is the acceleration of gravity. This force, which tends to accelerate the body falling through the fluid medium, is opposed by frictional forces within the medium which increase with increase in velocity of the falling body. Eventually a uniform rate of fall is reached at which the frictional forces become equal to the gravitational force, and thereafter the body will continue to fall with a *constant velocity* v. Sir George G. Stokes showed that, for a spherical body falling under the conditions of constant uniform velocity, the force of friction, f_2, is given by

$$f_2 = 6\,\pi r \eta v \tag{41}$$

Equating the gravitational and frictional forces, we see that

$$\frac{4}{3}\pi r^3(d - d_m)g = 6\,\pi r\eta v$$

$$\eta = \frac{2\,r^2(d - d_m)g}{9\,v} \tag{42}$$

This equation, known as *Stokes's law*, is applicable to the fall of spherical bodies in all types of fluid media provided the radius of the falling body r is large compared to the distance between the molecules of the fluid. When r is smaller than the distance between molecules there is a tendency for the falling body to "drop" or "channel," and the equation is no longer applicable.

Stokes's law is the basis of the falling sphere viscometer. The viscometer consists of a vertical cylindrical tube filled with the liquid under test and immersed in a thermostat at the desired temperature. A steel ball, of density d and a diameter suitable to give a slow rate of fall, is now dropped through the neck of the tube, and the time of fall between two marks is determined with a stopwatch. The viscosity coefficient of the liquid is calculated from the equation

$$\eta = \frac{2\,r^2(d - d_m)g}{9\,(s/t)(1 + 2.4\,r/R)} \tag{43}$$

where s is the distance of timed fall, d_m is the density of the liquid, r is the radius of the ball, t is the time required for fall through the distance s, and R is the radius of the viscometer tube. The last term in the denominator is a correction for the influence of the size of the container and becomes negligible when R is very much greater than r. Then equation (43) reduces to the simple Stokes's law equation (42). From either equation (43) or (42) the viscosity coefficient of a liquid relative to a standard is given by

$$\frac{\eta_1}{\eta_2} = \frac{(d - d_{m_1})t_1}{(d - d_{m_2})t_2} \tag{44}$$

Hence, the relative viscosity of a liquid may be determined from the times of fall of the same ball and the densities of the two liquids without the knowledge of s, r, or R.

A term frequently employed in connection with viscosity is *fluidity*. The fluidity, ϕ, of a substance is merely the reciprocal of the viscosity coefficient, namely, $\phi = 1/\eta$.

VARIATION OF VISCOSITY WITH TEMPERATURE

Table 6 gives the viscosity coefficients in centipoises of several liquids at various temperatures. With very rare exceptions (liquid carbon dioxide at low temperatures), the viscosity of a liquid decreases with increase in temperature. Various equations have been proposed to represent η as a function of T, of which the simplest is

$$\log \eta = \frac{A}{T} + B \tag{45}$$

A and B are constants, and T is the absolute temperature. This equation holds quite well for a large number of pure liquids. A more elaborate equation

$$\log \eta = \frac{A}{T} + B \log T + C \tag{46}$$

where A, B, and C are constants, has been found to give very good results for a wide variety of liquid systems.

TABLE 6

VISCOSITY COEFFICIENTS OF LIQUIDS*

(Centipoises)

Liquid	0° C	20° C	40° C	60° C	80° C	100° C
H_2O	1.794	1.009	0.654	0.470	0.357	0.284
CH_3OH	0.808	0.593	0.449	0.349		
$CHCl_3$	0.699	0.563	0.464	0.389		
C_8H_{18}	0.7060	0.5419	0.4328	0.3551	0.2971	
Toluene	0.7719	0.5903	0.4713	0.3874		
C_2H_5OH	1.772	1.200	0.834	0.592		
Benzene	0.900	0.647	0.492	0.389		
Nitrobenzene	3.083	2.013	1.438	1.094	0.875	0.705

* *International Critical Tables*, McGraw-Hill Book Company, Inc., New York, 1929–30, Vols. V and VII.

The viscosity of liquids is a question of considerable industrial importance. In practice various methods of measuring viscosity have been evolved, and various schemes for representing the variations of viscosity with temperature have been proposed. These, however, are beyond the scope of this book.

REFERENCES FOR FURTHER READING

1. G. Barr, *Monograph on Viscometry*, Oxford University Press, Oxford, 1931.
2. E. C. Bingham, *Fluidity and Plasticity*, McGraw-Hill Book Company, Inc., New York, 1922.
3. S. Glasstone, *Textbook of Physical Chemistry*, D. Van Nostrand Company, Inc., New York, 1946, Chap. VII.

4. H. S. Green, *The Molecular Theory of Fluids*, Interscience Publishers, Inc., New York, 1952.
5. W. Swietoslawski, *Ebulliometric Measurements*, Reinhold Publishing Corporation, New York, 1945.
6. H. S. Taylor and S. Glasstone, *Treatise on Physical Chemistry*, D. Van Nostrand Company, Inc., New York, 1951, Vol. II, Chap. III.
7. A. Weissberger, *Physical Methods of Organic Chemistry*, Interscience Publishers, Inc., New York, 1949, Vol. I, Chaps. IV, V, VIII, and IX.

PROBLEMS

1. Calculate the van der Waals constants for C_2H_6 from the critical temperature and pressure listed in Table 1. Using the constants thus calculated find the pressure exerted by 10 g of C_2H_6 when contained in a liter flask at $13°$ C.

2. The van der Waals constants for HCl are $a = 3.67$ atm-liter^2 mole^{-2}, and $b = 40.8$ cc mole^{-1}. Find the critical constants of this substance.

3. A modified form of the van der Waals equation (Berthelot) is

$$\left(P + \frac{n^2\alpha}{TV^2}\right)(V - n\beta) = nRT$$

where all the terms have their usual significance, and α and β are constants. Deduce the expressions for α, β, and R in terms of the critical constants.

4. Calculate the critical density of methyl alcohol from the following data:

$t°$ C	P (atm)	$d_{liq.}$ (g/cc)	$d_{vap.}$ (g/cc)
150	13.57	0.6495	0.01562
225	61.25	0.4675	0.1003

The critical temperature is $240.0°$ C.

5. Compare the reduced pressures of N_2 and NH_3 when each exerts a pressure of 100 atm.   *Ans.* N_2: 2.99; NH_3: 0.90.

6. Compare the reduced temperatures of ethylene and H_2 at $27°$ C.

7. Set up the reduced equation of state for the modified van der Waals equation given in problem 3.

8. In measuring the vapor pressure of a liquid by means of the isoteniscope, the height of the Hg in the manometer was found to be 53.32 cm at $40°$ C, and 39.40 cm at $55°$ C. The barometric pressure was 741.0 mm. What are the vapor pressures of the liquid at the two temperatures?

9. In measuring the vapor pressure of ethanol by the gas saturation method, the following data were taken:

> Volume of N_2 at 740 mm and $30°$ C = 5.6 liters
> Barometric pressure   = 740 mm
> Temperature   = $30°$ C
> Loss in weight of alcohol   = 1.193 g

Find the vapor pressure of ethanol at $30°$ C.   *Ans.* 78.2 mm Hg.

10. At the normal boiling point, $61.5°$ C, the heat of vaporization of $CHCl_3$ is 59.0 cal/g. Assuming that the vapor behaves as an ideal gas and that the volume of the liquid is negligible compared to that of the vapor, what is ΔE per mole for the vaporization process?

11. The vapor pressure of ethanol is 135.3 mm at 40° C and 542.5 mm at 70° C. Calculate the molar heat of vaporization and the vapor pressure of ethanol at 50° C.   *Ans.* ΔH_v = 9880 cal/mole; $P_{50°\ C}$ = 221.0 mm.

12. The heat of vaporization of ethyl ether is 83.9 cal/g while its vapor pressure at 30° is 647.3 mm. What will be the vapor pressure at 0° C?

13. The vapor pressure of CH_3Cl between −47° C and −10° C can be represented by the equation:

$$\log_{10} P_{mm} = \frac{-1149}{T} + 7.481$$

What is the heat of vaporization of this liquid in calories per gram?
                                                          Ans. 104.1 cal/g.

14. At the normal boiling point of isopropanol, 82.3° C, its heat of vaporization is 159 cal/g. Calculate the vapor pressure of this liquid at 27° C.

15. For $CHCl_3$ the normal boiling point is 61.5° C, while the heat of vaporization is 59.0 cal/g. At what temperature will $CHCl_3$ boil under a pressure of 700 mm?
                                                          Ans. 58.9° C.

16. A liquid is observed to boil at 120° C under a pressure of 725 mm. Its molar heat of vaporization is 8200 cal/mole. Calculate the normal boiling point of the liquid.

17. The normal boiling point of C_6H_5Br is 156.15° C. Using Trouton's rule, find the vapor pressure at 100° C, and compare with the observed value of 141.1 mm.

18. CCl_4 exhibits the following vapor pressures at the indicated temperatures:

t (° C)	30	50	70	100
P (mm Hg)	142.3	314.4	621.1	1463.0

Set up the equation giving $\log_{10} P$ as a function of the temperature.

19. Beattie and Marple [*J. Am. Chem. Soc.*, **72**, 1450 (1950)] give the following equation for the vapor pressure of 1-butene as a function of the temperature between −75° and 125° C:

$$\log_{10} P \text{ (atm)} = 5.475462 - \frac{1343.516}{T} - 167.515 \times 10^{-5}\ T$$

Find: (a) the expression for ΔH_v as a function of the temperature; (b) ΔH_v at 300° K; (c) the normal boiling point of the liquid.

20. The heat of vaporization of a certain liquid as a function of the temperature is given by the relation

$$\Delta H_v = a + bT + cT^2$$

where a, b, and c are constants. What will be the expression for $\ln P$ as a $f(T)$?

21. To measure the heat of vaporization of a liquid calorimetrically, 13.5200 g of vapor of the liquid, initially at 45.35° C, were passed into a calorimeter and condensed there. During this process the temperature of the calorimeter rose from 25.015° C to 26.525° C. If the heat capacity of the calorimeter is 453.25 cal/degree, and if the specific heat of the vapor is 0.180 cal g^{-1} degree^{-1}, what is the heat of vaporization of the liquid in calories per gram?
                                                          Ans. 47.1 cal/g.

22. The radius of a given capillary is 0.105 mm. A liquid whose density is 0.80 g/cc rises in this capillary to a height of 6.25 cm. Calculate the surface tension of the liquid.

23. From the following data calculate the critical temperature of CO_2:

Temperature (° C)	Density (g/cc)	Surface Tension (dynes/cm)
0	0.927	4.50
20	0.772	1.16

24. In measuring the surface tension of a liquid by the drop-weight method, 12 drops of the liquid falling from a tip whose diameter is 0.8 cm are found to weigh 0.971 g. If $f(r/V^{1/3}) = 0.6$ under these conditions, what is the surface tension in dynes per centimeter?   *Ans.* 52.60 dynes/cm.

25. The surface tension of mercury at 0° C is 480.3 dynes/cm while the density is 13.595 g/cc. If it is desired to obtain a *fall* in height of 10.0 cm, what radius of glass capillary tube will have to be used?

26. From the following data for CH_3Cl

t (° C)	0	10	20
γ (dynes/cm)	19.5	17.8	16.2
d_l (g/cc)	0.955	0.937	0.918
d_v (g/cc)	0.00599	0.00820	0.0110

determine the constant k in the Ramsay-Shields equation and the critical temperature of the liquid.

27. Using the data given in the preceding problem, determine the constant k' in the Katayama equation and t_c of CH_3Cl.

28. A steel ball of density 7.9 g/cc and 4 mm diameter requires 55 sec to fall a distance of 1 m through an oil of density 1.1 g/cc. Neglecting the correction due to the radius of the viscometer tube, calculate the viscosity of the oil in poises.

29. The time of efflux of H_2O through an Ostwald viscometer is 1.52 min. For the same volume of an organic liquid of density 0.800 g/cc the time is 2.25 min. Find the viscosity of the liquid relative to that of water and its absolute viscosity in millipoises. The temperature is 20° C.

30. Using the data for the viscosity coefficients of C_2H_5OH as a function of temperature given in Table 6, find for this substance the constants A and B in equation (45).

4

The Solid State

Solids differ from liquids and gases in possessing both definite volume and definite shape. The geometric stability of a solid is not due to any difference in compactness between the solid and liquid states, for the density of a substance in the solid state may actually be less than that of the corresponding liquid, as in the case of ice and water. The definite shape of a solid is to be ascribed rather to the fact that the structural units, instead of being in random motion like the molecules of a liquid or gas, are confined to definite positions of equilibrium within the crystal of the solid, positions about which the particles may vibrate but which they cannot readily leave.

Solid substances are frequently classed as either *crystalline* or *amorphous*. A crystalline solid is one in which the constituent structural units are arranged in a definite geometrical configuration characteristic of the substance. Amorphous substances, on the other hand, although possessing many of the attributes of a solid, such as definite shape, a certain rigidity, and hardness, do not show under test a definite configurational arrangement. For that reason they are not considered to be true solids but rather highly supercooled liquids of very high viscosity. Further, crystalline substances such as ice, sodium chloride, or naphthalene melt sharply at a constant and definite temperature, while amorphous substances like glass or asphalt melt gradually and over a temperature interval. However, under certain conditions an amorphous substance may acquire crystalline characteristics. Thus glass may crystallize on long standing or heating. Again, natural rubber when stretched exhibits a definite pattern on examination with x rays, an indication of the production of a definite configurational arrangement.

CRYSTALLIZATION AND FUSION

A pure liquid on being cooled suffers a decrease in the average translational energy of its molecules, and hence its temperature drops until the freezing point is reached. At this temperature the attractive forces of the molecules are sufficient to overcome the translational energy, and the molecules are forced to arrange themselves in a geometric pattern which is characteristic for each substance. When crystallization starts, heat is evolved in amount equal to the difference in heat content between solid and liquid, namely,

$$\Delta H_c = H_s - H_l \tag{1}$$

where ΔH_c is the *heat of crystallization*, while H_s and H_l are the heat contents of solid and liquid respectively, all per mole. This heat evolution arrests further temperature drop, and the temperature of the mixture of solid and liquid remains constant as long as both phases are present. Further removal of heat results merely in the crystallization of more liquid, until finally the whole mass solidifies; only then does the temperature begin to fall again on cooling.

The reverse of crystallization is the fusion or melting of the solid. As the pure solid is heated, its average vibrational energy increases, until at the melting point some particles are vibrating with sufficient energy to overcome the confining forces. The solid then begins to fuse. The temperature at which this occurs is the *same* as the crystallization temperature. To accomplish further fusion, heat must be supplied to compensate for the loss of the particles with high energy. The amount of heat which must be *absorbed* to accomplish the transition of 1 mole of solid to 1 mole of liquid is known as the *heat of fusion*, ΔH_f. This amount of heat must represent the difference in heat contents of 1 mole of liquid and solid respectively and must therefore be *equal in magnitude* but *opposite in sign* to the heat of crystallization of the substance, namely,

$$\Delta H_f = (H_l - H_s) = -\Delta H_c \tag{2}$$

The melting point of a solid is constant only at a fixed confining pressure and will be displaced by a change in external pressure in a direction which is determined by the relative densities of solid and liquid. The variation of melting point with pressure is given by the Clapeyron equation,

$$\frac{dT}{dP} = T\frac{(V_l - V_s)}{\Delta H_f} \tag{3}$$

where dT is the change in melting point produced by the change in pressure dP, T is the melting point, and V_l and V_s are the molar volumes of

liquid and solid respectively. If the volumes are expressed in cubic
centimeters and the pressures in atmospheres, ΔH_f must be expressed in
cubic centimeter-atmospheres per mole. To convert ΔH_f in calories to this
unit it is merely necessary to multiply ΔH_f by 41.2. From equation (3) it is
seen that, since ΔH_f and T are always positive, an increase in pressure (dP
positive) will result in a rise in melting point if V_l is greater than V_s, and a
lowering in melting point if V_s is greater than V_l. In other words, increase
in external pressure will favor the state having the higher density.

Equation (3) cannot be integrated unless both ΔH_f and $(V_l - V_s)$ are
known as functions of the temperature or pressure. Since such data are
usually not available, it is customary to employ the equation in differential form. Its use can be illustrated by an example. The melting
point of acetic acid is 16.60° C at atmospheric pressure, while ΔH_f and
$(V_l - V_s)$ are 46.42 cal and 0.1601 cc per gram respectively. Designating by M the molecular weight of acetic acid, we obtain for the change
in melting point per atmosphere change in pressure

$$\frac{\Delta T}{\Delta P} = T \frac{(V_l - V_s)}{\Delta H_f} = \frac{289.8(0.1601)M}{(46.42 \times 41.2)M}$$
$$= 0.0242 \text{ degree/atm}$$

At 11 atm total pressure, for instance, $\Delta P = 10$, and the melting point
at that pressure would be

$$t = 16.60 + 0.0242 \times 10$$
$$= 16.84° \text{ C}$$

It will be observed that the effect of pressure on the melting point is not
very large, and for small pressure variations may be disregarded.

Water is the interesting example of a substance having V_s greater
than V_l, and hence the melting point of water is lowered by the application of pressure.

SUBLIMATION PRESSURE OF SOLIDS

Many solids when placed in an evacuated space are found to exhibit
discernible and measurable vapor pressures. At any given temperature
the vapor pressure established is constant and unique for each substance.
The equilibrium vapor pressure of a solid, known as the *sublimation pres-*
sure, is entirely analogous to the saturated vapor pressure of a liquid. As
in liquids, the sublimation pressure represents an equilibrium between
the rate of evaporation of atoms or molecules from the surface of the solid
and the rate of return of molecules or atoms to the solid.

The effects of the direct evaporation or sublimation of solids are frequently directly observable. In winter snow will slowly disappear even

though the temperature remains considerably below freezing. Naphthalene (moth balls) exposed in a room will vanish with time, and the presence of the vapor can be detected by the odor. Iodine is customarily purified by sublimation of the solid and condensation of the vapors. Many other solids, however, exhibit no odor or measurable vapor pressures. Still, from a theoretical point of view it is convenient to ascribe to a solid a sublimation pressure at each temperature, no matter how small it may be, and whether it is measurable or not.

The process of sublimation, like that of vaporization of a liquid, is associated with a thermal change. The molar *heat of sublimation* is the number of calories required to vaporize 1 mole of solid at any given temperature. More precisely the heat of sublimation, ΔH_s, is defined as

$$\Delta H_s = H_v - H_s \tag{4}$$

where H_s is the molar heat content of the solid and H_v that of the vapor.

The sublimation pressure of solids increases with temperature. The effect of temperature on the sublimation pressure is readily deducible from the Clapeyron equation, which for the equilibrium solid-vapor takes the form

$$\frac{dP}{dT} = \frac{\Delta H_s}{T(V_g - V_s)} \tag{5}$$

V_g and V_s are the volumes of 1 mole of vapor and solid respectively, and P is the sublimation pressure at any absolute temperature T. V_s is negligibly small compared to V_g. Again, if we assume the ideal gas laws to be valid for the vapor, then $V_g = RT/P$, and

$$\frac{dP}{dT} = \frac{\Delta H_s}{T(V_g)} = \frac{\Delta H_s P}{RT^2}$$
$$\frac{d \ln P}{dT} = \frac{\Delta H_s}{RT^2} \tag{6}$$

Integrating this equation on the assumption that ΔH_s is constant, once without limits, and again between the limits P_1 and P_2 at the temperature T_1 and T_2, we obtain

$$\log_{10} P = -\frac{\Delta H_s}{2.303\ R}\left(\frac{1}{T}\right) + C \tag{7a}$$

$$\log_{10}\left(\frac{P_2}{P_1}\right) = \frac{\Delta H_s}{2.303\ R}\left[\frac{T_2 - T_1}{T_1 T_2}\right] \tag{7b}$$

These equations represent integrated forms of the Clausius-Clapeyron equation as applied to sublimation. They are exactly analogous to the equations developed in the preceding chapter for the vapor pressure of a liquid and are manipulated in the same way. They may be employed to represent the sublimation pressure of a solid as a function of temperature, to evaluate the heat of sublimation when the vapor pressures are known at at least two temperatures, or to calculate the sublimation pressure at a desired temperature when ΔH_s and P at some given temperature are known.

THE HEAT CAPACITY OF SOLIDS

The variation of the heat capacity with temperature for several solid elements is shown in Fig. 1. It will be observed that the heat capacities

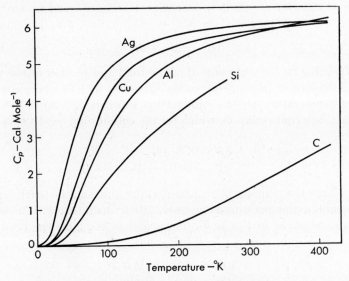

Fig. 1.   Variation of Heat Capacity with Temperature.

of elements like aluminum, copper, and silver are zero at 0° K, and increase very rapidly with temperature, approaching a value of 3 R = 5.97 cal mole⁻¹ at or near room temperature. Carbon and silicon, on the other hand, show a much more gradual increase in heat capacity with temperature and do not attain the 3 R value until very much higher temperatures. In fact, the heat capacity of carbon does not become 3 R until above 1300° C.

The first satisfactory approach to the theory of specific heats of crystalline monatomic solids was made by Albert Einstein in 1907. Einstein pointed out that the atoms constituting a crystal may be considered to be oscillators executing simple harmonic motion about their mean positions of equilibrium in the crystal. He ascribed to each substance a constant and characteristic frequency of vibration, ν, and postulated that absorption of energy by the oscillators does not take place continuously as called for by classical mechanics but discontinuously as postulated in the quantum theory of Planck (see Chapter 21). With these assumptions Einstein was able to show that the heat capacity per mole at constant volume C_v, at any temperature T, should be given for a monatomic crystalline solid by the equation

$$C_v = 3\,kN\left(\frac{h\nu}{kT}\right)^2 \frac{e^{h\nu/kT}}{(e^{h\nu/kT} - 1)^2} \qquad (8)$$

Here N is Avogadro's number, $k = R/N = 1.380 \times 10^{-16}$ erg degree^{-1}, e the base of natural logarithms, h a universal constant known as Planck's constant and equal to 6.625×10^{-27} erg-sec, while ν is the characteristic frequency. This equation predicts that C_v will approach zero at $T = 0$ and that at high temperatures C_v will approach asymptotically the value 3 R. In both these respects the equation is in general agreement with the facts. In the intermediate range, however, the equation gives C_v values considerably lower than those actually observed.

A more successful theory of specific heats of solids is that of Peter Debye (1912). Debye assumed that a solid does not vibrate with a single characteristic frequency but may be capable of vibrating with any frequency from zero up to a limiting frequency ν_m. By introducing certain principles from the theory of elasticity, and by employing the quantum theory, he was able to derive an equation for C_v as a function of temperature which, although more complicated than Einstein's, is in excellent accord with experiment for a large group of crystalline solids. Debye's theory also predicts that C_v will become zero at $T = 0$ and will approach asymptotically the value 3 R at high temperatures. Further, the equation has been found to be applicable not only to elementary crystalline solids but also to such substances as sodium, potassium, lead, and silver chlorides.

Another valuable contribution of the Debye theory is that it predicts at very low temperatures a linear relation between C_v and T^3, namely,

$$C_v = A\,T^3 \qquad (9)$$

where A is a constant. This equation, known as the *Debye third power law*, has been repeatedly verified. Since experimental determinations of specific heats cannot be carried conveniently below 15 to 20° K, the Debye third power law is employed to estimate the heat capacities of solids between 0 and say 20° K.

A shortcoming of the Debye theory is that it accounts only for heat capacities up to 3 R. Yet certain elements, particularly the alkali metals, reach values of C_v considerably above this limit at high temperatures. The excess absorption of energy is usually ascribed to electrons, of whose displacement by thermal means the simple Debye theory takes no account.

CRYSTALLOGRAPHY

Crystallography is the branch of science which deals with the geometry, properties, and structure of crystals and crystalline substances. Geometric crystallography is concerned with the outward spatial arrangement of crystal planes and the geometric shape of crystals, and is based on three fundamental laws, namely: (a) the law of constancy of interfacial angles; (b) the law of rationality of indices; and (c) the law of symmetry. The law of constancy of interfacial angles states that for a given substance the corresponding faces or planes forming the external surface of a crystal always intersect at a definite angle and that this angle remains constant no matter how the faces develop. Commonly, it is observed that the crystal planes are unequally developed so as to produce faces of variable size and shape; but the angle of intersection of any two corresponding faces is always found to be the same for any crystal of the same substance.

For any crystal a set of three coordinate axes can be so chosen that all the faces of the crystal will either intercept these axes at definite distances from the origin, or be parallel to some of the axes, in which case the intercepts are at infinity. The law of rationality of indices or intercepts, proposed in 1784 by Haüy, states that it is possible to choose along the three coordinate axes unit distances (a, b, c), not necessarily the same length, such that the ratio of the three intercepts of any plane in the crystal is given by $(ma:nb:pc)$, where m, n, and p are either integral whole numbers, including infinity, or fractions of whole numbers. The law may be illustrated with data on crystals of the mineral topaz, $Al_2(FOH)_2SiO_4$, for which four different planes have the parameters,

$$
\begin{array}{llll}
1. & m = 1 & n = 1 & p = 1 \\
2. & m = 1 & n = 1 & p = \infty \\
3. & m = 1 & n = 1 & p = \tfrac{2}{3} \\
4. & m = 2 & n = 1 & p = \infty
\end{array}
$$

and hence the intercept ratios are

$$
\begin{array}{ll}
1. & a:b:c \\
2. & a:b:\infty c \\
3. & a:b:\tfrac{2}{3} c \\
4. & 2a:b:\infty c
\end{array}
$$

For any particular plane these ratios characterize the plane and may consequently be used to represent it. The coefficients of a, b, and c are known as the *Weiss indices* of a plane. However, Weiss indices are rather awkward in use and have consequently been replaced by Miller indices. The Miller indices of a plane are obtained by taking the reciprocals of the Weiss coefficients and multiplying through by the smallest number that will express all the reciprocals as integers. Thus a plane which in the Weiss notation is given by $a:b: \infty c$ becomes in the Miller notation $a:b:0\ c$, or simply (110), since the order a, b, c is understood. Similarly, a face $a: \infty b: \frac{1}{4} c$ becomes (104). As an exercise the student may verify the statement that the four planes mentioned above for topaz are respectively (111), (110), (223), and (120) in the Miller system of crystal face notation.

The third law of crystallography states simply that all crystals of the same substance possess the same elements of symmetry. There are three possible types of symmetry. First, if a crystal can be divided by an imaginary plane passed through its center into two equal portions each of which is a mirror image of the other, the crystal is said to possess a *plane of symmetry*. Second, a crystal is said to possess *line symmetry* if it is possible to draw an imaginary line through the center of the crystal and then revolve the crystal about this line through 360° in such a way as to cause the crystal to appear unchanged two, three, four, or six times. Depending on the number of times the crystal appears unchanged on revolution, the crystal is said to possess two-, three-, four-, or sixfold symmetry. Finally, a crystal is said to possess a center of symmetry if every face has an identical face at an equal distance on the opposite side of this center. The total number of plane, line, and center symmetries possessed by a crystal is termed the *elements of symmetry* of the crystal.

THE CRYSTAL SYSTEMS

There are 230 crystal forms possible, and practically all have been observed. On the basis of their symmetry these 230 crystal forms may be grouped into 32 classes, and these in turn may be referred to six crystal systems. All the crystals belonging to a particular system are characterized by the fact that, although they may not all have the same elements of symmetry, they can all be referred to a particular set of crystallographic axes which differ from system to system in length of the various axes and the angles of inclination between axes. Table 1 lists the six crystal systems, their axial characteristics, the *maximum* symmetry which may be expected in each system, and some examples of substances crystallizing in the various systems. For a discussion of the various geometric forms which correspond to each of these systems the student must be referred to treatises on the subject.[1]

Such elementary forms as the cube, the octahedron, and the dodecahedron, a figure possessing 12 sides each of which is a rhombus, are all forms corresponding to the regular system, and all possess the maximum

---

[1] See Kraus, Hunt, and Ramsdell, *Mineralogy*, McGraw-Hill Book Company, Inc., New York, 1951.

TABLE 1

CRYSTAL SYSTEMS AND THEIR CHARACTERISTICS

System	Axial Characteristics	Maximum Symmetry	Examples
1. Regular (cubic or isometric)	Three axes at right angles. Unit distances: $a = b = c$	Nine planes Thirteen axes	NaCl KCl Alums Diamond CaF_2 (Fluorspar)
2. Tetragonal	Three axes at right angles, only two of equal length. Unit distances: $a = b \neq c$	Five planes Five axes	TiO_2 (Rutile) $ZrSiO_4$ (Zircon) SnO_2 (Cassiterite)
3. Hexagonal	Three axes of equal length in one plane making angles of 60° with each other, and a fourth axis at right angles to these and of unequal length. Unit distances: $a = b \neq c$	Seven planes Seven axes	PbI_2 Mg Beryl CdS (Greenockite) ZnO (Zincite)
4. Orthorhombic (rhombic)	Three axes at right angles, but all of different length. Unit distances: $a \neq b \neq c$	Three planes Three axes	KNO_3 Rhombic sulfur K_2SO_4 $BaSO_4$ (Baryte) $PbCO_3$ (Cerrusite)
5. Monoclinic	Three axes, all unequal. Two axes at right angles, the third inclined to these at an angle other than 90°. Unit distances: $a \neq b \neq c$	One plane One axis	$Na_2SO_4 \cdot 10\ H_2O$ $Na_2B_4O_7 \cdot 10\ H_2O$ $CaSO_4 \cdot 2\ H_2O$ Monoclinic sulfur
6. Triclinic	Three axes of unequal length, all inclined at angles other than 90°. Unit distances: $a \neq b \neq c$	No planes No axes	$CuSO_4 \cdot 5\ H_2O$ $K_2Cr_2O_7$ H_3BO_3

symmetry. A form of lower symmetry, but still in the same system, is the tetrahedron.

PROPERTIES OF CRYSTALS

For gases, liquids, and unstrained amorphous solids, such properties as index of refraction, coefficient of thermal expansion, thermal and electrical conductivity, and rate of solubility are all independent of direction. The same is true of substances crystallizing in the regular system. Such substances exhibiting the same properties in all directions are said to be *isotropic.* However, for substances crystallizing in the other crystal systems the properties enumerated above may vary according to the axis along which observation is made. Substances exhibiting directional differences in properties are said to be *anisotropic.* For such substances the coefficients of thermal expansion may not only differ in different directions along the crystal but may actually be positive in one direction and negative in another, as is the case with silver iodide. Again, unlike isotropic solids, anisotropic solids exhibit more than one index of refraction for the same crystal. From the standpoint of optics, anisotropic substances are subdivided into *uniaxial* and *biaxial* crystals. Uniaxial crystals, embracing the tetragonal and hexagonal systems, possess two indices of refraction, according to the axis along which observation is made. Thus ice, which is hexagonal, has the refraction indices 1.3090 and 1.3104, both for sodium D-line. Biaxial crystals, on the other hand, embracing the orthorhombic, monoclinic, and triclinic systems, have three indices of refraction, as for instance the triclinic potassium dichromate, for which the indices of refraction, depending on the axis of observation, are 1.7202, 1.7380, and 1.8197, all for the sodium D-line.

The anisotropic character of certain crystals is also responsible for directional differences in solubility observed with many solids. In such solids certain faces of the crystal will dissolve faster than others to produce characteristic patterns on the surface called *etch figures.* These etch figures are quite typical and may be employed to characterize the nature and even composition of the substance. This method of identification and estimation is employed very extensively in metallographic analysis.

POLYMORPHISM

Many substances exist only in a single solid crystalline form. Quite frequently it is found, however, that certain substances occur in more than one solid modification or undergo a change of crystalline form on heating or under pressure. The existence of a substance in more than one modification is known as *polymorphism.* Thus carbon exists in crystalline form as either diamond or graphite, calcium carbonate occurs as calcite or aragonite, while sulfur has been found to exist in a variety of solid modifications. Polymorphism occurring in elements, as in the last illustration, is more commonly referred to as *allotropy.* Some polymorphs exist as modifications in the same crystal system, as in ammonium chloride where both forms are cubic, or they may crystallize in different crystal systems, as in rhombic and monoclinic sulfur, or hexagonal and cubic silver iodide.

Each polymorphic form of a substance is thermodynamically stable within a particular temperature and pressure range, and the transformation from one form to another takes place at any given pressure at a fixed temperature known as the *transition temperature* or *transition point*. The rhombic variety of sulfur is stable at atmospheric pressure up to 95.6° C, at which temperature it is transformed into the monoclinic form. Conversely, on cooling slowly monoclinic sulfur, rhombic sulfur will not appear until the temperature of 95.6° C has been reached. At this temperature monoclinic and rhombic sulfur are in equilibrium, and the temperature will not change until *all* the monoclinic sulfur has been transformed to the rhombic variety. In this respect the transition temperatures bear a very striking similarity to fusion points and are sometimes employed as fixed points in thermometry.

In instances like the preceding the change is entirely reversible, i.e., it proceeds in both directions, and the temperature at which both forms are in equilibrium is definite and constant. However, the change from one form to the other often is not reversible but proceeds in one direction only. The fact is that if more than one form of a substance is found to exist within the same temperature and pressure range, only one of these is stable. All others are unstable and *tend* to change continuously and irreversibly into the stable form. Nevertheless, the rate of change is often extremely slow, and the unstable form or forms may exhibit to all appearances all the attributes of stability. An instance of such a metastable substance is aragonite ($CaCO_3$), which, although apparently stable, may be transformed into the more stable calcite. However, the reverse transformation is impossible at ordinary pressures, a fact which speaks for the thermodynamic instability of aragonite.

TABLE 2

TRANSITION POINTS OF POLYMORPHIC SUBSTANCES AT ATMOSPHERIC PRESSURE

Substance	Transition	Transition Temp.
Sulfur	Rhombic ⇌ Monoclinic	95.6°
Tin	Gray ⇌ White (tetragonal)	18°
	White ⇌ Rhombic	170°
Ammonium nitrate	Tetragonal ⇌ (Rhombic)$_1$	−17°
	(Rhombic)$_1$ ⇌ (Rhombic)$_2$	32.1°
	(Rhombic)$_2$ ⇌ Rhomboheral	84.2°
	Rhombohedral ⇌ Cubic	125.2°
Potassium nitrate	Rhombic ⇌ Rhombohedral	128.5°
Silver iodide	Hexagonal ⇌ Cubic	146.5°
Silver nitrate	Rhombic ⇌ Rhombohedral	159.5°

Table 2 lists several polymorphic substances, the transformations which they undergo, and the transition temperatures at 1 atm pressure.

VARIATION OF TRANSITION TEMPERATURE WITH PRESSURE

The transition temperature, like the melting point, is a function of the pressure. For any transformation $A \rightleftharpoons B$ the variation of the transition temperature with pressure is given by the Clapeyron equation,

$$\frac{dT}{dP} = \frac{T(V_B - V_A)}{\Delta H_t} = \frac{T \Delta V}{\Delta H_t} \tag{10}$$

where T is the temperature of transition, P the pressure, ΔV the volume change on transition, and ΔH_t is the heat of transition, namely,

$$\Delta H_t = H_B - H_A$$

ΔH_t is always positive where the transformation is from the form stable at low temperatures to that at high temperature, and negative for the reverse change. Equation (10) is handled in calculations in exactly the same way as the similar equation (3) for the variation of the melting point with pressure.

THE STRUCTURE OF CRYSTALS

Space Lattices and Space Groups. We have seen above that on purely geometrical grounds crystallographers have found it possible to classify all crystals into 32 classes of symmetry and into 6 crystal systems. However, such a classification tells nothing about the *internal* structure of the crystals. To gain insight on the latter point, crystallography postulates that any macroscopic crystal of a substance is built up by repetition and extension in all directions of a fundamental structural unit known as a *unit crystal lattice* or *space group*. Each unit lattice, in turn, must be constituted of atoms, molecules, or ions, as the case may be, arranged to give the particular geometrical configuration of the lattice. Further, the geometric shape of the unit lattice must be the same as that of the macroscopic crystal; i.e., if the crystal is a cube, the unit lattice will also have its constituents arranged so as to give a tiny cube.

A mathematical analysis of these ideas, combined with the fundamental laws of crystallography, has shown that there are only 14 basic arrangements, known as *space lattices*, in terms of which the internal structure of crystals can be described. The number of these basic arrangements or space lattices falling within a given system is listed in the second column of Table 3. Starting with the space lattices in a particular system, it is possible to combine these into a definite number of more intricate groupings, the space groups, whose number is shown in the last column of the table. Thus the three space lattices occurring in the cubic system may be elaborated into 36 space groups without violating the symmetry requirements, while the two basic designs of the tetragonal system may be combined to give 68 possible patterns of arrangement. Table 3 shows that the 14 space lattices can yield a total of 230 space groups, a number practically identical with that of the kinds of crystals actually observed.

TABLE 3

DISTRIBUTION OF SPACE LATTICES AND GROUPS

System	Number of Space Lattices	Number of Space Groups
Cubic	3	36
Tetragonal	2	68
Hexagonal	2	52
Orthorhombic	4	59
Monoclinic	2	13
Triclinic	1	2
	14	230

Although crystallography has been able to delimit the number of space groups occurring in a given system, it could not define the specific space group exhibited by a particular crystal. Thus it was known that a crystal in the cubic system had one of 36 possible space groups, but there were no means available to distinguish among these. It remained for the advent of x rays and their application to this field to supply the powerful means for this differentiation, and thereby for the elucidation of the structure of crystals.

X RAYS

X rays, discovered by Roentgen in 1895, are generated by electron bombardment of heavy metal targets. Like ordinary light, they are a form of electromagnetic radiation, but of very much shorter wave length. The position of x rays in the electromagnetic radiational spectrum can

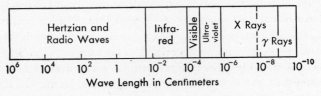

Fig. 2. Spectrum of Electromagnetic Radiation.

be judged from Fig. 2, where the various forms of such radiation are arranged in order of decreasing wave length. It will be observed that the wave lengths of x rays center approximately about 10^{-8} cm, or 1 angstrom (Å), a distance which is of the same order of magnitude as molecular diameters in gases and the roughly estimated interatomic distances in a solid.

THE LAUE METHOD OF X-RAY ANALYSIS

When x rays were first investigated, the problem arose of measuring their wave length. It is a well-known fact that, if light is permitted to

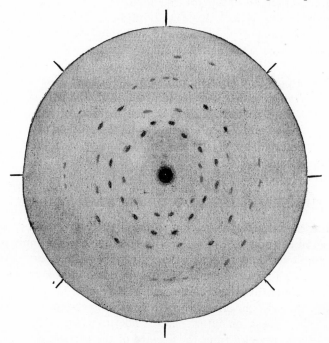

Fig. 3.   Laue Diffraction Pattern of Zinc Blende. (From Davey, W. P., *A Study of Crystal Structure and Its Applications*. (McGraw-Hill Book Company, Inc.)

strike a surface consisting either of a series of edges or of lines spaced closely enough to be of the same order of magnitude as that of the wave length of the light, the beam of light is diffracted, and the various radiations are dispersed into a series of spectra known as the first, second, third, etc., order spectra. Furthermore, there is a definite relation between the angle of diffraction, the wave length of the radiation, and the spacing of the lines on the ruled grating. Since x rays are of the same nature as light, it should be theoretically possible to determine the wave length of this radiation in the same way. However, it is impossible by mechanical means to rule a grating with about 10^8 lines per centimeter. To overcome this difficulty, Max von Laue in 1912 made the brilliant suggestion that, if a crystal consists actually of an orderly arrangement of atoms, then the atomic planes in the crystal should be spaced at intervals of about 10^{-8} cm, and the crystal should act then as a natural and very fine three-dimensional diffraction grating for x rays. He further predicted that, if a beam of inhomogeneous x rays were directed against a crystal and a photographic plate placed behind it, the image obtained on the latter would show a series of spots arranged in a geometrical fashion about the center of the beam.

Experimental investigation of the idea in 1913 verified von Laue's predictions in every respect. A series of diffraction patterns were obtained for various substances which showed differences characteristic of the materials examined. One of these Laue diagrams, that of zinc blende (ZnS), is shown in Fig. 3. These diagrams speak for a definite arrangement of the atoms in a crystal, and actually permit a reconstruction of the crystal arrangement which would account for the particular distribution of each Laue pattern. However, the method of reconstruction is highly complicated and difficult. A much simpler method of crystal analysis is that suggested by W. H. and W. L. Bragg, and this will be discussed now in some detail.

THE BRAGG METHOD OF CRYSTAL ANALYSIS

The Braggs first called attention to the fact that, since a crystal may be considered as composed of a series of equally spaced atomic planes, it may be employed not only as a transmission grating, as in the Laue method, but also as a reflection grating. A beam of x rays striking the atoms which constitute these planes will be diffracted then in such a manner as to cause either interference with or reinforcement of the beam diffracted from the first, or outer, plane, and the whole beam will behave as if it had been *reflected* from the surface of the crystal.

To understand better the theory of this method consider, as shown in Fig. 4, a wave front $GG'G''$ of x rays approaching at an angle θ a series of parallel, equidistant planes, W, X, Y, Z, etc., which constitute the atomic planes of the crystal. Part of the beam HGO will be reflected at O along OE at the angle of reflection θ, which is the same as the angle of incidence. Similarly, the beam $H'G'O'$ will be reflected partly at O' along $O'E'$, and then again at C on the second plane along COE. In order to emerge along OE the second beam has to travel a longer distance than the first, namely, the distance $H'G'O'CO$ as against the distance HGO. If the difference in distance of the two paths is exactly equal to an integral multiple of the wave length of the radiation, the two beams will be in phase at O, will reinforce each other, and the intensity of the reflected rays will be at a maximum. When the two beams are out of phase, however, interference will result, and the intensity of the reflected beam will be less than the maximum. The condition for maximum reflection intensity is then that the distance

$$G'CO - GO = n\lambda$$

where λ is the wave length of the x rays employed, while n is an integer taking on the values 1, 2, 3, $\cdot \cdot \cdot$ and known as the *order of reflection*.

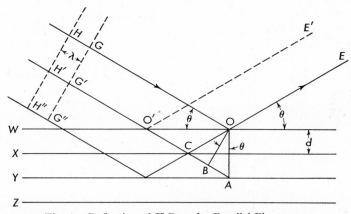

Fig. 4.   Reflection of X Rays by Parallel Planes.

If a perpendicular is drawn now from O to the extension of the line $G'O'C$, while another is dropped from O to A perpendicular to W, X, and Y, it follows that

$$G'CO = G'A - CA + CO$$
$$= G'A$$

since $CO = CA$ from the construction of the figure. But

$$GO = G'B$$

Therefore, $$G'CO - GO = G'A - G'B$$
$$= BA$$

and hence, $$BA = n\lambda$$

It can readily be shown that the angle BOA is also θ.   Then, since OB was constructed perpendicular to $G'A$,

$$\sin \theta = \frac{BA}{OA}$$

and $$BA = OA \sin \theta$$
$$= 2 d \sin \theta$$

where d is the distance between any two atomic planes in the crystal.

Therefore, $$n\lambda = 2 d \sin \theta \qquad (11)$$

This simple equation connects directly the wave length and order of reflection of the x rays with the interplanar distance d and the angle of maximum reflection θ. Without any further information the ratio λ/d is deducible by measuring n and θ. On the other hand, if λ is known, d may be calculated; or vice versa, if d is known, the crystal may be employed to determine the wave length of the x rays.

The reflection angles θ and the intensities of the reflected beams corresponding to these angles can be determined with the Bragg x-ray spectrometer, a diagram of which is shown in Fig. 5. The x rays generated in tube A by bombardment of a suitable target B are passed through a

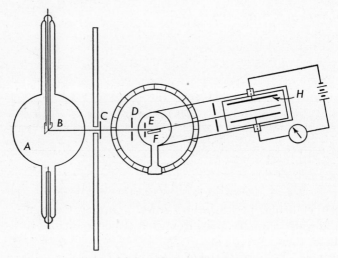

Fig. 5.   Bragg X-Ray Spectrometer.

series of slits and screen (C, D, E) to give a sharp and monochromatic beam and are then directed to strike the face of a crystal which is suitably mounted on a turntable F. The graduated turntable may be rotated to give any angle of incidence desired. Coaxially with the table and crystal is mounted an ionization chamber H, into which the reflected beam is passed. The ionization of the gas filling the chamber, usually sulfur dioxide, is proportional to the intensity of the x rays passing through the chamber. Since the current passing through the ionization chamber is proportional to the ionization of the gas, the intensity of such a current as measured by an electrometer gives directly a measure of the relative intensities of the x rays that are reflected from the crystal. By determining the intensities of the reflected beam at various angles of reflection, the angles at which maximum reflection occurs may be readily found.

THE X-RAY ANALYSIS OF SODIUM CHLORIDE

The procedure employed to elucidate the structure of sodium chloride will now be described in some detail, and this example may be taken as a general indication of the methods involved in studying other types of crystals. Sodium chloride has been chosen because it belongs to the cubic system, exhibits the highest type of symmetry in crystals, and is the simplest to study.

Simple Cubic Lattice

The unit lattice of sodium chloride, like the macroscopic crystal, must be a cube, and the atoms of sodium and chlorine must be arranged, as we have seen, in some combination of only three possible space lattices. These are known respectively as the *simple cubic*, the *face-centered cubic*, and the *body-centered cubic* arrangements. They are illustrated in Fig. 6. In the simple cubic lattice an atom is located at each of the corners of the cube. The face-centered cubic lattice in turn involves a simple cubic arrangement modified by the location of an atom in the center of each of the six faces of the cube. Finally, the body-centered cubic lattice is again a simple cubic arrangement but modified this time by the presence of a single atom in the *center* of the cube.

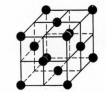

Face-Centered Cubic Lattice

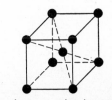

Body-Centered Cubic Lattice

Fig. 6.

In the cubic system the planes that can be passed through the atoms have the Miller indices (100), (110), or (111), as may be seen from Fig. 7. However, the ratios of the distances among the (100), (110), and (111) planes in the three types of cubic lattices are not the same. If we arbitrarily designate by a the distance between 100 planes in the simple cubic lattice, then the perpendicular distance between (110) planes will be $a/\sqrt{2}$, and the distance between (111) planes will be $a/\sqrt{3}$. In the face-centered cubic lattice, on the other hand, parallel planes can be interposed halfway between the (100) and the (110) planes in the simple cubic lattice, and hence the interplanar distances in this case are respectively $a/2$, $a/(2\sqrt{2})$, and $a/\sqrt{3}$. Finally, in the body-centered cubic lattice parallel planes can be interposed halfway between any (100) or (111) planes in the simple cubic lattices, so that in terms of a the respective distances become $a/2$, $a/\sqrt{2}$, and $a/(2\sqrt{3})$. These distances for the various planes in the three types of cubic lattices are summarized in

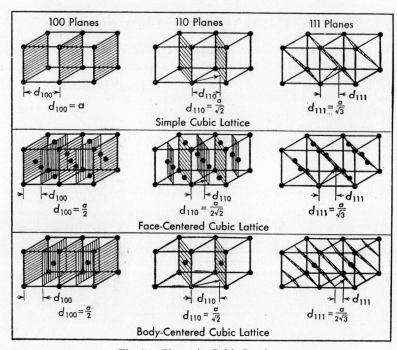

Fig. 7.   Planes in Cubic Lattices.

TABLE 4

DISTANCE BETWEEN ATOMIC PLANES FOR CUBIC CRYSTALS

	(100)	(110)	(111)
Simple cubic	a	$\dfrac{a}{\sqrt{2}}$	$\dfrac{a}{\sqrt{3}}$
Face-centered cubic	$\dfrac{a}{2}$	$\dfrac{a}{2\sqrt{2}}$	$\dfrac{a}{\sqrt{3}}$
Body-centered cubic	$\dfrac{a}{2}$	$\dfrac{a}{\sqrt{2}}$	$\dfrac{a}{2\sqrt{3}}$

Table 4. The ratios $d_{100}:d_{110}:d_{111}$ for the simple cubic, face-centered cubic, and body-centered cubic lattices are then:

Simple cubic: $d_{100}:d_{110}:d_{111} = a:\dfrac{a}{\sqrt{2}}:\dfrac{a}{\sqrt{3}} = 1:0.707:0.577$

Face-centered cubic: $d_{100}:d_{110}:d_{111} = \dfrac{a}{2}:\dfrac{a}{2\sqrt{2}}:\dfrac{a}{\sqrt{3}} = 1:0.707:1.154$

Body-centered cubic: $d_{100}:d_{110}:d_{111} = \dfrac{a}{2}:\dfrac{a}{\sqrt{2}}:\dfrac{a}{2\sqrt{3}} = 1:1.414:0.577$

It will be observed that the ratios of the distances in the three cases are all different, and hence a determination of the interplanar distance ratios in sodium chloride should permit a decision as to the type of lattice to which this substance belongs. Since for any given reflection order and wave length of x rays $d = (n\lambda)/(2 \sin \theta)$, then for nth order reflection maxima from the (100), (110), and (111) planes we have

$$d_{100}:d_{110}:d_{111} = \frac{n\lambda}{2 \sin \theta_1}:\frac{n\lambda}{2 \sin \theta_2}:\frac{n\lambda}{2 \sin \theta_3}$$

$$= \frac{1}{\sin \theta_1}:\frac{1}{\sin \theta_2}:\frac{1}{\sin \theta_3}$$

and a knowledge of the angles at which maximum intensities of reflection occur for the three types of planes is sufficient to determine the type of lattice to which sodium chloride belongs. In Table 5 are given the

TABLE 5

Glancing Angles for NaCl Using K Line from Palladium

Planes	First Order		Second Order		Third Order	
	θ_1	Sin θ_1	θ_2	Sin θ_2	θ_3	Sin θ_3
(100)	5.9	0.103	11.9	0.208	18.2	0.312
(110)	8.4	0.146	17.0	0.292	—	—
(111)	5.2	0.0906	10.5	0.182	—	—

values of θ, the angle of maximum reflection, for several values of n for each of the three types of planes, as well as sin θ. Considering first order reflections only, we see that

$$d_{100}:d_{110}:d_{111} = \frac{1}{\sin \theta_1}:\frac{1}{\sin \theta_2}:\frac{1}{\sin \theta_3} = \frac{1}{0.103}:\frac{1}{0.146}:\frac{1}{0.0906}$$

$$= 1:0.705:1.14$$

Comparing these ratios with those previously established for the three possible types of arrangement of cubic lattices, it follows that in sodium chloride the atoms must be arranged in a face-centered cubic lattice. The same conclusion may be arrived at by considering the results for second order reflection maxima.

THE RELATIVE POSITIONS OF SODIUM AND CHLORIDE ATOMS IN LATTICE

Determining the type of lattice along which the atoms in sodium chloride are arranged does not solve completely the problem of the structure of sodium chloride, for the question of the relative arrangement of the atoms of sodium and chlorine in the lattice still remains. This question can be resolved only by considering the relative intensities of the reflection maxima for the different orders and planes. In Table 6 are given

TABLE 6

RELATIVE INTENSITIES FOR REFLECTION MAXIMA IN NaCl

Order	Intensities for (100) Planes	Intensities for (110) Planes	Intensities for (111) Planes
First	100.00	50.4	9.00
Second	19.90	6.10	33.1
Third	4.87	0.71	0.58
Fourth	0.79		2.82
Fifth	0.12		0.14

the intensities for various orders of reflection for the (100), (110), and (111) planes, the intensity of the first order maximum for the (100) plane being taken as 100.

The intensity of a diffracted beam depends, in the first place, on the mass of the particle responsible for the diffraction the larger the mass the greater being the intensity; and, second, on the order of diffraction, the intensity decreasing in a definite manner with increase in order. These two facts are employed to explain the results of Table 6. It will be observed that in the (100) and (110) planes the intensities decrease progressively with order. This systematic decrease can be accounted for quantitatively by assuming that such planes contain equal numbers of sodium and chlorine atoms. In the (111) planes, however, an alternation of intensities is observed, the first order being weaker than the second and the third weaker than both first and second, while the fourth is weaker than the second but stronger than the third. It is possible to account for this by postulating that the (111) planes are composed alternately of sodium atoms and chlorine atoms, and that the planes containing sodium atoms only are interposed halfway between the (111) planes containing only chlorine atoms.

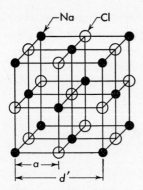

Fig. 8. The Sodium Chloride Lattice.

Exhaustive study has shown that the only possible arrangement of sodium and chlorine atoms which will satisfy the facts elicited from the study of the intensities is that shown in Fig. 8. In this arrangement atoms of sodium, shown by black circles, are located in the corners of the cube and in the center of each of the six faces. Halfway between every two sodium atoms is located a chlorine atom, shown by open circles. A moment's reflection will show that the indicated structure meets the required conditions and that it consists essentially of two interpenetrating face-centered cubic lattices, one composed entirely of sodium atoms, the other of chlorine atoms. The chlorine lattice is merely displaced the distance *a* along any edge of the cube.

Although for purposes of discussion we have considered the structural units of sodium chloride to be sodium and chlorine atoms, general consensus at present is that the sodium chloride in the crystal is ionized and that the units are rather sodium and chloride *ions*. Again, in terms of the x-ray interpretation of the structure as outlined here, the designation "molecule of sodium chloride" loses a great deal of its definite meaning. It can hardly be said that any particular chloride ion belongs to any definite sodium ion; rather, each sodium is shared equally by six chloride ions, and each chloride is held equally by six sodium ions. All that can be said is that to each sodium corresponds *one-sixth* of *six* chloride ions, so that each sodium has the equivalent of a chloride, but not any one ion exclusively.

CALCULATION OF *d* AND λ

The cube indicated in Fig. 8 is considered to be the unit crystal, or unit lattice, of sodium chloride, and the edge of the cube is then the distance between any two sodium or any two chloride ions which lie on the edge. This is *twice* the distance between (100) planes. The macroscopic crystal is built up by the extension of unit lattices in all directions.

Once the nature of the unit lattice is established, it is a simple matter to calculate the length of the edge of the unit cube and the distance between (100) planes from the molar volume and Avogadro's number. Each of the sodium ions at the corners is shared by eight cubes, hence to each cube may be ascribed $\frac{1}{8} \times 8$, or one sodium ion. Further, each of the sodium ions in the centers of the faces is shared by two cubes. This adds $\frac{1}{2} \times 6$ or three sodium ions more, making a total of four sodium ions. Similarly, each of the chloride ions along the edges is shared by four cubes, and since there are 12 of these, $\frac{1}{4} \times 12$ or three chloride ions are part of the cube. Adding to these the one in the center of the cube, we obtain $3 + 1 = 4$ chloride ions as the average chloride content of the cube. It may be said, therefore, that each unit lattice of sodium chloride contains on the average four sodium ions and four chloride ions, or a *total equivalent to four molecules of sodium chloride*.

The molar volume of sodium chloride is the gram molecular weight,

58.45, divided by the density, 2.17 g/cc, or

$$V_m = \frac{58.45}{2.17} = 26.93 \text{ cc}$$

This is the volume occupied by $N = 6.023 \times 10^{23}$ molecules. The volume occupied by four molecules, V, which is also the volume of the unit cube, is, then,

$$V = \frac{V_m \times 4}{6.023 \times 10^{23}} = \frac{26.93 \times 4}{6.023 \times 10^{23}} = 178.8 \times 10^{-24} \text{ cc}$$

From this volume the edge of the unit cube follows as

$$d' = \sqrt[3]{178.8 \times 10^{-24}}$$
$$= 5.63 \times 10^{-8} \text{ cm}$$

Since the edge of the unit cube is twice the distance between (100) planes, the distance d to be employed in the Bragg equation is $d'/2$, or,

$$d = \frac{5.63 \times 10^{-8}}{2} = 2.815 \times 10^{-8} \text{ cm}$$

The best value accepted at present for this distance is $2.8140 \pm 0.0010 \times 10^{-8}$ cm.

Once the interplanar distance for sodium chloride is known, the crystal may be employed to determine the wave length of any x rays which may be directed against it. Thus in the Bragg experiments $\sin \theta$ was found to be 0.103 for $n = 1$. Consequently the x rays employed in these experiments had a wave length of

$$\lambda = \frac{2d \sin \theta}{n} = \frac{2(2.814 \times 10^{-8})0.103}{1}$$
$$= 0.58 \times 10^{-8} \text{ cm} = 0.58 \text{ Å}$$

THE POWDER METHOD OF CRYSTAL ANALYSIS

Debye and Scherrer in 1916, and Hull independently in 1917, devised a method of x-ray crystal analysis which permits the use of a substance in *powder* form. In this method a monochromatic beam of x rays is focused upon a small tube containing the finely ground substance to be examined. Since in the powder the crystal planes are oriented at all possible angles to the beam, there will be always some crystals with just the proper orientation to give reinforced diffraction images, and from all the planes simultaneously. These diffraction maxima are photographed on a film fixed behind the sample in the form of a circular arc.

The diffracted rays obtained in this manner form concentric cones originating from the powder under examination. Photographed on a narrow strip of film, these images appear as nearly vertical lines arranged on each side of a bright center spot due to the undiffracted beam, although actually these lines are portions of arcs of circles whose center is the point of focus of the x-ray beam. Each pair of lines equidistant to the right and left of the center spot corresponds to a single order of diffraction for a family of planes, a pair being obtained for each order of diffraction for each type of plane present.

A powder diffraction pattern of zinc oxide is shown in Fig. 9.

The diffraction patterns obtained from various solid substances all are characteristic of the substances responsible for the particular patterns. For this reason the Debye-Scherrer-Hull method of x-ray diffraction is frequently employed in qualitative and quantitative chemical analysis to identify and estimate both pure substances and mixtures. When used

Fig. 9.   Powder Diffraction Diagram of ZnO. (*Courtesy Dr. Allen S. Powell, Case Institute of Technology.*)

for analytical purposes a comparison plate is prepared showing the position of various lines for the various substances which may be expected in the unknown sample. Then several milligrams of the unknown sample are also exposed, and the diffraction plate thus obtained is compared with the reference plate. Occurrence of identical lines in both plates testifies to the presence of the particular substance exhibiting those lines in both samples. The identity of each line is determined by comparison of plates with diagrams obtained from the pure constituents.

For quantitative estimation of the amount of each substance present the intensity of each line must be determined and compared with the intensities obtained from definite amounts of the pure constituents under identical operating conditions. Since the intensity of a line is proportional to the amount of substance present, such a comparison gives directly an estimate of amount. In the more elaborate installations intensities are evaluated with photoelectric comparators.

In one respect an x-ray analysis supplies more information than a chemical analysis. From a qualitative chemical analysis of a mixture of, say, calcium chloride and sodium bromide, it is impossible to tell whether the constituents are calcium chloride and sodium bromide or calcium bromide and sodium chloride. The x-ray method answers this question directly, for it will show the lines of calcium chloride and sodium bromide and no lines for the reciprocal salts.

RESULTS OF X-RAY STUDY OF CRYSTALS

Studies similar to that described for sodium chloride have been made upon a great many solid substances to determine their structure. Some of the results of these studies will now be summarized.

Many metals crystallize in the cubic system, with the atoms arranged in face-centered or body-centered lattices. As examples of the first may be cited aluminum, calcium, nickel, cobalt, copper, silver, platinum,

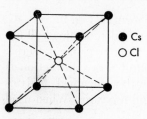

● Cs
○ Cl

Fig. 10.   The Cesium Chloride Lattice.

gold, and lead, while of the second lithium, chromium, sodium, potassium, iron, and tungsten. The simple cubic arrangement does not appear to be overly favored. On the other hand, the sodium chloride structure of two interpenetrating face-centered lattices is very common among compounds falling in the regular system. It is exhibited by oxides such as those of magnesium, calcium, strontium, barium, nickel, and cobalt, sulfides such as

those of magnesium, barium, manganese, and lead, and all of the halides of the alkali metals except those of cesium. The cesium halides occur as two simple cubic lattices, one of cesium and another of the halide, interlocking to form a resultant body-centered lattice with the equivalent of one molecule of cesium halide per unit cube. This structure is shown in Fig. 10.

Another type of cubic arrangement is found in zinc sulfide, diamond, silicon, germanium, and gray tin. Here we have a face-centered lattice which also contains an atom in the center of each alternate small cube within the larger lattice. On this basis each atom is equidistant from four other atoms. A modification of this scheme is the arrangement found in calcium, strontium, and barium fluorides. In these salts the metal ions are located on a face-centered lattice, while the nonmetal ions are situated in the centers of each of the eight small cubes composing the metallic lattice. The nonmetallic ions thus form a simple cubic lattice inside the face-centered lattice of the metal ions.

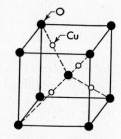

O
Cu

Fig. 11.   The Cuprous Oxide Lattice.

A still different cubic structure is that shown by cuprous oxide and silver oxide, Fig. 11. In crystals of these the oxygens lie on a body-centered cubic lattice, while the metal atoms interpenetrate this lattice to fall at the center of each alternate small cube within the oxygen framework.

As an example of a noncubic arrangement may be given the close-packed hexagonal lattice, Fig. 12, which occurs in elements such as magnesium, zinc, cadmium, and titanium. The compounds zinc oxide, beryllium oxide, cobalt sulfide, and stannous sulfide appear as two such interpenetrating hexagonal lattices, one composed of the metal, the other of the nonmetal. On the other hand, calcium, magnesium, manganese, and iron carbonates and sodium nitrate have a rhombohedral lattice in which the axes are all equal but inclined at equal angles other than 90°. If we imagine this lattice to be a distorted cube, then the metal ions and the anions are on two interpenetrating distorted face-centered lattices comparable to the undistorted sodium chloride lattice. It is of interest to point out that the anions CO_3^{--} and NO_3^- have been shown to be present in the crystal as a unit, with the oxygens distributed about the central atom. The same is true of other inorganic anions like SO_4^{--}, PO_4^{---}, ClO_3^-, and MnO_4^-. These findings are excellent evidence for the dissociation of salts in the solid state and for the existence of these radicals as individual entities.

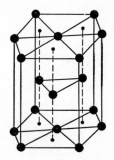

Fig. 12. Close-Packed Hexagonal Arrangement.

LATTICE STRUCTURAL UNITS

Depending on the nature of the substance in question, the units entering into the construction of a crystal lattice may be ions, atoms, or molecules. Inorganic compounds generally have ionic lattices. In such lattices the binding forces are the electrostatic attractions between the oppositely charged ions. As has already been pointed out, for such substances the ordinary definition of a molecule is meaningless, for no particular negative ion, say, may be said to belong exclusively to any particular positive ion. Rather, because of the requirements of electroneutrality, each positive ion has associated with it on the average a sufficient number of negative charges to balance the positive charge. Ionic lattices are generally very stable, and crystals constituted of these melt at relatively high temperatures.

In diamond and graphite the lattice-building units are atoms. Within the diamond lattice each atom of carbon is surrounded by four others in the form of a tetrahedron, an arrangement which confirms the valency of carbon and the directionality of the valence bonds as postulated by the organic chemists. The atoms are held together by covalent forces, and, as these are very strong, the crystals are hard, strong, and high melting. The graphite structure, on the other hand, consists of planar hexagonal rings in which the carbon atoms are tetrahedrally joined by covalent bonds. These planes, in turn, are held together by van der Waals forces. Since the latter are much weaker than covalent forces, the planes separate readily. This fact accounts for the flakiness of graphite.

Metals also have atoms as structural units. Since electrons in metals are loosely held, metals are good conductors of electricity. Again, most metallic crystals are strong, and generally malleable and ductile.

In substances like carbon dioxide, hydrogen chloride, and stannic iodide the complete molecule acts as a structural unit within the lattice. X-ray evidence indicates that such molecules occupy the key spatial positions, while the atoms within the molecules are arranged in a definite configuration about the mean position of equilibrium for each molecule. The molecules are held in their geometrical distribution within the lattice by van der Waals forces. These forces are much weaker than the electrostatic attractions in ionic lattices, and consequently such crystals are less strong and melt at considerably lower temperatures. The lower rigidity and higher vapor pressure of these substances as compared with ionic crystals may also be ascribed to the relative weakness of the van der Waals forces as compared to the electrostatic attractions between ions.

ELECTRON AND NEUTRON DIFFRACTION

DeBroglie in 1924 first called attention to the fact that moving electrons, besides exhibiting their corpuscular properties, should also possess properties characteristic of wave motion of the type associated with light. He showed that an electron moving with velocity v should have associated with it a wave of length λ given by

$$\lambda = \frac{h}{mv} \tag{12}$$

where m is the mass of the electron, 9.11×10^{-28} g, while h is Planck's constant, namely, 6.62×10^{-27} erg-sec. The velocity of an electron depends on the potential drop through which the electron falls. For the potential drop, ε, in volts it is given as

$$v = 5.94 \times 10^7 \sqrt{\varepsilon} \tag{13}$$

Inserting equation (13) in equation (12), we obtain for the wave length λ

$$\begin{aligned}
\lambda &= \frac{h}{m \times 5.94 \times 10^7 \sqrt{\varepsilon}} \\
&= \frac{6.62 \times 10^{-27}}{9.11 \times 10^{-28} \times 5.94 \times 10^7 \sqrt{\varepsilon}} \\
&= \frac{12.2 \times 10^{-8}}{\sqrt{\varepsilon}}
\end{aligned} \tag{14}$$

For potentials between 10 and 10,000 volts, λ should vary, then, between 3.86 and 0.12 Å, and hence such electrons should behave like x rays toward crystals.

This prediction of DeBroglie's was confirmed in a beautiful manner by Davisson and Germer in 1925. Davisson and Germer investigated the diffraction of electrons by a nickel surface and found that the electron diffraction pattern thus obtained was very similar to the one given with x rays. Further, the wave length of the electrons calculated from the diffraction pattern agreed remarkably well with that calculated from the DeBroglie equation.

These experiments and others carried out since 1925 not only provide excellent confirmation of DeBroglie's theory but also make available a new tool for investigation of solids. Compared to x rays, electron beams are much less penetrating. Consequently, whereas x rays are diffracted by atomic planes deep within a crystal, electrons are diffracted primarily by planes lying near the surface. Electron diffraction offers, then, a convenient means of investigating the nature of solid surfaces and surface films, and a great deal of work in this field is directed thus toward an elucidation of the nature of oxide and other surface films on solids.

Solids bombarded with high speed neutrons also give diffraction patterns. The wave length of the neutrons is again given by equation (12), but m is now 1.67×10^{-24} g. Neutrons are strongly scattered by hydrogen atoms, and hence neutron diffraction is very effective in locating the position of such atoms in crystals.

REFERENCES FOR FURTHER READING

1. C. W. Bunn, *Chemical Crystallography*, Oxford University Press, New York, 1945.
2. R. C. Evans, *An Introduction to Crystal Chemistry*, Cambridge University Press, Cambridge, 1946.
3. S. Glasstone, *Textbook of Physical Chemistry*, D. Van Nostrand Company, Inc., New York, 1946, Chap. V.
4. Kraus, Hunt, and Ramsdell, *Mineralogy*, McGraw-Hill Book Company, Inc., New York, 1951.
5. K. Lonsdale, *Crystals and X-Rays*, D. Van Nostrand Company, Inc., New York, 1949.
6. A. Weissberger, *Physical Methods of Organic Chemistry*, Interscience Publishers, Inc., New York, 1949, Chaps. III, XVI, XVII, XVIII, and XIX.
7. R. W. G. Wyckoff, *Crystal Structure*, Interscience Publishers, Inc., New York, 1948–1953.

PROBLEMS

1. The densities of liquid and solid Hg are respectively 13.70 and 14.19 g/cc at the melting point, $-38.87°$ C. The heat of fusion is 566 cal/g atom. Find the change in melting point per atmosphere change in pressure.

Ans. 0.0051° C/atm.

2. *m*-Dinitrobenzene melts at 89.8° C under a pressure of 1 atm, and at 114.8° C under a pressure of 968 atm. If the heat of fusion is 24.7 cal/g, what is the change in volume on fusion?

3. The heat of fusion of ice is 79.7 cal/g at 0° C. The densities of ice and water at the same temperature are, respectively, 0.9168 and 0.9999 g/cc. Calculate the melting point of ice at 325 atm pressure, and compare your answer with the observed value of −2.5° C.

4. The vapor pressure of solid CO_2 is 76.7 mm at −103° C, and 1 atm at −78.5° C. Calculate the heat of sublimation of CO_2.　　*Ans.* 6160 cal/mole.

5. At 630° K the heat of sublimation of $ZrBr_4$ is 25,800 cal/mole, while the vapor pressure is 1 atm. What will be the sublimation pressure at 700° K?

6. At 0° C the heat of sublimation of ice is 675.7 cal/g, while the heat of vaporization of water is 595.9 cal/g. Calculate the rates of change of vapor pressure with temperature for water and ice at 0° C. At this temperature the vapor pressure of water is 4.58 mm Hg.

7. Ice is in equilibrium with *air-free* liquid water at 0.0023° C under a pressure of 1 atm, while under its own vapor pressure the melting point is 0.0075° C higher. Using the data given in problem 3, find the sublimation pressure of the ice.

8. The sublimation pressure of N_2O is given by the relation

$$\log_{10} P_{atm} = \frac{-1294}{T} + 1.405 \log_{10} T - 0.0051\ T + 4.800$$

Find the expression for the heat of sublimation of N_2O as a function of the temperature.

9. The vapor pressure of liquid arsenic is given by the equation

$$\log_{10} P_{mm} = \frac{-2460}{T} + 6.69$$

that of solid arsenic by

$$\log_{10} P_{mm} = \frac{-6947}{T} + 10.8$$

Find the temperature at which the two forms of As have the same vapor pressure. What is the value of this pressure?

10. NH_4NO_3 undergoes a transition from one solid modification to another at 125.5° C at 1 atm, and at 135.0° C at 1000 atm pressure. The form stable at higher temperatures has an average volume of 0.0126 cc/g greater than the other modification over the pressure range studied. From these data calculate the heat of transition.　　*Ans.* 1040 cal/mole.

11. AgI exists in two forms, α and β, which are in equilibrium at 146.5° C at 1 atm pressure. For the change of α to β $\Delta H_t = 1530$ cal/mole, while $\Delta V = -2.2$ cc/mole. Find the pressure at which the transition temperature will be 145.0° C.

12. At 20° K the heat capacity per gram atom of silver is 0.39 cal/° K. Assuming the validity of the Debye third power law for this substance, estimate what will be the heat capacity per gram atom at 1° K.

13. A crystal plane intercepts the three crystallographic axes at the following multiples of the unit distances: $\frac{3}{2}$, 2, and 1. What will be the Miller indices of the plane?　　*Ans.* (436).

14. The first order reflection of a beam of x rays from a given crystal occurs at 5° 15′. At what angle will be the third order reflection?   *Ans.* 15° 56′.

15. The first order reflection of a beam of x rays from the (100) face of NaCl occurs at an angle of 6° 30′. What is the wave length of the x rays used?

16. If x rays of $\lambda = 1.540$ Å are used, find the angle at which will be obtained the second order reflection maxima from the (111) planes of NaCl.

17. The first order reflections from the (100), (110), and (111) planes of a given cubic crystal occur at angles of 7° 10′, 10° 12′, and 12° 30′ respectively. To what type of cubic lattice does the crystal belong?

18. The density of CaF_2 is 3.180 g/cc at 20° C. Calculate the dimensions of a unit cube of the substance containing 4 Ca^{++} and 8 F^- ions.   *Ans.* 5.45 Å.

19. Al crystallizes in a face-centered cubic lattice. Its density is 2.70 g/cc at 20° C. Calculate the distance between successive (100) planes and the distance of closest approach of Al atoms in the crystal.

20. Cesium chloride, whose density is 3.97 g/cc, crystallizes in a body-centered cubic lattice 4.12 Å on edge, and the equivalent of one CsCl molecule per unit cube. From these data calculate the value of Avogadro's number.

21. Tungsten crystallizes in a body-centered cubic lattice with a unit cube side length of 3.16 Å. (a) How many atoms of tungsten are present in a unit lattice? (b) What is the density of the metal?

22. Electrons emitted from a hot filament are accelerated in an electric field until their velocity is 5×10^9 cm/sec. Find the wave length of the electrons, and the potential drop required to obtain this wave length.

Ans. 0.145 Å; 7090 volts.

23. What will have to be the velocity of neutrons in order for them to have a wave length of 0.60 Å?

5

Solutions

When several nonreacting substances are mixed, three possible types of mixtures may be obtained: (a) a coarse mixture, such as that of salt and sugar; (b) a colloidal dispersion, such as results when fine clay is shaken with water; or (c) a true solution, obtained when a substance like sugar dissolves in water. In the coarse mixture, the individual particles are readily discernible and may be separated from each other by mechanical means. Although in a colloidal dispersion the particles are much finer and the heterogeneity is not so readily apparent, the dispersion is, nevertheless, not homogeneous. On the other hand, in the true solution the constituents cannot be separated from each other by mechanical means, and every part of the solution is found to be like every other part; i.e., a true solution constitutes a homogeneous phase.

We may, therefore, define a true solution as *a physically homogeneous mixture of two or more substances*. This definition of a solution places no restriction on either the state of aggregation or the relative amounts of the constituents, and consequently a solution may be gaseous, liquid, or solid and may vary in composition within wide limits. It is this latter fact which excludes pure compounds from the classification of solutions, for a fixed and definite ratio persists among the constituents in a compound.

It is frequently convenient to refer to the substance that dissolves as the *solute* and to the substance in which solution takes place as the *solvent*. For the solubility of solids in liquids, where the liquid is usually present in large excess over the solid, there is no ambiguity in these terms, the solid being the solute, the liquid the solvent. However, when dealing with the solubility of such liquids as acetone and water or diox-

ane and water, which dissolve in each other in all proportions, it is difficult to differentiate between solute and solvent. Here these terms will be
employed only when there is no ambiguity as to meaning.

A solution which contains at a given temperature as much solute as it
can hold in presence of the dissolving substance is said to be *saturated*.
Any solution which contains less than this amount of solute is *unsaturated*,
while if it contains more than this amount it is *supersaturated*. A supersaturated solution can exist only in the absence of dissolving substance
and is at best very unstable. Jarring and stirring may, and introduction of
solute will, cause the precipitation of excess solute in solution, leading to
the formation of a saturated solution. To determine the state of a solution
with respect to saturation it is only necessary to introduce some of the
dissolving substance. If the substance dissolves, the solution is unsaturated; if no further solubility takes place, the solution is saturated; while
if precipitation takes place, the original solution was supersaturated.

FACTORS AFFECTING SOLUBILITY

The extent to which a substance will dissolve in another varies greatly
with different substances and depends on the nature of the solute and
solvent, the temperature, and the pressure. In general the effect of pressure on solubility is small unless gases are involved. However, the effect
of temperature is usually very promounced. The direction in which the
solubility of a substance in a solvent changes with temperature depends on
the heat of solution. If a substance dissolves at saturation with evolution
of heat, the solubility decreases with rising temperature. On the other
hand, if a substance dissolves with absorption of heat, the solubility
increases as the temperature is raised.

In general compounds of similar chemical character are more readily
soluble in each other than are those whose chemical character is entirely
different. When a similarity of chemical nature exists between two substances, the solution of the two will have an environment not too different
from that of the pure substances, and the two can tolerate each other in
solution. On the other hand, when the chemical nature of the two substances is considerably different, the substances may not be able to
tolerate each other, and hence there may be little tendency to dissolve.
Between these two extremes a considerable number of intermediate stages
of similarity is possible, and this will account for the wide ranges of solubility of various substances in each other.

These points may be illustrated with the phenomena encountered in
the mutual solubility of liquids. When ethyl alcohol and water, which
are closely related chemically, are mixed, the two dissolve in each other
in all proportions, i.e., there is no saturation limit. Such substances are

said to be *completely miscible*. In distinction to these, two liquids such as water and mercury, which are very different chemically, do not dissolve in each other at all and are said to be *completely immiscible*. Between these two limiting types there are liquid pairs, such as ether and water, which dissolve in each other to a limited extent only. Thus, pure ether dissolves a certain amount of water to form a saturated solution of water in ether, while water dissolves a limited amount of ether to form a saturated solution of ether in water. Consequently, with high proportions of one or the other of these liquids, a completely miscible solution can be obtained. When the proportions taken are outside these saturation limits, however, two layers are obtained, one composed of a solution of ether in water, the other of water in ether. Liquid pairs of this sort are said to be *partially miscible*.

CONCENTRATION OF SOLUTIONS

The concentration of the constituents of a solution can be expressed in many different ways. The following list enumerates the more common of these:

1. Per cent by weight
2. Per cent by volume
3. Weight of solute per definite weight of solvent
4. Weight of solute per definite weight of solution
5. Molarity—number of moles of solute per liter of solution
6. Normality—number of equivalents of solute per liter of solution
7. Molality—number of moles of solute per *1000 grams of solvent*
8. Mol fraction

All these schemes are either self-explanatory or familiar to the student. As in gas mixtures, the mol fraction of any constituent of a solution is defined as the number of moles of the particular substance present divided by the *total* number of moles of all constituents of the solution. If instead of the number of moles the weights of the constituents are given, the mole fractions can be calculated provided the molecular weights are known, for

$$N_A = \frac{n_A}{n_A + n_B + \cdots} = \frac{W_A/M_A}{W_A/M_A + W_B/M_B + \cdots} \tag{1}$$

where the W's are the weights of the various species and the M's the respective molecular weights.

The choice of a particular method for expressing concentrations depends entirely on convenience and the purpose at hand. Of the various methods listed above, those expressed on a weight basis, namely, the first, third, fourth, seventh, and eighth, are temperature independent, i.e., the concentrations will be the same at all temperatures. The concentrations expressed on a volume basis, however, such as percentage by volume, normality, and molarity, will vary with temperature in a manner dependent upon the thermal expansion of the volume of solution.

TYPES OF SOLUTIONS

Although solutions with many components can be prepared, attention will be confined to binary solutions, i.e., solutions containing two components only. Since the solvent and solute may be either gaseous, liquid, or solid, the number of possible types of binary solutions that may be expected is nine, namely:

1. Solution of a gas in a gas
2. Solution of a liquid in a gas
3. Solution of a solid in a gas
4. Solution of a gas in a solid
5. Solution of a liquid in a solid
6. Solution of a solid in a solid
7. Solution of a gas in a liquid
8. Solution of a solid in a liquid
9. Solution of a liquid in a liquid

Of these types the solutions of gases in gases, gases in liquids, liquids in liquids, and solids in liquids are especially important.

SOLUTIONS OF GASES IN GASES

All gases are miscible in all proportions, yielding solutions whose physical properties are very nearly additive provided the total pressure is not too high. Under the latter conditions the partial and total pressures are governed by Dalton's law, the partial and total volumes by Amagat's law. Both of these principles have already been discussed.

SOLUBILITY OF LIQUIDS AND SOLIDS IN GASES

The vaporization of a liquid and the sublimation of a solid into a gas phase may be considered as solution of these substances in a gas. These processes involve first the conversion of the liquid or solid to vapor, and the subsequent solution of the vapor in the gas. Because the vaporization and sublimation pressures of a substance are fixed at any given temperature, the amounts of liquid and solid that can vaporize into a given volume of gas are limited to the amount necessary to establish the equilibrium pressures.

SOLUBILITY OF GASES AND LIQUIDS IN SOLIDS

Gases and liquids may dissolve in solids to form apparently true homogeneous solutions. Examples are the solubility of hydrogen in palladium and the solubility of liquid benzene in solid iodine. Both solutions formed are solid.

SOLUBILITY OF SOLIDS IN SOLIDS

When two solids dissolve in each other, the solutions formed may be completely or partially miscible, depending on the nature of the substances involved and the temperature. Examples of salts forming solid solutions are potassium and ammonium sulfates, copper and ferrous sulfates, and the alums of ammonium and potassium. Many metal pairs likewise form solid solutions, as for instance gold and platinum, gold and palladium, silver and palladium, and copper and nickel. Since the formation of a solid solution would occur extremely slowly while both materials remained solid, it is necessary to resort to crystallization, either from solution in the case of salts or from the molten materials in the case of metals, in order to obtain these solid solutions.

Temperature has no influence on the solubility when both substances involved in the solid solution formation are completely miscible in the solid state. When the two are only partially miscible, however, the extent of solubility depends on the temperature. Some substances may be completely miscible in the solid state at higher temperatures and only partially miscible at lower ones, a transition occurring from one type to the other. There are also other possibilities, but these will be discussed in greater detail in the chapter on the Phase Rule.

SOLUTIONS OF GASES IN LIQUIDS

Gases dissolve in liquids to form true solutions. The degree of solubility depends on the nature of the gas, the nature of the solvent, the pressure, and the temperature. Gases like nitrogen, hydrogen, oxygen, and helium dissolve in water only to a slight extent, while gases like hydrogen chloride and ammonia are very soluble. The large solubility in the latter cases is accounted for by the chemical reaction of these gases with the solvent to form hydrochloric acid and ammonium hydroxide, respectively. In the first-mentioned gases there is no chemical interaction between solute and solvent, solution being due rather to the effect of attractive molecular forces of the solvent for the molecules of solute.

Solubility depends greatly also on the nature of the solvent. Gases like nitrogen, oxygen, and carbon dioxide are much more soluble in

ethyl alcohol than they are in water at the same pressure and temperature, while hydrogen sulfide and ammonia are more soluble in water than
in ethyl alcohol. Frequently, chemical similarity between solute and
solvent leads to a higher solubility, as is evidenced by the fact that hydrocarbon vapors dissolve more readily in hydrocarbon and other organic
solvents than they do in water. Still, chemical similarity is not an infal-
lible criterion of solubility. Thus acetylene, which is quite different in
chemical characteristics from water, dissolves to a greater extent in
water at 0° C than does oxygen.

HENRY'S LAW

At any given temperature *the solubility of a gas in a liquid is directly
proportional to the pressure of the gas above the liquid at equilibrium.* This
principle is known as *Henry's law,* and may be formulated as

$$C = kP \qquad (2)$$

where C is the concentration of the gas in solution, P the pressure of the
gas above the solution at equilibrium, and k a proportionality constant
known as *Henry's law constant.* From equation (2) it is evident that, when
the pressure of a gas is doubled, the solubility is also doubled, etc. The
magnitude of the constant k depends on the nature of the gas and solvent,
the temperature, and the units in which C and P are expressed. It must be
determined experimentally in each case.

When several gases are being dissolved simultaneously in a solvent,
equation (2) is valid for each gas independently, provided C is the concentration and P the *partial pressure* of each gas. We may say, therefore, that *the solubility of each gas from a mixture of gases is directly
proportional to the partial pressure of the gas in the mixture.* The proportionality constant k will, of course, be different for each gas.

The validity of Henry's law is illustrated by the data given in Table 1

TABLE 1

SOLUBILITY OF OXYGEN IN WATER AT 25° C

P (cm Hg)	C (g/liter H_2O)	$\dfrac{C}{P} = k_{O_2}$
17.5	0.0095	0.000543
30.0	0.0160	0.000533
41.4	0.0220	0.000531
61.0	0.0325	0.000533
76.0	0.0408	0.000537

for the solubility of oxygen in water at 25° C. If the law is correct the ratio $C/P = k$ should be constant at all pressures. This is actually the case, as may be seen from column 3 of the table.

The strict applicability of Henry's law is limited to the lower pressures. At high pressures the law becomes less exact, and the proportionality constants exhibit considerable variation. Generally, the higher the temperature and the lower the pressure, the more closely is the law obeyed. Furthermore, the law as given above is not applicable where the dissolved gas reacts with the solvent, or where the dissolved gas ionizes. When the ionization in solution is complete, the law breaks down altogether. The deviations in case of chemical reaction and partial dissociation can be readily understood and corrected for when it is realized that Henry's law, which is a special case of a more general principle known as the Nernst distribution law, is valid only when it is applied to the concentration in solution of the *same molecular species* as exists in the gas phase and not to the total concentration in solution. Thus, when ammonia dissolves in water, part of the dissolved gas reacts to form ammonium hydroxide, which in turn dissociates partially to $NH_4^+ + OH^-$. The reactions involved may be written as

$$NH_3 \text{ (gas)} = NH_3 \text{ (dissolved)}$$
$$NH_3 \text{ (dissolved)} + H_2O = NH_4OH$$
$$NH_4OH = NH_4^+ + OH^-$$

In the light of the above limitation, Henry's law, to be applicable to the solubility of ammonia in water, must be expressed not as $C_{total}/P_{NH_3} = k$, but as $C_{NH_3}/P_{NH_3} = k$, where C_{NH_3} is the concentration of ammonia in solution present as NH_3.

EFFECT OF TEMPERATURE ON GAS SOLUBILITY

The solubility of most gases in liquids decreases with increase in temperature, and consequently the Henry's law constants have smaller values at the higher temperatures. The extent of this decrease may be judged from Table 2, where the *solubility coefficients* for several gases in water are given at various temperatures. The solubility coefficient of a gas is defined as the number of cubic centimeters of gas, reduced to standard conditions, which dissolves in 1 cc of the solvent at a particular temperature and under a pressure of 1 atm.

Because of the decrease in solubility at higher temperatures, liquids containing many types of dissolved gases may be purged of these by boiling. But this is not always the case. Some gases are more soluble at higher temperatures than at lower, and hence these are not readily removable by heating. In fact, dilute solutions of hydrogen chloride in

TABLE 2

SOLUBILITY COEFFICIENTS OF GASES IN WATER AT VARIOUS TEMPERATURES

Gas	0° C	10° C	25° C	50° C	100° C
CO_2	1.713	1.194	0.759	0.436	—
H_2	0.02148	0.01955	0.01754	0.01608	0.0160
N_2	0.02354	0.01861	0.01434	0.01088	0.0095
O_2	0.04758	0.03802	0.02831	0.02090	0.0170

water become more concentrated on boiling, until eventually a solution containing about 20 per cent hydrogen chloride is attained.

SOLUTIONS OF SOLIDS IN LIQUIDS

The extent to which solids dissolve in liquids varies greatly with the nature of the solid and liquid, the temperature, and to a much lesser degree the pressure on the system. In all cases the limit of solubility is the concentration of the *saturated* solution. For any particular solute and solvent the concentration of the *saturated* solution at any given temperature and pressure is constant and does not depend on the manner in which the solution is prepared.

The concentrations of various solutes in a solvent necessary for saturation range over wide limits. Thus, at 20° C 100 g of water dissolve 192 g of ammonium nitrate, 222 g of silver nitrate, 6.5 g of mercuric chloride, and only 8.4×10^{-6} g of silver bromide. In ethyl alcohol, on the other hand, the order of solubility of mercuric chloride and ammonium nitrate is reversed, 100 g of the solvent dissolving 47.6 g of mercuric chloride and only 3.8 g of ammonium nitrate. As a rule most inorganic substances are more soluble in water than in organic solvents, while the reverse holds true for organic substances. There are, however, many exceptions.

The influence of temperature on the solubility of a solute in a particular solvent is, in general, quite pronounced, as may be seen from Table 3. Because most substances absorb heat on solution they tend to become more soluble at higher temperatures. On the other hand, when the solution process is exothermic, a decrease of solubility with temperature may be expected, as is the case with sodium sulfate. However, for some substances the solubility behavior is not so regular. Thus the solubility of $CaSO_4 \cdot 2 H_2O$ increases up to 40° C, passes through a maximum at this temperature, and then decreases at higher temperatures.

When the solubility of any substance is plotted against temperature, the curve obtained is continuous as long as there is no change in the nature of the saturating solid phase. As soon as the solid phase changes, however, a break in the solubility curve appears, and a new solubility curve, originating at the point of break, is obtained, which gives now the solubility of the solid phase formed as a function of the temperature. For substances exhibiting such changes in solid phase the temperatures at which the breaks in the solubility curve occur are definite and characteristic of the substances involved; they represent the temperatures at which the original solid phase and the new phase are in equilibrium with the same solution. In other words, such a break occurs at the temperature at which the solution is saturated with respect to both solid phases.

TABLE 3

SOLUBILITY OF SOLIDS IN WATER AT VARIOUS TEMPERATURES
(g/100 g H_2O)

Solid	0° C	20° C	40° C	60° C	100° C
NH_4Cl	29.4	37.2	45.8	55.2	77.3
$CaSO_4 \cdot 2\ H_2O$	0.176	—	0.210	0.205	0.162
$CuSO_4 \cdot 5\ H_2O$	14.3	20.7	28.5	40.0	75.4
$MgSO_4 \cdot 6\ H_2O$	40.8	44.5	—	53.5	74.0
KCl	27.6	34.0	40.0	45.5	56.7
KNO_3	13.3	31.6	63.9	110.0	246.
$AgNO_3$	122.	222.	376.	525.	952.
NaCl	35.7	36.0	36.6	37.3	39.8
Na_2SO_4	—	—	48.8	45.3	42.5

The particular change in the nature of the solid phase involved may be a transformation of one crystalline form to another, a change from a hydrate to the anhydrous salt, or a transformation of one hydrate to another. These changes will be discussed more fully in Chapter 14. At present only one example will be given, namely, the transformation of β-rhombic ammonium nitrate to the γ-rhombic solid modification, which leads to a discontinuity in the water solubility curve at 32° C. Each of these forms of ammonium nitrate has its own solubility curve, but each form is stable over a different temperature interval. Below 32° C the β-form is stable and is the saturating phase, while above 32° C the γ-modification is the stable form. At 32° C, the transition temperature, both forms are stable. Hence the solubility curves of the two intersect, and the solution is saturated with respect to both. Any break in a solubility curve may be viewed, therefore, as the intersection of two distinct solubility curves, each corresponding to and characteristic of its particular saturating phase.

The effect of pressure on the solubility of solids in liquids is generally quite small. A change of 500 atm in pressure increases the solubility of sodium chloride in water by only 2.3 per cent and decreases the solubility of ammonium chloride by only 5.1 per cent. It has also been observed that the solubility of a solid in a liquid is increased when the particle size of the saturating phase becomes very small. Thus, when the particle size of calcium sulfate is decreased from 2 to 0.3 micron the solubility in water at 25° C goes up from 2.085 to 2.476 g per liter. This fact explains why it is necessary in analytical procedures to digest a precipitate in order to increase the particle size and thereby decrease the solubility. Any solution saturated with respect to fine particles will be supersaturated with respect to any coarser ones, and hence the tendency will be for solute to precipitate onto the coarser particles. The result will be that the crystal size of the larger particles will increase, while the finer particles will disappear by solution.

SOLUBILITY OF LIQUIDS IN LIQUIDS

Two liquids on being brought into contact with each other may be completely miscible, partially miscible, or completely immiscible. As the classifications imply, completely miscible liquids dissolve in each other in all proportions, partially miscible liquids only in limited proportions, and immiscible liquids not at all. Strictly speaking, there probably is no pair of entirely immiscible liquids. The distinction between partial miscibility and complete immiscibility is one of degree and depends on the sensitivity of the analytical methods available for the detection of the substances involved.

The degree of miscibility of two liquids depends on their nature and the temperature. In general, two liquids will be the more miscible the closer their chemical similarity. Thus liquid pairs like benzene and toluene, water and ethyl or methyl alcohol, and water and acetone are completely miscible in each other, while water and nitrobenzene or water and chlorobenzene are not. Increased solubility or even complete miscibility sometimes can be attained by increasing the temperature, as with the liquid pair phenol and water. This, however, is not generally true. Triethylamine and water are completely miscible below 18.5° C, and only partially miscible above this temperature. Again, mixtures of nicotine and water are completely miscible below 60° C and above about 210° C but are only partially miscible between these two temperatures. Finally, solutions of ether and water exhibit only partial miscibility over the entire range of existence of the solutions. These various types of partial miscibility will be discussed in greater detail later.

The properties of binary liquid solutions in which we are particularly interested here are the vapor pressures and the distillation behavior at a constant pressure. These can be understood best in terms of the concept of an *ideal solution* to which all real solutions can be compared.

IDEAL SOLUTIONS

Just as it was possible to set up an ideal gas as a criterion and to predict its properties from theoretical considerations, so, too, is it possible to define an ideal solution whose properties can be predicted on the basis of certain simple laws. An ideal solution may be defined as a solution in which the various pure constituents involved do not experience any modification of properties beyond that of dilution. In the formation of an ideal solution no heat will be evolved or absorbed on solution, and no heat effects will accompany the dilution of the solution with either constituent. For such solutions, also, the total volume will be equal to the sum of the volumes of the individual constituents, while other physical properties will be the average, depending on amounts present, of the properties of the pure constituents. And further, ideal solutions must obey strictly *Raoult's law of vapor pressures*, to be discussed in the next section, throughout the complete range of concentrations. As we shall see, some solutions approximate quite closely to these requirements; others, however, meet them only in dilute solutions.

RAOULT'S LAW

Raoult's law deals at any given temperature with the partial vapor pressures above a solution of the constituents in solution. The law states that the *partial vapor pressure of any volatile constituent of a solution is equal to the vapor pressure of the pure constituent multiplied by the mol fraction of that constituent in solution.* Thus, if we have a solution of two volatile and miscible liquids of composition N_A and N_B, where N_A and N_B are the mol fractions of the two constituents, then the vapor pressures of the two constituents above the solution are, respectively,

$$P_A = P_A^0 N_A \qquad (3a)$$
$$P_B = P_B^0 N_B \qquad (3b)$$

where P_A^0 and P_B^0 are the vapor pressures of the *pure* substances A and B. Equations (3) are a mathematical statement of Raoult's law. From these equations the total vapor pressure above such a solution follows as

$$P = P_A + P_B$$
$$= P_A^0 N_A + P_B^0 N_B \qquad (4)$$

Since, however, $N_A + N_B = 1$, then $N_A = 1 - N_B$, and

$$P = P_A^0(1 - N_B) + P_B^0 N_B$$
$$= (P_B^0 - P_A^0)N_B + P_A^0 \qquad (5)$$

Equation (5) gives the total vapor pressure above a solution as a function of the vapor pressures of the two pure substances and the mol fraction of one of these, N_B. This equation is of the form $P = mx + b$, where $m = (P_B^0 - P_A^0)$ and $b = P_A^0$, and hence it predicts that, when the total pressure of the solution is plotted against the mol fraction N_B, the curve should be a straight line with the indicated slope and an intercept at $N_B = 0$ of $b = P_A^0$. To show this graphically, it is convenient to use for binary mixtures a plot such as shown in Fig. 1. The ordinate is pressure, while the abscissa is N_B. Since N_B can have only values between zero and one, these must be the limits of the diagram. Further, since at $N_B = 0$ only pure A is present, and at $N_B = 1$ only pure B, the ordinate at $N_B = 0$ represents the relations for pure A, while the ordinate at $N_B = 1$ does the same for pure B. The ordinates between these two limits represent the properties of all possible proportions of A and B, and

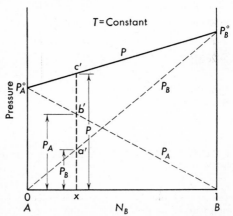

Fig. 1.   Vapor Pressure of Miscible Liquids According to Raoult's Law.

hence a plot such as is shown in Fig. 1 gives the complete vapor pressure relations of all possible mixtures of the two substances.

In line with these requirements, the ordinates in Fig. 1 at $N_B = 0$ and $N_B = 1$ give P_A^0 and P_B^0, respectively. Since the pressures of all intermediate concentrations lie on a straight line that includes these points, the solid line in the diagram must represent the total vapor pressures of all possible mixtures of A and B. We see, therefore, that for binary solutions obeying Raoult's law the vapor pressures are intermediate between those of the pure components and lie on a straight line between these points.

The dotted lines in the diagram represent the *partial* pressures of the individual components and are, similarly, the plots of equations (3a) and (3b). These vary linearly from $P_A = P_A^0$ and $P_B = 0$ at $N_B = 0$, to $P_A = 0$ and $P_B = P_B^0$ at $N_B = 1$. At all intermediate mol fractions the total pressure is the sum of the partial pressure ordinates. Thus, at

$N_B = x$, P_B is equal to the distance $a'x$, $P_A = b'x$, and the total pressure $P = c'x = a'x + b'x$.

The above relationships demanded by Raoult's law apply to the total and partial vapor pressures as a function of the mol fractions of the constituents *in solution*. To obtain the relation between the composition of a solution and the composition of the vapor above it, let Y_B be the mol fraction of B *in the vapor* above a solution of composition N_B. Then, according to Dalton's law of partial pressures,

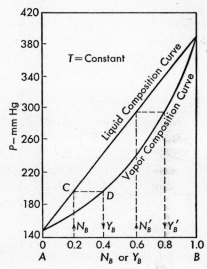

Fig. 2. Liquid and Vapor Composition Curves for an Ideal Solution.

$$Y_B = \frac{P_B}{P} \qquad (6)$$

But $P_B = P_B^0 N_B$, while P is given by equation (5). Consequently,

$$Y_B = \frac{P_B^0 N_B}{(P_B^0 - P_A^0)N_B + P_A^0} \qquad (7)$$

Equation (7) gives the mol fraction of B *in the vapor* above a solution of composition N_B in terms of the vapor pressures of the pure substances and N_B. It is readily seen that there is a definite composition of vapor corresponding to each composition of solution but that the two are not the same and cannot be the same unless $P_A^0 = P_B^0$.

With the aid of equation (7) a vapor pressure-vapor composition curve can be constructed for solutions obeying Raoult's law which will show the composition of the vapor corresponding to any particular composition of solution. Such a curve calculated at a constant temperature for $P_A^0 = 147$ mm and $P_B^0 = 396$ mm Hg is shown in Fig. 2. The straight line gives the total pressure above the solution as a function of the mol fraction of B in solution, N_B, while the curve lying below it represents the total vapor pressure as a function of the mol fraction of B in the vapor, Y_B. To obtain the composition of vapor corresponding to, say, a solution for which $N_B = 0.2$, we move vertically to point C to obtain the total vapor pressure of the solution. This same pressure is given also on the vapor composition curve by point D, corresponding to a composition $Y_B = 0.402$, and hence for the liquids in question when $N_B = 0.2$, $Y_B = 0.402$. Similarly, when $N_B' = 0.6$, $Y_B' = 0.803$. It will be observed that the vapor is always richer in B than the solution, i.e., the vapor is richer in the more volatile component.

VAPOR PRESSURE OF ACTUAL LIQUID PAIRS

A few binary miscible liquid systems obey Raoult's law strictly throughout the complete range of concentrations. One of these, the pair ethylene dibromide-propylene dibromide at 85.05° C, is shown in Fig. 3. Others are the pairs benzene-ethylene dichloride, carbon tetrachloride-stannic chloride, and chlorbenzene-brombenzene. Most systems, however, deviate from Raoult's law to a greater or lesser degree dependent on the nature of the liquids and the temperature.

The character of the deviations from Raoult's law may be judged from Figs. 4, 5, and 6, which show the total and partial pressures of several systems in their dependence on the mol fraction. In the pair carbon tetrachloride-cyclohexane, shown in Fig. 4, the total pressure as well as the partial pressures exhibit positive deviations from Raoult's law, but the total pressure is at all times intermediate between the vapor pressures of the two pure components. Similarly, in the system carbon disulfide-methylal, Fig. 5, the deviations from Raoult's law are positive, but the total vapor pressure curve rises to a *maximum* which is above the

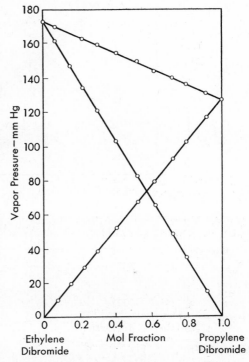

Fig. 3.   Vapor Pressures of the System Ethylene Dibromide-Propylene Dibromide at 85.05° C.

vapor pressure of either pure constituent. On the other hand, the pair chloroform-acetone, Fig. 6, exhibits negative deviations from Raoult's law which lead to a *minimum* in the total vapor pressure of the system, i.e., the vapor pressures of certain concentrations of the solution are *below* the vapor pressures of either of the pure constituents.

The vapor pressure curves given in Figs. 4, 5, and 6 are typical of the vapor pressure behavior of volatile liquid pairs. On the basis of these diagrams, all miscible liquid pairs can be classified into three general types, namely:

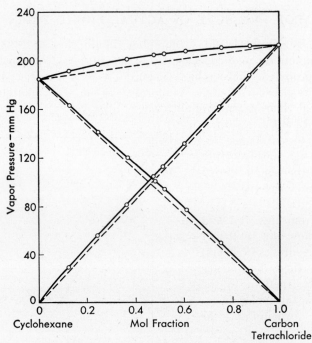

Fig. 4.   Vapor Pressures of the System Cyclohexane-Carbon Tetrachloride at 40° C.
[Scatchard, Wood, and Mochels, *J. Am. Chem. Soc.*, **61**, 3208 (1939).]

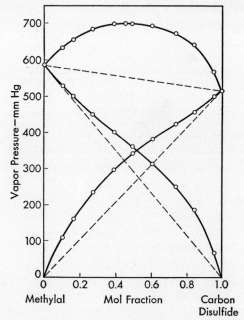

Fig. 5.   Vapor Pressures of the System Methylal-Carbon Disulfide at 35.2° C.

Type I: Systems whose total vapor pressure is *intermediate* between those of the pure components. Examples: Carbon tetrachloride-cyclohexane, carbon tetrachloride-benzene, benzene-toluene, water-methyl alcohol.

Type II: Systems exhibiting a *maximum* in the total vapor pressure curve. Examples: Carbon disulfide-methylal, carbon disulfide-acetone, benzene-cyclohexane, benzene-ethyl alcohol, chloroform-ethyl alcohol, and water and ethyl or *n*-propyl alcohol.

Type III: Systems exhibiting a *minimum* in the total vapor pressure curve. Examples: Chloroform-acetone, methyl ether-hydrogen chloride, pyridine–acetic acid, and water and formic, nitric, hydrochloric, or hydrobromic acids.

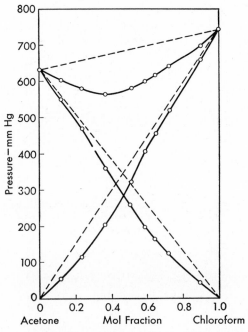

Fig. 6.   Vapor Pressures of the System Acetone-Chloroform at 55.1° C.

The vapor pressure-*liquid* composition curves of these various types, along with the corresponding vapor pressure-*vapor* composition curves, are illustrated in Fig. 7. All these curves correspond to a constant temperature.

It will be observed that for all types the vapor composition curves lie *below* the liquid composition curves and that in types II and III the two curves are in contact at the points of maximum and minimum vapor pressure respectively. At these points, therefore, the compositions of the solution and vapor are identical, and the diagrams of types II and III may be thought of as being composed of two curves of type I, one for pure *A* and solution of maximum or minimum vapor pressure, *C* or *D*, the other of solution of maximum or minimum vapor pressure. *C* or *D*, and pure B. The position of the vapor composition curves with respect to the liquid composition curves follows from the fact that out of a mixture of two volatile substances in solution the one of higher vapor pressure will volatilize to a greater extent than the one of lower vapor pressure, yielding a vapor of composition richer in the more volatile constituent than is the solution. Thus, in the liquid pair of type I shown in Fig. 7, B is more volatile than A, and consequently the vapor above all concentrations of solution must be richer in B than is the solution. Hence, the composition of vapor corresponding to point a on the diagram must lie closer to B than point a, and this is possible only if the vapor composition curve is below the liquid composition curve. As the diagram indicates, the composition of vapor corresponding to a is a', a mixture

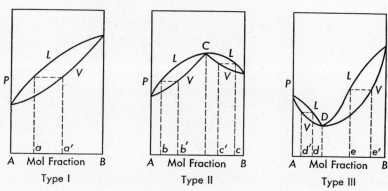

Fig. 7.   Types of Binary Vapor Pressure Diagrams (Temperature Constant).

considerably richer in B than is a. For the same reason all mixtures between A and C in type II must have vapors richer in B than the solution, while all mixtures between C and B must be richer in A than the solution. These conditions are satisfied by the diagram as drawn, for the vapor composition corresponding to a point such as b is b', richer in B than b, while that of composition c is c', richer in A than c. Similarly, the compositions of vapor in type III must be richer in A than the solutions between A and D, while richer in B between D and B. These conditions are again satisfied by the diagram drawn, as may be verified by the two points indicated, d with vapor composition d', and e with vapor composition e'.

BOILING POINT DIAGRAMS OF MISCIBLE BINARY MIXTURES

Because at any given temperature the vapor above any solution is richer in the more volatile substance than the solution, a solution can be made to shift in composition toward the less volatile constituent by removing the vapor above it. Again, if the vapors are condensed, and the new vapor above the condensate removed, the new vapors will be found considerably richer in the more volatile constituent than are the solutions from which they came. By repeating this process it is possible to obtain a concentration of the more volatile constituent in the vapor and a concentration of the less volatile constituent in the solution. Such a process of concentrating the constituents is known as fractional distillation; and, since the process described takes place at constant temperature, it may be designated as an isothermal fractional distillation.

In practice it is much more convenient to conduct a distillation at *constant pressure* rather than at constant temperature; i.e., it is much easier to conduct a distillation such that the temperature varies while the pressure remains constant than it is to hold the temperature constant and let the pressure vary. At a given confining pressure any solution of definite composition will boil at a temperature at which its *total* vapor pressure becomes equal to the confining pressure. If we designate by P the confining pressure, then the condition for boiling may be written as

$$P_A + P_B = P \qquad\qquad (8)$$

Thus, at atmospheric pressure a solution will boil at the temperature at which its total vapor pressure becomes equal to 760 mm Hg. Since different compositions of a solution have different vapor pressures, it must follow that the various solutions will not reach a total vapor pressure equal to the confining pressure at the same temperature, and therefore solutions of various concentrations will boil at different temperatures. In general, solutions of *low* vapor pressure will boil at temperatures *higher* than solutions whose vapor pressure is high, for solutions of high vapor pressure can reach a total pressure equal to the confining pressure at relatively lower temperatures than solutions whose vapor pressure is low.

This latter fact permits the construction of the various types of temperature-composition diagrams which will correspond to the three general types of vapor pressure-composition diagrams already discussed. These are shown in Fig. 8. In type I the vapor pressure of A is the lowest pressure in the system, that of B is the highest, while the vapor pressure of all possible compositions of A and B are intermediate between the two. Consequently, at constant pressure the boiling point of A will be the highest in the system and that of B the lowest, while those of all compositions of A and B will be intermediate and will be given by the liquid composition curve in the figure. Since the vapor coming off from any particular composition of solution must be richer in the more volatile constituent B, the vapor composition at any temperature must lie *closer* to B than the corresponding liquid composition, and hence the vapor composition curve must lie now *above* the liquid composition curve, as shown. The same considerations apply to the other two types. In type II the vapor pressure of the system is a maximum for composition *C*, and hence such a solution will boil at the lowest temperature, leading to a minimum in the boiling point curve. Again, since in type III

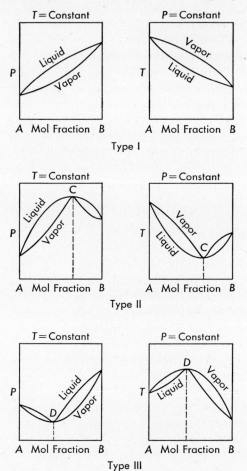

Fig. 8. Types of Distillation Diagrams Corresponding to Various Vapor Pressure Diagrams.

the solution of composition *D* has the lowest vapor pressure in the system, it will boil at the highest temperature, and consequently the boiling point curve exhibits a *maximum*. In all cases the vapor composition curves lie above the liquid composition curves for the reasons given. We see, therefore, that any system whose vapor pressures are intermediate between those of the pure constituents will have a distillation diagram with intermediate boiling points, such as type I. On the other hand, any system of the maximum vapor pressure type will give a distillation diagram with minimum boiling point, while any system of the minimum vapor pressure type will have a distillation diagram with a maximum in the boiling point curve.

The concentrations for points C and D in the vapor pressure and temperature diagrams are generally not identical. With change in temperature there is a tendency for the compositions at which the vapor pressure maxima or minima occur to shift toward A or B, depending on the system involved.

DISTILLATION OF BINARY MISCIBLE SOLUTIONS

Because of the differences in the distillation diagrams of the three types of solutions, the behavior of these on constant pressure distillation will be different. Consider first the behavior of a system of type I (Fig. 9). If we heat a solution of composition a, no boiling will start until temperature T_a is reached. At this temperature the vapor coming off from a and in equilibrium with it will have the composition a'. Since a' is richer in B than a, the composition of the residue must become richer in A, say b. The new composition of residue, b, cannot boil, however, until temperature T_b is reached, which is higher than T_a. In turn the vapor coming off from b will have the composition b', again richer in B, and consequently the composition of the residue will again be enriched in A, and again the temperature must rise before the residue will

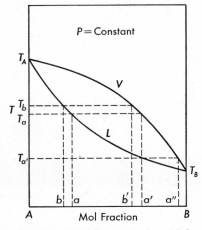

Fig. 9.   Distillation Behavior of Solutions of Type I.

boil. We see, therefore, that if the process described is continued the boiling point of the solution will rise from the initial boiling point T_a toward the boiling point, T_A, of pure A. At the same time the composition of the residue becomes richer in A than the original solution, and if the process is continued sufficiently long, a final residue of pure A can be obtained.

Consider now what can be done with the vapors. If the initial vapors obtained from the solution, namely, a', are condensed and again distilled, the boiling point of the new solution will be T_a', and the composition of the distillate will be given by a''. This distillate is again richer in B than the original. If the process of condensing and redistilling is continued, eventually a vapor can be obtained composed essentially of pure *B*. Therefore, on distillation of any mixture of type I it is possible to separate eventually the constituents into a residue of the less volatile constituent *A* and a distillate of the more volatile component *B*; i.e., *the two constituents forming a solution of type I can be separated by fractional distillation into the pure components.*

Such a separation into the pure components is impossible, however, with solutions of either type II or type III. Consider the distillation behavior of a solution of type II, Fig. 10, of which the system water (*A*)-ethyl alcohol (*B*) is an outstanding example. If a solution of com-

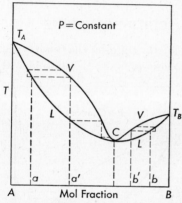

Fig. 10. Distillation Behavior of Solutions of Type II.

position between *A* and *C*, such as *a*, is distilled, the vapor coming off will have the composition *a'* and will be richer in *B* than the residue. Because of this fact the composition of the residue will shift toward *A*, and hence the residue will have to boil at a temperature higher than the original solution *a*. If the distillation is continued, the same argument as was employed for solutions of type I indicates that eventually a residue of pure *A*, boiling at temperature T_A, will be obtained. On the other hand, if the vapors from the original solution, *a'*, are condensed and redistilled repeatedly, a vapor of composition *C* will eventually be obtained. Such vapor when condensed and distilled will again yield vapor of composition *C*; i.e., the vapors coming off from the solution will have the same composition as the solution, and hence no further separation is possible by distillation. Consequently, *any mixture having a composition between A and C can be separated by fractional distillation only into a residue of pure A and a final distillate of composition C.* No pure *B* can be recovered. Thus, in the system water-ethyl alcohol point *C* corresponds to a minimum boiling temperature of 78.13° C and a composition of 95.57 per cent ethyl alcohol by weight, and hence any solution having a composition between that of pure water and 95.57 per cent ethyl alcohol can be separated only into a residue of pure water and a constant minimum boiling mixture of 95.57 per cent alcohol in the distillate. No pure ethyl alcohol can be recovered.

On the other hand, if a solution of composition between *C* and *B* is distilled, for example, *b*, the vapor coming off, *b'*, will be *richer in A* than the original solution, and hence on repeated distillation the residue will tend toward pure *B*, while the distillate will tend toward *C*. Such solutions on complete distillation will yield, therefore, pure B in the residue and constant boiling mixture C in the distillate. No A can be recovered by distillation. Thus alcohol-water mixtures richer in alcohol than 95.57 per cent can be separated by distillation only into pure alcohol in the residue and constant minimum boiling mixture C, 95.57 per cent alcohol, in the distillate. No amount of distillation will yield pure water.

Boiling solutions of composition C will yield, of course, vapor of exactly the same composition as the solution. Hence no separation of such solutions can be accomplished by distillation.

In summary it may be stated that all starting solutions belonging to type II will yield eventually a distillate of composition C. The residue will be either pure A or pure B, depending on whether the starting composi-tion is between A and C or between C and B. A starting composition C, however, cannot be separated by distillation.

The behavior of solutions of type III on distillation will be analogous to that of solutions of type II, with the exception that *the residues tend toward the maximum boiling mixture, while the distillates tend toward the pure constituents* (Fig. 11). If the starting mixture has a composition between A and D, such as a, the vapor obtained on distillation, a', will be richer in A than the solution. Hence the com-position of the residue will shift toward D and will eventually reach it. A redistilla-tion of the vapor, on the other hand, will finally yield a distillate of pure A. A

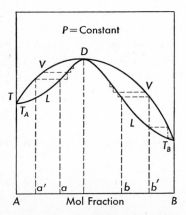

Fig. 11. Distillation Behavior of Solutions of Type III.

mixture between D and B, such as b, however, will yield on distillation a vapor of composition b', richer in B than the solution. Hence again the residue will shift toward D, while on redistillation the vapors will tend toward pure B. Consequently, complete distillation of a mixture such as b will eventually yield a residue of composition D and a distillate of pure B. We see, therefore, that any binary system of this type can be separated on complete fractional distillation into a residue of composition D, the constant maximum boiling mixture, and a distillate of either pure A or pure B, depending on whether the starting composition is between A and D or D and B. But a mixture of composition D cannot be separated further by distillation.

An example of a binary system exhibiting such a behavior is the pair water-hydrochloric acid. Although water boils at 100° C and hydrogen chloride at −85° C under a pressure of 1 atm, a solution of 20.24 per cent hydrochloric acid in water boils at 108.5° C. Any solution containing less than 20.24 per cent hydrochloric acid can be separated on distillation into a constant boiling mixture of 20.24 per cent hydrochloric acid and a final distillate of pure water, but no pure hydrogen chloride can be recovered from such solutions. On the other hand, any solution richer in hydrochloric acid than 20.24 per cent can be distilled to yield again the same constant composition residue, and, if the distillation is carried down to −85° C, pure hydrogen chloride.

AZEOTROPIC MIXTURES

The constant boiling mixtures described above are referred to either as *azeotropes* or *azeotropic mixtures*. At one time it was believed that such mixtures correspond to the formation of definite compounds between the two constituents. However, a definite compound should have a definite composition over a given temperature and pressure range. This is not the case with azeotropic mixtures. When the total pressure at which the solution boils is changed, it is found that not only the temperature at which the azeotrope is obtained but also the *composition* changes, as may be seen from Table 4. This is not the behavior to be expected from a definite compound. Rather, the particular behavior observed is the result of the interplay of intermolecular forces in solution.

TABLE 4

EFFECT OF PRESSURE ON COMPOSITION OF AZEOTROPE
IN SYSTEM H_2O-HCl

Pressure (mm Hg)	Weight % of HCl in Constant Boiling Mixture
730	20.314
740	20.290
750	20.266
760	20.242
770	20.218

The composition of azeotropic mixtures is remarkably constant at any given pressure. Advantage is taken of this constancy to prepare solutions of hydrochloric acid of accurately known composition. A solution of hydrochloric acid of composition lower than that of the maximum boiling mixture is distilled until the azeotropic composition is reached. The azeotrope is then collected, and the barometric pressure at which distillation took place is observed. From tables, such as Table 4, the composition of the azeotrope is then known, and any desired composition of hydrochloric acid can be prepared by dilution with an accuracy high enough for direct use in quantitative analysis.

Table 5 lists the boiling points and compositions of some azeotropes, all for a total pressure of 760 mm Hg.

TABLE 5

BOILING POINTS AND COMPOSITIONS OF AZEOTROPIC MIXTURES
($P = 760$ mm Hg)

Type	A	B	Boiling Point (° C)	Weight % of B in Azeotrope
Minimum boiling point	Water	Ethyl alcohol	78.15	95.57
	Water	n-Propyl alcohol	87.72	71.70
	Ethyl alcohol	Benzene	68.24	67.63
	Acetic acid	Benzene	80.05	98.
	Carbon disulfide	Ethyl acetate	46.1	3.
	Pyridine	Water	92.6	43.
Maximum boiling point	Water	Nitric acid	120.5	68.
	Water	Hydrochloric acid	108.5	20.24
	Water	Hydrobromic acid	126.0	47.5
	Water	Hydriodic acid	127.0	57.
	Water	Hydrofluoric acid	120.0	37.
	Water	Formic acid	107.1	77.
	Chloroform	Acetone	64.7	20.
	Pyridine	Formic acid	149.0	18.

THE FRACTIONATING COLUMN

The type of distillation described heretofore, in which the vapor removed is in equilibrium with the total mass of boiling liquid, is designated as *equilibrium distillation*. The process of separating mixtures by distillation would be extremely complicated and tedious if it had to be performed by repeated distillations and condensations in a discontinuous manner. Instead, the separation is performed in a continuous operation, known as *fractional distillation*, utilizing a distilling apparatus called a *fractionating column*, Fig. 12. The fractionating column consists essentially of three parts: a heated still A; the column proper D, composed of a series of plates whose detailed construction is shown in the figure; and a condenser F. The preheated mixture to be distilled is admitted through E onto one of these plates, and overflows through 2 to the plate below. On this lower plate the liquid comes in contact with vapor moving upward from the still through the "bubble caps" 3' and 4'. These caps are so designed that the vapor must bubble through the layer of liquid on each plate before it can escape. In doing so, part of the less volatile constituent is condensed out of the vapor, and part of the more volatile constituent is vaporized

out of the liquid. The vapor moving on to the next higher plates through
3 and 4 is richer, then, in the more volatile constituent than the vapor
which approached the plate from below, while the liquid overflowing to

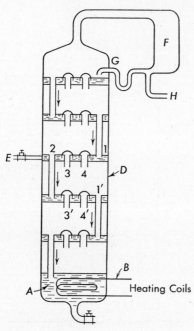

Fig. 12. Schematic Diagram of Fractionating Column.

the next lower plate through 1' is
richer in the less volatile constituent
than the liquid which reached the
plate from above. The net result of
the interaction between vapor and
liquid at the plate is, therefore, a
redistribution in favor of the more
volatile constituent in the vapor and
the less volatile constituent in the
liquid; i.e., each plate acts essentially
as a miniature still.

Since this process repeats itself at
each plate, it is possible with a sufficient number of plates to separate the
mixture into two end fractions, a
residue of the less volatile component
running into still *A*, where it can be
drawn off, and a vapor passing from
the top of the column containing
essentially the more volatile constituent. This vapor is fed into a condenser
F, where it is liquefied. Part of this
liquid is drawn off through *H*, while
part, the reflux, is returned to the column through *G* in order to maintain
the stock of essentially pure distillate on the upper plates.

RATIO OF DISTILLATE TO RESIDUE ON DISTILLATION

For various chemical and chemical engineering calculations it is frequently necessary to know the ratio of weight of distillate to weight of
residue at each stage of an equilibrium distillation. For a binary mixture
this information is readily available from the distillation diagram.

Consider a binary system wholse distillation diagram is given by Fig.
13. The abscissa is expressed now as weight per cent rather than mol
fraction. If we start with a mixture whose weight per cent is x, the system
will be entirely liquid until temperature T_1 is reached. At T_1 the solution
will begin to boil, and since the liquid becomes less concentrated in B,
the boiling point will gradually rise as distillation proceeds. At a temperature such as T_2, if no vapor is removed from the system, the latter
will still have the same over-all composition as the starting mixture x,
but it will be composed now of liquid of composition x_1 and vapor of

composition x_2. Under such conditions the weight of liquid present, w_1, is proportional to the linear distance bc, while the weight of vapor present, w_2, is proportional to the distance ab; i.e.,

$$\frac{w_1}{w_2} = \frac{bc}{ab} \qquad (9)$$

The argument leading to equation (9) is as follows. If we let w be the total weight of mixture of composition x, then

$$w = w_1 + w_2$$

Again, a material balance on constituent B yields

$$wx = w_1 x_1 + w_2 x_2$$

and hence we get on substitution for w,

$$(w_1 + w_2)x = w_1 x_1 + w_2 x_2$$
$$w_1(x - x_1) = w_2(x_2 - x)$$
$$\frac{w_1}{w_2} = \frac{(x_2 - x)}{(x - x_1)}$$

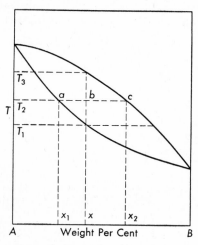

Fig. 13. Ratio of Distillate to Residue on Distillation.

But, $(x_2 - x) = bc$ and $(x - x_1) = ab$. Therefore equation (9) follows. This relation between weights and distances is perfectly general and can be applied to any portion of the diagram at all temperatures. It must be remembered, however, that, when the abscissa is not weight per cent but mol fraction, the ratios of the distances represent the ratios of the number of *moles* of liquid and vapor rather than the weights.

SOLUBILITY OF PARTIALLY MISCIBLE LIQUID PAIRS

Maximum Solution Temperature Type. When a small quantity of aniline is added to water at room temperature and the mixture is shaken, the aniline dissolves in the water to form a single liquid phase. However, when larger quantities of aniline are added, two liquid layers are formed. One of these, the lower, consists of a small amount of water dissolved in the aniline, while the upper consists of a small amount of aniline dissolved in water. Further addition of aniline to the system causes the water-rich layer to diminish in size until finally it disappears, leaving only a single liquid phase composed of water in the aniline.

If this experiment is performed at constant temperature, it is found that the compositions of the two layers, although different from each other, remain constant as long as two phases are present. The addition of small amounts of either aniline or water merely changes the relative volumes of the two layers, not their composition. As the temperature is raised, this behavior is found to persist except that the mutual solubility of the two liquids increases. When the temperature finally reaches 168° C, the compositions of the two layers become identical, and thereafter the two liquids are completely miscible. In other words, at 168° C and above aniline and water dissolve in each other in all proportions and yield only a single liquid layer on mixing.

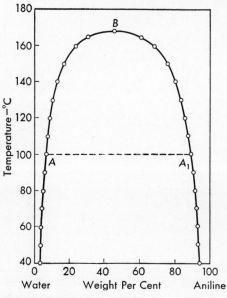

Fig. 14. Mutual Solubility of Water and Aniline at Various Temperatures.

This variation of the mutual solubility of water and aniline with temperature is illustrated in Fig. 14. At a temperature such as 100° C, point A represents the composition of the water-rich layer and point A_1 the composition of the aniline-rich layer in equilibrium with A. Between A and A_1 all mixtures yield two layers of compositions A and A_1. Outside these compositions the two liquids are mutually soluble at 100°; i.e., all compositions between pure water and A yield a solution of aniline in water, while all compositions between A_1 and pure aniline yield a solution of water in aniline.

Since the same argument holds at other temperatures, it must follow that the dome-shaped area represents the range of existence of two liquid phases, the area outside the dome that of a single liquid layer. The temperature corresponding to point B, i.e., the temperature at which solubility first becomes complete, is called either the *critical solution temperature* or the *consolute temperature*.

Minimum Solution Temperature Type. Figure 15 shows the effect of temperature on the mutual solubility of triethylamine and water. The two liquids are completely miscible at or below 18.5° C, but only partially miscible above this temperature. Thus at 30° C, for instance, a solution of 5.6 per cent triethylamine in water is in equilibrium with one containing 4 per cent water in triethylamine. The temperature at which the two liquids become completely miscible is called in this case the minimum critical solution temperature, since the curve confining the area of partial miscibility exhibits a minimum.

Maximum and Minimum Solution Temperature Type. The system nicotine-water exhibits two critical solution temperatures, an upper and a lower, as may be seen from Fig. 16. Within the enclosed area the liquids are only partially miscible, while outside the enclosed area they are completely miscible. The upper or maximum solution temperature, point C, is 208° C, while the lower, or minimum solution temperature, point C', is 60.8° C. The compositions corresponding to C and C' are the same, 34 per cent nicotine. At 94 to 95° C, point A, nicotine is least soluble in water, while water is least soluble in nicotine at 129 to 130° C, point B.

It has been found that on applying external pressure to this system the upper and lower critical solution temperatures approach each other, until a pressure is finally reached at which the two liquids become completely miscible.

Type Without Critical Solution Temperature. A final variation of these types is exhibited by the system ethyl ether-water, which has neither an upper nor a lower critical solution temperature. The two liquids are therefore only partially soluble in each other at all the temperatures over which the solution exists.

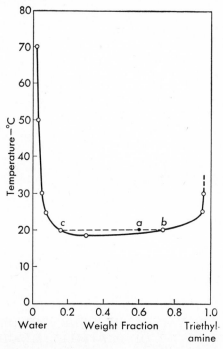

Fig. 15. Solubility of Triethylamine in Water at Various Temperatures.

It is always possible to deduce from solubility diagrams such as those given in Figs. 14, 15 and 16 the proportions by weight of the two layers present at equilibrium at the various temperatures. Consider specifically a system composed of 60 g of triethylamine and 40 g of water present in equilibrium at 20° C. Since the percentage of amine by weight is 60 per cent, the over-all composition is represented in Fig. 15 by point a. But this system is composed of solutions of compositions b and c, and hence, by the method used before,

$$\frac{Wt \text{ amine layer}}{Wt \text{ water layer}} = \frac{\text{distance } ca}{\text{distance } ab}$$

$$= \frac{60 - 15.5}{73 - 60}$$

$$= 3.42$$

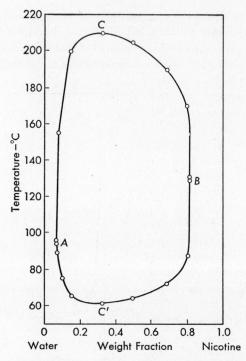

Fig. 16. Solubility of Nicotine in Water at Various Temperatures.

VAPOR PRESSURE AND DISTILLATION DIAGRAMS OF PARTIALLY MISCIBLE LIQUID PAIRS

Although three types of vapor pressure and distillation diagrams are possible for partially miscible liquid pairs, only one of these will be discussed here.

A total vapor pressure-composition diagram for the partially miscible liquid pair *n*-butyl alcohol-water is shown in Fig. 17(a). Starting with pure butyl alcohol, whose vapor pressure is D', we observe an increase in the total pressure of the system on addition of water. This increase continues until the pressure given by point C', corresponding to a saturated solution of water in butyl alcohol, is reached. Similarly, starting with pure water of vapor pressure A', addition of butyl alcohol raises the vapor pressure until a saturated solution of butyl alcohol in water, point B', is reached. The vapor pressure corresponding to C' is *exactly the same* as that of B'; i.e., the saturated solution of butyl alcohol in water has exactly the same vapor pressure as a saturated solution of water in butyl alcohol. And, furthermore, the total vapor pressure above the system in the region of partial miscibility, between B' and C', where two

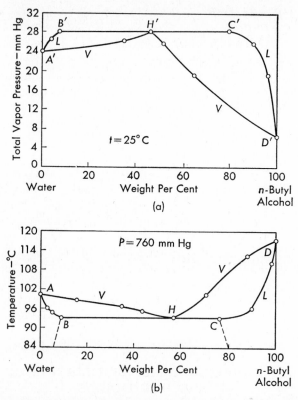

Fig. 17.   Vapor Pressure and Distillation Diagrams for the System *n*-Butyl Alcohol-Water. [(a) Butler, *J. Chem. Soc.*, **674**, (1933); (b) Stockhardt and Hull, *Ind. Eng Chem.*, **23**, 1438 (1931).]

layers are present, is *constant and equal to that of either of the two layers and not the sum of the two.* This state of affairs is a direct consequence of the thermodynamic conditions of equilibrium in such a system. For equilibrium to exist in a system involving the distribution of a particular component between two phases, such as butyl alcohol between the upper and lower layers, the vapor pressure of the particular constituent above each of the layers must be the same, and the vapor pressure above both must be that of any one. Consequently, the vapor pressure of butyl alcohol above B' must be equal to that above C', and the total must be the same as *either* that of B' or C'. Since the same considerations apply to the water in the two phases, the total pressure above both layers is the same as that of B' or C' and is constant as long as both phases are present.

The curves $A'H'$ and $D'H'$ give the compositions of vapor in equilibrium with $A'B'$ and $D'C'$, respectively. For all compositions of liquid between B' and C' the composition of vapor is constant and equal to H'.

The distillation diagram which corresponds to a system exhibiting the vapor pressure behavior shown by butyl alcohol-water is shown in Fig. 17(b). The curve CD gives the boiling points of all solutions of water in butyl alcohol, while HD gives the compositions of vapor corresponding to the various compositions of the liquid phase. Similarly, AB gives the boiling points of all solutions of butyl alcohol in water, while AH gives the corresponding vapor compositions. The boiling points of all over-all compositions that yield two layers, namely, between B and C, are given by BC, while the composition of vapor that corresponds to BC is given by point H; i.e., as long as the two saturated layers are present, the boiling point of the system is *constant,* and the composition of the vapor coming off is also *constant and independent of the over-all composition.*

The dotted lines emanating from B and C in Fig. 17(b) indicate the variation of the mutual solubility of the two liquids with temperature, and are part of the solubility diagram.

Other examples of systems exhibiting behavior similar to that of butyl alcohol-water are aniline-water, *iso*-butyl alcohol-water, and ethyl acetate-water.

VAPOR PRESSURE AND DISTILLATION OF IMMISCIBLE LIQUIDS

Since immiscible liquids are mutually insoluble, addition of one liquid to the other does not affect the properties of either liquid. Hence each will behave as if the other were not present. Consequently, in a mixture of two immiscible liquids each will exert the vapor pressure corresponding to the pure liquid at the given temperature, and the *total* vapor pressure above the mixture will be the sum of the vapor pressures of the two pure constituents, namely,

$$P = P_A^0 + P_B^0 \tag{10}$$

where P is the total vapor pressure, and P_A^0, P_B^0 are the vapor pressures of the two pure liquids A and B.

The boiling point of any system is the temperature at which the total vapor pressure is equal to the confining pressure. Since the two liquids together can reach any given total pressure at a lower temperature than either liquid alone, it must follow that any mixture of two immiscible liquids must boil at a temperature *lower* than the boiling point of *either* of the two liquids. Furthermore, since at any given temperature there is no change in total vapor pressure with change in over-all composition, the boiling point of all possible mixtures of the two must remain *constant* as long as both liquids are present. As soon as one of the liquids is boiled away, however, the boiling temperature will rise abruptly from that of the mixture to either T_A or T_B, depending on whether one or the other is boiled away first.

At any boiling temperature for the mixture, T, the partial vapor pressures of the two constituents are P_A^0 and P_B^0 corresponding to the given temperature. If we let N_A and N_B be the mol fractions of the two constituents in the vapor, then $P_A^0 = N_A P$, $P_B^0 = N_B P$, and hence,

$$\frac{P_A^0}{P_B^0} = \frac{N_A P}{N_B P} = \frac{N_A}{N_B} \tag{11}$$

But $N_A = n_A/(n_A + n_B)$, and $n_B = n_B/(n_A + n_B)$, where n_A and n_B are the number of moles of A and B in any given volume of vapor. Consequently,

$$\frac{P_A^0}{P_B^0} = \frac{n_A}{n_B} \tag{12}$$

and, since the ratio of the partial pressures at T is constant, n_A/n_B must also be constant; i.e., the composition of the vapor is at all times constant as long as both liquids are present. Further, since $n_A = W_A/M_A$, and $n_B = W_B/M_B$, where W_A, W_B are the weights in any given volume and M_A, M_B are the molecular weights of A and B respectively, equation (12) becomes

$$\frac{P_A^0}{P_B^0} = \frac{n_A}{n_B} = \frac{W_A}{W_B} \cdot \frac{M_B}{M_A}$$

and

$$\frac{W_A}{W_B} = \frac{M_A P_A^0}{M_B P_B^0} \tag{13}$$

Equation (13) relates directly the weights of the two constituents distilled from a mixture of two immiscible liquids to the molecular weights and the vapor pressures of the two pure constituents. It will be observed that the weight of any constituent distilled over depends on both its vapor pressure and molecular weight, and hence the effect of a low vapor pressure is counteracted by a high molecular weight as far as weight of a particular substance distilled over is concerned.

Distillation of immiscible liquids is utilized industrially and in the laboratory for the purification of organic liquids which either boil at high temperatures or tend to decompose when heated to their normal boiling point. The other liquid frequently is water, and the whole process is generally referred to as *steam distillation*. The immiscible mixture of the liquid and water is heated either directly or by injection of steam, and the vapors coming off are condensed and separated. In this manner it is possible to distill many liquids of high boiling point at temperatures below 100° C, the boiling point of water.

Distillation of immiscible liquids can also be utilized in determining the approximate molecular weight of one of the liquids involved. When the vapor pressures and weight ratios of distillates of two liquids are determined, and the molecular weight of one of the liquids is known, the molecular weight of the other can readily be calculated from equation (13). The manner in which the necessary data are obtained can best be explained through an example. When the two immiscible liquids chlorbenzene and water are boiled at a pressure of 734.4 mm Hg, the boiling point is 90° C, while the ratio of weight of chlorbenzene to water collected in the distillate is 2.47. Since at 90° C the vapor pressure of water is 526.0 mm Hg, the vapor pressure of chlorbenzene must be 734.4 − 526.0 = 208.4 mm Hg. Therefore, letting A be chlorbenzene and B water, and applying equation (13),

$$M_A = \left(\frac{W_A}{W_B}\right)\left(\frac{P_B^0}{P_A^0}\right) M_B$$

$$= 2.47 \times \frac{526.0}{208.4} \times 18.02$$

$$= 112.3$$

The molecular weight of chlorbenzene calculated from atomic weights is 112.6

REFERENCES FOR FURTHER READING

1. S. Glasstone, *Textbook of Physical Chemistry*, D. Van Nostrand Company, Inc., New York, 1946, pp. 693–735.
2. Hildebrand and Scott, *Solubility of Non-Electrolytes*, Reinhold Publishing Corporation, New York, 1950.
3. Robinson and Gilliland, *Elements of Fractional Distillation*, McGraw-Hill Book Company, Inc., New York, 1950.
4. A. Weissberger, *Physical Methods of Organic Chemistry*, Interscience Publishers, Inc., New York, 1949, Vol. I, Chaps. IV, V, and VII.
5. A. Weissberger, *Distillation*, Interscience Publishers, Inc., New York, 1951.

PROBLEMS

1. A solution contains 50% of water, 35% of ethyl alcohol, and 15% of acetic acid by weight. Calculate the mol fraction of each component in the mixture.
   Ans. $N_{H_2O} = 0.733$; $N_{HAc} = 0.066$; $N_{C_2H_5OH} = 0.201$.
2. A Na_2CO_3 solution is made up by dissolving 22.5 g of $Na_2CO_3 \cdot 10\ H_2O$ in H_2O and adding H_2O until the total volume is 200 cc. The density of the resulting solution is 1.040 g/cc. Calculate the molarity, normality, and mol fraction of Na_2CO_3 in the solution.
   Ans. 0.393 m; 0.786 N; 0.00704 mol fraction.

3. A solution containing 10% of NaCl by weight has a density of 1.071 g/cc. Calculate the molality and molarity of NaCl in the solution.

4. A gaseous solution was analyzed and found to contain 15% of H_2, 10% of CO, and 75% of N_2 by volume. What is the mol fraction and percentage by weight of each gas in the mixture?

5. Assuming dry air to contain 21% by volume of O_2, calculate the weight O_2 dissolved in 1 liter of H_2O saturated with air under 1 atm pressure at 25° C. Use for Henry's law constant the average value computed from Table 1.
$Ans.$ 0.0085 g/liter.

6. Using the solubility coefficient listed in Table 2, estimate the solubility of CO_2 in H_2O at 25° C and a partial pressure of 5 atm.

7. A mixture of H_2 and N_2 is agitated with 100 cc of water until equilibrium is established. At equilibrium it is found that the total pressure of the gas phase is 840 mm Hg and that the gas, after drying, consists of 35.3% H_2 by volume. Assuming the vapor pressure of water above the solution is the same as that for pure water, namely, 95.5 mm Hg at 50° C, calculate the weights of dissolved H_2 and N_2.

8. Expressed in grams of anhydrous salt per 100 g H_2O, the solubilities of $MnSO_4 \cdot 5\ H_2O$ and $MnSO_4 \cdot 4\ H_2O$ in water as a function of the temperature are as follows:

	Solubility	
$t°$ C	$MnSO_4 \cdot 5\ H_2O$	$MnSO_4 \cdot 4\ H_2O$
10	59.5	—
20	62.9	64.5
30	67.8	66.4
40	—	68.8
50	—	72.6

From a plot of solubilities vs. temperature ascertain the transition temperature of $MnSO_4 \cdot 5H_2O$ to $MnSO_4 \cdot 4\ H_2O$. Which of these phases is stable at 25° C?

9. A mixture of $C_6H_5CH_3$ and C_6H_6 contains 30% by weight of $C_6H_5CH_3$. At 30° C the vapor pressure of pure $C_6H_5CH_3$ is 36.7 mm Hg while that of pure C_6H_6 is 118.2 mm. Assuming that the two liquids form ideal solutions, calculate the total pressure and the partial pressure of each constituent above the solution at 30° C. $Ans.$ $P_{C_6H_6} = 86.7$ mm; $P_{total} = 96.5$ mm.

10. At 60° C the vapor pressure of ethyl alcohol is 352.7 mm Hg and that of methyl alcohol 625 mm Hg. A mixture of the two, which may be assumed to be ideal, contains 50% by weight of each constituent. What will be the composition of the vapor above the solution at 60° C?

11. At 140° C the vapor pressure of C_6H_5Cl is 939.4 mm and that of C_6H_5Br is 495.8 mm. Assuming that these two liquids form an ideal solution, what will be the composition of a mixture of the two which boils at 140° C under 1 atm pressure? What will be the composition of the vapor at this temperature?

12. Solutions of two volatile liquids, A and B, obey Raoult's law. At a certain temperature it is found that when the total pressure above a given solution is 400 mm Hg, the mol fraction of A in the vapor is 0.45 and in the liquid, 0.65. What are the vapor pressures of the two pure liquids at the given temperature?

13. Kretschmer and Wiebe [$J.\ Am.\ Chem.\ Soc.$, **71**, 3176 (1949)] give the following liquid-vapor equilibrium data for ethanol-methylcyclohexane solutions at 55° C:

Mol fraction of ethanol in		Total pressure
Liquid	Vapor	(mm Hg)
0.0000	0.0000	168.1
0.0528	0.4835	319.8
0.1251	0.5375	352.8
0.2205	0.5645	368.0
0.3621	0.5846	376.3
0.5071	0.5988	379.8
0.6832	0.6244	380.1
0.7792	0.6528	375.8
0.9347	0.7879	337.5
1.0000	1.0000	279.9

Prepare a plot giving the total and partial pressures of the constituents as a function of the mol fraction of ethanol in the liquid phase, and determine the mol fraction at which the vapor pressure is a maximum. Assume that the vapor behaves as an ideal gas.

14. Using the data given in the preceding problem, plot the mol fractions of the liquid phase against those of the vapor with which they are in equilibrium. From the plot determine the mol fraction of liquid phase corresponding to the point of maximum vapor pressure.

15. What weight of HCl-H_2O azeotrope prepared at 740 mm Hg pressure will have to be added to water in order to prepare 2 liters of 0.50 molar HCl solution?

16. At 30° C a mixture of C_6H_5OH and H_2O is made up containing 60% by weight of H_2O. The mixture splits into two layers, the C_6H_5OH layer containing 70% by weight of C_6H_5OH and the H_2O layer containing 92% by weight of H_2O. Calculate the relative weights of the two layers.
Ans. $W_{H_2O}/W_{Ph} = 0.934$.

17. A mixture of aniline and H_2O is made up containing 30% by weight of aniline. From Fig. 14 determine graphically the relative weights of the two layers which form and the proportion of the total amount of aniline present in each layer at 40° C.

18. Using data from a suitable handbook, plot on the same graph the vapor pressures of H_2O, C_6H_6, and the total pressure of a mixture of the two against temperature between 40° and 80° C. From this plot, find the boiling point of the immiscible system C_6H_6–H_2O under 1 atm pressure.

19. A totally immiscible liquid system composed of H_2O and an organic liquid boils at 90° C when the barometer reads 734 mm Hg. The distillate contains 73% by weight of the organic liquid. What is the molecular weight and vapor pressure at 90° C of the organic liquid? *Ans.* 122.9 g/mole; 208.2 mm Hg.

20. Naphthalene may be steam distilled at 99.3° C under atmospheric pressure. What weight of steam will be required to carry 2 lb of naphthalene into the distillate at atmospheric pressure?

21. If the specific heat of steam is 0.5 cal/g and the heat of vaporization of the liquid in problem 19 is 78 cal/g, calculate the total amount of heat and the minimum amount of steam, delivered at 99° C, required to steam-distill 500 g of the liquid at 90° C.

6

Colligative Properties of Solutions

In this chapter we shall consider four properties of solutions containing *nonvolatile* solutes, namely: (a) the vapor pressure lowering of the solvent, (b) the freezing point lowering, (c) the boiling point elevation, and (d) the osmotic pressure of the solution. These properties of a solution are referred to as the *colligative properties*. A colligative property is any property which depends only on the number of particles in solution and not in any way on the nature of these. As we shall see, this is the essential attribute of the four phenomena mentioned above, at least in dilute solutions.

On theoretical grounds it is convenient to subdivide solutions into (a) solutions of nonelectrolytes and (b) solutions of electrolytes. In nonelectrolytic solutions the solute dissolved in the solvent persists in molecular, uncharged form and exhibits no tendency to dissociate into electrically charged ions. For such solutions certain general laws have been developed which will be discussed below. In electrolytic solutions, on the other hand, the solute dissociates to a greater or lesser degree into ions, increasing thereby the total number of particles in solution. The behavior of the solution with respect to certain properties, therefore, is changed, and the simple laws deduced for nonelectrolytic solutions require modification. For this reason these two types of solutions will be discussed in this chapter in separate sections.

Solutions of Nonelectrolytes

The colligative properties of nonelectrolytic solutions deserve serious consideration, not only because they are of interest, but also because a study of these supplies valuable methods for estimating the molecular weight of the dissolved substance and for evaluating a number of highly important thermodynamic quantities. Here attention will be confined primarily to the presentation of the basic principles involved and their use for arriving at the molecular weights of the solutes.

LOWERING OF VAPOR PRESSURE OF SOLVENT BY SOLUTES

It has long been known that a dissolved solute lowers the vapor pressure of a liquid solvent in which it is dissolved. The vapor pressure lowering suffered by the solvent can be readily understood in terms of Raoult's law as developed in the preceding chapter. Let N_1 be the mol fraction of the solvent, N_2 the mol fraction of the solute, P^0 the vapor pressure of the pure solvent, and P the vapor pressure of the solvent above a given solution. Then according to Raoult's law P is given by

$$P = P^0 N_1 \tag{1}$$

Since N_1 in any solution is always less than unity, P must always be less than P^0. Consequently, *solution of a solute in a solvent leads to a lowering of the vapor pressure of the latter below that of the pure solvent.* Furthermore, when the solute is nonvolatile it does not contribute to the total vapor pressure, and hence equation (1) gives as well the total vapor pressure above the solution, which in this case is due to solvent only and is always less than P^0.

The extent of the vapor pressure lowering, ΔP, is

$$\begin{aligned} \Delta P = P^0 - P &= P^0 - P^0 N_1 \\ &= P^0(1 - N_1) \\ &= P^0 N_2 \end{aligned} \tag{2}$$

According to equation (2), the vapor pressure lowering of the solvent depends both on the vapor pressure of the solvent and the mol fraction of solute in solution. In other words, it depends on the nature of the solvent and on the concentration of solute, but not on the nature of the latter. However, if we consider the *relative vapor pressure lowering*, i.e., the ratio $\Delta P / P^0$, then from equation (2)

$$\frac{\Delta P}{P^0} = \frac{P^0 - P}{P^0} = N_2 \tag{3}$$

and the relative vapor pressure lowering of the solvent depends only on the mol fraction of solute and is *completely independent* of either the nature of solute or solvent. Equation (3), the form Raoult's law takes for solutions of nonvolatile solutes, shows that the relative vapor pressure lowering of a solvent is a colligative property, because it depends only upon the concentration of the solute and upon nothing else.

The validity of Raoult's law applied to vapor pressure lowering may be judged from the data given in Table 1 for water solutions of mannite at 20° C. Considering the difficulties involved in measuring small vapor pressure differences, the concordance between theory and experiment is satisfactory.

TABLE 1

VAPOR PRESSURE LOWERING FOR AQUEOUS MANNITE SOLUTIONS AT 20° C
(P^0 = 17.51 mm Hg)

Moles of Mannite per 1000 g H_2O	ΔP Observed (mm Hg)	ΔP Calculated (mm Hg)
0.0984	0.0307	0.0311
0.1977	0.0614	0.0622
0.2962	0.0922	0.0931
0.4938	0.1536	0.1547
0.6934	0.2162	0.2164
0.8922	0.2792	0.2775
0.9908	0.3096	0.3076

CALCULATIONS INVOLVING RAOULT'S LAW

Equations (2) or (3) may be employed to calculate the vapor pressure lowering and the vapor pressure of solutions of nonvolatile solutes; or, knowing the vapor pressure lowering, they may be utilized to calculate the molecular weight of the dissolved substance. Consider the problem of calculating the vapor pressure of solvent above a solution containing 53.94 g of mannite (molecular weight = 182.11) per 1000 g of water at 20° C. At this temperature the vapor pressure of water is 17.51 mm Hg. According to equation (2),

$$\Delta P = P^0 - P = P^0 N_2$$

$$= P^0 \left[\frac{W_2/M_2}{W_1/M_1 + W_2/M_2} \right] \tag{4}$$

where W_2 and M_2 are the weight and molecular weight respectively of the solute, while W_1 and M_1 are the same quantities for the solvent. Substituting the given data into equation (4), we obtain

$$\Delta P = 17.51 \left[\frac{53.94/182.11}{1000/18.016 + 53.94/182.11} \right]$$

$$= 17.51 \times 0.0053$$

$$= 0.0929 \text{ mm Hg}$$

The vapor pressure of the solution is, therefore,

$$P = P^0 - \Delta P = 17.51 - 0.09 = 17.42 \text{ mm Hg}$$

When the vapor pressure lowering is known, the calculation may be reversed and equation (4) utilized to calculate M_2, the molecular weight of the solute. Further, for very dilute solutions W_2/M_2 is small compared to W_1/M_1, and equation (4) can be reduced to

$$\frac{P^0 - P}{P^0} = \frac{W_2 M_1}{W_1 M_2} \tag{5}$$

DETERMINATION OF VAPOR PRESSURE LOWERING

The vapor pressures of the solvent in solutions containing nonvolatile solutes may be measured by essentially the same methods as those used for pure liquids. The vapor need not be analyzed for it is composed of solvent only. However, the solution composition in equilibrium with the vapor must be known or determined by some appropriate method.

These methods yield the vapor pressure of the solution directly. The vapor pressure lowering is then obtained by subtracting this pressure from that of the pure solvent at the same temperature. With concentrated solutions and with solvents of high volatility this procedure is fairly satisfactory. It leads to serious errors, however, when applied to dilute solutions in solvents of relatively low volatility, such as water at room temperature. For such solutions it is preferable to employ one of a number of *differential* methods which yield directly the vapor pressure lowering of the solvent in any particular solution. The simplest of these involves the use of the Frowein tensimeter. This tensimeter consists essentially of a U-tube manometer with two flasks attached to its upper ends. In one of these flasks is placed the pure solvent, while the other holds the solution whose vapor pressure lowering is to be determined. As a manometric fluid, some liquid of very low volatility and relatively low density is used, for example, β-bromonaphthalene, n-dibutyl phthalate, or Apiezon oil. To remove any dissolved air the two vessels are first connected together, and the whole apparatus is thoroughly evacuated. The vessels are then isolated from each other, the apparatus is placed in a constant temperature bath, and, after establishment of equilibrium, the difference in pressure between the two sides is read on the manometer. This difference is directly the vapor pressure lowering of the solvent in the given solution at the temperature of the thermostat. With careful attention and precautions an accuracy of 0.01 mm Hg can be attained.

BOILING POINT ELEVATION OF SOLUTIONS

Solutions containing nonvolatile solutes boil at temperatures *higher* than the boiling point of the pure solvent. The difference between the boiling points of the solution and pure solvent at any given constant pressure is referred to as the *boiling point elevation* of the solution. The boiling point elevation of a solution depends on the nature of the solvent and the concentration of solute, but is independent, at least in dilute solutions, of the nature of the solute as long as the latter is not ionized.

This elevation of the boiling point is readily understood in terms of the vapor pressure lowering and is a direct consequence of it. Consider the vapor pressure-temperature diagram shown in Fig. 1. In this diagram curve AB represents the vapor pressure of the pure solvent as a function of temperature. Since the vapor pressure of the solution is at all temperatures lower than that of the solvent, the vapor pressure-temperature curve of the solution must lie below that of the pure solvent and hence must be represented by some curve such as CD in the figure. In order to reach the boiling point at some given external pressure P^0, the solvent and the solution must be heated to temperatures at which their respective vapor pressures become equal to the given confining pressure. As the diagram indicates, the solvent can attain the pressure P^0 at the temperature

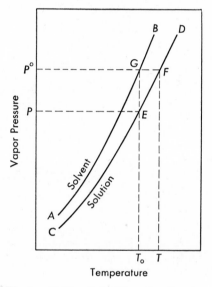

Fig. 1.   Boiling Point Elevation Due to Solutes.

T_0, but the solution must be raised to temperature T, higher than T_0, before the same pressure is reached. Consequently, at the same external pressure the solution must boil at a temperature higher than the pure solvent; and, the elevation of the boiling point of the solution, ΔT_b, is given by $\Delta T_b = T - T_0$. These considerations are perfectly general and apply to any solution of a nonvolatile solute.

DEPENDENCE OF ΔT_b ON CONCENTRATION

By applying the Clausius-Clapeyron equation and Raoult's law to the conditions depicted in Fig. 1, it is possible to deduce a relation between the boiling point elevation of the solution and its concentration. Since points E and F lie on the vapor pressure curve of the solution, they are both given by the Clausius-Clapeyron equation,

$$\ln \frac{P^0}{P} = \frac{\Delta H_v}{R}\left(\frac{T - T_0}{TT_0}\right) \tag{6}$$

where P is the vapor pressure of the solution at temperature T_0, while P^0 is the vapor pressure at temperature T. ΔH_v is heat of vaporization per mole of the solvent from the solution. When the solution is dilute, this is essentially the heat of vaporization per mole of the pure solvent. Again, when the solution is dilute T is not much different from T_0, and hence we may write $TT_0 = T_0^2$. Consequently equation (6) becomes

$$\ln \frac{P^0}{P} = -\ln \frac{P}{P^0} = \frac{\Delta H_v}{R}\cdot\frac{\Delta T_b}{T_0^2} \tag{7}$$

In equation (7) P is the vapor pressure of the solution at T_0, whle P^0 is also the vapor pressure of the pure solvent at the same temperature. When Raoult's law is applicable to the solution, these two pressures are related through

$$\frac{P}{P^0} = N_1 = 1 - N_2 \tag{8}$$

where N_2 is the mol fraction of solute in the solution. Hence equation (7) becomes

$$\ln(1 - N_2) = -\frac{\Delta H_v}{R}\cdot\frac{\Delta T_b}{T_0^2} \tag{9}$$

An expansion of $\ln(1 - N_2)$ in series yields the expression,

$$\ln(1 - N_2) = -N_2 - \frac{N_2^2}{2} - \frac{N_2^3}{3} - \cdots$$

and since the solution was already specified to be dilute, N_2 must be small, and all terms in the expansion beyond the first can be considered negligible. Writing, then, $-N_2$ for $\ln(1 - N_2)$ in equation (9), we have

$$-N_2 = -\frac{\Delta H_v}{R}\cdot\frac{\Delta T_b}{T_0^2}$$

and therefore,

$$\Delta T_b = \frac{RT_0^2}{\Delta H_v}\cdot N_2 \tag{10}$$

Equation (10) gives the boiling point elevation of a solution in terms of the boiling point and heat of vaporization of the solvent, and the mol fraction of the solute in solution. Since for any given solvent T_0 and ΔH_v are constant, the boiling point elevation for dilute solutions is seen to be directly proportional to the mol fraction of the solute only and is in no way dependent on the nature of the solute. The boiling point elevation of a solution is thus a colligative property.

The common practice in boiling point elevation work is to express the concentration not in mol fractions but in *moles of solute per 1000 g of solvent*, i.e., the molality m. If we now let n_1 be the number of moles of solvent in 1000 g, then,

$$N_2 = \frac{m}{n_1 + m} = \frac{m}{n_1}$$

since for dilute solutions m is small compared to n_1 and may be disregarded. Therefore,

$$\Delta T_b = \left[\frac{RT_0^2}{\Delta H_v n_1}\right] m \tag{11}$$

For any given solvent all the quantities in the brackets of equation (11) are constant, and hence the whole term is constant. Writing

$$K_b = \frac{RT_0^2}{\Delta H_v n_1} \tag{12}$$

equation (11) finally reduces to

$$\Delta T_b = K_b m \tag{13}$$

According to equation (13) the boiling point elevation of any dilute solution is directly proportional to the *molality of the solution*. The proportionality constant K_b is called either the *molal boiling point elevation constant*, or *the ebullioscopic constant*, and signifies the rise in boiling point for a 1 molal solution of a solute in a solvent provided the laws of dilute solutions are applicable to such a concentration. Actually it is the boiling point elevation per mole calculated by proportion from the boiling point elevation of much more dilute solutions.

VALIDITY OF EQUATION (13)

The validity of equation (13) deduced theoretically for dilute solutions on the assumption of Raoult's law may be tested in a number of ways. First, the equation demands that for a given solvent the boiling point elevation be proportional to the molality of the solute irrespective of its nature. Second, the equation demands that for any given solvent the proportionality constant K_b be independent of the nature or concentration of the solute. In both these respects the equation is in good agreement with experimental results on dilute solutions. A third, and more crucial, test can be made by comparing the observed values of K_b with those predicted by equation (12). If equation (12) is valid, it should be possible to calculate the molal boiling point elevation constant from a knowledge of the normal boiling point and heat of vaporization of the solvent. For instance, for water $T_0 = 373.2°$ K, while the heat of vaporization at the boiling point is 539 cal per gram. Applying equation (12), the molal boiling point elevation constant for water as a solvent follows as

$$K_b = \frac{RT_0^2}{\Delta H_v n_1}$$
$$= \frac{1.987 \times (373.2)^2}{(18.02 \times 539)(1000/18.02)}$$
$$= 0.513°$$

This value compares very well with the experimentally observed $K_b = 0.52°$.

Table 2 lists the normal boiling points and observed ebullioscopic constants for a number of solvents. The molal elevation constants for these solvents calculated by equation (12) are also included for comparison.

TABLE 2

MOLAL BOILING POINT ELEVATION CONSTANTS

Solvent	Boiling Point (° C)	K_b (obs.)	K_b (calc.)
Acetone	56.5	1.72	1.73
Carbon tetrachloride	76.8	5.0	5.02
Benzene	80.1	2.57	2.61
Chloroform	61.2	3.88	3.85
Ethyl alcohol	78.4	1.20	1.19
Ethyl ether	34.6	2.11	2.16
Methyl alcohol	64.7	0.80	0.83
Water	100.0	0.52	0.51

The agreement between calculated and observed values is highly satisfactory when uncertainties involved in boiling point determinations are considered. In view of this concordance between theory and experiment, equation (12) may be employed also to evaluate heats of vaporization of the solvent from experimental values of K_b.

DETERMINATION OF BOILING POINT ELEVATION

If we let ΔT_b be the boiling point elevation for a solution containing w_2 g of solute of molecular weight M_2 dissolved in w_1 g of solvent, then the weight of solute per 1000 g of solvent is

$$\frac{w_2 \times 1000}{w_1}$$

and hence m, the molality of the solution, is

$$m = \frac{w_2 \times 1000}{w_1 M_2} \tag{14}$$

Equation (13) in terms of equation (14) is, therefore,

$$\Delta T_b = K_b \left(\frac{1000\ w_2}{w_1 M_2}\right) \tag{15}$$

In order to obtain K_b from this relation it is necessary to measure ΔT_b, w_1, and w_2 with a solute of known molecular weight. On the other hand, in order to determine M_2, it is necessary to ascertain ΔT_b, w_1, and w_2 for a solvent of known K_b. In both instances the data to be obtained are the weights of solute and solvent, and the boiling point elevation of the solution. A method for obtaining this information will now be described.

In Fig. 2 is shown the Cottrell apparatus for determining boiling point elevations. It consists of a vessel A fitted with a vapor condenser D and a ground glass joint from which extends a glass shield B, whose function is to prevent the condensed vapors from D from coming into contact with the thermometer. The thermometer itself is suspended in the vapor above the liquid and inside the shield. To assure equilibrium between vapor and boiling liquid at the thermometer bulb, a "siphon pump" C is incorporated into the apparatus. This "pump" consists of a glass tube

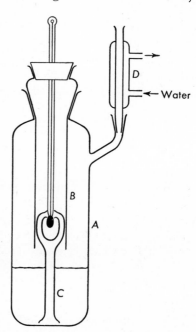

Fig. 2.   Cottrell Boiling Point Apparatus.

having a funnel-shaped base and a bent U-shaped top which fits around the thermometer stem as shown. When the liquid is boiling, bubbles of vapor formed at the bottom rise upward and force any liquid trapped in the tube to be spilled over the thermometer bulb. By this simple device the thermometer is always bathed by a mixture of boiling liquid and vapor and reaches a steady equilibrium temperature in a very short time. The liquid may be boiled either with a small gas flame or electrically.

For a determination a weighed quantity of solvent, w_1, is introduced into the boiling tube. Heating is then started and continued until the solvent boils uniformly and the temperature becomes constant. This temperature is read and is the boiling point of the solvent. Heating is now stopped, a weighed quantity, w_2, of solute pressed into a pellet is introduced, and the heating is repeated until a constant boiling point is again attained. The reading on the thermometer at this point minus the reading for the boiling point of the pure solvent gives the boiling point elevation ΔT_b of the solution.

Among a number of other types of apparatus described in the literature may be mentioned those of Beckmann, McCoy, Davis and Brandt, Saxton and Smith, and Swietoslawski. The various modifications in design and technique have all been aimed at the prevention of superheating of the liquid, the more rapid attainment of equilibrium, and greater accuracy of temperature and concentration determination. Some of the changes introduced have involved the use of manostats for pressure control on the boiling system, the use of thermocouples for temperature measurement, and the use of dual vessels for the simultaneous ebullition of solvent and solution.

CALCULATION OF MOLECULAR WEIGHTS FROM BOILING POINT ELEVATION

When the ebullioscopic constant of a solvent is known, a determination of the boiling point elevation of a solution containing the unknown solute in definite concentration is sufficient to yield the molecular weight of the solute. When the ebullioscopic constant is unknown, however, an independent determination of ΔT_b must be made with a solute of known molecular weight. The calculations involved can best be seen from the following example. A solution containing 0.5126 g of naphthalene (molecular weight = 128.16) in 50.00 g of carbon tetrachloride yields a boiling point elevation of 0.402° C, while a solution of 0.6216 g of an unknown solute in the same weight of solvent gives a boiling point elevation of 0.647° C. Find the molecular weight of the unknown solute.

For finding K_b of carbon tetrachloride, the given data are

$$w_1 = 50.00 \text{ g} \qquad \Delta T_b = 0.402° \text{ C}$$
$$w_2 = 0.5126 \text{ g} \qquad M_2 = 128.16$$

Substituting these into equation (15) and solving for K_b, we obtain

$$
\begin{aligned}
K_b &= \frac{\Delta T_b \, w_1 M_2}{1000 \, w_2} \\
&= \frac{0.402 \times 50.00 \times 128.16}{1000 \times 0.5126} \\
&= 5.03° \text{ C/mole/1000 g of solvent}
\end{aligned}
$$

Using now the found value of K_b along with the information for the unknown,

$$w_1 = 50.00 \text{ g} \qquad w_2 = 0.6216 \text{ g} \qquad \Delta T_b = 0.647° \text{ C}$$

equation (15) yields for M_2 of the unknown,

$$M_2 = \frac{1000 \ w_2 K_b}{w_1 \cdot \Delta T_b}$$

$$= \frac{1000 \times 0.6216 \times 5.03}{50.00 \times 0.647}$$

$$= 96.7 \text{ g mole}^{-1}$$

FREEZING POINT LOWERING OF SOLUTIONS

When a dilute solution is cooled, a temperature is eventually reached at which *solid solvent* begins to separate from solution. The temperature at which this separation begins is called *the freezing point of the solution.*
More generally the freezing point of a solution may be defined as the temperature at which a particular solution is in equilibrium with solid solvent.

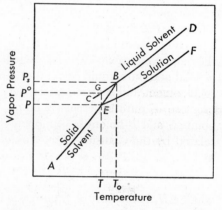

Solutions freeze at *lower* temperatures than the pure solvent. The freezing point lowering of a solution is again a direct consequence of the vapor pressure lowering of the solvent by dissolved solute. To appreciate this, consider the vapor pressure-temperature diagram shown in Fig. 3. In this diagram AB is the sublimation curve of the solid solvent, while CD

Fig. 3.   Depression of Freezing Point by Solutes.

is the vapor pressure curve of pure liquid solvent. At the freezing point of the pure solvent the solid and liquid phases are in equilibrium, and consequently they must both have at this temperature identical vapor pressures. The only point on the diagram at which the two forms of the pure solvent have the same vapor pressure is B, the intersection of AB and CD, and therefore T_0, the temperature corresponding to B, must be the freezing point of the pure solvent. When a solute is dissolved in the solvent, however, the vapor pressure of the latter is lowered, and equilibrium can no longer exist at T_0. To ascertain the new point of equilibrium between the solution of the solute and the solid solvent, the temperature must be found at which the vapor pressure of the solution becomes equal to that of the solid, i.e., the temperature at which the vapor pressure curve of the solution intersects the sublimation curve, and this will be the freezing point of the solution. Since the vapor pressure curve of the solution, EF, always lies below that of the pure solvent, the intersection of EF and AB can occur only at a point such as E for which the temperature is lower than T_0. Hence any solution of the solute in the solvent must have a freezing point, T, lower than that of the solvent, T_0.

DEPENDENCE OF FREEZING POINT DEPRESSION ON CONCENTRATION

The freezing point depression of a solution is defined as $\Delta T_f = T_0 - T$ and represents the number of degrees by which the freezing point of a solution is lower than that of the pure solvent. The magnitude of ΔT_f depends both on the nature of the solvent and the concentration of the solution. For dilute solutions of various solutes in a given solvent ΔT_f varies linearly with concentration irrespective of the nature of the solute. The proportionality constant of this concentration variation is, however, a function of the solvent and varies considerably for different solvents.

To relate mathematically the freezing point depression of a solution to the factors mentioned, consider again Fig. 3. Let P_s be the vapor pressure of solid and pure liquid solvent at T_0 and P be the vapor pressure of both solid solvent and solution at temperature T. Again, let P^0 be the vapor pressure of pure supercooled liquid solvent at T, point G. Then, since points G and B lie on the same vapor pressure curve, they must both be related by the Clausius-Clapeyron equation,

$$\ln \frac{P_s}{P^0} = \frac{\Delta H_v(T_0 - T)}{RT_0 T} \tag{16}$$

where ΔH_v is the heat of vaporization of the pure solvent. Similarly, since points E and B lie on the same sublimation curve, they must be given by the equation

$$\ln \frac{P_s}{P} = \frac{\Delta H_s(T_0 - T)}{RT_0 T} \tag{17}$$

where ΔH_s is the heat of sublimation of the solid solvent. Subtracting now equation (17) from equation (16), we obtain

$$\ln P_s - \ln P^0 - \ln P_s + \ln P = \frac{\Delta H_v(T_0 - T)}{RT_0 T} - \frac{\Delta H_s(T_0 - T)}{RT_0 T}$$

$$\ln P - \ln P^0 = -\frac{(\Delta H_s - \Delta H_v)(T_0 - T)}{RT_0 T}$$

$$\ln \frac{P}{P^0} = -\frac{(\Delta H_s - \Delta H_v)(T_0 - T)}{RT_0 T} \tag{18}$$

But $(\Delta H_s - \Delta H_v) = \Delta H_f$, the heat of fusion of the solvent. Therefore,

$$\ln \frac{P}{P^0} = -\frac{\Delta H_f(T_0 - T)}{RT_0T} = -\frac{\Delta H_f \Delta T_f}{RT_0T} \tag{19}$$

Equation (19) relates the vapor pressure of solid solvent at temperature T to the vapor pressure of pure liquid solvent at the same temperature. But since the vapor pressures of solid solvent and solution are equal at temperature T, the freezing point of the solution, equation (19) also relates the vapor pressure of the *solution* to that of the pure solvent at the temperature T. If we assume now that Raoult's law is applicable to the solution, then $P/P^0 = N_1 = (1 - N_2)$, where N_1 and N_2 are the mol fractions of the solvent and solute in solution, and equation (19) becomes

$$\ln (1 - N_2) = -\frac{\Delta H_f \Delta T_f}{RT_0T} \tag{20}$$

When N_2 is small, i.e., when the solution is dilute, $\ln (1 - N_2)$ is equal essentially to $-N_2$ and T_0T to T_0^2. Hence,

$$-N_2 = -\frac{\Delta H_f \Delta T_f}{RT_0^2}$$

and

$$\Delta T_f = \left(\frac{RT_0^2}{\Delta H_f}\right) N_2 \tag{21}$$

Finally, designating by m the *molality* of the solution, by n_1 the number of moles of solvent in 1000 g, $N_2 = m/n_1$ (approximately), and

$$\Delta T_f = \left(\frac{RT_0^2}{\Delta H_f \, n_1}\right) m$$
$$= K_f \, m \tag{22}$$

where

$$K_f = \frac{RT_0^2}{\Delta H_f \, n_1} \tag{23}$$

Equation (22) is the fundamental relation of cryoscopy and is directly analogous to equation (13) for boiling point elevation. K_f, called the *molal freezing point lowering* or *cryoscopic constant* of a solvent, is defined in terms of quantities characteristic of the solvent only and in no way depends on either the concentration or nature of the solute. It is the freezing point depression counterpart of the boiling point elevation constant K_b. Since for any given solvent K_f is a constant, the freezing point depression of a solution is determined by the concentration of solute only, and hence the freezing point depression, like the vapor pressure lowering and boiling point elevation, is a colligative property.

VALIDITY OF EQUATION (22)

An important test of this equation is the constancy of K_f with concentration for a given solvent. Table 3 shows some experimental data for the freezing point lowering of solutions of urea in water and the value of $K_f = \Delta T_f/m$ calculated therefrom. As the last column indicates, K_f is constant throughout the given concentration range and equal to 1.85. Essentially identical values for the cryoscopic constant of water have

TABLE 3

FREEZING POINT DEPRESSIONS FOR SOLUTIONS OF UREA IN WATER

m	ΔT_f	$K_f = \Delta T_f/m$
0.000538	0.001002	1.862
0.004235	0.007846	1.851
0.007645	0.01413	1.849
0.012918	0.02393	1.850
0.01887	0.03496	1.853
0.03084	0.05696	1.848
0.04248	0.07850	1.848
		1.852

been obtained with numerous other solutes. Furthermore, the observed value of this constant is in good agreement with the value predicted for water as a solvent by equation (23). For water, $T_0 = 273.2$, $\Delta H_f = 79.71 \times 18.02$, and $n_1 = 1000/18.02$. Therefore,

$$K_f = \frac{1.987(273.2)^2}{(79.71 \times 18.02)(1000/18.02)}$$
$$= 1.857° \text{ C/mole/1000 g } H_2O$$

Similar concordance between theory and experiment has been obtained with many other solvents. Table 4 lists a number of solvents, their freezing points, and their cryoscopic constants. It will be observed that, of those listed, the cryoscopic constant of water is the lowest. Hence, for a given concentration of solute, more pronounced freezing point depressions may be obtained in the various other solvents, and this fact is of importance in the practical use of these solvents for molecular weight determination.

Because of the assumptions made in its derivation, equation (22) can be expected to be valid only in dilute solutions. In more concentrated solutions K_f deviates considerably from constancy, and the deviation is the more pronounced the more concentrated the solution. Thus the cryoscopic constant of benzene as evaluated from freezing point determinations of carbon tetrachloride in the solvent is 5.09° C per mole in a 0.1184 molal solution and only 4.82° C per mole in a 1.166 molal solution.

TABLE 4

CRYOSCOPIC CONSTANTS FOR VARIOUS SOLVENTS

Solvent	Freezing Point (° C)	K_f
Acetic acid	16.7	3.9
Benzene	5.5	5.12
Bromoform	7.8	14.4
Camphor	178.4	37.7
Cyclohexane	6.5	20.0
1,4-Dioxane	10.5	4.9
Naphthalene	80.2	6.9
Phenol	42	7.27
Tribromophenol	96	20.4
Triphenylphosphate	49.9	11.76
Water	0.00	1.86

DETERMINATION OF FREEZING POINT LOWERING

Of the various methods developed for freezing point lowering measurements, only three will be described, namely: (a) the Beckmann method, (b) the Rast method, and (c) the equilibrium method.

The Beckmann Method. A simple Beckmann freezing point apparatus is shown in Fig. 4. The freezing point tube A has a side arm B for introduction of solute, and is fitted with a stopper carrying a Beckmann thermometer and stirrer. To prevent too rapid cooling of the contents of the freezing tube, A is surrounded with a guard tube C so as to leave an air space between A and C. The whole assembly is supported in the large beaker D, which contains the cooling mixture. This mixture should be at a temperature no lower than 5° below the freezing point of the solvent used.

For a determination a definite weight of solvent is placed in A, and cooled with stirring to a temperature about 0.5° below the freezing point. Rapid stirring of the supercooled liquid initiates crystallization and the temperature rises rapidly to the freezing point, which is recorded. Tube A is now removed, warmed to melt and solid, and a definite weight of solute added through B. After the solute has dissolved A is replaced, and the freezing point is redetermined in exactly the same manner as for the solvent. The difference in the two freezing points is the freezing point lowering of the solution.

Rast Method. The Rast method is particularly convenient for molecular weight determinations of solutes that are soluble in camphor. It takes advantage of the fact that the cryoscopic constant of camphor is very high, 37.7° C per mole per 1000 g of solvent. The Rast procedure is essentially a micromethod, for a freezing point lowering determination can be made with only a few milligrams of solute. Some solid camphor is first dusted into a small capillary tube, and a melting point determination is made by the same technique as is ordinarily employed in organic chemistry. A solution of the solute in camphor is prepared, then, as follows: A small weight of solute and about 10 to 15 times that weight of camphor are mixed and melted by heating over a flame. The melt is permitted to

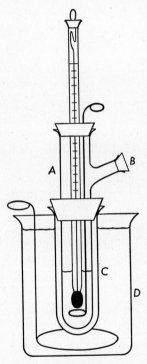

Fig. 4.   Beckmann Freezing Point Apparatus.

solidify, the solid is ground to a fine powder, and a small quantity of the powder is transferred into a clean capillary tube. The tube is heated now slowly until the solid begins to melt, and the temperature at which the last crystals of camphor disappear is taken as the freezing point of the solution. Since the lowerings obtained with this method are usually of the order of 10° or more, an ordinary thermometer whose readings can be estimated to 0.1 or 0.2° is satisfactory for the accuracy required.

Equilibrium Method. Practically all accurate freezing point lowering data are obtained at present by the equilibrium method. In this method an intimate mixture of solid and liquid solvent is first prepared and then agitated until equilibrium between the two is established. The temperature at this point is read, usually with a multijunction thermocouple. A volume of concentrated solution of the solute in the solvent is now added to yield approximately some desired concentration, and equilibrium is again permitted to be reestablished. The temperature is then read, and a sample of the liquid phase is removed and analyzed. By this procedure the tendency to supercool is reduced to a minimum, and the concentration of solution obtained is that at equilibrium.

The method can be improved even further by employing two similar containers, such as Dewar vessels, in one of which is placed an intimate mixture of pure solid and liquid solvent and in the other a mixture of solid solvent and solution. By inserting now one end of a multijunction thermocouple in the solvent and the other in the solution, it is possible to read directly the temperature difference between the two. Employing such methods precisions as high as 0.00001 to 0.00002° C have been reported in some researches.

CALCULATION OF MOLECULAR WEIGHTS FROM FREEZING POINT LOWERING

In view of the ease with which fairly precise freezing point data can be obtained, such data are particularly suitable for determining molecular weights of solutes in solution. The calculations involved are exactly analogous to those made in conjunction with boiling point elevation, as are also the equations and data required. If the expression for m from equation (14) is substituted into equation (22), we get

$$\Delta T_f = K_f \left(\frac{1000\ w_2}{w_1 M_2} \right) \tag{24}$$

From which the molecular weight follows as

$$M_2 = K_f \left(\frac{1000\ w_2}{\Delta T_f\ w_1} \right) \tag{25}$$

Therefore, to calculate the molecular weight, K_f for the solvent must be known, and ΔT_f, w_1 and w_2 must be measured. If K_f is not known, it can be either calculated by means of equation (23) or determined by making first a freezing point determination with a solution of a solute of known molecular weight in the same solvent.

SEPARATION OF SOLID SOLUTIONS ON FREEZING

These freezing point depression considerations and the equations deduced are valid only when the solid separating from solution is the pure solvent. Occasionally cases are encountered, such as solutions of iodine or thiophene in benzene, where the solid crystallizing out contains solute dissolved in it in the form of solid solutions. For such cases equation (22), and all others based on it, are no longer applicable. It can be shown by theoretical argument that when the separating solid phase is a solid solution, equation (22) must be replaced by

$$\Delta T_f = K_f(1 - k)m \tag{26}$$

where the symbols have the same significance as before, and k is the ratio of mol fraction of solute in the solid to mol fraction of solute in solution. When the solid phase is pure solvent, k is zero, and equation (26) reduces to equation (22). When the solid phase is not pure, however, two conditions may be distinguished. If the solute is more soluble in the liquid solvent than in the solid, k is a positive fraction, and hence $(1 - k)$ is less than unity. The effect will be, therefore, to give a freezing point depression less than would be anticipated for separation of pure solid solvent. If, on the other hand, the solute is more soluble in the solid phase than in the liquid, $k > 1$ and $(1 - k)$ is negative. Under these conditions ΔT_f is also *negative;* i.e., a freezing point *elevation* rather than a lowering is observed for the solution. Such behavior is rarely encountered under ordinary circumstances, but it is not at all unusual with metals and salts that form solid solutions.

OSMOSIS AND OSMOTIC PRESSURE

When an aqueous solution of a solute is separated from pure water by a semipermeable membrane, i.e., a membrane that permits the passage of water but not of dissolved solute, the water always tends to pass through the membrane into the solution, diluting it. The phenomenon, called *osmosis,* was first reported by the Abbe Nollet in 1748. In earlier studies animal membranes of various kinds were used, but it was found that these were not truly semipermeable.

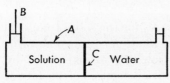

Fig. 5.   Osmotic   Pressure   of Solutions.

Finally, Traube (1864) was able to show that the membrane most nearly meeting the condition of semipermeability was a film of copper ferrocyanide, $Cu_2Fe(CN)_6$, prepared by contacting a solution of a cupric salt with one of potassium ferrocyanide. But the first quantitative measurements of the osmotic pressure of solutions were made by the botanist Pfeffer in 1877.

Before discussing Pfeffer's work or any of the subsequent refinements, it is necessary to define the osmotic pressure. For this purpose consider the diagram shown in Fig. 5. A is a chamber open at one end and fitted at the other with a movable piston B. The chamber is divided by means of a semipermeable membrane C into two sections, of which the right one is filled with pure water, the other with some aqueous solution. Because of osmosis, water will tend to pass through the membrane into the solution and displace the piston upward. The motion of the piston and osmosis of water can be prevented, however, by the application of pressure to the piston in order to keep it in its original position. The mechanical pressure which must be applied on a solution to prevent osmosis of the solvent into the solution through a semipermeable membrane is called the *osmotic pressure* of the solution. This pressure for a given solution depends on a number of factors, as we shall see later, but it does not depend on the nature of the membrane so long as the membrane is truly semipermeable. Hence the osmotic pressure of a solution must be considered as a measure of some real difference, expressible in pressure units, in the natures of the pure solvent and the solution, rather than as a phenomenon for which the membrane is responsible. The membrane is merely the artifice by which this difference is made manifest.

MEASUREMENT OF OSMOTIC PRESSURE

Pfeffer's original apparatus for measuring the osmotic pressure of solutions was rather crude, the membranes were not too strong, and consequently his measurements had to be confined to dilute solutions where the osmotic pressures are low. Little further progress in this field was forthcoming until H. N. Morse, J. C. W. Frazer, and their collaborators (1901–1923) in America, and the Earl of Berkeley and E. G. J. Hartley (1906–1909) in England, began their celebrated researches on osmotic pressure determination. These men developed methods of preparing osmotic cells in which the membranes were more truly semipermeable and which could withstand much higher pressures than Pfeffer's cells. They also improved the technique of pressure measurement to a point where highly accurate data could be obtained even with concentrated solutions. Thus, with the apparatus used by Frazer and Morse osmotic

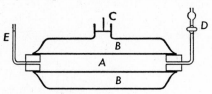

Fig. 6.   Osmotic Pressure Apparatus of Berkeley and Hartley.

pressures could be determined up to 270 atm, while with that of Berkeley and Hartley, up to 150 atm.

Only the method of Berkeley and Hartley will be described. A schematic diagram of their apparatus is shown in Fig. 6. *A* was a porous tube on the outside of which was deposited by a special technique a layer of copper ferrocyanide. This tube was mounted by means of water-tight joints within an outer metal jacket *B*, which carried an attachment *C* through which pressure could be applied. *A* was filled through *D* with pure water up to a definite mark on the capillary *E*, *B* with the solution under test. The apparatus was then immersed in a thermostat. As a result of osmosis the liquid level in *E* tended to drop. By applying pressure through *C* the liquid level at *E* could be restored to its initial position, and the pressure necessary to accomplish this restoration was taken as the osmotic pressure of the solution. With this method equilibrium is established rapidly, and the concentration of the solution is not changed by dilution with solvent.

RESULTS OF OSMOTIC PRESSURE MEASUREMENTS

Some of Pfeffer's data on the osmotic pressures of solutions of sucrose in water are reproduced in Tables 5 and 6. Table 5 gives the dependence

TABLE 5

OSMOTIC PRESSURE OF AQUEOUS SUCROSE SOLUTIONS AT 14° C

C (moles/liter of solution)	Π (atm)	Π/C
0.0588	1.34	22.8
0.0809	2.00	24.7
0.1189	2.75	23.2
0.1794	4.04	22.5

TABLE 6

OSMOTIC PRESSURE OF AQUEOUS SUCROSE SOLUTIONS
AT VARIOUS TEMPERATURES
(1 % Solution by Weight)

T	Π (atm)	Π/T
273.0	0.649	0.00238
279.8	0.664	0.00237
286.7	0.691	0.00241
288.5	0.684	0.00237
295.0	0.721	0.00244
305.0	0.716	0.00235
309.0	0.746	0.00241

TABLE 7

OSMOTIC PRESSURES OF AQUEOUS SUCROSE SOLUTIONS

m (moles/1000 g H_2O)	Osmotic Pressures (atm)				
	0°	20°	40°	60°	80°
0.1	2.46	2.59	2.66	2.72	
0.2	4.72	5.06	5.16	5.44	
0.3	7.09	7.61	7.84	8.14	
0.4	9.44	10.14	10.60	10.87	
0.5	11.90	12.75	13.36	13.67	
0.6	14.38	15.39	16.15	16.54	
0.7	16.89	18.13	18.93	19.40	
0.8	19.48	20.91	21.80	22.33	23.06
0.9	22.12	23.72	24.74	25.27	25.92
1.0	24.83	26.64	27.70	28.37	28.00

of the osmotic pressure Π on the concentration at constant temperature, while Table 6 gives the variation of osmotic pressure with temperature at constant concentration. The significant facts to be observed about these data are: (a) that at any given temperature the osmotic pressure is directly proportional to concentration, as is indicated by the constancy of the ratio Π/C in the last column of Table 5; and (b) that for any given concentration the osmotic pressure is directly proportional to the absolute temperature, as is evidenced by the constancy of the ratio Π/T in Table 6.

More extended and accurate data on the osmotic pressures of aqueous sucrose solutions at various temperatures are shown in Table 7. They are based on the measurements of Berkeley and Hartley and of Morse, Frazer, and their co-workers and are typical of the results obtained with nonelectrolytes in water solutions.

THE VAN'T HOFF EQUATION FOR OSMOTIC PRESSURE

van't Hoff first called attention to the fact that the osmotic pressure of a solution varies with concentration and temperature in exactly the same manner as does the pressure of an ideal gas. Since Pfeffer's data indicated that the osmotic pressure is proportional to concentration and temperature, it must follow that

$$\Pi = kCT \tag{27}$$

But $C = n/V$, where n is the number of moles of solute contained in V liters of solution. Therefore,

$$\Pi = \frac{knT}{V}$$
$$\Pi V = nkT \tag{28}$$

The analogy between equation (28) and the ideal gas law $PV = nRT$ is extremely striking. The analogy becomes even more striking when it is found that the constant k is essentially identical with the gas constant R, as may be seen from the following calculation. The osmotic pressure of a solution containing 45.0 g of sucrose per liter of solution at 0° C is 2.97 atm. Consequently, $\Pi = 2.97$ atm, $V = 1$ liter, $n = 45.0/342.2$, $T = 273.2$, and

$$k = \frac{\Pi V}{nT} = \frac{2.97 \times 1}{(45.0/342.2) \times 273.2} = 0.0827 \text{ liter-atm degree}^{-1} \text{ mole}^{-1}$$

This value of k agrees quite closely with $R = 0.0821$ liter-atm degree^{-1} mole^{-1}, and hence equation (28) may be written as

$$\Pi V = nRT \tag{29}$$

to yield for the osmotic pressure of solutions of nonelectrolytes an equation identical with that for the ideal gas law. The only difference is that equation (29) contains the osmotic pressure Π of the solution instead of the gas pressure P.

According to the van't Hoff equation the osmotic pressure of a solution at any given temperature should depend only on the concentration and not at all on the nature of the solute; i.e., the osmotic pressure should be a colligative property of the solution. This, however, is strictly true only for very dilute solutions. In more concentrated solutions the observed osmotic pressures are considerably higher than those predicted by equation (29). Hence the van't Hoff equation, like the ideal gas law, must be considered to be essentially a limiting law for osmotic pressure rather than one of general validity. This point will be brought out more clearly when the relation of osmotic pressure to vapor pressure lowering is considered.

RELATION OF OSMOTIC PRESSURE TO VAPOR PRESSURE

From purely thermodynamic considerations it is possible to derive a relation between osmotic pressure and the vapor pressure lowering of a solution. This relation is given by

$$\Pi = \frac{RT}{v} \ln \frac{P^0}{P} \tag{30}$$

where Π is the osmotic pressure, R the gas constant, T the absolute temperature, v the volume of *1 mole* of solvent, P^0 the vapor pressure of pure solvent at temperature T, and P the vapor pressure of solvent above the solution whose osmotic pressure is Π. The only assumptions involved in the derivation of equation (30) are that the solvent vapor behaves ideally and that the molar volumes of pure solvent and solvent in solution are

TABLE 8

COMPARISON OF OBSERVED AND CALCULATED OSMOTIC PRESSURES
OF SUCROSE SOLUTIONS AT 30° C

Moles of Sucrose per 1000 g H_2O	Π Obs. (atm)	Π Calc. ($\Pi V = nRT$)	Π Calc. (equation 30)
0.1	2.47	2.40	2.44
1.0	27.22	20.4	27.0
2.0	58.37	35.1	58.5
3.0	95.16	45.5	96.2
4.0	138.96	55.7	138.5
5.0	187.3	64.5	183.0
6.0	232.3	—	231.0

equal. As the error introduced by these assumptions is not serious, equation (30) may be expected to reproduce the osmotic pressures up to fairly high concentrations. Table 8 shows that such is actually the case.

A word concerning the units of equation (30) is in order. The units in which Π is obtained depend on the units employed for v and R. If v is expressed in liters and R in liter-atm mole^{-1} degree^{-1}, then Π will be given in atmospheres. The same result can be obtained for v in cubic centimeters and R in cc-atm mole^{-1} degree^{-1}.

The van't Hoff equation can readily be deduced from equation (30) for the special case of dilute solutions obeying Raoult's law. For a solution obeying Raoult's law, $P/P^0 = N_1$, and hence

$$\Pi v = RT \ln \frac{P^0}{P}$$
$$= -RT \ln N_1$$
$$= -RT \ln (1 - N_2)$$

If $\ln (1 - N_2)$ is expanded now in series as before, then for dilute solutions all terms beyond the first can be neglected, and $\ln (1 - N_2)$ becomes $-N_2 = -n/n_1$. Therefore,

$$\Pi v = \frac{RTn}{n_1}$$
$$\Pi(vn_1) = nRT$$

But vn_1 is the total volume of solvent containing n moles of solute, which for dilute solutions is essentially the volume V of the solution. Consequently,

$$\Pi V = nRT$$

which is identical with equation (29). In the light of this derivation of equation (29) from equation (30) it is readily understandable why the van't Hoff equation is limited in applicability only to very dilute solutions. It is, in essence, the limiting law for the osmotic pressure of solutions just as $PV = nRT$ is the limiting law for the behavior of gases.

MOLECULAR WEIGHT CALCULATION FROM OSMOTIC PRESSURES

Since the van't Hoff equation is valid for dilute solutions, it may be employed to calculate the molecular weight of the solutes from osmotic pressure measurements on such solutions. Substituting for n the equivalent W/M, where W is the weight of solute of molecular weight M dissolved in V liters of solution, equation (29) becomes

$$\Pi V = \frac{W}{M} RT \tag{31}$$

and therefore,

$$M = \frac{WRT}{\Pi V} \tag{32}$$

To illustrate the calculation of molecular weights from osmotic pressures, we may take the data of Flusin on the osmotic pressure of a solution of antipyrine in water. Flusin found that a solution of 10 g of antipyrine ($C_{11}H_{12}N_2O$) in a liter of solution gave an osmotic pressure of 1.18 atm at 0° C. Inserting these data into equation (32), we find for the molecular weight

$$M = \frac{WRT}{\Pi V}$$

$$= 10 \times \frac{0.0821 \times 273.2}{1.18 \times 1}$$

$$= 190 \text{ g mole}^{-1}$$

The molecular weight calculated from the atomic weights is 188.2.

Although this method may be employed for molecular weight determinations, it is rarely used except in high polymer work because of the extreme difficulty in obtaining accurate osmotic pressure data for dilute solutions. The same information can be obtained more readily by, say, a freezing point lowering determination with an accuracy that can hardly be attained in osmotic pressure measurements.

THEORIES OF OSMOTIC PRESSURE

Several theories have been proposed to explain the nature and cause of osmosis and osmotic pressure. One of these, the solvent bombardment theory, ascribes osmosis and osmotic pressure to the unequal bombardment of the semipermeable membrane by solvent molecules in the solution and in the pure solvent. On the pure solvent side every molecule that hits the membrane exerts solvent pressure and has a chance of passing through the membrane. On the solution side, however, only part of the collisions with the membrane are due to solvent molecules, the rest being due to solute. Consequently, the pressure exerted by solvent molecules in the solution must be less than the pressure exerted by solvent molecules in the pure solvent, and a tendency develops for solvent to pass into the solution. The difference in the solvent pressures exerted in the pure solvent and in the solution is taken as the osmotic pressure of the solution. Since the difference in solvent pressures developed will be greater the greater the concentration of solute molecules in solution, the osmotic pressure, on this basis, should also be greater the higher the concentration, as is actually observed.

The vapor pressure theory, in turn, ascribes osmosis to the fact that the vapor pressure of the solvent is greater in the pure solvent than in solution. As a result of this difference there is a tendency for solvent to distill through the membrane into the solution until the two pressures become equal. This distillation can be prevented by applying pressure to the solution. Since it can be shown thermodynamically that the vapor pressure of a liquid increases with increase in total applied pressure, application of pressure to the solution raises the vapor pressure of the solvent in the latter until it becomes equal to that of the pure solvent. Under these conditions osmosis stops, and the pressure required to accomplish this is taken as the osmotic pressure.

At present there is no way of distinguishing between the solvent bombardment and the vapor pressure theories of osmotic pressure. It may well be that both are merely different aspects of the same phenomenon, and are equally valid explanations of osmosis and osmotic pressure.

Solutions of Electrolytes

Solutions of nonelectrolytes in water or other solvents do not conduct electricity. Such solutions exhibit the colligative behavior described in the preceding section and obey in dilute solutions the various relations deduced there. These are also the solutions which yield for the dissolved substances normal molecular weights, i.e., the molecular weights expected from their chemical formulas, or, occasionally, some simple multiple of it. On the other hand, there is a class of substances, particularly salts and inorganic acids and bases, which when dissolved in water or other appropriate solvents yields solutions which conduct electricity to a greater or lesser extent. Such solutions are said to be *electrolytes*. Solutions of electrolytes, like those of nonelectrolytes, exhibit the colligative properties of vapor pressure lowering, boiling point elevation, freezing point lowering, and osmotic pressure, but they do not obey the simple relations deduced for nonelectrolytes. The colligative effects observed are always *greater* than those to be expected from the concentration. Stated differently, solutions of electrolytes behave as if the dissolved substance had in solution a molecular weight *lower* than the simplest formula weight of the substance.

This difference in the colligative behavior of electrolytes and nonelectrolytes led some early research workers to ascribe to electrolytes "anomalous" colligative properties. However, when certain effects present in electrolytes but absent in nonelectrolytes are taken into account, a great deal of the "anomaly" disappears, and the behavior of electrolytes becomes more understandable. This section will be devoted to a discussion of the colligative properties of electrolytic solutions and to an exposition of some of the theories which have been advanced to explain their "anomaly." Other aspects of electrolyte behavior will be elaborated on in later chapters.

COLLIGATIVE PROPERTIES OF ELECTROLYTES

As was indicated above, the freezing point lowering, boiling point elevation, vapor pressure lowering, and osmotic pressure of solutions of electrolytes all are higher than the corresponding effects for solutions of nonelectrolytes of the same total concentration. The freezing point data shown in Table 9 may be taken as typical of the nature of the devia-

TABLE 9

$\Delta T_f/m$ FOR AQUEOUS SOLUTIONS OF ELECTROLYTES

m	HCl	HNO$_3$	NH$_4$Cl	CuSO$_4$	H$_2$SO$_4$	CoCl$_2$	K$_2$SO$_4$	K$_3$Fe(CN)$_6$
0.0005	—	—	—	—	—	—	—	7.3
0.001	3.690	—	—	—	—	—	5.280	7.10
0.002	3.669	—	—	—	—	5.35	—	6.87
0.0025	—	—	—	3.003	5.052	—	5.258	—
0.005	3.635	3.67	3.617	2.871	4.814	5.208	5.150	6.53
0.01	3.601	3.64	3.582	2.703	4.584	5.107	5.010	6.26
0.05	3.532	3.55	3.489	2.266	4.112	4.918	4.559	5.60
0.10	3.523	3.51	3.442	2.08	3.940	4.882	4.319	5.30
0.20	3.54	3.47	3.392	1.91	3.790	4.946	4.044	5.0
0.40	—	3.46	—	—	3.68	5.170	3.79	—
1.00	3.94	3.58	3.33	1.72	4.04	6.31	—	—
2.00	4.43	3.79	3.34	—	5.07	8.51	—	—
4.00	5.65	4.16	3.35	—	7.05	—	—	—

tions. This table lists the ratios of observed freezing point lowering, ΔT_f, to molality, m, at various concentrations for a number of electrolytes in water solution. According to the arguments developed in the preceding chapter, this ratio should approach for dilute aqueous solutions the value of K_f for water, namely, 1.86° per mole per 1000 g of solvent. Inspection of the table reveals, however, that the limiting values approached by the various electrolytes are considerably higher than 1.86°. Furthermore, the limit approached is not the same throughout but varies from approximately $2 \times 1.86 = 3.72°$ for substances like hydrochloric acid and ammonium chloride to $3 \times 1.86 = 5.58°$ for cobalt chloride and $4 \times 1.86 = 7.44°$ for potassium ferricyanide.

To represent the colligative properties of electrolytes by means of the relations for nonelectrolytes, van't Hoff suggested the use of a factor i, which is defined as *the ratio of the colligative effect produced by a concentration m of electrolyte divided by the effect observed for the same concentration of non-electrolyte.* The van't Hoff factor indicates the number of times the colligative property of an electrolyte is greater than the effect which would be produced by the same concentration of nonelectrolyte. Applying this definition of i to freezing point depression of electrolyte solutions, it follows that

$$i = \frac{\Delta T_f}{(\Delta T_f)_0} \tag{33}$$

where ΔT_f is the freezing point lowering for the electrolyte and $(\Delta T_f)_0$ is the freezing point depression for a nonelectrolyte of the same concentration. Since according to equation (22) $(\Delta T_f)_0 = K_f m$, then

$$i = \frac{\Delta T_f}{K_f m}$$

and therefore, $\qquad\qquad \Delta T_f = i K_f m \tag{34}$

The values of i must be calculated from experimental data for each electrolyte at various concentrations. It has been found, however, that once i is known for a particular concentration of an electrolyte for one of the colligative properties, say freezing point lowering, the same value of i, within a small temperature correction where necessary, is essentially valid for the other properties at the same concentration. Consequently, we may write

$$i = \frac{\Delta T_f}{(\Delta T_f)_0} = \frac{\Delta T_b}{(\Delta T_b)_0} = \frac{\Delta P}{(\Delta P)_0} = \frac{\Pi}{(\Pi)_0} \tag{35}$$

where the quantities without subscripts refer to the electrolyte and those with subscripts to the nonelectrolyte of the same concentration. On substitution of equations (2), (13), and (29) into equation (35), the expressions for the boiling point elevation, vapor pressure lowering, and osmotic pressure for solutions of electrolytes become:

$$\Delta T_b = i(\Delta T_b)_0 = i K_b m \tag{36}$$

$$\Delta P = i(\Delta P)_0 = i P^0 N_2 \tag{37}$$

$$\Pi = i(\Pi)_0 = \frac{inRT}{V} \tag{38}$$

These equations may be expected to be applicable only to dilute solutions.

Table 10 lists the values of i calculated from Table 9 by means of equation (34). A perusal of this table reveals that in dilute solutions i increases as the molality is lowered and approaches a limit of two for electrolytes such as hydrochloric acid, nitric acid, ammonium chloride, and copper sulfate, a limit of three for electrolytes of the type sulfuric acid, cobalt chloride, and potassium sulfate, and a limit of four for potassium ferricyanide. In more concentrated solutions, on the other hand, i passes through a minimum and then increases, the increase frequently rising above the limits established in dilute solutions, as is the case with hydrochloric acid, nitric acid, sulfuric acid, and cobalt chloride. Obviously, such large divergences cannot be ascribed to deviations from the conditions prevailing in solutions of nonelectrolytes, and hence a more fundamental explanation of the nature of electrolytic solutions is necessary. Such an explanation was first supplied by the Arrhenius theory of electrolytic dissociation.

TABLE 10

VAN'T HOFF FACTORS, i, FOR VARIOUS ELECTROLYTES

m	HCl	HNO_3	NH_4Cl	$CuSO_4$	H_2SO_4	$CoCl_2$	K_2SO_4	$K_3Fe(CN)_6$
0.0005	—	—	—	—	—	—	—	3.92
0.001	1.98	—	—	—	—	—	2.84	3.82
0.002	1.97	—	—	—	—	2.88	—	3.70
0.0025	—	—	—	1.61	2.72	—	2.83	—
0.005	1.95	1.97	1.95	1.54	2.59	2.80	2.77	3.51
0.01	1.94	1.96	1.92	1.45	2.46	2.75	2.70	3.31
0.05	1.90	1.91	1.88	1.22	2.21	2.64	2.45	3.01
0.10	1.89	1.89	1.85	1.12	2.12	2.62	2.32	2.85
0.20	1.90	1.87	1.82	1.03	2.04	2.66	2.17	2.69
0.40	—	1.86	—	—	1.98	2.78	2.04	—
1.00	2.12	1.92	1.79	0.93	2.17	3.40	—	—
2.00	2.38	2.04	1.80	—	2.73	4.58	—	—
4.00	3.04	2.24	1.80	—	3.79	—	—	—

THE ARRHENIUS THEORY OF ELECTROLYTIC DISSOCIATION

The "anomalies" encountered in the colligative properties of electrolytes and the fact that solutions of electrolytes conduct electricity led Svante Arrhenius to propose in 1887 his celebrated *theory of electrolytic dissociation*. The essential points of this theory are already familiar to the student from his elementary chemical studies. Arrhenius postulated that electrolytes in solution are dissociated into electrically charged particles, called ions, in such a manner that the total charge on the positive ions is equal to the total charge on the negative ions. The net result is, therefore, that the solution as a whole is neutral in spite of the presence of electrically charged particles in it.

Once the presence of ions in an electrolytic solution is granted, the conductance of electricity through such a solution can readily be explained. If a pair of electrodes is dipped into a solution of an electrolyte and a potential applied across them, the positive ions will be attracted to the negative electrode and will migrate toward it, while the negative ions will be attracted toward the positive electrode and will move in that direction. Such a migration of ions through a solution constitutes a flow of electricity through the solution. Since nonelectrolytes do not yield ions, no migration of charged particles is possible, and hence solutions of this type are nonconducting.

Arrhenius pointed out further that an electrolyte in solution need not necessarily be completely dissociated into ions; instead it may be only partially dissociated to yield ions in *equilibrium* with unionized molecules of the substance. It may then be anticipated from the laws of chemical equilibrium that the extent of dissociation will vary with concentration, becoming greater as the concentration of dissolved substance becomes lower. In view of this, complete dissociation may be expected to take place only in infinitely dilute solutions. At finite concentrations, however, the electrolyte will be only partially ionized to a degree dependent on the nature of the substance and the concentration.

This idea of partial electrolytic dissociation was employed by Arrhenius to explain the colligative behavior of solutions of electrolytes. The colligative properties of a dilute solution depend on the number of particles, irrespective of kind, present in a given quantity of solvent. When there is no dissociation, dilute solutions exhibit the properties described and formulated for nonelectrolytes. When a substance in solution dissociates into ions, however, the number of particles in solution is increased. If it is assumed now that an ion acts with respect to the colligative properties in the same manner that an unionized molecule does, the increase in the number of particles in solution should cause an increase in the colligative effects. Thus, since the molal freezing point depression for a nonelectrolyte in water is 1.86°, it may be anticipated that for an electrolyte like hydrochloric acid, which yields on complete dissociation two ions for every molecule, the molal freezing point depression should be twice as great, namely $2 \times 1.86° = 3.72°$. Similarly, for an electrolyte like potassium sulfate, yielding three ions, the molal freezing point depression should be $3 \times 1.86° = 5.58°$, while for potassium ferricyanide, with four ions, $4 \times 1.86° = 7.44°$. These molal lowerings for the types of electrolytes mentioned are the ones to be anticipated on complete dissociation, and hence these are the values to be observed only in extremely dilute solutions. That such is actually the case is evident from an inspection of Table 9. Electrolytes which yield two ions, such as hydrochloric acid, nitric acid, ammonium chloride, and copper sulfate, approach the value of $\Delta T_f/m = 2 \times 1.86° = 3.72°$ as the molality approaches zero; electrolytes which yield three ions, namely, sulfuric acid, cobalt chloride, and potassium sulfate, approach $3 \times 1.86° = 5.58°$ as a limit; while potassium ferricyanide approaches on dilution a value of $\Delta T_f/m = 4 \times 1.86°$ $= 7.44°$. It is seen, therefore, that the observed limiting molal depressions for the various electrolytes are in accord with the predictions of the Arrhenius theory.

THE DEGREE OF DISSOCIATION OF ELECTROLYTES

From what has been said above it is evident that in terms of this theory any observed values of molal freezing point depressions higher than $1.86°$ and lower than the limits which would be reached on complete dissociation are to be accounted for by partial dissociation of the electrolyte. If this be the case, it is possible to calculate the degree of ionization of an electrolyte from the observed colligative data or from the values of i calculated from these. Consider an electrolyte A_xB_y which dissociates into x ions of A, each of charge z_+, and y ions of B, each of charge z_-, according to the equation

$$A_xB_y = xA^{z+} + yB^{z-} \tag{39}$$

If the original molality of the electrolyte is m, and if we let α be the fraction of 1 mole dissociated into ions, i.e., the *degree of dissociation*, then the number of moles of A_xB_y that dissociate is $m\alpha$, and the number of moles that remain unionized is $m - m\alpha = m(1 - \alpha)$. But for each mole of A_xB_y that dissociates, x moles of positive ions and y moles of negative ions are obtained. Consequently, for $m\alpha$ moles dissociating, $x(m\alpha)$ moles of A^{z+} and $y(m\alpha)$ moles of B^{z-} are obtained. The total number of moles, m_t, of substances of all types present in solution is then

$$\begin{aligned} m_t &= m(1 - \alpha) + x(m\alpha) + y(m\alpha) \\ &= m[1 - \alpha + x\alpha + y\alpha] \\ &= m[1 + \alpha(x + y - 1)] \end{aligned} \tag{40}$$

Designating by ν the *total number of ions yielded by a molecule of the electrolyte*, $\nu = x + y$, and equation (40) becomes

$$m_t = m[1 + \alpha(\nu - 1)] \tag{41}$$

Now, for a total molality m_t the freezing point depression must be given by $\Delta T_f = K_f m_t$, and hence, in terms of equation (41),

$$\Delta T_f = K_f m[1 + \alpha(\nu - 1)] \tag{42}$$

Solving for α we obtain

$$\begin{aligned} \alpha &= \frac{(\Delta T_f/K_f m - 1)}{(\nu - 1)} \\ &= \frac{\Delta T_f - K_f m}{(\nu - 1)(K_f m)} \end{aligned} \tag{43}$$

A more general relation for α follows by comparing equation (42) with equation (34). Since according to (34) $\Delta T_f = i K_f m$, i must be given by

$$i = 1 + \alpha(\nu - 1) \tag{44}$$

and, therefore,

$$\alpha = \frac{i - 1}{\nu - 1} \tag{45}$$

Equation (45) is applicable to any of the colligative properties and can just as readily be derived from boiling point elevation, vapor pressure lowering, or osmotic pressure considerations. It gives the degree of dissociation of an electrolyte from a knowledge of i and the type of electrolyte in question. Thus, according to Table 10, i for 0.005 molal ammonium chloride is 1.95; and, as $\nu = 2$ for this salt,

$$\alpha = \frac{i - 1}{\nu - 1} = \frac{1.95 - 1}{2 - 1}$$
$$= 0.95$$

or, ammonium chloride is 95 per cent dissociated in 0.005 molal solution according to the Arrhenius theory.

CLASSIFICATION OF ELECTROLYTES

Calculations of the degree of dissociation for various electrolytes in aqueous solutions show that practically all salts are highly dissociated into ions. The same is true for strong acids, such as nitric, hydrochloric, hydrobromic, hydriodic, sulfuric, and perchloric, and the bases of the alkali and alkaline earth metals. As may be expected from their high degree of dissociation, aqueous solutions of these substances are good conductors of electricity. On the other hand, there are many substances whose aqueous solutions exhibit relatively poor conductivity and whose colligative behavior indicates that they are only slightly dissociated even at fairly low concentrations. Among these are included a large number of organic acids such as acetic, propionic, and benzoic; inorganic acids such as carbonic, hydrosulfuric, hydrocyanic, orthoarsenic, boric, and hypochlorous acids; and bases such as ammonium, zinc, and lead hydroxides. Solutions of substances that show good conductance and which indicate a high degree of dissociation in solution are designated as *strong electrolytes*. In turn, solutions of substances that exhibit only poor conductance and a low degree of dissociation are called *weak electrolytes*.

However, not all electrolytes can be classified clearly as being either strong or weak. There are some electrolytes, such as aqueous solutions of *o*-chlorbenzoic, *o*-nitrobenzoic, 3,5-dinitrobenzoic, and cyanoacetic acids, whose behavior indicates that they are intermediate in properties between the strong and weak electrolytes. Still, the number of substances of intermediate strength is not very large, and hence such electrolytes will not be considered further.

It is frequently convenient to subdivide strong electrolytes further according to the charge of the ions produced. An electrolyte that yields two singly charged ions, such as sodium chloride or nitric acid, is called a uni-univalent electrolyte or an electrolyte of the 1–1 type. Again, an electrolyte that yields univalent positive ions and bivalent negative ions, such as potassium sulfate or sulfuric acid, is called a uni-bivalent electrolyte, or 1–2 type, while one that yields bivalent positive ions and univalent negative ions, such as barium chloride or magnesium nitrate, is called a bi-univalent electrolyte, or 2–1 type. Similarly, copper sulfate is a bi-bivalent electrolyte, or 2–2 type, while potassium ferricyanide is a uni-trivalent electrolyte, or one of 1–3 type. In this method of classification of strong electrolytes the charge of the positive ions is given first followed by the charge of the negative ions.

CRITICISM OF THE ARRHENIUS THEORY

Applications of the Arrhenius theory to the colligative behavior, electrical conductance, and ionic equilibria of *weak electrolytes* have shown that the theory is essentially satisfactory for these. However, in attempting to apply this theory to *strong electrolytes* so many anomalies and inconsistencies have been encountered that serious questioning arose early as to the validity of some of Arrhenius's postulates in respect to the nature of strong electrolytes.

Arrhenius showed that the degree of dissociation of an electrolyte may be determined not only from the colligative properties but also from conductance measurements by means that will be described in Chapter 15. The values of α obtained by these two methods agree quite well for weak electrolytes, but for strong electrolytes the agreement is not what is to be expected from the accuracy of the measurements. Again, application of the laws of equilibrium to the partial dissociation equilibrium postulated for electrolyte solutions by Arrhenius shows that these are obeyed quite well by weak electrolytes but not at all by strong electrolytes.

Another factor which militates against the simple dissociation theory when applied to strong electrolytes is the fact that Arrhenius considered solutions containing ions to behave essentially as ideal solutions containing the same number of neutral molecules. Yet such an assumption is hardly plausible. Whereas the forces between neutral molecules in fairly dilute solutions may be relatively small, the electrostatic attractions between electrically charged particles in solutions of electrolytes may exercise a significant effect on the motion and distribution of ions. Consequently such solutions can hardly be ideal in behavior, and ions can hardly be expected to act as if they were neutral and ideal molecules. Still, the effect produced by interionic attractions may be quite small in solutions of weak electrolytes where the number of ions is not large. Such solutions may behave, therefore, in line with Arrhenius's expectations. But, in strong electrolytes, where the number of ions is large, the effect of interionic attractions should be appreciable and should be the more pronounced the more concentrated the solution and the higher the valence of the ions.

These considerations, and others, point to the conclusion that the Arrhenius theory, although essentially valid for weak electrolytes, does not represent the true situation in solutions of strong electrolytes. The consensus is that the α's calculated from colligative effects and conductance data do give a close approximation to the degree of dissociation of weak electrolytes. On the other hand, the belief is that solutions of strong electrolytes are *completely ionized* even at moderate concentrations and that the α's calculated for strong electrolytes merely give an indication of the interionic forces of attraction operating in such solutions.

THE COMPLETE IONIZATION OF STRONG ELECTROLYTES

That interionic attraction rather than partial dissociation is the dominant effect in strong electrolytes at moderate concentrations can be shown by the use of a quantity called the *osmotic coefficient*, g, introduced by Bjerrum.[1] This quantity, analogous to the van't Hoff factor i, centers attention on deviations from complete dissociation rather than from no dissociation, as does i. It is defined as the ratio of an observed colligative property to what the property would be if dissociation were complete, i.e.,

$$g = \frac{\Delta T_f}{\nu(\Delta T_f)_0} = \frac{\Delta T_b}{\nu(\Delta T_b)_0} = \frac{\Delta P}{\nu(\Delta P)_0} = \frac{\Pi}{\nu(\Pi)_0} \tag{46}$$

where ν, as before, is the number of ions resulting from a molecule of electrolyte. From the definition of i in equation (35) it is also evident that

$$g = \frac{i}{\nu} \tag{47}$$

For completely dissociated electrolytes exhibiting no interionic attraction, $g = 1$. Deviation of g from unity, i.e., $(1 - g)$, is a measure, therefore, of either partial dissociation, or interionic attraction, or both. A study of the variation of $(1 - g)$ with the concentration of ions in solution should give then some indication of the nature of these deviations.

Figure 7 shows a plot of $(1 - g)$ against νC, the concentration of ions

[1] N. Bjerrum, *Zeit. für Elektrochemie*, **24**, 259 (1907).

in solution, for a number of electrolytes of various types. Since at zero ionic concentration dissociation is complete and no interionic attractions are operative, $g = 1$, $(1 - g) = 0$, and all curves start from the origin. These curves not only are applicable to the electrolytes shown in the figure but are representative also of other electrolytes of the given types. Thus, if the $(1 - g)$ values for sodium chloride were plotted on the same graph, they would coincide at the lower concentrations with those for potassium chloride, those for sulfuric acid would coincide with the potassium sulfate plot, while those for calcium sulfate would fall along the magnesium sulfate curve, etc. In brief, the $(1 - g)$ values for strong electrolytes of a particular ion type when plotted against the ionic concentration all lie on the same curve at the lower concentrations; and individual differences between electrolytes of a given ion type appear only at higher concentrations.

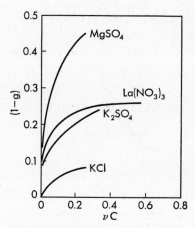

Fig. 7. Plot of $(1 - g)$ vs. νC for Strong Electrolytes.

This dependence of the deviations of strong electrolytes in dilute solution on the charges of the ions only is not what may be anticipated from the Arrhenius theory of partial dissociation. This theory makes no allowance for ionic charge, and hence there is no reason why the $(1 - g)$ plots should exhibit the regularity shown. Yet, this is just the type of behavior to be expected if interionic attraction is the determining factor. The electrostatic attraction between charged particles follows the Coulomb law of force, which states that the electrostatic attraction between two charged bodies is directly proportional to their charges and inversely proportional to the square of the distance between them. Since the charges of the ions are determined by their valences, interionic attraction should follow parallel with the valence types of the ions involved, as is the case. We are led to the conclusion, therefore, that *in strong electrolytes*, at least at moderate concentrations, *interionic attraction and not partial dissociation is the important influence* and that the deviations exhibited by strong electrolytes are due to electrostatic attractions between ions rather than to incomplete ionization of the electrolyte.

Other evidence which lends considerable credence to the concept of complete ionization of strong electrolytes is supplied by the results of x-ray analysis of crystals. A study of the structure of crystals of potassium and sodium chloride, sodium sulfate, etc., indicates that in such crystals the units composing the lattice are ions. There is no entity which corresponds to our ordinary concept of a molecule. In other words, such substances are already *completely ionized* in the solid state. Consequently, when, say, a crystal of sodium chloride is disintegrated by solution in water, the particles breaking away from the crystal and passing into solution are ions and not molecules. If any molecules of sodium chloride are to be present in solution, they must be formed there by *association* of ions rather than by dissociation of molecules already in existence. Since such an association is not very probable at very low concentrations, we again arrive at the deduction that at least in dilute solutions strong electrolytes are completely ionized. And again, if molecules of electrolytes like barium or sodium chloride or potassium sulfate are to be postulated in more concentrated solutions, these must be formed as secondary products through association of ions and cannot be considered as the initial substances from which ions result by partial dissociation.

The result of these considerations, and others, is that strong electrolytes are believed now to be completely ionized at least up to moderate concentrations and that in such solutions no unionized molecules are present. What the situation is in concentrated solutions is not so definite. Some of the difficulties and complexities of such solutions will be elaborated on a little later.

THE DEBYE-HÜCKEL THEORY OF INTERIONIC ATTRACTION

The first successful *quantitative* approach to the problem of interionic attraction in strong electrolytes was made by S. R. Milner.[1] However, Milner's treatment was so involved mathematically that his work attracted little attention among chemists. It was not until 1923, when P. Debye and E. Hückel[2] first published an alternate and much simpler treatment of the subject, that the theory of interionic attraction came to the fore. Since then this theory has grown to occupy a dominant position in all considerations involving electrolytes and their kinetic and thermodynamic behavior.[3]

At this time attention will be confined to the presentation of the salient qualitative details of the theory, without any attempt at mathematical formulation. Like Arrhenius, Debye and Hückel postulate that strong electrolytes exist in solution as ions of the types mentioned, but, unlike

---

[1] S. R. Milner, *Phil. Mag.*, **23**, 551 (1912); **25**, 742 (1913); **35**, 214, 352 (1918); *Trans. Farad. Soc.*, **15**, 148 (1919).

[2] Debye and Hückel, *Physikalische Zeitschrift*, **24**, 185 (1923).

[3] Although this theory will be discussed briefly at this point and will be elaborated on at several other stages in the book, no complete and rigid exposition is possible in an elementary text. Any student interested in further and more complete details is advised to read some of the references mentioned at the end of the chapter.

Arrhenius, they believe that strong electrolytes, at least in dilute solutions, are completely ionized and that the effects observed are due to the unequal distribution of ions resulting from interionic attraction. Debye and Hückel showed that, because of electrostatic attractions between charged ions, each positive ion in solution must be surrounded on an average with more negative ions than ions of like charge; and conversely, each negative ion must be surrounded on an average with more positive than negative ions. In other words, each ion in solution is surrounded by an *ionic atmosphere whose net charge is opposite to that of the central ion.* They showed, further, that the properties of the electrolyte are determined by the interaction of the central ion with its atmosphere. Since the nature of the atmosphere is determined by the valences of the ions in solution, their concentration, the temperature, and the dielectric constant of the medium, it must follow that these are also the factors controlling the thermodynamic properties of the electrolyte. At any given temperature and in any given solvent, the temperature and dielectric constant are fixed, and hence the properties of the electrolyte should depend only on the charges of the ions and their concentration and not at all on the specific nature of each electrolyte. These conclusions are strictly valid only for very dilute solutions. This limitation arises from the fact that Debye and Hückel were forced to make certain mathematical simplifications which in essence reduce the applicability of their equations to such solutions.

In the Debye-Hückel theory of interionic attraction the effect of the concentration of the ions enters through a quantity called the *ionic strength* of the solution. This quantity, first introduced by G. N. Lewis even before the advent of the Debye-Hückel theory, is a measure of the electrical environment of the solution and plays in this theory a role analogous to concentration in the Arrhenius theory. It is defined as

$$\mu = \frac{1}{2}\,(C_1 z_1^2 + C_2 z_2^2 + C_3 z_3^2 + \cdot\cdot\cdot)$$

$$= \frac{1}{2}\,\Sigma C_i z_i^2 \tag{48}$$

where μ is the ionic strength of the solution, C_1, C_2, C_3, $\cdot\cdot\cdot$ the concentrations of the various ions in gram ionic weights per liter, while z_1, z_2, z_3, $\cdot\cdot\cdot$ are the valences of the respective ions. The ionic strength of a solution is equal to the molarity only in the case of 1–1 electrolytes. In all other instances the two are not equal. This may be illustrated with the calculation of the ionic strength of C molar solutions of potassium chloride, barium chloride, and lanthanum sulfate. In potassium chloride, $C_+ = C_- = C$, $z_+ = z_- = 1$, and therefore

$$\mu_{KCl} = \frac{1}{2}[C(1)^2 + C(1)^2]$$

$$= \frac{2\,C}{2} = C$$

For barium chloride, $C_+ = C$, $C_- = 2\,C$, $z_+ = 2$, $z_- = 1$. Hence,

$$\mu_{BaCl_2} = \frac{1}{2}[C(2)^2 + 2\,C(1)^2]$$

$$= \frac{6\,C}{2} = 3\,C$$

Finally, for lanthanum sulfate, $C_+ = 2\,C$, $C_- = 3\,C$, $z_+ = 3$, $z_- = 2$, and therefore

$$\mu = \frac{1}{2}[2\,C(3)^2 + 3\,C(2)^2]$$

$$= \frac{30\,C}{2} = 15\,C$$

These examples show that the ionic strength of a solution is determined not only by the stoichiometric concentration of the electrolyte but also by the valences of its ions. It should also be emphasized that in calculating the ionic strength of a solution the summation called for in equation (48) must include any and all ionic species present, no matter what their source. Thus the ionic strength of a solution containing $C = 0.10$ potassium chloride in presence of $C = 0.01$ barium chloride is

$$\mu = \frac{1}{2}[0.1(1)^2 + 0.1(1)^2 + 0.01(2)^2 + 2(0.01)(1)^2]$$

$$= 0.13$$

Various indications of the ability of the Debye-Hückel theory to explain the behavior of dilute solutions of strong electrolytes will be given at appropriate stages in this book. At present it is sufficient to point out the superiority of this theory over that of Arrhenius in explaining the cource of the $(1 - g)$ vs. ionic concentration curves shown in Fig. 7. The Debye-Hückel theory predicts that $(1 - g)$ for very dilute solutions of strong electrolytes in water at 0° C should be given by

$$(1 - g) = 0.264(z_+z_-)^{3/2}\sqrt{\nu C} \qquad (49a)$$
or
$$(1 - g) = 0.373\,z_+z_-\sqrt{\mu} \qquad (49b)$$

According to these equations $(1 - g)$ should vary with $\sqrt{\nu C}$ or $\sqrt{\mu}$ with slopes dependent upon the valence type of the electrolyte in question. The extent to which these predictions are verified may be judged from Fig. 8, where a plot of $(1 - g)$ vs. $\sqrt{\nu C}$ is given. The solid lines are the plots of equation (49a) for the various ionic types, while the dotted lines show the course of the experimentally determined values. The significant facts to be observed in this comparison are (a) that the Debye-Hückel theory demands that the $(1 - g)$ curves follow the valence type of the electrolyte, as is actually the case, and (b) that the experimentally observed data approach the theoretically predicted curves at the low concentrations. These facts are strong confirmation of the essential validity of the concept of interionic attraction as the cause of the deviations in strong electrolytes.

In conclusion, the present status of the problem of electrolytes may be summarized as follows. For weak electrolytes the Arrhenius theory of partial dissociation is, within minor corrections, adequate. On the other hand, for strong electrolytes this theory is not satisfactory, for in these interionic attraction is the dominant factor. On the quantitative and theoretical side the Debye-Hückel theory supplies the explanation for the thermodynamic properties of very dilute and moderately dilute solutions, but this theory has not been extended as yet to concentrated solutions. It is quite probable that for concentrated solutions the treatment presented by the Debye-Hückel theory is considerably oversimplified. In order to understand the properties of concentrated solutions it may be necessary to consider not only interionic attraction,

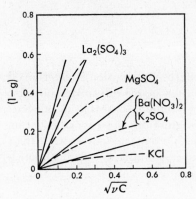

Fig. 8.   Plot of $(1 - g)$ vs. $\sqrt{\nu C}$ for Various Electrolytes.

but also such phenomena as interaction between ions resulting in association, interaction of the solvent with ions, and the change in the nature of the solvent as a result of the presence of charged particles. Although the importance of these factors is appreciated, and although some of them have been investigated both theoretically and experimentally, no complete analysis of the complex problems involved here has as yet been made.

REFERENCES FOR FURTHER READING

1. H. Falkenhagen, *Electrolytes*, Oxford University Press, New York, 1934.
2. Harned and Owen, *The Physical Chemistry of Electrolytic Solutions*, Reinhold Publishing Corporation, New York, 1950.
3. K. Jellinek, *Lehrbuch der physikalischen Chemie*, Ferdinand Enke, Stuttgart, 1930, Vols. II and III.
4. V. K. La Mer, *Trans. Am. Electrochem. Soc.*, **41**, 507 (1927).
5. G. Scatchard, *Chem. Rev.*, **13**, 7 (1933).

6. Shedlovsky, Brown, and MacInnes, *Trans. Am. Electrochem. Soc.*, **66**, 237 (1934).
7. A. Weissberger, *Physical Methods of Organic Chemistry*, Interscience Publishers, Inc., New York, 1949, Vol. I, Chaps. III, IV, V, and XI.

PROBLEMS

1. A solution contains 5 g of urea per 100 g of water. What will be the vapor pressure of this solution at 25° C? The vapor pressure of pure H_2O at this temperature is 23.756 mm.   *Ans.* 23.404 mm.

2. A solution composed of 10 g of a nonvolatile organic solute in 100 g of diethyl ether has a vapor pressure of 426.0 mm at 20° C. If the vapor pressure of the pure ether is 442.2 mm at the same temperature, what is the molecular weight of the solute?

3. A 25° C 10.50 liters of pure N_2, measured at 760 mm Hg, are passed through an aqueous solution of a nonvolatile solute, whereby the solution loses 0.2455 g in weight. If the total pressure above the solution is also 760 mm, what is the vapor pressure of the solution and the mol fraction of solute?

4. At 50° C the vapor pressures of pure water and ethyl alcohol are, respectively, 92.5 and 219.9 mm Hg. If 6 g of a nonvolatile solute of molecular weight 120 are dissolved in 150 g of each of these solvents, what will be the relative vapor pressure lowerings in the two solvents?

5. If 30 g of diphenyl are dissolved in 250 g of benzene, what will be the boiling point of the resulting solution under atmospheric pressure?   *Ans.* 82.1° C.

6. A solution consisting of 5.00 g of an organic solute per 25.00 g of CCl_4 boils at 81.5° C under atmospheric pressure. What is the molecular weight of the solute?

7. Select the proper data and calculate the ebullioscopic constant for C_6H_6.

8. From the data given in Table 2 calculate the molar heat of vaporization of ethyl alcohol.   *Ans.* 9420 cal/mole.

9. A certain weight of a nonvolatile solute dissolved in chloroform gives a boiling point elevation of 3° C at 760 mm pressure. Assuming the solution to be ideal, calculate the mol fractions of solute in the solution by equations (9), (10), and (13). Which of these results would be nearest the correct value?

10. In deriving equation (9) it has been assumed that ΔH_v is a constant. Suppose, however, that ΔH_v in calories/mole is not constant, but varies with temperature according to the equation

$$\Delta H_v = A + BT + CT^2 + DT^3$$

where A, B, C, and D are constants. Starting with the unintegrated Clausius-Clapeyron equation, and without making any assumptions other than that Raoult's law is valid, derive the relation between $\ln (1 - N_2)$, T, and T_0.

11. For water the constants in the heat of vaporization equation given in problem 10 are: $A = 13,425$, $B = -9.81$, $C = 7.5 \times 10^{-5}$, and $D = 4.46 \times 10^{-7}$. Using these constants and the equation derived in problem 10, calculate the mol fraction of solute in solution when the boiling point elevation is 0.50° C. Compare the result with those given by equations (9), (10), and (13).

12. What weight of glycerol would have to be added to 1000 g of water in order to lower its freezing point 10° C?   *Ans.* 495 g.

13. An aqueous solution contains 5% by weight of urea and 10% by weight of glucose. What will be its freezing point?

14. Compare the weights of methanol and glycerol which would be required to lower the freezing point of 1000 g of water 1° C.

15. Select the necessary data and calculate the cryoscopic constant of cyclohexane.

16. From the data given in Table 4, calculate the heat of fusion per mole of phenol.

17. A sample of CH_3COOH is found to freeze at 16.4° C. Assuming that no solid solution is formed, what is the concentration of impurities in the sample?

18. A mixture which contains 0.550 g of camphor and 0.045 g of an organic solute freezes at 157.0° C. The solute contains 93.46% of C and 6.54% by weight of H. What is the molecular formula of the compound?   *Ans.* $C_{12}H_{10}$.

19. When dissolved in 100 g of a solvent whose molecular weight is 94.10 and whose freezing point is 45.0° C, 0.5550 g of a solute of molecular weight 110.1 gave a freezing point depression of 0.382° C. Again, when 0.4372 g of solute of unknown molecular weight were dissolved in 96.50 g of the same solvent, the freezing point lowering was found to be 0.467° C. From these data find (a) the molecular weight of the unknown solute, (b) the cryoscopic constant of the solvent, and (c) the heat of fusion of the solvent per mole.

20. In the derivation of equation (20) it has been assumed that ΔH_v and ΔH_s are constant. Suppose, however, that both are dependent upon the temperature, and given by the relations

$$\Delta H_v = A + BT + CT^2 + DT^3$$
$$\Delta H_s = a + bT + cT^2 + dT^3$$

where A, B, C, D, a, b, c, and d are constants. Starting with the unintegrated Clausius-Clapeyron equation, derive the relation between $\ln (1 - N_2)$, T, and T_0. Make no assumptions other than that Raoult's law is valid.

21. For water the constants A, B, C, and D are given in problem 11. Again, for this substance $a = 11,260$, $b = 7.66$, $c = -15.6 \times 10^{-3}$, and $d = 4.46 \times 10^{-7}$. Using these constants and the equation derived in problem 20, calculate the mol fraction of solute in solution when the freezing point lowering is 1.000° C. Compare the result with those given by equations (20), (21), and (22).

22. An aqueous solution contains 20 g of glucose per liter. What is its osmotic pressure at 25° C?   *Ans.* 2.72 atm.

23. An aqueous solution freezes at −1.50° C. Calculate (a) the normal boiling point, (b) the vapor pressure at 25° C, and (c) the osmotic pressure at 25° C of the given solution.

24. The average osmotic pressure of human blood is 7.7 atm at 40° C. What should be the total concentration of various solutes in the blood? Assuming this concentration to be essentially the same as the molality, find the freezing point of blood.

25. The vapor pressure of an aqueous solution at 25° C is 23.45 mm. Using equation (30), calculate its osmotic pressure given that the vapor pressure of pure H_2O is 23.756 mm at 25° C.

26. A 0.2 molal aqueous solution of KCl freezes at −0.680° C. Calculate i and the osmotic pressure at 0° C. Assume volume to be that of pure H_2O.   *Ans.* $i = 1.83$; $\Pi = 8.2$ atm.

27. A 0.4 molal aqueous solution of K_2SO_4 freezes at −1.52° C. Assuming that i is constant with temperature, calculate the vapor pressure at 25° C and the normal boiling point of the solution.

28. From the data listed in Table 10, calculate the freezing point and the vapor pressure at 25° C of a 2.00 molal $CoCl_2$ solution.

29. A solution of HCl, 0.72% by weight, freezes at $-0.706°$ C. Calculate the apparent molality and the apparent molecular weight of the HCl.

30. A 0.01 molal solution of $K_3Fe(CN)_6$ freezes at $-0.062°$ C. What is the apparent percentage of dissociation?   *Ans.* 78%.

31. A 2.00 molal HCl solution freezes at $-8.86°$ C. Calculate the apparent percentage of dissociation and explain your answer.

32. A 0.1 molal solution of a weak electrolyte ionizing into two ions freezes at $-0.208°$ C. Calculate the degree of dissociation.   *Ans.* 0.118.

33. At 25° C at 0.1 molal solution of CH_3COOH is 1.35% dissociated. Calculate the freezing point and osmotic pressure of the solution. Compare your results with those which you would obtain if the acid did not dissociate.

34. What is the osmotic coefficient of the $K_3Fe(CN)_6$ solution given in problem 30?   *Ans.* 0.833.

35. At 25° C the vapor pressure of a 2.00 molal $CoCl_2$ solution is 20.00 mm Hg. Calculate the osmotic coefficient.

36. Compare the ionic strengths of 0.1 N solutions of HCl, $SrCl_2$, $AlCl_3$, $ZnSO_4$, and $Fe_2(SO_4)_3$.

37. A solution is 0.5 molar in $MgSO_4$, 0.1 molar in $AlCl_3$, and 0.2 molar in $(NH_4)_2$-SO_4. What is the total ionic strength?   *Ans.* 3.2.

38. Using the Debye-Hückel equation, calculate what will be the values of g and i at 0° C for 0.0005 molar aqueous solutions of HCl, $BaCl_2$, H_2SO_4, $CuSO_4$, and $La(NO_3)_3$.

39. According to the Debye-Hückel theory what will be the osmotic coefficient of NaCl in an aqueous solution containing 0.001 molar NaCl and 0.0001 molar K_2SO_4 at 0° C?

7

Surface Phenomena

Attention has already been directed to the fact that the molecular forces at the surface of a liquid are in a state of unbalance or unsaturation. The same is true of the surface of a solid, where the molecules or ions in the surface of a crystal do not have all their forces satisfied by union with other particles. As a result of this unsaturation, solid and liquid surfaces tend to satisfy their residual forces by attracting onto and retaining on their surfaces gases or dissolved substances with which they come in contact. This phenomenon of concentration of a substance *on* the surface of a solid or liquid is called *adsorption*. The substance thus attracted to a surface is said to be the *adsorbed phase*, while the substance to which it is attached is the *adsorbent*.

*Ad*sorption should be carefully distinguished from *ab*sorption. In the latter process a substance is not only retained on the surface, but passes through the surface to become distributed throughout the body of a solid or liquid. Thus water is *ab*sorbed by a sponge, or water vapor is *ab*sorbed by anhydrous calcium chloride to form a hydrate; but acetic acid in solution and various gases are *ad*sorbed by charcoal. Where doubt exists as to whether a process is true adsorption or absorption, the noncommittal term *sorption* is sometimes employed.

ADSORPTION OF GASES BY SOLIDS

Although it is probable that all solids adsorb gases to some extent, adsorption as a rule is not very pronounced unless an adsorbent possesses a large surface for a given mass. For this reason silica gel and charcoals

214

obtained from various sources, such as wood, bone, coconut shells, and lignite, are particularly effective as adsorbing agents. These substances have a very porous structure and with their large exposed surfaces can take up appreciable volumes of various gases. The extent of adsorption can further be increased by "activating" the adsorbents in various ways. Thus wood charcoal can be "activated" by heating between 350 and 1000° C in a vacuum or in air, steam, and certain other gases to a point where the adsorption of carbon tetrachloride at 24° C can be increased from 0.011 g per gram of charcoal to 1.48 g. The activation involves apparently a distilling out of hydrocarbon impurities from a charcoal and leads thereby to exposure of a larger free surface for possible adsorption.

TABLE 1

ADSORPTION OF GASES BY CHARCOAL AT 15° C
(1 g of adsorbent)

Gas	Volume Adsorbed (cc)	Critical Temperature (°K)
H_2	4.7	33
N_2	8.0	126
CO	9.3	134
CH_4	16.2	190
CO_2	48	304
HCl	72	324
H_2S	99	373
NH_3	181	406
Cl_2	235	417
SO_2	380	430

The amount of gas adsorbed by a solid depends on the natures of the adsorbent and gas being adsorbed, the area of the adsorbent, the temperature, and the pressure of the gas. The specificity with which certain gases are adsorbed by a given solid can be seen from Table 1, where the volumes of various gases adsorbed by a gram of charcoal at 15° C are given. The volumes of gas have all been reduced to 0° C and 1 atm pressure. A comparison of the relative volumes of various gases adsorbed by a solid reveals that in general the extent of adsorption parallels the increase in the critical temperature of the gases. This parallelism suggests that gases which liquefy easily are more readily adsorbed, but it does not necessarily indicate that the gases exist as liquids on the surface. A similar correlation is obtained with boiling points.

As may be expected, an increase in the surface area of adsorbent increases the total amount of gas adsorbed. Since the surface area of adsorbing agents cannot always be determined readily, common practice is to employ the mass of adsorbent as a measure of the surface available and to express the amount of adsorption per unit mass of adsorbing agent used.

In adsorption a true equilibrium is established between the gas in contact with a solid and the gas on the surface; i.e., for a given gas and adsorbent the extent of adsorption under any condition of temperature and pressure is definite and reproducible. Like all equilibria, the adsorption process is strongly affected by temperature. Invariably an increase in temperature leads to a decrease in the amount adsorbed, and vice versa. Thus, at 600 mm pressure a gram of charcoal adsorbs about 10 cc of nitrogen at $0°$ C, 20 cc at $-29°$ C, and 45 cc at $-78°$ C. These data indicate that adsorption of gas by a solid is accompanied by evolution of heat which is called the *heat of adsorption*.

TYPES OF ADSORPTION

Study of adsorption of various gases on solid surfaces has revealed that the forces operative in adsorption are not the same in all cases. Two types of adsorption are generally recognized, namely, *physical* or van der Waals adsorption and *chemical* or activated adsorption. Physical adsorption is characterized by low heats of adsorption, of the order of 10,000 cal or less per mole of adsorbate, and by the fact that the adsorption equilibrium is reversible and is established rapidly. This is the type observed in the adsorption of various gases on charcoal. The forces responsible for the adsorption here are of the same kind as are involved in deviations of gases from ideal behavior and in liquefaction, i.e., van der Walls forces. On the other hand, activated or chemical adsorption is accompanied by much higher heat changes, ranging from 20,000 to as high as 100,000 cal, and leads to a much firmer attachment of the gas to the surface. As these heats are of the same order of magnitude as those involved in chemical reactions, it is quite certain that the adsorption consists of a combination of gas molecules with the surface to form a surface compound. In the adsorption of oxygen on tungsten it has actually been found that tungsten trioxide distills from the surface at about $1200°K$; however, even above this temperature oxygen remains on the surface apparently as WO. As other examples of chemical adsorption may be mentioned that of carbon monoxide on tungsten, oxygen on silver, gold, platinum, and carbon, and hydrogen on nickel.

Many cases of adsorption are neither one type nor the other, but a combination of both. Again, some systems show physical adsorption at low temperatures and chemisorption as the temperature is raised. This is true with the adsorption of hydrogen on nickel. In general chemical adsorption is more specific in nature than physical and is to be found only where there is tendency toward compound formation between a gas and adsorbent, However, since van der Waals forces are not specific in nature, physical adsorption may be found in all instances, although it may possibly be masked by the stronger chemical type.

ADSORPTION ISOTHERMS

The relation between the amount of substance adsorbed by an adsorbent and the equilibrium pressure or concentration at constant temperature is called an *adsorption isotherm*. Five general types of isotherms have

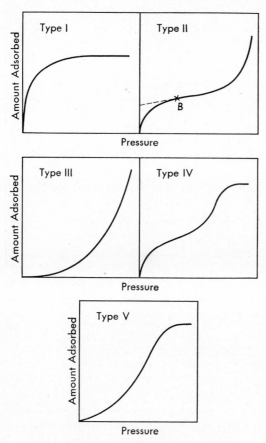

Fig. 1.   Types of Adsorption Isotherms.

been observed in the adsorption of gases on solids. These are shown in Fig. 1. In cases of chemisorption only isotherms of type I are encountered, while in physical adsorption all five types occur.

In isotherms of type I the amount of gas adsorbed per given quantity of adsorbent increases relatively rapidly with pressure and then much more slowly as the surface becomes covered with gas molecules. To represent the variation of the amount of adsorption per unit area or unit mass with pressure, Freundlich proposed the equation

$$y = kP^{1/n} \qquad (1)$$

Here y is the weight or volume of gas adsorbed per unit area or unit mass of adsorbent, P is the equilibrium pressure, and k and n are empir-

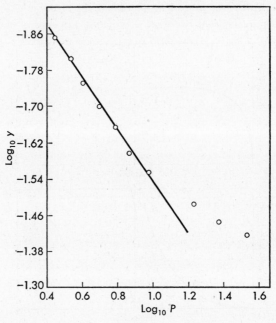

Fig. 2.   Application of Freundlich Equation to Adsorption of N_2 on Mica at 90° K.

ical constants dependent on the nature of solid and gas and on the temperature. This equation may be tested as follows. Taking logarithms of both sides, equation (1) becomes

$$\log_{10} y = \log_{10} k + \frac{1}{n} \log_{10} P \qquad (2)$$

If $\log_{10} y$ is plotted now against $\log_{10} P$, a straight line should result with slope equal to $1/n$ and ordinate intercept equal to $\log_{10} k$. Figure 2 shows such a plot for the adsorption of nitrogen on mica at 90° K. In this plot y is in mg/cm², while P is in dynes/cm². Although the requirements of the equation are met satisfactorily at the lower pressures, at higher pressures the experimental points curve away from the straight line, indicating that this equation does not have general applicability in reproducing adsorption of gases by solids.

THE LANGMUIR ADSORPTION EQUATION

A much better equation for type I isotherms was deduced by Irving Langmuir[1] from theoretical considerations. Langmuir postulated that gases in being adsorbed by a solid surface cannot form a layer more than a *single molecule* in depth. Further, he visualized the adsorption process as consisting of two opposing actions, a condensation of molecules from the gas phase onto the surface and an evaporation of molecules from the surface back into the body of the gas. When adsorption first starts, every molecule colliding with the surface may condense on it. However, as adsorption proceeds, only those molecules may be expected to be adsorbed which strike a part of the surface not already covered by absorbed molecules. The result is that the initial *rate* of condensation of molecules on a surface is highest and falls off as the area of surface available for adsorption is decreased. On the other hand, a molecule adsorbed on a surface may, by thermal agitation, become detached from the surface and escape into the gas. The rate at which desorption will occur will depend, in turn, on the amount of surface covered by molecules and will increase as the surface becomes more fully saturated. These two rates, condensation and desorption, will eventually become equal, and when this happens an adsorption equilibrium will be established.

These ideas can be formulated mathematically. If we let θ be the *fraction* of the total surface covered by adsorbed molecules at any instant, then the fraction of surface bare and available for adsorption is $(1 - \theta)$. Since, according to kinetic theory, the rate at which molecules strike unit area of a surface is proportional to the pressure of the gas, the rate of condensation of molecules should be determined both by the pressure and the fraction of surface bare, or,

$$\text{Rate of condensation} = k_1(1 - \theta)P$$

where k_1 is a constant of proportionality. On the other hand, if we let k_2 be the rate at which molecules evaporate from unit surface when the surface is fully covered, then for a fraction θ of surface covered the rate of evaporation will be

$$\text{Rate of evaporation} = k_2\theta$$

For adsorption equilibrium these rates must be equal. Therefore,

$$k_1(1 - \theta)P = k_2\theta$$
$$\theta = \frac{k_1P}{k_2 + k_1P}$$
$$= \frac{bP}{1 + bP} \tag{3}$$

[1] I. Langmuir, *J. Am. Chem. Soc.*, **38**, 2221 (1916); **40**, 1361 (1918).

where $b = k_1/k_2$. Now, the amount of gas adsorbed per unit area or per unit mass of adsorbent, y, must obviously be proportional to the fraction of surface covered, and hence,

$$y = k\theta = \frac{kbP}{1 + bP}$$

$$= \frac{aP}{1 + bP} \tag{4}$$

where the constant a has been written for the product kb.

Equation (4) is the *Langmuir adsorption isotherm*. The constants a and b are characteristic of the system under consideration and are evaluated

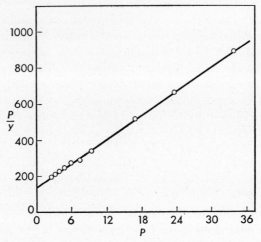

Fig. 3.   Application of Langmuir Equation to Adsorption of N_2 on Mica at 90° K.

from experimental data. Their magnitude depends also on the temperature. At any one temperature the validity of the Langmuir adsorption equation can be verified most conveniently by first dividing both sides of equation (4) by P and then taking reciprocals. The result is

$$\frac{P}{y} = \frac{1}{a} + \left(\frac{b}{a}\right) P \tag{5}$$

Since a and b are constants, a plot of P/y vs. P should yield a straight line with slope equal to b/a and an ordinate intercept equal to $1/a$. In Fig. 3 is given such a plot of the same data as used for Fig. 2. This excellent straight line confirms the Langmuir adsorption equation and indicates its superiority to the Freundlich isotherm. Furthermore, this test, and many similar ones, lend support to the correctness of Langmuir's mechanism of the adsorption process and to his assumption that the adsorbent is covered only by a unimolecular layer of gas molecules.

From a graph such as Fig. 3 the constants in equation (4) or (5) are readily determined by taking the slope and the y intercept. Thus from the plot we find that the slope is $b/a = 22.0$, while the y intercept $1/a = 140$. Hence $a = 0.00714$, $b = 0.157$, and the adsorption of nitrogen on mica at 90° K can be represented by the formula

$$y = \frac{0.00714\,P}{1 + 0.157\,P}$$

TYPE II-V ISOTHERMS

The explanation proposed for type II and type III isotherms is that in these the adsorption is *multimolecular*, i.e., the adsorption involves the formation of many molecular layers on the surface rather than a single one. On this postulate Brunauer, Emmett, and Teller[1] derived for these two types of isotherms the relation

$$\frac{P}{v(P^0 - P)} = \frac{1}{v_m c} + \left(\frac{c - 1}{v_m c}\right)\frac{P}{P^0} \tag{6}$$

In this equation v is the volume, reduced to standard conditions, of gas adsorbed at pressure P and temperature T, P^0 the saturated vapor pressure of the adsorbate at temperature T, v_m the volume of gas, reduced to standard conditions, adsorbed when the surface is covered with a unimolecular layer, and c is a constant at any given temperature equal approximately to

$$c = e^{(E_1 - E_L)/RT} \tag{7}$$

Here E_1 is the heat of adsorption of the first layer, and E_L is the heat of liquefaction of the gas. The isotherms of type II follow when $E_1 > E_L$ and those of type III when $E_1 < E_L$.

Equation (6) can be tested by plotting $P/v(P^0 - P)$ vs. P/P^0. The plot should be a straight line with slope given by $(c - 1)/v_m c$ and intercept by $1/v_m c$. From these v_m and c can be found.

To explain types IV and V isotherms it has been suggested that substances exhibiting such behavior undergo not only multilayer adsorption but also condensation of gas in the pores and capillaries of the adsorbent. The two types arise again from the relative magnitudes of E_1 and E_L. When $E_1 > E_L$, isotherms of type IV are obtained here, whereas when $E_1 < E_L$ isotherms of type V follow.

Although these theories have proved fairly successful in explaining the more complex types of isotherms, they are still insufficient to account quantitatively for all the phenomena observed.

[1] Brunauer, Emmett, and Teller, *J. Am. Chem. Soc.*, **60**, 309 (1938); *ibid.*, **62**, 1723 (1940); S. Brunauer, *The Adsorption of Gases and Vapors*, Princeton University Press. Princeton, 1943, Vol. I.

DETERMINATION OF SURFACE AREA OF ADSORBENTS

The question of the surface area possessed by finely divided solids is important not only in adsorption, but also in contact catalysis and many other fields. Brunauer, Emmett, and Teller[1] showed how it is possible to use the adsorption of gases by such materials for determination of their surface areas, and furnished thus a very powerful tool being very widely used at present.

The B-E-T method is based on the postulate, for which there is considerable justification, that in adsorption of gases exhibiting type II isotherms point B in Fig. 1 corresponds to the adsorbed volume necessary to yield a monolayer of gas on the surface. This point is equal to v_m in equation (6). If such be the case, then the area of the solid per definite weight of adsorbent is given by

$$\Sigma = \left(\frac{P_0 v_B}{RT_0}\right) NS \tag{8}$$

In this equation Σ is the area in Å^2, $P_0 = 1$ atm, $T_0 = 273.2°$ K, R is the gas constant, v_B the volume corresponding to point B, N Avogadro's number, and S the area occupied on the surface by a single gas molecule. The general practice is to convert Σ to square meters per gram or to acres per pound.

For area determinations the gas most commonly used is nitrogen at its normal boiling point ($-195.8°$ C) or at liquid air temperature ($-183°$ C). At these temperatures the area of the nitrogen molecule is generally taken to be 16.2 Å^2.

Another method for determining the areas of solids was proposed by Harkins and Jura.[2] This method involves plotting $\log_{10} P/P^0$ vs. $1/v^2$, where all the symbols have the same significance as before, and taking the slope of the linear portion of the curve. The area follows then from the slope, A, as

$$\Sigma = k \sqrt{-A} \tag{9}$$

where k is a constant for a given gas and temperature. For areas in square meters per gram of adsorbent k is equal to 4.06 for N_2 at $-195.8°$ C, 13.6 for *n*-butane at $0°$ C, 16.9 for *n*-heptane at $25°$ C, and 3.83 for water vapor at the same temperature. This method gives generally very good agreement with the results obtained by the B-E-T method.

[1] See Brunauer and Emmett, *J. Am. Chem. Soc.*, **57**, 1754 (1935); *ibid.*, **59**, 1553 (1937); *ibid.*, **59**, 2682 (1937); Emmett in *Advances in Colloid Science*, Interscience Publishers, Inc., New York, 1942, pp. 1–35. Also the references listed on p. 229.
[2] Harkins and Jura, *J. Am. Chem. Soc.*, **66**, 1366 (1944).

Recently, Maron, Bobalek, and Fok[1] described a procedure for the determination of the surface area of carbon blacks by adsorption of soap from aqueous solution. The method involves the ascertaining of the amount of soap required to cover the surface of a unit mass of the black with a monolayer of soap. From a knowledge of this quantity and the area occupied on the surface by a soap molecule, the surface area of the carbon black can be calculated.

ADSORPTION OF SOLUTES BY SOLIDS

Solid surfaces can adsorb also dissolved substances from solution. When a solution of acetic acid in water is shaken with activated carbon, part of the acid is removed by the carbon and the concentration of the solution is decreased. Similarly, activated carbon can be used to remove ammonia from solutions of ammonium hydroxide, phenolphthalein from solutions of acids or bases, etc. Again, freshly precipitated silver chloride tends to adsorb either silver or chloride ions, depending on which are in excess, while arsenic trisulfide tends to adsorb sulfide ions from solutions in which they are precipitated.

As a rule activated carbon is much more effective in adsorbing nonelectrolytes from a solution than electrolytes, and the extent of adsorption is usually the greater the higher the molecular weight of the adsorbate. Conversely, inorganic solids tend to adsorb electrolytes more readily than nonelectrolytes. This tendency of adsorbents to attract certain substances in preference to others occasionally leads to the phenomenon of *negative adsorption*, i.e., the concentration of a solute is actually increased after treatment with the adsorbing agent. Dilute solutions of potassium chloride agitated with blood charcoal offer a case in point. The explanation suggested for negative adsorption is that the solvent, in this case water, is adsorbed in preference to the electrolyte, and as a consequence the concentration of the solute is raised. However, at high concentrations potassium chloride exhibits positive adsorption, with the salt being adsorbed rather than the water.

Adsorption from solution follows generally the principles laid down for adsorption of gases and is subject to the same factors. As was pointed out, some adsorbents are specifically more effective in attracting certain substances to their surface than others. Again, an increase in temperature operates to decrease the extent of adsorption, while an increase in surface area increases it. Adsorption of solutes, like that of gases, involves the establishment of an equilibrium between the amount adsorbed on the surface and the concentration of the substance in solution. The variation of extent of adsorption with concentration of solute is usually

[1] Maron, Bobalek, and Fok, *J. Colloid. Sci.*, **11**, 21 (1956).

represented by the Freundlich equation, which seems to work better with this type of adsorption than with gases. For this purpose, equation (1) is written in the form

$$y = kC^{1/n} \tag{10}$$

where y is the mass of substance adsorbed per unit mass of absorbent, C is the equilibrium concentration of the solute being adsorbed, while k and n are again empirical constants. By taking as before logarithms of both sides of equation (10), we obtain

$$\log_{10} y = \log_{10} k + \frac{1}{n} \log_{10} C \tag{11}$$

and hence a plot of $\log_{10} y$ vs. $\log_{10} C$ should be linear with slope equal to $1/n$ and intercept equal to $\log_{10} k$. Figure 4 shows such a plot of data on

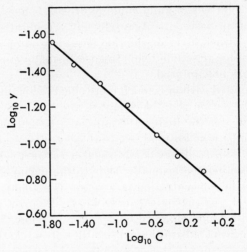

Fig. 4. Application of Freundlich Equation to Adsorption of Acetic Acid on Charcoal.

the adsorption at 25° C of acetic acid from aqueous solution by blood charcoal. In the figure y is expressed in grams of acid adsorbed per gram of charcoal, while C is in moles per liter. From the slope and intercept of the satisfactory straight line we find $n = 2.32$, $k = 0.160$, and hence these data may be represented at 25° C by the equation $y = 0.160 \, C^{1/2.32}$.

ADSORPTION AT SOLUTION SURFACES

Addition of soap to water lowers greatly the surface tension of the latter. Thus the surface tension of a 0.0035 molar solution of sodium oleate in water is about 30 dynes cm^{-1} at 25° C, while that of pure water is 72 dynes cm^{-1}. Substances which have the ability to produce an appre-

ciable reduction in the surface tension of a liquid on being dissolved in it
are called *surface active agents*. In this category are included the soaps,
certain sulfonic acids, and various other types of organic compounds. On
the other hand, some solutes, particularly electrolytes, have the faculty
of increasing the surface tension of water, and these substances are said
to exhibit negative surface activity.

As early as 1878 J. Willard Gibbs indicated that surface activity is due
to unequal distribution of a solute between the surface and body of a solution. By a purely thermodynamic argument he showed that if a solute so
distributes itself that unit area of the surface contains q moles of solute
in excess of that present in the body of the solution, then for dilute solutions q at equilibrium should be given by

$$q = - \frac{C}{RT} \frac{d\gamma}{dC} \tag{12}$$

where C is the concentration of the solution, T the absolute temperature,
R the gas constant, and $d\gamma/dC$ the rate of variation of the surface tension of the solution with concentration. When $d\gamma/dC$ is positive, i.e.,
when the surface tension of a solution increases with concentration, q
must be negative, and the body of the solution is richer in the solute than
the surface, as is the case with many electrolytes. However, when the
surface tension of a solution decreases with concentration, $d\gamma/dC$ is negative, q is positive, and the surface contains a higher concentration of
solute than the solution. The latter is the case with surface active agents.
Positive surface activity, therefore, is associated with what may be considered to be an adsorption of solute from solution by the surface of the
solution, while negative surface activity is due to an expulsion of solute
from the surface.

Equation (12) has been subjected to direct test by McBain and his
co-workers.[1] The results obtained on solutions of phenol in water, which
show positive surface excess, and on sodium chloride in water, with negative surface adsorption, confirm in an excellent manner the demands of
the Gibbs adsorption equation.

INTERFACIAL TENSION AND SPREADING OF LIQUIDS

When two immiscible or partially miscible liquids A and B are con-
tacted, it is found that an *interfacial tension* exists at the boundary between the two layers. This interfacial tension, γ_{AB}, can be measured by
methods very similar to those employed to determine the surface tension
of pure liquids. Its value is generally intermediate between the surface
tensions of the two liquids, γ_A and γ_B, but sometimes it is lower than both.

[1] McBain and Swain, *Proc. Roy. Soc.* (London), **154A**, 608 (1936).

The interfacial tension of liquids is very sensitive to impurities, since these concentrate in the contact surface and thereby lower appreciably the interfacial tension. However, whereas the interfacial tension can be reduced readily by surface active agents, it cannot be increased significantly even by addition of electrolytes.

If a column of pure liquid 1 cm² in cross section is pulled apart, two surfaces are created, each of which is 1 cm² in area. Since the surface tension is also the work necessary to create unit surface area, the work done in pulling the liquid apart is then

$$w_c = 2\gamma \tag{13}$$

where w_c is the *work of cohesion* of the liquid. In a like manner, if we consider a column composed of two immiscible or partially miscible liquids, then it can be shown that the work required to separate one liquid from the other against the acting interfacial tension is given by

$$w_a = \gamma_A + \gamma_B - \gamma_{AB} \tag{14}$$

where w_a is now the *work of adhesion*. These two types of work lead to a very important quantity, called the *spreading coefficient*, and given by

$$S_{BA} = w_a - w_{c_B} \tag{15a}$$
$$= \gamma_A - \gamma_B - \gamma_{AB} \tag{15b}$$

S_{BA} is the coefficient for the spreading of liquid B on the surface of A, while w_{c_B} is the work of cohesion of liquid B. A positive value of S_{BA} indicates that when a small quantity of liquid B is placed on the surface of A, it will spread across the surface like oil on water. On the other hand, when S_{BA} is negative no spreading will take place, and the added liquid will remain as a drop on the surface.

INSOLUBLE SURFACE FILMS

Palmitic acid ($C_{15}H_{31}COOH$) is insoluble in water. When a small quantity of the acid dissolved in a volatile solvent is placed upon a clean water surface, the solvent evaporates and the palmitic acid spreads over the surface until a film only *1 molecule thick* results. The surface tension, γ, of the surface covered by this unimolecular film is less than that of pure water, γ_0. The difference between the two, namely,

$$f = \gamma_0 - \gamma \tag{16}$$

is defined as the *surface pressure, f,* which is the force acting per unit length of the film.

Unimolecular films analogous to those of palmitic acid can be obtained with many substances which are insoluble or only slightly soluble in water. The surface pressure of such films depends on the area occupied per molecule. In 1917 Irving Langmuir showed how the surface pressure can be determined as a function of molecular area by means of a *surface balance*. This apparatus consists essentially of a shallow trough containing water. Near one end of the trough is a fixed barrier extending across the trough and floating on the water. The barrier is equipped with a mechanism for determining any horizontal pressure exerted upon it. Near

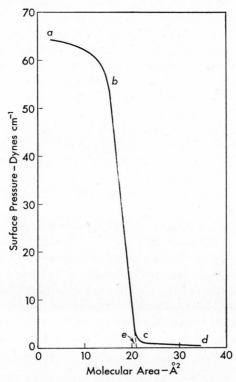

Fig. 5.   Force-Area Plot for Palmitic Acid on Water at 16° C.

the other end of the trough is a movable bar also touching the water and capable of compressing the film against the fixed barrier. If the number of molecules placed on the surface is known, the area they occupy is given by the area between the fixed and movable barriers. Further, the total force exerted on the fixed bar divided by its length gives the surface pressure. By varying the positions of the movable bar and observing the corresponding pressures, it is possible to obtain f values for various areas, σ, occupied by a molecule in the unimolecular surface film.

An f—σ plot for palmitic acid films on water at 16° C is shown in Fig. 5. At large molecular areas, as along *cd*, the surface pressure is low.

Between *c* and *b* the pressure climbs rapidly on compression and then tapers off again along *ab*. The reasons for the observed behavior are as follows. For areas between *d* and *c* the molecules on the surface are sufficiently separated from each other to allow considerable compression without appreciable increase in surface pressure. However, as point *c* is approached the unimolecular film becomes tightly packed, and hence further reduction in area requires considerable force. As a consequence the pressure rises sharply along *cb*. Finally, between *b* and *a* the molecules in the film are so tightly packed that any attempt at still greater reduction of the area causes the film to buckle. The extension of the line *bc* to $f = 0$, point *e*, is taken, therefore, to be the area occupied by a molecule of palmitic acid in a closely packed monolayer on the water surface.

This area of 21 Å² corresponds to the cross section of the linear palmitic acid molecule. Hence the molecules in a tightly packed monolayer must be aligned vertically like straws in a bundle, with the hydrophilic (water-loving) —COOH group oriented towards the water and the hydrophobic (water-hating) hydrocarbon end sticking straight up. That this is the correct picture of the packed monolayer is confirmed by calculations of the length of the molecule, and from it the C—C bond distance. The bond length thus obtained is in very good agreement with values deduced from x-ray diffraction.

Measurements similar to those on palmitic acid have been made on various types of compounds ranging from the higher paraffin hydrocarbons to complex organic structures. By supplying information on the size and shape of molecules, the study of surface films has proved very valuable in the elucidation of the structure of many organic compounds. At the same time considerable knowledge has been gained on the nature of the films themselves. It has thus been found that many substances on the surface behave at low pressures as if the films were two-dimensional ideal gases obeying the relation

$$f\sigma = kT \tag{17}$$

where $k = R/N$ is the Boltzmann constant, i.e., the gas constant per molecule. Other films, on the other hand, behave as two-dimensional nonideal gases, or even liquids or solids, In fact, detailed f—σ plots for some substances resemble strikingly the isothermals for carbon dioxide shown in Fig. 1 of Chapter 3.

APPLICATIONS OF ADSORPTION

Adsorption finds very extensive application both in the research laboratory and in industry. Adsorption of gases on solids is utilized in the laboratory to preserve the vacuum between walls of Dewar containers designed for the storage of liquid air or liquid hydrogen. Activated charcoal, placed between the walls, tends to adsorb any gases which appear due to glass imperfections or diffusion through the glass. Again, adsorption plays a very important part in various aspects of catalysis of gaseous reactions by solid surfaces. This subject will be developed in more detail in a later chapter. Further, all gas masks are merely devices containing an adsorbent or a series of adsorbents which, by preferentially removing poisonous gases from the atmosphere, purify the air for breathing. In a similar manner various adsorbents are used in industry to recover solvent vapors from air, or particular solvents from mixtures of other gases.

As applications of adsorption from solution may be mentioned the clarification of sugar liquors by charcoal, the removal of coloring matter from various other types of solutions, and the recovery of dyes from dilute solutions in a number of solvents. Adsorption has also been used for the recovery and concentration of vitamins and other biologic substances and finds utility now in a method called *chromatographic analysis*. This scheme for estimation of small quantities of substance depends on progressive and selective adsorption of a number of constituents present simultaneously in a solution.

Surface active agents find extensive application in detergents, paints, waterproofing, lubrication, and a host of other fields. All surfaces are covered with layers of either gaseous, liquid, or solid films, and the problem of displacing these frequently becomes very important. Substances that can displace these adhering materials are called *wetting agents*. Wetting agents lower the interfacial tensions by preferential adsorption and permit thereby the wetting of a surface by a liquid. When the wetting involves also a dispersion of the displaced film, we have a *detergent*, i.e., a substance suitable for removal of dirt and grime. Typical among the wetting agents used commercially are aliphatic alcohols, sulfonated higher alcohols, sulfonated alkyl naphthalenes, and soaps of various kinds.

REFERENCES FOR FURTHER READING

1. N. K. Adam, *The Physics and Chemistry of Surfaces*, Oxford University Press, New York, 1941.
2. S. Brunauer, *The Adsorption of Gases and Vapors*, Princeton University Press, Princeton, 1943.
3. W. D. Harkins, *The Physical Chemistry of Surface Films*, Reinhold Publishing Corporation, New York, 1952.
4. A. Weissberger, *Physical Methods of Organic Chemistry*, Interscience Publishers, Inc., New York, 1949, Chaps. IX and X.

PROBLEMS

1. From their critical temperatures arrange the following gases in the order in which you would expect them to be most readily adsorbed by charcoal at 15° C: Ethane, ethylene, *n*-pentane, argon, nitrogen, and chlorine.

2. The following data are given for the adsorption of CO on wood charcoal at
$0°$ C. The pressure P is in mm Hg, while x is the volume of gas in cc, measured
at standard conditions, adsorbed by 2.964 g of charcoal.

P	x	P	x
73	7.5	540	38.1
180	16.5	882	52.3
309	25.1		

Find graphically the constants k and n of the Freundlich equation.

Ans. $k = 0.088$ cc/g; $n = 1.26$.

3. Find graphically the constants a and b in the Langmuir equation which fit the
data given in problem 2.

4. From the results of the preceding problem calculate the volume of CO at
standard conditions adsorbed by 1 g of wood charcoal at $0°$ C when the partial
pressure of CO is 400 mm. *Ans.* 10.5 cc.

5. In a laboratory experiment 50 cc of a solution originally 0.2 molar in CH_3-
COOH was permitted to come to equilibrium with a 5 g sample of charcoal.
At equilibrium 25 cc of the CH_3COOH solution required 30.0 cc of 0.1 N
NaOH for neutralization. Calculate the weight of CH_3COOH adsorbed per
gram of charcoal and the equilibrium concentration of the acid.

6. The following data were obtained for the adsorption of acetone on charcoal
from an aqueous solution at $18°$ C:

y (millimoles/g)	C (millimoles/liter)
0.208	2.34
0.618	14.65
1.075	41.03
1.50	88.62
2.08	177.69
2.88	268.97

By plotting the proper functions, evaluate the constants k and n of the
Freundlich equation.

7. For the adsorption of a substance A from aqueous solution by charcoal at
$25°$ C the Freundlich constants are $n = 3.0$ and $k = 0.50$ for y in grams per
gram and C in grams per liter. What weight of A will be adsorbed by 2 g of
charcoal from 1 liter of a solution containing originally 2 g of the substance?

Ans. 1 g.

8. In the adsorption of N_2 at $90.1°$ K on a certain solid, the following volumes of
gas, reduced to standard conditions, were found to be adsorbed per gram of
solid at the indicated relative pressures:

P/P^0	v (in cc)
0.05	51.3
0.10	58.8
0.15	64.0
0.20	68.9
0.25	74.2

Show that these data follow a type II isotherm, and evaluate the constants v_m
and c in equation (6). *Ans.* $v_m = 57.3$ cc/g; $c = 109$.

9. From the results of the preceding problem find the area of the solid in square
meters per gram, and the value of $E_1 - E_L$ in calories per mole.

10. Using the data given in problem 8, find the area of the solid in square meters per gram by the Harkins-Jura method.

11. At 19° C the surface tensions of solutions of butyric acid in water, γ, can be represented accurately by the equation

$$\gamma = \gamma_0 - a \ln (1 + bC)$$

where γ_0 is the surface tension of water, while a and b are constants. Set up the expression for the excess surface concentration q as a function of C.

12. For butyric acid the constants in the preceding problem are $a = 13.1$ and $b = 19.62$. Calculate q at a concentration of 0.20 mole per liter.

Ans. 4.32×10^{-10} mole cm^{-2}.

13. From the data given in problems 11 and 12 calculate the limiting value of q as C becomes large. (Hint: Assume $bC \gg 1$.)

14. Assuming that the only molecules present in the surface are those corresponding to the excess, calculate from the result of problem 13 the area in Å^2 occupied by a molecule of butyric acid in the solution surface. *Ans.* 30.5 Å^2.

15. At 20° C the surface tensions of water and mercury are, respectively, 72.8 and 483 dynes cm^{-1}, while the interfacial tension between the two is 375 dynes cm^{-1}. Calculate (a) the work of cohesion of mercury, (b) the work of adhesion, and (c) the spreading coefficient of mercury on water. Will mercury spread on water?

16. Using the data given in problem 15, find (a) the work of cohesion of water and (b) the spreading coefficient of water on mercury. Will water spread over a mercury surface?

17. In a surface balance experiment involving the spreading of myristic acid on water, 1.53×10^{-7} mole of the acid was spread over an area 12.00 cm wide and 24.40 cm long. The force exerted on the fixed barrier, whose effective length was 11.20 cm, was found to be 122.0 dynes. Find (a) the surface pressure and (b) the area in Å^2 occupied by a molecule of the acid.

Ans. (a) 10.9 dynes cm^{-1}; (b) 31.8 Å^2.

18. The density of the straight-chain paraffin hydrocarbon n-dodecane ($C_{12}H_{26}$) is 0.751 g cc^{-1} at 20° C. If the cross-sectional area of the molecule is 20.7 Å^2, find (a) the length of the molecule and (b) the average distance between two adjacent carbon atoms, both in Å.

19. At 25° C and a surface pressure of 0.10 dyne cm^{-1}, lauric acid occupies an area of 3100 Å^2 per molecule on a water surface. Assuming the film to be a two-dimensional ideal gas, calculate the gas constant in ergs mole^{-1} degree^{-1}, and compare the result with the accepted value.

8

Colloids

The size of solute particles in ordinary solutions is generally between 1 and 10 Å, or 0.1–1 mμ.[1] There are many systems, however, where the particles are considerably larger and may in fact range from the upper limit for ordinary solutions up to several microns in size. Systems which consist of media with dissolved or dispersed particles ranging approximately from 1 mμ up to several microns in size are called *colloids*. Dispersions with particles larger than several microns are considered to be coarse mixtures. Colloids occupy, then, an intermediate position between solutions of relatively low molecular weight substances on the one hand, and coarse mixtures on the other. The dividing line between ordinary solutions and colloids, or between the latter and coarse mixtures, is not sharp, since many of the characteristics of the systems shade into each other without discontinuity. Consequently classification is frequently difficult, and the designation used becomes a matter of arbitrary choice.

Colloids may be grouped into three general classes, each of which depends on the manner in which the large size of the particles arises. These are (a) colloidal dispersions, (b) solutions of macromolecules, and (c) association colloids. The dispersions consist of suspensions in a medium of insoluble substances in masses containing many individual molecules. Examples are colloidal dispersions of gold, As_2S_3, or oil in water. The macromolecular solutions, on the other hand, are true solutions of molecules so large that they fall into the colloidal range. Examples of these are aqueous solutions of proteins and polyvinyl alcohol, or solutions of rubber and various other high-polymeric materials in organic solvents.

[1] 1 μ (micron) = 10^{-6} meter = 10^{-4} cm = 10,000 Å
  1 mμ (millimicron) = 10^{-3} micron = 10^{-7} cm = 10 Å.

Finally, the association colloids consist of solutions of soluble and relatively low molecular weight substances which, at a particular concentration in each instance, associate to form aggregates of colloidal size. Soap solutions are an outstanding example of this category.

In the following discussion these three classes of colloids and their properties will be considered in turn.

COLLOIDAL DISPERSIONS

Dispersions of all kinds of substances in various media can be prepared, be these substances crystalline or noncrystalline, and be they electrolytes or nonelectrolytes. The particles in dispersion are usually beyond the range of the ordinary microscope, and as a rule they will not be retained by ordinary filters. Unlike true solutions, which are homogeneous, colloidal dispersions are considered to be heterogeneous, with the medium as one phase and the dispersed substance as the other. The medium in which the dispersion takes place is called the *disperse medium*, the substance dispersed the *disperse phase*, while the complete colloidal solution is referred to as a *disperse system*. These terms are analogous to solvent, solute and solution in ordinary solutions. Furthermore, dispersions are thermodynamically unstable and tend to coagulate and precipitate on standing unless suitable precautions are taken. Once a disperse phase precipitates, it will not redisperse spontaneously; i.e., the precipitation of the disperse phase is an irreversible process. Since both the disperse phase and disperse medium may be solid, liquid, or gaseous, dispersions may be classified, like solutions, according to the state of the two to yield the nine types of disperse systems given in Table 1. Actually these reduce to

TABLE 1

TYPES OF COLLOIDAL DISPERSIONS

Disperse Phase	Disperse Medium	Name	Examples
Solid	Gas	Aerosol	Smokes
Solid	Liquid	Sol or Suspensoid	AgCl, Au, As_2S_3, or S in H_2O
Solid	Solid	—	Glasses colored with dispersed metals (ruby glass)
Liquid	Gas	Aerosol	Fogs, mists, clouds
Liquid	Liquid	Emulsion or Emulsoid	Dispersions of H_2O in oil or oils in H_2O
Liquid	Solid	Gels	Jellies, minerals with liquid inclusions (opal)
Gas	Gas	—	Unknown
Gas	Liquid	Foam	Whipped cream
Gas	Solid	—	Pumice stone

eight, since no colloidal dispersion of one gas in another has ever been observed. The names generally ascribed to some of these types as well as examples of each category are included.

Of the eight types observed, those of particular importance and interest are the sols or suspensoids, emulsions, gels, aerosols, and foams. However, as an extended discussion of all these would take us too far afield, only sols, emulsions, and gels will be considered here.

SOLS AND THEIR PREPARATION

Dispersions of solids in liquids can be subdivided broadly into *lyophobic* and *lyophilic* sols. Lyophobic (solvent-hating) sols are those dispersions in which there is very little attraction between disperse phase and medium, as in dispersions of various metals and salts in water. Lyophilic (solvent-loving or -attracting) sols, on the other hand, are dispersions in which the disperse phase exhibits a definite affinity for the medium, and as a result extensive solvation of the colloidal particles takes place. Examples of lyophilic sols are dispersions of the lyophobic type to which have been added, say, gelatin, glue, or casein. The latter substances are adsorbed by the disperse phase and impart to it lyophilic character. For dispersions in water the terms *hydrophobic* and *hydrophilic* are generally substituted for the more inclusive designations.

As dispersions involve a state of subdivision of matter intermediate between true solutions and coarse particles, they may be prepared either by *condensation* of particles in true solution or by *dispersion* of coarse particles into smaller aggregates. Within each of these general methods of preparation are a number of specific means of bringing about colloid formation. Some of these are chemical in nature and involve reactions like double exchange, oxidation, and reduction. Others in turn are physical, like change of solvent, use of an electric arc, or of a *colloid mill* for disintegration of bulk solids. A detailed discussion of the preparation of sols is given by McBain.[1]

PURIFICATION OF SOLS

In preparing suspensoids, sols frequently result which contain besides the colloidal particles appreciable quantities of electrolyte. To obtain the pure colloid this electrolyte has to be removed. For this purification of a sol three methods are available, namely, (a) dialysis, (b) electrodialysis, and (c) ultrafiltration. In *dialysis* the sol is purified by permitting the electrolyte to diffuse through a porous membrane, such as parchment, cellophane, or collodion, which is permeable to molecules of solvent and

[1] J. W. McBain, *Colloid Science*, D. C. Heath and Company, Boston, 1950, Chap. 5.

low molecular weight solutes, but not to colloidal particles. The usual procedure for dialyzing a sol is to enclose it in a sack made of the material chosen for a dialyzing membrane and then to immerse the membrane in distilled water. On prolonged contact with the water the ions in solution pass through the membrane into the water; but the colloidal particles, not able to pass through the membrane, remain behind to yield a pure sol. Sometimes a continuous stream of water is kept passing about the membrane to assure a maximum concentration gradient for diffusion.

Dialysis is, at best, a very slow process, requiring days, and occasionally weeks, for its completion. It is usually not carried to a point where all of the electrolyte is removed, since highly dialyzed sols, by losing too much electrolyte, become unstable and tend to precipitate readily.

In *electrodialysis* the dialyzing process is accelerated by applying a potential difference across the membrane. Under the influence of this applied field ions migrate faster and are thereby removed from a sol much more readily.

Ultrafiltration is a process similar to filtration of an ordinary precipitate, except that a membrane is used which will permit passage of electrolytes and medium but not of colloid. For this purpose the diaphragms mentioned previously, or ordinary filter paper impregnated with collodion, may be employed. Other filter media are unglazed porcelain and finely sintered glass. Since as a rule ultrafiltration proceeds very slowly, pressure or suction is used to speed the process. By these means it is possible to separate, in the form of a slime, colloid particles from media containing electrolytes. These slimes may be suspended, then, in pure media.

PROPERTIES OF SUSPENSOIDS

The properties of suspensoids are best considered under a number of specific heads, namely, (a) physical, (b) colligative, (c) optical, (d) kinetic, and (e) electrical properties.

The *physical properties* of sols depend on whether the sols are lyophobic or lyophilic. For dilute lyophobic sols such properties as density, surface tension, and viscosity are not very different from those of the medium. This is to be anticipated, since such sols, by showing very slight interaction between suspended matter and medium, affect the properties of the latter little. On the other hand, lyophilic sols show a high degree of solvation of the suspensoid, and as a consequence the physical properties of the medium are modified. This is particularly noticeable in the viscosity, which is much higher for the sol than for the medium. Furthermore, the surface tension of the sol is frequently lower than that of the pure medium.

Sols exhibit *colligative properties*, but the effects observed are *very much smaller* than for ordinary solutions. In fact, with the exception of osmotic pressure, the effects are practically negligible. The reason for this lies in the difference in particle size of the two types of dispersions. When, say, 0.01 mole of solute is dissolved in 1000 g of solvent to form a true solution, the number of particles resulting is 0.01 N, where N is Avogadro's number. However, if the same amount of substance is colloidally dispersed in the same amount of medium to form aggregates containing 1000 molecules per particle, the number of particles present will be only $\frac{1}{1000}$ of that present in the true solution, and hence the colligative effect will be reduced by the same amount. In freezing point lowering, boiling point elevation, and vapor pressure lowering such a decrease in number of particles leads to practically no observable difference between the properties of the sol and the pure medium. But the osmotic pressure, being larger in magnitude than the others, still manifests itself, although again considerably reduced below that of a true solution of the same concentration.

OPTICAL PROPERTIES OF SOLS

A beam of light passed through an ordinary solution may be partly absorbed and partly transmitted, but very little of the light is scattered. On the other hand, a light beam directed at a colloidal dispersion has its path through the sol illuminated by the light scattered by the colloidal particles. This tendency of colloids to scatter light is called the *Tyndall effect*, while the illuminated path is referred to as a *Tyndall beam*. We are all familiar with the Tyndall beams shown by dust particles in air when a ray of sunlight enters a darkened room, or with the beam thrown by searchlights or headlights of a car on a foggy night. These are all due to scattering of light either by dust particles or by water droplets in colloidal suspension in air.

Scattering of light is pronounced only when light strikes a medium which contains reasonably large particles. Further, the intensity of the scattered light depends on the difference in the refractive indices of the disperse medium and the disperse phase and is greater the larger the difference. For this reason the Tyndall effect is particularly well defined in lyophobic colloids, where the difference in refractive indices of the two phases is large. However, in lyophilic colloids, where extensive solvation of the disperse phase tends to obliterate to an appreciable extent the difference in refractive indices, the Tyndall effect may be relatively weak.

The ability of colloids to scatter light is the basis of the *ultramicroscope* invented by Siedentopf and Zsigmondy in 1903 for making colloidal particles visible. A schematic diagram of this instrument is shown in Fig. 1. A beam of light from an arc lamp or some other strong source, A, is condensed by the projection lens B onto a knife-edge slit C, whose function it is to control the width of the beam. This beam is focused by means of projective lens D onto objective lens E, which reduces the image of the slit appreciably before permitting the light to enter the cell F containing the colloid. The light scattered by the colloidal particles is observed then through a microscope G, located at an angle of 90° to the original path of the beam. With this arrangement the colloidal particles appear as pinpoints of light moving about against a dark background of the disperse medium. An ultramicroscope can resolve particles as small as 3–5 mμ.

The size of the pin points of light seen in the ultramicroscope is not an indication of the actual diameter of the particles. However, it is possible to deduce the dimensions of the particles as follows. The mass of disperse

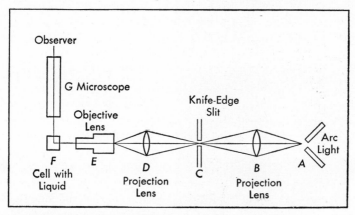

Fig. 1.   Schematic Arrangement of Slit Ultramicroscope.

phase present in a given volume of sol is first determined by some suitable means, such as evaporation of the sol and weighing of the residue. Next the sol is placed in the ultramicroscope, and the number of particles present in a definite volume, as determined by means of an ocular micrometer, is counted. Assuming now that all particles have the same size, that they are spherical in shape, and that their density is the same as for the disperse phase in bulk, the volume of a single particle V follows as

$$V = \frac{m}{nd} \tag{1}$$

where m is the mass of particles present in the volume in which n particles were found, while d is their density. Since the volume of a sphere is $\frac{4}{3} \pi r^3$, the average diameter of the particles l follows from equation (1) as

$$l = 2 \sqrt[3]{\frac{3\,V}{4\,\pi}}$$

$$= 2 \sqrt[3]{\frac{3\,m}{4\,\pi nd}} \tag{2}$$

Using this procedure Burton[1] found that in dispersions of noble metals in water the particle size ranged from 0.2 to 0.6 μ in diameter.

Various other light-scattering methods have been described for the determination of the particle size of colloids.[2] These cannot be discussed here, but suffice it to say that they find extensive application in many fields and in the study of many types of colloids.

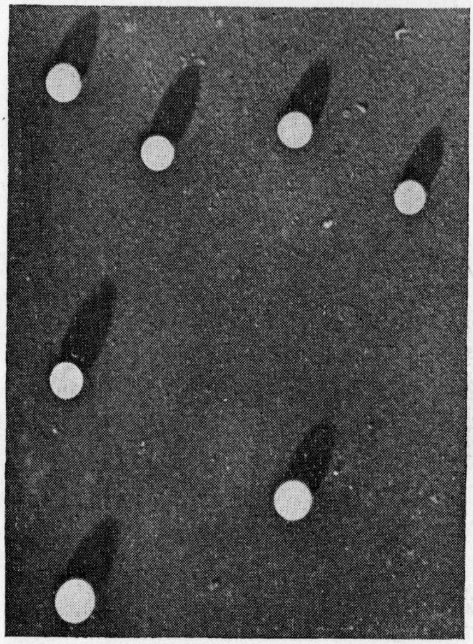

Still another means of getting at the size and shape of dispersed particles is the *electron* microscope. In this instrument a beam of electrons is used instead of ordinary light to observe and photograph the colloidal particles. In Fig. 2 is shown an electron photomicrograph of synthetic rubber latex particles[3] whose average diameter is 2300 Å. With suitable enlargement of such photomicrographs magnifications as high as 100,000 diameters have been obtained.

In certain systems, such as synthetic rubber latices, particle size can also be determined by adsorption methods.[4] These involve titration of the colloid with a soap solution until the surface of the particles is covered with a monolayer of soap. From the amount of soap required per unit weight of disperse phase and the area occupied by a soap molecule on the surface is calculated then the average diameter of the particles.

Fig. 2. Electron Photomicrograph of Synthetic Rubber Latex Particles. (*Courtesy Dr. Allen S. Powell, Case Institute of Technology.*)

KINETIC PROPERTIES OF SOLS

The properties of sols which can be discussed conveniently under this heading are diffusion, Brownian motion, and sedimentation.

[1] E. F. Burton, *Phil. Mag.*, **11**, 425 (1906).

[2] G. Mie, *Ann. Physik* (4), **25**, 377 (1908); R. Gans, *ibid.*, **62**, 331 (1920); P. Debye, *J. Appl. Physics*, **15**, 338 (1944); *J. Phys. and Colloid Chem.*, **51**, 18 (1947); V. K. LaMer and co-workers, *J. Colloid Sci.*, **1**, 71, 79 (1946); *ibid.*, **2**, 349 (1947); *ibid.*, **4**, 163 (1949); *ibid.*, **5**, 471 (1950); *J. Am. Chem. Soc.*, **69**, 1184 (1947); Doty and Steiner, *J. Chem. Phys.*, **18**, 1211 (1950).

[3] Maron, Moore, and Powell, *J. Appl. Phys.*, **23**, 900 (1952).

[4] Maron, Elder, and Ulevitch, *J. Colloid Sci.*, **9**, 89 (1954); Maron, Elder, and Moore, *ibid.*, **9**, 104 (1954).

Graham observed that colloidal particles diffuse much more slowly than solutes in true solution. Albert Einstein and others showed that it is possible to derive an expression for the diffusion of colloidal particles in a medium provided it is assumed that the van't Hoff equation for osmotic pressure applies and that the colloid particles are spherical and large compared to the molecules of the medium. With these assumptions the equation for the diffusion coefficient D, i.e., the number of moles of colloid diffusing across unit area per unit time under a concentration gradient of unity, follows as

$$D = \frac{RT}{N} \left(\frac{1}{6 \pi \eta r} \right) \tag{3}$$

where R is the gas constant in ergs mole^{-1} degree^{-1}, T the absolute temperature, N Avogadro's number, η the viscosity of the medium in poises, and r the radius of the colloidal particles in centimeters. This equation has been employed to estimate from diffusion measurements either r, when N was assumed, or N when r was known, and has been found to hold well for various types of dispersions.

Colloidal particles observed in the ultramicroscope are found to be in a ceaseless random and swarming motion. This kinetic activity of particles suspended in a liquid is called *Brownian motion*. Brownian motion is due to bombardment of the dispersed particles by molecules of the medium. As a result the particles acquire at equilibrium a kinetic energy equal to that of the medium at the given temperature. Since the particles in dispersion are considerably heavier than the molecules of the medium, this acquired kinetic energy manifests itself in a Brownian movement which is considerably slower than that of the molecules of the medium and may thus be observed in the ultramicroscope.

The validity of this explanation of Brownian motion is borne out by mathematical considerations again due to Einstein. He showed that, on the basis of the assumptions mentioned in connection with diffusion, the diffusion coefficient of a colloid should be related to the *average displacement* Δ, produced by Brownian movement in time t along the x axis, by the equation

$$D = \frac{\Delta^2}{2 t} \tag{4}$$

Eliminating D between equations (3) and (4), Δ^2 follows as

$$\Delta^2 = \frac{RT}{N} \left(\frac{t}{3 \pi \eta r} \right) \tag{5}$$

This equation was used by Perrin in his classical experiments on suspensions of gamboge and mastic in water for the determination of Avogadro's number. The displacements Δ were estimated by charting with the aid of the ultramicroscope the positions of a specific particle at various time intervals and calculating therefrom the average horizontal displacements. The radius of the particles was determined from sedimentation experiments in a manner to be described shortly. These data were substituted then in equation (5) to calculate N. From a large number of experiments with particles ranging from 0.2 to 11.5 μ Perrin found N to be 6.85×10^{23}, as compared with the present best value of 6.02×10^{23}. Considering the difficulties involved in these experiments, Perrin's work constitutes an excellent confirmation both of the applicability of the kinetic theory to colloids and of the postulated nature of Brownian motion.

SEDIMENTATION OF SUSPENSOIDS

Although colloidal dispersions may be stable over long periods of time, sometimes years, they nevertheless tend to settle out slowly under the influence of gravity on prolonged standing. The rate of settling can usually be followed quite readily, for the boundary between clear medium and sol is, as a rule, quite distinct. From the observation of such rates it is possible to arrive at the dimensions of the suspended particles and their masses.

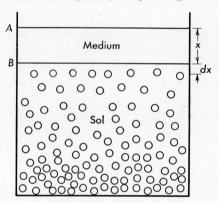

Fig. 3.   Sedimentation Under Gravity.

Consider a tube such as shown in Fig. 3 containing a disperse phase of density d suspended in a medium of density d_m and viscosity η. If d is greater than d_m, the particle will settle; otherwise, the particle will be displaced upward. Any particle of radius r tending to settle under gravity will be opposed by the frictional force of the medium. Now, it was shown in Chapter 3, equation (49), that when equilibrium is established between these two forces a spherical particle will fall according to Stokes's law with a constant velocity v, given by

$$v = \frac{2\,r^2 g(d - d_m)}{9\,\eta} \tag{6}$$

where g is the acceleration of gravity. Since v at a point such as x from the top, A, is obviously dx/dt, the rate at which the height of level B changes with time, equation (6) may be written as

$$\frac{dx}{dt} = \frac{2\,r^2 g(d - d_m)}{9\,\eta} \tag{7}$$

Integrating this equation between the limits $x = x_1$ at $t = t_1$, and $x = x_2$ at $t = t_2$, we obtain

$$(x_2 - x_1) = \frac{2\ r^2 g(d - d_m)(t_2 - t_1)}{9\ \eta} \tag{8}$$

By knowing d, d_m, and η, and by measuring the distances x_2 and x_1 at two different times t_2 and t_1, it is possible to calculate from equation (8) the radius of the settling particles. This is the procedure Perrin used in his experiments. Once the radius is known, the mass of a single particle follows from $m = \frac{4}{3}\ \pi r^3 d$, and the molar weight of the disperse phase from $M = Nm$.

Unless the suspended particles are large, sedimentation under gravity is an extremely slow process. However, it is possible to accelerate greatly the sedimentation by means of *ultracentrifuges*. An ultracentrifuge is essentially a very high-speed centrifuge in which the centrifugal force of rotation is substituted for the force of gravity. By whirling colloidal dispersions in cells placed in specially designed rotors, accelerations as high as one million times that of gravity have been achieved. Under these conditions even finely dispersed sols can be sedimented in a relatively short time. To observe the rate of settling, optical methods have been developed which permit photographing the level of the sol at various stages of settling without stopping the ultracentrifuge.

Since the acceleration of a centrifugal field at a distance x from the axis of rotation is $\omega^2 x$, where ω is the angular velocity of rotation in radians per second, substitution of this quantity into equation (7) in place of g gives immediately the rate of settling, namely,

$$\frac{dx}{dt} = \frac{2\ r^2 \omega^2 x(d - d_m)}{9\ \eta} \tag{9}$$

Separating the variables, and integrating between the same limits as before, we have

$$\ln \frac{x_2}{x_1} = \frac{2\ r^2 \omega^2 (d - d_m)}{9\eta}\ (t_2 - t_1) \tag{10}$$

Through equation (10) r may again be calculated from the values of x and t at two stages of the sedimentation and from a knowledge of the speed of rotation of the ultracentrifuge, ω. This procedure for obtaining r, and therefrom the molar weight of a suspensoid, is called the *sedimentation velocity* method.

An alternate procedure for obtaining these quantities is the *sedimentation equilibrium* method. If a suspensoid is whirled sufficiently long in an ultracentrifuge, a stage is reached at which the sol no longer settles. At this point an equilibrium is reached between the rate of sedimentation and the rate at which the suspended particles tend to diffuse back into the more dilute portions of a cell against the centrifugal force. By equating these two rates, it is possible to arrive at the distribution of concentration with distance in various parts of the sedimentation cell. This distribution is given by the relation

$$\ln \frac{C_2}{C_1} = \frac{M\omega^2(d - d_m)(x_2^2 - x_1^2)}{2\,RTd} \tag{11}$$

where C_1 and C_2 are the concentrations of colloid at levels x_1 and x_2, while $M = (\frac{4}{3}\pi r^3)Nd$ is the weight of Avogadro's number of particles, or *the molecular weight of the colloid*. By determining the concentrations C_1 and C_2 at the two levels x_1 and x_2 in the settling cell at sedimentation equilibrium, M can readily be calculated from equation (11).

Equation (10) is applicable to dilute dispersions of uniform spherical particles, while equation (11) applies to dilute dispersions of particles of any shape so long as they are all of the same size. When the particles are nonspherical, a more involved analysis of the sedimentation velocity data is required. Again, when systems are heterogeneous in particle size, it is possible by sedimentation studies to determine the particle size distribution for the systems.

Most of the sedimentation studies have been made on proteins in aqueous solution and on substances of biological interest. Some results obtained are given in Table 2.

TABLE 2

MOLECULAR WEIGHTS OF PROTEINS DETERMINED BY ULTRACENTRIFUGE

Protein	M (g mole^{-1})	Protein	M (g mole^{-1})
Trypsin	15,000	Urease	480,000
Insulin	35,100	Thyroglobulin (pig)	650,000
Egg albumin	40,500	Hemocyanin (octopus)	2,800,000
Serum albumin (horse)	66,900	Hemocyanin (helix)	8,900,000
Diphtheria antitoxin	92,000	Tobacco mosaic virus	31,400,000
Catalase	250,000	Rabbit virus	47,000,000

ELECTRICAL PROPERTIES OF SOLS

Colloidal dispersions possess electrical properties which are intimately associated with their ability to absorb from solution ions, molecules of medium, or both. Study of colloids has established that lyophobic sols adsorb primarily ions of electrolyte from the solutions in which they are prepared. On the other hand, the particles in lyophilic sols attract onto themselves first a layer of medium to which, depending on the conditions

existing in the solution, may or may not be adsorbed **ions**. Although the
nature of the dispersoid particles determines whether a colloid is to be
lyophobe or lyophile, it is the character of the adsorbed phase on the
final particle which eventually controls the stability of the sol and establishes the manner in which the particles are to behave in an electric field.

Any solid in contact with a liquid tends to develop a difference in potential across the interface between the two. Thus, when water is brought
into contact with a glass surface,
the latter adsorbs hydroxyl ions
and becomes negatively charged
with respect to the water. To
counterbalance this charge, hydrogen ions are attracted to the
surface to form a double layer of
charges, with the negative charges
on the glass and positive charges
in the water immediately adjacent
to these, as shown in Fig. 4(a).
Such an arrangement of charges,
called a *Helmholtz double layer*,
leads to a difference of electric
potential between the solid and
liquid.

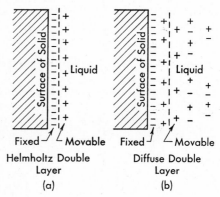

Fig. 4. Helmholtz and Diffuse Double
Layers.

In the original concept of the double layer the charges next to the surface were considered to be fixed, while the compensating charges in the
liquid, along with the latter, were thought to be movable. However, more
recent considerations indicate that the layer is more diffuse in character
and extends part way into the liquid in the manner illustrated in Fig.
4(b). Here the charges shown immediately adjacent to the surface are
probably on the surface, with some of the compensating charges held in
a stationary liquid layer adhering to the surface. The remaining charges
are distributed through the electrolyte next to this layer in the form of
a diffuse and movable atmosphere analogous to the one postulated by
Debye and Hückel for electrolytes. In terms of this concept the potential drop between the surface and the liquid occurs in two parts, (a) between the surface and the stationary compensating layer and (b) between
the latter and the body of the solution. The second of these potential
drops, called the *electrokinetic* or *zeta potential*, is the one involved in various nonstatic electrical properties of solid-liquid interfaces and is the one
responsible for the electrical effects observed in colloids.

Since dispersions of solids in liquids produce solid-liquid interfaces, a
diffuse double layer of the type described above should be established at
the particle boundary, and this should lead to the appearance of a zeta

potential. Further, selective adsorption of ions must result in an electric charge on the particle of sign equal and opposite to that of the surrounding medium; i.e., both the particles and medium must become electrically, though oppositely, charged. Consequently both the particle and the medium should respond to applied electric fields and should migrate under these in opposite directions. This is actually so. When experimental contions are adjusted to permit the migration of dispersoid but not of medium, we encounter the phenomenon of *electrophoresis*. On the other hand, when migration of dispersoid but not that of medium is prevented, we have *electroosmosis*.

ELECTROPHORESIS

The migration of electrically charged colloidal particles under an applied electric potential is called *electrophoresis*. This effect can be followed

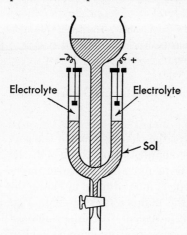

Fig. 5. Burton Tube for Electrophoresis.

readily in the apparatus shown in Fig. 5, called a *Burton tube*. This apparatus consists of a U-tube fitted with a stopcock for drainage and a funnel-shaped filling tube with stopcock (not shown) attached to the back of the U-tube. A solution of some suitable electrolyte of lower density than the sol is first placed in the tube, and the sol next introduced through the funnel so as to displace the electrolyte upward and produce sharp boundaries in the two arms. Electrodes are then inserted, as shown, and connected to a source of potential, such as a high-voltage battery. When the colloidal particles are negatively charged it is observed that the level of the sol falls gradually on the negative electrode side and rises simultaneously on the positive side, i.e., the colloidal particles move toward the positive electrode. Conversely, when the particles are positively charged, the reverse occurs. If the electrophoresis is permitted to proceed until the appropriate electrode is reached, the sol will discharge and precipitate.

By noting whether colloid particles migrate in an electric field and the direction of migration, it is readily possible to determine whether the particles in a given colloid are charged, and what is the sign of the charge. Through such means it has been established that lyophobic colloids are specific in their adsorption of either positive or negative ions. Thus sulfur, metallic sulfide, and noble metal sols are negatively charged. On the other hand, metal oxide sols, such as iron and aluminum oxide, are positively charged. This same specificity of charge is observed also with some lyophilic sols. However, with certain sols of the latter type, particularly the proteins, the sign of the charge depends on the pH (hydrogen ion concentration) of the solution. Above a certain pH value, characteristic for each sol, the particles are negatively charged, while below this pH they have a positive charge. At the pH value in question, called the *isoelectric point*, the particles are uncharged and consequently do not migrate in an electric field. As a rule the isoelectric point does not come at a definite pH but covers a pH range, being, for instance, 4.1-4.7 for casein from human milk, and 4.3-5.3 for hemoglobins from various sources.

Electrophoresis can also be utilized for quantitative measurement of the rate with which colloid particles migrate. By determining the time necessary for a sol to migrate a definite distance under a potential difference applied over a given length of conducting path, the *electrophoretic mobility* can be calculated, i.e., the rate in centimeters per second under a potential drop of 1 volt per centimeter. Such calculations show that the migration velocities of colloidal particles are not much different from those of ions under the same conditions, and are of the order of 10 to 60×10^{-5} cm^2 sec^{-1} volt^{-1}.

Since different colloidal species in a mixture migrate at different rates, electrophoresis may be employed for their separation. For this reason electrophoresis is used extensively for the fractionation and analysis of proteins, nucleic acids, polysaccharides, and other complex substances of biologic interest and activity.

ELECTROOSMOSIS

When electrophoresis of a dispersoid is prevented by some suitable means, the medium can be made to move under the influence of an applied potential. This phenomenon is referred to as *electroosmosis* and is a direct consequence of the existence of a zeta potential between the colloid particles and the medium. Figure 6 shows a simple apparatus for observing electroosmosis. The colloid is placed in compartment A, separated from compartments B and C by dialyzing membranes D and D'. B and C are filled with water up to the marks indicated on the sidearms. When a potential is applied across the two electrodes placed close to the membranes in B and C, the liquid level is observed to fall on one side and rise on the other owing to passage of water through D and D'. The direction of flow of the water depends on the charge of the colloid. For positively charged sols the medium is negatively charged, and hence the flow will take place from C to B. For negatively charged colloids the reverse will be true, and the level on the C side will rise.

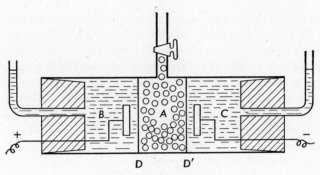

Fig. 6. Electroosmosis.

STABILITY OF SUSPENSOIDS

A question of considerable interest and importance is: Why are colloidal dispersions stable? The answer can be found for lyophobic colloids in their electric charge, for lyophilic colloids in both their electric charge and their extensive solvation. To bring about precipitation of a dispersion the particles must coalesce on collision into aggregates large enough to settle out. In lyophobic sols such agglomeration is prevented by the electric charges on the particles which are all of the same sign, and hence on approach they are repelled by the electrostatic forces between them. The result is that as long as these charges are present each particle is protected from every other by an electric field, and approach close enough for coalescence into larger aggregates is difficult. In lyophilic colloids the same type of electrostatic repulsion is operative, along with the added factor of solvation. The colloidal particle becomes encased in a sheath of solvent which acts as a further barrier to contact between aggregates of disperse phase. Removal of the surface charge in lyophobic colloids would be sufficient to bring about coagulation. In lyophilic colloids, on the other hand, charge removal may decrease stability, but it does not necessarily lead to precipitation. This fact is well illustrated by proteins at their isoelectric point, where the particles are uncharged. Although in this state the protein dispersions are least stable, they do not always precipitate because they are still protected by a surrounding layer of water. However, as soon as this layer is removed by some appropriate means, coagulation takes place, and the protein settles as a precipitate.

The added stability of lyophilic colloids is frequently utilized to increase the stability of lyophobic sols by adding to them lyophilic colloidal substances. These substances are adsorbed by the lyophobic particles, impart to them lyophilic character, and as a result the sols acquire greater resistance to precipitation. Lyophilic colloids used in this manner to increase the stability of lyophobic ones are called *protective colloids*.

PRECIPITATION OF SOLS

To bring about precipitation of a disperse phase, conditions must be created which are opposite to those which lead to stability. For lyophobic sols this means that the charge on the particles must be removed, while with lyophilic sols removal of both the charge and the adhering layer of solvent is necessary.

Neutralization of electric charges on lyophobic particles may be accomplished by an applied electric field such as is used in electrophoresis. The charged particle on coming in contact with an electrode of sign opposite to itself is discharged and precipitated. A more common method of producing precipitation is by the addition of electrolytes, which, though essential in small concentrations for stability, produce in higher concentrations flocculation of the disperse phase. The amount of electrolyte required to precipitate a given sol depends on the nature of both the sol and the electrolyte added. For a given sol the precipitating power of electrolytes is determined primarily by the valence of the ions opposite in sign to that of the colloid. Table 3 gives some results for the precipitation of a positive and negative sol by various electrolytes. The concentrations refer to the minimum amounts of electrolyte required to produce precipitation in 2 hours. From this table it is evident that, although some specificity does exist, the precipitating action of various electrolytes depends essentially on the valence of the anions in the positive sol and on the valence of the cations in the negative sol. Further, the precipitating

TABLE 3

PRECIPITATION OF HYDROSOLS BY ELECTROLYTES

Ferric Hydroxide Sol (positive)		Arsenious Sulfide Sol (negative)	
Electrolyte	Concentration (millimoles/liter)	Electrolyte	Concentration (millimoles/liter)
NaCl	9.3	NaCl	51
KCl	9.0	KCl	50
KI	16.2	HNO_3	50
$BaCl_2$	9.6	HCl	31
		$MgCl_2$	0.72
K_2SO_4	0.20	$CaCl_2$	0.65
$MgSO_4$	0.22	$BaCl_2$	0.69
$K_2C_2O_4$	0.24	$ZnCl_2$	0.69
$K_2Cr_2O_7$	0.19	$Al(NO_3)_3$	0.095
		$AlCl_3$	0.093
$K_3Fe(CN)_6$	0.096	$Ce(NO_3)_3$	0.080

power of an electrolyte increases very rapidly with increase in the valence of the anion or cation, the ratios being approximately $1:40:90$ for the ferric hydroxide and $1:70:500$ for the arsenious sulfide.

Frequently a sol may be coagulated by adding to it a colloid of charge opposite to itself. In the process both sols may be partially or completely precipitated. A case in point is the precipitation of the negative arsenious sulfide sol by the positive ferric hydroxide hydrosol. Again, flocculation can occasionally be effected by boiling or freezing. In boiling, the amount of electrolyte adsorbed by the sol is reduced; and, if this reduction is sufficient to produce coagulation, the sol can be destroyed. Freezing, on the other hand, results in removal of medium. If carried far enough, there may not be enough medium left to keep the dispersoid suspended.

Flocculation in lyophilic sols may be accomplished in two ways. First, if solvents such as alcohol or acetone, which have a high affinity for water, are added to a hydrophilic colloid, the disperse phase undergoes dehydration to yield particles whose stability is due solely to their charge. A small quantity of electrolyte added to the sol in this condition produces ready flocculation. Again, precipitation can also be brought about by the use of sufficiently high concentrations of certain ions. This "salting out" of lyophilic colloids by high concentrations of electrolyte is due, apparently, to the tendency of the ions to become solvated, causing the removal of adsorbed water from the dispersed particles. The "salting out" power of various ions is given by the *Hofmeister* or *lyotropic series*, in which the ions are arranged in order of *decreasing* precipitating effectiveness. For anions this series gives

$$\text{Citrate}^{---} > \text{Tartrate}^{--} > \text{SO}_4^{-} > \text{PO}_4^{-} -- > \text{Acetate}^{-} > \text{Cl}^{-} >$$
$$\text{NO}_3^{-} > \text{I}^{-} > \text{CNS}^{-}$$

while for cations,

$$\text{Mg}^{++} > \text{Ca}^{++} > \text{Sr}^{++} > \text{Ba}^{++} > \text{Li}^{+} > \text{Na}^{+} > \text{K}^{+} > \text{Cs}^{+}$$

However, this order is not always valid. Depending on the nature of the colloid being precipitated, the relative positions of various anions and cations may be changed.

EMULSIONS

A colloidal dispersion of one liquid in another immiscible with it is called an *emulsion*. Emulsions can be prepared by agitating a mixture of the two liquids or, preferably, by passing the mixture through a colloid mill referred to as a homogenizer. Such emulsions prepared from the pure liquids only are generally not stable and settle out on standing. To prevent this, small quantities of substances called *emulsifying agents* or *emulsifiers* are added during preparation to stabilize the emulsions. These are usually soaps of various kinds, long-chain sulfonic acids and sulfates, or lyophilic colloids.

If we employ the term *oil* to designate any liquid immiscible with water and capable of forming an emulsion with it, we may classify emulsions into two classes, namely, (a) emulsions of oil in water, in which the disperse phase is the oil while water is the medium and (b) emulsions of water in oil, in which the functions of the two are reversed. The type of emulsion that results on agitation of two liquids depends on the relative proportions of the two in the mixture. As a rule the one in excess will act as the "outside phase" or medium, the other as the "inner phase" or dispersoid. The exact excess required for the formation of a particular type of emulsion is hard to define. In fact, Stamm and Kraemer[1] showed that emulsions of oleic acid in water can be prepared as long as the proportion of acid in the mixture does not exceed 40 per cent. Once this percentage is exceeded, an emulsion of water in the acid results. The type of emulsion obtained depends also on the nature of the emulsifying agent used. Water-soluble alkali metal soaps and basic metal sulfates generally favor the formation of emulsions of oil in water. On the other hand, water-insoluble soaps, such as those of zinc, aluminum, iron, and the alkaline earth metals, favor the formation of emulsions of water in oil. Frequently the first type of emulsion can be converted to the second by addition of heavy metal ions. Under these conditions a water-soluble emulsifier is converted to one that is water insoluble, and a reversal of phase is brought about.

Whether a particular emulsion belongs to one type or another can be ascertained in several ways. If water is the outside phase, then any water added to the emulsion will be readily miscible with it, while oil will not. Similarly, for oil as the outside phase the miscibility will be with oil but not water. By observing the behavior on such additions under a microscope, it is readily possible to identify the nature of the emulsion. Another means of distinguishing the two depends on the fact that a small amount of electrolyte added to an emulsion will make the latter conducting if water is the outside phase but will have very little effect on the conductance if oil is the disperse medium.

The particle size of the distributed phase is usually larger in emulsions than in sols, ranging from 0.1 to more than 1 μ in diameter. Otherwise the properties of emulsions are not very different from those of lyophobic sols. They show the Tyndall effect, and Brownian motion can be observed provided the particles are not too large. Again, the globules are generally negatively charged, migrate in an electric field, and exhibit sensitivity to added electrolytes, particularly those containing multivalent positive ions.

[1] Stamm and Kraemer, *J. Phys. Chem.*, **30**, 992 (1926).

Emulsions can be broken to yield the constituent liquids by heating, freezing, severe jarring, centrifuging, by addition of appreciable quantities of electrolyte to salt out the disperse phase, or by chemical destruction of the emulsifying agent. Centrifuging is commonly resorted to for the separation of cream from milk and the separation of water from oil. Because of the negative charge of the globules, electrolytes containing divalent and trivalent positive ions are particularly effective in bringing about a salting out of the emulsified substance. The means employed for the destruction of the emulsifying agent depend on its nature. As an example may be mentioned the precipitation of an oil in water emulsion stabilized by a sodium or potassium soap through addition of a strong acid. The acid hydrolyzes the soap to liberate the free fatty acid, and, since the latter is not a good emulsifying agent, the emulsion separates. The same result can be accomplished by careful addition of positive ions which tend to bring about a reversal of phase. If an excess is avoided, a segregation of the two phases will take place before reversal of the oil in water to a water in oil emulsion becomes possible.

GELS

Coagulation of a lyophobic or lyophilic sol yields usually a precipitate which may or may not be gelatinous. However, if the conditions are right, it is possible to obtain the disperse phase as a more or less rigid mass enclosing within it all of the liquid. The product in this form is called a *gel*, while the process by which it is formed is called *gelation*.

Depending on their nature, gels may be prepared generally by one of the following three methods: (a) cooling, (b) double decomposition or metathesis, or (c) change of solvents. Gels of agar-agar, gelatin, and other substances of this kind are prepared readily by cooling a not too dilute dispersion of these substances in hot water. As the sol cools the highly hydrated dispersed particles lose stability, agglomerate into larger masses, and eventually mat together to form a semirigid gel structure that entraps any free medium. The second method is illustrated by the formation of silicic acid gels on addition of an acid to a water solution of sodium silicate. The free silicic acid thus liberated is highly gelatinous due to hydration and sets more or less rapidly to a solid gel. Finally, some gels are formed on changing rather suddenly the solvent in which a substance is dissolved to one in which it is insoluble. An example of this is a gel of calcium acetate. When alcohol is added rapidly to a solution of calcium acetate in water, the salt is suddenly thrown out of solution as a colloidal dispersion which subsequently sets to a gel containing all of the liquid.

Gels may be subdivided into two kinds, *elastic*, of which agar-agar and gelatin are examples, and *nonelastic*, such as silica gel. A completely dehydrated elastic gel can be regenerated by addition of water; however, once a nonelastic gel is freed of moisture, addition of water will not bring about gelation. This difference in hydration behavior seems to lie in a difference in the structure of the dried gels. In elastic gels the fibrils composing the gel are flexible, and on hydration they can expand again to reform the gel. In nonelastic gels, on the other hand, the structure is much more rigid, and though the gel can take on some water, it cannot expand sufficiently to enclose all of the liquid. In some cases, also, heating brings about chemical changes which modify the nature of the substance. An example is the hardening of eggs on boiling, caused by the irreversible denaturation of certain proteins.

Partially dehydrated elastic gels can imbibe water when immersed in the solvent. The amount of water absorbed may be large, leading to an appreciable expansion or *swelling*. Many gels, both elastic and nonelastic, experience also a shrinkage in volume on standing with an attendant exudation of solvent. This process is called *syneresis*. Again, some gels, particularly those of hydrous oxides and gelatin, liquefy readily when shaken to form a sol which on standing reverts to a gel. The sol-gel transformation is reversible and is referred to generally as *thixotropy*. Such reversibility is observed also in gels that can be prepared by cooling, except that the liquefaction is brought about by heating, the gelation by reducing the temperature. The temperature at which the latter type of transformation occurs is usually quite definite and reproducible.

SOLUTIONS OF MACROMOLECULES

Through polymerization reactions it is possible to join by primary valence linkages a large number of relatively low molecular weight molecules into single, giant molecules. Such *macromolecules* may consist of hundreds or thousands of smaller molecules combined into the final structure in a more or less repetitive manner. Thus molecules of butadiene ($M = 54$) can be joined to yield polybutadiene of molecular weights as high as 5–6 million. High polymer molecules of this type are generally linear, with small cross section and very great length. Furthermore, the molecules are very flexible. As a result they can take on various shapes ranging all the way from spheres when completely folded to rods on complete extension. However, the most probable configuration of such coiling chains is neither a sphere nor a rod, but a randomly coiled arrangement intermediate between the two.

High-polymeric materials such as synthetic rubbers, polystyrene, polyethylene, lucite, nylon, etc., are prepared synthetically. But, many high polymers occur naturally, and these include the proteins, polysaccharides, gums and resins of various kinds, and natural rubber. Some of these high polymers are crystalline, but most are amorphous. Again, some are quite soluble in suitable solvents, while others are practically insoluble. Apparently the length of the chain is no drawback to solubility, but cross-linking of chains to form a three-dimensional network leads to insoluble polymers or *gels*.

Polymers dissolve to form true solutions just as do solutes of lower molecular weight. The solutions are formed spontaneously and they are thermodynamically stable. Further, a polymer precipitated from a solution can be redissolved, whereas in dispersions this is not the case. However, because of the large size of the solute molecules the solutions behave as colloids, and this is the reason they are considered here.

PROPERTIES OF MACROMOLECULAR SOLUTIONS

Solutions of high polymers behave in many ways like lyophilic sols. Their physical properties are generally quite different from those of the solvents, and there may be present considerable interaction between the polymer molecules and the medium. Particularly noticeable is the relatively high viscosity of the solutions, especially at higher concentrations. Further, these solutions exhibit non-Newtonian flow at all but the lower concentrations, i.e., the viscosity coefficient of a given solution is not a constant, but depends on the shear conditions under which it is measured. Thus a solution of a polymer in a good solvent may become non-Newtonian at a concentration as low as 1–2 per cent by weight, whereas in lyophobic dispersions non-Newtonian behavior may not appear until a concentration of 25 per cent by volume is reached.

The colligative behavior of solutions of high polymers is very similar to that described for dispersions. The only property measured frequently is the osmotic pressure, although some determinations of the vapor pressures of polymer solutions have been made. Polymer solutions also scatter light and sediment in ultracentrifuges. Both of these phenomena are employed for determination of the molecular weight of the macromolecules, with sedimentation supplying a means of obtaining molecular weight distributions as well.

High-polymeric molecules in solution do not carry an electric charge and hence do not migrate in an electric field, unless the molecules themselves form ions. To do this they must contain carboxyl, sulfonic, amino, and other groups of this type. In the proteins, where both carboxyl and amino groups are present, the charge above the isoelectric point is due to the ionization of the —COOH group, while below the isoelectric point to the conversion of the amino group into an ammonium ion by acceptance of a hydrogen ion from solution. Hence the charge is negative above the isoelectric point and positive below it. Macromolecules forming ions in solution are called *polymeric or colloidal electrolytes.*

Macromolecules can be precipitated from solution by evaporation of the solvent or by addition to the solution of a solvent in which the polymer is insoluble. In the latter instance the largest molecules precipitate first, followed by the lighter molecules in order of decreasing molecular weight. Consequently, controlled addition of a nonsolvent to a solution of a polymer containing different molecular weights can be used to separate the whole polymer into fractions, each of which has a more or less narrow range of molecular weights.

DETERMINATION OF MOLECULAR WEIGHT BY OSMOMETRY

The methods employed most frequently to determine the molecular weights of polymers in solution are: (a) osmotic pressure, (b) light scattering, (c) viscosity, and (d) sedimentation. Since the procedure with the sedimentation method is very similar to that described for dispersions, only the first three will be considered here.

Thermodynamic theory of dilute high-polymer solutions predicts that at any given temperature the dependence of osmotic pressure, Π, on concentration, C, should be given by

$$\frac{\Pi}{C} = \frac{RT}{M} + AC + BC^2 + \cdots \tag{12}$$

where R is the gas constant, M the molecular weight of the solute, while A and B are constants. Consequently, if Π/C be plotted vs. C and extrapolated to $C = 0$, the limiting value of the ordinate, $(\Pi/C)_0$, should equal

$$\left(\frac{\Pi}{C}\right)_0 = \frac{RT}{M} \tag{13a}$$

and

$$M = \frac{RT}{(\Pi/C)_0} \tag{13b}$$

A very common type of osmometer consists of a small glass or stainless steel chamber fitted at the top with a true-bore capillary tube, while across the open bottom is clamped a membrane. The membranes most frequently used are denitrated nitrocellulose or nonwaterproofed cellophane. The chamber is filled with the solution to be studied until the level projects into the lower end of the capillary, and the osmometer is introduced into a larger tube containing pure solvent. The level of solvent is kept just a short distance above the membrane. The entire assembly is then placed in a thermostat, and an initial reading of the solution level is made followed by a final reading when osmotic equilibrium has been established.

The rise in height of the solution level is a measure of the osmotic pressure of the solution.

Figure 7 shows a plot of Π/C vs. C for polystyrene in toluene at 25° C. Here Π is expressed in centimeters of toluene, and the concentration in grams per cubic centimeter. From the graph $(\Pi/C)_0$ follows as 1.77×10^2. To apply equation (13b) the pressure in $(\Pi/C)_0$ has to be converted from centimeters of toluene to atmospheres. To do this we multiply $(\Pi/C)_0$ by

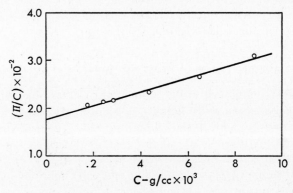

Fig. 7. Osmotic Pressures of Polystyrene Solutions in Toluene at 25° C.

the density of toluene, 0.8610 at 25° C, and divide it by the weight of 76 cm of mercury at 0° C, namely, 76×13.60. For Π in atmospheres and volume in cubic centimeters $(\Pi/C)_0$ is then

$$\left(\frac{\Pi}{C}\right)_0 = \frac{1.77 \times 10^2 \,(0.8610)}{76(13.60)}$$

and therefore

$$M = \frac{(82.06)(298.2)(76)(13.60)}{1.77 \times 10^2 \,(0.8610)}$$

$$= 166{,}000 \text{ g mole}^{-1}$$

If the polymer contains molecules of varying molecular weight, as is usually the case, the value of M obtained is an average given by

$$M_n = \frac{\Sigma n_i M_i}{\Sigma n_i} \tag{14}$$

In this equation n_i is the number of molecules having molecular weight M_i, while M_n is the *number average molecular weight* of the polymer.

MOLECULAR WEIGHTS BY LIGHT SCATTERING

The determination of the molecular weights of polymers in solution by observation of the intensity of scattered light depends on the following equation due to Debye,[1] namely,

$$\frac{HC}{\tau} = \frac{1}{M'} + A'C + B'C^2 + \cdots \tag{15}$$

Here C is the concentration in grams per cubic centimeter, A' and B' are constants, and τ is the turbidity, i.e., the fraction of the incident light scattered by the *solute* in all directions per centimeter of path. The quantity H is defined by the relation

$$H = \frac{32\pi^3 n_0^2 (dn/dC)^2}{3N\lambda^4} \tag{16}$$

where n_0 = refractive index of solvent, N = Avogadro's number, dn/dC = variation of refractive index of the solution with concentration, and λ = wave length *in vacuo* of the light used, in centimeters. Finally, M' is an apparent molecular weight of the solute related to the correct molecular weight, M, by the relation

$$M = M'\alpha\beta \tag{17}$$

The quantities α and β are correction terms necessitated by the size and nature of the solute molecules. The first, α, is called the dissymmetry correction and the second the depolarization correction.

To use these equations it is necessary to determine the turbidity at several dilute concentrations of the solution, n_0, dn/dC, and the correction factors α and β, all for the wave length of light involved. The turbidity is obtained generally from the intensity of the light scattered at 90° to the direction of the incident beam.[2] n_0 is measured with a refractometer and dn/dC with special differential refractometers. The correction α follows from measurements of the intensities of the scattered light at angles of 45° and 135° to the primary beam[3] and β from the ratio of the horizontal to the vertical components of the light scattered by the solute at 90° to the direction of the incident beam.

The procedure for getting M from these data is as follows. First are calculated the quantities HC/τ, these are then plotted against C, and the plot extrapolated to $C = 0$. According to equation (15) this extrapolated value of HC/τ is $1/M'$, and hence M' is obtained. The latter, used along with the values of α and β in equation (17), gives then the correct molecular weight M.

In Fig. 8 is shown a plot of HC/τ vs. C for polystyrene in methyl ethyl ketone[4] at 25° C. When $C = 0$ this plot yields $1/M' = 1.19 \times 10^{-6}$, and

[1] P. Debye, *J. Applied Phys.*, **15**, 338 (1944); *J. Phys. and Colloid Chem.*, **51**, 18 (1947).

[2] See, for instance, Maron and Lou, *J. Polymer Sci.*, **14**, 29 (1954).

[3] Doty and Steiner, *J. Chem. Phys.*, **18**, 1211 (1950).

[4] Maron and Lou, *J. Polymer Sci.*, **14**, 29 (1954).

therefore $M' = 0.840 \times 10^6$. For these solutions $\alpha = 1.25$ and $\beta = 0.961$. Hence

$$M = 0.840 \times 10^6 (1.25)(0.961)$$
$$= 1.01 \times 10^6 \text{ g mole}^{-1}$$

The average obtained by light scattering for M is different from that given by osmotic pressure and is defined by

$$M_w = \frac{\Sigma n_i M_i^2}{\Sigma n_i M_i} \tag{18}$$

where M_w is the *weight average molecular weight*. For polymers containing a distribution of molecular weights $M_w > M_n$. Only when the molecular

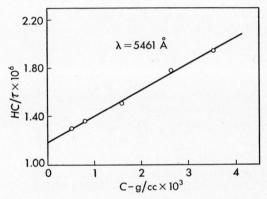

Fig. 8. *HC/τ* Plot for Polystyrene in Methyl Ethyl Ketone at 25° C.

species are all the same, or when the distribution is very narrow, are M_n and M_w identical.

Light-scattering measurements are considerably more difficult and involved than osmotic pressure determinations. However, the light-scattering method is much more versatile. Thus, whereas osmotic pressure measurements are generally limited to molecular weights of solutes between about 20,000 and 600,000, light scattering has been used to determine molecular weights of substances ranging all the way from sucrose,[1] with $M = 342$, to polymers of M greater than 5,000,000.

MOLECULAR WEIGHTS FROM VISCOSITY MEASUREMENTS

Osmometry, light scattering, and sedimentation are absolute methods for arriving at the molecular weights of macromolecules. The viscosity method, however, is empirical and requires calibration, as will become apparent from what follows.

[1] Maron and Lou, *J. Phys. Chem.*, **59**, 232 (1955).

The relative viscosity of a solution, η_r, is the ratio $\eta_r = \eta/\eta_o$, where η is the viscosity of the solution and η_o that of the pure solvent, both at the same temperature. Again, the *specific viscosity*, η_{sp}, is given by $\eta_{sp} = \eta_r - 1$. In terms of these the *intrinsic viscosity*, $[\eta]$, is defined as either

$$[\eta] = \lim_{C \to 0} \left(\frac{\eta_{sp}}{C} \right) \tag{19a}$$

$$[\eta] = \lim_{C \to 0} \left(\frac{\ln \eta_r}{C} \right) \tag{19b}$$

where C is the concentration of solute, expressed generally in grams per 100 cc of solution. Both of these expressions lead to the same value for

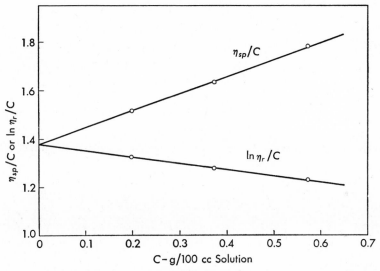

Fig. 9.   Plots of η_{sp}/C and $\ln \eta_r/C$ vs. C for Polyvinyl Chloride in Cyclohexanone at 25° C.

$[\eta]$. Now, the intrinsic viscosity has been shown to be related to the molecular weight M by the expression

$$[\eta] = KM^a \tag{20}$$

where at a given temperature K and a are constants for a specific polymer in a specific solvent. Consequently, once K and a are known for a polymer-solvent combination, M may be calculated from a determined value of $[\eta]$.

To obtain $[\eta]$, viscosities of several dilute solutions of a polymer in a solvent as well as η_0 are measured, and the data are then plotted as either η_{sp}/C or $(\ln \eta_r)/C$ vs. C. Extrapolation to $C = 0$ yields then the intrinsic viscosity. Such a plot for polyvinyl chloride in cyclohexanone[1] at 25° C is shown in Fig. 9. In turn, to obtain K and a, intrinsic viscosities are determined for a series of fractionated samples of the polymer. Next the molecular weights of these fractions are ascertained by either light scattering or osmometry. Finally, log $[\eta]$ is plotted vs. log M to yield usually a straight line of slope a and intercept log K.

When the intrinsic viscosities of polymers heterogeneous in molecular weight are substituted into equation (20), the M obtained is an average dependent upon the value of a. Most observed values of a lie between 0.5 and 1.0. For $a = 1$, M is the weight average molecular weight M_w. However, for $a < 1$, M lies between M_n and M_w, but much closer to the latter.

Because of its convenience, the viscosity method is employed very extensively for characterization of polymers.

MOLECULAR WEIGHTS OF POLYMERIC ELECTROLYTES

The above methods as described are applicable only to polymers that are nonelectrolytes. When polymeric electrolytes are involved, anomalous effects are observed in all the methods unless suitable precautions are taken. It has been shown[2] that in such cases it is necessary to work in the presence of appreciable quantities of added neutral electrolyte, and sometimes also controlled pH, in order to suppress either the effect of the charge or the extent of ionization.

ASSOCIATION COLLOIDS

When potassium oleate is added incrementally to water at 50° C, it dissolves to form potassium and oleate ions, and the surface tension of the solution decreases continuously from that of pure water. However, when a concentration 0.0035 molar in oleate is reached a break appears in the surface tension-concentration curve, and thereafter the surface tension levels off at an almost constant value of about 30 dynes cm^{-1}. Similar discontinuities at this concentration can be observed also in the osmotic pressure, conductance, turbidity, and the specific volume of the solution. It has been established that the reason for the discontinuities is an association of oleate ions into clusters called *micelles*. The initial concentration at which the micelles appear is designated as the *critical micellization concentration* (cmc). Below the cmc the oleate ions exist in solution as individual entities; but above the cmc they are associated into

---

[1] Mead and Fuoss, *J. Am. Chem. Soc.*, **64**, 277 (1942). In the plot the concentration units given in the paper have been changed to grams per 100 cc of solution.

[2] See A. Weissberger, *Physical Methods of Organic Chemistry*, Interscience Publishers, Inc., New York, 1949, Vol. I, p. 494.

micelles of a size sufficient to be classified as colloids. The change from ions to micelles is reversible, and the micelles can be destroyed by diluting the solution.

Potassium oleate typifies the behavior of a whole class of substances known as *association colloids*. These include the soaps, higher alkyl sulfates, sulfonates, and amine salts, certain dyes, long chain esters of glycerides, and polyethylene oxides. Some of these substances yield anions which micellize, like the soaps, sulfates, and sulfonates. Others, like the amine salts, yield micellizing cations. Finally, substances like the polyethylene oxides are nonionic, and in these the whole molecule undergoes micellization. These various types are referred to as anionic, cationic, and nonionic association colloids.

The micellization of an association colloid occurs at a definite concentration at each temperature. Increase in temperature raises the cmc; and, if the temperature is made high enough micellization can actually be prevented in some cases. On the other hand, presence of electrolytes has a tendency to lower the cmc.

The molecular weights of some association colloids at the cmc have been determined by light scattering. The values found range from about 10,000–30,000 g mole^{-1}. Compared to dispersed particles and polymer solutes, micelles represent, therefore, rather small aggregates.

Association colloids are of great practical utility because of the properties which they exhibit. Many anionic, cationic, and nonionic colloids are excellent emulsifying agents, detergents, and dispersion stabilizers. Some also are excellent solubilizers of many types of organic compounds in water. Finally, micellizing substances have been found to be of great importance in emulsion polymerization, where the presence of micelles has been shown to be essential for rapid initiation of the process.

IMPORTANCE OF COLLOIDS

Colloids play such an important role in our everyday life and in industry that a further word on their extensive occurrence is in order. Many of our foods are colloids. Preeminent among these is milk, which is an emulsion of butterfat in water stabilized by casein as an emulsifying agent. Others are salad dressings, clear soups, jello, fruit jellies of various kinds, and whipped cream. Many medicinal preparations are either emulsions or suspensions. Soap, our most useful detergent, is a colloidal electrolyte whose detergent action is ascribed to its ability to emulsify dirt, grime, and surface oils with water and cause their removal by rinsing.

Latex, from which rubber is made, is a colloidal suspension of negatively charged rubber particles. Paints, lacquers, varnishes, and enamels are dispersions of paint pigments or gums in suitable vehicles or solvents.

Silica and alumina gels find application as sorbents for various gases and as drying agents. All of our new plastics and rubbers are colloids, as are the celluloses, resins, gums, and glues. Though this list could be continued, it is sufficient to point out that from dispersions of cellulose alone we obtain such important products as rayon, Cellophane, and paper.

Finally, smokes, dusts, clouds, mists, and fogs are all suspensions of either solids or liquids in gases. Although some of these, such as clouds, are of benefit, fogs are a hazard, while dusts and smokes create sanitary and health problems.

REFERENCES FOR FURTHER READING

1. Alexander and Johnson, *Colloid Science*, Oxford University Press, New York, 1949, 2 vols.
2. P. Flory, *Principles of Polymer Chemistry*, Cornell University Press, Ithaca, N. Y., 1953.
3. H. R. Kruyt, *Colloid Science*, Elsevier Publishing Company, New York, 1949–1952, 2 vols.
4. Mark and Tobolsky, *Physical Chemistry of High Polymeric Systems*, Interscience Publishers, Inc., New York, 1950.
5. J. W. McBain, *Colloid Science*, D. C. Heath and Company, Boston, 1950.
6. A. Weissberger, *Physical Methods of Organic Chemistry*, Interscience Publishers, Inc., New York, 1949, Vol. I, Chaps. VIII, XI, XIII, and XXVI.

PROBLEMS

1. A 1-cc cube of a substance is subdivided into tiny cubes 100 Å on edge. Find the ratio of the final to the initial areas. *Ans.* 1×10^6.
2. If a cube l_0 cm on edge is subdivided into small cubes of length l, find the expression for the final area of the cubes.
3. A solution containing 0.2 mg/liter of a suspended material whose density is 2.2 g/cc is observed under the ultramicroscope in a field of view 0.04 mm in diameter and 0.03 mm in depth. On the average the field of view was found to contain 8.5 particles. Assuming them to be spherical, what is the diameter of the particles? *Ans.* 9.2×10^{-6} cm.
4. The average diameter of the spherical latex particles shown in Fig. 2 is 2300 Å, while their density is 0.930 g/cc. What is the molecular weight of the latex particles?
5. A certain substance in colloidal dispersion is found to adsorb at 50° C 2.45×10^{-4} mole of sodium oleate per gram. The particles in dispersion have a density of 0.930 and are known to be spherical. If the area of the sodium oleate molecule is 28.2 Å^2, find (a) the surface area of the solid in Å^2 per gram, and (b) the diameter of the particles in Å.
   Ans. Area = 4.16×10^{21} Å^2; $l = 1550$ Å.
6. How many dispersed particles of the substance described in problem 5 will be present in 1 ml of a solution containing 10 g of disperse phase per liter of dispersion?
7. Using the data listed in Table 2, estimate the freezing point and osmotic pressure at 27° C of a solution containing 1 g of egg albumin per 100 g of H_2O.

8. Calculate the freezing point depression and osmotic pressure at 20° C of a solution containing 1 g of polystyrene (M = 200,000 g mole^{-1}) in 100 cc of benzene. Assume the density of the solution to be the same as that of benzene, 0.879 g/cc.   *Ans.* ΔT_f = 0.00029°C; Π = 0.0012 atm.

9. The mean diameter of the particles in a certain aqueous colloidal solution is 42 Å. Assuming the viscosity of the solution to be the same as that of pure water, calculate the diffusion coefficient at 25° C.

$$Ans.\ D = 1.16 \times 10^{-6}\ cm^2\ sec^{-1}.$$

10. What will be the average displacement along an x axis produced by Brownian motion in 1 sec on the particles described in problem 9?

11. A portion of a certain suspension at 20° C requires 80 min to fall under the influence of gravity through a column of H_2O 1 m in height. If the density of the suspended particles is 2.0 g/cc, what is the radius of the individual particles? Assume the viscosity to be that of water.

12. How many times that of gravity will be the acceleration of a body revolving at 10,000 rpm at a distance of 5 cm from the axis of rotation?

13. In measuring particle size in an aqueous suspension at 25° C by the sedimentation velocity method in a centrifugal field, the boundary of the suspension moves from a position 10 cm from the axis of rotation to a position 16 cm away in a period of 30.0 min when the centrifuge performs 20,000 rpm. If the density of the suspended material is 1.25 g/cc, what is the radius of the suspended particles?   *Ans.* 3.10×10^{-6} cm.

14. The molecular weight of a substance was determined by sedimentation equilibrium. After equilibrium was established it was found that the aqueous sol was 1.90 times as concentrated at a distance 10.0 cm from the axis of rotation as at a distance of 6.0 cm. The rotor was run at 6000 rpm, the temperature was 25° C, and the density of the dispersed substance was 1.2 g/cc. From these data find the molecular weight of the substance.

15. In an electrophoretic velocity experiment it is observed that a colloid moves toward the negative electrode a distance of 3.82 cm in 60 min when the potential gradient is 2.10 volts/cm. Calculate the electrophoretic mobility of the colloid.

16. Assuming the polybutadiene molecule to be linear, and its cross-sectional area to be 20 Å^2, calculate the fully extended length in Å of the molecules in the polymer when the molecular weight is 100,000 g mole^{-1}. The density of polybutadiene may be taken as 0.92 g cc^{-1}.   *Ans.* 9030 Å.

17. Using the data given in problem 16, and assuming the molecules to be spherical, calculate the diameter in Å of each polybutadiene sphere. Consider the volume occupied by the spheres to be 74% of the total volume.

18. For a certain polymer dissolved in CCl_4 were obtained the following osmotic pressure data at 20° C:

C (g/cc)	0.002	0.004	0.006	0.008
Δh (cm of CCl_4)	0.40	1.00	1.80	2.80

The density of CCl_4 at 20° C is 1.594 g/cc. Find the molecular weight of the polymer.   *Ans.* $M = 1.04 \times 10^5$ g mole^{-1}.

19. At a wave length of 5461 Å and a temperature of 25° C, Maron and Lou obtained the following light-scattering data for sucrose solutions in water:

C (g/cc)	0.0352	0.0614	0.106	0.163
$(HC/\tau) \times 10^3$	2.84	2.91	3.08	3.32

For sucrose solutions $\alpha = 1.00$ and $\beta = 0.935$. Determine the molecular weight of the sucrose, and compare with the expected value of 342.3 g mole^{-1}.

20. At 25° C and a wave length of 4358 Å, the refractive index, n, of sucrose solutions can be represented by the equation

$$n = 1.3397 + 0.1453\,C - 0.00265\,C^2$$

where C is the concentration in grams per cubic centimeter. Find the value of H in equation (16) for a sucrose solution of $C = 0.100$ g/cc.

Ans. $H = 5.74 \times 10^{-6}$.

21. At 25° C and $\lambda = 4358$ Å, the following light-scattering data were obtained for a sample of polystyrene in toluene:

$C \times 10^3$ (g/cc)	0.750	1.670	3.330	5.000
$(HC/\tau) \times 10^6$	2.94	3.51	4.87	6.27

For these solutions $\alpha = 1.248$ and $\beta = 0.970$. Find the molecular weight of the polystyrene.

22. A polymer contains the following distribution of molecular weights:

f_n	0.10	0.30	0.40	0.10	0.10
$M \times 10^{-5}$ (g mole^{-1})	1	2	3	4	6

where f_n is the fraction of the total number of molecules. Find the number and weight average molecular weights of the polymer.

23. The following relative viscosities were measured for a polymer in a given solvent at 25° C:

C (g/100 cc)	0.152	0.271	0.541
η_r	1.226	1.425	1.983

Find the intrinsic viscosity of the polymer. *Ans.* $[\eta] = 1.36$ deciliters g^{-1}.

24. For polyisobutylene in cyclohexane at 30°C $[\eta] = 2.60 \times 10^{-4}\,M^{0.70}$. What is the molecular weight of a polymer whose intrinsic viscosity in cyclohexane at 30° C is 2.00 deciliters g^{-1}?

25. Fractions of a polymer, when dissolved in an organic solvent, gave the following intrinsic viscosities at 25° C:

M (g mole^{-1})	34,000	61,000	130,000
$[\eta]$	1.02	1.60	2.75

Determine a and K in equation (20) for this system.

Ans. $a = 0.73$; $K = 5.1 \times 10^{-4}$.

9

Thermochemistry

Thermochemistry is the branch of physical chemistry which deals with the thermal changes accompanying chemical and physical transformations. Its aims are the determination of the quantities of energy emitted or absorbed as heat in various processes, as well as the development of methods of calculating these thermal readjustments without recourse to experiment.

From a practical point of view it is essential to know whether heat is evolved or absorbed in a particular reaction, and how much, for in one case provision must be made for removing that heat in order to effect the reaction, while in the second case provision must be made for supplying the necessary quantity of heat. Again, the heats of various metamorphoses are required for many types of physicochemical calculations. Thus we have already seen how the heats of vaporization, sublimation, and fusion enter into calculations involving the Clapeyron equation and the colligative properties of solutions. Further, such data are also necessary for calculations involving the variation of equilibrium constants with temperature, the entropy and free energy change, and other thermodynamic quantities. For these reasons it is imperative to consider how heats of reaction are determined experimentally, as well as some of the methods and principles that have been deduced from thermodynamics for evaluation of such thermal changes without appeal to experiment in each case.

The energy units in which thermal changes are usually expressed are the *calorie*, the *joule*, and the *large* or *kilocalorie*. A kilocalorie is equal to 1000 small calories.

MEASUREMENT OF THERMAL CHANGES

To determine directly the heat change involved in a reaction calorim-
eters are employed. A calorimeter consists essentially of an insulated container filled with water in which is immersed the reaction chamber. In an
exothermic reaction the heat generated is transferred to the water, and
the consequent temperature rise of the water is read from an accurate
thermometer immersed in it. Knowing the quantity of water present, its
specific heat, and the change in temperature, the amount of heat evolved
in the reaction may be calculated. Special corrections must be applied
for radiation, rate of cooling of the calorimeter, temperature rise of the
vessels, stirrer, etc. To avoid the latter corrections it is best to determine
the heat capacity of the calorimeter by burning a definite amount of substance whose heat of combustion has been accurately measured. For this
purpose specially prepared samples of benzoic acid, naphthalene, or sugar
may be used. An alternate means of avoiding these corrections is to reproduce by electrical heating the temperature change produced in the calorimeter by the process being studied. The amount of electrical energy
required to do this is equal to the heat evolved in the process.

A similar apparatus may serve also with endothermic reactions, except
that the temperature drop instead of temperature increase is measured.

HEAT OF REACTION AT CONSTANT VOLUME AND AT CONSTANT PRESSURE

There are two general conditions under which thermochemical measurements are made, namely, (a) constant volume and (b) constant pressure. Under the first of these conditions the volume of the system whose
thermal change is sought is kept constant during the whole course of the
measurement. In experiments at constant pressure, however, the system
is kept either open to the atmosphere or is confined within a vessel upon
which a constant external pressure is exerted. Under these conditions any
volume change which accompanies the transformation or reaction can
take place, and the system is able to adjust itself to the constant external pressure.

The magnitudes of the thermal changes obtained under these two conditions are, in general, different. At constant volume any thermal change
taking place must be due only to the difference in the sum of the internal
energies of the products and the sum of the internal energies of the reactants. At constant pressure, however, not only does the change in the internal energy take place, but work is also involved. This work must modify
the amount of heat observed in the calorimeter at constant volume.

The exact significance of both types of measurement can best be obtained by applying the first law of thermodynamics to the thermal change occurring within the calorimeter. According to the first law, any heat q added to a system will in general go to increase the internal energy of the system and to perform external work, namely,

$$q = \Delta E + w = \Delta E + \int_{V_1}^{V_2} P dV \tag{1}$$

Since at constant volume $dV = 0$, no work can be performed. Hence

$$(q)_V = \Delta E \tag{2}$$

i.e., any thermal change occurring in the calorimeter at constant volume must be the change in the internal energy due to the chemical reaction or physical transformation. On the other hand, when the pressure is kept constant,

$$w = \int_{V_1}^{V_2} P dV = P(V_2 - V_1) = P \Delta V$$

and, therefore, $$(q)_P = \Delta E + P \Delta V \tag{3}$$

According to equation (3) the thermal change observed in the calorimeter at constant pressure involves not only the change in the internal energy, but also the work performed in any expansion or contraction of the system.

Equation (3) may be rewritten to

$$(q)_P = (E_p - E_r) + P(V_p - V_r)$$
$$= (E_p + PV_p) - (E_r + PV_r) \tag{4}$$

where the subscripts p and r refer to products and reactants respectively. But, since H, the enthalpy or heat content, is defined by $H = E + PV$, $H_p = E_p + PV_p$, $H_r = E_r + PV_r$, and equation (4) becomes

$$(q)_P = H_p - H_r$$
$$= \Delta H \tag{5}$$

We see, therefore, that the thermal change which at constant volume measures the change in the internal energy of products and reactants, at constant pressure gives the change in the heat contents of products and reactants. Equation (2) defines the *heat of reaction at constant volume* and shows that it is equal to the thermodynamic quantity ΔE. Similarly, equation (5) defines the *heat of reaction at constant pressure* and shows that it is equal to ΔH. The relation between the two is of course,

$$\Delta H = \Delta E + P \Delta V \tag{6}$$

In line with the conventions established in Chapter 2 a *positive value of ΔH or ΔE shows that heat is absorbed* during the process, while a *negative value of ΔH or ΔE shows that heat is evolved.*

THERMOCHEMICAL EQUATIONS

The heat associated with a process depends not only on whether the change occurs at constant volume or constant pressure, but also on the amounts of substances considered, their physical state, the temperature, and the pressure. The effect of pressure on the heat of reaction is usually small; and, since considerations of the variation of heat of reaction with pressure involve a more complete knowledge of thermodynamics than the student possesses at present, they will be omitted here. The variation of heat of reaction with temperature will be discussed later in the chapter. At present we shall consider the effects on the heat of reaction of the quantities of substances involved and their physical state.

The quantity of heat obtained in a reaction depends on the amount of substance reacted and is directly proportional to it. Thus, when 2 g of hydrogen are burned in oxygen to form liquid water, 68,320 cal of heat are evolved. For 4 g the amount of heat evolved would be twice 68,320 cal, and so on. Instead of recording the amount of heat evolved per gram of substance reacted, it is customary, rather, to give the heat for a particular reaction, namely,

$$H_2 + \frac{1}{2} O_2 = H_2O \qquad \Delta H = -68,320 \text{ cal} \tag{7a}$$

Equation (7a) is called a *thermochemical equation*. It indicates that when 1 mole of hydrogen reacts with 0.5 mole of oxygen to form 1 mole of water 68,320 cal of heat are evolved at constant pressure. If it is desired to indicate the interaction of 2 moles of hydrogen with oxygen to form 2 moles of water, then equation (7a) becomes

$$2 H_2 + O_2 = 2 H_2O \qquad \Delta H = 2(-68,320) = -136,640 \text{ cal} \tag{7b}$$

In writing a thermochemical equation it is essential that the equation be *balanced* and that the values of ΔE or ΔH indicated in the reaction correspond to the quantities of substance given by the equation.

Equation (7a) is still incomplete in two respects. In the first place, the heat of reaction given corresponds to a definite temperature, in this instance 25° C, and this must be stated. Second, the equation as it stands does not tell us anything about the physical state of reactants and products, and yet such information is necessary to define the conditions for which ΔH is given. There is not much ambiguity about the states of hydrogen and oxygen, for both are definitely gaseous at this temperature, but the water may be liquid or gaseous. For the formation of liquid water from the elements at 25° C, $\Delta H = -68,320$ cal per mole. However, if a mole of gaseous water is formed from the elements at the same temperature, $\Delta H = -57,800$ cal per mole, the two values of ΔH differing from each other by the heat of vaporization of a mole of water at 25° C, namely, 10,520 cal. To make the thermochemical equation complete, therefore, we write, instead of equation (7a),

$$H_2(g) + \frac{1}{2} O_2(g) = H_2O(l) \qquad \Delta H_{25° C} = -68,320 \text{ cal} \qquad (8)$$

The symbols (g) and (l) indicate that the hydrogen and oxygen are gaseous, the water is liquid, while the subscript on the ΔH shows that the heat of reaction given is for 25° C. In a similar manner the symbol (s) is used to designate a solid phase, while the symbol (aq) is used to represent a dilute aqueous solution.

It is very important that the student appreciate the physical significance of a thermochemical equation. Since in general $\Delta H = H_{(products)} - H_{(reactants)}$, ΔH for the reaction given in equation (8) defines the difference in heat content of 1 mole of liquid water and the sum of the heat contents of 1 mole of gaseous hydrogen and 0.5 mole of gaseous oxygen, namely,

$$\Delta H = H_{H_2O(l)} - \left(H_{H_2(g)} + \frac{1}{2} H_{O_2(g)} \right)$$

As this ΔH is negative, the sum of the heat contents of the reactants must exceed that of the product by 68,320 cal, and consequently when a mole of liquid water is formed from the elements that amount of heat is *evolved.* Conversely, if we were to consider the reverse reaction, namely, the decomposition of a mole of water to form the elements, the sum of the heat contents of products would exceed that of the reactant by the same amount, and 68,320 cal of heat would have to be *absorbed* to accomplish the reaction. It is evident, therefore, that once ΔH for a particular reaction is known, the ΔH for the reverse reaction is also known from the relation

$$\Delta H_{\text{direct reaction}} = -\Delta H_{\text{reverse reaction}} \qquad (9)$$

CALCULATION OF ΔE FROM ΔH AND VICE VERSA

According to equation (6), the difference between ΔH and ΔE is given by $P\Delta V$, where P is constant. The significant factor determining the difference is, therefore, ΔV, the change in volume which occurs during a reaction. For reactions involving solids and liquids only, the volume changes are usually very slight and may be disregarded if the pressure is not very high. For such reactions, then, ΔH is equal to ΔE. In reactions involving gases, however, the volume changes may be large and cannot be disregarded. For such reactions the difference $\Delta H - \Delta E$ can be calculated very simply if we assume that the gases are ideal. If in general we have a reaction in which are involved n_r moles of *gaseous* reactants and n_x moles of *gaseous* products, then $PV_r = n_r RT$, $PV_p = n_p RT$, and, since the pressure is constant,

$$
\begin{aligned}
P\Delta V &= P(V_p - V_r) \\
&= (n_p - n_r)RT \\
&= \Delta n_g RT
\end{aligned}
\tag{10}
$$

where $\Delta n_g = (n_p - n_r)$, i.e., *the difference between the number of moles* of *gaseous products and reactants*. If equation (10) is inserted into equation (6), we obtain

$$
\Delta H = \Delta E + \Delta n_g RT
\tag{11}
$$

The usefulness of this equation in converting ΔH into ΔE, and vice versa, can best be illustrated by an example. For the combustion of 1 mole of liquid benzene, the heat of reaction at constant volume is given by

$$
C_6H_6(l) + 7\tfrac{1}{2}\, O_2(g) = 6\ CO_2(g) + 3\ H_2O(l) \qquad \Delta E_{25°C} = -780{,}980 \text{ cal}
$$

In this reaction there is a contraction in volume from 7.5 to 6 moles of gas, and hence $\Delta n_g = 6 - 7.5 = -1.5$. From equation (11) we obtain, then, for ΔH,

$$
\begin{aligned}
\Delta H_{25°C} &= \Delta E_{25°C} + \Delta n_g RT \\
&= -780{,}980 - 1.5(1.99)(298.2) \\
&= -780{,}980 - 894 \\
&= -781{,}870 \text{ cal}
\end{aligned}
$$

HESS'S LAW OF HEAT SUMMATION

A very important principle of thermochemistry, based on the first law of thermodynamics but discovered independently, was enunciated by Hess in 1840. Hess showed that *the heat evolved or absorbed in a given reaction is independent of the particular manner in which the reaction takes place*. It depends only on the initial and final states of the system and is not affected by the number of steps which may intervene between the reactants and products. Stated differently, if a reaction proceeds in several steps, the heat of the over-all reaction will be the algebraic sum of the heats of the various stages, and this sum in turn will be identical with the heat the reaction would evolve or absorb were it to proceed in a single step. This generalization is known as *Hess's law of constant heat summation*, or simply as *Hess's law*.

This principle makes it possible to calculate the heats of many reactions which either do not lend themselves to direct experimental determination or which it is not desired to measure. In these calculations thermochemical equations are handled as if they were ordinary algebraic equations, being added, subtracted, and multiplied or divided. The manner in which this is done can be illustrated by the following example. Suppose it is desired to find ΔH for the reaction

$$2\ C(s) + 2\ H_2(g) + O_2(g) = CH_3COOH(l) \qquad \Delta H_{25°C} = ? \quad (12)$$

The heat of this reaction cannot be determined directly. However, calorimetric measurements are available for the reactions:

$$CH_3COOH(l) + 2\ O_2(g) = 2\ CO_2(g) + 2\ H_2O(l)$$
$$\Delta H_{25°C} = -208,300 \text{ cal} \quad (12a)$$

$$C(s) + O_2(g) = CO_2(g) \qquad\qquad \Delta H_{25°C} = -94,050 \text{ cal} \quad (12b)$$

$$H_2(g) + \frac{1}{2} O_2(g) = H_2O(l) \qquad\quad \Delta H_{25°C} = -68,320 \text{ cal} \quad (12c)$$

If we multiply now equations (12b) and (12c) by 2 and then add, we have:

$$2\ C(s) + 2\ O_2(g) = 2\ CO_2(g) \qquad\quad \Delta H_{25°C} = -188,100 \text{ cal}$$
$$2\ H_2(g) + O_2(g) = 2\ H_2O(l) \qquad\quad \Delta H_{25°C} = -136,640 \text{ cal}$$
$$\overline{2\ C(s) + 2\ H_2(g) + 3\ O_2(g) = 2\ CO_2(g) + 2\ H_2O(l)}$$
$$\Delta H_{25°C} = -324,740 \text{ cal} \quad (12d)$$

On subtracting (12a) from (12d), we obtain

$$2\ C(s) + 2\ H_2(g) + O_2(g) - CH_3COOH(l) = 0 \qquad \Delta H_{25°C} = -116,440 \text{ cal}$$

and, therefore,

$$2\ C(s) + 2\ H_2(g) + O_2(g) = CH_3COOH(l) \qquad \Delta H_{25°C} = -116,440 \text{ cal}$$

$\Delta H_{25°C} = -116,400$ cal is then the heat of reaction at constant pressure for equation (12).

HEATS OF FORMATION

A substance at any temperature is said to be in its *standard state* when its activity is equal to one. The activity,[1] symbol a, may be looked upon as a thermodynamically corrected pressure or concentration. For pure solids, liquids, and ideal gases the standard state corresponds to the substances at 1 atm pressure. For real gases the pressure in the standard state is not 1 atm, but the difference from unity is not large. In the case of dissolved substances the standard state is the concentration in each instance at which $a = 1$. The enthalpies of substances in their standard states are designated by the symbol H^0, while the ΔH of a reaction where all reactants and products are at unit activity is represented by the symbol ΔH^0.

---

[1] The activity will be defined more fully in Chapter 11. Here the mere statement that the activity in the standard state is one will suffice.

The thermal change involved in the formation of *1 mole of a substance from the elements* is called the *heat of formation* of the substance. Again, the *standard heat of formation* is the heat of formation when *all* the substances involved in the reaction are each at unit activity. Thus the thermochemical equation

$$C(s) + 2 H_2(g) = CH_4(g) \qquad \Delta H^0_{25° C} = -17,890 \text{ cal} \qquad (13a)$$

gives the standard heat of formation of a mole of methane at 25° C. By definition ΔH^0 in equation (13a) is given by

$$\Delta H^0_{25° C} = -17,890 = H^0_{CH_4(g)} - (H^0_{C(s)} + 2H^0_{H_2(g)}) \qquad (13b)$$

where the H^0's are the standard enthalpies per mole.

Were the enthalpies of the elements known, the above information would be sufficient to calculate the absolute heat content of the methane. However, such information is not available. To get around this difficulty, the assumption is arbitrarily made that *the enthalpies of all elements in their standard states at 25° C are zero.* When an element can exist in more than one allotropic form under these conditions, the form most stable at 1 atm pressure and 25° C is chosen to have zero enthalpy. Thus for carbon graphite rather than diamond is selected, and for sulfur the rhombic rather than the monoclinic modification, since graphite and rhombic sulfur are the stable forms. On the basis of this assumption the enthalpies of $H_2(g)$ and $C(s)$ are zero at 25° C provided the latter is graphite. Therefore, $\Delta H^0_{25° C} = H^0_{CH_4(g)}$, i.e., the standard heat of formation of the compound may be considered to be its heat content at 25° C.

The heat of formation of a compound may be obtained either by measuring the ΔH of the reaction involving the direct formation of the compound from the elements or by calculating the heat of formation from heats of reactions involving the compound. For instance, to find the standard heat of formation of $Fe_2O_3(s)$, the reactions

$$3 C(s) + 2 Fe_2O_3(s) = 4 Fe(s) + 3 CO_2(g)$$
$$\Delta H^0_{25° C} = +110,800 \text{ cal} \quad (14a)$$
$$C(s) + O_2(g) = CO_2(g) \qquad \Delta H^0_{25° C} = -94,050 \text{ cal} \quad (14b)$$

are available. In terms of the assumption made above, the enthalpies of $C(s)$, $Fe(s)$, and $O_2(g)$ are zero. Therefore,

$$\Delta H^0 = +110,800 = 3 \Delta H^0_{CO_2} - 2 \Delta H^0_{Fe_2O_3}$$

and
$$\Delta H^0_{Fe_2O_3} = \frac{3 \Delta H^0_{CO_2} - \Delta H^0}{2}$$

$$= \frac{3(-94,050) - 110,800}{2}$$

$$= -196,500 \text{ cal/mole of } Fe_2O_3$$

The standard heats of formation for a number of compounds at 25° C are given in Table 1. With the aid of such a table heats of reaction may be easily calculated. Thus, for the reaction

$$Na_2CO_3(s) + 2\ HCl(g) = 2\ NaCl(s) + CO_2(g) + H_2O(l) \qquad (15)$$

$$\Delta H^0_{25°\,C} = (2\ \Delta H^0_{NaCl} + \Delta H^0_{CO_2} + \Delta H^0_{H_2O}) - (\Delta H^0_{Na_2CO_3} + 2\ \Delta H^0_{HCl})$$

Substituting the appropriate heats of formation from the table, we obtain

$$\Delta H^0_{25°\,C} = [2(-98{,}230) + (-94{,}050) + (-68{,}320)]$$
$$-[(-270{,}000) + 2(-22{,}060)]$$
$$= -44{,}700\ cal$$

Hence ΔH^0 of reaction (15) is $-44{,}700$ calories at 25° C.

Compounds formed from their elements with evolution of heat are called exothermic compounds and those formed with absorption of heat endothermic compounds. The first type is much more common.

TABLE 1

STANDARD HEATS OF FORMATION OF COMPOUNDS AT 25° C

Substance	ΔH^0 (cal mole^{-1})	Substance	ΔH^0 (cal mole^{-1})
H_2O(l)	$-68{,}320$	Ag_2O(s)	$-7{,}310$
H_2O(g)	$-57{,}800$	CuO(s)	$-38{,}500$
HCl(g)	$-22{,}060$	FeO(s)	$-64{,}300$
HBr(g)	$-8{,}660$	Fe_2O_3(s)	$-196{,}500$
HI(g)	$6{,}200$	Fe_3O_4(s)	$-267{,}000$
HNO_3(l)	$-41{,}400$	$NaCl$(s)	$-98{,}230$
H_2SO_4(l)	$-193{,}910$	KCl(s)	$-104{,}180$
H_2S(g)	$-4{,}820$	$AgCl$(s)	$-30{,}360$
CO(g)	$-26{,}420$	$NaOH$(s)	$-102{,}000$
CO_2(g)	$-94{,}050$	KOH(s)	$-102{,}000$
NH_3(g)	$-11{,}040$	$AgNO_3$(s)	$-29{,}400$
NO(g)	$21{,}600$	Na_2SO_4(s)	$-330{,}500$
NO_2(g)	$8{,}090$	$PbSO_4$(s)	$-218{,}500$
SO_2(g)	$-70{,}960$	Na_2CO_3(s)	$-270{,}000$
SO_3(g)	$-94{,}450$	$CaCO_3$(s)	$-288{,}450$
Methane(g), CH_4	$-17{,}890$	Acetylene(g), C_2H_2	$54{,}190$
Ethane(g), C_2H_6	$-20{,}240$	Benzene(l), C_6H_6	$11{,}720$
Propane(g), C_3H_8	$-24{,}820$	Naphthalene(s), $C_{10}H_8$	$14{,}400$
n-Butane(g), C_4H_{10}	$-29{,}810$	Methanol(l), CH_3OH	$-57{,}040$
n-Hexane(g), C_6H_{14}	$-39{,}960$	Ethanol(g), C_2H_5OH	$-56{,}300$
n-Octane(g), C_8H_{18}	$-49{,}820$	Ethanol(l), C_2H_5OH	$-66{,}360$
Ethylene(g), C_2H_4	$12{,}500$	Acetic Acid(l), CH_3COOH	$-116{,}400$

HEATS OF COMBUSTION

The heats evolved in the complete combustion of many organic compounds in oxygen have been carefully determined. The method ordinarily used is to burn the substance in a combustion bomb and to measure the heat evolved. Since heats of combustion are obtained at constant volume, the experimentally measured ΔE's are converted and corrected to ΔH^0's.

The term *heat of combustion* refers to the amount of heat liberated *per mole* of substance burned.

Heats of combustion may be employed directly to calculate heats of formation of organic compounds. If the organic compounds contain only carbon, hydrogen, and oxygen, the supplementary information required is the heats of formation of carbon dioxide and liquid water, the usual final oxidation products of such compounds. The method of calculation may be illustrated with the data on the combustion of propane. For gaseous propane, the heat of combustion is

$$C_3H_8(g) + 5\ O_2(g) = 3\ CO_2(g) + 4\ H_2O(l)$$
$$\Delta H^0_{25°C} = -530,600 \text{ cal} \quad (16)$$

Therefore,

$$\Delta H^0_{25°C} = -530,600 = (3\ \Delta H^0_{CO_2} + 4\ \Delta H^0_{H_2O(l)}) - \Delta H^0_{propane}$$
$$\Delta H^0_{propane} = 530,600 + 3(-94,050) + 4(-68,320)$$
$$= -24,830 \text{ cal}$$

The standard heat of formation of propane from the elements is thus

$$3\ C(s) + 4\ H_2(g) = C_3H_8(g) \quad \Delta H^0_{25°C} = -24,830 \text{ cal/mole} \quad (17)$$

Another direction in which heats of combustion have proved of value is in the study of the energy differences of allotropic forms of the elements. Carbon exists in two crystalline forms, diamond and graphite. When these two forms of carbon are burned, the heats evolved are found to be

$$C\ (diamond) + O_2(g) = CO_2(g) \quad \Delta H^0_{25°C} = -94,500 \text{ cal} \quad (18)$$
$$C\ (graphite) + O_2(g) = CO_2(g) \quad \Delta H^0_{25°C} = -94,050 \text{ cal} \quad (19)$$

Therefore, carbon in the diamond form has the higher heat content, and in the transition,

$$C\ (graphite) = C\ (diamond) \quad \Delta H^0_{25°C} = 450 \text{ cal} \quad (20)$$

450 cal of heat would be absorbed per gram atom.

Further information supplied by heats of combustion pertains to the energy associated with certain atomic groups in the molecule. It has been observed, for instance, that the heat of combustion in a homologous series of compounds varies by more or less constant amount as we pass from one member to the next higher one in the series. Thus for addition of a CH_2 group to a normal saturated paraffin hydrocarbon chain, the increase in ΔH^0 of combustion is approximately 157,000 cal, as may be seen from Table 2. Similar regularities have been observed for other groupings and linkages, and not only in the heats of combustion, but also in heats of formation. As may be anticipated, the thermal increments vary both with the nature of the group and the character of the bond.

TABLE 2

HEATS OF COMBUSTION OF HOMOLOGOUS PARAFFIN
HYDROCARBONS AT 25° C

Substance	ΔH^0 (cal/mole)	Increase in ΔH^0 per CH_2 Group
Methane(g)	$-212,800$	
		160,000
Ethane(g)	$-372,820$	
		157,800
Propane(g)	$-530,600$	
		157,400
n-Butane(g)	$-687,980$	
		157,200
n-Pentane(g)	$-845,160$	

Heats of combustion of some compounds in addition to those already given are compiled in Table 3.

TABLE 3

HEATS OF COMBUSTION OF ORGANIC COMPOUNDS AT 25° C

Substance	Formula	ΔH^0 (cal/mole)
Ethylene(g)	C_2H_4	$-337,230$
Benzene(g)	C_6H_6	$-787,200$
Benzene(l)	C_6H_6	$-780,980$
Toluene(l)	C_7H_8	$-934,500$
Naphthalene(s)	$C_{10}H_8$	$-1,228,200$
Sucrose(s)	$C_{12}H_{22}O_{11}$	$-1,348,900$
Methanol(l)	CH_3OH	$-173,600$
Ethanol(l)	C_2H_5OH	$-326,700$
Formic acid(l)	$HCOOH$	$-62,800$
Acetic acid(l)	CH_3COOH	$-207,900$
Oxalic acid(s)	$(COOH)_2$	$-60,100$
Benzoic acid(s)	C_6H_5COOH	$-771,400$
Salicylic acid(s)	HOC_6H_4COOH	$-723,100$

THERMONEUTRALITY OF SALT SOLUTIONS

Since salts of strong acids and bases are considered to be completely ionized in dilute solutions, it might be expected that, if solutions of such salts were mixed without the incidence of chemical action, the heat effect observed should be essentially zero. Such is actually the case. Thus, when a dilute solution of potassium nitrate is mixed with a dilute solution of sodium bromide.

$$KNO_3(aq) + NaBr(aq) = KBr(aq) + NaNO_3(aq) \qquad \Delta H = 0 \quad (21a)$$

That the exchange indicated in equation (21a) involves no chemical reaction may be seen more readily when the equation is written in ionic form:

$$K^+(aq) + NO_3^-(aq) + Na^+(aq) + Br^-(aq) =$$
$$K^+(aq) + Br^-(aq) + Na^+(aq) + NO_3^-(aq) \qquad \Delta H = 0 \quad (21b)$$

Since the products and reactants are identical, no thermal change is to be expected. If a slight thermal effect is observed, it is to be ascribed to the change in interionic attractions produced by the dilution on mixing.

The principle that dilute solutions of neutral salts of strong acids and strong bases may be mixed without absorption or evolution of heat is termed the *principle of thermoneutrality of salt solutions.*

When a chemical reaction does occur on mixing, the principle of thermoneutrality is no longer valid. Thus, when a dilute solution of barium chloride is mixed with a dilute solution of sodium sulfate, barium sulfate precipitates, and the heat of reaction instead of being zero is actually

$$BaCl_2(aq) + Na_2SO_4(aq) = BaSO_4(s) + 2\,NaCl(aq)$$
$$\Delta H_{20°\,C} = -5800 \text{ cal} \quad (22a)$$

or, in ionic form,

$$Ba^{++}(aq) + SO_4^{--}(aq) = BaSO_4(s) \qquad \Delta H_{20°\,C} = -5800 \text{ cal} \quad (22b)$$

HEATS OF NEUTRALIZATION OF ACIDS AND BASES

When dilute solutions of strong acids are neutralized with dilute solutions of strong bases at room temperature, the *heat of neutralization* per mole of water formed is essentially constant and independent of the nature of the acid or base, as may be seen from the following data:

$$HCl(aq) + NaOH(aq) = NaCl(aq) + H_2O(l) \qquad \Delta H = -13,680 \text{ cal}$$
$$HCl(aq) + LiOH(aq) = LiCl(aq) + H_2O(l) \qquad \Delta H = -13,700 \text{ cal}$$
$$HNO_3(aq) + KOH(aq) = KNO_3(aq) + H_2O(l) \qquad \Delta H = -13,870 \text{ cal}$$

This constancy of the heat of neutralization is readily understood when it is remembered that strong acids, bases, and salts are completely dissociated in their dilute solutions and that consequently the neutralization process involves only the combination of hydrogen and hydroxyl ions to form unionized water. Since this process is the same in all neutralizations, ΔH of neutralization should be essentially constant per mole of water formed. The value of this thermal quantity is $-13,600$ cal at 25° C. Hence

$$H^+(aq) + OH^-(aq) = H_2O(l) \qquad \Delta H_{25° C} = -13,600 \text{ cal} \qquad (23)$$

Equation (23) represents the heat of formation of a mole of liquid water from the two ions H^+ and OH^- at essentially infinite dilution. However, $\Delta H^0_{25° C}$ for the process, i.e., when the two ions are at unit activity, is

$$H^+(a = 1) + OH^-(a = 1) = H_2O(l) \qquad \Delta H^0_{25° C} = -13,520 \text{ cal} \qquad (24)$$

TABLE 4

HEATS OF NEUTRALIZATION OF ACIDS AND BASES
IN DILUTE SOLUTIONS
(Room temperature)

Acid	Base	ΔH (cal)
HCl	NaOH	$-13,680$
HCl	NH₄OH	$-12,400$
CH₃COOH	NaOH	$-13,300$
CH₃COOH	NH₄OH	$-12,000$
HCOOH	NaOH	$-13,400$
HCOOH	NH₄OH	$-11,900$
½H₂S	NaOH	$-3,800$
½H₂S	NH₄OH	$-3,100$
HCN	NaOH	$-2,900$
HCN	NH₄OH	$-1,300$

This constancy of heat of neutralization does not carry over to the neutralization of weak acids by strong bases, weak bases by strong acids, or weak acids by weak bases, as may be seen from Table 4. The behavior of the reactions mentioned is explicable on the ground that in such neutralizations the combination of hydrogen and hydroxyl ions to form water is not the only reaction taking place. Take the case of hydrocyanic acid and sodium hydroxide as an example. In water solution the hydrocyanic acid is practically unionized. Before the hydrogen ion of the acid can react with the hydroxyl ion of the base ionization must take place. Since this ionization occurs while the neutralization is proceeding, the thermal change observed is the sum of the heat of ionization of the acid and the heat of neutralization of the ionized hydrogen ion; i.e., the over-all reaction,

$$HCN(aq) + NaOH(aq) = NaCN(aq) + H_2O(l)$$
$$\Delta H = -2900 \text{ cal} \quad (25a)$$

is in reality composed of the two reactions:

$$HCN(aq) = H^+(aq) + CN^-(aq) \qquad \Delta H = \Delta H_i \qquad (25b)$$
$$H^+(aq) + NaOH(aq) = Na^+(aq) + H_2O(l)$$
$$\Delta H = -13,600 \text{ cal} \quad (25c)$$

The sum of equations (25b) and (25c) gives equation (25a), and consequently,

$$\Delta H_i + (-13,600) = -2900$$
$$\Delta H_i = +10,700 \text{ cal} \qquad (26)$$

ΔH_i is the heat of ionization of the hydrocyanic acid per mole. For the purpose at hand, the slight ionization in water of an acid as weak as hydrocyanic acid may be disregarded.

Similarly may be explained the results on the neutralization of weak bases by strong acids and weak bases by weak acids. In the first instance the heat of ionization of the weak base must be considered and in the latter the heats of ionization of both the weak acid and the weak base.

THE HEATS OF FORMATION OF IONS

For the calculation of heats of reactions involving electrolytes in aqueous solution, a knowledge of the heats of formation of the electrolytes in solution from the elements is required. Such data can be obtained from a combination of the heat of formation of the pure substance from the elements and the heat of solution of the substance in the solvent. The sum of these two is the heat involved in the formation of the substance in solution. Thus, for instance, the heat of formation of $HCl(g)$ from the elements at 25° C is $-22,060$ cal mole^{-1}, while the heat of solution of a mole of $HCl(g)$ in sufficient water to form essentially an infinitely dilute solution at the same temperature is $-17,880$ cal mole^{-1}. Consequently,

$$\frac{1}{2} H_2(g) + \frac{1}{2} Cl_2(g) = HCl(g) \qquad \Delta H^0_{25° C} = -22,060 \text{ cal}$$
$$HCl(g) + aq = HCl(aq) \qquad \Delta H_{25° C} = -17,880 \text{ cal}$$

On adding the two equations we get

$$\frac{1}{2} H_2(g) + \frac{1}{2} Cl_2(g) + aq = HCl(aq) \qquad \Delta H_{25° C} = -39,940 \text{ cal}$$

and this is the heat liberated on formation of a mole of HCl in dilute solution at 25° C.

To present complete thermal data on aqueous solutions of electrolytes, it would be necessary to give heats of formation at various concentrations. The task could be simplified by listing only the standard heats of formation of the electrolytes, i.e., when all the species are at unit activity. However, it would be much more desirable to tabulate standard heats of formation of the ions themselves. Then, for any given electrolyte in water the standard heat of formation would be the sum of the heats of formation of the individual ions. Further, these heats could be used to calculate thermal changes for reactions in which the ions participate.

The approach to this problem can be made through equation (24). Since the standard heat of formation of a mole of water from hydrogen and hydroxyl ions at 25° C involves the evolution of 13,520 cal of heat, this amount of heat must be supplied in order to dissociate a mole of water into these two ions, namely,

$$H_2O(l) = H^+(a = 1) + OH^-(a = 1) \qquad \Delta H^0_{25°C} = 13,520 \text{ cal} \quad (27)$$

If equation (27) is combined with the equation for the standard heat of formation of 1 mole of $H_2O(l)$, we obtain the standard heat of formation of the hydrogen and hydroxyl ions,

$$H_2(g) + \frac{1}{2} O_2(g) = H^+(a = 1) + OH^-(a = 1)$$

$$\Delta H^0_{25°C} = -54,800 \text{ cal} \quad (28)$$

This sum cannot be resolved at present without some assumption with respect to the heat of formation of one of these ions. The convention generally adopted is that *the heat of formation of the hydrogen ion in aqueous solution is zero at 25° C and unit activity*, i.e., that for the reaction

$$\frac{1}{2} H_2(g) = H^+(a = 1) \qquad \Delta H^0_{25°C} = 0 \quad (29)$$

With this convention equation (28) gives directly the heat of formation of the hydroxyl ion, or

$$\frac{1}{2} H_2(g) + \frac{1}{2} O_2(g) = OH^-(a = 1) \qquad \Delta H^0_{25°C} = -54,800 \text{ cal} \quad (30)$$

Once the heats of formation of these two ions are known, those for other ions may be readily calculated. Since the standard heat of formation of HCl in water at 25° C is $\Delta H^0 = -39,900$ cal, and since $\Delta H^0 = 0$ for H^+, $\Delta H^0 = -39,900$ cal must represent the heat of formation of the chloride ion. Again in the reaction

$$Na(s) + \frac{1}{2} O_2(g) + \frac{1}{2} H_2(g) = Na^+(a = 1) + OH^-(a = 1)$$

$$\Delta H^0_{25°C} = -112,300 \text{ cal} \quad (31)$$

Combining this equation with (30), we see that

$$-112{,}300 = \Delta H^0_{Na^+} + \Delta H^0_{OH^-}$$
$$= \Delta H^0_{Na^+} - 54{,}800$$
$$\Delta H^0_{Na^+} = -57{,}500 \text{ cal at } 25°\text{ C}$$

By similar procedures have been evaluated the heats of formation of many other ions in aqueous solution. Some of these are summarized in Table 5. The use of this table in the calculation of heats of reactions in-

TABLE 5

STANDARD HEATS OF FORMATION OF IONS AT 25° C

Ion	ΔH^0 cal (g ion)$^{-1}$	Ion	ΔH^0 cal (g ion)$^{-1}$
H^+	0	Cd^{++}	$-17{,}600$
Li^+	$-66{,}600$	Hg^{++}	$+41{,}600$
Na^+	$-57{,}500$	Pb^{++}	-200
K^+	$-60{,}300$	OH^-	$-54{,}800$
NH_4^+	$-31{,}500$	Cl^-	$-39{,}900$
Ag^+	$+25{,}200$	Br^-	$-28{,}700$
Hg^+	$+20{,}100$	I^-	$-13{,}600$
Mg^{++}	$-110{,}200$	HSO_4^-	$-213{,}300$
Ca^{++}	$-129{,}500$	NO_3^-	$-49{,}500$
Sr^{++}	$-130{,}000$	HCO_3^-	$-164{,}800$
Ba^{++}	$-128{,}400$	CH_3COO^-	$-117{,}600$
Mn^{++}	$-49{,}200$	S^{--}	$+10{,}000$
Fe^{++}	$-20{,}600$	SO_3^{--}	$-149{,}000$
Co^{++}	$-16{,}500$	SO_4^{--}	$-216{,}300$
Ni^{++}	$-15{,}200$	CO_3^{--}	$-160{,}500$
Zn^{++}	$-36{,}300$	PO_4^{---}	$-254{,}500$

volving strong acids, bases, or salts in aqueous solutions can best be shown by an example. Suppose it is desired to calculate ΔH^0 for the reaction

$$\frac{1}{2} H_2(g) + AgCl(s) = Ag(s) + H^+(a = 1) + Cl^-(a = 1)$$

$$\Delta H^0_{25°C} = ? \quad (32)$$

Since the enthalpies of $H_2(g)$, $Ag(s)$, and H^+ are all zero, ΔH^0 is given by

$$\Delta H^0 = \Delta H^0_{Cl^-} - \Delta H^0_{AgCl(s)}$$

On inserting the value of $\Delta H^0_{Cl^-}$ from Table 5 and $\Delta H^0_{AgCl(s)}$ from Table 1, we get

$$\Delta H^0_{25°C} = -39{,}900 - (-30{,}360)$$
$$= -9540 \text{ cal}$$

INTEGRAL HEATS OF SOLUTION AND DILUTION

Solution of a substance in a solvent is accompanied by absorption or evolution of heat, and this thermal effect is termed the *integral heat of solution* of the substance. Per mole of dissolved substance the integral heat of solution at any given temperature depends upon the amount of solvent in which solution takes place, as may be seen from Table 6. For

TABLE 6

INTEGRAL HEATS OF SOLUTION OF 1 MOLE OF H_2SO_4
IN WATER AT 18° C

Moles of Water (n_1)	ΔH (cal)
0.00	0
0.11	−920
0.25	−1,970
0.43	−3,300
0.67	−4,890
1.00	−6,740
1.50	−8,630
2.33	−10,680
4.00	−13,010
9.00	−15,110
19.00	−16,900
∞	−20,200

this reason it is essential to specify the number of moles of solvent per mole of solute in giving a heat of solution, as in the following:

$$H_2SO_4(l) + 9\ H_2O(l) = H_2SO_4(9\ H_2O) \qquad \Delta H_{18°C} = -15,110\ \text{cal} \qquad (33)$$

However, when the amount of solvent per mole of substance is large, it is usually found that further dilution will produce no significant thermal effect. Once this state of a dilute solution has been reached, the symbol *aq* is employed to indicate this fact. Thus the limiting value of the integral heats of solution in Table 6 would be represented by

$$H_2SO_4(l) + aq = H_2SO_4(aq) \qquad \Delta H_{18°C} = -20,200\ \text{cal} \qquad (34)$$

The difference between any two integral heats of solution gives the heat involved in the *dilution* of a substance from the initial state to the final state and is termed the *integral heat of dilution* of the substance. According to Table 6 the heat recoverable on diluting with 8 moles of water a solution containing 1 mole of sulfuric acid in 1 mole of water is

$$H_2SO_4(1\ H_2O) + 8\ H_2O(l) = H_2SO_4(9\ H_2O)$$
$$\Delta H_{18°C} = -15,110 - (-6740) = -8370\ \text{cal} \qquad (35)$$

Similarly, the heat evolved on diluting the same solution with a very large quantity of water is

$$H_2SO_4(1\ H_2O) + aq = H_2SO_4(aq)$$
$$\Delta H_{18°C} = -20{,}200 + 6740 = -13{,}460\ \text{cal} \quad (36)$$

The latter value represents the maximum heat obtainable from dilution of the given solution.

DIFFERENTIAL HEATS OF SOLUTION AND DILUTION

The integral heat of solution, ΔH, obtained on solution of n_2 moles of solute in n_1 moles of solvent at constant temperature and pressure will depend on the values of both n_1 and n_2; i.e.,

$$\Delta H = f(n_1, n_2) \quad (37)$$

Differentiation of this expression yields

$$d(\Delta H) = \left[\frac{\partial(\Delta H)}{\partial n_1}\right]_{n_2} dn_1 + \left[\frac{\partial(\Delta H)}{\partial n_2}\right]_{n_1} dn_2$$
$$= \overline{\Delta H}_1 dn_1 + \overline{\Delta H}_2 dn_2 \quad (38)$$

where $\overline{\Delta H}_1 = [\partial(\Delta H)/\partial n_1]_{n_2}$ and $\overline{\Delta H}_2 = [\partial(\Delta H)/\partial n_2]_{n_1}$. The quantities $\overline{\Delta H}_1$ and $\overline{\Delta H}_2$ are called respectively the *differential heats of solution* of solvent and solute. $\overline{\Delta H}_1$ is the change in the heat of solution produced when *one mole* of solvent is added to a quantity of solution so large that its addition produces no significant change in the concentration of the solution. Likewise $\overline{\Delta H}_2$ is the change produced in the heat of solution on addition of *one mole* of solute under the same conditions. From the thermodynamics of solutions it can be shown that

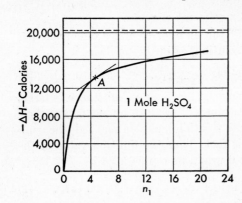

Fig. 1. Integral Heat of Solution of H_2SO_4 in Water at 18° C.

$$\Delta H = \overline{\Delta H}_1 n_1 + \overline{\Delta H}_2 n_2 \quad (39)$$

The differential heats of solution can be obtained from the integral heats in a number of ways, only one of which will be indicated here. Consider a plot of the data in Table 6 shown in Fig. 1. The derivative of this curve at any point such as A is $[\partial(\Delta H)/\partial n_1]_{n_2}$, where $n_2 = 1$ mole. Hence the slope of the tangent to the curve at point A is $\overline{\Delta H}_1$. With $\overline{\Delta H}_1$ known, equation (39) can be used to find $\overline{\Delta H}_2$. On the other hand, if we were to prepare a plot of ΔH as a function of n_2 at some constant n_1, say 1 mole, then the derivative of the curve at any point would yield $\overline{\Delta H}_2$ directly.

The *differential heat of dilution* of the solvent is the difference between the $\overline{\Delta H}_1$ values for two different concentrations, namely,

$$(\overline{\Delta H}_1)_d = (\overline{\Delta H}_1)_2 - (\overline{\Delta H}_1)_1 \tag{40}$$

where the subscripts 1 and 2 outside the parentheses represent respectively initial and final concentrations. Similarly, the differential heat of dilution of the solute is

$$(\overline{\Delta H}_2)_d = (\overline{\Delta H}_2)_2 - (\overline{\Delta H}_2)_1 \tag{41}$$

HEATS OF HYDRATION

Integral heats of solution may also be employed to calculate *heats of hydration*, i.e., the heats for reactions of the type

$$CaCl_2(s) + 2\ H_2O(l) = CaCl_2 \cdot 2\ H_2O(s) \tag{42}$$
$$CaCl_2 \cdot 2\ H_2O(s) + 2\ H_2O(l) = CaCl_2 \cdot 4\ H_2O(s) \tag{43}$$

The integral heats of solution at 18° C for the various solid modifications of calcium chloride in the indicated quantities of water are given by

$$CaCl_2(s) + 400\ H_2O(l) = CaCl_2(400\ H_2O) \qquad \Delta H = -17{,}990\ \text{cal} \tag{44}$$
$$CaCl_2 \cdot 2\ H_2O(s) + 398\ H_2O(l) = CaCl_2(400\ H_2O)$$
$$\Delta H = -10{,}030\ \text{cal} \tag{45}$$
$$CaCl_2 \cdot 4\ H_2O(s) + 396\ H_2O(l) = CaCl_2(400\ H_2O)$$
$$\Delta H = -1830\ \text{cal} \tag{46}$$
$$CaCl_2 \cdot 6\ H_2O(s) + 394\ H_2O(l) = CaCl_2(400\ H_2O)$$
$$\Delta H = +4560\ \text{cal} \tag{47}$$

It will be noticed that all the final solutions formed are the same. Consequently the difference between any two of the equations (44) to (47) gives directly the *heat of hydration* of one solid phase to another. Thus, equation (44) minus equation (45) yields

$$CaCl_2(s) + 2\ H_2O(l) = CaCl_2 \cdot 2\ H_2O(s) \qquad \Delta H = -7960\ \text{cal} \tag{48}$$

Similarly, equations (45) − (46) and equations (46) − (47) give

$$CaCl_2 \cdot 2\ H_2O(s) + 2\ H_2O(l) = CaCl_2 \cdot 4\ H_2O(s)$$
$$\Delta H = -8200\ \text{cal} \tag{49}$$
$$CaCl_2 \cdot 4\ H_2O(s) + 2\ H_2O(l) = CaCl_2 \cdot 6\ H_2O(s)$$
$$\Delta H = -6390\ \text{cal} \tag{50}$$

On the other hand, the heat evolved in the direct hydration of $CaCl_2(s)$

to $CaCl_2 \cdot 6 \ H_2O(s)$ follows from the difference between equations (44) and (47), namely,

$$CaCl_2(s) + 6 \ H_2O(l) = CaCl_2 \cdot 6 \ H_2O(s) \qquad \Delta H = -22,500 \ cal \quad (51)$$

Equations (44) to (47) emphasize the influence of the nature of the solid phase on the heat of solution. Whereas a mole of anhydrous calcium chloride will dissolve in water with the *evolution* of a large quantity of heat, dissolution of a mole of $CaCl_2 \cdot 6 \ H_2O$ can take place only with the *absorption* of 4560 cal of heat per mole of salt. The difference in the two heats of solution is due, of course, to the heat of hydration of $CaCl_2(s)$ and is given by equation (51).

OTHER HEATS OF REACTION

There are many types of heats of reaction besides those mentioned. Some of these have been discussed in other chapters, as heats of fusion, vaporization, and sublimation. Others, like heats of dissociation, hydrogenation, and polymerization are merely particular types of heats of reaction. All of them are subject to the same treatment and thermodynamic requirements as the heats discussed in this chapter.

VARIATION OF HEAT OF REACTION WITH TEMPERATURE

The heat of a reaction obtained calorimetrically or by calculation from heats of formation corresponds to some one definite temperature. At other temperatures the heat of the reaction will in general not be the same. As reactions are carried out at various temperatures, it is very frequently necessary to know heats of reaction at temperatures other than those at which they were determined. A method of calculating the heat of reaction at one temperature from that at another is, therefore, highly desirable.

In such calculations heat capacities play a very important part, and hence a word about these is in order. We have seen that there are two types of heat capacities, C_p and C_v. For gases $C_p - C_v = R$ cal per mole. On the other hand, since the volume changes accompanying the heating of solids and liquids are small, these two heat capacities may be taken as essentially equal for these. Furthermore, heat capacities vary with temperature. This variation is generally expressed by empirical formulas of the type

$$C_p = a + bT + cT^2 + dT^3 \quad \text{cal mole}^{-1} \text{ degree}^{-1} \qquad (52)$$

or $$C_p = a' + b'T + \frac{c'}{T^2} \quad \text{cal mole}^{-1} \text{ degree}^{-1} \qquad (53)$$

TABLE 7

CONSTANTS FOR MOLAR HEAT CAPACITY EQUATIONS OF VARIOUS SUBSTANCES*

Substance	Range (°K)	a	$b \times 10^3$	$c \times 10^7$	$d \times 10^9$
$H_2(g)$	300–2500	6.62	0.81		
$N_2(g)$	300–2500	6.76	0.606	1.3	
$O_2(g)$	300–2500	6.76	0.606	1.3	
$CO(g)$	300–2500	6.60	1.2		
$HCl(g)$	300–1500	6.70	0.84		
$H_2O(g)$	300–1500	7.219	2.374	2.67	
$H_2S(g)$	300–1800	6.955	3.675	7.40	−0.585
$NH_3(g)$	300–1000	6.189	7.887	−7.28	
$CO_2(g)$	300–1500	5.166	15.177	−95.78	2.260
$CH_4(g)$	300–1500	3.422	17.845	−41.65	
$C_2H_4(g)$	300–1500	2.706	29.160	−90.59	
$C_2H_6(g)$	300–1000	1.375	41.852	−138.27	
		a'	$b' \times 10^3$	$c' \times 10^{-5}$	
$Cl_2(g)$	300–1500	8.76	0.271	−0.656	
$NO(g)$	300–2500	8.05	0.233	−1.56	
$C(s, graphite)$	300–1400	2.673	2.617	−1.169	
$C(s, diamond)$	300–1300	2.162	3.059	−1.303	

* For compilations of such data see: Spencer and Justice, *J. Am. Chem. Soc.*, **56**, 2311 (1934); Spencer and Flannagan, *ibid.*, **64**, 2511 (1942); H. M. Spencer, *Ind. Eng. Chem.*, **40**, 2152 (1948); and K. K. Kelley, U.S. Bureau of Mines Bulletins No. 371 (1934), No. 383 (1935), No. 384 (1935), No. 406 (1937), and No. 407 (1937).

where a, b, c, and d, or a', b', and c', are constants for a given substance. Values of these constants for various substances are given in Table 7. The temperature range over which the constants hold is also indicated.

The differential equation for the variation of heat of reaction with temperature may be obtained as follows. Since

$$\Delta H = H_{\text{products}} - H_{\text{reactants}} \qquad (54)$$

differentiation of both sides with respect to absolute temperature at constant pressure yields

$$\left[\frac{\partial(\Delta H)}{\partial T}\right]_P = \left[\frac{\partial H_{\text{products}}}{\partial T}\right]_P - \left[\frac{\partial H_{\text{reactants}}}{\partial T}\right]_P$$

But the second and third terms are, respectively, $C_{p_{\text{products}}}$ and $C_{p_{\text{reactants}}}$. Therefore,

$$\left[\frac{\partial(\Delta H)}{\partial T}\right]_P = C_{p_{\text{products}}} - C_{p_{\text{reactants}}} = \Delta C_p \qquad (55)$$

Equation (55) is known as *Kirchhoff's equation*. In the same manner can be obtained the equation for the variation of ΔE with temperature, namely,

$$\left[\frac{\partial(\Delta E)}{\partial T}\right]_V = C_{v_{\text{products}}} - C_{v_{\text{reactants}}} = \Delta C_v \tag{56}$$

The integration of equation (55) depends on whether ΔC_p is constant or temperature dependent. When ΔC_p is constant, then integration between two temperatures T_1 and T_2 yields

$$\int_{\Delta H_1}^{\Delta H_2} d(\Delta H) = \int_{T_1}^{T_2} \Delta C_p dT$$
$$\Delta H_2 - \Delta H_1 = \Delta C_p(T_2 - T_1)$$

and
$$\Delta H_2 = \Delta H_1 + \Delta C_p(T_2 - T_1) \tag{57}$$

Here ΔH_1 is the heat of reaction at T_1 and ΔH_2 that at T_2. However, when ΔC_p is not constant, then

$$\int d(\Delta H) = \int \Delta C_p dT + \Delta H_0$$

and
$$\Delta H = \int \Delta C_p dT + \Delta H_0 \tag{58}$$

where ΔH_0 is a constant of integration. To evaluate the integral in equation (58), ΔC_p must be available as a function of the temperature.

The use of equations (57) and (58) can best be illustrated by examples. Suppose it is desired to calculate ΔH^0 at 348° K for the reaction

$$\frac{1}{2} H_2(g) + \frac{1}{2} Cl_2(g) = HCl(g) \qquad \Delta H^0_{298°\,K} = -22{,}060 \text{ cal} \tag{59}$$

The mean heat capacities over this temperature interval are

$$H_2(g): \quad C_p = 6.82 \text{ cal mole}^{-1} \text{ degree}^{-1}$$
$$Cl_2(g): \quad C_p = 7.71 \text{ cal mole}^{-1} \text{ degree}^{-1}$$
$$HCl(g): \quad C_p = 6.81 \text{ cal mole}^{-1} \text{ degree}^{-1}$$

from which we get

$$\Delta C_p = 6.81 - \frac{1}{2}(6.82) - \frac{1}{2}(7.71) = -0.46$$

Therefore, $\Delta H^0_{348°\,K} = -22{,}060 + (-0.46)(348 - 298)$
$$= -22{,}080 \text{ cal}$$

However, suppose it is desired to find the heat of formation of ammonia at 1000° K from the following data:

$$\frac{1}{2}\,N_2(g) + \frac{3}{2}\,H_2(g) = NH_3(g) \qquad \Delta H^0_{298.2°\,K} = -11,040 \text{ cal} \qquad (60)$$

$N_2(g)\colon C_p = 6.76 + 0.606 \times 10^{-3}\,T + 1.3 \times 10^{-7}\,T^2$

$$\text{cal mole}^{-1}\text{ degree}^{-1} \quad (61a)$$

$H_2(g)\colon C_p = 6.62 + 0.81 \times 10^{-3}\,T \text{ cal mole}^{-1}\text{ degree}^{-1} \qquad (61b)$

$NH_3(g)\colon C_p = 6.189 + 7.887 \times 10^{-3}\,T - 7.28 \times 10^{-7}\,T^2$

$$\text{cal mole}^{-1}\text{ degree}^{-1} \quad (61c)$$

Now $C_{p_{\text{products}}} = C_{p_{NH_3}}$. Again, $C_{p_{\text{reactants}}}$ is given by

$$
\begin{aligned}
C_{p_{\text{reactants}}} &= \frac{1}{2}\,C_{p_{N_2}} + \frac{3}{2}\,C_{p_{H_2}} \\
&= 3.38 + 0.303 \times 10^{-3}\,T + 0.65 \times 10^{-7}\,T^2 + 9.93 \\
&\quad + 1.22 \times 10^{-3}\,T \\
&= 13.31 + 1.523 \times 10^{-3}\,T + 0.65 \times 10^{-7}\,T^2 \qquad (62)
\end{aligned}
$$

Subtracting equation (62) from equation (61c), we obtain for ΔC_p

$$\Delta C_p = -7.12 + 6.364 \times 10^{-3}\,T - 7.93 \times 10^{-7}\,T^2 \qquad (63)$$

On substitution of equation (63) for ΔC_p in equation (58) and integration, we get

$$
\begin{aligned}
\Delta H^0 &= \int \Delta C_p dT + \Delta H_0 \\
&= \int (-7.12 + 6.364 \times 10^{-3}\,T - 7.93 \times 10^{-7}\,T^2)dT + \Delta H_0 \\
&= -7.12\,T + 3.182 \times 10^{-3}\,T^2 - 2.64 \times 10^{-7}\,T^3 + \Delta H_0 \quad (64)
\end{aligned}
$$

In order to evaluate the constant of integration, a known value of ΔH^0 at some definite temperature must be substituted in equation (64), and ΔH_0 solved for. Since we have given that at 298.2° K $\Delta H^0 = -11,040$ cal, then

$$-11,040 = -7.12(298.2) + 3.182 \times 10^{-3}(298.2)^2 - 2.64 \times 10^{-7}(298.2)^3$$
$$+ \Delta H_0$$

and $\Delta H_0 = -11,040 + 2120 - 280 + 10$
$$= -9190 \text{ cal}$$

Inserting the found value of ΔH_0 into equation (64), the expression for ΔH^0 becomes

$$\Delta H^0 = -9190 - 7.12\,T + 3.182 \times 10^{-3}\,T^2 - 2.64 \times 10^{-7}\,T^3 \quad (65)$$

This equation gives ΔH^0 for the formation of ammonia as a function of the temperature. Equations of this type are very useful, for they permit calculation of the heat of reaction merely by inserting the temperature at which ΔH^0 is sought. Thus for the present case we have at 1000° K

$$\Delta H^0 = -9190 - 7.12(1000) + 3.182 \times 10^{-3}(1000)^2 - 2.64$$
$$\times 10^{-7}(1000)^3$$
$$= -9190 - 7120 + 3180 - 260$$
$$= -13,390 \text{ cal at } 1000° \text{ K}$$

Hence 2350 more calories of heat are evolved at 1000° K than at 298° K.

The accuracy of these equations is determined by the precision with which the specific heats and the heats of reaction have been determined. Discretion should be exercised as to the temperature range over which these equations are used, since they are valid only for the temperature interval over which the specific heats have been determined.

REFERENCES FOR FURTHER READING

1. Bichowsky and Rossini, *The Thermochemistry of Chemical Substances*, Reinhold Publishing Corporation, New York, 1936.
2. S. Glasstone, *Thermodynamics for Chemists*, D. Van Nostrand Company, Inc., New York, 1947.
3. Hougen and Watson, *Chemical Process Principles*, John Wiley & Sons, Inc., New York, 1947, Vol. II.
4. K. K. Kelley, U. S. Bureau of Mines Bulletins No. 324, 371, 383, 384, 393, 406, and 407.
5. Parks and Huffman, *The Free Energies of Some Organic Compounds*, Reinhold Publishing Corporation, New York, 1932.
6. Rossini, Pitzer, Taylor, Ebert, Kilpatrick, Beckett, Williams, and Werner, *Selected Values of Properties of Hydrocarbons*, Circ. Natl. Bur. Standards C 461, U.S. Government Printing Office, Washington, D. C., 1947.
7. Rossini, Wagman, Evans, Levine, and Jaffe, *Selected Values of Chemical Thermodynamic Properties*, Circ. Natl. Bur. Standards 500, U.S. Government Printing Office, Washington, D. C., 1952.
8. R. R. Wenner, *Thermochemical Calculations*, McGraw-Hill Book Company, Inc., New York, 1941.
9. A. Weissberger, *Physical Methods of Organic Chemistry*, Interscience Publishers, Inc., New York, 1949, Chap. XIV.

PROBLEMS

1. The molar heat of combustion of naphthalene (M.W. = 128.16) is -1228.2 kilocal/mole. If 0.550 g of naphthalene burned in a calorimeter cause a rise in temperature of 2.050° C, what is the total heat capacity of the calorimeter?
   Ans. 2571 cal/° C.
2. If 1.52 g of an organic compound burned in the calorimeter in problem 1 cause the temperature to rise 1.845° C, what is the heat of combustion in calories per gram of the compound?
3. Calculate the difference between ΔH and ΔE at 25° C for the reaction

$$CH_3COOH(l) + 2 O_2(g) = 2 CO_2(g) + 2 H_2O(l) \qquad Ans. \text{ Zero.}$$

4. A 0.500-g sample of *n*-heptane burned in a bomb calorimeter causes a temperature rise of 2.94° C. If the heat capacity of the calorimeter and its accessories is 1954 cal/degree and the mean temperature of the calorimeter is 25° C, calculate the heat of combustion of heptane at 25° C in calories per mole.

5. For the following reactions state whether ΔH will be significantly different from ΔE, and tell whether ΔH will be greater or less than ΔE in each case. Assume that all reactants and products are in their normal states at 25° C.

   a. The complete combustion of sucrose $(C_{12}H_{22}O_{11})$
   b. The oxidation of solid naphthalene $(C_{10}H_8)$ with gaseous O_2 to solid phthalic acid, $C_6H_4(COOH)_2$
   c. The complete combustion of ethyl alcohol
   d. The oxidation of PbS with O_2 to PbO and SO_2

6. From the following equations and heats of reaction, calculate the standard molar heat of formation of AgCl at 25° C.

$$Ag_2O(s) + 2\,HCl(g) = 2\,AgCl(s) + H_2O(l) \qquad \Delta H^0 = -77{,}610 \text{ cal}$$

$$2\,Ag(s) + \frac{1}{2}\,O_2(g) = Ag_2O(s) \qquad \Delta H^0 = -7{,}310 \text{ cal}$$

$$\frac{1}{2}\,H_2(g) + \frac{1}{2}\,Cl_2(g) = HCl(g) \qquad \Delta H^0 = -22{,}060 \text{ cal}$$

$$H_2(g) + \frac{1}{2}\,O_2(g) = H_2O(l) \qquad \Delta H^0 = -68{,}320 \text{ cal}$$

Ans. $-30{,}360$ cal.

7. The heats of the following reactions at 25° C are:

$$Na(s) + \frac{1}{2}\,Cl_2(g) = NaCl(s) \qquad \Delta H^0 = -98{,}230 \text{ cal}$$

$$H_2(g) + S(s) + 2\,O_2(g) = H_2SO_4(l) \qquad \Delta H^0 = -193{,}910 \text{ cal}$$
$$2\,Na(s) + S(s) + 2\,O_2(g) = Na_2SO_4(s) \qquad \Delta H^0 = -330{,}500 \text{ cal}$$
$$\frac{1}{2}\,H_2(g) + \frac{1}{2}\,Cl_2(g) = HCl(g) \qquad \Delta H^0 = -22{,}060 \text{ cal}$$

From these data find the heat of reaction at constant volume at 25° C for the process

$$2\,NaCl(s) + H_2SO_4(l) = Na_2SO_4(s) + 2\,HCl(g)$$

8. From the data of Table 1 calculate the heats of the following reactions at 25° C:

   (a) $Fe_2O_3(s) + CO(g) = CO_2(g) + 2\,FeO(s)$
   (b) $2\,NO_2(g) = 2\,NO(g) + O_2(g)$
   (c) $3\,C_2H_2(g) = C_6H_6(l)$

9. For the reaction

$$2\,NaHCO_3(s) = Na_2CO_3(s) + CO_2(g) + H_2O(g) \qquad \Delta H^0_{25°C} = 30{,}920 \text{ cal}$$

Find the standard heat of formation at 25° C of $NaHCO_3(s)$ in calories per mole.

10. From the heat of combustion of *n*-butane in Table 2 calculate the standard heat of formation of this compound per mole at 25° C.

Ans. $-29{,}820$ cal/mole.

11. From the data in Table 1 calculate the heat of combustion at 25° C of $C_2H_5OH(g)$ in calories per mole.

12. The following compounds originally in dilute aqueous solution are mixed together as indicated:

    (a) $CH_3COONa + HCl \longrightarrow$
    (b) $KCl + MgSO_4 \longrightarrow$
    (c) $NH_4Cl + Ba(OH)_2 \longrightarrow$
    (d) $CaCl_2 + K_2CO_3 \longrightarrow$

    In which cases may an appreciable thermal effect be expected? Explain your answer.

13. A 150.0-cc portion of 0.40 N HCl is neutralized with an excess of NH_4OH in a Dewar vessel with a resulting rise in temperature of 2.36° C. If the heat capacity of the Dewar and its contents after the reaction is 315 cal/degree, calculate the heat of neutralization in calories per mole.

14. $Na_2CO_3(s)$ dissolves in a large excess of H_2O with the evolution of 5500 cal of heat per mole at 25° C. Calculate the heat of formation per mole of Na_2CO_3 in a dilute solution.   *Ans.* $-275,500$ cal/mole.

15. From the following reactions and thermal data at 25° C

$$2\,Fe(s) + \frac{3}{2}\,O_2(g) = Fe_2O_3(s) \qquad\qquad \Delta H^0 = -196,500 \text{ cal}$$

$$2\,FeO(s) + \frac{1}{2}\,O_2(g) = Fe_2O_3(s) \qquad\qquad \Delta H^0 = -67,900 \text{ cal}$$

$$Fe(s) + 2\,H^+(a = 1) = Fe^{++}(a = 1) + H_2(g) \qquad \Delta H^0 = -20,600 \text{ cal}$$

$$\frac{1}{2}\,H_2(g) = H^+(a = 1) \qquad\qquad \Delta H^0 = 0 \text{ cal}$$

$$H_2(g) + \frac{1}{2}\,O_2(g) = H_2O(l) \qquad\qquad \Delta H^0 = -68,320 \text{ cal}$$

calculate ΔH^0 of the reaction:

$$FeO(s) + 2\,H^+(a = 1) = H_2O(l) + Fe^{++}(a = 1)$$

16. From the data of Tables 1 and 5, calculate the heats of the following reactions at 25° C:

    (a) $Ca^{++} + CO_3^{--} = CaCO_3(s)$
    (b) $CO_3^{--} + 2\,H^+ = H_2O(l) + CO_2(g)$

17. From the data in Table 6 calculate the integral heat of solution of 2 moles of H_2SO_4 in 3 moles of H_2O.   *Ans.* $-17,260$ cal.

18. By interpolation of the data in Table 6 estimate the heat effect resulting (a) when 100 g of H_2SO_4 are added to 100 g of H_2O, and (b) when 100 g H_2O are added to 100 g of solution containing 70% of H_2SO_4 by weight.

19. From a plot of the data given in Table 6 determine the differential heats of solution of solute and solvent per mole (a) in a solution containing 1 mole of H_2SO_4 in 2 moles of H_2O, and (b) in a solution containing 1 mole of H_2SO_4 in 10 moles of H_2O.

20. From the results of the preceding problem determine the differential heats of dilution per mole for solvent and solute between the two concentrations of solutions given there.

21. At 18° C the heat of solution of anhydrous $CuSO_4$ in a large volume of water is $-15,800$ cal/mole, while that of $CuSO_4 \cdot 5\ H_2O$ is 2750 cal/mole. What is the heat of the reaction

$$CuSO_4(s) + 5\ H_2O(l) = CuSO_4 \cdot 5\ H_2O(s)$$

at 18° C?

22. Using the heat capacity constants in Table 7, calculate the amount of heat required to raise the temperature of 200 g of $CO_2(g)$ from 27° to 227° C at (a) constant pressure and (b) constant volume. Assume $C_p - C_v = R$.

Ans. (a) 8883 cal; (b) 7084 cal.

23. One mole of $N_2(g)$ and 3 moles of $H_2(g)$ at 25° C are heated to 450° C and subjected to a pressure which results in the conversion of 0.1 mole of the N_2 into $NH_3(g)$. The gases are then cooled rapidly back to 25° C. From the thermal data given in this chapter find how much heat is given up or absorbed in the whole process.

24. A mixture of gases contains 40% of CO_2, 30% of CO, and 30% of N_2 by volume. Calculate the amount of heat necessary to raise the temperature of 1000 g of this mixture from 27° C to 227° C at constant pressure.

25. Calculate the heat of vaporization of H_2O at 120° C and 1 atm pressure. The heat capacity of $H_2O(l)$ may be taken as 1.0 cal/g-degree, C_p for the vapor as 0.45 cal/g-degree, and the heat of vaporization at 100° C as 536 cal/g.

26. Calculate ΔH^0 at 1000° C for the reaction

$$2\ CO(g) + O_2(g) = 2\ CO_2(g) \qquad \Delta H^0_{293°\,K} = -135,800\ \text{cal}$$

27. Find ΔH^0 as a function of T for the reaction

$$CO_2(g) + C(s,\ \text{graphite}) = 2\ CO(g)$$

given that $\Delta H^0_{293°\,K} = 41,400$ calories.

Ans. $\Delta H^0 = 40,810 + 5.361\ T - 7.697 \times 10^{-3}\ T^2 + 31.93 \times 10^{-7}\ T^3$
$$-0.565 \times 10^{-9}\ T^4 - \frac{1.169 \times 10^5}{T}.$$

28. The expression for ΔH^0 of formation of CO_2 as a function of temperature is

$$\Delta H^0 = -93,480 - 0.603\ T - 0.675 \times 10^{-4}\ T^2 - \frac{1.091 \times 10^5}{T}$$

Find ΔC_p for this reaction as a function of T.

29. Find the expression for ΔH^0 as a function of the temperature for the reaction

$$N_2(g) + O_2(g) = 2\ NO(g)$$

given that $\Delta H^0_{293°\,K} = 43,000$ cal.

10

The Second and Third Laws
of Thermodynamics

Although the first law of thermodynamics establishes the relationship between the heat absorbed and the work performed by a system, it places absolutely no restrictions on the source of this heat or on the direction of its flow. According to the first law there is nothing impossible about a process in which, without any external aid, ice may be used to heat water by extracting heat from the former at a lower temperature and supplying it to the latter at a higher temperature. Yet we know from experience that such a transfer of heat from a lower to a higher temperature will not take place spontaneously. Instead heat is always found to flow of its own accord from the warmer to the colder body; i.e., *the spontaneous flow of heat is always unidirectional from the higher to the lower temperature.*

A similar unidirectionality of change is observed in all natural phenomena. Thus electricity tends to flow only from a point of higher electric potential to one of lower, water will move by itself only from a higher level to a lower, diffusion will occur only from the point of higher concentration to the lower, and all chemical systems under given conditions will tend to undergo reaction in a direction which will lead to the establishment of equilibrium. In fact, all the above observations can be summarized by the statement that *all naturally occurring processes always tend to change spontaneously in a direction which will lead to equilibrium.*

There is still another respect in which the first law is insufficient. In demanding the conservation of energy in all types of transformations, the first law of thermodynamics does not define the ease or extent of convertibility of one form of energy into another. Still, it is an empirical fact that, whereas various forms of energy can be converted readily and completely into heat, the converse process, the conversion of heat into work, can be accomplished only under severely limited conditions. At constant temperature heat can be transformed into work only at the expense of some permanent change in the system involved. For instance, heat may be converted into work by the isothermal reversible expansion of a gas in a cylinder. But to retain this work the gas must remain expanded. If we attempt to return the gas to its original condition, we find that the work obtained in the expansion must be utilized in the compression, and as a result we wind up with the original quantity of heat and no work. To obtain work from heat by means of a periodically operating machine, such as a heat engine, it is essential that a temperature drop take place and that a flow of heat occur from a higher to a lower temperature. Furthermore, even under such conditions not all the heat absorbed by the system can be converted to work, but only a fraction of it determined, under ideal conditions, by the two temperatures between which the operation takes place.

THE SECOND LAW OF THERMODYNAMICS

To express the limitations inherent in the convertibility of heat into work and to indicate the direction of change of all naturally occurring processes, the second law of thermodynamics has been promulgated, largely through the efforts of Clausius and Lord Kelvin. In its general and concise form this law will be stated later in the chapter in terms of the entropy. At present we may take as statements of the law the italicized passages given above or the following statement by Clausius that *"it is impossible for a self-acting machine, unaided by external agency, to convey heat from a body at one temperature to another body at a higher temperature."* The latter pronouncement merely states that the natural tendency of heat is to flow from the higher temperature to the lower. However, it should be realized that nothing implied in this statement would preclude the possibility of cooling a body below the temperature of its surroundings. Such a cooling can be accomplished, but in order to bring it about work has to be expended.

The second law of thermodynamics is a statistical law applicable to systems containing large numbers of individual units. For instance, in observing in a colloid the random motion of particles which constitutes the Brownian movement, it is found that most of the particles move from the more concentrated portion of the field to the less concentrated, as may be expected. Occasionally, however, just the reverse takes place, and a particle moves toward the more concentrated portion of the field. This behavior may at first glance appear to be a violation of the second law. However, it has been shown that the second law cannot be violated by such a fluctuation, since for the system as a whole the Brownian movement is from the region of higher to lower concentration. Further, the statistical nature of the second law is borne out by the connection which has been established between this law and the laws of probability governing the behavior of systems containing large numbers of atoms or molecules.

ENTROPY

In order to express the second law of thermodynamics in mathematical terms, let us define a new thermodynamic quantity S, called the *entropy* of the system. As we shall see later, *the entropy of a system depends only on the initial and final states of the system*, and hence, as in the case of E and H, we may write that the change in entropy of a process, ΔS, is

$$\Delta S = S_2 - S_1 \tag{1}$$

where S_2 and S_1 are, respectively, the entropies of the system in the final and initial states. Further, let us specify that the differential change in S, dS, is given by

$$dS = \frac{dq_r}{T} \tag{2}$$

where dq_r is the infinitesimal quantity of heat absorbed in a process taking place under *reversible* conditions at temperature T. In the case of a finite reversible change at constant temperature, dS becomes ΔS, dq_r becomes q_r, and equation (2) takes then the form

$$\Delta S = \frac{q_r}{T} \tag{3}$$

Therefore, for any isothermal reversible process in which an amount of heat q_r is absorbed at temperature T, the entropy change involved is simply the absorbed heat divided by the absolute temperature. When q_r is positive, i.e., heat is absorbed, ΔS is also positive, indicating an increase in the entropy of the system. On the other hand, when heat is evolved q_r is negative and so is ΔS, and the system experiences a decrease in entropy.

Entropies and entropy changes are expressed in calories per degree per given amount of substance. The quantity *calorie per degree* is called an *entropy unit* (eu).

ENTROPY CHANGE IN ISOTHERMAL PROCESSES

Consider a cylinder containing a gas and fitted with a frictionless and weightless piston. Let the cylinder be enclosed in a large heat reservoir which is so thoroughly insulated from its surrounding that no heat can enter or leave the reservoir. Such an arrangement of a system and heat reservoir adiabatically insulated from their surroundings is called an *isolated system*. Let now the temperature in the isolated system be constant and equal to T, and suppose that the gas in the cylinder undergoes an isothermal and reversible expansion from volume V_1 to V_2. During this process the gas will absorb from the reservoir a quantity of heat q_r, and so the entropy change suffered by the gas, ΔS_g, will be, according to equation (3)

$$\Delta S_g = \frac{q_r}{T} \tag{4a}$$

At the same time the reservoir loses a quantity of heat q_r, and hence the entropy change of the reservoir, ΔS_r, is

$$\Delta S_r = \frac{\bar{q}_r}{T} \tag{4b}$$

where the bar over q_r indicates a loss of heat. The total change in entropy for the gas and the reservoir, ΔS_1, is then

$$\Delta S_1 = \Delta S_g + \Delta S_r$$
$$= \frac{q_r}{T} + \frac{\bar{q}_r}{T}$$
$$= 0 \tag{4c}$$

If we compress the gas now isothermally and reversibly from V_2 back to V_1, the heat rejected by the gas will be q_r and so will be the heat gained by the reservoir. The entropy changes involved are

$$\Delta S_g' = \frac{\bar{q}_r}{T} \tag{5a}$$

$$\Delta S_r' = \frac{q_r}{T} \tag{5b}$$

and the total entropy change for the gas and reservoir, ΔS_2, is thus

$$\Delta S_2 = \Delta S_g' + \Delta S_r'$$
$$= \frac{\bar{q}_r}{T} + \frac{q_r}{T}$$
$$= 0 \tag{5c}$$

Further, the total change in entropy for the complete cycle, ΔS, is the sum of ΔS_1 and ΔS_2, or

$$\Delta S = \Delta S_1 + \Delta S_2$$
$$= 0 \tag{6}$$

The above considerations lead to two very important conclusions. First, even though parts of an isolated system may experience a change in entropy, the entropy change for the entire isolated system when a reversible isothermal change occurs in it is zero. Second, the total entropy change for a reversible isothermal cycle is zero, and hence at the end of the cycle the system has the same entropy as it had initially. The entropy behaves, then, as a property of the state of the system only, and this fact justifies equation (1). These conclusions are valid for all types of processes and cycles performed under isothermal and reversible conditions in isolated systems.

Consider again the isothermal expansion of the gas from volume V_1 to V_2, but let the change be now irreversible. Since the expansion is irreversible, the heat absorbed by the gas will be q, where $q < q_r$. However, *the entropy change* of the gas must still be the same as it was in the reversible expansion, for it *is determined by the reversible heat and not by the heat actually absorbed*. The actual value of q in an irreversible process depends on the manner of conducting the process and will vary anywhere from $q = 0$ to $q = q_r$ when complete reversibility obtains. Therefore, for an irreversible process ΔS cannot equal q/T, for, if ΔS were equal to q/T in all these cases, we should obtain a series of different values of ΔS between any two given states of the system. As this is impossible for a property characteristic of the states of the system only, it must follow that even in an irreversible process ΔS must be given by q_r/T. On the basis of these arguments the entropy change for the isothermal but irreversible expansion of the gas from V_1 to V_2 is still given by equation (4a). However, the loss of q cal of heat by the reservoir can be considered to take place reversibly, and so the entropy change of the reservoir is $\Delta S_r = \bar{q}/T$. The total entropy change of the isolated system is then

$$\Delta S_1 = \frac{q_r}{T} + \frac{\bar{q}}{T} \tag{7a}$$

But, $q_r > \bar{q}$ and $q_r/T > \bar{q}/T$. Consequently,

$$\Delta S_1 = \frac{q_r}{T} + \frac{\bar{q}}{T} > 0 \tag{7b}$$

and hence *an irreversible process occurring isothermally in an isolated system leads to an increase in the total entropy of the system.*

If we recompress the gas to its original state isothermally and reversibly at temperature T, then the entropy change of the process will again be that given in equation (5c), or $\Delta S_2 = 0$. As a result the total entropy change for the irreversible cycle will be the sum of $\Delta S_2 = 0$ and equation (7b), namely,

$$\Delta S = \frac{q_r}{T} + \frac{\bar{q}}{T} > 0 \tag{8}$$

Therefore, whereas for a complete isothermal and reversible cycle carried out in an isolated system $\Delta S = 0$, for an irreversible cycle $\Delta S > 0$. This conclusion is again valid for all types of irreversible processes, and not just for the example cited.

The increase in entropy which occurs in the irreversible cycle is the result of conversion of work to heat. At the end of the cycle the working gas, by being returned to its initial state, suffers no change of any kind. The reservoir, however, has lost a quantity of heat q and regained q_r. The net heat gained by the reservoir is thus $q_r + \bar{q}$, and hence its entropy gain is $q_r/T + \bar{q}/T$, a quantity greater than zero. At the same time the work performed on the gas was w_m, while that performed by the gas was w. The difference $w_m - w$ was converted into the heat gained by the reservoir and caused the entropy increase.

ENTROPY CHANGE IN NONISOTHERMAL PROCESSES

Any nonisothermal process may be considered to be composed of a successive series of isothermal steps, each occurring at a temperature infinitesimally different from the preceding. If each of these isothermal steps takes place reversibly, the entropy change for each will be given by the heat absorbed in the step, dq_r, divided by T, the temperature at which the heat absorption takes place. The total entropy change for a process occurring between the temperatures T_1 and T_2 will be, then, the sum of the small continuous isothermal entropy changes, or

$$\Delta S = \int_{T_1}^{T_2} \frac{dq_r}{T} \tag{9}$$

From what has been said before it is evident that equation (9) is applicable also to irreversible nonisothermal processes provided the q's employed are not the heats actually observed but the heats evaluated for the corresponding reversible processes between the same two states.

When equation (9) is applied, in a manner similar to the one used in the preceding section, to the changes which take place in an isolated system under nonisothermal conditions, it is found that:

1. For any *reversible* process or cycle $\Delta S = 0$
2. For any *irreversible* process or cycle $\Delta S > 0$

These conclusions are identical to those reached for isothermal processes. Therefore, whether an increase in entropy does or does not occur for processes taking place in isolated systems depends entirely on whether the processes are irreversible or reversible.

ENTROPY AND THE SECOND LAW OF THERMODYNAMICS

The results of the two preceding sections can be summarized into the statement that for any process performed in an isolated system

$$\Delta S \gtreqless 0 \tag{10}$$

the equality applied to reversible processes and the inequality to irreversible ones. Completely reversible processes, involving as they do a balance of driving and opposing forces, must of necessity occur very slowly. In fact, to carry out any change in a completely reversible manner would require infinite time. Consequently, any process that does take place in a finite time must be irreversible, and it must be attended by an increase in the total entropy of all the bodies involved. The latter conclusion permits a statement of the second law of thermodynamics in its most general form, namely, *that all processes in nature tend to occur only with an increase in entropy and that the direction of change is always such as to lead to the entropy increase.* The several forms of the second law given earlier in the chapter are merely special cases of this general statement.

Suppose we consider the universe as an isolated system, as Clausius did, and apply to it the second law. Since all processes in nature are irreversible, the entropy of the universe must be a unidirectional property which continually increases and tends to reach a maximum. On the other hand, the first law of thermodynamics states that the energy of the universe is constant. These facts led Clausius to the enunciation of the first two laws of thermodynamics in the oft-quoted statement that "the energy of the universe is constant, the entropy of the universe tends to a maximum."

J. W. Gibbs, one of the greatest scientific minds America has produced, referred to entropy as a measure of the "mixtupness" of a system. This term is both descriptive and illuminating. What he meant is this. Energy in useful form, such as electrical, mechanical, or chemical energy, is organized and directed energy which can be utilized for the performance of work. On the other hand, heat is a form of energy due to the random motions of the atoms or molecules in a body and is thus chaotic in character. Therefore, when energy which is organized and which can be utilized for performance of work is converted to heat, the chaos or "mixtupness" of the system is increased. Since entropy is a measure of this "mixtupness," it must also increase. The idea that entropy is a measure of the disorder in a system is the basis of the relations which can and have been established between entropy and probability, and which are the concern of the field of science known as statistical mechanics.

From the above discussion the essence of the second law of thermodynamics can be summarized in the statement that our stockpile of available energy in the universe is continually decreasing and is being converted into the disordered form of energy we call heat.

CALCULATION OF ENTROPY CHANGE

The entropy of an isolated system can either remain constant or increase. On the other hand, the entropy of individual bodies or systems considered without their reservoirs or surroundings can increase, decrease, or remain constant. Most entropy change calculations deal with the latter situation, since usually interest is centered on what is happening to a particular substance or process when conditions are varied, and not on the surroundings.

To illustrate the calculation of ΔS, we shall consider two examples, one dealing with an isothermal reversible process and the other with the same process performed irreversibly.

Example (a): Calculate the entropy change involved in the isothermal reversible expansion of 5 moles of an ideal gas from a volume of 10 liters to a volume of 100 liters at 300° K. Since the process is isothermal, $\Delta E = 0$. Hence by the first law of thermodynamics $q = w$. Further, since the process is reversible, the work done must be w_m, and therefore $w_m = q_r$. The entropy change for this process is given then by

$$\Delta S = \frac{q_r}{T} = \frac{w_m}{T}$$

But, according to equation (31), Chapter 2, w_m is

$$w_m = nRT \ln \frac{V_2}{V_1}$$

Therefore, $\Delta S = nR \ln \dfrac{V_2}{V_1} = 5 \times 1.987 \times 2.303 \log \dfrac{100}{10}$

$$= 22.88 \text{ cal degree}^{-1}$$
$$= 22.88 \text{ eu}$$

Example (b): Calculate the entropy change involved in the isothermal expansion of 5 moles of an ideal gas against a constant pressure of 1 atm from a volume of 10 liters to a volume of 100 liters at 300° K. The expansion described in this problem is irreversible, but again isothermal. For such a process q equals w, but w now is not the maximum work, and hence q does not equal q_r. To find q_r we must imagine the same process conducted reversibly. For the reversible process, however, q_r is given by the same equation as in the preceding problem, and consequently we have again that

$$\Delta S = nR \ln \frac{V_2}{V_1}$$

$$= 5 \times 2.303 \, R \log \frac{100}{10}$$

$$= 22.88 \text{ eu}$$

The entropy change is the same for both processes because the initial and final states are the same, although different paths were followed in the two cases in passing from one point to the other.

DEPENDENCE OF ENTROPY ON VARIABLES OF A SYSTEM

Since the entropy is a function of the state of a system, its value for any pure substance will depend on any two of the three variables T, V, and P. Commonly, T is selected as one of the independent variables, and hence the combinations of variables to be dealt with are T and V, or T and P.

Variables T and V. If the entropy of a substance is a function of T and V, then

$$dS = \left(\frac{\partial S}{\partial T}\right)_V dT + \left(\frac{\partial S}{\partial V}\right)_T dV \tag{11}$$

Again, the first law states that under reversible conditions

$$dE = dq_r - dw_m \tag{12}$$

But, by equation (2) $dq_r = TdS$. Also, $dw_m = PdV$ where P is the pressure equal to that of the system. Therefore,

$$dE = TdS - PdV \tag{13}$$

However, E is also a function of T and V, and hence

$$dE = \left(\frac{\partial E}{\partial T}\right)_V dT + \left(\frac{\partial E}{\partial V}\right)_T dV \tag{14}$$

On eliminating dE between equations (13) and (14) we get for dS

$$dS = \frac{1}{T}\left(\frac{\partial E}{\partial T}\right)_V dT + \frac{1}{T}\left[\left(\frac{\partial E}{\partial V}\right)_T + P\right] dV \tag{15}$$

$(\partial E/\partial T)_V$ is, of course, C_v. Again, it can be shown that

$$\frac{1}{T}\left[\left(\frac{\partial E}{\partial V}\right)_T + P\right] = \left(\frac{\partial P}{\partial T}\right)_V \tag{16}$$

Equation (15) may thus be written as

$$dS = \frac{C_v}{T} dT + \left(\frac{\partial P}{\partial T}\right)_V dV \tag{17}$$

and, on comparison of equations (11) and (17), we see that

$$\left(\frac{\partial S}{\partial T}\right)_V = \frac{C_v}{T} \tag{18}$$

and

$$\left(\frac{\partial S}{\partial V}\right)_T = \left(\frac{\partial P}{\partial T}\right)_V \tag{19}$$

Variables T and P. With independent variables T and P, dS is given by

$$dS = \left(\frac{\partial S}{\partial T}\right)_P dT + \left(\frac{\partial S}{\partial P}\right)_T dP \tag{20}$$

Since $H = E + PV$, complete differentiation yields

$$dH = dE + PdV + VdP$$

or $$dE + PdV = dH - VdP \tag{21}$$

Substitution of equation (21) in equation (13) gives then

$$TdS = dH - VdP \tag{22}$$

However, H is also a function of T and P, and so

$$dH = \left(\frac{\partial H}{\partial T}\right)_P dT + \left(\frac{\partial H}{\partial P}\right)_T dP \tag{23}$$

On elimination of dH between equations (22) and (23), we obtain thus

$$dS = \frac{1}{T}\left(\frac{\partial H}{\partial T}\right)_P dT + \frac{1}{T}\left[\left(\frac{\partial H}{\partial P}\right)_T - V\right] dP \tag{24}$$

Now, $(\partial H/\partial T)_P = C_p$. Again, it can be proved that

$$\frac{1}{T}\left[\left(\frac{\partial H}{\partial P}\right)_T - V\right] = -\left(\frac{\partial V}{\partial T}\right)_P \tag{25}$$

Therefore,

$$dS = \frac{C_p}{T} dT - \left(\frac{\partial V}{\partial T}\right)_P dP \tag{26}$$

Finally, comparison of equations (20) and (26) shows that

$$\left(\frac{\partial S}{\partial T}\right)_P = \frac{C_p}{T} \tag{27}$$

and $$\left(\frac{\partial S}{\partial P}\right)_T = -\left(\frac{\partial V}{\partial T}\right)_P dP \tag{28}$$

Equations (17) and (26) are perfectly general and apply to any substance, whether solid, liquid, or gaseous. However, we shall use them here only for calculating entropy changes in ideal gases.

ENTROPY CHANGE IN IDEAL GASES

Variables T and V. In equation (17) C_v refers to the heat capacity of whatever quantity of substance is being considered. If we are dealing with n moles of gas, it is more convenient to write for it nC_v, where C_v

is now the heat capacity per mole. Again, for an ideal gas, $PV = nRT$, and differentiation yields

$$\left(\frac{\partial P}{\partial T}\right)_V = \frac{nR}{V} \tag{29}$$

Hence for ideal gases equation (17) becomes

$$dS = \frac{nC_v dT}{T} + \frac{nR dV}{V} \tag{30}$$

and on integration of equation (30) between the indicated limits, we get for ΔS,

$$\begin{aligned} \Delta S &= \int_{T_1}^{T_2} \frac{nC_v dT}{T} + \int_{V_1}^{V_2} \frac{nR dV}{V} \\ &= \int_{T_1}^{T_2} \frac{nC_v dT}{T} + nR \ln \frac{V_2}{V_1} \end{aligned} \tag{31}$$

When C_v is constant over the temperature interval in question, equation (31) reduces to

$$\Delta S = nC_v \ln \frac{T_2}{T_1} + nR \ln \frac{V_2}{V_1} \tag{32}$$

If, however, it is not constant, then C_v has to be substituted as a function of T, and the expression integrated between the limits T_1 and T_2.

The first term on the right in equation (31) or equation (32) gives the change in entropy of n moles of an ideal gas on change of temperature at constant volume. In turn, the second term gives the ΔS due to change of volume at constant temperature. When T is constant the first term vanishes, and only the second applies. Again, at constant V the second term is zero, and only the first term is used to get ΔS.

To illustrate the use of equation (31), consider the problem of finding the change in entropy suffered by 2 moles of hydrogen gas on being heated from 300° K and a volume of 25 liters to 600° K and a volume of 100 liters. For $H_2(g)$ $C_v = 4.63 + 0.81 \times 10^{-3}T$ cal mole^{-1} degree^{-1}. Inserting these data into equation (31) we have

$$\begin{aligned} \Delta S &= 2 \int_{300° \text{ K}}^{600° \text{ K}} \left(\frac{4.63 + 0.81 \times 10^{-3}T}{T}\right) dT + 2 \times 1.987 \times 2.303 \log \frac{100}{25} \\ &= 2 \left[4.63 \ln \frac{T_2}{T_1} + 0.81 \times 10^{-3}(T_2 - T_1) \right] + 5.51 \\ &= 2 \left[4.63 \times 2.303 \log \frac{600}{300} + 0.81 \times 10^{-3}(600 - 300) \right] + 5.51 \\ &= 6.91 + 5.51 \\ &= 12.42 \text{ eu} \end{aligned}$$

Of this total 6.91 eu is the ΔS resulting from the temperature change at constant volume, while 5.51 eu is due to the change in volume at constant temperature.

Variables T and P. In this case we may substitute for C_p in equation (26) nC_p, when C_p is now the heat capacity per mole of gas. Again, from differentiation of $PV = nRT$ we obtain

$$\left(\frac{\partial V}{\partial T}\right)_P = \frac{nR}{P} \tag{33}$$

Substituting these into equation (26), dS for n moles of an ideal gas becomes

$$dS = \frac{nC_p}{T}\,dT - \frac{nR}{P}\,dP \tag{34}$$

and hence on integration between the indicated limits

$$\begin{aligned}
\Delta S &= \int_{T_1}^{T_2} \frac{nC_p dT}{T} - \int_{P_1}^{P_2} \frac{nR dP}{P} \\
&= \int_{T_1}^{T_2} \frac{nC_p dT}{T} - nR \ln \frac{P_2}{P_1}
\end{aligned} \tag{35}$$

If C_p is or may be considered constant, then equation (35) yields

$$\Delta S = nC_p \ln \frac{T_2}{T_1} - nR \ln \frac{P_2}{P_1} \tag{36}$$

These relations are handled in the same way as those given for T and V as variables. The first term in equation (35) or equation (36) gives the entropy change suffered by n moles of an ideal gas due to variation of temperature at constant pressure, while the second term gives the ΔS resulting from changing the pressure at constant temperature.

ENTROPY CHANGE IN PHYSICAL TRANSFORMATIONS

Changes in entropy accompany not only variations in the temperature, pressure, or volume of a system, but also physical transformations such as fusion, vaporization, or transition from one crystalline form to another. For all such processes the change in entropy is defined as

$$\Delta S = S_2 - S_1 \tag{37}$$

where S_2 is the entropy of the final form and S_1 the entropy of the initial form.

The transitions enumerated take place reversibly at constant temperature T and pressure P and are accompanied by an absorption or evolution of ΔH cal of heat for a given quantity of substance. Therefore, for all such processes

$$\Delta S = \frac{q_r}{T} = \frac{\Delta H}{T} \tag{38}$$

i.e., the change in entropy is given by the heat necessary to accomplish the transition divided by the temperature at which the transition takes place. Of necessity equation (38) is valid only when reversible conditions obtain during the transformation, i.e., when equilibrium exists between the two forms.

As an illustration of the use of equation (38), consider the problem of finding the entropy difference for the transition

$$H_2O(l, 1 \text{ atm}) = H_2O(g, 1 \text{ atm}) \qquad \Delta H_{373.2°\,K} = 9710 \text{ cal mole}^{-1}$$

Since at 373.2° K and 1 atm pressure, the normal boiling point of water, $H_2O(l)$ is in equilibrium with $H_2O(g)$, then

$$\Delta S = S_g - S_l = \frac{\Delta H}{T}$$
$$= \frac{9710}{373.2}$$
$$= 26.02 \text{ eu mole}^{-1}$$

Entropy changes may also be calculated for irreversible transitions, but the change in entropy will no longer be given by equation (38). Consider first the process

$$H_2O(l, 1 \text{ atm}) = H_2O(g, 0.1 \text{ atm})$$

at 373.2° K. Since the change in entropy does not depend on the manner of accomplishing the change, we may first vaporize the water isothermally and reversibly to steam at 1 atm pressure and then expand the steam reversibly and isothermally from 1 to 0.1 atm. The total change in entropy will then be

$$\Delta S = \Delta S_{\text{vaporization}} + \Delta S_{\text{expansion}}$$
$$= \frac{\Delta H}{T} + R \ln \frac{P_1}{P_2}$$
$$= \frac{9710}{373.2} + 4.58 \log \frac{1}{0.1}$$
$$= 30.60 \text{ eu mole}^{-1}$$

Again, suppose it is desired to calculate the entropy change involved in an irreversible process such as the conversion of a mole of water to ice at −15° C and 1 atm pressure. At this pressure water and ice are in equilibrium only at 0° C, and hence equation (38) will not give the entropy change at $-15°$ C. However, if we determine the entropy changes involved in the following steps:

1. The heating of a mole of water from $-15°$ C to $0°$ C
2. Reversible conversion of a mole of water to a mole of ice at $0°$ C
3. Cooling of a mole of ice from $0°$ C to $-15°$ C

then the sum of these entropy changes should be the same as the entropy change of the irreversible process $H_2O(l) = H_2O(s)$ at $-15°$ C, since the net process is the same in both cases.

ENTROPY CHANGE IN CHEMICAL REACTIONS

The entropy change accompanying a chemical reaction is defined as the difference between the sum of the entropies of all the products and the sum of the entropies of all reactants. For any reaction such as

$$aA + bB + \cdots = cC + dD + \cdots$$

the entropy change is given by

$$\Delta S = (cS_C + dS_D + \cdots) - (aS_A + bS_B + \cdots) \qquad (39.$$

Where S_A, S_B, etc., are the entropies *per mole* of the various species. When the entropies of the individual substances correspond to a state of unit activity they are called *standard entropies* and are designated by the symbol S^0. Again, in a reaction where all the substances involved are at unit activity ΔS is written ΔS^0, and the latter is the *standard entropy change* of the reaction.

Entropy changes of chemical reactions are evaluated at constant temperature and pressure. For any given reaction and at any given temperature and pressure the entropy change is definite and just as characteristic of the reaction as the change in the internal energy or heat content. The manner in which the entropy change of a reaction depends on the temperature at constant pressure may readily be deduced from equations (39) and (27). If equation (39) be differentiated with respect to temperature at constant pressure, then

$$\left[\frac{\partial(\Delta S)}{\partial T}\right]_P = \left[c\left(\frac{\partial S_C}{\partial T}\right)_P + d\left(\frac{\partial S_D}{\partial T}\right)_P + \cdots\right]$$
$$- \left[a\left(\frac{\partial S_A}{\partial T}\right)_P + b\left(\frac{\partial S_B}{\partial T}\right)_P + \cdots\right]$$

But, according to equation (27) $(\partial S/\partial T)_P = C_p/T$. Hence,

$$\left[\frac{\partial(\Delta S)}{\partial T}\right]_P = \frac{(cC_{p_C} + dC_{p_D} + \cdots)}{T} - \frac{(aC_{p_A} + bC_{p_B} + \cdots)}{T}$$
$$= \frac{\Delta C_p}{T} \qquad (40)$$

ΔC_p is the difference between the C_p's of products and reactants. On integration of equation (40) between the limits T_1 and T_2, we obtain

$$\int_{\Delta S_1}^{\Delta S_2} d(\Delta S) = \int_{T_1}^{T_2} \frac{\Delta C_p}{T}\, dT$$

$$\Delta S_2 - \Delta S_1 = \int_{T_1}^{T_2} \frac{\Delta C_p}{T}\, dT \tag{41}$$

ΔS_2 is the entropy change at T_2, while ΔS_1 is the entropy change of the reaction at T_1. The difference between the two is given by the integral in equation (41). When ΔC_p may be assumed constant over the temperature interval in question, then equation (41) becomes

$$\Delta S_2 - \Delta S_1 = \Delta C_p \int_{T_1}^{T_2} \frac{dT}{T}$$

$$= \Delta C_p \ln \frac{T_2}{T_1} \tag{42}$$

If ΔC_p is not constant, however, the expression for ΔC_p as a function of T must be obtained in the same manner as described in the chapter on thermochemistry, and the integration must be carried out term by term between the given temperature limits.

The isothermal entropy change of a reaction is calculated by means of equation (39), or, more commonly, from ΔH and ΔF of the reaction. ΔF, the free energy change, will be discussed in the next chapter. To obtain ΔS with the aid of equation (39), the entropies of the individual substances at the temperature in question must be available. These are obtained at present through the *third law of thermodynamics*.

THE THIRD LAW OF THERMODYNAMICS

As a result of the researches of T. W. Richards, Walter Nerst, Max Planck, and others, another fundamental principle of thermodynamics, which deals with the entropy of pure crystalline substances at the absolute zero of temperature, has come into being. This principle, called the third law of thermodynamics, states that the *entropy of all pure crystalline solids may be taken as zero at the absolute zero of temperature*. The statement is confined to pure crystalline solids because theoretical argument and experimental evidence have shown that the entropy of solutions and supercooled liquids is not zero at 0° K. For pure crystalline solids the law has been verified repeatedly, and at present little doubt remains as to general validity of the above statement of the law.

The importance of the third law lies in the fact that it permits the calculation of absolute values of the entropy of pure substances from heat capacity data alone. Entropy changes with temperature at constant pressure may be calculated from equation (27). Since, however, according to the third law $S = 0$ for a pure crystalline substance at $T = 0$, equation (27) may be integrated from this lower limit to any temperature T, namely,

$$\int_{S=0}^{S=S} dS = \int_{T=0}^{T=T} \frac{C_p dT}{T}$$

$$S_T = \int_0^T \frac{C_p dT}{T}$$

$$= 2.303 \int_0^T C_p d \log_{10} T \tag{43}$$

S_T, known as the *absolute entropy* of the substance, is always a positive quantity. All that is necessary for the integration of equation (43) in order to obtain absolute entropies is a knowledge of the heat capacities of the substance from $T = 0$ to any temperature desired.

CALCULATION OF ABSOLUTE ENTROPIES

The integral in equation (43) is practically always evaluated graphically by plotting experimental C_p data vs. $\log_{10} T$ or C_p/T vs. T, and determining the area under the curve. Since the area under the curve is equal to the integral, the entropy of any substance is given by

$$S_T = 2.303 \int_0^T C_p d \log_{10} T = 2.303 \left[\text{Area} \right]_{T=0}^{T=T} \tag{44}$$

In practice heat capacities are usually measured from approximately 20° K to room temperature, and extrapolation is resorted to from ca. 20° K to $T = 0$. Such extrapolations may be made graphically, but more usually are made with the aid of Debye third power law (see Chapter 4), which yields heat capacities of solids at low temperatures. The uncertainty involved in such extrapolations is usually quite small, for the area between $T = 0$ and $T = $ ca. 20° is very small compared to the total area under the curve.

A plot of C_p vs. $\log_{10} T$ for anhydrous sodium sulfate is shown in Fig. 1. The area under the curve between $T = 14°$ and $T = 298.15°$ K is 15.488, while the area from $T = 0$ to $T = 14°$ is 0.026. Hence the absolute entropy per mole of sodium sulfate at 298.15° K is

$$S^0_{298.15° K} = 2.303(15.488 + 0.026)$$
$$= 35.73 \text{ eu mole}^{-1}$$

Absolute entropies, not only of solids but also of substances that are liquid or gaseous at room temperatures, can be obtained with the third law. The total absolute entropy of a substance in a particular state at a given temperature will be the sum of all the entropy changes the substance has to undergo in order to reach the particular state from the crystalline solid at absolute zero. Thus, if a substance is gaseous at 1 atm pressure and 25° C, the entropy of the gas must be the sum of the entropies involved in (a) heating the crystalline solid from $T = 0$ to $T = T_f$, the fusion point; (b) the entropy of fusion, $\Delta H_f / T_f$; (c) the entropy of heating the liquid from T_f to T_b, the normal boiling point; (d) the entropy of vaporization, $\Delta H_v / T_b$; and (e) the entropy of heating the

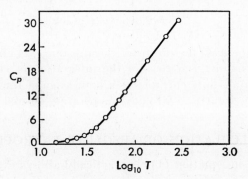

Fig. 1. Heat Capacity of Na_2SO_4 at Various Temperatures.[1]

gas from T_b to 298° K. These changes and the attendant entropies are shown in the following scheme:

$$\text{Solid} \xrightarrow[\;T=0\;]{\Delta S_1 = \int_0^{T_f} C_{p_s} d \ln T} \text{Solid} \xrightarrow[\;T=T_f\;]{\Delta S_f = \frac{\Delta H_f}{T_f}} \text{Liquid} \xrightarrow[\;T=T_f\;]{\Delta S_2 = \int_{T_f}^{T_b} C_{p_l} d \ln T}$$

$$\text{Liquid} \xrightarrow[\;T=T_b\;]{\Delta S_v = \frac{\Delta H_v}{T_b}} \text{Gas} \xrightarrow[\;T=T_b\;]{\Delta S_3 = \int_{T_b}^{298°} C_{p_g} d \ln T} \text{Gas}_{\;T=298°\,K}$$

It follows, therefore, that the absolute entropy of any substance at a temperature T may be written as

$$S_T = \int_0^{T_f} C_{p_s} d \ln T + \frac{\Delta H_f}{T_f} + \int_{T_f}^{T_b} C_{p_l} d \ln T + \frac{\Delta H_v}{T_b} + \int_{T_b}^{T} C_{p_g} d \ln T$$

$$(45)$$

If a substance is solid at temperature T, only the first integral applies with $T_f = T$; when it is liquid, the first three terms are used with $T_b = T$ now; when it is gaseous, the full equation must be used. Equation (45) may further be complicated if the solid undergoes any crystalline modifications between $T = 0$ and $T = T_f$. When such transitions occur, the

[1] Pitzer and Coulter, *J. Am. Chem. Soc.*, **60**, 1310 (1938).

entropy or entropies of transition must be added to the others in equation (45).

The steps involved in the calculation of the absolute entropy of a substance that is gaseous at 25° C may be illustrated with the following example. Messerly and Aston[1] have shown that at 1 atm pressure methyl chloride is solid between 0° K and 175.44° K, liquid between 175.44° K and 248.94° K, and gaseous thereafter, and that the entropies accompanying the heating of the solid, liquid, and gas between the temperatures indicated are

$$\Delta S_{\text{solid}} = \int_0^{175.44°} C_{p_s} d \ln T = 18.48 \text{ eu mole}^{-1}$$

$$\Delta S_{\text{liquid}} = \int_{175.44°}^{248.94°} C_{p_1} d \ln T = 6.24 \text{ eu mole}^{-1}$$

$$\Delta S_{\text{vapor}} = \int_{248.94°}^{298.15°} C_{p_g} d \ln T = 1.67 \text{ eu mole}^{-1}$$

Further, since the heat of fusion at 175.44° K is 1537 cal per mole, and the heat of vaporization at 248.94° K is 5147 cal per mole, the entropy changes accompanying fusion and vaporization must be

$$\Delta S_{\text{fusion}} = \frac{\Delta H_f}{T_f} = \frac{1537}{175.44} = 8.76 \text{ eu mole}^{-1}$$

$$\Delta S_{\text{vaporization}} = \frac{\Delta H_v}{T_b} = \frac{5147}{248.94} = 20.68 \text{ eu mole}^{-1}$$

On adding these entropies we obtain for the standard absolute entropy of methyl chloride at 298.15° K

$$S^0_{298.15° \text{ K}} = 18.48 + 8.76 + 6.24 + 20.68 + 1.67$$
$$= 55.83 \text{ eu mole}^{-1}$$

USE OF ABSOLUTE ENTROPIES IN CALCULATIONS

Absolute entropies are generally calculated at 25° C and 1 atm pressure. Values of these thermodynamic constants are available at present for most elements and for many compounds, both inorganic and organic. Tabulations may be found in books on thermodynamics, in some of the references listed at the end of the chapter and in the chemical literature.

In Table 1 are given standard absolute entropies at 25° C for a representative number of elements and compounds. From such individual entropies the entropy changes involved in chemical reactions may readily

---

[1] Messerly and Aston, *J. Am. Chem. Soc.*, **62**, 889 (1940).

TABLE 1

STANDARD ABSOLUTE ENTROPIES OF ELEMENTS AND COMPOUNDS AT 25° C
(Entropy units per gram atom or mole)

Substance	S^0	Substance	S^0
$H_2(g)$	31.21	$H_2O(l)$	16.72
C (diamond)	0.583	$H_2O(g)$	45.11
C (graphite)	1.36	$CO(g)$	47.30
$N_2(g)$	45.77	$CO_2(g)$	51.06
$O_2(g)$	49.00	$HgCl_2(s)$	34.6
Na(s)	12.2	$HgCl(s)$	23.5
Mg(s)	7.77	$CuI(s)$	23.1
S (rhombic)	7.62	$AgCl(s)$	22.97
S (monoclinic)	7.78	$AgI(s)$	27.6
$Cl_2(g)$	53.29	$Fe_2O_3(s)$	21.5
Fe(s)	6.49	$MgO(s)$	6.55
Cu(s)	7.97	$NaCl(s)$	17.3
$Br_2(g)$	58.64	$C_2H_6(g)$	54.85
Ag(s)	10.21	$CH_3OH(l)$	30.3
$I_2(s)$	27.9	$C_2H_5OH(l)$	38.4
$I_2(g)$	62.29	$C_6H_6(l)$	41.30
Hg(l)	18.5	$C_6H_5OH(l)$	34.0
Hg(g)	41.80	$CH_3COOH(l)$	38.2

be calculated. Suppose the entropy change is required for the reaction

$$C(s, \text{graphite}) + 2\ H_2(g) + \frac{1}{2}\ O_2(g) = CH_3OH(l) \qquad \Delta S^0_{25°C} = ? \quad (46)$$

Using the molar entropies given in Table 1, we get

$$\Delta S^0_{25°C} = S^0_{CH_3OH} - \left(S^0_C + 2\ S^0_{H_2} + \frac{1}{2}\ S^0_{O_2} \right)$$
$$= 30.3 - 1.36 - 62.42 - 24.50$$
$$= -58.0 \text{ eu}$$

In a similar manner may be calculated ΔS^0 values for other reactions at 25° C provided the necessary absolute entropies are known. To obtain the entropy changes at temperatures other than 25° C, we need only apply equation (41). In terms of this equation the entropy change for any reaction at a temperature T in relation to ΔS^0 at 298° K is given by

$$\Delta S^0_T - \Delta S^0_{298°K} = \int_{298°K}^{T} \frac{\Delta C_p dT}{T}$$
$$\Delta S^0_T = \Delta S^0_{298°K} + \int_{298°K}^{T} \frac{\Delta C_p dT}{T} \qquad (47)$$

The evaluation of the integral has already been discussed.

REFERENCES FOR FURTHER READING

1. B. F. Dodge, *Chemical Engineering Thermodynamics*, McGraw-Hill Book Company, Inc., New York, 1944.
2. S. Glasstone, *Thermodynamics for Chemists*, D. Van Nostrand Company, Inc., New York, 1947.
3. K. K. Kelley, Bureau of Mines Bulletins Nos. 350, 384, 394, 406, and 434.
4. I. M. Klotz, *Chemical Thermodynamics*, Prentice-Hall, Inc., New York, 1950.
5. G. N. Lewis and M. Randall, *Thermodynamics and the Free Energy of Chemical Substances*, McGraw-Hill Book Company, Inc., New York, 1923.
6. F. D. Rossini, *Chemical Thermodynamics*, John Wiley & Sons, Inc., New York, 1950.
7. F. D. Rossini and associates, *Selected Values of Properties of Hydrocarbons*, Circ. Natl. Bur. Standards C461, 1947; *Selected Values of Chemical Thermodynamic Properties*, Circ. Natl. Bur. Standards 500, 1952, U.S. Government Printing Office, Washington, D. C.
8. L. Steiner, *Introduction to Chemical Thermodynamics*, McGraw-Hill Book Company, Inc., New York, 1948.
9. Taylor and Glasstone, *Treatise on Physical Chemistry*, D. Van Nostrand Company, Inc., New York, 1942, Vol. I.

PROBLEMS

1. A quantity of ideal gas in an isolated system is expanded isothermally and reversibly at 400° K from a volume V_1 to V_2. During the expansion the gas absorbs 200 cal of heat from the reservoir in contact with it. Find (a) the entropy change of the gas, (b) the entropy change of the reservoir, and (c) the entropy change of the whole system.

   Ans. (a) 0.50 eu; (b) 0.50 eu; (c) zero.

2. If the gas in problem 1 is expanded from V_1 to V_2 isothermally but irreversibly at 400° K with an absorption of 100 cal of heat, what will be the entropy changes for (a) the gas, (b) the reservoir, and (c) the complete system?

3. Suppose the gas in problem 1 expands freely from V_1 to V_2 at 400° K. What will be the entropy changes for (a) the gas, (b) the reservoir, and (c) the entire system?

4. Calculate the change in entropy suffered by 3 moles of an ideal gas, for which $C_p = \frac{5}{2} R$ cal mole^{-1} degree^{-1}, on being heated at constant pressure from a temperature of 27° to 327° C.   *Ans.* $\Delta S = 10.35$ eu.

5. For an ideal gas $C_p = \frac{5}{2} R$ cal mole^{-1} degree^{-1}. Find the change in the entropy of 3 moles of the gas on being cooled from 175° to 25° C at a constant volume of 50 liters.

6. Assuming C_p for N_2 to be constant and equal to $\frac{7}{2} R$, what will be the change in entropy upon heating 10 g of the gas from 0 to 100° C (a) at constant pressure, (b) at constant volume?

7. Using the equation for C_p as a function of T for $CH_4(g)$ given in the last chapter, calculate the entropy change which results from heating 2 moles of the gas from 300° to 600° K at constant pressure.   *Ans.* $\Delta S = 14.33$ eu.

8. Assuming that for $CH_4(g)$ $C_p - C_v = R$, repeat the calculation of the preceding problem to find the entropy change resulting from heating 2 moles of the gas from 300° to 600° K at constant volume.

9. The atomic heat capacity of solid Mo is given by the equation

$$C_p = 5.69 + 1.88 \times 10^{-3}\, T - \frac{0.503 \times 10^5}{T^2}$$

Find the change in entropy which accompanies the heating of 1 atomic weight of Mo from 0° C to its melting point, 2620° C.   *Ans.* ΔS = 18.6 eu.

10. What is the entropy change in the isothermal compression of 200 g of N_2 from a pressure of 1 to 5 atm at 25° C? Assume that N_2 is a perfect gas.

11. One mole of a perfect gas contained in a 10-liter vessel at 27° C is permitted to expand freely into an evacuated vessel of 10-liter capacity so that the final volume is 20 liters. What amount of work is done and what amount of heat is absorbed in the process? What is the change in the entropy accompanying the process?

12. Calculate the change in entropy suffered by 2 moles of an ideal gas on being heated from a volume of 100 liters at 50° C to a volume of 150 liters at 150° C. For the gas C_v = 7.88 cal mole^{-1} degree^{-1}.   *Ans.* ΔS = 5.88 eu.

13. What is the difference in entropy between 1 mole of N_2 at standard conditions and 1 mole of N_2 at 200° C when the molar volume is 50 liters? Assume that C_p is $\frac{7}{2}R$ and that N_2 behaves ideally.

14. Calculate the change in entropy experienced by 2 moles of an ideal gas on being heated from a pressure of 5 atm at 50° C to a pressure of 10 atm at 100° C. For the gas C_p = 9.88 cal mole^{-1} degree^{-1}.   *Ans.* ΔS = 0.08 eu.

15. For a certain gas C_p = 12.0 cal mole^{-1} degree^{-1}. What will be the change in entropy of 10 moles of the gas when it is expanded from a volume of 200 liters at 3 atm pressure to a volume of 400 liters at 1 atm pressure?

16. C_p = 7.05 + 35.60 × 10^{-3} T − 216.9 × 10^{-7} T^2 cal mole^{-1} degree^{-1} for $CHCl_3(g)$. Assuming this gas to be ideal, calculate the change in entropy involved in heating 2 moles of the gas from a volume of 100 liters at 500° K to a volume of 70 liters at 700° K.

17. CH_3COOH melts at 16.6° C with a heat of fusion of 44.0 cal/g. Calculate the entropy of fusion per mole.   *Ans.* 9.13 eu.

18. The heat of sublimation of CO_2 is 6260 cal/mole, while the sublimation temperature is 194.6° K. Find the entropy of sublimation for 2 moles of CO_2.

19. In the transformation $AgI(\alpha) = AgI(\beta)$ the heat of transition is +1530 cal/mole, while the transition temperature is 146.5° C. What will be the entropy of transition?

20. A certain liquid obeys Trouton's rule. What will be the entropy change on vaporization of 1 mole of the liquid at its normal boiling point?

21. The heat of fusion of a certain solid is 4000 cal/mole. What will be the net change in entropy involved in melting and then resolidifying 2 moles of the substance at its melting point, 80° C?

22. One g of ice at 0° C is added to 10 g of H_2O at the boiling point. What will be the final temperature, and what is the entropy change accompanying the process? Assume that the heat of fusion of H_2O is 80 cal/g and the specific heat 1 cal/g-degree.   *Ans.* t = 83.6° C; ΔS = 0.11 eu.

23. What is the entropy change involved in transforming 1 g of ice at 0° C and 1 atm pressure into vapor at 150° C and 0.1 atm pressure? Assume that the specific heats of liquid and gaseous water are respectively 1.0 and 0.45 cal/g-degree.

24. The heat capacities of the solid and liquid forms of a compound A are respectively 18.3 and 25.2 cal mole^{-1} degree^{-1}. The compound melts under 1 atm

pressure at a temperature of 160° C with a heat of fusion of 2460 cal/mole. What will be the entropy change of the process $A(l) \longrightarrow A(s)$ at 150° C?

25. Eastman and McGavock [*J. Am. Chem. Soc.*, **59**, 145 (1937)] list the atomic heat capacities of rhombic S from 15° K to 360° K. From the data of Table II in this article determine by a graphical method the entropy of rhombic S per mole at 298.2° K.

26. Kemp and Egan [*J. Am. Chem. Soc.*, **60**, 1521 (1938)] found that for propane $\Delta H_f = 842.2$ cal/mole at 85.45° K, the melting point, and $\Delta H_v = 4487$ cal/mole at 231.04° K, the normal boiling point. They further found that for heating solid propane from 0° K to 85.45° K $\Delta S^0 = 9.95$ eu, while for heating the liquid from 85.45° K to 231.04° K $\Delta S^0 = 21.06$ eu. From these data find the standard entropy of gaseous propane at 231.04° K. *Ans. $S^0 = 60.29$ eu.*

27. From the data of Table 1 find the standard entropy changes accompanying the following reactions at 25° C:

    (a) $CO(g) + 2 H_2(g) = CH_3OH(l)$
    (b) $2 HgCl(s) = 2 Hg(l) + Cl_2(g)$
    (c) $MgO(s) + H_2(g) = H_2O(l) + Mg(s)$.

28. For a certain reaction $\Delta S^0_{298.2° K} = -59.20$ eu, and

$$\Delta C_p = -7.58 + 17.42 \times 10^{-3} T - \frac{3.985 \times 10^5}{T^2}$$

Find from these data ΔS^0 of the reaction of 400° K.

11

The Free Energy

MAXIMUM WORK AND TENDENCY TOWARD CHANGE

All changes in nature are due to the tendency on the part of systems to reach a condition of maximum stability commensurate with the state of each system, i.e., equilibrium. Once equilibrium has been reached, the propensity toward further change disappears, and we say that the system is stable. As long as a system is away from equilibrium it will experience a tendency to reach that state, and the tendency will be greater the greater the distance from equilibrium.

Work results only when the tendency of systems to attain equilibrium is harnessed in some way. From a system in equilibrium no work can be obtained, but a system on the way to equilibrium may be made to yield useful work. The amount of work that can be recovered from any system undergoing a change depends both on the nature of the change and the manner in which the system is harnessed. However, for each particular process there is a maximum amount of work the system can possibly do, and this maximum work may be taken as a measure of the tendency of the system in question to undergo change.

A system undergoing change can perform maximum work only when the change is carried out reversibly. If the process is not completely reversible, the amount of work obtainable is always below the maximum, the difference appearing as heat. The driving force behind the change is still, however, the maximum work difference between the final and initial states, for this difference still represents the highest possible quantity of energy that *tends* to appear in utilizable form as a result of the process. Whether it does appear or not depends entirely on the manner in which the process is conducted, and in no way affects the conclusion that the maximum work a process *may* perform, if conducted properly, is the true measure of the driving tendency behind the process.

THE FREE ENERGY

The maximum work a process may yield is not necessarily the amount of energy available for doing useful work, even though the process is conducted reversibly. Of the total amount of work available, a certain amount has to be utilized for the performance of pressure-volume work against the atmosphere due to contraction or expansion of the system during the process. For a process taking place at constant temperature and pressure, and involving a volume change from V_1 to V_2, the work done against the atmosphere is $P(V_2 - V_1) = P\Delta V$. Since this work is accomplished at the expense of the maximum work yielded by the process, the *net* amount of energy available for work other than pressure-volume against the confining atmosphere must be

$$\text{Net available energy at } T \text{ and } P = w_m - P\Delta V \tag{1}$$

To bring out more precisely the nature of the maximum net energy available from a process, let us define a new quantity F, called the *free energy* of a system, by the relation

$$F = H - TS \tag{2}$$

where H is the enthalpy and S the entropy of the system. Since H, S, and T are characteristic of the state of the system, F must also have this attribute; i.e., *F must be a function characteristic of the state of the system only and be independent of the manner of arriving at that state.* The change in free energy between any two states will be, therefore,

$$\Delta F = F_2 - F_1 \tag{3a}$$
$$= (H_2 - T_2 S_2) - (H_1 - T_1 S_1) \tag{3b}$$

and when the temperature is constant equation (3b) becomes

$$\Delta F = (H_2 - H_1) - T(S_2 - S_1)$$
$$= \Delta H - T\Delta S \tag{4}$$

At constant temperature $T\Delta S = q_r$. Again, when the pressure is also constant, $\Delta H = \Delta E + P\Delta V$. Inserting these quantities into equation (4) we get

$$\Delta F = \Delta E + P\Delta V - q_r$$
$$= -(q_r - \Delta E - P\Delta V)$$

But, by the first law $q_r - \Delta E = w_m$, and therefore,

$$\Delta F = -(w_m - P\Delta V) \tag{5}$$

Comparison of equations (1) and (5) shows that $-\Delta F$ represents the maximum net energy at constant T and P available for doing useful work; i.e., the net available energy under the specified conditions results from a *decrease* in the free energy content of the system on passing from the initial to the final state.

An alternate, but equivalent, way of defining F is through the relation

$$F = A + PV \tag{6}$$

where A is the maximum work content or Helmholtz free energy, and P and V are the pressure and volume of the system. From equation (6) ΔF follows as

$$\Delta F = \Delta A + P_2 V_2 - P_1 V_1 \tag{7}$$

which at constant pressure becomes

$$\Delta F = \Delta A + P \Delta V \tag{8}$$

However, at constant temperature $\Delta A = -w_m,$[1] and hence for constant T and P equation (8) reduces to equation (5).

DEPENDENCE OF F ON VARIABLES OF SYSTEM

The free energy of any pure substance is a function of temperature and pressure. Therefore,

$$dF = \left(\frac{\partial F}{\partial T}\right)_P dT + \left(\frac{\partial F}{\partial P}\right)_T dP \tag{9}$$

Again, from complete differentiation of equation (2) we get

$$dF = dH - TdS - SdT \tag{10}$$

Now, it was shown in the last chapter, equation (22), that

$$TdS = dH - VdP$$

and so equation (10) becomes

$$\begin{aligned} dF &= dH - (dH - VdP) - SdT \\ &= -SdT + VdP \end{aligned} \tag{11}$$

Finally, comparison of equations (9) and (11) shows that

$$\left(\frac{\partial F}{\partial T}\right)_P = -S \tag{12}$$

and

$$\left(\frac{\partial F}{\partial P}\right)_T = V \tag{13}$$

---

[1] See Chapter 2, p. 66.

Equation (12) is difficult to apply directly, but equation (13) is not. The use of the latter equation will be considered later in the chapter.

THE FREE ENERGY CHANGE

The free energy change for any process, being a function of the initial and final states of the system only, is a definite quantity at any given temperature and pressure and varies as these two variables are changed. As in the case of heat contents and internal energies, the absolute values of the free energies of substances are not known, and hence only differences can be dealt with. The free energy changes of processes are expressed in equations similar to thermochemical ones and can be similarly added and subtracted. Thus, for instance, the free energy changes for the two reactions below are:

$$SO_2(g) + Cl_2(g) = SO_2Cl_2(g) \qquad\qquad \Delta F_{298°K} = -2{,}270 \text{ cal} \qquad (14a)$$
$$S(\text{rhom.}) + O_2(g) + Cl_2(g) = SO_2Cl_2(g) \quad \Delta F_{298°K} = -74{,}060 \text{ cal} \quad (14b)$$

If equation (14b) is subtracted from (14a), we find that

$$SO_2(g) + Cl_2(g) - S(\text{rhom.}) - O_2(g) - Cl_2(g) = 0$$
$$\Delta F_{298°K} = +71{,}790 \text{ cal}$$

or $S(\text{rhom.}) + O_2(g) = SO_2(g)$ $\qquad \Delta F_{298°K} = -71{,}790 \text{ cal} \quad (14c)$

Consequently, the formation of sulfur dioxide from rhombic sulfur and gaseous oxygen proceeds with a free energy decrease of 71,790 cal; i.e., the free energy content of $(S + O_2)$ is greater than that of SO_2 by this amount.

The sign of the free energy change of a process is very significant. When the driving tendency of a reaction is from left to right, energy is emitted on reaction, and the sign of ΔF is negative. A minus sign denotes, therefore, that the reaction tends to proceed spontaneously. When the tendency is from right to left, however, net work equivalent to ΔF has to be absorbed in order for the reaction to proceed in the direction indicated, and ΔF is positive. A positive sign for ΔF signifies, therefore, that the reaction in the given direction is not spontaneous. Finally, when the system is in equilibrium, there is no tendency to proceed in either direction, no work can be done by the system, and hence $\Delta F = 0$. These three possible conditions for the free energy change of a process *at constant temperature and pressure* may be summarized as follows:

$$
\begin{array}{llll}
A + B \longrightarrow C + D & \Delta F = - & \text{(spontaneous)} & (15a) \\
A + B \longleftarrow C + D & \Delta F = + & \text{(nonspontaneous)} & (15b) \\
A + B \rightleftharpoons C + D & \Delta F = 0 & \text{(equilibrium)} & (15c)
\end{array}
$$

The arrows indicate the directions the reaction tends to follow spontaneously for the given sign of the free energy change.

A negative free energy change for a process does not necessarily mean that the process will take place. It is merely an indication that the process *can* occur provided the conditions are right. Thus oxygen and hydrogen in the ratio of 1:2 can coexist indefinitely at room temperature without combining, although ΔF for the reaction at 25° C is $-56,690$ cal per mole of water. When a catalyst like platinized asbestos is introduced, however, the reaction proceeds with explosive violence. Even with a catalyst the reaction would have been impossible had not the potentiality to react been present. It is the sign of the free energy change which determines whether the potentiality to react exists, and it is the magnitude of the free energy change which tells us how large that potentiality is.

RELATION BETWEEN ΔF AND ΔH

The relation between ΔF and ΔH at any temperature T is given by equation (4). An alternate relation between the two quantities can be obtained as follows. If equation (4) be differentiated with respect to T at constant P, then

$$\left[\frac{\partial(\Delta F)}{\partial T}\right]_P - \left[\frac{\partial(\Delta H)}{\partial T}\right]_P = -T\left[\frac{\partial(\Delta S)}{\partial T}\right]_P - \Delta S \qquad (16)$$

Since, however, $\qquad \left[\frac{\partial(\Delta H)}{\partial T}\right]_P = \Delta C_p \qquad \left[\frac{\partial(\Delta S)}{\partial T}\right]_P = \frac{\Delta C_p}{T}$

equation (16) becomes

$$\left[\frac{\partial(\Delta F)}{\partial T}\right]_P - \Delta C_p = -\frac{T\Delta C_p}{T} - \Delta S$$

and therefore, $\qquad \left[\frac{\partial(\Delta F)}{\partial T}\right]_P = -\Delta S \qquad (17)$

On substitution of equation (17) into equation (4) we obtain the *Gibbs-Helmholtz equation*

$$\Delta F - \Delta H = T\left[\frac{\partial(\Delta F)}{\partial T}\right]_P \qquad (18)$$

The physical significance of equations (4) or (18) is best illustrated by an example. Consider the reaction

$$Zn(s) + CuSO_4 \text{ (solution)} = ZnSO_4 \text{ (solution)} + Cu(s)$$

When this reaction is permitted to take place in an open beaker by adding zinc to a solution of copper sulfate, heat of reaction equal to ΔH is obtained. If, on the other hand, the same reaction is carried out reversibly by allowing the process to proceed in an electromotive cell, and forcing the voltage established to do work against another voltage only infinitesimally smaller than that of the cell, then, instead of all heat, work equivalent to ΔF will be obtained. The difference between the work so obtained and the heat which would have been liberated had the reaction been carried out completely irreversibly, as in an open beaker, is given by the Gibbs-Helmholtz equation, and is equal to either $-T\Delta S$ or $T[\partial(\Delta F)/\partial T]_P$.

The term $-T\Delta S = T[\partial(\Delta F)/\partial T]_P$ represents the heat interchange between the system and its surroundings when the process is conducted *isothermally and reversibly*, for

$$-T\Delta S = -T\frac{q_r}{T} = -q_r$$

and hence, $\Delta H - \Delta F = q_r$ (19)

When ΔH is greater than ΔF, the difference q_r is positive, and energy is absorbed as heat from the surroundings. On the other hand, when ΔF is greater than ΔH, q_r is negative, and heat is evolved to the surroundings. Finally, in the special case when $\Delta H = \Delta F$, heat is neither absorbed nor evolved by the system, and hence there is no change in entropy.

VARIATION OF ΔF WITH TEMPERATURE

The manner in which ΔF varies with temperature may be obtained by differentiating the quantity $\Delta F/T$ with respect to T at constant pressure. Then

$$\left[\frac{\partial(\Delta F/T)}{\partial T}\right]_P = \frac{T[\partial(\Delta F)/\partial T]_P - \Delta F}{T^2}$$

But, according to equation (18)

$$T\left[\frac{\partial(\Delta F)}{\partial T}\right]_P = \Delta F - \Delta H$$

Therefore, $$\left[\frac{\partial(\Delta F/T)}{\partial T}\right]_P = \frac{\Delta F - \Delta H - \Delta F}{T^2}$$

$$= -\frac{\Delta H}{T^2}$$ (20)

Equation (20) gives the variation of ΔF with temperature in terms of ΔH and may be employed to calculate ΔF at one temperature from that at another. To do this, ΔH as a function of temperature, deduced by the method outlined in Chapter 9, must be available, as well as one value of

ΔF at a known temperature. With such information at hand, equation (20) can be integrated in the manner illustrated below.

Example: Suppose ΔF is sought at 1000° K for the reaction

$$\frac{1}{2} N_2(g) + \frac{3}{2} H_2(g) = NH_3(g) \qquad \Delta F_{298.2° K} = -3980 \text{ cal} \tag{21}$$

For this reaction it was already shown, p. 285, that ΔH is given by

$$\Delta H = -9190 - 7.12 T + 3.182 \times 10^{-3} T^2 - 2.64 \times 10^{-7} T^3$$

Substituting this value of ΔH in equation (20), we have

$$\left[\frac{\partial(\Delta F/T)}{\partial T} \right]_P = -\frac{\Delta H}{T^2} = \frac{9190}{T^2} + \frac{7.12}{T} - 3.182 \times 10^{-3} + 2.64 \times 10^{-7} T$$

On integration this expression becomes

$$\frac{\Delta F}{T} = -\frac{9190}{T} + 7.12 \ln T - 3.182 \times 10^{-3} T + 1.32 \times 10^{-7} T^2 + I$$

where I is a constant of integration. Hence,

$$\Delta F = -9190 + 7.12 T \ln T - 3.182 \times 10^{-3} T^2 + 1.32 \times 10^{-7} T^3 + IT$$

Inserting now the value of $\Delta F = -3980$ cal at $T = 298.2°$ K from equation (21), and solving for I, we find that

$$-3980 = -9190 + 7.12(298.2) \ln (298.2) - 3.182 \times 10^{-3}(298.2)^2$$
$$+ 1.32 \times 10^{-7}(298.2)^3 + I(298.2)$$
$$I = -21.61$$

Consequently ΔF as a function of the temperature follows as

$$\Delta F = -9190 + 7.12 T \ln T - 3.182 \times 10^{-3} T^2 + 1.32 \times 10^{-7} T^3 - 21.61 T \tag{22}$$

and hence at $T = 1000°$ K ΔF is

$$\Delta F = -9190 + 7.12(1000) \ln (1000) - 3.182 \times 10^{-3}(1000)^2$$
$$+ 1.32 \times 10^{-7}(1000)^3 - 21.61(1000)$$
$$= +15,340 \text{ cal}$$

We see, therefore, that although the formation of ammonia will proceed spontaneously at 298° K, for ΔF is negative, the same process at 1000° K will be nonspontaneous to the extent of 15,340 cals.

The method described for calculating ΔF at one temperature from that at another is thermodynamically exact and is conditioned only by the accuracy of the data employed. As in the case of heat of reaction, great care must be exercised that calculations made are within the range over which the thermal data have been determined. Only with precise data and with due regard for the limits of their validity can great trust be placed in the result of such calculations.

OTHER APPLICATIONS OF ΔF EQUATIONS

ΔF equations such as equation (22) are useful not only for calculating the free energy change at any temperature T, but also for evaluating ΔS and ΔH. ΔS is readily obtained by differentiation with respect to temperature at constant pressure of the ΔF expression in accordance with equation (17). In turn, ΔH may be obtained either by differentiating $\Delta F/T$ with respect to T and using equation (20) or by evaluating first both ΔF and ΔS, and subsequently employing equation (4) to find ΔH.

Example: Suppose ΔS and ΔH for the ammonia synthesis, equation (21), are to be calculated at 1000° K. To obtain ΔS we differentiate first equation (22) with respect to T. Then,

$$\left[\frac{\partial(\Delta F)}{\partial T}\right]_P = -\Delta S = 7.12 + 7.12\ln T - 6.364 \times 10^{-3}\,T + 3.96 \times 10^{-7}\,T^2 - 21.61$$
$$\Delta S = 14.49 - 7.12\ln T + 6.364 \times 10^{-3}\,T - 3.96 \times 10^{-7}\,T^2$$

On substituting $T = 1000°$ K, we find thus $\Delta S_{1000°\,K} = -28.74$ eu. Having now ΔF and ΔS at 1000° K, equation (4) yields for ΔH

$$\Delta H = T\Delta S + \Delta F$$
$$= (1000)(-28.74) + 15,340$$
$$= -13,400 \text{ cal at } 1000° \text{ K}$$

This result is identical with the one found for the heat of this reaction at 1000° K on p. 286 in Chapter 9.

FREE ENERGY AND PRESSURE

It has already been shown that the variation of the free energy of a substance with pressure at constant temperature is given by equation (13), namely,

$$\left(\frac{\partial F}{\partial P}\right)_T = V \tag{13}$$

where V is the volume of the substance at temperature T and pressure P. From equation (13) the change in free energy attending a change in total pressure on a substance from P_1 to P_2 at the constant temperature T follows as

$$\int_{F_1}^{F_2} dF = \int_{P_1}^{P_2} V\,dP$$
$$\Delta F = F_2 - F_1 = \int_{P_1}^{P_2} V\,dP \tag{23}$$

To evaluate the integral between the given limits, V must be known as a function of P.

For ideal gases equation (23) is readily integrable. Since for an ideal gas $V = nRT/P$, equation (23) becomes

$$\Delta F = \int_{P_1}^{P_2} V \, dP$$

$$= \int_{P_1}^{P_2} \frac{nRT \, dP}{P}$$

$$= nRT \ln \frac{P_2}{P_1} \tag{24}$$

Equation (24) gives the change in free energy of n moles of an ideal gas due to change in pressure from P_1 to P_2 at the constant temperature T.

Equation (24) is also applicable for obtaining the free energy change with change in osmotic pressure of ideal solutions obeying van't Hoff's law, $\Pi V = nRT$. When n moles of solute are transferred from a solution of osmotic pressure Π_1 to a solution where the pressure is Π_2, the change in free energy involved is

$$\Delta F = nRT \ln \frac{\Pi_2}{\Pi_1} \tag{25}$$

But, since $\Pi = (nRT/V) = CRT$, ΔF is also

$$\Delta F = nRT \ln \frac{C_2}{C_1} \tag{26}$$

where C is the concentration in moles per liter. As will become apparent from the discussion given later in the chapter, equation (26) is valid not only for dilute solutions obeying van't Hoff's law, but also for *ideal* solutions of any concentration.

As solids and liquids are only slightly compressible, their volume may be considered essentially constant over appreciable pressure ranges. Equation (23) integrates, then, simply to

$$\Delta F = \int_{P_1}^{P_2} V \, dP$$

$$= V(P_2 - P_1) \tag{27}$$

where ΔF is the free energy change of the solid or liquid due to change in pressure from P_1 to P_2. Such free energy changes with pressure usually are small compared to the free energy changes in gases and solutions and may be disregarded; i.e., the free energies of pure solids and liquids may be considered to be constant over a fairly wide pressure range at any given temperature.

THE FUGACITY AND ACTIVITY CONCEPTS

When equation (24) is applied either to real gases at high pressures or to nonideal solutions, especially those containing electrolytes even at low concentrations, it is found that the change in free energy is not reproduced by this simple relation. The difficulty is, of course, that in cases of nonideal behavior V is no longer given by nRT/P, but by some more complicated function of the pressure. To obtain the free energy change with pressure for the nonideal substance, the exact dependence of the volume on the pressure must be known before equation (23) can be integrated. Since such volume dependence may be highly individual, the result would be that ΔF in each case would be given by an equation different in form, and the simplicity and generality of equation (24) would be destroyed.

G. N. Lewis first showed how nonideal systems may be handled without discarding the simple free energy equations deduced for ideal systems. To do this he introduced two new thermodynamic quantities, *fugacity* and *activity*. To understand these quantities, consider first a system composed of liquid water and its vapor. At constant temperature there is a definite pressure of water vapor above the liquid. This vapor comes from the liquid phase and represents a tendency of the liquid to pass into the vapor phase. In turn, the vapor tends to escape the gaseous state by condensing to liquid. When these two *escaping tendencies* become equal, the system reaches equilibrium, i.e., the vapor pressure becomes constant at constant temperature. We may, say, therefore, that a state of equilibrium is the point at which the escaping tendency of a constituent is the same in all parts of the system.

The idea that each substance in a particular state has a definite tendency to escape from that state is perfectly general. Lewis pointed out that this escaping tendency can be measured by a quantity f, called the *fugacity*, which is related to the free energy content of the substance *per mole*, F, by the expression

$$F = RT \ln f + B \qquad (28)$$

where B is a constant dependent only on the temperature and the nature of the substance. Since absolute values of the free energy are not known, B cannot be evaluated. However, we can get around this difficulty by referring all free energy measurements to a standard reference point. If we designate by F^0 the free energy and by f^0 the fugacity in this standard state, then F^0 is given by

$$F^0 = RT \ln f^0 + B \qquad (29)$$

and the free energy difference between any state in which the free energy is F and the standard state is given by

$$F - F^0 = RT \ln \frac{f}{f^0} \tag{30}$$

Consequently, the free energy content of a substance in any state in terms of the free energy in the standard state follows as

$$F = F^0 + RT \ln \frac{f}{f^0} \tag{31}$$

If we write now

$$\frac{f}{f^0} = a \tag{32}$$

equation (31) becomes

$$F = F^0 + RT \ln a \tag{33}$$

The quantity a is called the *activity*. From equation (33) we see that the free energy per mole of any substance at a teperature T may be

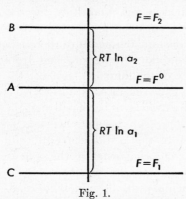

Fig. 1.

written as the free energy of the substance in the standard state at temperature T, and the quantity $RT \ln a$. In the standard state $F = F^0$, $RT \ln a = 0$, and hence $a = 1$; i.e., in the standard state the activity must be unity. In any other state the value of the activity will depend on the difference $(F - F^0)$, or in other words, on the distance of the particular state from the standard state. This relation between F and F^0 can best be understood from Fig. 1. Let the vertical line represent a free energy axis.

On this axis A represents the arbitrary point chosen as standard state, while B represents another point where the free energy is F_2. Then equation (33) states that the difference in free energies of a substance between points B and A is $RT \ln a_2$. Similarly, the free energy difference between a point like C and the reference state is given by $RT \ln a_1$.

In terms of equation (33) the difference in free energy per mole occasioned on passing from one state where the free energy is F_1 and the activity is a_1, to another state where the free energy is F_2 and the activity is a_2, must be

$$\Delta F = F_2 - F_1 = (F^0 + RT \ln a_2) - (F^0 + RT \ln a_1)$$

$$\Delta F = RT \ln \frac{a_2}{a_1} \tag{34a}$$

or, for n moles,

$$\Delta F = nRT \ln \frac{a_2}{a_1} \tag{34b}$$

The striking similarity of equations (34a) and (34b) to equations (24) and (25) suggests that we may consider the activity as the thermodynamic counterpart of the concentration or pressure. When activities of gases and solutions, as determined according to well-worked-out thermodynamic methods, are substituted for pressures and concentrations in equations (24) and (25), exact free energy calculations are possible. The reason for this exactness is that evaluation of activities, unlike that of concentrations and pressures, takes into account not only stoichiometric relationships, but also any mutual attractions between molecules, interactions between solute and solvent in a solution, and ionization. These effects complicate ideal behavior and are the factors responsible for the breakdown of the thermodynamic equations for ideal systems when applied to real substances.

Before activities of gases, liquids, solids, and solutions can be evaluated, the particular state to be chosen as standard must be defined. This definition may be purely arbitrary, but certain established conventions are in general use at present, and these will now be discussed.

STANDARD STATE FOR GASES

As the standard state for a gas at any given temperature is taken the state in which the fugacity is equal to unity, namely, $f^0 = 1$. On the basis of this definition, the activity of any gas becomes equal to the fugacity, for

$$a = \frac{f}{f^0} = \frac{f}{1} = f \qquad (35)$$

and hence for a gas equation (33) may be written as

$$F = F^0 + RT \ln f \qquad (36)$$

For an ideal gas the fugacity is equal to the pressure. Since, however, any gas can be brought into an ideal state by reducing its pressure to zero, we can complete the definition of the fugacity of any gas by stating that, in general,

$$f = P \text{ as } P \to 0 \qquad (37a)$$

or that

$$\lim_{P \to 0} \frac{f}{P} = 1 \qquad (37b)$$

As long as a gas is ideal the ratio f/P remains equal to unity. However, as soon as a gas deviates from ideal behavior f is no longer equal to P, and the ratio f/P becomes something other than one. The further this ratio is from unity the greater is the nonideality. Consequently, this ratio, called the *activity coefficient* of a gas, and represented by the symbol γ, gives a direct measure of the extent to which any real gas deviates from ideality at any given pressure and temperature.

DETERMINATION OF ACTIVITY COEFFICIENTS OF GASES

Determination of the activity coefficients of gases at any temperature T is based on equation (13), namely, $dF = VdP$. Since F^0 is a constant at at any given temperature, differentiation of equation (36) yields $dF = RTd \ln f$, and so

$$d \ln f = \frac{V}{RT} dP \qquad (38)$$

Let us define now a quantity α as

$$\alpha = V - \frac{RT}{P} \qquad (39)$$

and therefore

$$V = \frac{RT}{P} + \alpha \qquad (40)$$

Insertion of equation (40) into (38) yields

$$d \ln f = d \ln P + \frac{\alpha}{RT} dP$$

or

$$d \ln \gamma = d \ln \frac{f}{P} = \frac{\alpha}{RT} dP \qquad (41)$$

Equation (41) may be integrated now between the limits $P = 0$, where $\gamma = 1$, and P with its value of γ. We get thus

$$\int_{\gamma=1}^{\gamma} d \ln \gamma = \frac{1}{RT} \int_{P=0}^{P} \alpha dP$$

and

$$\ln \gamma = \frac{1}{RT} \int_{P=0}^{P} \alpha dP \qquad (42)$$

Equation (42) is the expression used for obtaining γ. To do this, when an equation of state for the gas is available, α is substituted as a function of P and the integration performed between $P = 0$ and any desired pressure. If, however, only P–V data are available at a given temperature, then α is plotted against P, and the integration is performed graphically.

The general conclusions deduced from such calculations may be summarized as follows. For all gases at relatively low pressures, pressure may be substituted for fugacity in thermodynamic equations without the introduction of any serious error. The exact pressure up to which this is permissible cannot be specified, for it will depend on the nature of the gas in question, the temperature, and the accuracy required. At higher pressures, however, such a substitution may lead to considerable, and even very large, errors, as may be judged from Table 1. An idea of the error that may be involved in the substitution of pressure for fugacity in ΔF calculations can be gathered from the following example.

TABLE 1

RELATION BETWEEN FUGACITY AND PRESSURE FOR SOME GASES

P (atm)	H₂ at 100° C		NH₃ at 200° C		CO₂ at 60° C	
	f (atm)	γ	f (atm)	γ	f (atm)	γ
0	0	1.00	0	1.000	0	1.000
25	25.3	1.01	23.9	0.954	23.2	0.928
50	51.5	1.03	45.7	0.913	42.8	0.856
100	105	1.05	84.8	0.848	70.4	0.704
200	222	1.11	144	0.720	91.0	0.455
300	351	1.17	193	0.642	112	0.373
400	492	1.23	—	—	—	—
500	650	1.30	—	—	—	—

Example: Calculate the free energy change accompanying the compression of 1 mole of CO_2 at 60° C from 25 to 300 atm. Using pressures first, we obtain

$$\Delta F = nRT \ln \frac{P_2}{P_1}$$

$$= 1 \times 1.987 \times 333 \times 2.303 \log_{10} \frac{300}{25}$$

$$= 1640 \text{ cal}$$

Using instead the fugacities given in Table 1 and equation (34b)

$$\Delta F = nRT \ln \frac{a_2}{a_1} = nRT \ln \frac{f_2}{f_1}$$

$$= 1 \times 1.987 \times 333 \times 2.303 \log_{10} \frac{112}{23.2}$$

$$= 1040 \text{ cal}$$

The approximate calculation gives here, therefore, a result 57.7% too high.

STANDARD STATES FOR SOLIDS AND LIQUIDS

As the standard state of a pure solid or liquid is taken the solid or liquid at 1 atm pressure at each temperature. In this state of the solid or liquid $a = 1$ and $F = F^0$. Since, as we have seen, the free energies of solids and liquids are not very dependent on pressure, for these $a = 1$, to a near approximation, at all temperatures and for wide ranges of pressure.

STANDARD STATES FOR COMPONENTS OF A SOLUTION

The activity of each component of a solution is unity in the standard state of the given component, but the particular concentration of a solution that corresponds to each of these standard states is different. This difference is due to the manner in which the standard states of solute and solvent are defined. As the standard state of the solvent is chosen the *pure solvent*. On the other hand, as the standard state of the solute is taken the concentration of solution in which $a = 1$, the activity being evaluated on the basis that $a/C = 1$ as $C \to 0$, C being the concentration of solute in solution. In other words, in the infinitely dilute solution the activity of solute is set equal to the concentration; then, whatever concentration of solution contains solute at unit activity is the defined standard state of the solute. So long as the activity coefficient of the solute, i.e., the ratio a/C, remains one, the solution behaves ideally, and C may be substituted for a. For solutions of nonelectrolytes in many systems the activity coefficients may actually stay quite close to one up to fairly high concentrations. However, such is not the case with electrolytes, and hence the problem of the activity coefficients for these will be considered separately in Chapter 16.

Activities of dissolved substances may be determined from vapor pressure, freezing point lowering, solubility, electromotive force, and other data. Some of the methods involved are quite complicated, others are relatively simple. At this point it may be of interest to know that for a solution whose solvent vapor pressure is P_1, the activity of the *solvent in solution* is given by

$$a_1 = \frac{f_1}{f_1^0} = \frac{P_1}{P_1^0} \tag{43}$$

where P_1^0 is the vapor pressure of the pure solvent. This equation is valid provided the vapor at the pressures in question behaves ideally.

THE REACTION ISOTHERM

With the free energy of a substance defined in terms of the free energy in the standard state and the activity, we may proceed to deduce the equation for the free energy change involved in a chemical reaction. For a reaction such as

$$aA + bB + \cdots = cC + dD + \cdots \tag{44}$$

if the activities of A and B at the *start* are a_A and a_B, while the activities of C and D at the *end* of the reaction are a_C and a_D respectively, then the free energies of each of these substances *per mole* at a temperature T are given by the expressions,

$$F_A = F_A^0 + RT \ln a_A \tag{45a}$$
$$F_B = F_B^0 + RT \ln a_B \tag{45b}$$
$$F_C = F_C^0 + RT \ln a_C \tag{45c}$$
$$F_D = F_D^0 + RT \ln a_D \tag{45d}$$

where the F^0's with the given subscripts represent the free energies at unit activity of the respective species. By definition the free energy change of the reaction, ΔF, is

$$\Delta F = (cF_C + dF_D + \cdots) - (aF_A + bF_B + \cdots)$$

and hence,

$$\Delta F = (cF_C^0 + cRT \ln a_C + dF_D^0 + dRT \ln a_D + \cdots)$$
$$- (aF_A^0 + aRT \ln a_A + bF_B^0 + bRT \ln a_B + \cdots)$$
$$= [(cF_C^0 + dF_D^0 + \cdots) - (aF_A^0 + bF_B^0 + \cdots)]$$
$$+ [(cRT \ln a_C + dRT \ln a_D + \cdots)$$
$$- (aRT \ln a_A + bRT \ln a_B + \cdots)]$$
$$= [(cF_C^0 + dF_D^0 + \cdots) - (aF_A^0 + bF_B^0 + \cdots)]$$
$$+ RT \ln \frac{a_C^c a_D^d \cdots}{a_A^a a_B^b \cdots} \quad (46)$$

The first term on the right of equation (46) gives the free energy change of the reaction in the standard state; i.e., the free energy change involved when the starting materials at *unit* activity react to form products also at *unit* activity. If this free energy change in the standard state be designated by ΔF^0, then equation (46) becomes

$$\Delta F = \Delta F^0 + RT \ln \frac{a_C^c a_D^d \cdots}{a_A^a a_B^b \cdots} \quad (47)$$

Equation (47) gives the free energy change of a reaction in terms of the free energy change in the standard state and the starting and final activities at any *constant temperature T*. For this reason this most fundamental thermodynamic equation is referred to as the *reaction isotherm*. When the activities of the starting and final materials are all one, the second term on the right of equation (47) is zero, and $\Delta F = \Delta F^0$. On the other hand, when the initial and final activities are other than unity, the second term is not zero, and ΔF is given then by the full equation (47).

For any reaction ΔF^0 is constant at any given temperature and completely independent of pressure. The variation of ΔF^0 with temperature, like that of ΔF, is given by equations (17) or (20), except that in this case the ΔH's and ΔS's are ΔH^0's and ΔS^0's; i.e., the heat and entropy changes are for the reactions in the standard states. Outside of this one difference, calculations involving ΔF^0's are handled in exactly the same manner as those involving ΔF's.

STANDARD FREE ENERGIES OF FORMATION

Because of the direct relation of ΔF^0 to the conditions prevailing at equilibrium, to be discussed in the next chapter, the evaluation of the standard free energy change of a reaction is a problem of prime concern in physical chemistry. Free energy changes may be obtained from the ΔH^0 and ΔS^0 of a reaction at a particular temperature through equation (4), and by other methods to be developed further in the text. At this time will be presented a scheme employed to tabulate free energies of formation of compounds, from which free energy changes for all types of reactions may be calculated.

TABLE 2

STANDARD FREE ENERGIES OF FORMATION AT 25° C

Substance	ΔF^0 (cal/mole)	Substance	ΔF^0 (cal/mole)
$HCl(g)$	$-22,770$	$Ag_2O(s)$	$-2,590$
$H_2O(l)$	$-56,690$	$HgO(s)$	$-13,940$
$H_2O(g)$	$-54,640$	$PbSO_4(s)$	$-193,890$
$CO(g)$	$-32,810$	$CH_4(g)$	$-12,140$
$CO_2(g)$	$-94,260$	$C_2H_6(g)$	$-7,860$
$NO(g)$	$20,720$	$C_2H_4(g)$	$16,280$
$NO_2(g)$	$12,390$	$C_2H_2(g)$	$50,000$
$N_2O_4(g)$	$23,400$	$C_6H_6(g)$	$30,990$
$H_2S(g)$	$-7,890$	$C_6H_6(l)$	$29,760$
$SO_2(g)$	$-71,790$	$CH_3OH(l)$	$-39,730$
$NH_3(g)$	$-3,980$	$C_2H_5OH(l)$	$-41,770$
$NaCl(s)$	$-91,790$	$HCOOH(l)$	$-82,700$
$AgCl(s)$	$-26,220$	$CH_3COOH(l)$	$-93,800$

The standard free energy of formation of a compound is defined as the free energy change accompanying the formation of the compound at unit activity from the elements also at unit activity. The equation

$$H_2(g) + \frac{1}{2} O_2(g) = H_2O(l) \qquad \Delta F^0_{298°K} = -56,690 \text{ cal} \qquad (48)$$

gives the change in free energy on formation of 1 mole of $H_2O(l)$ at unit activity from $H_2(g)$ and $\frac{1}{2} O_2(g)$, both at unit activity. *Assuming now arbitrarily*, as in heats of formation, *that the free energies of formation of the elements in their standard states at 25° C are zero*, $\Delta F^0_{298°K}$ above becomes the standard free energy of formation of liquid water from the elements, and we may write simply that

$$H_2O(l): \qquad \Delta F^0_{298°K} = -56,690 \text{ cal mole}^{-1} \qquad (49)$$

Table 2 lists the standard free energies of formation per mole for a number of compounds at 25° C. These free energies of formation may be used to calculate ΔF^0 of reactions in the same manner that heats of formation are used to calculate heats of reaction. Thus, for instance, taking the data from the table, we find at 25° C for the standard free energy change of the reaction

$$NO(g) + \frac{1}{2} O_2(g) = NO_2(g)$$

$$\Delta F^0_{25°C} = \Delta F^0_{NO_2} - \left[\Delta F^0_{NO} + \frac{1}{2} \Delta F^0_{O_2} \right]$$
$$= 12{,}390 - 20{,}720 - 0$$
$$= -8330 \text{ cal}$$

REFERENCES FOR FURTHER READING

See list at end of Chapter 10. Also:

1. K. K. Kelley, Bureau of Mines Bulletins Nos. 383 and 407.

PROBLEMS

1. For the reaction, H_2 (1 atm) $+ \frac{1}{2} O_2$ (1 atm) $= H_2O(l)$, calculate the difference in calories between ΔF and ΔA at 25° C. *Ans.* $\Delta F - \Delta A = -888$ cal.

2. For a certain process at 400° K $\Delta F = -12{,}200$ cal while $\Delta H = -17{,}500$ cal. Find ΔS of the process at 400° K.

3. For a certain reaction $\Delta F = 13{,}580 + 16.1\, T \log_{10} T - 72.59\, T$. Find ΔS and ΔH of the reaction at 25° C.   *Ans.* $\Delta S = 25.74$ eu; $\Delta H = 11{,}490$ cal.

4. Assuming that the process mentioned in problem 2 is carried out reversibly, how much heat is evolved during its performance?

5. Assuming N_2 to be an ideal gas, find the free energy change involved in compressing 7 g of N_2 at 27° C from a pressure of 0.5 to 3 atm.   *Ans.* 267 cal.

6. Calculate the free energy change for the transfer of 1 mole of naphthalene from a 0.01 molar solution in C_6H_6 to a 0.05 molar solution in the same solvent at 27° C. What is the significance of the sign of ΔF?

7. Assuming the water vapor to behave as an ideal gas, find at 25° C ΔF of the reaction

$$H_2O(l) = H_2O(g, 760 \text{ mm Hg})$$

given that

$$H_2O(l) = H_2O(g, 23.76 \text{ mm Hg}) \qquad \Delta F_{25°C} = 0 \qquad \text{\textit{Ans.} } \Delta F = 2050 \text{ cal.}$$

8. For the reaction, $H_2(g, 1 \text{ atm}) + Cl_2(g, 1 \text{ atm}) = 2\, HCl(g, 1 \text{ atm})$ ΔF at 25° C is $-45{,}400$ cal. Find ΔF for the process

$$H_2(g, 2 \text{ atm}) + Cl_2(g, 1 \text{ atm}) = 2\, HCl(g, 0.1 \text{ atm})$$

9. Using Table 1, find ΔF for the isothermal compression of 1 mole of $H_2(g)$ from 50 to 500 atm at 100° C. Compare the result with the value obtained on assumption that $H_2(g)$ behaves as an ideal gas.

10. A certain gas at temperature T obeys the relation $PV = RT + BP + CP^2$. Deduce the expression for ln γ of the gas as a function of P at this temperature.

11. If in problem 10 $T = 223.2°$ K, $B = -3.69 \times 10^{-2}$, and $C = 1.79 \times 10^{-4}$ for volume in liters and pressure in atmospheres, what will be the activity coefficient of the gas at $P = 100$ atm?   *Ans.* $\gamma = 0.858$.

12. At $-50°$ C the molar volumes of $N_2(g)$ at various pressures are as follows:

P (atm)	V (l/mole)
1	18.28
20	0.890
40	0.434
60	0.284
100	0.167
200	0.0879
300	0.0671
400	0.0579
500	0.0526

Determine the activity coefficients of the gas at 100, 200, and 500 atm.
13. The molar volume of $C_6H_6(l)$ at $20°$ C is 88.9 cc. Assuming the volume to be constant, find ΔF in calories for compression of the liquid from 1 to 100 atm.
14. From the result of problem 13, calculate the activity of $C_6H_6(l)$ at $20°$ C and 100 atm pressure.   *Ans. a* = 1.44.
15. A solution of a nonvolatile solute in diethyl ether shows at $20°$ C a vapor pressure of 426.0 mm Hg. At the same temperature the pure solvent has a vapor pressure of 442.2 mm Hg. What is the activity of the solvent in the given solution?
16. The standard free energy of formation of $H_2O(l)$ at $25°$ C is $-56,690$ cal. Find the free energy of formation of H_2O at $25°$ C from H_2 at a partial pressure of 0.01 atm and O_2 at a partial pressure of 0.25 atm.   *Ans.* $\Delta F = -53,550$ cal.
17. For the formation of $C_2H_5OH(l)$ $\Delta F^0_{25°C} = -41,770$ cal. Find ΔF at $25°$ C for the reaction

$$2 C(s) + 3 H_2(g, f = 50 \text{ atm}) + \frac{1}{2} O_2(g, f = 100 \text{ atm}) = C_2H_5OH(l)$$

18. From the data of Table 2, calculate ΔF^0 for the following reactions at $25°$ C:

(a) $C_2H_5OH(l) + O_2(g) = CH_3COOH(l) + H_2O(l)$
(b) $2 CO_2(g) = 2 CO(g) + O_2(g)$

Which of the above reactions as written is spontaneous in the standard state?
                    Ans. (*a*) $\Delta F^0 = -108,720$ cal.
19. Using the absolute entropies from Table 2 of the preceding chapter, calculate ΔH^0 at $25°$ C for reactions given in the preceding problem.
20. From the following series of reactions find the free energy of formation of $N_2O_4(g)$ at $25°$ C:

$$\frac{1}{2} N_2(g) + \frac{1}{2} O_2(g) = NO(g) \qquad \Delta F^0_{298°K} = 20,720 \text{ cal}$$

$$NO(g) + \frac{1}{2} O_2(g) = NO_2(g) \qquad \Delta F^0_{298°K} = -8330 \text{ cal}$$

$$2 NO_2(g) = N_2O_4(g) \qquad \Delta F^0_{298°K} = -1380 \text{ cal}$$

21. From the appropriate absolute entropies and heats of formation calculate the standard free energy change at $25°$ C for the reaction:

$$CO(g) + H_2O(l) = CO_2(g) + H_2(g)$$

22. For the sublimation $Au(s) = Au(g)$ $\Delta H^0_{298.2^\circ K} = 90,500$ cal/mole and $\Delta F^0_{298.2^\circ K} = 81,000$ cal/mole. Further,

$$Au(g): \quad C_p = 5.00 \text{ cal mole}^{-1} \text{ degree}^{-1}$$
$$Au(s): \quad C_p = 5.61 + 1.44 \times 10^{-3}\, T \text{ cal mole}^{-1} \text{ degree}^{-1}$$

From these data find an expression for ΔF^0 as a function of T, and calculate ΔF^0 at 1000° K.

$Ans.$ $\quad \Delta F^0 = 90,740 + 1.40\, T \log_{10} T - 36.23\, T + 0.72 \times 10^{-3}\, T^2$
$\Delta F^0_{1000^\circ K} = 59,430$ cal.

23. For the reaction $MoS_2(s) + 2\,H_2(g) = Mo(s) + 2\,H_2S(g)$ $\Delta H^0_{25^\circ C} = 46,670$ cal, $\Delta F^0_{25^\circ C} = 38,460$ cal, and ΔC_p is given by

$$\Delta C_p = -12.95 + 3.75 \times 10^{-3}\, T - \frac{0.503 \times 10^5}{T^2}$$

Deduce the expression for ΔF^0 as a function of T.

24. For the reaction $Cu(s) = Cu(g)$

$$\Delta H^0 = 81,730 - 0.47\, T - 0.731 \times 10^{-3}\, T^2$$
$$\Delta S^0 = 34.94 - 1.08 \log_{10} T - 1.46 \times 10^{-3}\, T$$

(a) Set up the expression for ΔF^0 as a function of T. (b) Find the value of ΔF^0 at 1000° K.

25. For the reaction $FeCO_3(s) = FeO(s) + CO_2(g)$

$$\Delta F^0 = 18,660 - 14.42\, T \log_{10} T - 6.07\, T + 8.24 \times 10^{-3}\, T^2$$

Find ΔH^0 and ΔS^0 for the reaction at 25° C.

$Ans.$ $\Delta H^0 = 19,790$ cal/mole; $\Delta S^0 = 43.1$ eu.

26. At high temperatures ΔF^0 for the dissociation

$$CaCO_3(s) = CaO(s) + CO_2(g)$$

is given by the expression:

$$\Delta F^0 = 42,500 - 1.52\, T \log_{10} T - 34.6\, T + 2.15 \times 10^{-3}\, T^2$$

Calculate ΔF^0 at 100° intervals between 700 and 1200° C, plot the values as a function of T, and determine from the curve the temperature at which ΔF^0 changes sign.

27. For the reaction $C(s, \text{graphite}) + S_2(g) = CS_2(g)$

$$\Delta F^0 = -5040 - 7.67\, T \log_{10} T + 1.51 \times 10^{-3}\, T^2 + \frac{1.106 \times 10^5}{T} + 21.58\, T$$

Further, $C(s, \text{graphite})$: $\quad C_p = 2.673 + 2.617 \times 10^{-3}\, T - \dfrac{1.169 \times 10^5}{T^2}$ cal mole^{-1} degree^{-1}

$CS_2(g)$: $C_p = 13.75 + 0.49 \times 10^{-3}\, T - \dfrac{3.38 \times 10^5}{T^2}$ cal mole^{-1} degree^{-1}

From these data find the equation for C_p of $S_2(g)$ as a function of the temperature.

12

Homogeneous Chemical Equilibrium

A knowledge of the laws governing chemical reactions is of inestimable value to the chemist, chemical engineer and metallurgist. Without theoretical guidance the intelligent planning of experimental and development work on any chemical process would be extremely difficult and would require the determination of a tremendous amount of data. With the aid of theoretical principles, however, the experimental work necessary for the definition of a process or reaction can be reduced to the bare minimum required for the application of established thermodynamic and kinetic equations.

An important question to be answered about any chemical reaction is: To what extent can the reaction in question take place? To answer this question fully it is necessary to ascertain the effects of temperature, pressure, foreign substances, and the state of the substances involved in the reaction, i.e., whether the reaction can take place better in the gaseous, liquid, or solid state, or in solution. The problem involved here is one of chemical equilibrium and is purely thermodynamic in nature. It can frequently be solved by a study of the free energy relations involved, provided the necessary data are available. This is the problem that will concern us in this and the following chapter.

CHEMICAL EQUILIBRIUM

It is a familiar and well-established fact that many reactions do not go to completion. They proceed to a certain point and then apparently stop, often leaving considerable amounts of unaffected reactants. Under any given set of conditions of temperature, pressure, and concentration, the point at which any reaction seems to stop is always the same; i.e., there exists at this point among the concentrations of the various reactants and products of any reaction a relationship which is definitely fixed. When a reaction reaches this stage in its course, it is said to be in *equilibrium*.

A state of chemical equilibrium should not be considered the state of a reaction at which all motion ceases. It is much more fruitful to consider the point of equilibrium as the state in which the *rate* at which reactants disappear to form products is exactly equal to the *rate* at which the products interact to reform the reacting substances. Under these conditions no perceptible transformation can be detected in the system, and the net effect is an *apparent* state of complete rest. Such an equilibrium is designated as a *dynamic* one, in contrast to a *static* equilibrium where there is no motion whatsoever. All chemical equilibria and physical equilibria between states are considered to be dynamic in nature.

In terms of this concept every reaction may be considered to have a point of equilibrium. In reactions going spontaneously to completion, the state of equilibrium is far on the side of the products, the quantities of unreacted materials being so small as to escape detection by ordinary laboratory methods. On the other hand, in reactions designated as not taking place, the equilibrium is almost completely in favor of the reactants, the concentrations of products being beyond detection. The fact that we may not be able to detect the presence of reactants in one case or products in the other does not militate against the concept of dynamic equilibrium. It is generally believed that the extremely small concentrations of substances demanded by some equilibria could be found if more sensitive and precise methods were at our disposal. In all instances where the principle has been tested it has been found to be valid in every detail.

Chemical equilibria may be classified into two groups: (a) *homogeneous* equilibria and (b) *heterogeneous* equilibria. A homogeneous equilibrium is one established in a system in which only one phase occurs, as in a system containing only gases, or a single liquid or solid phase. A heterogeneous equilibrium, on the other hand, is one established in a system in which more than a single phase appears, as equilibrium between solid and gas, liquid and gas, solid and liquid, or solid and solid.

THERMODYNAMICS OF EQUILIBRIUM

For any reaction such as

$$\alpha A + bB + \cdots = cC + dD + \cdots \tag{1}$$

the change in free energy, ΔF, at any temperature T is given by the reaction isotherm, equation (47) of the last chapter, namely,

$$\Delta F = \Delta F^0 + RT \ln \left(\frac{a_C^c a_D^d \ \cdots}{a_A^a a_B^b \ \cdots} \right) \tag{2}$$

The activities indicated are those of the products at the end and of reactants at the start of the reaction. However, we have seen in the last chapter that the criterion of equilibrium is that $\Delta F = 0$ at constant temperature and pressure. Hence, at equilibrium equation (2) becomes

$$0 = \Delta F^0 + RT \ln \left(\frac{a_C^c a_D^d \ \cdots}{a_A^a a_B^b \ \cdots} \right)$$

and $$\Delta F^0 = -RT \ln \left(\frac{a_C^c a_D^d \ \cdots}{a_A^a a_B^b \ \cdots} \right) \tag{3}$$

The activities now are those of reactants and products *at equilibrium*. Since at any given temperature ΔF^0, the free energy change in the standard state, for any reaction is a constant, it follows that the activity ratio in equation (3) must also be constant, i.e.,

$$K_a = \frac{a_C^c a_D^d \ \cdots}{a_A^a a_B^b \ \cdots} \tag{4}$$

and equation (3) may be written as

$$\Delta F^0 = -RT \ln K_a \tag{5}$$

Equation (4) defines K_a, *the thermodynamic equilibrium constant* of a reaction. It also shows that the indicated ratio of the activities of products and reactants at equilibrium must be *constant and independent of all factors except temperature*. Again, equation (5) relates directly the thermodynamic equilibrium constant of a reaction at a temperature T to the free energy change in the standard state for the reaction. It permits, therefore, the calculation of K_a from ΔF^0 values, and vice versa, the calculation of ΔF^0 of reactions from their thermodynamic equilibrium constants. This highly important equation makes possible reduction of the free energy change calculations described in the last chapter to equilibrium constants, and allows prediction of the behavior of chemical reactions under various conditions without recourse to direct experiment. Thus, we have seen in the last chapter that for the reaction

$$\frac{1}{2} N_2(g) + \frac{3}{2} H_2(g) = NH_3(g) \qquad \Delta F^0_{298.2^\circ K} = -3980 \text{ cal}$$

Using equation (5), we find for the equilibrium constant of this reaction at 298.2° K,

$$\log_{10} K_a = -\frac{\Delta F^0}{2.303\ RT}$$

$$= \frac{3980}{2.303 \times 1.987 \times 298.2}$$

$$= 2.917$$

$$K_a = 826.1$$

In writing the expression for the equilibrium constant the *activities of products must always be placed in the numerator* and those of the reactants in the denominator. Inversion of the ratio will not give the constant for the reaction as written, but its reverse; for, as may be seen from equation (4), the two constants are reciprocally related to each other, i.e.,

$$K_{\text{direct reaction}} = \frac{1}{K_{\text{reverse reaction}}} \qquad (6)$$

K_p AND K_c

Before proceeding it is necessary to relate the thermodynamic equilibrium constant to experimentally measurable quantities. These are the partial pressures of reactants and products at equilibrium in the case of gaseous reactions, and concentrations for reactions in solution.

We have seen in the preceding chapter that the activity of a gas, which is identical with the fugacity, is given by $a = P\gamma$, where γ is the activity coefficient and P the pressure of the gas. If this expression be substituted for the activity of each substance in equation (4), then we get for K_a of a gaseous reaction at equilibrium

$$K_a = \frac{(P_C\gamma_C)^c(P_D\gamma_D)^d \cdots}{(P_A\gamma_A)^a(P_B\gamma_B)^b \cdots}$$

$$= \left(\frac{P_C^c P_D^d \cdots}{P_A^a P_B^b \cdots}\right)\left(\frac{\gamma_C^c \gamma_D^d \cdots}{\gamma_A^a \gamma_B^b \cdots}\right) \qquad (7)$$

The first term on the right in equation (7) may be represented by K_p, namely,

$$K_p = \frac{P_C^c P_D^d \cdots}{P_A^a P_B^b \cdots} \qquad (8)$$

and the second term by K_γ, where

$$K_\gamma = \frac{\gamma_C^c \gamma_D^d \cdots}{\gamma_A^a \gamma_B^b \cdots} \qquad (9)$$

With these definitions equation (7) becomes

$$K_a = K_p K_\gamma \qquad (10)$$

K_p is the *equilibrium constant of a reaction expressed in pressures.* For evaluating K_p any desired pressure units may be used. However, for substitution in equation (10) or equation (5) the pressures must be in atmospheres.

In equation (10) K_a is a true constant for a reaction at a given temperature. On the other hand, K_γ is a quantity whose magnitude depends on the gases involved and the pressure. For ideal gases, or for real gases at zero pressure, $\gamma = 1$ for each gas, and hence K_γ is also equal to unity. Under such conditions $K_a = K_p$, and the two types of equilibrium constants are identical. However, for nonideal gases at pressures above zero the γ's will deviate from unity, and so will K_γ; in fact, for any given reaction the value of K_γ will be determined by the total pressure of the system and will vary as the latter is changed. Therefore, it must follow from equation (10) that, whereas for any given reaction and temperature K_a is a true constant, K_p may not be a constant but a quantity whose value may depend on the total pressure at equilibrium.

A similar argument applies to reactions in solution. The activity of a dissolved substance is related to the concentration C by the expression $a = Cf$, where f is the activity coefficient. If this relation be substituted for the activity of each species in equation (4), then we obtain for K_a of a reaction in solution

$$K_a = \frac{(C_C f_C)^c (C_D f_D)^d \cdots}{(C_A f_A)^a (C_B f_B)^b \cdots}$$
$$= \left(\frac{C_C^c C_D^d \cdots}{C_A^a C_B^b \cdots}\right)\left(\frac{f_C^c f_D^d \cdots}{f_A^a f_B^b \cdots}\right) \tag{11}$$

If we write now

$$K_c = \frac{C_C^c C_D^d \cdots}{C_A^a C_B^b \cdots} \tag{12}$$

and

$$K_f = \frac{f_C^c f_D^d \cdots}{f_A^a f_B^b \cdots} \tag{13}$$

then equation (11) becomes

$$K_a = K_c K_f \tag{14}$$

Equation (12) defines K_c, the *concentration equilibrium constant* of a reaction. K_c may be expressed in any concentration units desired, but for use in equation (14) or equation (5) C must be in moles per liter.

In equation (14) K_a is again a true constant for a given reaction and temperature, while K_f is a factor dependent on the nature of the dissolved substances and their concentration. For ideal solutions, or real solutions at zero concentration, $f = 1$, $K_f = 1$, and therefore $K_a = K_c$. However, for nonideal solutions at concentrations other than zero K_f may not equal unity, and hence K_c will not be identical with K_a. Further, since K_f is a function of the concentration, K_c will also have to vary with the concentration of the solution at equilibrium.

The limits within which pressures and concentrations may be substituted for activities have been discussed in the preceding chapter. Since no electrolytic equilibria will be considered here, we shall proceed on the supposition, unless it is indicated otherwise, that K_a is synonymous with K_p for gaseous reactions and with K_c for reactions in solution. In most of the cases to be cited this assumption will not introduce errors which are too serious for our purposes.

K_c FOR GASEOUS REACTIONS

Although equilibria involving gases are formulated most frequently in terms of partial pressures to yield K_p, they may also be expressed in concentration terms as K_c in line with equation (12). The values of K_p and K_c thus obtained for a given reaction are generally different numerically. However, a relation between these two at any temperature T can readily be deduced provided the gases involved may be considered to behave ideally. Since for an ideal gas $P = (n/V)RT = CRT$, we obtain on substitution of this relation in equation (8),

$$
\begin{aligned}
K_p &= \frac{C_C^c(RT)^c C_D^d(RT)^d \, \cdots}{C_A^\alpha(RT)^\alpha C_B^b(RT)^b \, \cdots} \\
&= \left(\frac{C_C^c C_D^d \, \cdots}{C_A^\alpha C_B^b \, \cdots}\right) \frac{(RT)^{c+d+\cdots}}{(RT)^{\alpha+b+\cdots}} \\
&= K_c(RT)^{(c+d+\cdots)-(\alpha+b+\cdots)} \qquad (15a)
\end{aligned}
$$

But, $(c + d + \cdots) - (\alpha + b + \cdots)$ represents the change in the total number of moles of gaseous products and reactants during the reaction. Letting this difference be Δn_g, we obtain for the relation between the two constants

$$
K_p = K_c(RT)^{\Delta n_g} \qquad (15b)
$$

It is apparent from equation (15) that $K_p = K_c$ only when $\Delta n_g = 0$; i.e., when there is no change in volume on reaction. However, when there is a volume change, $K_p \neq K_c$. For an increase in volume on reaction Δn_g is positive, and hence K_p is numerically larger than K_c. On the other hand, when Δn_g is negative, corresponding to a volume decrease, K_p is less than K_c. In using equation (15) R must be expressed in the same units as are the pressures and volumes involved in K_p and K_c.

PROPERTIES OF EQUILIBRIUM CONSTANTS

Because of the fundamental importance of equilibrium calculations in physical chemistry and chemical engineering, it may not be amiss to recapitulate and emphasize the properties of the equilibrium constant of a reaction. In the discussion which follows it will be assumed that K_p or K_c for a reaction is a true constant identical with K_a.

First, the equilibrium constant principle is valid only at *equilibrium*. The relation called for between the concentrations of products and reactants does not apply to all possible concentrations that may be encountered in a reacting system, but only to those which correspond to the point of true equilibrium. Unless true equilibrium concentrations are substituted in equation (8) or (12), these equations cannot be expected to yield constants.

Again, the equilibrium constant for any reaction should, at a fixed temperature, be a constant independent of concentration or pressure at all concentrations and pressures. On the other hand, the equilibrium constant of a reaction will not be the same at all temperatures but will vary from temperature to temperature in a manner predictable by thermodynamics.

The magnitude of the equilibrium constant determines the extent to which any particular reaction can proceed under given conditions. A large value of K_p or K_c indicates that the numerator in the equilibrium constant expression is large compared to the denominator, i.e., that the concentrations of products are large compared to those of the reactants and hence that the reaction favors the formation of products. On the other hand, when K_p or K_c is small, the concentrations of reactants are large compared to those of products, and the indications are that the particular reaction does not proceed to any appreciable extent under the given conditions.

Further, the equilibrium constant defines *quantitatively* the effect of concentrations of reactants and products on the extent of reaction. The manner of calculating such effects will be discussed later in the chapter. At present we may deduce qualitatively certain conclusions of general validity. For this purpose consider the reaction

$$\text{H}_2(\text{g}) + \text{Cl}_2(\text{g}) = 2\,\text{HCl}(\text{g}) \tag{16}$$

for which the equilibrium constant is given by

$$\frac{P_{\text{HCl}}^2}{P_{\text{H}_2} P_{\text{Cl}_2}} = K_p \tag{17}$$

Since K_p is a constant at all pressures, the relation among the partial pressures of H_2, Cl_2, and HCl in equation (17) should also remain constant under all conditions at a given temperature. If now hydrogen is added to an equilibrium mixture of the three gases, the pressure of this gas is increased, and hence the existing relationship among the partial pressures as given in equation (17) is disturbed. To accommodate the added hydrogen without violating the constancy of K_p, the partial pressure of chlorine must decrease, while that of hydrogen chloride must increase. This can be accomplished by further interaction of hydrogen and chlorine to form hydrogen chloride, the process continuing until the relationship called for by K_p is reestablished and the gases are again in equilibrium. The same effect may be produced by adding chlorine. Conversely, addition of hydrogen chloride will increase the numerator, and hence the denominator must also be increased to preserve the constancy of K_p. This time the adjustment is brought about by dissociation of HCl into H_2 and Cl_2 until equilibrium is again reestablished and K_p returns to its constant value.

From this behavior of an equilibrium mixture on addition of excess reactants or products may be drawn the following two generalizations:

1. Presence of excess of some of the reactants over others tends to drive a reaction further to completion with respect to the reactants not in excess.
2. Initial presence of products tends to decrease the extent of conversion of reactants to products.

EQUILIBRIA IN GASEOUS SYSTEMS

Many direct experimental studies of gaseous equilibria have been made. Several examples of these will be discussed in detail to indicate some of the methods employed, as well as to illustrate the application of equilibrium constants.

THE AMMONIA EQUILIBRIUM

The equilibrium

$$\frac{3}{2} H_2(g) + \frac{1}{2} N_2(g) = NH_3(g) \tag{18}$$

has been extensively investigated by Haber and co-workers, Nernst and Jellinek, and more recently by Larson and Dodge.[1] The last named passed a mixture of nitrogen and hydrogen, in the ratio of 1:3 by volume, through an iron coil immersed in a constant temperature bath. To speed the approach of equilibrium, the coil was lined with finely divided iron to act as a catalyst, i.e., a substance which accelerated the attainment of equilibrium without affecting it. The exit gases were analyzed, then, for hydrogen, nitrogen, and ammonia to determine the composition of the equilibrium mixture. To check their results and to assure themselves that true equilibrium had been attained, Larson and Dodge approached equilibrium also from the ammonia side by passing through the coil mix-

[1] Larson and Dodge, *J. Am. Chem. Soc.*, **45**, 2918 (1923).

tures of ammonia, nitrogen, and hydrogen. Some of their results for the direct formation of ammonia from nitrogen and hydrogen at various pressures and temperatures are given in Table 1. The first column gives the

TABLE 1

EQUILIBRIUM CONSTANTS FOR FORMATION OF NH_3

$t°$ C	$P = 10$ atm		$P = 30$ atm		$P = 50$ atm	
	% NH_3	K_p	% NH_3	K_p	% NH_3	K_p
350	7.35	0.0266	17.80	0.0273	25.11	0.0278
400	3.85	0.0129	10.09	0.0129	15.11	0.0130
450	2.04	0.00659	5.80	0.00676	9.17	0.00690

temperature at which equilibrium was determined, column 2 the mol percentage of ammonia found in the equilibrium mixture under a total equilibrium pressure of 10 atm and column 3 the value of the equilibrium constants K_p as calculated from

$$K_p = \frac{P_{NH_3}}{P_{H_2}^{3/2} P_{N_2}^{1/2}} \tag{19}$$

The other columns give the same information under different total equilibrium pressures.

From the percentage of ammonia at equilibrium at a total pressure P, K_p is calculated with the aid of Dalton's law of partial pressures. Taking the data for 30 atm and 400° C, we see that the percentage of ammonia at equilibrium is 10.09, and hence the partial pressure of ammona is

$$P_{NH_3} = 30 \times 0.1009 = 3.03 \text{ atm}$$

The pressure of hydrogen plus nitrogen is, therefore,

$$P_{H_2} + P_{N_2} = 30.00 - 3.03 = 26.97 \text{ atm}$$

Since, however, the nitrogen and hydrogen are present in the ratio of 1:3, then,

$$P_{H_2} = \frac{3}{4} \times 26.97 = 20.22 \text{ atm}$$

$$P_{N_2} = \frac{1}{4} \times 26.97 = 6.75 \text{ atm}$$

and
$$K_p = \frac{P_{NH_3}}{P_{H_2}^{3/2} P_{N_2}^{1/2}}$$
$$= \frac{3.03}{(20.22)^{3/2}(6.75)^{1/2}}$$
$$= 0.0129$$

Table 1 clearly substantiates equation (19) as the expression for the equilibrium constant of this reaction. Although the variation in total pressure is quite large, 10 to 50 atm, still K_p at any *given temperature* is essentially constant. The total pressure merely determines the relative percentages of hydrogen, nitrogen, and ammonia present at equilibrium, but does not affect the constancy of K_p. On the other hand, variation of temperature produces significant changes both in the percentage of ammonia and in K_p. At all the given pressures increase of temperature operates to decrease the yield of ammonia and hence to decrease K_p.

THE LE CHATELIER-BRAUN PRINCIPLE

To foretell qualitatively the effect of variation in pressure or temperature on a system in equilibrium, use is made of the *Le Chatelier-Braun principle*. This principle states that *whenever stress is placed on any system in a state of equilibrium, the system will always react in a direction which will tend to counteract the applied stress*. Thus, if pressure is applied to a system, the tendency of the stress will be to decrease the volume, and hence that reaction in the system will take place which will favor the smaller volume. In the ammonia equilibrium the combination of nitrogen and hydrogen to form ammonia is attended by a volume *decrease* from two molar volumes to one, and hence according to the Le Chatelier-Braun principle we may expect the formation of ammonia to be favored by an increase in total pressure. That this is actually the case is borne out by Table 1.

Again, when a reaction is endothermic, i.e., absorbs heat, addition of heat should favor it, and the reaction should proceed to a greater extent at higher temperatures. Conversely, when a reaction is exothermic we may expect that addition of heat would tend to inhibit the reaction, and hence at higher temperatures the reaction should tend to reverse itself. The latter behavior is shown by the exothermic ammonia synthesis reaction. Table 1 indicates, in line with the Le Chatelier-Braun prediction, that the yield of ammonia is higher the lower the temperature.

THE PHOSGENE EQUILIBRIUM

The formation of phosgene,

$$CO(g) + Cl_2(g) = COCl_2(g) \qquad (20)$$

has been fully studied by Max Bodenstein and Heinrich Plaut[1] by a static method, as contrasted to the flow, or dynamic, method employed by Larson and Dodge for the ammonia equilibrium. The apparatus used consisted of a glass reaction bulb set in a cylindrical, electrically heated oven which was kept at a constant temperature. The top of the

[1] Bodenstein and Plaut, *Z. physik. Chem.*, **110**, 399 (1924).

glass bulb was connected by capillary glass tubing to tanks in which the various gases were stored and to a specially constructed manometer made of quartz. All pressure measurements were made with this manometer. At the start of an experiment chlorine was first admitted, then carbon monoxide, and the pressure of each was recorded. After equilibrium had been established, the total pressure as recorded on the manometer was also read.

K_p can be calculated directly from the pressure readings. In a typical experiment Bodenstein and Plaut found at 394.8° C that for an initial pressure of chlorine equal to 351.4 mm and carbon monoxide equal to 342.0 mm, the total pressure at equilibrium was 439.5 mm. Since the volume was constant throughout the experiment, the partial pressures are directly proportional to the numbers of moles of each constituent present, and hence we may deal with these directly. If, then, we let x be the drop in the partial pressure of chlorine during the experiment, the drop in partial pressure of carbon monoxide is also x, while the partial pressure of phosgene formed is x. This relation is apparent from the stoichiometry of equation (20), where the two gases, chlorine and carbon monoxide, interact mole for mole to form 1 mole of phosgene. We may write, therefore, for the partial pressures of the three gases at equilibrium:

$$P_{Cl_2} = 351.4 - x \quad mm$$
$$P_{CO} = 342.0 - x \quad mm$$
$$P_{COCl_2} = x \quad mm$$

The total pressure at equilibrium must be the sum of these partial pressures and must equal in turn to 439.5 mm as found by experiment. Then

$$P = P_{Cl_2} + P_{CO} + P_{COCl_2} = 439.5 \ mm$$
$$= (351.4 - x) + (342.0 - x) + x = 439.5 \ mm$$
$$= 693.4 - x = 439.5 \ mm$$
$$x = 693.4 - 439.5 = 253.9 \ mm$$

Substituting this value of x into the expressions for the partial pressures, we find

$$P_{Cl_2} = 351.4 - 253.9$$
$$= 97.5 \ mm = 0.128 \ atm$$
$$P_{CO} = 342.0 - 253.9$$
$$= 88.1 \ mm = 0.116 \ atm$$
$$P_{COCl_2} = 253.9 \ mm = 0.334 \ atm$$

Hence at 394.8° C

$$K_p = \frac{P_{COCl_2}}{P_{Cl_2}P_{CO}} = \frac{0.334}{(0.128)(0.116)}$$
$$= 22.5$$

When the equilibrium constant for a forward reaction is known, the equilibrium constant for the reverse reaction is also known through equation (6). Thus, since the equilibrium constant for the formation of phosgene from chlorine and carbon monoxide is $K_p = 22.5$ at $394.8°$ C, the equilibrium constant for the *dissociation* of phosgene into carbon monoxide and chlorine, namely,

$$COCl_2(g) = CO(g) + Cl_2(g) \qquad (21)$$

must be
$$K'_p = \frac{P_{CO}P_{Cl_2}}{P_{COCl_2}} = \frac{1}{K_p} \qquad (22)$$

$$= \frac{1}{22.5} = 0.0444$$

This new constant may be employed to calculate the extent to which phosgene dissociates into the given products at any specified pressure and $394.8°$ C. If we start with n moles of phosgene, and let α be the degree of dissociation at equilibrium, i.e., the *fraction of each mole* that dissociates, the number of moles of phosgene undissociated at equilibrium must be $n(1 - \alpha)$, while the number of moles of chlorine and carbon monoxide formed must each be $n\alpha$. Hence the total number of moles of gas present at equilibrium is

$$n_t = n(1 - \alpha) + n\alpha + n\alpha$$
$$= (n + n\alpha)$$
$$= n(1 + \alpha)$$

If the total equilibrium pressure is P, the partial pressures of the three gases, using Dalton's law, must be

$$P_{COCl_2} = \left(\frac{n_{COCl_2}}{n_t}\right) P = \left(\frac{1 - \alpha}{1 + \alpha}\right) P$$

$$P_{Cl_2} = \left(\frac{n_{Cl_2}}{n_t}\right) P = \left(\frac{\alpha}{1 + \alpha}\right) P$$

$$P_{CO} = \left(\frac{n_{CO}}{n_t}\right) P = \left(\frac{\alpha}{1 + \alpha}\right) P$$

and therefore,
$$K'_p = \frac{P_{CO}P_{Cl_2}}{P_{COCl_2}} = \frac{\left(\frac{\alpha}{1 + \alpha}\right) P \cdot \left(\frac{\alpha}{1 + \alpha}\right) P}{\left(\frac{1 - \alpha}{1 + \alpha}\right) P}$$

$$= \frac{\alpha^2 P}{(1 - \alpha)(1 + \alpha)}$$

$$= \frac{\alpha^2 P}{(1 - \alpha^2)} \qquad (23)$$

Substituting $K'_p = 0.0444$, and assuming $P = 1$ atm, solution for α yields

$$\frac{\alpha^2}{1 - \alpha^2} = 0.0444$$

$$\alpha = 0.206$$

Consequently, pure phosgene dissociates into chlorine and carbon monoxide to the extent of 20.6 per cent at 1 atm pressure and a temperature of 394.8° C.

This typical calculation illustrates the general procedure followed in setting up expressions for the equilibrium constant in terms of the total pressure and the degree of dissociation.

THE DISSOCIATION OF ANTIMONY PENTACHLORIDE

In the phosgene equilibrium the α's were ascertained from pressure measurements. In dissociations the α's may be deduced also from density or apparent molecular weight data. To illustrate this method of calculation, consider the equilibrium

$$SbCl_5(g) = SbCl_3(g) + Cl_2(g) \tag{24}$$

If we start with n moles of antimony pentachloride in a volume of V liters, and let α be the degree of dissociation at temperature T and total equilibrium pressure P, then the number of moles of antimony pentachloride left undissociated is $n(1 - \alpha)$, the number of moles each of antimony trichloride and chlorine formed is $n\alpha$, and the total number of moles of gas present at equilibrium is thus $n_t = n(1 + \alpha)$. For such an equilibrium gas mixture, the ideal gas law gives the relation

$$PV = n_t RT$$
$$= n(1 + \alpha)RT \tag{25}$$

Since n is the weight W of antimony pentachloride started with divided by the molecular weight M of this substance, and since the total mass of gas does not change, $W = W_{\text{mixture}}$, $n = W_{\text{mixture}}/M$, and equation (25) becomes

$$PV = \frac{W_{\text{mixture}}}{M}(1 + \alpha)RT$$

or

$$P = \left(\frac{W_{\text{mixture}}}{V}\right)\frac{(1 + \alpha)RT}{M}$$
$$= \frac{d_a(1 + \alpha)RT}{M} \tag{26}$$

where d_a is the density of the mixture. Solving for α, we find that

$$\alpha = \frac{PM}{d_a RT} - 1 \tag{27}$$

and hence α can be calculated from the observed pressure, temperature, and density of the mixture. It should be remembered that in equation (27) M is the normal molecular weight of antimony pentachloride as obtained from atomic weights. Furthermore, reference to equation (54), Chapter 1, shows that PM/RT is what the density d of antimony pentachloride would have been at the given temperature and pressure if no dissociation had occurred. Substituting then d for PM/RT in equation (27), we obtain also for α

$$\alpha = \frac{d}{d_a} - 1$$

$$\alpha = \frac{d - d_a}{d_a} \tag{28}$$

Equation (28) may be cast into still another form. If the numerator and denominator are multiplied by the molar volume of a gas at the given temperature and pressure, dV_m becomes M, the molecular weight of the antimony pentachloride, $d_a V_m$ becomes the apparent molecular weight M_a of the gas mixture, and equation (28) is then

$$\alpha = \frac{M - M_a}{M_a} \tag{29}$$

The apparent molecular weight of the equilibrium mixture is what would be calculated for the molecular weight of the antimony pentachloride on the assumption that only n moles of gas were present at the temperature, pressure, and volume of the equilibrium gas mixture, i.e.,

$$M_a = \frac{WRT}{PV} \tag{30}$$

In Table 2 are given some data on the dissociation of antimony pentachloride at various temperatures and 1 atm pressure. Column 1 lists the temperature, column 2 the apparent molecular weight calculated from the observed data by means of equation (30), while in column 3 are the values of α obtained through equation (29). The molecular weight of undissociated antimony pentachloride is 299.05.

Equations (28) and (29) apply to dissociations in which one molecule decomposes to yield *two* molecules of product. More generally it can be shown that when a single molecule dissociated into ν moles of product, whether identical or not, equation (28) becomes

$$\alpha = \frac{d - d_a}{(\nu - 1)d_a} \tag{31}$$

and equation (29)

$$\alpha = \frac{M - M_a}{(\nu - 1)M_a} \tag{32}$$

TABLE 2

DISSOCIATION OF SbCl$_5$ AT VARIOUS TEMPERATURES*
(Total pressure = 1 atm)

Temperature (°C)	M_a	$\alpha = \dfrac{M - M_a}{M_a}$
128	276.2	0.082
141	265.5	0.126
157	252.7	0.183
169	245.3	0.219
182	231.5	0.292
191	221.3	0.351
206	204.4	0.462
221	194.2	0.540
233.5	179.3	0.668
248	174.0	0.718

* Calculated from the data of Braune and Tiedje, *Zeit. anorg. allgem. Chem.*, **152**, 39 (1926).

THE DISSOCIATION OF HYDROGEN SULFIDE

Hydrogen sulfide on being heated dissociates into hydrogen and sulfur according to the equation

$$2 \text{ H}_2\text{S(g)} = 2 \text{ H}_2\text{(g)} + \text{S}_2\text{(g)} \tag{33}$$

To determine the extent of this dissociation, Preuner and Schupp[1] utilized a very novel method. Hydrogen sulfide under a definite pressure was admitted into an elongated porcelain tube where it was allowed to dissociate at constant temperature. In the center of this tube was located a small platinum bulb which acted as a membrane permeable to hydrogen, but not to hydrogen sulfide or sulfur. This bulb was evacuated before each experiment. As the hydrogen sulfide dissociated, the hydrogen formed diffused rapidly into the platinum bulb until it built up within a pressure equal to the equilibrium pressure of hydrogen. This pressure was recorded on a manometer connected directly with the bulb and was used to calculate the degree of dissociation, α, of the hydrogen sulfide. Values of α obtained in this manner at several temperatures for a total equilibrium pressure of *1* atm are shown in Table 3.

To calculate K_p from these values of α we proceed as follows. Of each initial mole of hydrogen sulfide the amount left at equilibrium is $(1 - \alpha)$ and of n moles, $n(1 - \alpha)$. Since for each mole of hydrogen sulfide that dissociates 1 mole of hydrogen and 0.5 mole of sulfur are formed, then from

[1] Preuner and Schupp, *Z. physik. Chem.*, **68**, 157 (1909).

TABLE 3

DISSOCIATION OF H_2S AT 1 ATMOSPHERE PRESSURE

$t°$ C	α	K_p
750	0.055	0.000091
830	0.087	0.00038
1065	0.247	0.0118
1132	0.307	0.0260

a total of $n\alpha$ moles dissociated, $n\alpha$ moles of hydrogen and $n\alpha/2$ moles of sulfur are obtained. The conditions at equilibrium are, therefore,

$$2 H_2S \;=\; 2 H_2 + S_2$$
$$n(1 - \alpha) \qquad n\alpha \qquad \frac{n\alpha}{2}$$

and, instead of the initial n moles of gas, there are present at equilibrium

$$n_t = n(1 - \alpha) + n\alpha + \frac{n\alpha}{2}$$
$$= \frac{n(2 + \alpha)}{2} \quad \text{moles}$$

For a total equilibrium pressure P the partial pressures are, respectively,

$$P_{H_2S} = \left[\frac{n(1 - \alpha)}{n(2 + \alpha)/2}\right] P = \left[\frac{2(1 - \alpha)}{2 + \alpha}\right] P$$

$$P_{H_2} = \left[\frac{n\alpha}{n(2 + \alpha)/2}\right] P = \left[\frac{2\,\alpha}{2 + \alpha}\right] P$$

$$P_{S_2} = \left[\frac{(n\alpha/2)}{n(2 + \alpha)/2}\right] P = \left[\frac{\alpha}{2 + \alpha}\right] P$$

and, therefore,

$$K_p = \frac{P_{H_2}^2 P_{S_2}}{P_{H_2S}^2} = \frac{[2\,\alpha/(2 + \alpha)]^2 P^2 \cdot [\alpha/(2 + \alpha)]P}{[2(1 - \alpha)/(2 + \alpha)]^2 P^2}$$

$$= \frac{\alpha^3 P}{(2 + \alpha)(1 - \alpha)^2} \tag{34}$$

The values of K_p obtained by substituting $P = 1$ and the α's from Table 3 into the above expression are given in column 3 of the table.

Expressions for K_p such as equations (23) or (34) apply only to the equilibrium conditions for which they were derived. When the conditions under which equilibrium is established are varied, such as when products as well as reactants are present initially, the expressions are different in form and more complicated. Thus, consider the hydrogen sulfide equilibrium when n_{H_2S} moles of hydrogen sulfide, n_{H_2} moles of hydrogen, and n_{S_2} moles of sulfur are mixed at 1132° C. To obtain the equilibrium relations at a total pressure P, let x be the number of moles of hydrogen sulfide which react to form hydrogen and sulfur. The number of moles of each species at equilibrium is, then,

$$2\,H_2S \;=\; 2\,H_2 \;+\; S_2$$

$$(n_{H_2S} - x) \quad (n_{H_2} + x) \quad \left(n_{S_2} + \frac{x}{2}\right)$$

and
$$n_t = (n_{H_2S} - x) + (n_{H_2} + x) + \left(n_{S_2} + \frac{x}{2}\right)$$

$$= \left(n_{H_2S} + n_{H_2} + n_{S_2} + \frac{x}{2}\right)$$

Consequently the partial pressures are

$$P_{H_2S} = \left(\frac{n_{H_2S} - x}{n_{H_2S} + n_{H_2} + n_{S_2} + x/2}\right) P$$

$$P_{H_2} = \left(\frac{n_{H_2} + x}{n_{H_2S} + n_{H_2} + n_{S_2} + x/2}\right) P$$

$$P_{S_2} = \left(\frac{n_{S_2} + x/2}{n_{H_2S} + n_{H_2} + n_{S_2} + x/2}\right) P$$

and the expression for K_p becomes

$$K_p = \frac{P_{H_2}^2 P_{S_2}}{P_{H_2S}^2}$$

$$= \frac{\left(\dfrac{n_{H_2} + x}{n_{H_2S} + n_{H_2} + n_{S_2} + x/2}\right)^2 P^2 \cdot \left(\dfrac{n_{S_2} + x/2}{n_{H_2S} + n_{H_2} + n_{S_2} + x/2}\right) P}{\left(\dfrac{n_{H_2S} - x}{n_{H_2S} + n_{H_2} + n_{S_2} + x/2}\right)^2 P^2}$$

$$= \frac{(n_{H_2} + x)^2 (n_{S_2} + x/2) P}{(n_{H_2S} + n_{H_2} + n_{S_2} + x/2)(n_{H_2S} - x)^2} \tag{35}$$

For the *special* case of $n_{H_2S} = n_{H_2} = n_{S_2} = 1$, and $P = 1$ atm, the equilibrium constant expression at 1132° C, where $K_p = 0.0260$, reduces to

$$K_p = \frac{(1 + x)^2(1 + x/2)}{(3 + x/2)(1 - x)^2} = 0.0260 \tag{36}$$

Solution of this equation for x yields $x = -0.526$. The minus sign indicates that hydrogen sulfide does *not* dissociate under the conditions specified, but that hydrogen and sulfur must combine to form hydrogen sulfide before equilibrium can be established in a mixture containing initially 1 mole of each of the participants and at a total equilibrium pressure of 1 atm. At equilibrium there are present, therefore,

$$n_{H_2S} - x = 1 + 0.526 = 1.526 \text{ moles of } H_2S$$
$$n_{H_2} + x = 1 - 0.526 = 0.474 \text{ mole of } H_2$$
$$n_{S_2} + \frac{x}{2} = 1 - 0.263 = 0.737 \text{ mole of } S_2$$

and the partial pressures are, respectively,

$$P_{H_2S} = \frac{1.526}{2.737} \times 1 = 0.558 \text{ atm}$$
$$P_{H_2} = \frac{0.474}{2.737} \times 1 = 0.173 \text{ atm}$$
$$P_{S_2} = \frac{0.737}{2.737} \times 1 = 0.269 \text{ atm}$$

EFFECT OF INERT GASES ON EQUILIBRIUM

All the examples of equilibria considered so far involved only the gases which participate directly in the reaction. Frequently, however, equilibrium mixtures are encountered where gases are present other than those involved in the reaction. The question is: What, if any, will be the effect of gases not entering into the reaction on the extent of reaction? Obviously, the presence of these gases cannot affect in any way the thermodynamic equilibrium constant. But, the presence of these inert gases modifies the γ's, and thereby also K_γ. As a result K_p is changed. However, even if we neglect this effect on K_p, the presence of the inert gases still affects the *partial pressures* of the reactants and products at a given total equilibrium pressure, and hence we may expect a shift in the extent of reaction to permit a redistribution of the partial pressures in accord with the demands of the equilibrium constant.

To illustrate quantitatively the effect of an inert gas on an equilibrium, consider again the reaction

$$COCl_2(g) = CO(g) + Cl_2(g)$$

We have seen that at 394.8° C and at a total equilibrium pressure of 1 atm the degree of dissociation of the phosgene is $\alpha = 0.206$. Suppose now, however, that equilibrium is established in presence of nitrogen gas at a partial pressure of 0.40 atm in a total pressure of 1 atm. Then the sum of the partial pressures of phosgene, chlorine, and carbon monoxide is no longer

$P = 1$, but $1 - 0.40 = 0.60$ atm, and from equation (23) it follows that

$$K'_p = \frac{P_{CO} \times P_{Cl_2}}{P_{COCl_2}} = \frac{\alpha^2 P}{(1 - \alpha^2)}$$

$$0.0444 = \frac{\alpha^2(0.60)}{(1 - \alpha^2)}$$

$$\alpha = 0.262$$

The addition of nitrogen under the specified conditions leads, therefore, to an increase of 5.6 per cent in the dissociation of phosgene.

Qualitatively, the effect of inert gases on the extent of reaction can be foretold with the aid of the Le Chatelier-Braun principle. Since for any given total pressure the presence of inert gases decreases the partial pressure of reactants and products, the net effect will be the same as if the gases at equilibrium were subjected to a lower total pressure. Or, stated differently, the effect of an inert gas is to *dilute* the concentrations of reactants and products. Consequently, according to the Le Chatelier-Braun principle, presence of inert gases will favor the reaction that results in an *increase* in volume. Thus, when the volume of reactants is greater than that of products, the reaction will be displaced in favor of reactants, while when the opposite is true, the formation of products will be favored, as is substantiated by the above calculation. When there is no change in volume on reaction, however, neither side will be favored, and the equilibrium will be uninfluenced by the introduction of inert gases.

EQUILIBRIA IN LIQUID SYSTEMS

As an example of an equilibrium in a liquid solution may be taken the dissociation of the amyl ester of dichloracetic acid into the acid and amylene, namely,

$$CHCl_2COOC_5H_{11} = CHCl_2COOH + C_5H_{10} \tag{37}$$

for which the equilibrium constant K_c is given by

$$K_c = \frac{(C_{acid})(C_{amylene})}{C_{ester}} \tag{38}$$

In investigating this equilibrium Nernst and Hohmann[1] mixed various proportions of amylene and dichloracetic acid, sealed the mixtures in glass tubes, and kept the tubes at 100° C until equilibrium was established. The tubes were chilled then to "freeze" the equilibrium, opened, and the contents analyzed for the amount of ester present.

If we let a equal the initial number of moles of acid, b the initial number of moles of amylene, x the number of moles of ester at equilibrium,

[1] Nernst and Hohmann, Z. *physik. Chem.*, **11**, 352 (1893).

and V the total volume of mixture in liters, then the concentrations of the various substances at equilibrium in moles per liter are

$$C_{\text{ester}} = \frac{x}{V}$$

$$C_{\text{acid}} = \frac{a - x}{V}$$

$$C_{\text{amylene}} = \frac{b - x}{V}$$

and, therefore,

$$K_c = \frac{\left(\dfrac{a - x}{V}\right)\left(\dfrac{b - x}{V}\right)}{\left(\dfrac{x}{V}\right)}$$

$$= \frac{(a - x)(b - x)}{xV} \tag{39}$$

In all of Nernst and Hohmann's experiments a was kept at 1 mole, while b was varied. The values b, V, and x for a series of runs are shown in the first three columns of Table 4, while the fourth column shows the values of K_c calculated from these data by equation (39). The constancy in K_c is fairly satisfactory.

TABLE 4

DECOMPOSITION OF THE AMYL ESTER
OF DICHLORACETIC ACID AT 100° C
(a = 1 mole)

b (moles)	V (liters)	x	K_c
1.05	0.215	0.455	3.31
2.61	0.401	0.615	3.12
4.45	0.640	0.628	3.54
5.91	0.794	0.658	3.44
7.30	0.959	0.650	3.73
8.16	1.062	0.669	3.49
11.33	1.439	0.688	3.35
13.80	1.734	0.700	3.24
15.36	1.829	0.703	3.39

Often the values of K_c obtained in the study of equilibria in solutions show deviations from constancy which become more pronounced with increase in concentration. The deviations usually are not very serious with nonelectrolytes or weak electrolytes, but they are very large when strong electrolytes are involved. In such cases true equilibrium constants can be obtained only by the use of activities in place of concentrations.

Homogeneous equilibria involving strong electrolytes will be discussed in a subsequent chapter.

EQUILIBRIUM CONSTANTS AND TEMPERATURE

Although the equilibrium constant of a reaction is constant at any given temperature, its magnitude varies appreciably as the temperature is changed. The exact manner in which the equilibrium constant of any reaction depends on the temperature is readily deducible from thermodynamics. If equation (5) of this chapter be differentiated with respect to temperature, then

$$\Delta F^0 = -RT \ln K_a$$

$$\left[\frac{\partial \Delta F^0}{\partial T}\right] = -RT\left[\frac{\partial \ln K_a}{\partial T}\right] - R \ln K_a$$

But according to the Gibbs-Helmholtz equation,

$$\left[\frac{\partial \Delta F^0}{\partial T}\right] = \frac{\Delta F^0 - \Delta H^0}{T} = \frac{-RT \ln K_a - \Delta H^0}{T}$$

$$= -R \ln K_a - \frac{\Delta H^0}{T}$$

Therefore,

$$-R \ln K_a - \frac{\Delta H^0}{T} = -RT\left[\frac{\partial \ln K_a}{\partial T}\right] - R \ln K_a$$

and

$$\left[\frac{\partial \ln K_a}{\partial T}\right] = \frac{\Delta H^0}{RT^2} \tag{40}$$

Equation (40), known as the *van't Hoff reaction isobar*, defines the temperature coefficient of $\ln K_a$ in terms of the heat of reaction ΔH^0 and the temperature T. For gaseous reactions, when $K_a = K_p$, equation (40) may be written as

$$\left[\frac{\partial \ln K_p}{\partial T}\right] = \frac{\Delta H^0}{RT^2} \tag{41}$$

For exact integration of equation (41) ΔH^0 must be known as a function of T. However, when the temperature interval considered is not very large, ΔH^0 may be considered constant over the interval, and

$$\int_{K_{p_1}}^{K_{p_2}} d \ln K_p = \int_{T_1}^{T_2} \frac{\Delta H^0}{RT^2} dT$$

$$\ln K_p \Big]_{K_{p_1}}^{K_{p_2}} = \frac{\Delta H^0}{R}\left[-\frac{1}{T}\right]_{T_1}^{T_2}$$

$$\ln \frac{K_{p_2}}{K_{p_1}} = \frac{\Delta H^0}{R}\left[\frac{T_2 - T_1}{T_1 T_2}\right] \tag{42}$$

Equation (42) permits the calculation of K_{p_2} at T_2 when K_{p_1} at T_1 and ΔH^0 are available; or, when the equilibrium constants at two different temperatures are known, equation (42) may be used to obtain the average heat of the reaction over the temperature range T_1 to T_2. These calculations may be illustrated by the following two examples.

Example (a): The equilibrium constant for the dissociation

$$2\,H_2S(g) = 2\,H_2(g) + S_2(g)$$

is $K_p = 0.0118$ at $1065°$ C, while the heat of dissociation is $\Delta H^0 = 42,400$ cal. Find the equilibrium constant of the reaction at $1200°$ C. Applying equation (42)

$$\log_{10}\frac{K_{p_2}}{K_{p_1}} = \frac{\Delta H^0}{2.303 \times R}\left[\frac{T_2 - T_1}{T_1 T_2}\right]$$

$$\log_{10}\frac{K_{p_2}}{0.0118} = \frac{42,400}{4.57}\left[\frac{1473 - 1338}{1473 \times 1338}\right]$$

$$= 0.6350$$

$$\frac{K_{p_2}}{0.0118} = 4.30$$

$$K_{p_2} = 4.30 \times 0.0118$$
$$= 0.0507 \text{ at } 1200° \text{ C}$$

Example (b): For the reaction

$$SO_2(g) + \frac{1}{2}O_2(g) = SO_3(g)$$

$K_p = 6.55$ at $900°$ K and $K_p = 1.86$ at $1000°$ K. Calculate the heat of the reaction over the temperature interval 900 to $1000°$ K. Again applying equation (42), we find

$$\log_{10}\frac{1.86}{6.55} = \frac{\Delta H^0}{4.57}\left[\frac{1000 - 900}{900 \times 1000}\right]$$
$$\Delta H^0 = -22,500 \text{ cal}$$

Instead of integrating equation (41) between limits, a solution under the same conditions of constant ΔH^0 may be obtained in the form

$$d \ln K_p = \frac{\Delta H^0}{RT^2}dT$$

$$\ln K_p = -\frac{\Delta H^0}{RT} + C \tag{43}$$

C is an integration constant which can be evaluated for any reaction by substituting a known value of K_p at some given temperature. When several values of K_p at various temperatures are available and ΔH^0 is sought, it is preferable to determine ΔH^0 graphically rather than by use of equation (42). According to equation (43) a plot of $\log_{10} K_p$ vs. $1/T$ should be a straight line with slope equal to $-\Delta H^0/2.303R$, and hence ΔH^0

follows as

$$\Delta H^0 = -2.303 \, R \times \text{slope}$$
$$= -4.576 \times \text{slope} \tag{44}$$

Figure 1 shows such a plot for the reaction

$$SO_2(g) + \frac{1}{2} O_2(g) = SO_3(g)$$

between 800° and 1170° K. In agreement with equation (43) the plot is a

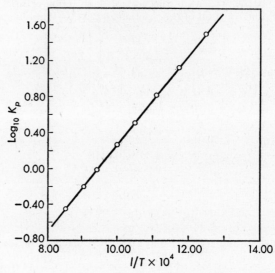

Fig. 1.   Plot of $Log_{10} \, Kp$ vs. $1/T$ for the Reaction $SO_2(g) + \frac{1}{2} O_2(g) = SO_3(g)$.

straight line with slope equal to 4930. Consequently over this temperature interval

$$\Delta H^0 = -4.576 \times 4930$$
$$= -22,600 \text{ cal}$$

K_c AND TEMPERATURE

An equation similar to (41) may also be derived for the variation of K_c of a gaseous reaction with temperature, namely,

$$\left[\frac{\partial \ln K_c}{\partial T} \right] = \frac{\Delta E^0}{RT^2} \tag{45}$$

where ΔE^0 is the heat of reaction at constant volume. This equation is integrated and handled in exactly the same manner as equation (41). As a general rule equations (45) and (41) will yield different results and will be identical only when $K_c = K_p$ and $\Delta H^0 = \Delta E^0$, i.e., when $\Delta n_g = 0$ and there is no volume change on reaction.

Equation (45) is valid also for reactions in solution. For such reactions the difference between ΔH^0 and ΔE^0 is negligible, and hence equation (45) may be written as well

$$\left[\frac{\partial \ln K_c}{\partial T}\right] = \frac{\Delta E^0}{RT^2} = \frac{\Delta H^0}{RT^2} \tag{46}$$

REFERENCES FOR FURTHER READING

See list at end of Chapters 10 and 11. Also:

1. Hougen and Watson, *Chemical Process Principles*, John Wiley & Sons, Inc., New York, 1947, Vol. II.
2. K. Jellinek, *Lehrbuch der physikalischen Chemie*, Ferdinand Enke, Stuttgart, 1930, Vol. III.

PROBLEMS

1. State which of the following equilibria are homogeneous and which are heterogeneous:

    (a) S (rhombic) = S (monoclinic)
    (b) $Fe_2O_3(s) + CO(g) = CO_2(g) + 2\ FeO(s)$
    (c) $2\ SO_2(g) + O_2(g) = 2\ SO_3(g)$
    (d) $CaCO_3(s) + H^+(aq) = HCO_3^-(aq) + Ca^{++}(aq)$

2. Formulate the equilibrium constant K_p for each of the following reactions:

    (a) $C_2H_6(g) = C_2H_4(g) + H_2(g)$
    (b) $2\ NO(g) + O_2(g) = 2\ NO_2(g)$
    (c) $NO_2(g) + SO_2(g) = SO_3(g) + NO(g)$
    (d) $3\ O_2(g) = 2\ O_3(g)$

3. In each of the reactions of the preceding problem determine the ratio of K_p to K_c at 27° C.

4. The standard free energy of formation of HCl(g) at 25° C is $-22,770$ cal/mole. Calculate the thermodynamic equilibrium constant for the dissociation of HCl into its elements at 25° C.   *Ans.* 2.06×10^{-17}.

5. For the synthesis of 1 mole of $NH_3(g)$ from the elements at 600° K, $\log_{10} K_\gamma$ as a function of the total equilibrium pressure P in atmospheres is given by the relation [Maron and Turnbull, *Ind. Eng. Chem.*, **33**, 69(1941)]:

$$\log_{10} K_\gamma = -6.360 \times 10^{-4} P - 10.484 \times 10^{-8} P^2 + 1.750 \times 10^{-10} P^3$$

    Determine the ratio of K_p to K_a at (a) 100 atm, (b) 300 atm, and (c) 500 atm total equilibrium pressure.   *Ans.* (a) $K_p/K_a = 1.16$.

6. In each of the following equilibria, predict qualitatively the effect of increasing the total pressure upon the percentage of products present at equilibrium:

(a) $2 SO_3(g) + heat = 2 SO_2(g) + O_2(g)$
(b) $2 HI(g) = H_2(g) + I_2(g) + heat$
(c) $2 NO_2(g) = N_2O_4(g) + heat$
(d) $CO(g) + H_2O(g) = CO_2(g) + H_2(g) + heat$

7. In the preceding problem, what effect will a decrease in temperature have upon the percentage of product present at equilibrium?

8. At 2155° C and 1 atm pressure steam is 1.18% decomposed into H_2 and O_2 according to the equation: $2 H_2O(g) = 2 H_2(g) + O_2(g)$. Calculate K_p for the decomposition of steam at this temperature.   *Ans.* 8.38×10^{-7}.

9. At a total pressure of 1 atm and at 184° C, NO_2 is 5% decomposed according to the equation:

$$2 NO_2(g) = 2 NO(g) + O_2(g)$$

Calculate K_p for the equilibrium.

10. PCl_5 dissociates as follows:

$$PCl_5(g) = PCl_3(g) + Cl_2(g)$$

At 250° C and a pressure of 1 atm the density of the equilibrium mixture of the above gases was observed to be 2.695 g/liter. Calculate the degree of dissociation, α, of PCl_5, and K_p for the reaction.   *Ans.* $\alpha = 0.80$; $K_p = 1.78$.

11. For the equilibrium

$$2 CO_2(g) = 2 CO(g) + O_2(g)$$

derive an expression for α, the degree of dissociation of CO_2, as a function of K_p for the reaction and the total pressure P. Assume that α is negligible compared to unity.

12. For the reaction

$$C_2H_5OH(l) + CH_3COOH(l) = CH_3COOC_2H_5(l) + H_2O(l)$$

let a be the number of moles of alcohol present initially per mole of acid and x the number of moles of acid esterified after equilibrium is established. Then from the following data

a	x
0.5	0.420
1.0	0.665
1.5	0.779

(a) calculate K_c in each case, and (b) from the average value of K_c find x when a is 0.1 mole.

13. At 3000° K and 1 atm, CO_2 is 40% dissociated into CO and O_2. (a) What will be the degree of dissociation if the pressure is raised to 2 atm? (b) What will be the degree of dissociation when a mixture of 50% CO_2 and 50% O_2 is heated to 3000° K, the pressure being 1 atm?   *Ans.* (a) 0.335; (b) 0.271.

14. From the average value of K_p in Table 1 calculate the percentage of NH_3 present at equilibrium at 450° C when the total pressure is 100 atm and the molar ratio of H_2 to N_2 is 3 to 1.

15. Repeat the calculation in the preceding problem, assuming that the initial molar ratio of H_2 to N_2 is 1 to 1 and the total equilibrium pressure is 10 atm.

16. At 30° C K_p in atmospheres for the dissociation

$$SO_2Cl_2(g) = SO_2(g) + Cl_2(g)$$

is 2.9×10^{-2}. Calculate the degree of dissociation when total pressure is 1 atm.

17. At 25° C ΔF^0 for the reaction

$$N_2O_4(g) = 2 NO_2(g)$$

is $+1380$ cal. What is the degree of dissociation at 25° C when the total pressure is 10 atm?

18. In the preceding problem calculate the degree of dissociation when the total pressure is maintained at 10 atm, but a partial pressure of CO_2 equal to 5 atm is present at equilibrium.   *Ans.* $\alpha = 0.0698$.

19. For the reaction

$$H_2(g) + I_2(g) = 2 HI(g)$$

$K_c = 50.0$ at 448° C, and $K_c = 66.9$ at 350° C. Calculate (a) the heat of reaction and (b) the degree of dissociation, α, at 400° C. Assume that ΔH^0 does not vary with temperature.   *Ans.* (a) -2660 cal; (b) 0.21.

20. For the reaction

$$2 SO_3(g) = 2 SO_2(g) + O_2(g)$$
$$\Delta H^0_{298.2° K} = 46,980 \text{ cal} \qquad \Delta F^0_{298.2° K} = 33,460 \text{ cal}$$

Calculate (a) ΔF^0 and (b) the degree of dissociation, α, of SO_3 at 600° K and 0.5 atm pressure. Assume ΔH^0 to be independent of temperature.

21. From the heat of formation and free energy of formation of NO and NO_2 given in the proper tables of the preceding chapters, find the degree of dissociation of NO_2 into NO and O_2 at 200° C and 1 atm pressure. Assume that ΔH^0 is constant.

22. For the reaction

$$CO(g) + H_2O(g) = CO_2(g) + H_2(g)$$

the following are the absolute entropies S^0, and heats of formation ΔH^0, at 25° C:

	S^0(eu)	ΔH^0 (cal)
CO	47.30	$-26,420$
H_2O	45.11	$-57,800$
CO_2	51.06	$-94,050$
H_2	31.21	—

Assuming that ΔH^0 is constant with T, calculate K_p for the reaction at 600° K.
                    Ans. 23.2.

23. By referring to Table 2 of the preceding chapter, predict which of the following reactions are thermodynamically possible in the standard state at 25° C:

(a) $3 C_2H_2(g) = C_6H_6(g)$
(b) $4 NH_3(g) + 5 O_2(g) = 4 NO(g) + 6 H_2O(g)$
(c) $N_2O_4(g) = 2 NO(g) + O_2(g)$
(d) $CO(g) + 2 H_2(g) = CH_3OH(l)$

24. For the reaction

$$(CH_3)_2CHOH(g) = (CH_3)_2CO(g) + H_2(g)$$

K_p at $457.4°$ K is 0.36, $\Delta C_p = 4.0$, and $\Delta H^0_{298.2°\,K} = 14{,}700$ cal. (a) Derive an expression for $\log_{10} K_p$ as a function of T, and (b) calculate K_p at $500°$ K.

$$Ans.\ (a)\ \log_{10} K_p = -\frac{2950}{T} + 2.01 \log_{10} T + 0.656;\ (b)\ K_p = 1.42.$$

25. For the reaction $2\,H_2(g) + S_2(g) = 2\,H_2S(g)$

$$\Delta F^0 = -38{,}810 + 15.41\,T \log_{10} T - 2.065 \times 10^{-3}\,T^2 - 25.02\,T$$

Deduce the expressions for $\ln K_p$, ΔH^0, ΔS^0, and ΔC_p of the reaction as a function of the temperature.

26. For the reaction $S_2(g) + 2\,O_2(g) = 2\,SO_2(g)$ $\Delta H^0_{25°\,C} = -172{,}900$ cal, $\Delta S^0_{25°\,C} = -33.67$ eu, and ΔC_p as a function of temperature is given by

$$\Delta C_p = -1.49 + 1.424 \times 10^{-3}\,T - \frac{0.336 \times 10^5}{T^2}$$

From these data find the value of K_p of the reaction at $1000°$ K.

27. For the reaction $S_2(g) = 2\,S(g)$ $\log_{10} K_p = -16.735$ at $1000°$ K, while

$$\Delta H^0 = 102{,}600 + 2.47\,T - 0.444 \times 10^{-3}\,T^2$$

Find the extent to which $S_2(g)$ will be dissociated into atoms at a temperature of $4000°$ K and 1 atm pressure.

13

Heterogeneous Equilibria

A heterogeneous system is characterized by the presence of several distinct phases. Each of these phases may be solid, liquid, or gas. Since gases are miscible in all proportions, there can be only one gas phase in a system. On the other hand, in a system containing several liquids or solids, or solids and liquids, several phases may occur. Hence we may have heterogeneous systems composed of two or more solid phases, two or more liquid phases, or combinations of solid, liquid, and gas phases. As examples of heterogeneous systems may be mentioned two partially miscible liquids in contact, a liquid and its vapor, a solid and its melt, a solid and its vapor, a solution in presence of its vapor or solid solvent, a saturated solution in contact with saturating solid phase, a salt like barium carbonate in presence of its thermal decomposition products, barium oxide and carbon dioxide, or a system in which cupric oxide reacts with hydrogen to form copper and water vapor.

From the examples cited it is readily apparent that the number of equilibria possible in heterogeneous systems is very large. In general, the various equilibria encountered may be classified as being either physical in nature, such as the equilibrium between a liquid and its vapor, or chemical, such as dissociation of barium carbonate, although there are cases of mixed type, as we shall see. In approaching the problem of equilibria in heterogeneous systems three methods of attack are available: (a) the equilibrium constant principle, (b) the Nernst distribution law, and (c) the Gibbs phase rule. The particular method employed depends on the nature of the problem at hand and the information sought. The equilibrium constant approach is employed when quantitative information is desired on heterogeneous *chemical* equilibria involving gases; the Nernst distribution law is used in problems involving the solubility of a substance in two mutually insoluble solvents; while the phase rule is a general principle valuable for the definition of conditions obtaining in heterogeneous equilibria. These delineations of the sphere encompassed by each of these principles will become clearer as soon as specific instances of the application of each are given.

This chapter will be devoted to treatment of heterogeneous equilibria in terms of the equilibrium constant and the distribution law. The phase rule in its various aspects will be discussed in the next chapter.

THE EQUILIBRIUM CONSTANT FOR HETEROGENEOUS REACTIONS

Consider the reaction

$$CuO(s) + H_2(g) = Cu(s) + H_2O(g) \tag{1}$$

The thermodynamic equilibrium constant K_a for this reaction is

$$K_a = \frac{a_{Cu} a_{H_2O}}{a_{CuO} a_{H_2}} \tag{2}$$

However, it was shown in Chapter 11 that *the activity of a pure solid or liquid may be taken as unity at all temperatures up to fairly high pressures.* Then $a_{Cu} = a_{CuO} = 1$, and

$$K_a = \frac{a_{H_2O}}{a_{H_2}} \tag{3}$$

When the gases involved may be considered to behave ideally the activity reduces to the pressure, and equation (3) becomes

$$K_p = \frac{P_{H_2O}}{P_{H_2}} \tag{4}$$

Thermodynamic reasoning indicates, therefore, that the equilibrium constant for a heterogeneous reaction should contain only the activities or pressures of the gaseous constituents and should not include terms for either pure solids or pure liquids; i.e., *the presence of pure solid or liquid phases is completely disregarded in writing the expression for the equilibrium constant.* K_p's of heterogeneous reactions are generally referred to as *condensed* equilibrium constants.

Below are given several typical examples of heterogeneous equilibria in order to illustrate some of the methods employed in their study and mathematical treatment.

THE DISSOCIATION OF CUPRIC OXIDE

At elevated temperatures cupric oxide dissociates into cuprous oxide and oxygen according to the reaction

$$4\,CuO(s) = 2\,Cu_2O(s) + O_2(g) \tag{5}$$

Since oxygen is the only gaseous constituent involved in this equilibrium, the condensed equilibrium constant K_p for this reaction should be

$$K_p = P_{O_2} \tag{6}$$

i.e., the pressure of oxygen above a mixture of cupric and cuprous oxides should be constant at each given temperature. This conclusion is verified by the experimental results of F. Hastings Smith and H. R. Robert.[1] These investigators placed a charge of pure cupric oxide in a silica tube, evacuated the system, and then heated the tube to the desired temperature in an electric furnace. The equilibrium pressure of oxygen developed as a result of dissociation of the cupric oxide was read on a manometer attached to the silica tube. To make sure that the pressures read were those at true equilibrium, the latter was approached from both lower and higher temperatures, and at each temperature some gas was removed and the equilibrium pressure permitted to reestablish itself. In this manner Hastings Smith and Robert proved that at each temperature the pressure of oxygen is constant in accord with equation (6). Some of their results at various temperatures are given in Table 1.

TABLE 1

Dissociation Pressures of CuO
at Various Temperatures

$t°$ C	$K_p = P_{O_2}$ (mm Hg)
900	12.5
940	29.2
980	65.0
1020	137.7
1060	278.0
1080	388.0

THE CARBON DISULFIDE EQUILIBRIUM

When gaseous sulfur is passed over carbon at high temperatures, carbon disulfide is formed according to the equation

$$C(s) + S_2(g) = CS_2(g) \tag{7}$$

[1] F. Hastings Smith and H. R. Robert, *J. Am. Chem. Soc.*, **42**, 2582 (1920).

For this reaction the condensed equilibrium constant is given by

$$K_p = \frac{P_{CS_2}}{P_{S_2}} \tag{8}$$

To study this equilibrium F. Koref[1] employed a dynamic method. Nitrogen gas saturated with sulfur vapor was passed over finely divided carbon kept at the desired temperature in an electric furnace. The exit gases were cooled rapidly to prevent the shift of equilibrium, the sulfur and carbon disulfide condensed out, while the nitrogen was collected in a gasometer. The equilibrium quantities of carbon disulfide and sulfur were then determined by weighing.

TABLE 2

K_p AT 1009° C FOR THE REACTION $C(s) + S_2(g) = CS_2(g)$

V_{CS_2}(cc)	V_{S_2}(cc)	K_p
458	84	5.45
607	109	5.57
738	130	5.68
814	142	5.73
1164	207	5.62
2057	371	5.54

From the data thus obtained the equilibrium constant was calculated as follows. If it is assumed that the sulfur and carbon disulfide vapors behave ideally, the volume of each of these at equilibrium at temperature T and total pressure P is

$$V_{S_2} = \frac{n_{S_2}RT}{P} \qquad V_{CS_2} = \frac{n_{CS_2}RT}{P}$$

where n_{S_2} and n_{CS_2} are the numbers of moles of these substances present in the condensates from the equilibrium mixture. If we let V be the total volume of gases at equilibrium, i.e., the sum of the volumes of sulfur, carbon disulfide, and nitrogen, then the mol fractions of the first two substances are $N_{S_2} = V_{S_2}/V$ and $N_{CS_2} = V_{CS_2}/V$, and hence, according to Dalton's law,

$$P_{S_2} = N_{S_2}P = \left(\frac{V_{S_2}}{V}\right)P \qquad P_{CS_2} = N_{CS_2}P = \left(\frac{V_{CS_2}}{V}\right)P$$

Substituting these expressions for the partial pressures into equation (8),

[1] F. Koref, *Z. anorg. Chem.*, **66**, 73 (1910).

we find

$$K_p = \frac{P_{\text{CS}_2}}{P_{\text{S}_2}} = \frac{(V_{\text{CS}_2}P)/V}{(V_{\text{S}_2}P)/V}$$
$$= \frac{V_{\text{CS}_2}}{V_{\text{S}_2}} \tag{9}$$

namely, the equilibrium constant should equal the ratio of the volumes of the two substances at equilibrium. Table 2 lists some of Koref's data at 1009° C and the values of K_p calculated from these. The constancy exhibited by K_p is satisfactory.

THE DISSOCIATION OF AMMONIUM CARBAMATE

Ammonium carbamate dissociates even at room temperature as follows

$$\text{NH}_2\text{COONH}_4(\text{s}) = 2\,\text{NH}_3(\text{g}) + \text{CO}_2(\text{g}) \tag{10}$$

The condensed equilibrium constant for this reaction is, therefore,

$$K_p = P_{\text{NH}_3}^2 P_{\text{CO}_2} \tag{11}$$

In studying this equilibrium by a static method T. R. Briggs and V. Migidichian[1] introduced solid ammonium carbamate along with definite quantities of ammonia and carbon dioxide into an evacuated glass vessel to which was attached a manometer. The apparatus was immersed then in a water thermostat, the mixture was allowed to reach equilibrium, and the total pressure at equilibrium was read on the manometer.

If we consider the experiments where only ammonia was introduced initially along with the ammonium carbamate, and if we let e_1 be the initial pressure of ammonia and P the total pressure at equilibrium, then the increase in pressure due to dissociation of the solid is $(P - e_1)$. From the stoichiometry of the reaction it follows that of this increase two-thirds must be due to the formation of ammonia, one-third to formation of carbon dioxide. Consequently,

$$P_{\text{NH}_3} = \frac{2}{3}(P - e_1) + e_1 = \left(\frac{2P + e_1}{3}\right)$$
$$P_{\text{CO}_2} = \frac{1}{3}(P - e_1)$$

and equation (11) becomes

$$K_p = \left(\frac{2P + e_1}{3}\right)^2 \left(\frac{P - e_1}{3}\right)$$
$$= \frac{(2P + e_1)^2(P - e_1)}{27} \tag{12}$$

[1] T. R. Briggs and V. Migidichian, *J. Phys. Chem.*, **28**, 1121 (1924).

TABLE 3

DISSOCIATION OF AMMONIUM CARBAMATE AT 30° C

e_1	P	P_{NH_3}	P_{CO_2}	K_p
0	125.0	83.3	41.7	2.89×10^5
13.6	124.9	87.8	37.1	2.86
27.3	125.4	92.7	32.7	2.81
52.5	129.5	103.8	25.7	2.77
141.1	174.2	163.2	11.0	2.93
168.6	194.2	185.7	8.5	2.93

Table 3 presents typical data obtained during a series of experiments at 30° C, as well as the equilibrium constants calculated according to equation (12). All pressures are given in mm Hg. From the latter equation it is apparent that when $e_1 = 0$, i.e., when no ammonia is present initially, the expression for K_p reduces to

$$K_p = \frac{(2\,P)^2 P}{27}$$
$$= \frac{4\,P^3}{27} \tag{13}$$

Other examples of heterogeneous equilibria which can be handled in the manner described are the thermal dissociations of metal carbonates, halides, and sulfides, the oxidation of carbon to carbon monoxide and dioxide, and the reduction of metal oxides by carbon monoxide.

EFFECT OF PRESSURE ON HETEROGENEOUS EQUILIBRIA

As in homogeneous equilibria, the influence of pressure on heterogeneous equilibria can be predicted by means of the Le Chatelier principle. Whenever a reaction proceeds with a decrease in volume, increase of pressure will favor the products, while for reactions occurring with an increase in volume, higher pressures will favor the reactants. In the special case of no volume change, the extent of reaction will be uninfluenced by the total equilibrium pressure. In considering the change in volume accompanying a reaction, the volumes of all condensed phases may be disregarded, since they are negligibly small compared to those of the gases involved.

To illustrate the application of the Le Chatelier principle to a heterogeneous equilibrium consider again the reaction

$$4\,CuO(s) = 2\,Cu_2O(s) + O_2(g) \tag{14}$$

Since this reaction proceeds with an increase in volume, any increase in the oxygen pressure above its equilibrium value will shift this reaction to the left, i.e., cuprous oxide and oxygen will interact to form cupric oxide until the pressure of oxygen is back to its equilibrium value. On the other hand, when the oxygen pressure is reduced below its equilibrium value, cupric oxide will dissociate, and the process will continue until the requisite oxygen pressure is reestablished.

Such equilibrium adjustments are possible only when *all the condensed phases participating in the equilibrium are present*. According to equation (6), the pressure of oxygen at equilibrium in this system should be constant at any given temperature. When the equilibrium is approached from the cupric oxide side, and when sufficient cupric oxide is taken to supply the given pressure of the gas in the volume involved, all the phases participating in the equilibrium are present, and the demands of the equilibrium constant can be satisfied. Suppose, however, that the equilibrium is approached from the other side, and that the initial pressure of oxygen is considerably above the equilibrium pressure. Then cuprous oxide will interact with the oxygen to form cupric oxide, and this reaction will proceed until the pressure of the gas has been reduced to the equilibrium pressure. But, this reaction can go this far only if sufficient cuprous oxide is present to react with all the excess oxygen. If such is not the case, all the cuprous oxide will be converted to cupric oxide, and still an excess of oxygen will remain to yield a pressure higher than that demanded by the equilibrium constant. Under such conditions no equilibrium is possible in the system, since no cuprous oxide is present, and hence the oxygen pressure may assume any value dependent on the amount of it present.

These conclusions apply to all heterogeneous equilibria. It must be remembered, therefore, that sufficient amounts of the solid phases involved in the equilibria must be present to permit regulation and adjustment of the conditions in the system necessary for the establishment of true equilibrium. Otherwise true equilibrium is impossible, and the equilibrium constant principle does not apply.

EFFECT OF TEMPERATURE ON HETEROGENEOUS EQUILIBRIA

The variation of condensed equilibrium constants with temperature is given by the same equations as for constants of homogeneous reactions, namely, the differential equations (41) and (45) of Chapter 12 and the integrated forms which correspond to these. The validity of these equations may again be tested by plotting $\log K_p$ vs. $1/T$ and observing whether a straight line is obtained. Figure 1 shows such a plot of the

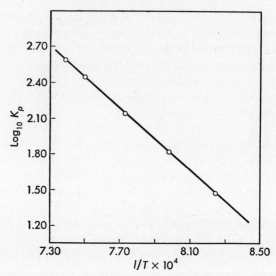

Fig. 1.   Plot of $Log_{10}\ K_p$ vs. $1/T$ for the Reaction $4\,CuO(s) = 2\,Cu_2O(s) + O_2(g)$.

data presented in Table 1 for the thermal dissociation of cupric oxide. The straight line has a slope of $-13{,}200$ and hence the heat of the dissociation reaction is

$$-\frac{\Delta H^0}{2.303\ R} = -13{,}200$$
$$\Delta H^0 = 4.576 \times 13{,}200$$
$$= 60{,}400\ cal$$

EQUILIBRIA IN HYDRATES

An interesting type of heterogeneous equilibrium is that exhibited by hydrates, or in general solvates, of various substances. Under proper conditions these hydrates are found to dissociate into lower hydrates, or the anhydrous substance, and water vapor which establishes a definite vapor pressure above the solid phases. Thus $Na_2HPO_4 \cdot 12\ H_2O$ dissociates into $Na_2HPO_4 \cdot 7\ H_2O$, the latter into $Na_2HPO_4 \cdot 2\ H_2O$, the dihydrate into Na_2HPO_4. The equilibria attending these dissociations are:

$$Na_2HPO_4 \cdot 12\ H_2O(s) = Na_2HPO_4 \cdot 7\ H_2O(s) + 5\ H_2O(g) \qquad (15)$$
$$Na_2HPO_4 \cdot\ 7\ H_2O(s) = Na_2HPO_4 \cdot 2\ H_2O(s) + 5\ H_2O(g) \qquad (16)$$
$$Na_2HPO_4 \cdot\ 2\ H_2O(s) = Na_2HPO_4(s) + 2\ H_2O(g) \qquad (17)$$

These heterogeneous equilibria can be treated by the methods described. The equilibrium constants of all such dissociations are given simply by

$$K_p = P^x \qquad (18)$$

where x is the number of moles of vapor resulting from the dissociation of the hydrate, i.e., 5 for equations (15) and (16) and 2 for equation (17), while P is the vapor pressure above the pair of solid phases. From equation (18) it follows that, since P^x is constant for a particular dissociation, P must also be constant, and therefore at any given temperature the vapor pressure above any *hydrate pair* must be constant as long as both phases are present. This conclusion is in accord with observation. In the presence of any given hydrate and its lower dissociation product the pressure is found to be definite and characteristic of the particular hydrate pair. This is not true, however, when only a single solid phase is present, as under such conditions the vapor pressure can vary within certain limits. It is erroneous, therefore, to speak of the vapor pressure of a hydrate. The vapor pressure is constant only for a hydrate pair or a hydrate and its anhydride.

TABLE 4

AQUEOUS VAPOR PRESSURE OF HYDRATE PAIRS AT 25° C
(In mm Hg)

Hydrate Pair	P
$MgSO_4 \cdot 7\ H_2O - MgSO_4 \cdot 6\ H_2O$	11.5
$6\ H_2O - 5\ H_2O$	9.8
$5\ H_2O - 4\ H_2O$	8.8
$4\ H_2O - H_2O$	4.1
$H_2O - MgSO_4$	1.0
$CuSO_4 \cdot 5\ H_2O - CuSO_4 \cdot 3\ H_2O$	7.80
$3\ H_2O - H_2O$	5.60
$H_2O - CuSO_4$	0.8(?)
$Na_2HPO_4 \cdot 12\ H_2O - Na_2HPO_4 \cdot 7\ H_2O$	19.13
$7\ H_2O - 2\ H_2O$	14.51
$2\ H_2O - Na_2HPO_4$	9.80

In Table 4 are given the vapor pressures at 25° C for the hydrate pairs of several salts. It will be observed that the vapor pressure is highest for the pair richest in water and decreases as the water content of the solid phase decreases. A clearer appreciation of the relation between the pressures of the various hydrated forms of a substance at a particular temperature can be obtained by plotting the pressure against the number of moles of water in the solid phase, n. Such a plot for disodium phosphate is shown in Fig. 2. The horizontal portions indicate the values of n over which the particular vapor pressures will remain constant, i.e., between $n = 0$ and 2, $n = 2$ and 7, and $n = 7$ and 12. The vertical portions, on the other hand, give the *vapor pressure ranges* over which the pure solid phases (anhydrous salt, 2 H_2O, 7 H_2O, and 12 H_2O) are stable. Thus between zero and 9.80 mm Hg water vapor pressure anhydrous disodium phosphate does not combine with water vapor. As soon as the latter pressure is reached, however, some $Na_2HPO_4 \cdot 2 H_2O$ is formed, and the pressure remains constant as long as any unconverted anhydrous salt is present. As soon as all of the disodium phosphate has been converted to the dihydrate, it is found that the aqueous tension can be varied between 9.80 and 14.51 mm Hg without formation of the heptahydrate; i.e., the range of stability of the dihydrate is from 9.80 to 14.51 mm Hg vapor pressure. At 14.51 mm Hg the heptahydrate phase begins to form, and the pressure again becomes constant, this time at 14.51 mm, until all of the dihydrate has been converted to the heptahydrate. The latter in turn remains stable between this pressure and 19.13 mm, at which pressure the 12 H_2O begins to form. Once the solid phase has been converted to the 12 H_2O, the pressure may be increased up to the pressure of the saturated solution

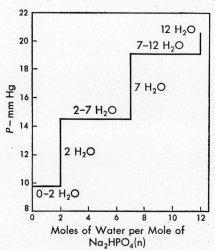

Fig. 2.   Vapor Pressures of the Hydrates of Na_2HPO_4 at 25° C.

of disodium phosphate in water. On reaching this pressure some of the solid will dissolve to form a solution in equilibrium with solid $Na_2HPO_4 \cdot 12 H_2O$.

On dehydration the phenomena described will be found to take place in reverse order, i.e., the 12 H_2O will break down to the 7 H_2O, the 7 H_2O to 2 H_2O, etc. From this discussion it is apparent that any particular hydrate can be preserved only as long as the aqueous tension lies between the limits of stability exhibited by the hydrate at the given temperature. Outside these limits the hydrate will either dissociate to a lower hydrate or the anhydrous salt, or it will take on water to form a water richer phase, depending on whether the vapor pressure is below or above the prescribed limits.

This behavior of the hydrates of disodium phosphate at various aqueous tensions is typical of that exhibited by all hydrates at a particular temperature, as well as by other solvates such as alcoholates and ammoniates of various salts.

The vapor pressures of hydrate and other solvate pairs increase with rise in temperature, as may be seen from Table 5, in a manner readily deducible from equation (18). Since $K_p = P^x$, then

$$\frac{d \ln P^x}{dT} = \frac{\Delta H^0}{RT^2} \tag{19}$$

and therefore,

$$\frac{d \ln P}{dT} = \frac{\Delta H^0}{xRT^2} \tag{20}$$

On integration, assuming ΔH^0 constant, this leads to

$$\log_{10} P = \left(\frac{-\Delta H^0}{2.303\, xR}\right) \frac{1}{T} + C \tag{21}$$

Equation (21) is identical with the Clausius-Clapeyron equation except that the slope of $\log_{10} P$ vs. $1/T$, instead of being $(-\Delta H^0/2.303\, R)$, is given by $(-\Delta H^0/2.303\, xR)$. From the slope of such a plot the heat of dissociation of a hydrate or solvate readily follows as

$$\Delta H^0 = -2.303\, xR \text{ (slope)} \tag{22}$$

TABLE 5

VAPOR PRESSURES OF SOME HYDRATE PAIRS AT VARIOUS TEMPERATURES
(P in mm Hg)

Hydrate Pair	0° C	15°	20°	25°	30°
$Na_2HPO_4 \cdot 12\, H_2O - 7\, H_2O$*	2.66	8.95	12.93	19.18	27.05
$SrCl_2 \cdot 6\, H_2O - 2\, H_2O$†	1.23	3.99	8.37	—	—
$Na_2SO_4 \cdot 10\, H_2O - Na_2SO_4$†	2.77	9.21	19.20	—	—

* Partington and Winterton, *J. Chem. Soc.*, **132**, 635 (1930); Baxter and Cooper, *J. Am. Chem. Soc.*, **46**, 927 (1924).
† Baxter and Lansing, *J. Am. Chem. Soc.*, **42**, 419 (1920).

HETEROGENEOUS EQUILIBRIA INVOLVING IONS

All the heterogeneous equilibria discussed thus far involved gases and condensed phases. Heterogeneous equilibria involving condensed phases and ions in solution are also quite common, but a discussion of these will be postponed until Chapter 16.

THE DISTRIBUTION LAW

Mercuric bromide is soluble in both water and benzene. When a solution of mercuric bromide in water is shaken with benzene, which is immiscible with water, it is found that the mercuric bromide distributes itself between the water and benzene layers in such a way that at equilibrium the *ratio of the concentrations* of mercuric bromide in the two layers *is a constant at any given temperature.* Such distribution of a solute between two immiscible or only slightly miscible solvents can be accomplished with any solute for which a pair of immiscible solvents can be found.

The above behavior is a direct consequence of the thermodynamic requirements for equilibrium. To show this, consider a pair of immiscible solvents in contact, A and B, both containing the same substance in solution. According to equation (33) of Chapter 11, the free energy of the solute in liquid A, F_A, can be represented by

$$F_A = F_A^0 + RT \ln a_A \tag{23}$$

where F_A^0 is the standard free energy and a_A the activity of the solute in solvent A. Similarly, the free energy of the solute in the second liquid, F_B, can be written as

$$F_B = F_B^0 + RT \ln a_B \tag{24}$$

where all the quantities have the same significance as in equation (23), except that they refer now to liquid B. Since for equilibrium between the layers $\Delta F = F_B - F_A$ must be zero at constant temperature and pressure, it follows that

$$F_B = F_A$$
$$F_B^0 + RT \ln a_B = F_A^0 + RT \ln a_A$$
$$\ln \frac{a_B}{a_A} = \frac{F_A^0 - F_B^0}{RT} \tag{25}$$

However, at any given temperature F_B^0 and F_A^0 are constants for a given substance in the particular solvents. Hence,

$$\ln \frac{a_B}{a_A} = k$$

and therefore,
$$\frac{a_B}{a_A} = K \tag{26}$$

Equation (26) is a mathematical statement of the *distribution law*, which states that a substance will distribute itself between two solvents until at equilibrium the *ratio* of the activities of the substance in the two layers is constant at any given temperature, irrespective of the absolute values of either a_B or a_A. When the solutions are dilute, or when the solute behaves ideally, the activity is essentially equal to the concentration C, and equation (26) reduces to

$$\frac{C_B}{C_A} = K \qquad (27)$$

The constant K is called either the *distribution* or *partition coefficient* of the solute between the two solvents.

The applicability of the simplified distribution law, equation (27), may be judged from the data given in Table 6. The essential constancy

TABLE 6

DISTRIBUTION COEFFICIENTS AT 25° C

(C in moles/liter)

I₂ Between H₂O and CCl₄*			HgBr₂ Between H₂O and C₆H₆†			H₃BO₃ Between H₂O and Amyl Alcohol‡		
C_{H_2O}	C_{CCl_4}	$K = \dfrac{C_{H_2O}}{C_{CCl_4}}$	C_{H_2O}	$C_{C_6H_6}$	$K = \dfrac{C_{H_2O}}{C_{C_6H_6}}$	C_{H_2O}	C_A	$K = \dfrac{C_{H_2O}}{C_A}$
0.000322	0.02745	0.0117	0.00320	0.00353	0.90	0.02602	0.00805	3.24
0.000503	0.0429	0.0117	0.00394	0.00436	0.90	0.05104	0.01545	3.31
0.000763	0.0654	0.0117	0.00634	0.00715	0.89	0.1808	0.0540	3.35
0.00115	0.101	0.0114	0.00953	0.01074	0.89	0.3012	0.0857	3.52
0.00134	0.1196	0.0112	0.01147	0.01303	0.88			
			0.017	0.0194	0.88			

* Jakowkin, *Z. physik. Chem.*, **18**, 585 (1895).
† Sherrill, *ibid.*, **43**, 730 (1903).
‡ Mueller and Abegg, *ibid.*, **57**, 514 (1907).

of the distribution coefficients for low concentrations shows that in dilute solutions equation (27) is valid. However, the last two values for iodine and the last for boric acid indicate that in more concentrated solutions activities must be employed instead of concentrations to obtain a true constant for the partition coefficient. Furthermore, K depends on the nature of the solute and the liquids involved. Other factors affecting the magnitude of this constant are the temperature and the manner in which the constant is written, i.e., C_A/C_B or C_B/C_A. As there is no generally agreed method of writing the partition coefficient, it is essential, in order to avoid ambiguity, to specify in each instance the equation for the constant and the temperature to which it applies.

Other examples of distribution which may be cited are the distributions of iodine between water and carbon disulfide, chloroform, and ethylene glycol, bromine between water and carbon disulfide or bromoform, hydrogen peroxide between water and various organic solvents, and phenol between water and amyl alcohol.

CHANGES IN SOLUTE AND THE DISTRIBUTION LAW

Walter Nernst[1] first called attention to the fact that the above statement of the distribution law is valid only when the solute undergoes no change such as dissociation or association. If a solute does dissociate into ions or simpler molecules or if it associates into more complex molecules, then the distribution law does not apply to the total concentrations in the two phases, but only to the concentrations of the particular species *common* to both. Thus, if a substance A dissolves in one solvent without any change in molecular form, and in another with partial association into, say, A_2, the partition coefficient for the distribution will not be given by the ratio of the total concentrations in the two phases, but rather by the total concentration in the first solvent divided by the concentration of unassociated molecules in the second solvent; i.e., by the ratio of the concentrations of the molecules having identical molecular weights in the two solvents. This limitation to the applicability of the distribution law was pointed out in conjunction with the use of Henry's law for gases that form new molecular or ionic species in solution.

TABLE 7

DISTRIBUTION OF BENZOIC ACID BETWEEN WATER AND CHLOROFORM AT 40° C
(C in moles/liter. $K = 0.442$)

C_W	C_C	$\dfrac{C_W}{C_C}$	α	$C_W(1-\alpha)$	m	$C_C - m$	$K_1 = \dfrac{m^2}{C_C - m}$
0.00211	0.00721	0.292	0.1548	0.00178	0.00404	0.00317	0.0052
0.00268	0.01084	0.247	0.1385	0.00231	0.00523	0.00561	0.0049
0.00353	0.01686	0.210	0.1220	0.00310	0.00701	0.00985	0.0050
0.00725	0.05700	0.127	0.0869	0.00662	0.01497	0.04203	0.0053
0.01272	0.16733	0.076	0.0660	0.01188	0.02687	0.14046	0.0052

To illustrate how the distribution law may be utilized in handling more complicated cases, consider the distribution of benzoic acid between water and chloroform, for which data are given in Table 7. Column 1 gives the total concentration of benzoic acid in the water layer, column 2 the same data for the chloroform layer at equilibrium, while column 3 shows the ratio of the two concentrations. Obviously there is no semblance of constancy in the ratio of total concentrations of benzoic acid in the two solvents. However, the observed results can be explained on the basis that the acid is partially *dissociated* in water into benzoate and hydrogen ions and *associated* in chloroform into double molecules $(C_6H_5COOH)_2$.

[1] W. Nernst, *Z. physik. Chem.*, **8**, 110 (1891).

Since the distribution law can be applied here only to the common species in the two phases, i.e., the single molecules of the acid, the equilibria occurring in both phases must be considered. To do this, let

C_W = total concentration of benzoic acid in water (moles per liter)
C_C = total concentration of benzoic acid in CHCl$_3$ (*expressed in moles per liter of single molecules*)
α = degree of dissociation of the acid in water
m = concentration of single molecules of the acid in CHCl$_3$.

In terms of these quantities the equilibrium constants for the several equilibria in the system are given by:

Water:

$$C_6H_5COOH = C_6H_5COO^- + H^+ \qquad (28)$$
$$C_W(1-\alpha) \qquad\qquad C_W\alpha \qquad\qquad C_W\alpha$$

$$K_i = \frac{(C_W\alpha)^2}{C_W(1-\alpha)}$$

$$= \frac{C_W\alpha^2}{(1-\alpha)} \qquad (29)$$

Chloroform:

$$(C_6H_5COOH)_2 = 2\ C_6H_5COOH \qquad (30)$$
$$C_C - m \qquad\qquad\qquad m$$

$$K_1 = \frac{m^2}{C_C - m} \qquad (31)$$

Distribution:

$$C_6H_5COOH\ (\text{in CHCl}_3) = C_6H_5COOH\ (\text{in H}_2O)$$
$$m \qquad\qquad\qquad C_W(1-\alpha) \qquad (32)$$

$$K = \frac{C_W(1-\alpha)}{m} \qquad (33)$$

Solving for m in equation (33) and substituting into equation (31), we obtain

$$K_1 = \frac{m^2}{C_C - m} = \frac{\left[\dfrac{C_W(1-\alpha)}{K}\right]^2}{\left[C_C - \dfrac{C_W(1-\alpha)}{K}\right]} \qquad (34)$$

Equation (34) involves three unknowns, K_1, K, and α. However, α for each value of C_W is available through equation (29) from the known value of K_i for benzoic acid in water, 6.6×10^{-5}. Furthermore, since K_1 should be a constant independent of concentration, it is possible to take two sets of values of C_W and C_C and the corresponding values of α and solve for K in equation (34). Once K is known, it may be employed to find

m through equation (33); and, as a check on the complete argument, m along with C_C may be used through equation (31) to see whether K_1, the dissociation constant for double molecules in benzene, comes out a true constant. In Table 7, columns 4 to 8, are given the concentrations of the various molecular and ionic species as deduced by W. S. Hendrixson[1] in the manner described. As may be seen from the last column of the table, K_1 does come out to be a good constant, and hence the explanation advanced does account for the observed distribution behavior. The actual distribution constant for single molecules is $K = 0.442$ at 40° C.

Other systems to which such analysis has been applied with success are the distribution of benzoic acid between water and benzene, salicylic acid between water and benzene or chloroform, and acetic acid between water and various organic solvents.

DISTRIBUTION COEFFICIENTS AND TEMPERATURE

Distribution coefficients, like other equilibrium constants, vary with temperature. Thus K for the distribution of benzoic acid between water and chloroform is 0.564 at 10° C and 0.442 at 40° C. The variation of these constants with temperature is given by equation (46), Chapter 12, where ΔH is now the heat of transfer per mole of the solute from one solution to the other.

APPLICATIONS OF THE DISTRIBUTION LAW

The distribution law has been applied to the study of problems of both theoretical and practical interest, such as extraction, analysis, and determination of equilibrium constants. Extraction is a subject of great importance both in the laboratory and in industry. In the laboratory occasion frequently arises for the removal of a dissolved substance from, say, a water solution, with solvents such as ether, chloroform, carbon tetrachloride, or benzene. Again, in industry extraction is used to remove various undesirable constituents of a product, such as harmful ingredients in petroleum oils, by treating the product with an immiscible solvent in which the impurity is also soluble. In all such processes it is important to know how much solvent and how many treatments are necessary in order to accomplish a particular degree of separation.

When a substance distributes itself between two solvents without the complications of association, dissociation, or reaction with the solvent, it is possible to calculate the weight of substance which can be removed

---

[1] W. S. Hendrixson, *Z. anorg. Chem.*, **13**, 73 (1897). Hendrixson gave his concentrations in grams per 200 cc of solution. In Table 7 these have all been converted to moles of single molecules per liter.

in a series of extractions. Suppose we have a solution containing w g of a substance in V_1 cc of solution, and suppose that this solution is shaken repeatedly with V_2 cc samples of pure immiscible second solvent until distribution equilibrium is attained. Then at the end of n extractions the weight w_n of solute remaining unextracted will be

$$w_n = w \left(\frac{KV_1}{KV_1 + V_2} \right)^n \tag{35}$$

and therefore the weight extracted will be

$$w - w_n = w - w \left(\frac{KV_1}{KV_1 + V_2} \right)^n$$
$$= w \left[1 - \left(\frac{KV_1}{KV_1 + V_2} \right)^n \right] \tag{36}$$

Here $K = C_1/C_2$. When K is known, equation (35) may be employed to estimate the number of extractions necessary with V_2 cc of extracting solvent for V_1 cc of the original solution in order to reduce w to some given value w_n. Another important deduction which can be made from equation (35) is that if a given volume V of a solvent is available for extraction, greater extracting efficiency can be obtained if this volume is utilized in a number of separate extractions than if it were all used once. In other words, greater extracting efficiency is obtained by keeping V_2 small and n large than the other way around, and hence it is better to extract with small volumes of solvent several times than once with a large volume. The same conclusions apply to washing of precipitates, in which case the process may be considered as the distribution of the impurity between the wash liquid and the precipitate.

Another application of distribution coefficients is in analysis. Suppose a substance is present in a solvent A, in which analysis for the substance is difficult, and suppose, further, that analysis in another solvent B is readily possible. Then a distribution of the substance between the two solvents can be carried out and the substance analyzed for in solvent B. From the result of analysis in B, the volumes of the two solvents used, and the distribution coefficient, K, for the substance between the two solvents, the weight of it present originally in A can be obtained.

REFERENCES FOR FURTHER READING

1. S. Glasstone, *Textbook of Physical Chemistry*, D. Van Nostrand Company, Inc., New York, 1946.
2. K. Jellinek, *Lehrbuch der physikalischen Chemie*, Ferdinand Enke, Stuttgart, 1930, Vol. III.
3. K. K. Kelley, U.S. Bureau of Mines Bulletins Nos. 383, 384, 406, and 407.

4. A. Weissberger, *Technique of Organic Chemistry*, Interscience Publishers, Inc., New York, 1950, Vol. III, chap. on Extraction and Distribution.

PROBLEMS

1. Formulate equilibrium constants for the following equilibria:

   (a) $O_2(g) + 2\,Hg(l) = 2\,HgO(s)$
   (b) $HCO_3^-(aq) + H^+(aq) = CO_2(g) + H_2O(l)$
   (c) $NH_3(g) + H_2O(l) = NH_4OH(aq)$
   (d) $MgO(s) + 2\,HCl(g) = MgCl_2(s) + H_2O(g)$

2. NH_4HS dissociates as follows:

$$NH_4HS(s) = NH_3(g) + H_2S(g)$$

At 25° C the dissociation pressure of the pure solid is 500 mm Hg. Calculate (a) K_p and (b) the total pressure at equilibrium when 300 mm of NH_3 are introduced into a flask containing solid NH_4HS.

Ans. (a) $6.25 \times 10^4\ mm^2$; (b) 583.0 mm.

3. For the equilibrium

$$C\ (graphite) + CO_2(g) = 2\,CO(g)$$

at 1123° K the mole per cent of CO in the vapor phase at equilibrium is 93.77% at 1 atm pressure. What is (a) K_p, and (b) the mole per cent of CO present at equilibrium when the total pressure is 10 atm?

4. In two experiments solid $NH_2CO_2NH_4$ is introduced at 30° C into a flask containing (a) a partial pressure of 200 mm of NH_3 gas and (b) a partial pressure of 200 mm of CO_2 gas. Using the average value of K_p in Table 3, find what will be the total pressure at equilibrium in each case.

5. For the reaction

$$H_2S(g) + I_2(s) = 2\,HI(g) + S(rh)$$

$K_p = 1.33 \times 10^{-5}$ atm at 60° C. What will be the mole fraction of HI in the vapor at 60° C when the total pressure is 1 atm? *Ans.* 0.00365.

6. At 713° K, K_p for the reaction

$$Sb_2S_3(s) + 3\,H_2(g) = 2\,Sb(s) + 3\,H_2S(g)$$

is 0.429. What is the mole fraction of H_2 in the vapor at 713° K? Will the result depend upon the total pressure? Explain.

7. For the reaction,

$$2\,CaSO_4(s) = 2\,CaO(s) + 2\,SO_2(g) + O_2(g)$$

$K_p = 1.45 \times 10^{-5}$ atm³ at 1625° K. What is the dissociation pressure of $CaSO_4$ in mm Hg at 1625° K?

8. One mole of H_2 and 1 mole of $Sb_2S_3(s)$ are introduced into a reaction vessel and heated to 713° K. From the data given in problem 6 find the number of moles of Sb formed and the number of moles of H_2 unconverted.

9. One g of $Na_2HPO_4 \cdot 7\,H_2O$ is placed in a 2-liter vessel at 25° C. What weight of H_2O would have to be added in order to convert practically completely

this hydrate into $Na_2HPO_4 \cdot 12\ H_2O$ and establish a condition of equilibrium in the vessel? Use the data given in Table 4.

10. For the transition

$$HgS\ (red) = HgS\ (black)$$

$\Delta F^0 = 4100 - 6.09\ T$. What is the stable modification of HgS at 100° C? What is the transition temperature?

11. For the reaction

$$2\ NaHSO_4(s) = Na_2S_2O_7(s) + H_2O(g)$$
$$\Delta H^0_{298.2°\ K} = 19,800\ cal \qquad \Delta F^0_{298.2°\ K} = 9000\ cal$$

Assuming that ΔH^0 is constant with temperature, calculate the dissociation pressure of $NaHSO_4$ at 700° K. *Ans.* 55.3 atm.

12. For the reaction

$$CuSO_4 \cdot 3\ H_2O(s) = CuSO_4 \cdot H_2O(s) + 2\ H_2O(g)$$

the dissociation pressure at 298.2° K is 7.37×10^{-3} atm, while $\Delta H^0_{298.2°\ K} = 27,000$ cal. Assuming that ΔH^0 does not vary with T, what is the dissociation pressure in mm Hg at 100° C?

13. For the reaction $2\ NaHCO_3(s) = Na_2CO_3(s) + CO_2(g) + H_2O(g)$

$$\Delta H^0 = 29,320 + 9.15\ T - 12.75 \times 10^{-3}\ T^2, \text{ and } \Delta F^0_{25°\ C} = 7080\ cal$$

What will be the partial pressure of $H_2O(g)$ at 400° K above a mixture of the two solids to which is added CO_2 at an initial pressure of 100 mm Hg?

14. For the reaction $MnCO_3(s) = MnO(s) + CO_2(g)$

$$\Delta F^0 = 27,660 - 14.16\ T\ log_{10}\ T + 10.7 \times 10^{-3}\ T^2 - 10.19\ T$$

Determine the temperature at which the dissociation pressure of $CO_2(g)$ will be 0.5 atm.

15. For the reaction $2\ Mo(s) + CH_4(g) = Mo_2C(s) + 2\ H_2(g)$ $K_p = 3.55$ at 973° K. What will have to be the initial pressure of methane in order to yield $H_2(g)$ at an equilibrium pressure of 0.75 atm?

16. The integral heat of solution of $MgCl_2(s)$ at 18° C is $-35,900$ cal, that of $MgCl_2 \cdot 6\ H_2O(s)$ is -2950 cal, while the heat of vaporization of H_2O is 587 cal/g. Find ΔH at 18° C for the reaction

$$MgCl_2 \cdot 6\ H_2O(s) = MgCl_2(s) + 6\ H_2O(g)$$

Ans. 96,350 cal.

17. At 20° C SO_2 was permitted to distribute itself between 200 cc of $CHCl_3$ and 75 cc of H_2O. When equilibrium was established, the $CHCl_3$ layer contained 0.14 mole of SO_2 and the H_2O layer 0.05 mole. What is the distribution coefficient of SO_2 between H_2O and $CHCl_3$ at 20° C? *Ans.* $C_{H_2O}/C_{CHCl_3} = 0.953$.

18. Using the average value of the distribution coefficients given in Table 6, calculate the number of moles of H_3BO_3 which may be extracted from 50 cc of a 0.2 molar aqueous solution (a) by a single extraction with 150 cc of amyl alcohol, and (b) by three extractions with 50-cc portions of amyl alcohol.

19. From the following data for the distribution of benzoic acid between H_2O and C_6H_6 at 20° C (a) show that benzoic acid is associated into double molecules in C_6H_6, and (b) calculate the distribution coefficients on the basis of this assumption. Neglect the dissociation of benzoic acid in water.

C_{H_2O}	$C_{C_6H_6}$
0.0150	0.242
0.0195	0.412
0.0289	0.970

20. Using the results of the preceding problem, calculate the number of moles of benzoic acid which may be extracted from 100 cc of a 0.2 molar aqueous solution by 10 cc of C_6H_6 at 20° C.

21. At 25° C the distribution coefficient of H_2S between H_2O and C_6H_6, defined as $[H_2S]_{H_2O}/[H_2S]_{C_6H_6}$, is 0.167. What is the minimum volume of C_6H_6 necessary at 25° C to extract in a single step 90% of the H_2S from 1 liter of a 0.1 molar aqueous solution of H_2S?   *Ans.* 1.50 liters.

22. Use the data of the preceding problem to find what total volume of C_6H_6 would be necessary to remove 90% of the H_2S from the given aqueous solution in three separate extractions using equal volumes of C_6H_6 in each.

23. At 25° C the distribution coefficient of C_2H_5OH between CCl_4 and H_2O, $K = [C_2H_5OH]_{CCl_4}/[C_2H_5OH]_{H_2O}$, is 0.0244. How will 1 g of C_2H_5OH distribute itself between 20 cc of H_2O and 50 cc of CCl_4?

14

The Phase Rule

Up to this point various types of heterogeneous equilibria were considered from a number of different points of view. Thus, heterogeneous equilibria such as vaporization, sublimation, fusion, transition of one solid phase to another, solubility of solids, liquids, and gases in each other, vapor pressure of solutions, chemical reaction between solids or liquids and gases, and distribution of solutes between phases all have been approached by methods suitable for each particular type of equilibrium. These involved empirical rules, kinetic considerations, Raoult's law, Henry's law, equilibrium constants, and the distribution law. However, it is possible to treat all heterogeneous equilibria from a unified standpoint by means of a principle called the *phase rule*. With this principle the number of variables to which each and every type of heterogeneous equilibrium is subject may be defined under various experimental conditions. By this definition the phase rule does not invalidate or supersede some of the methods of attack described for the quantitative study of such equilibria. The phase rule is merely able to fix the number of variables involved, but the quantitative relations among the variables must be established through supplementary expressions such as some of those mentioned above. The significance of this statement will become clearer as soon as the nature of the phase rule and the manner in which it is used are developed.

DEFINITIONS

Before proceeding to a statement of the phase rule, it will be necessary to define and explain in some detail certain terms which are employed frequently in this connection. These are system, phase, true, metastable, and unstable equilibrium, number of components, and degrees of freedom of a system.

A *system* is defined as a substance or mixture of substances isolated from all others in an inert container for the purpose of specific study of the effects of pressure, temperature, and the change of concentration on the state of the materials present. For example, the system "water" would consist of water placed alone in an inert container fitted with a movable piston and some heating or cooling device such that either the temperature of or the pressure on the system, or both of these variables, may be varied at will. Similarly, the system sodium chloride-water would consist of these two substances placed in such a container for study of the effect of the variables mentioned on the state of the mixture.

A *phase* is a homogeneous, physically distinct, and mechanically separable portion of a system. If in the system "water," ice, liquid water, and water vapor coexist, each form constitutes a separate phase. Each phase is separated from every other phase by a phase boundary. Furthermore, each phase may be continuous, such as a gas or liquid phase, or it may be broken up into a number of smaller portions, such as a group of ice crystals. The term "mechanically separable" in the definition means that each phase can be separated from every other phase by such operations as filtration, sedimentation, decantation, or by some other mechanical method of separation, say, hand picking of crystals. It does not include, however, such methods of separation as evaporation, distillation, adsorption, or extraction. Since all gases are completely miscible, only one gas phase is possible in a system. With liquids there appears to be no theoretical limit to the maximum number of phases possible, but eight[1] is the largest number observed in any one system. Apparently any number of solid phases is possible.

A state of *true equilibrium* is said to exist in a system when the same state can be realized by approach from either direction. Thermodynamically speaking, true equilibrium is attained when the free energy content of the system is at a minimum for the given values of the variables. An instance of such an equilibrium is ice and liquid water at 1 atm pressure and 0° C. At the given pressure, the temperature at which the two phases are in equilibrium is the same whether it is attained by partial melting of the ice or a partial freezing of the water. On the other hand, water at −5° C can be obtained by careful cooling of the liquid, but not by fusion of ice. Water at −5° C is said to be in a state of *metastable equilibrium*. Such a state can be realized only by careful approach from one direction and may be preserved provided the system is not subjected to sudden shock, stirring, or "seeding" by solid phase. As soon as a crystal of ice is

[1] Kittsley and Goeden, *J. Am. Chem. Soc.*, **72**, 4841 (1950).

introduced, solidification sets in rapidly, and the temperature rises to 0° C.

A state of *unstable equilibrium* is said to exist when the approach to equilibrium in a system is so slow that the system *appears* to undergo no change with time. An instance of such a situation is sodium chloride dissolving into a solution which is very nearly saturated with the salt. Insufficient time of observation might make it appear that equilibrium had been reached, whereas actually the process is still proceeding very slowly toward true saturation. It must be realized that, although a metastable equilibrium represents a state of at least partial stability, unstable equilibrium does not involve any equilibrium at all, but only a process of very slow change.

The *number of components* of a system is the *smallest number* of independently variable constituents, in terms of whose formulas equations may be written expressing the composition of each of the possible phases that may occur. The quantity desired here is the *smallest number*, and it is immaterial which particular constituents are chosen to express the compositions of the various phases. This point will become clearer from the following examples. In the system "water" the phases that occur are ice, liquid water, and water vapor. The composition of each of these phases can be expressed in terms of the single constituent water, and hence this is a one-component system. The variable could equally well be hydrogen or oxygen, for the specification of one of these automatically fixes the other through the formula H_2O. Similar considerations show that the minimum number of constituents necessary to describe the composition of all phases in the system sodium sulfate-water is two, and hence this is a two-component system. In this system the various phases that may occur are Na_2SO_4, $Na_2SO_4 \cdot 7\ H_2O$, $Na_2SO_4 \cdot 10\ H_2O$, solutions of Na_2SO_4 in water, ice, and water vapor. The composition of each of these phases in terms of the two components sodium sulfate and water may be stated as follows:

$$
\begin{aligned}
Na_2SO_4: &\quad Na_2SO_4 + 0\ H_2O \\
Na_2SO_4 \cdot 7\ H_2O: &\quad Na_2SO_4 + 7\ H_2O \\
Na_2SO_4 \cdot 10\ H_2O: &\quad Na_2SO_4 + 10\ H_2O \\
Na_2SO_4(aq.): &\quad Na_2SO_4 + x\ H_2O \\
H_2O(s),\ H_2O(l),\ H_2O(g): &\quad 0\ Na_2SO_4 + H_2O
\end{aligned}
$$

It will be noted that the composition of certain phases may be stated in terms of only one of these constituents, whereas certain others necessitate a knowledge of the amounts of both present in order to specify unambiguously the composition of the phase. Since two components are the smallest number by which the compositions of *all* the phases can be defined, sodium sulfate-water must be a two-component system.

The essential fact to remember in deciding upon the number of components of a system is that the particular constituents chosen as independent variables do not matter, but their *smallest* number does. If the number chosen is not the smallest, certain of these will not be independent of the others. Again, in writing the composition of a phase in terms of the components selected, plus, minus, and zero coefficients in front of a component are permissible. Thus, in a system in which solid magnesium carbonate dissociates according to

$$MgCO_3(s) = MgO(s) + CO_2(g) \tag{1}$$

the compositions of the various phases may be represented in terms of magnesium carbonate and magnesium oxide as follows:

$$
\begin{aligned}
MgCO_3: \quad & MgCO_3 + 0\ MgO \\
MgO: \quad & 0\ MgCO_3 + MgO \\
CO_2: \quad & MgCO_3 - MgO
\end{aligned}
$$

Finally, by the *degrees of freedom* or the *variance* of a system is meant the *smallest number* of independent variables (such as pressure, temperature, concentration) that must be specified in order to define completely the remaining variables of the system. The significance of the degrees of freedom of a system may be gathered from the following examples. In order to specify unambiguously the density of liquid water, it is necessary to state also the temperature and pressure to which this density corresponds; i.e., the density of water is 0.99973 g per milliliter at 10° C and 1 atm pressure. A statement of the density at 10° C without mention of pressure does not define clearly the state of the water, for at 10° C the water may exist at any and all possible pressures above its own vapor pressure. Similarly, mention of the pressure without the temperature leaves ambiguity. Hence, for complete description of the state of the water, two variables must be given, and this phase, when present alone in a system, possesses two degrees of freedom, or the system is said to be *bivariant.* When liquid and solid water exist in equilibrium, however, the temperature and the densities of the phases are determined only by the pressure, and a statement of some arbitrary value of the latter is sufficient to define all the other variables. Thus, if we know that ice and water are at equilibrium at 1 atm pressure, the temperature can be only 0° C and the densities are also established. The same applies to the choice of temperature as the independent variable. At each arbitrarily chosen temperature (within the range of existence of the two phases) equilibrium is possible only at a given pressure, and once again the system is defined in terms of one variable. Under these conditions the system possesses only one degree of freedom, or it is *monovariant.*

THE GIBBS PHASE RULE

That there is a definite relation in a system between the number of degrees of freedom, the number of components, and the number of phases present was first established by J. Willard Gibbs in 1876. This relation, known as the *phase rule*, is a principle of the widest generality, and its validity is in no way dependent on any concepts of atomic or molecular constitution. Credit is due to Ostwald, Roozeboom, van't Hoff, and others for showing how this generalization can be utilized in the study of problems in heterogeneous equilibrium.

To arrive at a formulation of the phase rule, consider in general a system of C components in which P phases are present. The problem now is to determine the total number of variables upon which such a system depends. First of all, the state of the system will depend upon the pressure and the temperature. Again, in order to define the composition of each phase, it is necessary to specify the concentration of $(C - 1)$ constituents of the phase, the concentration of the remaining component being determined by difference. Since there are P phases, the total number of concentration variables will be $P(C - 1)$, and these along with the temperature and pressure constitute a total of $[P(C - 1) + 2]$ variables.

The student will recall from his study of algebra that when an equation in n independent variables occurs, n independent equations are necessary in order to solve for the value of each of these. Similarly, in order to define the $[P(C - 1) + 2]$ variables of a system, this number of equations relating these variables would have to be available. The next question is then: How many equations involving these variables can possibly be written from the conditions obtaining in the system? To answer this query recourse must be had to thermodynamics. Thermodynamics tells us that equilibrium between the various phases in a system is possible only provided the free energy[1] per mole of each constituent of a phase is equal to the free energy of the *same* constituent in every other phase. Since the free energy of the constituent of a phase is a function of the pressure, temperature, and $(C - 1)$ concentration variables, it readily follows that the thermodynamic condition for equilibrium makes it possible to write *one equation* among the variables *for each constituent distributed between any two phases*. When P phases are present, $(P - 1)$ equations are available for each constituent, and for C constituents a total of $C(P - 1)$ equations.

If this number of equations is equal to the number of variables, the system is completely defined. However, generally this will not be the case, and the number of variables will exceed the number of equations by F,

---

[1] Strictly speaking, the *partial* free energy.

where

$$F = \text{Number of variables} - \text{Number of equations}$$
$$= [P(C - 1) + 2] - [C(P - 1)]$$
$$= C - P + 2 \tag{2}$$

Equation (2) is the celebrated phase rule of Gibbs. F is the number of degrees of freedom of a system and gives the number of variables whose values must be specified arbitrarily before the state of the system can be completely and unambiguously characterized. According to the phase rule the number of degrees of freedom of a system is determined by both the number of components and the number of phases present, or, rather, by $(C - P)$.

In this derivation it was assumed that each component is present in every phase. If a component is missing from a particular phase, however, the number of concentration variables is decreased by one. But at the same time the number of possible equations is also decreased by one. Hence the value of $(C - P)$, and therefore F, remains the same whether each constituent is present in every phase or not. This means that the phase rule is not restricted by the assumption made, and is generally valid under all conditions of distribution provided that equilibrium exists in the system.

CLASSIFICATION OF SYSTEMS ACCORDING TO PHASE RULE

The principal value of equation (2) is in its use as a check in the construction of various types of plots for the representation of the equilibrium conditions existing in heterogeneous systems. Before proceeding to a discussion of some specific systems and the application of the phase rule to these, it is convenient to classify all systems according to the number of components present. Thus we may have one-, two-, three-, etc., component systems. The advisability of this approach will become apparent from what follows.

ONE-COMPONENT SYSTEMS

The complexity of one-component systems depends on the number of solid phases that can exist in the system. The simplest case is one in which only a single solid phase occurs, as in water at the lower pressures and carbon dioxide. When more than one solid phase appears in a system the number of possible equilibria is considerably enhanced, and hence the phase diagram, or the plot showing the various equilibria, becomes more involved. The possibilities in such systems and their phase relations can best be brought out by the consideration of several specific examples.

The System: Water. Above about $-20°$ C and below 2000 atm pressure there is only one solid phase in this system, namely, ordinary ice. This solid phase, liquid water, and water vapor constitute the *three* possible single phases in the system. These phases may be involved in *three* possible-two-phase equilibria, namely,

1. Liquid-vapor
2. Solid-vapor
3. Solid-liquid

and *one* three-phase equilibrium, solid-liquid-vapor. Applying the phase rule to the system when only a single phase is present, we see that $F = C - P + 2 = 1 - 1 + 2 = 2$, and therefore each single phase at equilibrium possesses two degrees of freedom. If temperature and pressure are chosen as the independent variables, the phase rule predicts that both of these must be stated in order to define the condition of the phase. Since two independent variables are necessary to locate any point in an area, it must follow that each phase on a P–T diagram occupies an area; and, as three single phases are possible in this system, we may anticipate three such areas on the plot, one for each phase.

For two phases in equilibrium the phase rule predicts that $F = 1 - 2 + 2 = 1$, or one degree of freedom. Since a single variable determines a line, we may expect for each two-phase equilibrium a line on the P–T plot. As three such equilibria may occur in the system, the diagram will be characterized by the existence of three lines separating the various areas from each other. Finally, for the three-phase equilibrium $F = 1 - 3 + 2 = 0$, i.e., no variables need be specified. This must mean that when all three phases coexist the temperature and pressure are fixed, and the position of this equilibrium on the diagram is characterized by the intersection of the three lines at a common *point*.

Although the phase rule makes it possible to predict the general appearance of the diagram, the exact positions of all lines and points can be determined only by experiment. An inspection of the possible equilibria in this system shows that the data necessary for the construction of a P–T plot are: (a) the vapor pressure curve of water (liquid-vapor equilibrium), (b) the sublimation curve of ice (solid-vapor equilibrium), (c) the melting point curve of ice as a function of pressure (solid-liquid equilibrium), and (d) the position of the solid-liquid-vapor equilibrium point. These experimental data for the system water are shown in Fig. 1. In this phase diagram line AO gives the sublimation curve of ice, line OB the vapor pressure curve of liquid water, and OC the line along which equilibria between ice and liquid water occur at various pressures. O is the *triple point* at which ice, water, and water vapor are in equilibrium. This equilibrium is possible only at $0.0098°$ C and 4.58 mm pressure. As predicted by the phase rule, there are three areas on the diagram, disposed as shown, one such area corresponding to each of the single phases.

The vapor pressure curve of water, line OB, extends from the triple point O up to the critical point B, corresponding to 374° C and 220 atm pressure. However, under certain conditions it is possible to supercool water below point O to yield the metastable liquid-vapor equilibria shown by the dotted line OD. The fact that OD lies above AO shows that at temperatures below that of the triple point liquid water has a vapor pressure higher than the sublimation pressure of ice, and hence the supercooled liquid is unstable at these temperatures with respect to the ice. The sublimation curve of ice, line AO, may extend from absolute zero up to O. No superheating of ice beyond O has ever been realized. Line CO runs from O up to a point corresponding to 2000 atm pressure and about −20° C; at this point ordinary ice, type

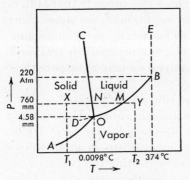

Fig. 1. The System Water at Moderate Pressures (Schematic).

I, in equilibrium with water undergoes a transformation into another solid modification, type III, in equilibrium with the liquid. The slope of this line indicates that the melting point of ice is *lowered* by increase in pressure in accord with the Le Chatelier principle and the fact that ice has a larger specific volume than liquid water. The slopes of the lines AO, OB, and OC are determined at each point by the Clapeyron equation or one of its modifications as applicable in each instance. From the slopes and this equation it is possible to evaluate the heats of vaporization from OB, the heats of sublimation from AO, and the heats of fusion from OC.

Since no liquid may exist above the critical temperature, dotted line BE has been inserted in the diagram to separate the liquid from vapor areas above the critical temperature. Consequently the vapor area lies below and to the right of $AOBE$, the liquid area above OB and between the lines OC and BE, while the solid area extends to the left of OC and above AO.

The manner in which a diagram such as Fig. 1 may be used to follow the changes that occur in the system with a change in the variables may be seen from the following example. Suppose it is desired to know the behavior of the system on heating ice at a pressure of 760 mm and temperature T_1, corresponding to point X in the diagram, to a point corresponding to point Y at the same pressure but temperature T_2. Starting with ice at X and heating it slowly at constant pressure, the system follows line XN with an increase in the temperature of the ice and a slight decrease in its density. However, once N is reached the ice begins to melt, the temperature remains constant until the fusion is complete, and only when this process is terminated does the temperature begin to rise again along NM. Between N and M the only change is an increase in the temperature of the liquid and a decrease in its density. But at M vaporization sets in, and the temperature again is constant until all the liquid is converted to vapor. On complete transformation of liquid to vapor, any further addition of heat results merely in an increase of the temperature of the vapor along MY until the latter point is reached. In

the same way it is possible with the aid of Fig. 1 to predict and outline any changes that may take place in this system with a variation of temperature, pressure, or both.

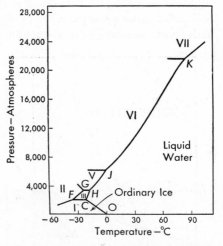

Fig. 2. The System Water at High Pressures.

At high pressures a number of other solid modifications besides the ordinary form have been observed.[1] The phase diagram of the system under these conditions is shown in Fig. 2. Figures 1 and 2 are parts of the same diagram, the latter figure being merely the high-pressure portion of the former. The manner in which the two diagrams tie in can be judged from the line OC, which is the same in both plots. It is of interest to observe in Fig. 2 that at very high pressures ice of types VI and VII may exist at temperatures above 0° C. In fact, at a pressure of about 40,000 atm ice VII is stable at 190° C.

The System: Sulfur. Sulfur exists in two solid modifications, the *rhombic* form stable at ordinary temperatures and the *monoclinic* variety stable at higher temperatures. These two solid phases along with the liquid and vapor give a possibility of existence of four single phases, which in turn can lead to the following equilibria:

Two-Phase Equilibria

1. S(r) — S(vapor)
2. S(m) — S(vapor)
3. S(r) — S(liquid)
4. S(m) — S(liquid)
5. S(liquid) — S(vapor)
6. S(r) — S(m)

Three-Phase Equilibria

1. S(r) — S(m) — S(liquid)
2. S(r) — S(liquid) — S(vapor)
3. S(m) — S(liquid) — S(vapor)
4. S(r) — S(m) — S(vapor)

Four-Phase Equilibria

1. S(r) — S(m) — S(liquid) — S(vapor)

[1] Tammann, *Zeit. physik. Chem.*, **72**, 609 (1910); Bridgman, *Proc. Am. Acad. Sci.*, **47**, 441 (1912); *J. Chem. Phys.*, **5**, 964 (1937).

Applying the phase rule to these possible equilibria, we may anticipate four separate divariant single-phase areas, six monovariant two-phase equilibrium lines, and four invariant three-phase equilibrium points. Since the maximum number of phases that may be present in equilibrium is given by the phase rule with $F = 0$, it follows that $P = 3$ for a one-component system, and hence the four-phase equilibrium cannot exist in this or any other one-component system.

Figure 3 shows the schematic phase diagram for this system. The four single-phase areas are disposed as indicated. Lines OP and PK are the sublimation curves of rhombic and monoclinic sulfur respectively, while KU is the vapor pressure curve of liquid sulfur. At point P rhombic sulfur undergoes a transition to monoclinic sulfur, and hence this is an invariant point corresponding to the equilibrium $S(r) - S(m) - S(vapor)$. At point K monoclinic sulfur melts, and thus this point corresponds to the three-phase equilibrium $S(m) - S(liquid) - S(vapor)$. Line PS shows the variation of the transition point with pressure, while line KS shows in a like manner the variation of the melting point of monoclinic sulfur with the same variable. These two lines intersect at S to yield the three-phase equilibrium $S(r) - S(m) - S(liquid)$. Finally, the line SW gives the melting point of rhombic sulfur. These are all the *stable* equilibria that occur. The monoclinic sulfur area is enclosed by the lines PS, PK, and KS, and therefore no monoclinic sulfur can exist in stable condition outside this area. Furthermore, no vapor can exist stably at pressures above those given by the lines OP, PK, and KU below the temperature of the critical point U. Above this temperature, however, no liquid is possible. Hence the liquid area is terminated along the vertical dotted line through U, and vapor may exist thereafter at high pressures.

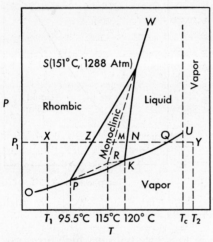

Fig. 3.   The System Sulfur (Schematic).

The remaining equilibria in this system are all *metastable*. By rapid heating it is possible to superheat rhombic sulfur along the extension of OP, the line PR, which is the equilibrium line for superheated $S(r)$ with $S(vapor)$. Similarly, it is possible to supercool liquid sulfur along the extension of KU to R. At point R the metastable $S(r) - S(vapor)$ line intersects the metastable $S(liquid) - S(vapor)$ line to yield the metastable invariant point $S(r) - S(liquid) - S(vapor)$. The line RS shows the variation of this metastable point with pressure and is, therefore, the melting point line for rhombic sulfur as a function of pressure. This line is an extension of the stable SW line into the metastable range. It should be clearly understood that, when these various metastable equilibria occur, monoclinic sulfur does not appear; instead rhombic sulfur is transformed directly to liquid along RS or to vapor along PR without passing through the monoclinic stage.

In order to clarify the relations in this system, consider conversion of rhombic sulfur at a pressure P_1 and temperature T_1, point X, to vapor at the same pressure but temperature T_2, point Y. If the rhombic sulfur is heated slowly at constant pressure, its temperature will rise until point Z is reached. At this point, allowing sufficient time for establishment of equilibrium, the rhombic sulfur will transform at constant temperature to the monoclinic form. When this transition is over, the temperature will again climb to N, the melting point, where the monoclinic sulfur is converted to liquid at constant temperature. Once this process is completed, further addition of heat will result in the heating of the liquid to Q, where vaporization takes place under isothermal conditions, and thereafter the temperature of the vapor will rise steadily to Y. Throughout all these operations only stable equilibria were encountered. If, however, the rhombic sulfur is heated rapidly, it may be carried past Z to M without transformation. At M the rhombic sulfur melts to liquid which subsequently vaporizes at Q. By operating in this manner with the metastable states between Z and N no monoclinic form is encountered, and the rhombic sulfur goes directly to the liquid.

Other One-Component Systems. The system *carbon dioxide* is very similar to the system water as shown in Fig. 1, except that the triple point occurs at $-56.4°$ C and a pressure of about 5 atm. Furthermore, the solid-liquid line slopes to the right instead of to the left as in the water diagram. Since the 1 atm line in this system cuts only the sublimation curve of the solid, solid carbon dioxide must change directly to vapor at this pressure without passing through the liquid state. Liquefaction of the solid can be attained only under pressures of about 5 atm or higher.

Other examples of one-component systems investigated are phosphorus and benzophenone. For details see Findlay, Campbell and Smith.[1]

TWO-COMPONENT SYSTEMS

When a single phase is present in a two-component system, the number of degrees of freedom is $F = 2 - 1 + 2 = 3$. This means that three variables must be specified in order to describe the condition of the phase:

[1] Findlay, Campbell, and Smith, *The Phase Rule and Its Applications*, Dover Publications, New York, 1951.

pressure, temperature, and the concentration of one of the components. To present these relations graphically, three coordinate axes at right angles to each other would be required, and the diagram thus resulting would be a solid figure. Since such figures are difficult to construct and use, the more common practice is to employ either a projection of such a solid diagram on a plane, or a planar cross section of the figure for a given constant value of one of the variables. In this manner it is possible to present the various relations in two-component systems in a two-dimensional plot of any two of the three variables mentioned.

Moreover, the discussion of two-component systems can be simplified further by considering the various possible types of equilibria separately. Thus the usual practice is to study liquid-gas, solid-gas, liquid-liquid, and solid-liquid equilibria individually and, when necessary, to combine the diagrams. Since the first three types of equilibria have already been considered in various places in the text, attention here will be devoted exclusively to an application of the phase rule to the very important category of solid-liquid equilibria.

SOLID-LIQUID EQUILIBRIA

Solid-liquid equilibria are of great importance because of their connection with all crystallization problems. Such equilibria are characterized generally by the absence of a gas phase and by the fact that they are little affected by small changes in pressure. Systems where the gas phase is absent are called *condensed systems*, and it is with condensed systems that we shall be concerned.

Measurements on solid-liquid equilibria in condensed systems are usually carried out at atmospheric pressure. Because of the relative insensitivity of such systems to small variations in pressure, the latter may be considered constant, and for such systems the phase rule takes the form

$$F = C - P + 1 \tag{3}$$

For two-component systems equation (3) becomes

$$\begin{aligned} F &= 2 + 1 - P \\ &= 3 - P \end{aligned} \tag{4}$$

where the only remaining variables are temperature and the concentration of one of the constituents. Solid-liquid equilibria are represented, therefore, on temperature-composition diagrams. For limited ranges of concentration any scheme of expressing concentration will do, but where the range may extend from 100 per cent of one constituent to 100 per cent of the other, it is preferable to employ as an abscissa either weight percentage or mol percentage, as in distillation diagrams.

DETERMINATION OF SOLID-LIQUID EQUILIBRIA

Of the many experimental procedures employed for the determination of equilibrium conditions between solid and liquid phases, the two of widest utility and applicability are the *thermal analysis* and *saturation or solubility methods*. These methods, supplemented when necessary by an investigation of the nature of the solid phases occurring in a system, can cover between them the study of any system which may be encountered.

The Thermal Analysis Method. The thermal analysis method involves a study of the cooling rates, i.e., temperature-time curves, of the various compositions of a system during solidification. From such curves it is possible to ascertain the temperature of initial and final solidification of a mixture and to detect the temperatures at which various transformations and transitions occur. Although thermal analysis is applicable under all temperature conditions, it is particularly suitable for equilibrium investigations at temperatures considerably above and below that of the room.

In order to illustrate the experimental steps involved in this procedure, the interpretation of the curves, and the plotting of the final diagram, consider specifically the problem of determining the condensed phase diagram for the binary system bismuth-cadmium. The first step involves the preparation of a number of mixtures of the two metals ranging in over-all composition from 100 per cent bismuth to 100 per cent cadmium. These mixtures may be spaced at 10 per cent intervals and should all be preferably of equal weight, say 100 to 300 g. Each of these mixtures of solids is placed in an inert crucible of, say, fireclay or graphite and is then melted in an electric furnace. To prevent oxidation of the metals it is advisable to maintain an inert or reducing atmosphere over them by passing hydrogen, nitrogen, or carbon dioxide through the furnace. A molten flux, such as borax, or a layer of powdered graphite may be used to cover the crucible charge as an added precaution. After melting and thorough agitation a thermocouple is inserted in the melt, and the furnace and contents are allowed to cool slowly. Temperature and time readings are taken until the charge in the crucible is completely solidified. For this purpose recording potentiometers are particularly convenient, as they yield a continuous record of temperatures at various times during the cooling. Finally, plots of the temperatures thus obtained against time are prepared. If a check on the composition is desired, the solidified alloys are removed and carefully analyzed.

Figure 4 shows a set of cooling curves thus obtained for various compositions of bismuth-cadmium mixtures. The explanation of these curves is as follows. When a body that liberates only sensible heat is cooled slowly and uniformly, a smooth cooling curve is obtained, and the temperature of the body approaches that of the room as a limit. However, when some transformation that liberates heat occurs during cooling, the slope of the cooling curve is reduced suddenly. The nature of the reduction depends on the degrees of freedom of the system. A single phase with $F = 2$ exhibits a continuous cooling curve. When a new phase appears, the variance of the system is reduced to one, and the heat generated by the formation of the new phase results in a discontinuity in the curve due to change of slope for the cooling of one phase to a lesser slope corresponding to the cooling of two phases. Again, when still a third phase appears, $F = 0$, and the temperature of the system must remain constant until one of the phases disappears. The result is a flat portion

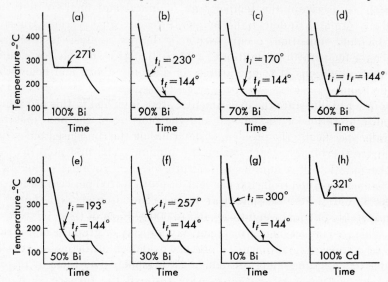

Fig. 4. Cooling Curves for the System Bismuth-Cadmium.

on the cooling curve. Finally, when solidification is complete, the system regains a degree of freedom, and the cooling curves once again exhibit continuous variation of temperature with time. In light of these facts a "break" or arrest in a cooling curve indicates the appearance of a second phase, usually the separation of a solid from the melt, while a horizontal portion indicates the coexistence of three phases. The third phase may result from the separation of two solids from the melt, the interaction of the melt with a solid to form another solid, or the separation of a solid from two liquid phases. The nature of the particular change occurring can be ascertained from an inspection of the final phase diagram and an analysis of the solids in the system.

With these considerations in mind we may conclude from the cooling curves in Fig. 4 that the arrests indicated by t_i signify the appearance of a second phase in the system, while the horizontal portions result from the coexistence of three phases. In this system the only solid phases are pure bismuth and pure cadmium, and hence the horizontal portions are the result of simultaneous occurrence of these solids and melt. However, in curves (a) and (h) the horizontal portions are due to two phases, since these are one-component systems.

To construct the equilibrium diagram from the cooling curves, the initial and final solidification temperatures, t_i and t_f, are taken off the cooling curves for the various over-all concentrations and are plotted on a temperature-composition diagram. Smooth curves are drawn then through all the t_i and t_f temperatures to yield the diagram shown in Fig. 5. Curve AB indicates the temperatures at which bismuth begins to separate from various concentrations of melt, while BC gives the same information for initial separation of cadmium. Line DE indicates the temperature at which all mixtures become completely solid. Further details of this type of diagram will be discussed later.

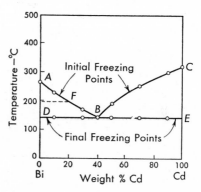

Fig. 5.   Phase Diagram for the System Bismuth-Cadmium.

The Saturation or Solubility Method. In Fig. 5 line AB may be looked upon not only as the initial freezing point curve for bismuth, but also as the *solubility* curve of bismuth in molten cadmium. Points on this curve represent then the solubilities of bismuth in the molten cadmium at various temperatures. Similarly, curve BC gives the solubilities at various temperatures of cadmium in molten bismuth, while at B the solution is saturated with respect to both solids.

In the saturation method the solubilities of one substance in another are determined at various constant temperatures, and the solubilities are then plotted as a function of the temperature. To obtain the composition of a solution of cadmium saturated with bismuth at say 200° C, point F in Fig. 5, excess powdered bismuth may be added to molten cadmium, the mixture brought to 200°, and the mass agitated until equilibrium is attained. The excess solid bismuth is now filtered off, and the saturated solution is analyzed for both constituents. By repeating this operation at various temperatures between 144 and 271° C, curve AB may be traced out. By a similar procedure, but employing molten bismuth and excess solid cadmium, curve BC may be obtained between 144 and 321° C. Although this method is rarely applied to the study of metallic systems, it is the principal means employed in systems containing water and similar solvents. Outside temperatures between $-50°$ C and $200°$ C this method is attended by many experimental difficulties, and the thermal analytical procedure is consequently preferred.

DETERMINATION OF NATURE OF SOLID PHASES

For a complete interpretation of the phase diagram it is essential to know the nature and composition of the solid phases which appear during crystallization and in the final solid. These may be:

1. *Pure components*, such as bismuth or cadmium in the system discussed above.
2. *Compounds* formed by reaction between the pure constituents. Examples are $MgZn_2$ in the system Mg-Zn, $Na_2SO_4 \cdot 10\ H_2O$ in the system Na_2SO_4-H_2O, and $FeCl_3 \cdot 6\ H_2O$ in the system $FeCl_3$-H_2O. Such compounds have definite composition, are stable over definite temperature and solution concentration intervals, possess definite melting or transition temperature, and have a definite crystal structure.
3. *Solid solutions*, homogeneous solids whose composition may vary within certain concentration intervals and is determined by the composition of the solution from which the solid crystallizes. Such variability in composition differentiates the solid solution from a compound.
4. *Mixtures* of solids which may be pure components, compounds, or solid solutions.

Frequently it is possible to deduce the nature of the solid phases from the shape of the phase diagram. However, in some instances it is necessary to subject the solids to a more careful scrutiny. To do this the completely solidified mass may be inspected under a microscope to determine the number of solids present and, if possible, their identity. Another possibility is the use of x rays. Direct separation of solids from a solution and their subsequent analysis may also be resorted to, but this procedure is attended by some uncertainty because of difficulty in obtaining a solid free from contamination by saturated solution. This difficulty may be circumvented sometimes by the use of a "telltale." The "telltale" is a substance that is soluble in the solution but not in the solid phase. On adding a definite small quantity of this substance to the solution and determining the amount of it present in the wet solid, it is possible to ascertain the quantity of solution adhering to the solid and thereby to arrive at the composition of the pure solid phase.

CLASSIFICATION OF TWO-COMPONENT
SOLID-LIQUID EQUILIBRIA

Every condensed phase diagram may be considered to be composed of a combination of a number of simple types of diagrams. In some systems only a single type occurs; in others a number of these simple types may occur combined to yield a more complicated complete diagram. In either case the phase relations in a system can readily be understood when the significance of the elementary types of diagrams is manifest. For this reason we proceed to a classification and discussion of various simple types of diagrams which may be encountered in condensed two-component systems.

All condensed two-component systems may be classified first according to the miscibility of the liquid phases, and these in turn according to the nature of the solid phases which crystallize from the solution. On this basis the important elementary types are:

Class A. The two components are completely miscible in the liquid state.
Type I.   The pure components only crystallize from the solution.
Type II. The two constituents form a solid compound stable up to its melting point.
Type III. The two components form a solid compound which decomposes before attaining its melting point.
Type IV. The two constituents are completely miscible in the solid state and yield thereby a complete series of solid solutions.
Type V.   The two constituents are partially miscible in the solid state and form stable solid solutions.
Type VI. The two constituents form solid solutions which are stable only up to a transition temperature.
Class B. The two components are partially miscible in the liquid state.
Type I.   Pure components only crystallize from solution.
Class C. The two components are immiscible in the liquid state.
Type I.   Pure components only crystallize from solution.

CLASS A: TYPE I. SIMPLE EUTECTIC DIAGRAM

Two-component condensed systems belonging to this class have a diagram of the general form shown in Fig. 6. They are characterized by the fact that two constituents A and B are completely miscible in the liquid state, and such solutions yield only pure A or pure B as solid phases. In this figure points D and E are the melting points of pure A and pure B respectively. Line DG gives the concentrations of solutions saturated with A at temperatures between D and F, or the freezing points of the solutions which yield A as a solid phase. Similarly, line EG gives the concentrations of solutions saturated with solid B at temperatures between E and F. At G the solution is saturated with both A and B, i.e., at G three phases are in equilibrium. It follows, therefore, that the lines DG and EG represent monovariant two-phase equilibria, while G is an invariant point. At this point the temperature F and the composition C of the solution must remain constant as long as three phases coexist. The temperature can be lowered below F only when one of the phases has disappeared, and on cooling this must be the saturated solution. In other words, at F solution G must solidify completely. Temperature F must consequently be the *lowest* temperature at which a liquid phase may exist in the system A–B; below this temperature the system is completely solid. Temperature F is called the *eutectic temperature*, composition C the *eutectic composition*, and point G the *eutectic point* of the system.

Above the lines DG and GE is the area in which unsaturated solution or melt exists. In this area only one phase is present and the system is divariant. In order to define any point in this area both the temperature and composition must be specified. The significance of the remaining portions of the diagram can be made clear by considering the behavior on cooling of several mixtures of A and B. Take first a mixture of over-all composition a. If such a mixture is heated to point a''' an unsaturated solution is obtained. On cooling this solution nothing beyond a drop of temperature of the liquid phase occurs until point a'', corresponding to temperature x'', is reached. At this point the solution becomes saturated with A; or, in other words, a'' is the freezing point of the solution at temperature x''. As cooling continues A keeps on separating out, and the composition of the saturated solution changes along the line $a''G$. Thus at a temperature such as x' solid A is in equilibrium with saturated solution of composition y', and so on. It

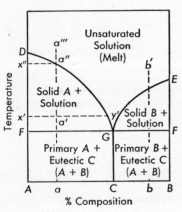

Fig. 6. Simple Eutectic Diagram.

is seen, therefore, that for any over-all composition falling in area DFG solid A is in equilibrium with various compositions of solution given by the curve DG at each temperature. However, at temperature F another solid phase, B, appears, and the system becomes invariant. On extracting heat from this system A and B must crystallize from the saturation solution in the fixed ratio C, and this crystallization will proceed until the solution has been completely solidified. Once this process is over and nothing but a *mixture* of solid A and solid B remains, the system becomes monovariant, and the cooling may be continued below F into area $FACG$, the area of coexistence of the two solids A and B.

Inspection of the solid in area $FACG$ under a microscope would reveal that it is composed of relatively large crystals of A which have had a chance to grow from temperature x'' to the temperature below F, and an intimate *mixture* of finer crystals of A and B which crystallized in definite proportion C at temperature F. The larger crystals of A are called *primary crystals*, since they appeared first. Area $FACG$ may be marked, therefore, as containing primary crystals of A and an intimate eutectic mixture of fine crystals of A and B.

Similar considerations applied to over-all compositions lying between C and B, such as b, for instance, show that in area EFG solid B is in equilibrium with saturated solutions along the line EG. At temperature F solid A also appears, the system becomes invariant, and it remains so until the solution at G solidifies. Once the solidification is complete, the mixture passes into area $FBCG$ where now primary B and eutectic mixture of over-all composition C are present. Finally, cooling a mixture of over-all composition C will yield no solid until point G is reached. At this point solids A and B appear simultaneously, and the system solidifies at constant temperature to yield only the eutectic mixture. In this respect composition C behaves like a pure substance on freezing. However, the result is not a single solid, but a mixture of two.

Once a phase diagram such as Fig. 6 is available for a binary system, it is possible to specify the conditions under which particular solid phases may be obtained and to describe the behavior of any given over-all mixture on cooling. Thus it is seen that pure A may be separated only from mixtures falling in area DFG, and only between the temperatures D and F. Similarly, pure B may be obtained only in area EFG from over-all compositions between C and B, and only between the temperatures E and F. The proportion of solid to saturated solution at each temperature can be estimated from the diagram. For over-all composition a at a temperature such as x', the distance $x'a'$ is a measure of the amount of saturated solution of composition y', while the distance $a'y'$ is a measure of the amount of solid A present in the mixture. Consequently the ratio $x'a'/a'y'$ is the weight ratio of y' to A if the composition is expressed in weight percentage, or of the number of moles of y' to A if the composition is expressed in mol percentage. From these ratios and any over-all weight it is possible to calculate the yield of solid phase to be anticipated at any given temperature.

Examples of systems exhibiting simple eutectic diagrams of the type shown in Fig. 6 are aluminum-tin, bismuth-cadmium, potassium chloride-silver chloride, sodium sulfate-sodium chloride, and benzene-methyl chloride. The behavior of all these systems on cooling will be similar to that described for the system bismuth-cadmium.

CLASS A: TYPE II. FORMATION OF COMPOUND WITH CONGRUENT MELTING POINT

When the two pure components react to form a compound stable up to its melting point, the phase diagram takes on the typical form shown in Fig. 7 for the system cuprous chloride-ferric chloride. If the compound, in

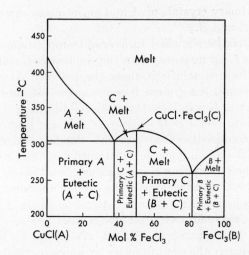

Fig. 7.   Formation of Compound with Congruent Melting Point.

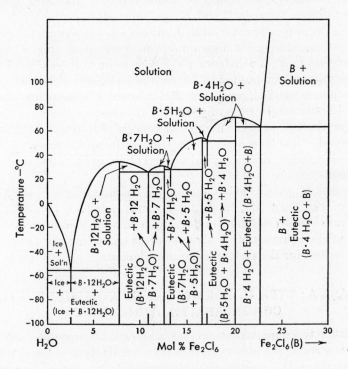

Fig. 8.   The System Fe_2Cl_6-H_2O.

this case $CuCl \cdot FeCl_3$, is considered as a separate component, the whole diagram may be thought of as being composed of two diagrams of the simple eutectic type, one for $CuCl-CuCl \cdot FeCl_3$, and the other for $CuCl \cdot FeCl_3-FeCl_3$. The discussion of type I diagrams can now be applied to each portion with the results shown in the figure.

A compound such as $CuCl \cdot FeCl_3$ which melts at a constant temperature to yield a liquid of the same composition as the solid compound is said to have a *congruent* melting point. Compounds with congruent melting points also appear in such binary systems as gold-tellurium ($AuTe_2$), aluminum-selenium (Al_2Se_3), calcium chloride-potassium chloride ($CaCl_2 \cdot KCl$), urea-phenol (1:1), and many others. When several compounds with congruent melting points are formed in a system a maximum is obtained for each, and the diagram takes on the appearance of Fig. 8 for the system $Fe_2Cl_6-H_2O$.[1] In this system four stable compounds have been observed, namely, $Fe_2Cl_6 \cdot 12 H_2O$, $Fe_2Cl_6 \cdot 7 H_2O$, $Fe_2Cl_6 \cdot 5 H_2O$, and $Fe_2Cl_6 \cdot 4 H_2O$. The occurrence of these compounds increases the number of areas and eutectic points but otherwise introduces nothing new. By employing the artifice of considering each compound as a constituent, the significance of the various areas, lines, and points can readily be deduced to be as indicated.

CLASS A: TYPE III. COMPOUND FORMATION AS RESULT OF PERITECTIC REACTION

In many systems compounds are formed whose stability does not extend all the way to the melting point. When such compounds are heated, it is found that instead of melting congruently they decompose to yield a new solid phase and a solution composition *different* from that of the solid phases. When this happens the compound is said to undergo a *transition*, or *peritectic reaction*, or *incongruent fusion*.

Any peritectic reaction can in general be represented by the equation

$$C_2 \rightleftharpoons C_1 + \text{solution (or melt)} \qquad (5)$$

where C_2 is the compound, and C_1 is the new solid phase which may be itself a compound or the pure constituent. As equation (5) indicates, the peritectic reaction is reversible, i.e., on heating the change from left to right will occur, while on cooling the reverse will take place. Since during the peritectic reaction three phases are present at equilibrium, the system is invariant, and hence the temperature as well as the compositions of all the phases are fixed. Temperature or composition can change only when one of the phases disappears, or, in other words, when the peritectic reaction is completed. The constant temperature at which the

[1] B. Roozeboom, Z. *physik. Chem.*, **10**, 477 (1892).

peritectic reaction takes place is called the *peritectic* or *transition temperature,* and for this temperature there will be obtained a horizontal portion on the cooling curves analogous to the eutectic portion.

The relations in a system in which a peritectic reaction occurs can be illustrated with the diagram for the binary condensed system calcium fluoride-calcium chloride shown in Fig. 9. Line AB gives the concentrations of melt in equilibrium with solid calcium fluoride. When point B, corresponding to 737° C, is reached, a peritectic reaction between the melt of composition B and solid calcium fluoride sets in to form the double compound $CaF_2 \cdot CaCl_2$ according to the equation

$$CaF_2(s) + \text{melt } (B) = CaF_2 \cdot CaCl_2(s) \qquad (6)$$

This reaction proceeds isothermally to form compound C until either all the calcium fluoride or all of the melt has been consumed. Whether one or the other of these phases dis-

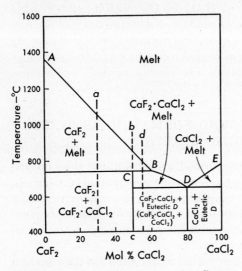

Fig. 9. Phase Diagram for the System CaF_2-$CaCl_2$.

appears depends on the over-all composition of the mixture. If the over-all composition lies between calcium fluoride and C, as a in the figure, there is more calcium fluoride present than is necessary to react with all of the melt B, and hence on completion of the reaction all the melt will be converted to $CaF_2 \cdot CaCl_2$, while the excess calcium fluoride will remain as such. Consequently, on passing into the area between the calcium fluoride axis and C below 737° C, only the two solid phases, CaF_2 and $CaF_2 \cdot CaCl_2$, will be present. If, however, the over-

all composition of the mixture lies between C and B, such as d, more melt is present than is required to react with all of the solid calcium fluoride, and hence the products of the peritectic reaction will be C and unreacted melt. On passing into the area immediately below CB we shall have, therefore, solid C and melt in equilibrium with the concentrations of the saturated solutions given by the line BD. It should be observed that the lines AB and BD are not continuous but show a break at B. This means that the solid phases calcium fluoride and $CaF_2 \cdot CaCl_2$ each have separate and distinct solubility curves which intersect at B, the concentration of solution saturated with both phases. Finally, should the over-all composition happen to be *b*, corresponding exactly to *C*, there is just sufficient calcium fluoride to react with all of the melt, and the result of the peritectic reaction is now only pure compound *C*.

The remainder of the diagram introduces nothing new. *CBDE* is merely a simple eutectic-type diagram involving the constituents *C* and calcium chloride. From the interpretation of such a diagram the area designations shown in the figure readily follow. It will be observed that the eutectic mixture is composed of calcium chloride, $CaF_2 \cdot CaCl_2$, and melt, with no pure calcium fluoride appearing.

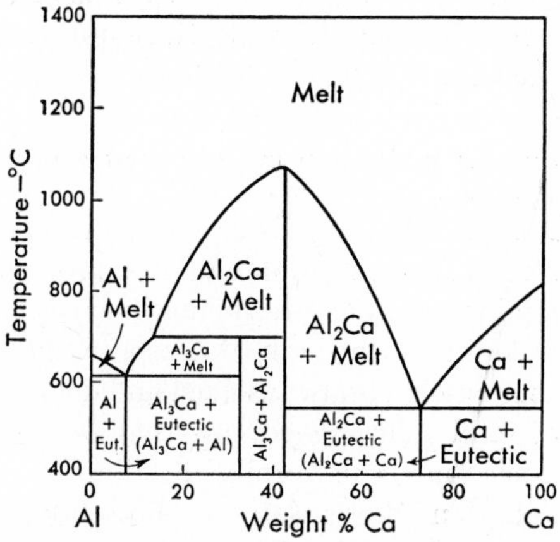

Peritectic reactions have been observed in many binary systems. As examples may be quoted the following, along with the compounds formed: gold-antimony ($AuSb_2$), potassium chloride-cupric chloride ($2\ KCl \cdot CuCl_2$), picric acid (*A*)-benzene (*B*) (*A* · *B*), sodium chloride-water ($NaCl \cdot 2\ H_2O$), and sodium sulfate-water ($Na_2SO_4 \cdot 10\ H_2O$). In some systems several compounds occur, some of which have congruent melting points while others do not. Thus in the system aluminum-calcium the compound Al_2Ca has a congruent melting point, while the compound Al_3Ca is formed by peritectic reaction. The phase diagram for this system, shown in Fig. 10, may be considered typical of the relations encountered under such conditions. Finally, in many systems several compounds are formed, none of which has a congruent melting point. Instances of this type are potassium sulfate-cadmium sulfate ($K_2SO_4 \cdot 2\ CdSO_4$, $K_2SO_4 \cdot 3\ CdSO_4$) and magnesium sulfate-water

Fig. 10.   Phase Diagram for the System Aluminum-Calcium.

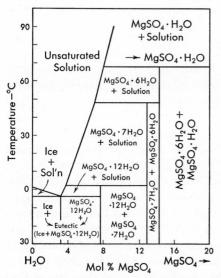

Fig. 11.   Phase Diagram for the System $MgSO_4$-H_2O.

($MgSO_4 \cdot H_2O$, $MgSO_4 \cdot 6 H_2O$, $MgSO_4 \cdot 7 H_2O$, $MgSO_4 \cdot 12 H_2O$). The water-end portion of the diagram for the latter system is shown in Fig. 11. Study of this diagram will reveal that its interpretation involves merely an extension of the principles employed for interpreting the simple diagram shown in Fig. 9.

CLASS A: TYPE IV. COMPLETE MISCIBILITY IN SOLID STATE

Just as two liquids may dissolve in each other to form a liquid solution, so one solid may dissolve in another to form a *solid solution*. Solid, like liquid, solutions are homogeneous and may vary in composition within wide limits. In the latter respect they differ from solid compounds whose composition is always fixed and definite. X-ray examination of the lattices of solid solutions reveals that one constituent enters the lattice of the other and is uniformly distributed through it. This uniformity of distribution differentiates a solid solution from a mixture of solids, for in the latter instance each constituent preserves its own characteristic crystal structure.

The condensed phase diagrams of binary systems where both the liquid and solid phases are completely miscible fall into three groups, for which:

1. The melting points of all solutions are intermediate between those of the pure constituents.
2. The melting point curve exhibits a minimum.
3. The melting point curve exhibits a maximum.

These various cases will now be discussed.

Intermediate Type of Diagram. Figure 12 shows the phase diagram for the system ammonium thiocyanate-potassium thiocyanate, where the two constituents are completely miscible in both the solid and liquid states. In this diagram the upper or *liquidus* curve gives the temperature of initial solidification, i.e., the compositions of melt saturated with solid solutions at various temperatures, while the lower or *solidus* curve gives the temperatures at which final solidification takes place. To follow the changes involved in the solidification of any given composition of melt, consider a point such as *a* in the liquid phase. On cooling this solution, no solid phase will separate until the temperature corresponding to point *b* is reached. At this point a small amount of *solid solution* of composition *c* will separate and change thereby the composition of the melt toward, say, *d*. On further cooling *d* will start freezing at *e*, and the composition of the solid phase will adjust itself to *g* by solution of some ammonium thiocyanate from the melt. At all times the composition of the liquid and solid solutions at equilibrium is given by the intersections of the horizontal isothermal lines with the liquidus and solidus curves. As cooling is continued the compositions of the melt will move along the liquidus curve toward ammonium thiocyanate, while the compositions of the solid solution will move in the same direction along the solidus curve. When point

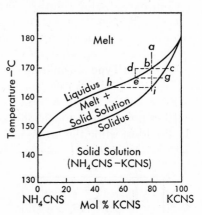

h is reached, the solid solution in equilibrium with the small amount of melt remaining has the over-all composition of the mixture, and hence at this point the mixture solidifies completely to yield a solid solution of composition *i* equal to the original composition of the melt. Further cooling will result merely in lowering the temperature of *i*.

Fig. 12. Phase Diagram for the System NH₄CNS-KCNS.

The same considerations apply to the cooling of any other over-all composition in the diagram. Although the cooling process described above has been considered to be stepwise, actually the changes in the compositions of solid and melt involve a continuous adjustment of the concentrations to the equilibrium values called for by the liquidus and solidus curves at each temperature. It should be pointed out, however, that this mode of solidification is obtained only if the cooling rate is sufficiently slow and there is sufficiently good contact between the phases to allow equilibrium to be reached. With rapid cooling and little agitation solid solutions of varying composition may separate, and the final congealing temperature may be lower than *hi*.

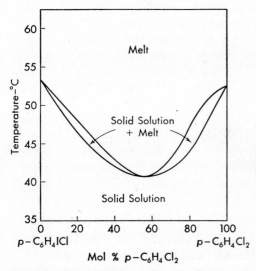

Fig. 13. Phase Diagram for the System *p*-C₆H₄ICl–*p*-C₆H₄Cl₂.

Since in this system no more than two phases are present at any time in equilibrium, there are no invariant points, and hence there are no horizontal portions on the cooling curves. The only discontinuities are an arrest when the liquidus curve is reached and solid starts separating, and another arrest when the over-all composition line crosses the solidus curve and the melt disappears; i.e., for a composition such as *a* arrests are observed at temperatures corresponding to points *b* and *i*.

Continuous solid solution formation of the type discussed is fairly common. Systems besides the above that exhibit such behavior are lead chloride-lead bromide, silver chloride-sodium chloride, copper-nickel, cobalt-nickel, silver-gold, and naphthalene–β-naphthol.

Minimum Type of Diagram. A variation of Fig. 12 is the diagram shown in Fig. 13 for the system *p*-iodochlorbenzene (*A*)–*p*-dichlorbenzene (*B*). Here, as before, *A* and *B* form a complete series of solid solutions, but the melting point curve now exhibits a minimum. Again the upper curve is the liquidus, while the lower curve is the solidus. Except for the fact that the melt composition corresponding to the minimum freezes at constant temperature to yield a solid solution, the relations in this system are similar to those described for ammonium thiocyanate-potassium thiocyanate.

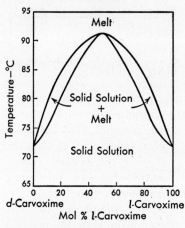

Fig. 14.   Phase Diagram for the System *d*-Carvoxime–*l*-Carvoxime.

Some other systems falling within this category are sodium carbonate-potassium carbonate, potassium chloride-potassium bromide, mercuric bromide-mercuric iodide, potassium nitrate-sodium nitrate, silver-antimony, and copper-gold.

Maximum Type of Diagram. Though rarely encountered, a third possible type of diagram is one in which the melting point curve of the system exhibits a maximum. Figure 14 shows such a diagram for the system *d*-carvoxime–*l*-carvoxime $(C_{10}H_{14}N \cdot OH)$. Again the liquidus is the upper curve, the solidus the lower. As in the preceding type, there is just one composition of melt which solidifies at constant temperature to yield a solid solution—the one corresponding to the maximum. All other over-all compositions behave as described.

CLASS A: TYPE V. PARTIAL MISCIBILITY IN SOLID STATE WITH EUTECTIC

When two solids are soluble in each other to a limited degree only, *A* will dissolve a given amount of *B* to yield a saturated solution of *B* in *A*, while *B* will dissolve some *A* to yield a saturated solution of *A* in *B*. As long as these limiting concentrations are not exceeded, the solid phase is homogeneous and constitutes a single solid solution. If the range of miscibility is exceeded, however, two solid phases result, each composed of a saturated solution of one constituent in the other. It follows from the phase rule, therefore, that for equilibria between a single solid solution and melt the system will be monovariant, while for equilibria between the two solid solutions and melt the system will be invariant. Any processes involving the coexistence of the two solid solutions and melt will have to take place then isothermally.

Systems in which partial miscibility in the solid state occurs exhibit two types of diagrams. In the first of these, type V, the cooling of melt within certain composition limits results in the appearance of a eutectic involving melt and the two solid solutions. The other possibility, type VI, is observed when the two solid solutions are not stable within certain concentration ranges, and one of these is transformed to the other through a peritectic reaction.

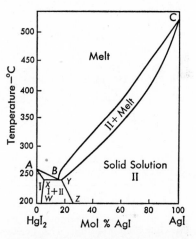

Figure 15 shows a typical phase diagram for a system in which the partial miscibility in the solid state leads to a eutectic B. Line AB is the liquidus curve for solid solutions of silver iodide in mercuric iodide (I), while line AX is the solidus curve for the same solutions. Similarly, line BC is the liquidus curve for solid solutions of mercuric iodide in silver iodide (II), while line YC is the solidus curve for these solutions.

Fig. 15. Phase Diagram for the System Mercuric Iodide–Silver Iodide.

The area enclosed by the lines AX, XB, and BA contains then solid solutions I and melt and the area enclosed by the lines BY, YC, and CB solid solutions II and melt. Below $AXYC$ no melt is present, only solid solutions. To the right of YZ and below CY the solid phase present is solid solution II, while to the left of WX and below AX the solid phase is solid solution I. The area below XY and between the lines WX and YZ is the range of partial miscibility of the solid solutions. In this area I and II coexist, with the lines WX and YZ showing the compositions of I and II respectively at each temperature. From the directions of these lines it is apparent that the partial miscibility of the solid iodides decreases as the temperature is lowered. The eutectic at B involves two solid solutions with the fixed compositions given by X and Y.

Other systems exhibiting diagrams of this type are silver chloride–cuprous chloride, potassium nitrate–thallium nitrate, azobenzene–azoxybenzene, naphthalene-monochloracetic acid, and the metal pairs lead-antimony, silver-copper, lead-tin, and cadmium-zinc.

CLASS A: TYPE VI. PARTIAL MISCIBILITY IN SOLID STATE WITH PERITECTIC

Instead of exhibiting a eutectic, two solid solutions may undergo a peritectic reaction in which a solid solution of one type is transformed to a solid solution of another type at a definite temperature. When this occurs, the phase diagram takes on the general form shown in Fig. 16. In this diagram JD and JF are the liquidus and solidus curves, respectively, of solid solutions of B in A, while DE and CE are the corresponding curves for solid solutions of A in B. As may be seen from the diagram, any over-all compositions lying between pure A and point F yield only solid solutions I; those lying between pure B and point D yield only solid solutions II. However, the solid phases resulting from mixtures between F and D depend on whether the over-all composition lies between F and C, or C and D.

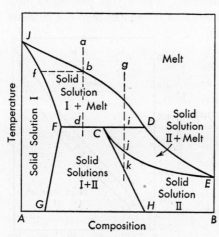

Fig. 16. Phase Diagram for Partially Miscible Solid Solutions with Peritectic.

Cooling any mixture between F and C, such as a, will yield first solid solution I of composition f when point b is reached. Further cooling will result in further separation of I of compositions along fF, while the melt composition adjustment will proceed along bD. But when the temperature corresponding to line FD is reached, point d, solid solution I of composition F becomes unstable and begins to react with melt of composition D to form solid solution II of composition C. Since this *peritectic* reaction between the two solid solutions and melt involves the coexistence of three phases, the process must occur isothermally until the melt is all consumed and only the two solid phases remain. Once the melt has disappeared the temperature begins to fall again, and we pass into the area of partial miscibility of the two solid solutions. The lines FG and CH give the compositions of I and II respectively at various temperatures below the peritectic.

For any composition falling between C and D, such as g, the behavior on cooling will be similar to that of a up to point i, the peritectic temperature. At i solid solution F and melt D again interact to form solid solution II of composition C; but, since now there is more melt present than is necessary to react with all of F to form C, F must disappear, and the end of the peritectic reaction must result in the presence of solid solution II and melt. This mixture of melt and II will eventually solidify at j to leave only solid solution II.

In the diagram under discussion the solid solution of composition j will be stable only between the temperatures corresponding to j and k. When the latter temperature is reached, j passes into the range of partial miscibility and breaks up into two solid solutions.

The appearance of peritectics involving solid solutions is found in such binary systems as silver chloride-lithium chloride, silver nitrate-sodium nitrate, cobalt-iron, indium-thalium, and p-iodo-chlorbenzene–p-diiodo-benzene.

CLASS B: PARTIAL MISCIBILITY IN LIQUID STATE

Although the discussion has centered so far on systems exhibiting a single liquid phase, there are systems in which the melt is only partially miscible over certain temperature and concentration ranges. When this separation of a liquid into two layers occurs, the number of phases is increased, and the phase relations are thereby modified. The case to be considered here is that in which the melt is partially miscible but the solid phases are the pure constituents, Fig. 17. This figure is essentially a simple eutectic-type diagram with an area of partial miscibility of the melt superimposed upon it. Outside the dome-shaped area and above the solid lines a single liquid phase is present. Within the

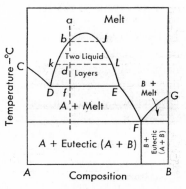

Fig. 17.   Phase Diagram for System with Partially Miscible Melt.

dome-shaped area and above line DE two liquid phases coexist whose compositions at each temperature are given by horizontal tie-lines such as bJ or kL. Since the relations below line DE have been discussed, we need elaborate only the behavior at and above this line.

For this purpose consider specifically a melt of composition a lying between D and E. Cooling of this melt will yield no new phases until at b a small amount of a second liquid layer J appears. Further cooling of these two layers to a point such as d merely changes the relative amounts of the two layers and brings about an adjustment in the concentrations along bk and JL. However, when the layer compositions reach D and E, corresponding to the over-all composition point f, layer D becomes saturated with A, and the latter begins to deposit according to the scheme

$$\text{Liquid } D \longrightarrow A \text{ (solid)} + \text{Liquid } E \qquad (7)$$

During this crystallization of A and transformation of liquid layer D into E, three phases are present in equilibrium, the system is invariant, and hence the temperature remains constant until all of D has disappeared. Once D is gone the system regains a degree of freedom, and the temperature falls to yield A in equilibrium with a single melt of composition given by EF. Final solidification takes place at F to yield a eutectic mixture of A and B.

For compositions between C and D the behavior will be somewhat different. Cooling of any such mixture will result first in a separation of A when line CD is crossed. Further cooling will shift the melt composition toward D, and when this point is reached a separation of the melt into D and E will occur. From this stage on, separation of A will proceed under isothermal conditions until D is gone, and thereafter the mixture of A and melt along EF will cool in the manner described. Since to the right of E only a single liquid phase is present the cooling behavior will be the same as that of any simple eutectic system.

In many systems the line CD is either extremely short or nonexistent. In the latter instance points D and C coincide; i.e., at the melting point of A the A-rich layer is practically pure A. Again, the eutectic point F may be displaced so close to the B axis as to obliterate practically the line FG and the $(B + \text{melt})$ area. Examples of all these various modifications of Fig. 17 may be found in the condensed binary pairs lithium-sodium, bismuth-zinc, bismuth-cobalt, chromium-copper, copper-lead, benzoic acid-water, and phenol-water.

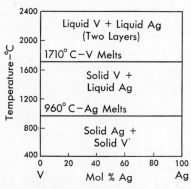

Fig. 18. Phase Diagram for the System Vanadium-Silver.

CLASS C: IMMISCIBILITY IN SOLID AND LIQUID STATES

When two constituents are completely immiscible in both the solid and liquid states, each of these substances will melt and freeze independently of the other. An example of such behavior is shown in Fig. 18 for the system vanadium-silver. Below 960° C the two elements exist as two solid phases. At 960° C the silver melts sharply to yield the liquid, which then coexists with the solid vanadium up to the melting point of the latter. At 1710° C the vanadium melts, and thereafter the system contains only the two pure liquids in two layers.

Similar behavior is observed also with the metal pairs bismuth-chromium, chromium-iron, aluminum-sodium, aluminum-lead, gallium-mercury, potassium-magnesium, and others. In practically all instances the melts become partially miscible at temperatures above the fusion point of the higher melting constituent.

COMPOSITE DIAGRAMS

As a rule binary solid-liquid diagrams are not of the simple types described but have the elements of several types combined into a single diagram. Such a more complicated phase relation for the system magnesium-zinc is shown in Fig. 19. By applying the general principles developed for the simple types it is readily possible to interpret the more complicated equilibria occurring in this system as a combination of solid solution formation, formation of compounds, both stable ($MgZn_2$) and unstable ($MgZn$ and $MgZn_5$), and eutectic. The student should verify for himself the validity of the legends in the various areas

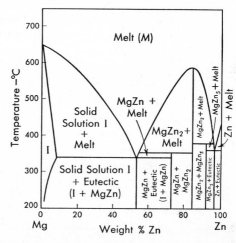

Fig. 19. Phase Diagram for the System Magnesium-Zinc.

and should sketch cooling curves for various over-all compositions in the system.

THREE-COMPONENT SYSTEMS

In three-component systems a single phase possesses four degrees of freedom, namely, temperature, pressure, and the compositions of two out of the three components. This number of variables poses great difficulty in the graphical presentation of the phase relations. For this reason data in ternary systems are generally presented at some fixed pressure, such as atmospheric, and at various constant temperatures. Under these conditions it is possible to show the concentration relations among the three components at any given temperature on a planar diagram. By combining such planar diagrams for various temperatures it is then possible, if desired, to construct a solid model having concentrations as a base and temperature as a vertical axis.

For a three-component system the phase rule takes the form $F = 5 - P$. At a fixed pressure and temperature the number of degrees of freedom is reduced by two, so that $F = 3 - P$, and the maximum number of phases which can occur simultaneously is thus three. This is the same number as is possible in two-component systems under a constant pressure only. Therefore, under the specified conditions an area will again indicate divariance, a line monovariance, and a point invariance.

METHOD OF GRAPHICAL PRESENTATION

Several schemes for plotting two-dimensional equilibrium diagrams for ternary systems have been proposed. Of these the equilateral triangle method suggested by Stokes and Roozeboom is most generally employed and will be used here. In this method concentrations of the three components at any given temperature and pressure are plotted on an equilateral triangle such as that shown in Fig. 20. Each apex of the triangle is taken as 100 per cent of the component with which it is designated. To obtain percentages other than 100 for A, the sides AB and AC are divided into 10 (or sometimes 100) equal parts, and lines parallel to the side BC are drawn. Each of these lines represents then a definite percentage of A ranging from zero on line BC to 100 at A. Similarly, lines dividing the sides BA and BC and parallel to AC give various percentages of B, while the lines along the sides CA and CB and parallel to AB represent various percentages of C. To plot any point on the diagram such as D, having 30 per cent A, 20 per cent B, and 50 per cent C, we locate first the 30 per cent A line, namely ab, and next the 20 per cent B line, or cd. The intersection of these two lines yields the desired point. This point should lie also on the 50 per cent C line, or ef, and this fact may be utilized as a check on the accuracy of location of the point.

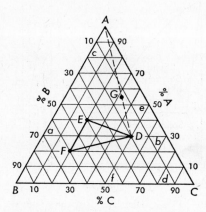

Fig. 20. Graphical Representation of Three-Component Systems.

From the nature of the diagram it is readily apparent that the sides of the triangle represent various proportions of constituents in two-component systems. Thus lines AB, BC, and AC give the concentration relations in the binary systems A–B, B–C, and A–C, respectively, and any point on these lines refers only to these binary systems. On the other hand, any mixture composed of A, B, and C must lie within the diagram. In fact, the argument may be extended to show that similar relations apply also to any line or smaller triangle within the diagram. Thus all mixtures that can be prepared from D and E will lie on DE, those prepared from E and F will lie on EF, while those composed of F and D will lie on the line FD; and all possible compositions that can be prepared from D, E, and F will fall within the small triangle DEF. From the same considerations it also follows that if a point such as G lies on a straight line connecting D and A, then D must lie on an extension of the straight line through G linking A and G.

Another relation to remember is this: Any mixture such as G, composed of A and D, will contain A and D in the length ratios $DG:AG$ by weight, if weight percentage is plotted, or by moles, if mole percentage is plotted. By knowing the total amount of any mixture present, and by determining these lengths from the diagram, it is possible to calculate the weights (or moles) of various phases present in a given system. Such calculations find wide application in all types of separation problems involving three components.

PARTIALLY MISCIBLE THREE-LIQUID SYSTEMS

Although many categories of three-component systems are possible and have been observed, prime attention will be devoted here to only two of these, namely, (a) systems composed of three liquid components which exhibit partial miscibility and (b) systems composed of two solid components and a liquid.

Systems composed of three liquids which show partial miscibility may be classified as follows:

Type I.   Formation of one pair of partially miscible liquids
Type II. Formation of two pairs of partially miscible liquids
Type III. Formation of three pairs of partially miscible liquids

These three types will be discussed now in turn.

TYPE I. ONE PARTIALLY MISCIBLE PAIR

Consider a pair of liquids, B and C, that are partially soluble in each other at a given temperature and pressure. If we mix relative amounts of the two so as to exceed the mutual solubility limits, two layers will be obtained, one composed of a solution of B in C, the other of C in B. Suppose we add now to the two-layer mixture a third liquid A, which is completely miscible with both B and C. Experience shows that A will distribute itself between the two layers and will promote thereby a greater miscibility of B and C. The increase in miscibility brought about by A depends on the amount of it added and on the amounts of B and C present. If sufficient A is introduced, the two layers can be changed into a single solution composed of the three liquids.

The changes in miscibility produced by progressive additions of A to mixtures of B and C can be followed on the diagram shown in Fig. 21. Points a and b designate the compositions of the two liquid layers resulting from mixing B and C in some arbitrary over-all proportion such as c, while line Ac shows the manner in which the over-all composition of c is changed by addition of A. When enough A is added to change c to c_1, the compositions of the two layers are shifted from a and b to a_1 and b_1. The line a_1b_1 through c_1 connects the compositions of the two layers in equilibrium, and is called a *tie-line*. In a similar manner the compositions are changed to a_2, a_3 and b_2, b_3 when the over-all compositions reach c_2 and c_3. Finally, at point b_4 sufficient A has been added to form only a single layer of this composition, and thereafter only a single solution is obtained.

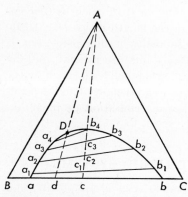

Fig. 21. Three Liquids with One Partially Miscible Pair.

The tie-line for b_4 shows that the composition of the B-rich layer at the point of complete miscibility is not identical with b_4 but is equal to a_4. This fact indicates that complete miscibility is brought about not by coalescence of the two layers into one, but rather by the disappearance of the B-rich layer. Complete miscibility by the merging of the two layers into one can occur only at one point on the diagram, D. At this point the compositions of the two layers become identical, and the two solutions coalesce into a single liquid phase of constant composition. Point D is called either the *isothermal critical point* of the system, or the *plait point*, and can be obtained only by adding A to a single mixture of B and C, namely, d.

From the preceding discussion it follows that any mixture of A, B, and C of over-all composition falling within the dome-shaped area will yield two liquid layers of compositions given by the appropriate tie-line through the composition of the mixture. On the other hand, any mixture of over-all composition outside this area will yield only a single homogeneous solution of the three liquids. Curve aDb is frequently referred to as a *binodal* curve. In general the plait point D will fall off the maximum of the binodal curve. Furthermore, since as a rule component A will not distribute itself equally between the two layers a and b, the tie-lines will not be parallel either to BC or to each other.

Examples of systems of the type under discussion are acetic acid-chloroform-water (A–B–C), and acetone-water-phenol (A–B–C).

TYPE II. TWO PARTIALLY MISCIBLE PAIRS

A system composed of three liquids such that A and B and A and C are partially miscible, while B and C are completely miscible, will exhibit a phase diagram with two binodal curves as shown in Fig. 22. Curve aDb gives the range of compositions in which mixtures of A and B containing C are partially miscible. Again the binodal curve cFd gives the area within

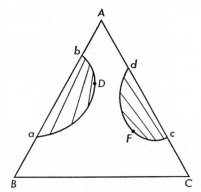

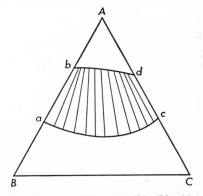

Fig. 22. Partially Miscible Liquids with Two Binodal Curves.

Fig. 23. Partially Miscible Liquids with Intersecting Binodal Curves.

which C and A containing B separate into two layers. Outside these areas the three components are completely miscible. D and F are the respective plait points of the two heterogeneous regions, while the indicated tie-lines show the compositions of the various layers in equilibrium. This type of diagram is shown by the liquids succinic nitrile-water-ethyl alcohol (A–B–C) between 18.5 and 31° C.

Although some ternary liquid systems exhibit this type of diagram at elevated temperatures, at lower temperatures, when the miscibility decreases, the two binodal curves may intersect to form the "band" type of diagram shown in Fig. 23. Here the partial miscibility area $abdc$ extends across the width of the diagram, with bd giving the composition of one layer and ac that of the other. The indicated tie-lines join solutions in equilibrium. Examples of "band" formation are found in the systems water-phenol-aniline (A–B–C) and water-ethyl acetate–n-butyl alcohol (A–B–C).

TYPE III. THREE PARTIALLY MISCIBLE PAIRS

When all three liquids are partially soluble in each other, three binodal curves (Fig. 24) result, provided the temperature is sufficiently high to prevent intersections. Here again the dome-shaped areas indicate two-phase liquid regions, while outside these only a single phase is present. However, when two of the binodal curves intersect, as may occur at lower temperatures, the diagram takes on the appearance of Fig. 25. Here in the areas designated as 1 only a single phase exists, while in the areas marked 2 two liquid phases coexist with the equilibrium concentrations given by the connecting tie-lines. But the area marked 3 contains now *three* liquid phases. Since for three phases in equilibrium the system must

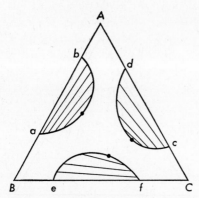

Fig. 24. Partially Miscible Liquids with Three Binodal Curves.

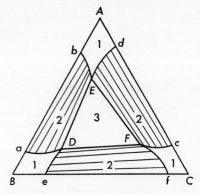

Fig. 25. Intersection of Three Binodal Curves.

be invariant at constant temperature and pressure, the compositions of the three layers must be fixed and independent of the over-all composition—as long as it falls within this area. These constant compositions for the three liquid layers in equilibrium are given by the points D, E, and F.

An example of a system yielding three liquid phases in equilibrium is succinic nitrile-water-ether. At higher temperatures this system goes over to the type shown in Fig. 24.

APPLICATION OF TERNARY LIQUID DIAGRAMS

Ternary liquid diagrams are of considerable value in various types of separation and solvent extraction problems. In certain binary mixtures where separation of the individual components is desired, extraction of one component by a third solvent frequently offers advantages over distillation, crystallization, or other possible methods of segregation. This is true in the removal of certain undesirable impurities from lubricating oils, where treatment with a solvent in which the impurity concentrates, but one in which the oil is either partially or totally insoluble, can bring about improvement in the quality and properties of the lubricant. By studying the diagrams for the components in question and various solvents, it is possible to deduce whether the separation sought can be accomplished and to define the best operating conditions for optimum results.

SYSTEMS COMPOSED OF TWO SOLIDS AND A LIQUID

This important class of three-component systems considers the crystallization of various solid phases from solutions of two solid components in a liquid solvent. Although the solvent may be any suitable liquid in which the solid components may be soluble, attention will be focused primarily on solutions in water, which is by far our most important crystallization medium. However, the relations developed will apply equally to any other systems of the general type under discussion.

All the systems to be described below will exhibit only a single liquid phase. For one liquid phase occurring in a system, the behavior of the solid phases may be classified as follows:

Type I.   Crystallization of pure components only
Type II.   Formation of binary compounds
Type III. Formation of ternary compounds
Type IV. Formation of complete series of solid solutions
Type V.   Partial miscibility of solid phases

TYPE I. CRYSTALLIZATION OF PURE COMPONENTS ONLY

When in a system composed of water and two solid components B and C only the two pure solid components appear on crystallization, the *isothermal* phase diagram has the general form shown in Fig. 26. In this diagram points D and E are solubilities in water of pure B and C respectively at the given temperature. As C is added to the solution saturated with B, the concentration of the latter changes and follows the line DF. Similarly, when B is dissolved in the water solution saturated with C, the composition of the solution changes along line EF. The line DF is, therefore, the saturation *solubility curve* of B in water containing C, while EF is the corresponding solubility curve of C in water containing B. At F, the point of intersection of the two solubility curves, the solution becomes saturated with both B and C. Since the system contains now three phases in equilibrium, B, C, and saturated solution of composition F, there are no degrees of freedom left, and hence the composition at this point must be constant. For this reason F is called the *isothermal invariant point*.

The area above the lines DF and FE contains only unsaturated solution. However, area DFB is a two-phase region in which solid B is in equilibrium with saturated solutions of compositions lying along DF. The particular concentration of saturated solution resulting from a given over-all composition, such as G, can readily be determined from the diagram. Any mixture G of B, C, and water within the indicated area will yield at equilibrium pure solid B and a saturated solution somewhere along DF. From the relations of the equilateral triangle it follows, therefore, that the concentration of solution sought must lie on a straight line from B through G, namely, G_1. By the same token any mixture such as H will have H_1 as a saturated solution. Lines such as G_1B and H_1B which connect the concentrations of the saturated solutions with the solid phases in equilibrium with them are called tie-lines. The points of convergence of various sets of these tie-lines on a diagram determine the nature of the solid phases with which various solutions are saturated.

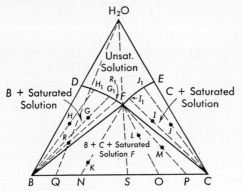

Fig. 26. Crystallization of Two Solid Components from Solution.

Corresponding to area DFB is the area EFC in which the saturating phase is C. Any mixtures falling within this area, such as I or J, yield at equilibrium solid C and saturated solutions along EF. On the other hand, the area BFC is a three-phase region. Anywhere within this area will be found solid B *and* solid C in equilibrium with saturated solution of composition F. A shift in over-all composition from a point K to L or M in this area merely changes the relative proportions of B and C present from N to O or P, but the composition of F remains unaffected. Diagrams of the type under discussion are exhibited by the systems ammonium chloride-ammonium nitrate-water, sodium chloride-sodium nitrate-water, and ammonium chloride-ammonium sulfate-water.

The manner in which a diagram such as Fig. 26 may be utilized in solving a crystallization problem may be illustrated with the following example. Suppose a mixture of the two solids B and C of over-all composition Q is available and it is desired to separate from this mixture pure B. In order to recover this solid it is necessary to bring the over-all composition into area DFB. This may be accomplished by the addition of water which will make the composition change along line Q–H_2O. When water is first added we enter area BFC in which both B and C are in equilibrium with solution F. However, as soon as line BF is crossed to a point such as R, all the C dissolves, and a solution R_1 is obtained saturated with solid B which can be filtered off, washed, and dried to obtain pure B. The amount of water necessary to dissolve all of C, and the yield of B, can be calculated with the aid of the diagram. From the distances QR and R–H_2O it follows that the ratio of the weight of Q to the weight of water to be added to reach R is

$$\frac{\text{Weight of } Q}{\text{Weight of water}} = \frac{R\text{–}H_2O}{RQ}$$

Knowing the original weight of Q, the weight of water to be added and the total weight of the mixture at R may be determined. Furthermore, since R is composed of B and R_1, we find in the same manner that

$$\frac{\text{Weight of } B}{\text{Weight of } R_1} = \frac{\overline{RR_1}}{\overline{BR}}$$

By using this ratio and the total weight of the mixture at R, the weight of B which can be recovered may be predicted.

The maximum amount of B is recovered when R is very close to the line BF. Farther along the line R–H_2O the proportion of saturated solution to B is greater, and hence the yield of B is less. Another significant fact is that B can be recovered by the addition of pure water only when the mixture of B and C does not exceed the composition S. Once this composition is exceeded toward C, the saturation area of C is entered, and consequently only this substance may be recovered from the mixture.

THE SCHREINEMAKERS "WET RESIDUE" METHOD

Experimental methods employed for the determination of phase diagrams of ternary systems containing solid and liquid phases are in general similar to those described for binary systems. Thermal analysis may be used, but it usually yields cooling curves that are more difficult to interpret than those encountered in binary mixtures. For this reason the saturation method is used almost exclusively in the study of equilibria at and near room temperatures. The procedure for this method is briefly as follows: Mixtures of various proportions of the solid components with water are prepared and agitated in a thermostat until equilibrium is established. The liquid phase is separated then from the wet crystals, and both are weighed and analyzed carefully. The compositions thus obtained for saturated solution and the wet residue are plotted finally on a triangular diagram.

Figure 27 shows a series of points arrived at in this manner. S_1, S_2, etc., are the compositions of saturated solutions, while R_1, R_2, etc., are the compositions of the corresponding wet residues. To ascertain the nature of the solid phases in equilibrium with the various solutions and present in the residues a graphical scheme is employed known as the *Schreinemakers method of wet residues*. This method is based on the fact that any wet residue composed of a given solid phase and a saturated solution must lie on a straight line joining the composition of the solid phase and that of the saturated solution. Consequently a tie-line drawn between any corresponding pair of R and S points must pass, on extension past R, through the composition of the solid phase. Moreover, as several solutions may have the same solid phase, all the tie-lines for such solutions

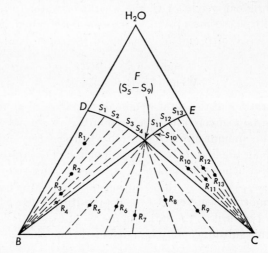

Fig. 27.   Schreinemakers' Method of Wet Residues.

must intersect at a common point, which is the composition of the common solid phase. By this reasoning we deduce that the solid phase for all solutions between D and F is B, for those between F and E is C, while F is saturated with various proportions of B and C.

TYPE II. FORMATION OF BINARY COMPOUNDS

In many systems composed of two salts and water compounds may be formed at a given temperature either between the salts and water, namely, hydrates, or between the two solid salts. Although a number of possible combinations can be envisaged, only several typical cases will be discussed to indicate the nature of the diagrams obtained under these conditions.

Hydrate Formation. Figure 28 shows the phase diagram for a system in which one of the components, B, forms a hydrate. Since the hydrate is composed of B and water, its composition must lie along the line B–H_2O and is given by D. E is the solubility of the hydrate in pure water at the given temperature, while line *EF* gives the solubility of the hydrate in solutions containing *C*. Within area *DEF* the hydrate *D* coexists with saturated solutions given by line *EF*. The area *FGC* contains again pure *C* in equilibrium with saturated solutions along *FG*. However, at *F*, the isothermal invariant point, the solution is saturated with both *D* and *C*. As all possible mixtures of the latter two lie along line *DC*, the tie-lines within the area *DFC* must terminate along this line, as shown. Since all of the liquid phase disappears when line *DC* is reached, below this line only a mixture of solids *D*, *B*, and *C* can exist. The system sodium sulfate-sodium chloride-water at 15° C is an example of this type of behavior, the hydrate formed being $Na_2SO_4 \cdot 10 H_2O$.

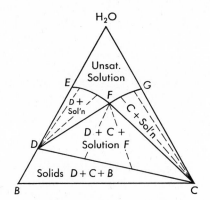

Fig. 28.   Formation of a Hydrate.

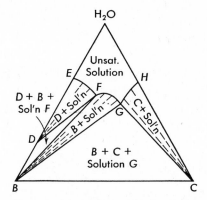

Fig. 29.   Appearance of Hydrate and Pure Components.

A system in which both solid components form a hydrate will have a diagram similar to Fig. 28 except that the tie-lines, instead of intersecting at *C*, will intercept the *C*–H_2O line at some point between *G* and *C*. The line *DC* will similarly be elevated above *C*. An example of such a system is magnesium chloride-calcium chloride-water at 0° C, where the hydrates $MgCl_2 \cdot 6 H_2O$ and $CaCl_2 \cdot 6 H_2O$ occur.

Under some temperature conditions in certain systems not only the hydrate of a component, but also the anhydrous salt, appears. The phase diagram then has the appearance of Fig. 29. Three saturation curves are now obtained, one for each of the solid phases, and two invariant points, *F* and *G*. The solution at the invariant point *F* is in equilibrium with *D* and *B*, and any mixture within area *DFB* will yield these three phases. On the other hand, any mixture falling within area *BGC* will have *B* and *C* in equilibrium with the solution at the isothermal invariant point *G*. A diagram similar to Fig. 29 is again exhibited by the system sodium sulfate-sodium chloride-water, but at 25° C. At this temperature both Na_2SO_4 and $Na_2SO_4 \cdot 10 H_2O$ appear as saturating phases.

Double Salt Formation. Two salts B and C, instead of forming hydrates, may react with each other to form a double salt of the general formula B_nC_m. When this happens the composition of the double salt will have to fall on the line BC, and a saturation curve for this new solid phase will have to appear in the phase triangle. The diagram for such a system is shown in Fig. 30. Here point D indicates the composition of the double salt, and line FG the compositions of solutions saturated with this compound. F and G are the two isothermal invariant points. The first of these solutions is saturated with B and D, the second with D and C.

The stability of the double salt in presence of water depends on where along BC the composition of the salt falls. If point D falls between the points I and J, it is possible to prepare stable solutions of the double salt by adding water to it, as is indicated by the line D–H_2O. Such a salt is said to be *congruently saturating*. On the other hand, if the composition of the salt falls either to the left of I or to the right of J, it is impossible to prepare a saturated solution of the salt in water by adding water to D. A line from D lying between B and I to the water apex will miss curve FG to yield a mixture either within areas BDF or BEF. Similarly, for D between J and C a line to the water point will miss FG to form either a mixture of D, C, and saturated solution G, or a mixture of C and saturated solution. In either eventuality the double salt undergoes partial or complete decomposition. Double salts behaving in this manner are said to be *incongruently saturating*.

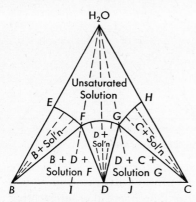

Fig. 30.   Double Salt Formation.

As an example of a congruently saturating double salt may be mentioned $NH_4NO_3 \cdot AgNO_3$ in the system ammonium nitrate-silver nitrate-water at 30° C. However, in the system potassium nitrate-silver nitrate-water at the same temperature the double salt formed, $KNO_3 \cdot AgNO_3$, decomposes on addition of water and hence is incongruently saturating.

TYPE III. FORMATION OF TERNARY COMPOUNDS

In certain systems not only can binary compounds be formed but ternary compounds involving all three components as well. Figure 31 shows the phase diagram for a system in which appear a binary compound, hydrate E, and ternary compound D, composed of B, E, and water.

Within area GHD compound D is in equilibrium with saturated solutions along GH, and may be recovered from these. G and H are the isothermal invariant points. G is saturated with mixtures of B and D, H with the solids D and E. All mixtures are completely solid below the lines BD and DE. Within the triangle BDE the solid phases are B, D, and E; but once line BE is crossed into area BEC, the solid phases become B, E, and C.

The ternary compound D shown in Fig. 31 is evidently of the incongruently saturating type and decomposes on addition of water. Examples of such a compound are $CaCl_2 \cdot MgCl_2 \cdot 12\ H_2O$ (tachydrite) in the system calcium chloride-magnesium chloride-water at 25° C, and $MgSO_4 \cdot Na_2SO_4 \cdot H_2O$ in the system magnesium sulfate-sodium sulfate-water at the same temperature. On the other hand, ternary compounds such as the alums, whose

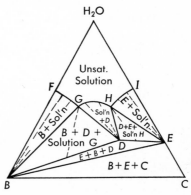

Fig. 31.   Formation of Ternary Compound.

general formula is $B_2SO_4 \cdot C_2(SO_4)_3 \cdot 24\ H_2O$, form congruently saturating salts which are stable in presence of water.

TYPE IV. FORMATION OF SOLID SOLUTIONS

When two solid components B and C are completely soluble in each other in the solid phase, a series of solid solutions ranging in composition from pure B to pure C can be recovered from a solution of these in water. Since under these conditions only two phases appear in the system, the solid solution and the liquid saturated solution, no invariant point is observed. Figure 32 shows the phase diagram for such a system. In this diagram line DE gives the compositions of saturated solutions in equilibrium with solid solutions of B and C of the compositions shown by the various tie-lines. In the area above DE only unsaturated solutions can be obtained. Below this line two phases occur, the saturated solutions along DE and the solid solutions in equilibrium with them.

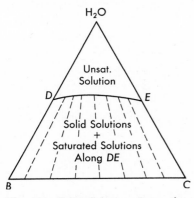

Fig. 32.   Solid Solution Formation.

TYPE V. PARTIAL MISCIBILITY OF SOLID PHASES

Finally, Fig. 33 shows the phase diagram for a system in which the solid phases B and C are only partially soluble in each other. Under these conditions two sets of solid solutions result, one of C in B, lying between points B and D, and another of B in C, between points E and C. Line FG gives the compositions of saturated solutions in equilibrium with the first series of these solid solutions and line GH those in equilibrium with the second. Between points D and E mixtures of B and C yield two solid phases of which one has the composition D, the other E. G is an isothermal invariant point such that any over-all composition falling within area DGE yields this solution and the two solid solutions, D and E, in equilibrium with it.

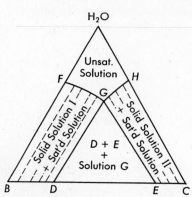

Fig. 33. Partial Miscibility of Solid Phases.

THE THREE-DIMENSIONAL PHASE DIAGRAM

The various triangular diagrams described heretofore are actually isothermal sections of a solid figure consisting of an equilateral triangular base, along which concentrations are plotted, and a vertical axis giving temperature. Such a solid diagram can be constructed from a study of a given ternary system at various temperatures and subsequent assembly of the isothermal sections into a three-dimensional model. The result of this kind of study for the system bismuth-tin-lead is shown schematically in Fig. 34. The relations in this system are the simplest that can be encountered, for here only the pure components appear as solid phases. In Fig. 34 points A, B, C give the melting points of pure bismuth, tin, and lead respectively. Each face of the prism indicates in turn the phase behavior of a two-component system. Thus the face ADB-Sn-Bi shows

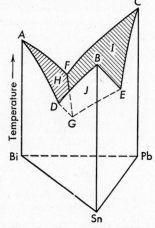

Fig. 34. The System Bi-Sn-Pb at Various Temperatures.

that the binary pair bismuth-tin yields a simple eutectic-type diagram with the eutectic point at D. Similarly points E and F show the eutectics for the systems tin-lead and bismuth-lead. As lead is added to the binary pair bismuth-tin, the position of point D changes along line DG according to the amount of lead added. In the same manner addition of tin to F changes its locus along FG, while addition of bismuth to E changes this point along line EG. All these lines eventually intersect at G.

Lines FG, DG, and GE divide the total surface area of the prism into three distinct surfaces H, I, and J. At all temperatures above these surfaces only melt exists. As soon as a surface is reached, however, a solid phase begins to separate. On H the solid phase is bismuth, on I lead, on J tin. These surfaces represent, therefore, two-phase equilibria involving a pure component and melt. Since FG is the line of intersection of surface H, involving an equilibrium between solid bismuth and melt, and surface I, involving solid lead and melt, this line must represent three phases in equilibrium, namely, bismuth, lead, and melt. By the same reasoning along line GE, tin, lead, and melt, and along line DG bismuth, tin, and melt, are in equilibrium. When these lines eventually meet at G, four phases coexist, the three solids and melt. As for four phases in equilibrium a three-component system at constant pressure possesses zero degrees of freedom, point G must be the absolute invariant point of the system. This invariant point can occur only at a fixed temperature and must correspond to a constant composition of the three components. For the system bismuth-tin-lead the coordinates of G are 97° C and approximately 51 per cent bismuth, 16 per cent tin, and 33 per cent lead. Below 97° C no melt can appear in this system, and hence below this temperature only the three solid phases coexist.

REFERENCES FOR FURTHER READING

1. S. T. Bowden, *Phase Rule and Phase Reactions*, The Macmillan Company, New York, 1939.
2. Findlay, Campbell, and Smith, *The Phase Rule and Its Applications*, Dover Publications, New York, 1951.
3. M. Hansen, *Der Aufbau der Zweistofflegierungen*, Julius Springer, Berlin, 1936.
4. *International Critical Tables*, McGraw-Hill Book Company, Inc., New York, 1923, Vol. II.
5. J. S. Marsh, *Principles of Phase Diagrams*, McGraw-Hill Book Company, Inc., New York, 1935.
6. Purdon and Slater, *Aqueous Solutions and Phase Diagrams*, Edward Arnold & Co., London, 1946.
7. J. E. Teeple, *The Industrial Development of Searles Lake Brines*, Reinhold Publishing Corporation, New York, 1929.

PROBLEMS

1. State how many components are present in each of the following systems:

    (a) $H_2(g) + N_2(g)$
    (b) $NH_3(g)$
    (c) A solution of $Ca(NO_3)_2$ in water

(d) An aqueous solution of NaCl + Na_2SO_4
(e) An aqueous solution of KCl + Na_2SO_4 *Ans.* (a) Two; (b) one.

2. How many degrees of freedom will each of the systems enumerated in problem 1 possess?
3. How many degrees of freedom will each of the following systems possess:

    (a) NaCl(s) in equilibrium with its saturated solution at 25° C and 1 atm pressure.
    (b) I_2(s) in equilibrium with its vapor
    (c) I_2(s) in equilibrium with its vapor at 50° C
    (d) HCl(g) and NH_3(g) in equilibrium with NH_4Cl(s) when the equilibrium is approached by starting with the two gases only
    (e) HCl(g) and NH_3(g) in equilibrium with NH_4Cl(s) when the equilibrium is approached by starting only with the solid

4. From the following information sketch and label the phase diagram for CH_3COOH. (a) The melting point of the solid is 16.6° C under its own vapor pressure of 9.1 mm; (b) solid CH_3COOH exists in two modifications, I and II, both of which are more dense than the liquid, and I is the stable modification at low pressure; (c) phases I, II, and liquid are in equilibrium at 55.2° C under a pressure of 2000 atm; (d) the transition temperature from I to II decreases as the pressure is decreased.
5. Suppose that a one-component system exhibits a gas phase, a liquid phase, and three solid modifications. How many one-, two-, three-, and four-phase equilibria are possible in the system?
6. The system *n*-heptane and 2,2,4-trimethyl pentane exhibits a simple eutectic point at −114.4° C corresponding to 24 mole per cent of *n*-heptane [Smittenberg, Hoog, and Henkes, *J. Am. Chem. Soc.*, **60**, 17 (1938)]. Determine analytically the maximum mole per cents of *n*-heptane which can be recovered by crystallization from mixtures of the two compounds containing 80, 90, and 95 mole per cent of *n*-heptane.   *Ans.* 92.1, 96.5, and 98.3%.
7. The following data are given by Andrews [*J. Phys. Chem.*, **29**, 1041 (1925)] for the system *o*-dinitrobenzene–*p*-dinitrobenzene:

Mol % of Para Compound	Initial Melting Point, ° C
100	173.5
90	167.7
80	161.2
70	154.5
60	146.1
50	136.6
40	125.2
30	111.7
20	104.0
10	110.6
0	116.9

Construct a temperature-composition diagram for the system, and determine therefrom the eutectic temperature and composition.
8. Using the plot constructed in the preceding problem, find graphically the maximum percentage of *p*-dinitrobenzene which can be recovered pure by crystallization from mixtures of the two compounds containing originally 95%, 75%, and 45% of the para compound.

9. From the phase diagram of the system Cd-Bi given in the text, estimate the solubility of Cd in Bi at 200° C.   *Ans.* 110.5 g/100 g Bi.

10. In the system $NaCl$-H_2O a simple eutectic is observed at $-21.1°$ C for a solution containing 23.3% by weight NaCl where $NaCl \cdot 2\,H_2O$ and ice crystallize out of the mixture. At a composition of 27% by weight of NaCl and at $-9°$ C a peritectic point exists where the dihydrate decomposes to form anhydrous NaCl. The temperature coefficient of solubility of anhydrous NaCl is very small and positive. Make a rough sketch for the system showing clearly the phases in equilibrium in the various areas and along the various curves of the diagram.

11. In Fig. 7 sketch and interpret the cooling curves which would result when melts corresponding to 20, 40, and 60 mol per cent of $FeCl_3$ are cooled.

12. By referring to Fig. 9, state the conditions of temperature and composition which must be met in order to crystallize in the pure state the compound $CaF_2 \cdot CaCl_2$ from the CaF_2-$CaCl_2$ system.

13. By referring to Fig. 11, explain how you would proceed to obtain the optimum amount of pure $MgSO_4 \cdot 6\,H_2O$ crystals from a dilute aqueous solution of $MgSO_4$.

14. The system SO_3-H_2O exhibits congruent melting points at compositions by weight of 68.96%, 81.63%, and 89.89% SO_3. What are the formulas of the corresponding compounds?   *Ans.* $H_2SO_4 \cdot H_2O$ for first.

15. Complete and interpret the phase diagram, Fig. 35, for the system Al-Ni, explaining what phases are in equilibrium under the various conditions represented by the areas and curves.

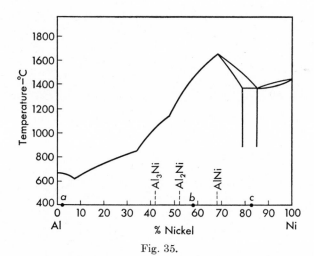

Fig. 35.

16. In the preceding problem sketch cooling curves showing the complete solidification of melts having compositions *a*, *b*, and *c*.

17. Will the addition of a small amount of impurity to a pure compound or element always lower its melting point? Explain your answer.

18. CCl_4 and H_2O may be assumed to be immiscible. Apply the phase rule to the system H_2O-CCl_4-I_2, and explain what variables must be specified in order to determine the state of the system.

19. The following data are for the system water-alcohol-benzene at 25° C. The first two columns give the percentages by weight of alcohol and benzene in one layer, while the third column gives the percentage by weight of water in the layer conjugate to these.

Layer I		Layer II
% C_6H_6	% C_2H_5OH	% H_2O
1.3	38.7	
9.2	50.8	
20.0	52.3	3.2
30.0	49.5	5.0
40.0	44.8	6.5
60.0	33.9	13.5
80.0	17.7	34.0
95.0	4.8	65.5

Construct a phase diagram for the system, and draw in the tie-lines.

20. An aqueous solution contains 46% by weight of ethyl alcohol. Using the diagram of the preceding problem, find how much alcohol would be extracted from 25 g of this solution by 100 g of C_6H_6.   *Ans.* 5.05 g.

21. The following data are given by Prutton, Brosheer, and Maron [*J. Am. Chem. Soc.*, **57**, 1656 (1935)] for the system $NH_4Cl-NH_4NO_3-H_2O$ at 25° C:

Saturated Solution		Wet Residue	
% NH_4NO_3	% NH_4Cl	% NH_4NO_3	% NH_4Cl
67.73	0	—	—
66.27	2.00	88.20	0.79
64.73	3.82	88.00	1.34
62.24	5.58	90.25	1.65
61.68	6.97	87.65	2.28
53.49	11.08	23.31	62.22
36.99	15.80	13.63	66.29
19.05	21.81	7.09	72.75
0	28.33	—	—

Construct and interpret the phase diagram for the system, and determine the ternary composition. Is there evidence of hydrate or double salt formation in this system?

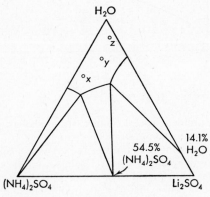

Fig. 36.

22. Using the plot constructed in the preceding problem, determine the maximum theoretical recovery of NH_4Cl from a dry salt mixture of NH_4Cl-NH_4NO_3 containing 80% by weight of NH_4Cl.   *Ans.* 96.1%.

23. For the system KNO_3-$NaNO_3$-H_2O a ternary point exists at 5° C at which the two anhydrous salts are in equilibrium with a saturated solution containing 9.04% by weight of KNO_3 and 41.01% $NaNO_3$. Determine analytically the maximum weight of KNO_3 which could be recovered pure from a salt mixture containing 70 g of KNO_3 and 30 g of $NaNO_3$ by crystallization from an aqueous solution at 5° C.   *Ans.* 90.5%.

24. Complete and interpret the phase diagram, Fig. 36, for the system $(NH_4)_2SO_4$-Li_2SO_4-H_2O at 25° C.

25. In the diagram of the preceding problem, what will be the composition of the first crystals formed by the evaporation of H_2O from solutions of compositions x, y, and z at 25° C?

26. The following hydrates may under proper conditions be crystallized from the system $Ba(OH)_2$-$NaOH$-H_2O at 30° C: $Ba(OH)_2 \cdot 8\ H_2O$, $Ba(OH)_2 \cdot 3\ H_2O$, $Ba(OH)_2 \cdot H_2O$, and $NaOH \cdot H_2O$. Sketch and interpret the phase diagram for this system.

15

Electrolytic Transference and Conductance

Electrochemistry is the branch of physical chemistry that concerns itself with the interrelation of chemical phenomena and electricity. It deals with the study of the electrical properties of solutions of electrolytes and with the elucidation of the relation between chemical action and electricity in such systems. The phenomena encountered in electrochemistry are of such theoretical and practical importance that this and the three chapters following are to be devoted to an exposition of various aspects of the subject.

OHM'S LAW AND ELECTRICAL UNITS

The strength of an electric current flowing through a conductor, i.e., the quantity of electricity flowing per second, is determined by the difference in potential applied across the conductor and by the resistance offered by the conductor to the current. According to Ohm's law the relation among these three quantities is given by

$$I = \frac{\varepsilon}{R} \tag{1}$$

where I is the strength of a current flowing through a resistance R under an applied potential ε. From this equation it is evident that the current strength is directly proportional to the difference in potential and inversely proportional to the resistance. By an appropriate choice of units the constant of proportionality is made unity.

Electrical quantities may be expressed in cgs *electromagnetic units* (*emu*), based on the law of attraction or repulsion of magnets, in cgs *electrostatic units* (*esu*), based on the Coulomb law of force between electric charges, or in *absolute units* derived from the emu units. As of January 1, 1948, the United States Bureau of Standards has adopted the last-named system as the official one for this country.[1] Before this date the official system of units was the one known as the *international*.

In the absolute system the units of current, potential, and resistance are respectively the absolute *ampere, volt,* and *ohm*. The corresponding units in the international system were the international *ampere, volt,* and *ohm*. The international ampere was defined as the invariable current of such strength that on passage through a water solution of silver nitrate it will deposit 0.00111800 g of silver in 1 sec. In turn, the international ohm was defined as the resistance at 0° C of a column of mercury of uniform cross section, 106.300 cm long, and containing 14.4521 g of mercury. From these two units and Ohm's law the international volt followed as the potential difference required to send a current of 1 amp through a resistance of 1 ohm.

Depending on the system, the unit of quantity of electricity is either the absolute or international *coulomb*. The coulomb is the quantity of electricity transported by a current of 1 amp in 1 sec. Since the quantity of electricity carried by a current must equal rate of transport times the time, the charge Q carried by a current I in t sec must be

$$Q = It \tag{2}$$

coulombs. Another unit of quantity of electricity which we shall employ frequently is the faraday, $\mathfrak{F}$. A faraday is equal to 96,496 absolute coulombs.

The electrical work w performed when a current of strength I passes for t sec through a resistance across which the potential drop is ε is given by Joule's law, namely,

$$w = \varepsilon It = \varepsilon Q \tag{3}$$

where w is expressed in *joules*. The *joule* is the electrical unit of energy and is defined as the amount of work performed by a current of 1 amp flowing for 1 sec under a potential drop of 1 volt. The work in joules is readily convertible to other energy units through the relations

$$1 \text{ joule(abs.)} = 1 \times 10^7 \text{ ergs} = 0.2390 \text{ cal} \tag{4}$$

Finally, the rate at which work is being done by an electric current is expressed in *watts*. A *watt* is work performed at the rate of 1 joule per second, and is obviously a unit of electrical power. From equation (3)

[1] National Bureau of Standards Circular C 459 (1947).

the power in watts p delivered by a current follows as

$$p = \varepsilon I = \frac{\varepsilon Q}{t} \tag{5}$$

A larger unit of power is the kilowatt, which is equal to 1000 watts.

In Table 1 is given a comparison of the magnitudes of the electrical units in the various systems. Since the difference between the values of the units for a given quantity in the international and absolute systems is generally negligible for our purposes, no distinction will be made between these except where necessary.

TABLE 1

COMPARISON OF ELECTRICAL UNITS IN VARIOUS SYSTEMS
(Each quantity in the first column is equal to all others on line with it)

Absolute	International	Electromagnetic (cgs emu)	Electrostatic (cgs esu)
1 volt	0.999670 volt	1×10^8	$\frac{1}{300}$
1 ampere	1.000165 ampere	1×10^{-1}	2.9978×10^9
1 ohm	0.999505 ohm	1×10^9	$\frac{1}{9} \times 10^{-11}$
1 coulomb	1.000165 coulomb	1×10^{-1}	2.9978×10^9
1 watt	0.999835 watt	1×10^7	0.9993×10^7
1 joule	0.999835 joule	1×10^7	0.9993×10^7

ELECTRONIC AND ELECTROLYTIC CONDUCTORS

All substances may in general be subdivided into conductors or non-conductors of electricity. The latter are frequently referred to also as *dielectrics* or *insulators*. The distinction between these two classes is not sharp, for there is a shading off in conductivity as we pass from one class to the other, making it sometimes very difficult to say whether a substance is to be considered a poor conductor or an insulator. This may be seen from Table 2, where the specific resistivity ρ for a number of substances is given. The specific resistivity is the electrical resistance of a block of the material 1 cm in length and 1 cm^2 in cross section. The substances with low resistivity are good conductors, while those with high resistivity are poor conductors or dielectrics.

Flow of electricity through a conductor involves a transfer of electrons from a point of higher negative potential to one of lower. However, the mechanism by which this transfer is accomplished is not the same for all conductors. On the basis of mechanism of current flow conductors may be classified into two types, namely, (a) electronic and (b) electrolytic conductors. In electronic conductors of which solid and molten metals and certain solid salts (cupric sulfide, cadmium sulfide) are examples, conduction takes place by direct migration of electrons through the conductor under the influence of an applied potential. Here the atoms or ions composing the conductor are not involved in the process, and, except for a vibration about their mean positions of equilibrium, they remain stationary. The only noticeable effect produced by the current in the conductor is a heating resulting from the dissipation of electrical energy in the form of heat. Another characteristic of electronic conductors is their increase in resistance as the temperature is raised. Thus, the specific resistance of platinum increases from 1×10^{-7} at $-265°$ C to 1×10^{-5} at $20°$ C and to 2.54×10^{-5} at $400°$ C. This fact is utilized in platinum resistance thermometers for estimating temperature by observing the change in resistance with change in temperature. The decrease in resistance becomes especially pronounced at temperatures of 3 or 4° K. Under these conditions the resistance of many metals becomes so low that there is practically no opposition left to electron flow. In this state the metals are said to be *superconducting*.

TABLE 2

Specific Resistivity of Various Substances

Substance	Temp. (° C)	ρ (ohm-cm)	Substance	Temp. (° C)	ρ (ohm-cm)
Silver	20	1.59×10^{-6}	Water		
Copper	20	1.72×10^{-6}	(conductivity)	20	1×10^6
Magnesium	20	4.6×10^{-6}	Slate	—	1×10^8
Mercury	20	9.58×10^{-5}	Celluloid	16	4×10^{10}
Bismuth	20	1.20×10^{-4}	Wood	—	$10^{10} - 10^{13}$
Graphite	0	8.00×10^{-4}	Glass (ordinary)	20	9×10^{13}
$CaCl_2$ (fused)	750	0.86	Sulfur	17	8×10^{15}
H_2SO_4 (1 M)	20	1.31	Paraffin oils	—	1×10^{16}
KCl (0.01 M)	20	7.83×10^2			
Acetic acid (0.001 M)	18	2.44×10^4			

Electrolytic conduction is encountered in solutions of strong and weak electrolytes, in fused salts, and also in some solid salts such as sodium chloride and silver nitrate. In distinction to electronic conductors, electron transfer in electrolytic conductors takes place not by the flow of free electrons, but by a *migration of ions*, both positive and negative, toward the electrodes. This migration involves not only a transfer of electricity from one electrode to the other, but also a transport of matter from one part of the conductor to another. Further, current flow in electrolytic conductors is always accompanied by chemical changes at the electrodes which are quite characteristic and specific for the substances composing the conductor and the electrodes. Finally, while the resistance of electronic conductors increases with temperature, that of electrolytic conductors always decreases as the temperature is raised.

MECHANISM OF ELECTROLYTIC CONDUCTION

The mechanism by which an electric current passes through a solution, with the attendant ionic migrations and chemical reactions, can best be understood from a specific example. For this purpose consider a cell, Fig. 1, composed of two inert electrodes, in this case platinum, connected to a source of current B and dipping into an aqueous solution of sodium chloride. The electrode C, connected to the negative side of B, is called the *cathode*. This is the electrode by which electrons from B, say a battery,

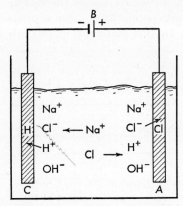

Fig. 1.   Electrolytic Conduction.

enter the solution. In turn, electrode A, connected to the positive side of the battery, is termed the *anode*. It is the electrode through which the electrons leave the solution to return to B. In solution we have sodium and chloride ions, and also some hydrogen and hydroxyl ions due to the very slight ionization of the water. Now, when the circuit is closed and a current passes through the solution, it is found that chlorine gas escapes at the anode and hydrogen gas at the cathode, while sodium hydroxide forms in the solution immediately adjacent to the cathode. The explanation of these changes is as follows. Electrons enter the solution at the cathode C by combining with hydrogen ions in solution to form monatomic hydrogen. Two atoms of hydrogen thus deposited on the electrode combine then to form a molecule of hydrogen which escapes from the electrode as a gas. The reactions involved can be represented by

$$2\,H^+ + 2\ominus \text{ (electrons)} = 2\,H$$
$$2\,H = H_2(g)$$

Again, electrons leave the solution at the anode by the discharge of chloride ions, with each chloride ion giving up one electron to the electrode and becoming a chlorine atom. The electrons thus liberated flow through the external circuit from the electrode to the source of potential, while the nascent chlorine atoms combine with each other to form gaseous chlorine which escapes. The reactions here are

$$2 \text{ Cl}^- = 2 \text{ Cl} + 2 \ominus$$
$$2 \text{ Cl} = \text{Cl}_2(\text{g})$$

We see, therefore, that two electrons are removed from the cathode to form a molecule of hydrogen, and simultaneously two electrons are given up to the anode by chloride ions to form a molecule of chlorine. The net result is a transfer of two electrons from the cathode side of the circuit to the anode side.

How the electrons get from the cathode to the anode may be surmised from the fact that negative ions, or *anions*, migrate when the circuit is closed toward the anode, while positive ions, or *cations*, migrate toward the cathode. As these particles are charged, their motion constitutes a flow of electricity, or an electric current. The anions move to the anode, and hence electrons are carried by these ions from the cathode to the anode. Again, since transport of positive electricity to the *left* may be considered a flow of negative electricity to the *right*, the migration of cations to the cathode is equivalent to a flow of electrons in the opposite direction. Consequently, the net result of the migration is a flow of electrons through the solution in the direction of the current, with each ion carrying part of the current and thus contributing its share to the transport of electricity through the solution.

The formation of sodium hydroxide in the cathode portion of the cell is understood when we remember that from this part of the solution hydrogen ions have been removed by discharge on the electrode, leaving in solution an excess of hydroxyl ions. Since these have no existence independent of positive ions, sodium ions migrate into the cathode compartment in quantity just sufficient to give an electrically neutral solution. When this solution of sodium and hydroxyl ions is evaporated, solid sodium hydroxide is obtained.

The process of current passage through an electrolytic conductor with all the accompanying chemical and migratory changes is called *electrolysis*. From the above discussion the mechanism of electrolysis may be summarized by saying that (a) electrons enter and leave the solution through chemical changes at the electrodes, and (b) electrons pass through the solution by migration of ions. Just as many electrons pass through the solution and leave it as entered it, no more, no less. The evidence for this statement follows from Faraday's laws of electrolysis.

FARADAY'S LAWS OF ELECTROLYSIS

The chemical reaction which occurs during electrolysis at the anode need not be necessarily a deposition of ions, but may be any *oxidation* reaction, as solution of a metal or oxidation of ferrous to ferric ions. Similarly, the reaction at the cathode may be any *reduction* possible under the circumstances, as solution of iodine to form iodide ions, or reduction of stannic to stannous tin. Still, no matter what the nature of the reaction may be, Michael Faraday found that the *mass of a substance involved in reaction at the electrodes is directly proportional to the quantity of electricity passed through the solution.* This statement is known as *Faraday's first law of electrolysis.* The law has been shown to hold very rigidly provided the passage of electricity takes place entirely by electrolytic conduction. It applies to molten electrolytes as well as to solutions of electrolytes and is independent of temperature, pressure, or the nature of the solvent, as long as the lattter can promote ionization of the solute.

From Faraday's first law of electrolysis the quantity of electricity necessary to deposit one equivalent weight of silver may readily be calculated. Since by definition 1 international coulomb deposits 0.00111800 g of silver, and since the mass deposited is directly proportional to the quantity of electricity, the number of coulombs required for deposition of 1 g atomic weight of silver, 107.880 g, must be

$$\frac{107.880}{0.00111800} = 96,494 \text{ coulombs}$$

The question that immediately arises is: What mass of other substances will this quantity of electricity deposit or form? If two cells, one composed of silver electrodes in silver nitrate, the other of copper electrodes in copper sulfate, are connected in series, any current passed through one cell must also pass through the other. With such a setup it can be shown that the weight of copper deposited per coulomb of electricity is 0.0003292 g. Therefore the quantity of electricity necessary to deposit 1 g atomic weight of copper, 63.54 g, is

$$\frac{63.54}{0.0003292} = 193,000 = 2(96,500) \text{ coulombs}$$

However, since copper is divalent, an equivalent is 63.54/2 g. Consequently, to deposit *one equivalent* of copper only one-half the above amount of electricity is required, or 96,500 coulombs.

From a series of such experiments Faraday arrived at his *second law of electrolysis,* namely, that *the masses of different substances produced during electrolysis are directly proportional to their equivalent weights.* Another way of stating this law is that *the same quantity of electricity will produce chemically equivalent quantities of all substances* resulting from the process. Moreover, since 96,500 coulombs will yield one equivalent of silver, a direct consequence of Faraday's second law is that *during electrolysis 96,500 coulombs of electricity will yield one equivalent weight of any substance.* To honor the man who discovered these laws, the name faraday (symbol $\mathfrak{F}$) has been given to this quantity of electricity, i.e., 1 faraday = 96,496 absolute coulombs. For ordinary calculations 1 faraday = 96,500 coulombs will be sufficiently exact.

It is essential to realize that 1 faraday will produce one equivalent of *each* of the primary products of electrolysis. A primary product is one formed directly by the current rather than by subsequent chemical action. To the latter Faraday's laws do not apply. For instance, 1 faraday passed through a sodium chloride cell will produce one equivalent each of chlorine, hydrogen, and sodium hydroxide. These are the primary products of the electrolysis. However, should the chlorine happen to diffuse into the cathode compartment and react with the sodium hydroxide to form sodium hypochlorite and sodium chlorate, the amounts of these formed will not depend on the quantity of electricity passed through the cell, but rather on the operating conditions. In fact, with proper care the formation of these *secondary* products can be avoided, but not that of the primary.

By applying Faraday's laws, the weight of primary products formed in any electrolytic process may be calculated very simply from a knowledge of the strength of the current and its time of passage. Thus, suppose a solution of silver nitrate is electrolyzed between silver electrodes with a current of 0.20 amp flowing for 30 min. The quantity of electricity delivered to the cell is $0.2 \times 30 \times 60 = 360$ coulombs, and hence the weight of silver deposited is 360/96,500 of an equivalent, or

$$\frac{107.88 \times 360}{96,500} = 0.4025 \text{ g}$$

SIGNIFICANCE OF FARADAY'S LAWS

Like the first law of electrolysis, the second law holds very rigidly for electrolytes both in solution and when fused. Its validity is again independent of temperature, pressure, and the nature of the solvent. The reason for the exactness of these laws, and an insight into their significance, may be gathered from the following simple calculation. Millikan and others have established that the charge on the electron is equal to 1.602×10^{-19} coulomb of electricity. Consequently the number of electrons in 1 faraday is

$$\frac{96,496}{1.602 \times 10^{-19}} = 6.023 \times 10^{23} \text{ electrons}$$

But, 6.023×10^{23} is exactly Avogadro's number. Hence, we must conclude that 1 faraday of electricity is associated with 6.023×10^{23} particles of unit charge, or, in general, with one equivalent of a chemical substance. One equivalent of positive ions lacks this number of electrons, while one equivalent of negative ions has this number of electrons in excess. When 1 faraday of electricity is passed through a solution, Avogadro's number of electrons is removed from the cathode by reduction of one equivalent of substance, and exactly the same number of electrons is donated to the anode as a result of some oxidation. Through the solution the equivalent of Avogadro's number of electrons is carried by the migration of positive and negative ions to the appropriate electrodes. In this way the whole process of electrolysis reduces itself to the transport of a given number of electrons through the electrolytic conductor. Since a given number of electrons does not depend on pressure, temperature, or other such factors, neither should the process of electrolysis, and this is the case.

COULOMETERS

As Faraday's laws are obeyed so rigidly, they may be utilized to determine the quantity of electricity passing through a circuit by observing the chemical changes produced by the same current in a suitable electrolytic cell. A cell used for this purpose is called a *coulometer*. The coulometer is placed in the circuit in series with any other apparatus and is allowed to remain there as long as the current is flowing. It is then removed, and the chemical changes produced by the current are determined by some appropriate means.

The silver coulometer is commonly employed for precise work. This coulometer consists of a platinum dish serving as both cathode and cell vessel, and pure silver as anode. The electrolyte is an aqueous solution of purified silver nitrate. The dish is weighed before electrolysis, and the cell is assembled. After electrolysis the electrolyte is carefully decanted, the deposit of silver on the dish is thoroughly washed with distilled water, and the dish plus silver are dried and weighed. From the increase in weight is calculated then the quantity of electricity passed through the coulometer. As an added precaution the anode is separated from the dish by a porous cup to prevent any silver which may chip off the electrode from falling into the dish. With care such coulometers can give results accurate to 0.05 per cent or better.

The iodine coulometer[1] can also yield high precision. In this coulometer the iodine liberated from a solution of potassium iodide by passage of current is estimated by titration with sodium thiosulfate or arsenious acid. For less accurate work copper coulometers, consisting of copper

---

[1] For details on this and other coulometers see the book by MacInnes listed at end of the chapter.

electrodes in a solution of copper sulfate, are quite suitable. Here the copper deposited is estimated by weighing.

TRANSFERENCE AND TRANSFERENCE NUMBERS

Although current is transported through a solution by migration of positive and negative ions, the fraction of the total current carried by each is not necessarily the same. Thus in dilute solutions of magnesium sulfate the magnesium ion carries about 0.38 of the total current, while the sulfate ion carries the balance, or 0.62. Similarly, in dilute nitric acid solutions the nitrate ion carries only 0.16 of the total current, the hydrogen ion 0.84. The sulfate and hydrogen ions transport the greater fraction of the total current because in their respective solutions they move faster than the other ions present. If both ions in a solution moved with the same speed, each would transfer past any fixed plane in the solution the same quantity of electricity in any given time. However, when the speeds of two ions are not the same, in any given period of time the faster ion will carry past any plane a greater fraction of the current, and hence will perform a greater percentage of the total work involved in current transfer.

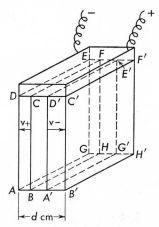

Fig. 2.   Relation of Current to Ionic Velocities.

The quantitative relation between the fraction of the current carried by an ion and its speed can be established as follows. Consider two parallel plates d cm apart, Fig. 2, across which is applied a potential of ε volts and between which is contained some volume of an electrolyte. Let the average migration velocity of the cation in this solution be v_+ cm per second, the charge of the ion be z_+, and the number of these ions n_+. Similarly, let the velocity of the anion be v_-, its charge z_-, and the number of these n_-. Then the quantity of electricity transported by the cation in 1 sec, i.e., the current due to the cation, is going to be all the electricity possessed by all the cations that lie within a distance v_+ of the negative plate, or, in other words, all those which lie within the volume $ABCDEFGH$. The number of these ions is obviously the fraction v_+/d of the total or n_+v_+/d. Again since the charge of each ion is z_+, and the quantity of electricity associated with unit charge is e, the electronic charge, the current carried by the positive ions, must be

$$I_+ = \frac{n_+v_+z_+e}{d} \qquad (6)$$

In a like manner, the current carried by the anions to the positive plate must be that corresponding to all the electricity possessed by the anions in the volume $A'B'C'D'E'F'G'H'$, namely,

$$I_- = \frac{n_- v_- z_- e}{d} \tag{7}$$

Consequently the total current carried by both ions is

$$I = I_+ + I_- = \frac{n_+ v_+ z_+ e + n_- v_- z_- e}{d} \tag{8}$$

But, the condition for electroneutrality of the solution demands that the total charge of the cations must be equal to that of the anions, namely,

$$n_+ z_+ = n_- z_- \tag{9}$$

Therefore,

$$I = \frac{n_+ z_+ e v_+ + n_+ z_+ e v_-}{d}$$

$$= \frac{n_+ z_+ e (v_+ + v_-)}{d} \tag{10}$$

From equations (6) and (10) the fraction of the total current carried by the cations, t_+, follows as

$$t_+ = \frac{I_+}{I} = \frac{n_+ v_+ z_+ e}{n_+ z_+ e (v_+ + v_-)}$$

$$= \left(\frac{v_+}{v_+ + v_-}\right) \tag{11}$$

while the fraction of the total current carried by the anions, t_-, follows from equations (7) and (10) as

$$t_- = \frac{I_-}{I} = \frac{n_- v_- z_- e}{n_+ z_+ e (v_+ + v_-)} = \frac{n_+ z_+ e v_-}{n_+ z_+ e (v_+ + v_-)}$$

$$= \left(\frac{v_-}{v_+ + v_-}\right) \tag{12}$$

t_+ and t_- are called the *transport* or *transference numbers* of the cation and anion respectively. These numbers give the fraction of the total current carried by a given ion in a solution. On dividing equation (11) by equation (12) we see that

$$\frac{t_+}{t_-} = \frac{v_+}{v_-} \tag{13}$$

and hence the transport numbers of the ions, and therefore the fractions of the total current they carry, are directly proportional to their absolute velocities. When these are equal, $t_+ = t_-$ and both ions contribute equally to the transport of current. However, when v_+ does not equal v_-, t_+ will not equal t_-, and the two ions will carry different proportions of the total current. Still, no matter what the ratio between t_+ and t_- may be, since the two ions carry between them all of the current, the sum of the two transference numbers must be unity, i.e.,

$$t_+ + t_- = 1 \qquad (14)$$

HITTORF'S RULE

As a result of passage of current through a solution concentration changes directly related to the velocities of the ions occur in the vicinity of the electrodes. To understand the nature of these changes and their dependence on the ionic speeds, consider the cell illustrated under I in Fig. 3. Let this cell be divided by the imaginary planes AA' and BB' into three compartments, anode, center, and cathode, and let each compartment contain five equivalents of positive ions and the same number of equivalents of negative ions. Assume, further, that the speeds of the two ions are equal. Now, if 4 faradays of electricity are passed through the cell, four equivalents of positive ions in the cathode compartment will accept electrons from the electrode and deposit. Again four equivalents of negative ions in the anode compartment will give up their electrons to

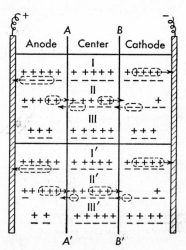

Fig. 3. Concentration Changes Due to Transference.

the anode and will also deposit. The result of these changes is summarized under II. But while these changes at the electrodes are taking place, the ions migrate through the solution. Since in this case both ions move with the same speed, each must carry one-half the current; i.e., past the planes AA' and BB' the cations must transport 2 faradays of electricity from left to right, the anions 2 faradays of electricity from right to left. Consequently, two equivalents of positive ions must move from the anode compartment into the center, and the same number of equivalents from the center into the cathode compartment. Simultaneously, two equivalents of negative ions must move past these planes from the cathode compartment to the center, and also two of these from the center into the anode compartment. When these migrations are added to the changes at the electrodes, the final result is III. From III it is evident that the concentration in the central compartment has not been affected by the passage of current. On the other hand, the concentrations in the cathode and anode compartments have both decreased, but the decrease, two equivalents, is the *same* for both.

However, the situation is different when the speeds of the ions are not the same. Brackets I′, II′, III′ in Fig. 3 illustrate what happens when the speed of the cation is three times that of the anion, the quantity of electricity being again 4 faradays. As before, four equivalents of each ion are deposited at the electrodes. But, since the cation carries here three times as much current as the anion, three equivalents of positive ions must migrate from anode to center, and from center to cathode compartments. At the same time only one equivalent of anions leaves the cathode section, and only one equivalent leaves the center for the anode compartment. From III′, where the final state of the cell is given, it is seen that again there is no change in concentration in the central compartment. Moreover, as before there are concentration changes at the two electrodes, but this time the two are not the same. In fact, the anode compartment has suffered a concentration change equal to three times that for the cathode. By repeating the above argument for various ionic speed ratios, it can readily be shown that the changes in concentration at the electrodes as a result of electrolysis will be equal only when the ionic speeds are the same. When these are different, so are the concentration changes at the electrodes.

An inspection of Fig. 3 reveals further that for the case of *equal* speeds the loss in concentration of cations due to migration from the anode compartment is equal to the loss in concentration of anions due to migration from the cathode compartment. On the other hand, when $v_+ : v_- = 3:1$, the loss in concentration of cations from the anode compartment due to migration is *three times* that of anions from the cathode section. This parallelism between concentration loss due to migration and the velocity of the ion responsible for it leads to *Hittorf's rule*, namely,

$$\frac{\text{Loss in cation equivalents at anode due to migration}}{\text{Loss in anion equivalents at cathode due to migration}} = \frac{v_+}{v_-} = \frac{t_+}{t_-}$$

$$(15)$$

Since the total current passed through the cell, expressed in equivalents, is proportional to $t_+ + t_- = 1$, direct consequences of this rule are also the statements:

$$\frac{\text{Loss in cation equivalents at anode due to migration}}{\text{Equivalents of current passed}} = \frac{t_+}{1} = t_+ \quad (16)$$

$$\frac{\text{Loss in anion equivalents at cathode due to migration}}{\text{Equivalents of current passed}} = \frac{t_-}{1} = t_- \quad (17)$$

DETERMINATION OF TRANSFERENCE NUMBERS

Experimentally, transference numbers may be determined by three different methods: (a) the *Hittorf method*, based on observation of the changes in concentration about the electrodes due to migration, (b) the *moving boundary method*, and (c) from *electromotive force measurements*. The first two of these will be described here, while the third will be explained in Chapter 17. A typical setup for determination of transference numbers by the Hittorf method is shown in Fig. 4. The apparatus consists of a transport cell A, in series with a silver coulometer C, both connected to a battery B through the variable resistance R. The milliammeter M in the circuit permits adjustment of the current to any desired value and makes possible a rough estimation of the quantity of electricity passed through the cell. The cell is filled with the electrolyte to be investigated, the current is turned on, and the solution is electrolyzed sufficiently long to give an appreciable change in concentration about the electrodes. The current is then stopped, and the solution is drained from one or both of the electrode compartments, weighed, and analyzed. The quantity of electricity passed through the cell is obtained from the increase in weight of the cathode in the coulometer. If the original concentration is known, the solution in the central compartment may be ignored or analyzed to see whether any diffusion has taken place.

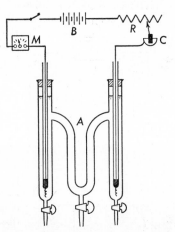

Fig. 4.   Transference Apparatus for Hittorf Method.

If it is not known, the central compartment must be drained, weighed, and analyzed to yield the original composition of the solution. The following example illustrates the steps in a typical calculation of transport numbers from observed data. It is based on the assumption usually made that only the ions migrate, but not the water.

Example: To determine the transport numbers of the ions in an exactly 0.2000 molal solution of copper sulfate, the cell was filled with the solution and electrolyzed between copper electrodes for some time. The cathode solution from the cell was found to weigh 36.4340 g and to contain 0.4415 g of copper. Further, the cathode in the coulometer showed an increase in weight of 0.0405 g due to deposited silver. From these data it is required to calculate the transference numbers of the copper and sulfate ions.

The 36.4340 g of final cathode solution contained 0.4415 g of copper, which is equivalent to $0.4415 \times CuSO_4/Cu = 1.1090$ g of copper sulfate. The weight of water in this solution was, then, $36.4340 - 1.1090 = 35.3250$ g. Now, since before electrolysis the solution was 0.2000 molal, each gram of water had associated with it $0.2000 \times CuSO_4/1000$ g of the salt. Hence 35.3250 g of water had associated with them initially

$$35.3250 \left(0.2000 \times \frac{CuSO_4}{1000} \right) = \frac{35.3250 \times 0.2000 \times 159.61}{1000}$$
$$= 1.1276 \text{ g } CuSO_4$$

Therefore, the loss in weight of the copper sulfate in cathode compartment is equal to $1.1276 - 1.1090 = 0.0186$ g, or $2 \times 0.0186/159.61 = 0.000233$ equivalent.

The total current passed through the cell is given by 0.0405 gram of silver, or $0.0405/107.88 = 0.000375$ equivalent. Consequently, the loss in copper sulfate due to deposition of copper on cathode should have been this number of equivalents. But, the actual loss was only 0.000233 equivalent, and hence the difference, $0.000375 - 0.000233 = 0.000142$ equivalent, must have migrated into this compartment. As the ion that migrates toward the cathode is Cu^{++}, this number of equivalents must have been transported by this ion, and therefore its transport number is

$$t_{Cu^{++}} = \frac{0.000142}{0.000375} = 0.379$$

while that of SO_4^{--} is

$$t_{SO_4^{--}} = 1 - 0.379 = 0.621$$

An independent check on these values could have been obtained by analyzing the anode solution and calculating the transport numbers therefrom. In this connection it should be remembered that copper dissolved at the anode, and hence an actual increase in copper concentration would have been observed there. However, owing to migration of copper ions out of the compartment, the increase will not be as large as may be anticipated from the quantity of electricity passed through the cell.

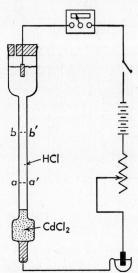

Fig. 5. Transference Numbers by Moving Boundary.

In the moving boundary method the motion of ions under the influence of an applied potential is observed directly rather than through the concentration changes at the electrodes. To understand the principle of this method, consider specifically the determination of the transference number of the hydrogen ion in hydrochloric acid. The apparatus required, Fig. 5, is the same as in the Hittorf method except for the cell. This time the cell consists of a tube mounted vertically and filled with cadmium chloride and the acid in the manner shown, so as to leave a sharp boundary between the two. The cathode, inserted at the top, is a platinum wire, while the anode at the bottom is a stick of cadmium metal. When current is turned on cadmium dissolves at the anode, hydrogen is evolved at the cathode, and hydrogen ions migrate upward through the cell. As these ions move toward the cathode their place is taken by cadmium ions, and hence the boundary between the two solutions also moves upward. By observing the volume swept out by the moving boundary for a given quantity of electricity passed through the cell, it is possible to calculate the transport number of the hydrogen ion as follows:

Suppose that the volume swept out by the boundary in moving from aa' to bb' during the passage of Q faradays of electricity, as measured in the coulometer, is V cc. Then, if the concentration of the acid is C equivalents per liter, the number of equivalents of acid carried toward the cathode by the current is $V \times C/1000$ equivalents. Since this number of equivalents is carried toward the cathode by hydrogen ions, and as the total current carried is Q equivalents, the transport number of the hydrogen ion, t_+, is given by

$$t_+ = \frac{V \times C}{1000\ Q} \tag{18}$$

Although as described here the method appears to be very simple, actually certain conditions must be met in choosing the solutions to be employed in connection with the one to be studied, and various corrections must be applied. For details the student is referred to the excellent discussion given by MacInnes,[1] who with Longsworth has made very valuable contributions to the technique and precision of this method.

RESULTS OF TRANSFERENCE MEASUREMENTS

In Table 3 are given the transference numbers of the cations for a number of electrolytes in aqueous solution. As far as can be observed, these numbers are not affected by current strength. They vary somewhat with concentration, but the variation is not large. As a rule the transference numbers that are large in dilute solution increase with rise in concentration, while those which are small decrease. However, there are exceptions to this rule. With increase in temperature the transport numbers of the cation and anion tend to equalize and approach a value of 0.5. Hence transference numbers greater than 0.5 decrease as the temperature is raised, while those less than 0.5 increase. This variation is illustrated in the data for hydrochloric acid and potassium chloride given in the table.

ELECTROLYTIC CONDUCTANCE

The resistance of an electrolytic conductor to current passage can be determined by the application of Ohm's law to such conductors. How-

---

[1] See reference at end of chapter.

TABLE 3

TRANSFERENCE NUMBERS OF CATIONS

Substance	Temp. (° C)	Concentration—Equivalents per Liter							
		0.005	0.01	0.02	0.05	0.10	0.20	0.50	1.00
HCl	0	0.847	0.846	0.844	0.839	0.834	—	—	—
	18	0.832	0.833	0.833	0.834	0.835	0.837	0.840	0.844
	25	—	0.825	0.827	0.829	0.831	0.834	—	—
	96	—	0.748	—	—	—	—	—	—
HNO$_3$	20	0.839	0.840	0.841	0.844	—	—	—	—
H$_2$SO$_4$	20	—	—	0.822	0.822	0.822	0.820	0.816	0.812
NH$_4$Cl	25	—	0.491	0.491	0.491	0.491	0.491	—	—
AgNO$_3$	25	—	0.465	0.465	0.466	0.468	—	—	—
LiCl	25	—	0.329	0.326	0.321	0.317	0.311	0.300	0.287
KCl	25	0.490	0.490	0.490	0.490	0.490	0.489	0.489	0.488
	30	0.498	0.498	0.498	0.498	0.497	0.496	—	—
NaCl	25	—	0.392	0.390	0.388	0.385	0.382	—	—
NaOH	25	—	0.203	—	0.189	0.183	0.177	0.169	0.163
NaC$_2$H$_3$O$_2$	25	—	0.554	0.555	0.557	0.559	0.561	—	—
CaCl$_2$	25	—	0.426	0.422	0.414	0.406	0.395	—	—
CdSO$_4$	18	—	0.389	0.384	0.374	0.364	0.350	0.323	0.294
CuSO$_4$	18	—	—	0.375	0.375	0.373	0.361	0.327	—

ever, instead of the resistance, it is customary to speak of the *conductance*, which is merely the *reciprocal* of the electrical resistance.

As is well known, the resistance of any conductor is proportional directly to its length and inversely to its cross-sectional area, namely,

$$R = \rho \frac{l}{A} \qquad (19)$$

where R is the resistance in ohms, l the length in centimeters, A the area in square centimeters, and ρ the *specific resistivity*. The value of ρ depends on and is characteristic of the nature of the conductor. From equation (19) the expression for the corresponding conductance L follows as

$$L = \frac{1}{R} = \frac{1}{\rho}\left(\frac{A}{l}\right)$$
$$= L_s \left(\frac{A}{l}\right) \qquad (20)$$

where $L_s = 1/\rho$ is the *specific conductance* of the conductor. This quantity may be considered the conductance of 1 cm cube (not cc) of material and is expressed in reciprocal ohms or *mhos*.

Although the specific conductance is a property of the conducting medium, in dealing with solutions of electrolytes a quantity of greater significance is the *equivalent conductance* Λ. The equivalent conductance of an electrolyte is defined as the conductance of a volume of solution containing one equivalent weight of dissolved substance when placed between two parallel electrodes 1 cm apart, and large enough to contain between them all of the solution. Λ is never determined directly, but is calculated from the specific conductance. If C is the concentration of a solution in gram equivalents per liter, then the concentration per cubic centimeter is $C/1000$, and the volume containing one equivalent of the solute is, therefore, $1000/C$ cc. Since L_s is the conductance of a centimeter cube of the solution, the conductance of $1000/C$ cc, and hence Λ, will be

$$\Lambda = \frac{1000\, L_s}{C} \qquad\qquad (21)$$

Equation (21) is the defining expression for the equivalent conductance. It must be remembered that C in this equation is in *equivalents of solute per liter of solution.*

DETERMINATION OF CONDUCTANCE

The problem of obtaining Λ reduces itself to a determination of the specific conductance of the electrolyte, and this, in turn, to a measurement of the resistance of the solution and use of equation (20). For measuring resistances of electrolytic solutions the Wheatstone bridge method is employed, a schematic diagram of which is shown in Fig. 6. R_x, the unknown resistance whose value is to be determined, is placed in one arm of the bridge, a variable known resistance R_s in the other. AB is a uniform slide wire across which moves a contact point C. To balance the bridge the contact is moved along this resistance until no current from the battery E flows through the galvanometer G. When this condition is reached, R_s, the resistance from A to C, R_1, and that from C to B, R_2, are read. R_x is then calculated from these according to the following considerations.

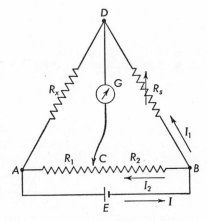

Fig. 6.   Principle of Direct Current Wheatstone Bridge.

When the current I from the battery reaches point B it divides into two parallel paths and into the two currents, I_1 and I_2. These currents lead to potential drops across the resistances they traverse. The purpose of balancing the bridge is to find a point along AB, namely C, such that the potential drop from B to C is equal to that from B to D. When this point is found, D and C are at the same potential and no current flows through the branch containing the galvanometer. The condition for bridge balance is, then,

$$R_s I_1 = R_2 I_2$$

But, when these IR drops are equal, those from D to A and from C to A must also be equal. Hence,

$$R_x I_1 = R_1 I_2$$

Dividing now the second of these equalities by the first, we obtain

$$\frac{R_x}{R_s} = \frac{R_1}{R_2}$$

and therefore,
$$R_x = R_s \left(\frac{R_1}{R_2} \right) \tag{22}$$

By reading R_s, R_1, and R_2 for the bridge balance, R_x can be calculated from equation (22).

Although the principle of the Wheatstone bridge as just given remains the same, several modifications in technique are necessary before resistances of electrolytic solutions can be measured by this method. In the first place, direct current cannot be used, as it would cause electrolysis and concentration changes at the electrodes. To avoid these, alternating current is employed usually at a frequency of 1000 cycles per second and supplied by either a vibrating tuning fork or a vacuum tube oscillator. This current should be close to a pure sine wave in form. Since a current of this frequency is within the range of the human ear, the galvanometer can be replaced by a set of earphones. Passage of the current through these produces a buzzing sound which decreases in intensity as balance is approached and is a minimum when the balance point is reached. Theoretically the sound should be zero at balance, but due to capacitance introduced by the cell, such an ideal state is not attained. However, by placing a variable condenser across the standard resistance, it is possible to sharpen the balancing by adjusting the condenser to the

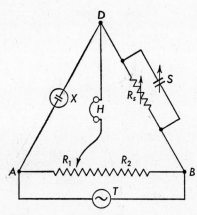

Fig. 7.   Assembly for Determination of Electrolytic Conductance.

capacitance of the cell, thus neutralizing the two to a degree. With these modifications the Wheatstone bridge assembly for electrolytic conductivity measurements takes on the form shown in Fig. 7. Here again R_s is the standard resistance, X is the conductivity cell, S is the variable capacitance, H are the headphones, and T is the source of the alternating current.

The cells employed for conductance work are of various types and shapes, depending on the purpose and on the accuracy required. They are constructed of glass, with electrodes of either platinum or gold. To overcome imperfections in the current and other effects at the electrodes, the latter are coated electrolytically from a solution of chloroplatinic acid with a thin layer of finely divided platinum, called *platinum black* because of its color. The distance apart the electrodes are placed in a cell is

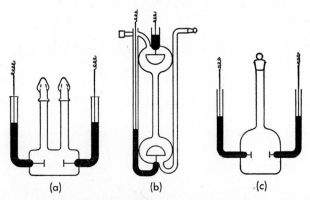

(a)   (b)   (c)

Fig. 8.   Types of Conductivity Cells.

determined by the conductance of the solution to be measured. For solutions of high conductance the electrodes are widely spaced, while for poorly conducting solutions the electrodes are mounted near each other. In Fig. 8 are shown several cells commonly encountered in the laboratory. Types (a) and (b) are used in research, while type (c) is frequently used for less precise work.

THE CELL CONSTANT

According to equation (20), the specific conductance of any electrolytic conductor is given by

$$L_s = \left(\frac{l}{A}\right)L = \left(\frac{l}{A}\right)\frac{1}{R} \qquad (23)$$

and hence before L_s can be calculated from the measured resistance the ratio (l/A) for the particular cell used is required. For any given cell this ratio is a fixed quantity called the *cell constant K*. To obtain the value of the cell constant it is not necessary to determine l and A. Instead, a solution of known L_s is placed in the cell, the resistance is measured, and K is calculated. Once K is available, the specific conductance of any other solution whose resistance is observed in the same cell follows from

$$L_s = \frac{K}{R} \tag{24}$$

To determine cell constants either 1, 0.1, or 0.01 *demal* solutions of potassium chloride are used. A demal solution is a solution containing 1 g mole of salt per *cubic decimeter* of solution at 0° C, or 76.6276 g of potassium chloride in 1000 g of water, both weighed in air. The 0.1 and 0.01 demal solutions contain, respectively, 7.47896 and 0.74625 g of potassium chloride per 1000 g of water. The conductances of these solutions have been measured with great accuracy in cells with electrodes of definite area and definite spacing, and their specific conductances are well known. The most concentrated solution is used only for cells with electrodes far apart, the other two for electrodes close together or intermediate in spacing. Table 4 gives the specific conductances of these solutions at several temperatures as determined by Jones and Bradshaw.[1] The calculation of cell constants, and specific and equivalent conductances from experimental data may be illustrated with the following example.

Example: In a particular cell a 0.01 demal solution of potassium chloride gave a resistance of 150.00 ohms at 25°, while a 0.01 N solution of hydrochloric acid

TABLE 4

SPECIFIC CONDUCTANCES OF KCl SOLUTIONS
(In int. ohm^{-1} cm^{-1})

Demal Conc.	Grams KCl per 1000 g H_2O (in air)	Grams KCl per 1000 g Solution (in air)	Specific Conductance		
			0° C	18° C	25° C
0.01	0.74625	0.74526	0.00077364	0.00122052	0.00140877
0.10	7.47896	7.41913	0.0071379	0.0111667	0.0128560
1.00	76.6276	71.1352	0.065176	0.097838	0.111342

gave a resistance of 51.40 ohms at the same temperature. At 25° C the specific conductance of 0.01 demal potassium chloride is 0.0014088, and hence the cell constant for the given cell is

$$K = L_s R = 0.0014088 \times 150.00$$
$$= 0.21132$$

[1] Jones and Bradshaw, *J. Am. Chem. Soc.*, **55**, 1780 (1933).

From this K and the resistance of the hydrochloric acid solution the specific conductance of the latter follows as

$$L_s = \frac{K}{R} = \frac{0.21132}{51.40}$$
$$= 0.004111 \text{ mho cm}^{-1}$$

and the equivalent conductance as

$$\Lambda = \frac{1000 \, L_s}{C}$$
$$= \frac{0.004111 \times 1000}{0.01}$$
$$= 411.1 \text{ mho cm}^{-1} \text{ equiv}^{-1}$$

VARIATION OF CONDUCTANCE WITH CONCENTRATION

Both the specific and equivalent conductances of a solution vary with concentration. For strong electrolytes at concentrations up to several equivalents per liter, the specific conductance increases sharply with increase in concentration. In contrast, the specific conductances of weak electrolytes start at lower values in dilute solutions and increase much more gradually. Thus, in passing from 0.001 to 0.05 N solutions the specific conductance at 25° C for hydrochloric acid changes from 4.21×10^{-4} to 199.5×10^{-4} mho, that of acetic acid from 0.49×10^{-4} to only 3.70×10^{-4} mho. In both instances the increase in conductance with concentration is due to the increase in the number of ions per unit volume of solution. In strong electrolytes the number of ions per cubic centimeter increases in proportion to the concentration. In weak electrolytes, however, the increase cannot be quite so large because of the changing partial ionization of the solute, and consequently the conductance does not go up so rapidly as in strong electrolytes.

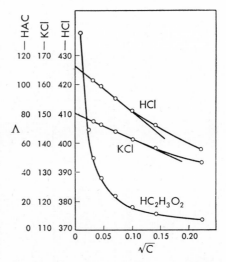

Fig. 9.   Plot of Λ vs. $\sqrt{C}$ for Strong and Weak Electrolytes.

Unlike the specific conductance, the equivalent conductance Λ of both strong and weak electrolytes increases *with dilution*. The reason for this

TABLE 5

Equivalent Conductances of Electrolytes in Aqueous Solution at 25° C

C Equiv./liter	NaCl	KCl	HCl	AgNO₃	HIO₃	NaC₂H₃O₂	½ H₂SO₄	½ Na₂SO₄	½ BaCl₂	½ CuSO₄	½ LaCl₃	HC₂H₃O₂	NH₄OH
0.0000	126.45	149.86	426.16	133.36	—	91.0	429.6	129.9	139.98	—	145.9	390.7	271.4
0.0001	—	—	—	—	386.3	—	—	—	—	—	—	134.7	93
0.0005	124.50	147.81	422.74	131.36	383.9	89.2	413.1	125.74	135.96	—	139.6	67.7	47
0.001	123.74	146.95	421.36	130.51	370.9	88.5	399.5	124.15	134.34	115.2	137.0	49.2	34
0.005	120.65	143.55	415.80	127.20	359.7	85.72	364.9	117.15	128.02	97.5	127.5	22.9	16
0.01	118.51	141.27	412.00	124.76	343.0	83.76	336.4	112.44	123.94	83.3	121.8	16.3	11.3
0.02	115.76	138.34	407.24	121.41	310.7	81.24	308.0	106.78	119.09	72.2	115.3	11.6	8.0
0.05	111.06	133.37	399.09	115.24	278.3	76.92	272.6	97.75	111.48	58.8	106.2	7.4	5.1
0.10	106.74	128.96	391.32	109.14	242.2	72.80	250.8	89.98	105.19	50.5	99.1	—	3.6
0.20	101.6	123.9	379.6	101.8	219.5	67.7	234.3	81.5	98.6	43.5	—	—	—
0.50	93.3	117.2	359.2	—	—	58.6	222.5	—	88.8	35.1	—	—	—
1.00	—	111.9	332.8	—	—	49.1	—	—	80.5	29.3	—	—	—

* Taken mostly from D. A. MacInnes, *Principles of Electrochemistry*, Reinhold Publishing Corporation, New York, 1939, p. 339.

is that the decrease in specific conductance is more than compensated by the increase in the value of $1/C$ on dilution, and hence Λ goes up. The manner in which Λ varies with concentration can be judged from Table 5, and from the plot of Λ vs. $\sqrt{C}$ given in Fig. 9. Why the $\sqrt{C}$ plot is used will be explained later. It may be seen from these that the Λ's for strong and weak electrolytes behave differently on decrease of concentration. On dilution of a strong electrolyte Λ rapidly approaches already in 0.001 or 0.0001 N solutions a value close to the limiting value of the conductance at zero concentration, Λ_0. On the other hand, although the equivalent conductance of weak electrolytes increases rapidly on dilution, at the concentrations mentioned it is still very far from its limit. For instance, Λ at 25° C for 0.001 N sodium chloride is 123.7 as against a Λ_0 of 126.5. At the same concentration and temperature Λ for acetic acid is only 49.2, while Λ_0 is 390.7. Because of this fundamental difference in the behavior of the equivalent conductances of strong and weak electrolytes on dilution, quite diverse procedures must be used for obtaining their limiting equivalent conductances.

EQUIVALENT CONDUCTANCES OF STRONG ELECTROLYTES AT INFINITE DILUTION

Attention was directed to the fact that on reduction of the concentration of a solution to zero the equivalent conductance approaches a constant limit. This limiting value of the equivalent conductance is known as the *equivalent conductance at infinite dilution* and is designated by the symbol Λ_0, the subscript indicating zero concentration. The Λ_0 value of an electrolyte is not the same as the equivalent conductance of the pure solvent, but is a characteristic of the electrolyte in question. As this quantity is of great import, its determination requires some consideration.

Kohlrausch was the first to point out that when Λ for *strong electrolytes* is plotted against $\sqrt{C}$ the curve approaches linearity in dilute solutions, i.e., in dilute solutions the variation of Λ with concentration can be represented by the equation

$$\Lambda = \Lambda_0 - b\sqrt{C} \tag{25}$$

where b is a constant. The validity of this finding may be seen from the plots for hydrochloric acid and potassium chloride in Fig. 9. Consequently, to obtain Λ_0 of such electrolytes the curve may be extrapolated to $\sqrt{C} = 0$ and the intercept read, or the slope of the linear portion of the curve may be obtained from the plot, and Λ_0 solved for from equation (25). Some of these Λ_0 values are given in the first horizontal column of Table 5.

EQUIVALENT CONDUCTANCES OF WEAK ELECTROLYTES AT INFINITE DILUTION

The above method for evaluation of Λ_0 cannot be used for weak electrolytes. As may be seen from Fig. 9, the plot of Λ vs. $\sqrt{C}$ for a weak electrolyte, acetic acid, does not approach linearity in solutions as dilute as 0.0001 N. Instead, Λ exhibits a very rapid increase with decrease in concentration. Again, it is not practicable to carry the measurements to concentrations much lower than 0.0001 N, for in such dilute solutions the conductance of the water becomes an appreciable part of the total. Although the conductance of the water may be subtracted from the specific conductance of the solution to yield that of the electrolyte, such corrections are not always satisfactory and introduce uncertainty into the final result.

Equivalent conductances at infinite dilution for weak electrolytes are obtained by application of *Kohlrausch's law of independent migration of ions*. This law states that at infinite dilution, where dissociation for all electrolytes is complete and where all interionic effects disappear, each ion migrates independently of its co-ion, and contributes to the total equivalent conductance of an electrolyte a definite share which depends only on its own nature and not at all on that of the ion with which it is associated. If this be the case, then Λ_0 of any electrolyte should be the sum of the equivalent conductances of the ions composing it, provided, of course, that the solvent and temperature are the same. Evidence for the validity of this statement is given in Table 6. According to this law the difference between the Λ_0's of electrolytes containing a common ion should be a constant equal to the difference in the equivalent conductances of the ions not in common. In line with this requirement we see that, irrespective of the nature of the co-ion, the difference between the conductances of K^+ and Li^+ is constant, and the same is true for the differ-

TABLE 6

KOHLRAUSCH'S LAW OF INDEPENDENT MIGRATION OF IONS

Electrolyte	Λ_0 (25° C)	Difference	Electrolyte	Λ_0 (25° C)	Difference
KCl	149.9		HCl	426.2	
LiCl	115.0	34.9	HNO$_3$	421.3	4.9
KNO$_3$	145.0		KCl	149.9	
LiNO$_3$	110.1	34.9	KNO$_3$	145.0	4.9
KOH	271.5		LiCl	115.0	
LiOH	236.7	34.8	LiNO$_3$	110.1	4.9

ence in conductance between the Cl^- and NO_3^- ions. The law has been tested on other ions as well, and with the same results.

From the law of independent migration of ions it follows that Λ_0 for any electrolyte may be written as

$$\Lambda_0 = l_+^0 + l_-^0 \tag{26}$$

where l_+^0 and l_-^0 are the *equivalent ionic conductances at infinite dilution* of the cation and anion respectively. Moreover, since the fraction of the total current carried by any ion is given by its transport number, this number must represent as well the fraction of the total conductance due to the ion. Consequently l_+^0 and l_-^0 are also related to Λ_0 by the relations

$$l_+^0 = t_+^0 \Lambda_0 \tag{27}$$

$$l_-^0 = t_-^0 \Lambda_0 \tag{28}$$

t_+^0 and t_-^0 being the transference numbers at infinite dilution as obtained by extrapolation. These equations permit ready calculation of the limiting ionic conductances from transference numbers and Λ_0 values of strong electrolytes. For example, Λ_0 for hydrochloric acid at 25° C is 426.16, while t_+^0 of the hydrogen ion is 0.821. Therefore,

$$l_{H^+}^0 = 0.821 \times 426.16 = 349.9$$
$$l_{Cl^-}^0 = 0.179 \times 426.16 = 76.3$$

The equivalent ionic conductances of other ions have similarly been evaluated. These are summarized in Table 7. The ionic conductances of ions of weak acids or bases were deduced from the Λ_0's of their salts, which are strong electrolytes.

Through equation (26) Λ_0 values of *strong and weak electrolytes* follow from Table 7 on addition of the appropriate ionic conductances of the cation and anion. Thus we find for Λ_0 of acetic acid, a weak electrolyte,

$$\begin{aligned}
\Lambda_{0(HAc)} &= l_{H^+}^0 + l_{Ac^-}^0 \\
&= 349.8 + 40.9 \\
&= 390.7 \text{ mhos}
\end{aligned}$$

In arriving at the equivalent ionic conductances given in Table 7, and from these at the Λ_0's of electrolytes, transference numbers were used. However, it is possible to obtain Λ_0's of electrolytes by direct addition and subtraction of appropriate Λ_0 values without using transport numbers. Thus, if Λ_0 for hydrochloric acid is added to that for sodium acetate, and that for sodium chloride subtracted, the result is Λ_0 for acetic acid. For

$$\begin{aligned}
\Lambda_{0(NaAc)} + \Lambda_{0(HCl)} - \Lambda_{0(NaCl)} &= l_{Na^+}^0 + l_{Ac^-}^0 + l_{H^+}^0 + l_{Cl^-}^0 - l_{Na^+}^0 - l_{Cl^-}^0 \\
&= l_{H^+}^0 + l_{Ac^-}^0 \\
&= \Lambda_{0(HAc)}
\end{aligned}$$

Similarly Λ_0 of nitric acid follows from the Λ_0's of potassium nitrate, potassium chloride, and hydrochloric acid. This method of calculating Λ_0 is particularly valuable with weak electrolytes for whose salt solutions transport numbers are not available, and neither are the equivalent ionic conductances at infinite dilution for both ions. From the example cited it is evident that all that is necessary to obtain Λ_0 for a weak acid for which no data are extant is Λ_0 of its sodium salt. Since the salt is a strong electrolyte, its Λ_0 can be evaluated from the measured equivalent conductances without any special difficulty. By combining this Λ_0 with

TABLE 7

Equivalent Ionic Conductances at Infinite Dilution*
(25° C)

Cations	l^0_+	Anions	l^0_-
K+	73.52	Cl−	76.34
Na+	50.11	Br−	78.4
Li+	38.69	I−	76.8
NH$_4$+	73.4	NO$_3$−	71.44
H+	349.82	HCO$_3$−	44.48
Ag+	61.92	OH−	198
Tl+	74.7	Acetate−	40.9
½ Ca++	59.50	Chloracetate−	39.7
½ Ba++	63.64	Propionate−	35.81
½ Sr++	59.46	ClO$_4$−	68.0
½ Mg++	53.06	½ SO$_4$−−	79.8
⅓ La+++	69.6	⅓ Fe(CN)$_6$−−−	101.0
		¼ Fe(CN)$_6$−−−−	110.5

* D. A. MacInnes, *op. cit.*, p. 342.

that of hydrochloric acid and sodium chloride, as shown above, the Λ_0 for the acid follows immediately. Similarly, Λ_0 for a weak base like ammonium hydroxide can be calculated from Λ_0 of ammonium chloride, sodium hydroxide, and sodium chloride.

EFFECT OF OTHER FACTORS ON CONDUCTANCE

The conductance of all electrolytes increases with temperature. The variation of Λ_0 with temperature can be represented by the equation

$$\Lambda_{0(t)} = \Lambda_{0(25° \text{ C})}[1 + \beta(t - 25)] \qquad (29)$$

where $\Lambda_{0(t)}$ is the limiting equivalent conductance at $t°$ C, $\Lambda_{0(25° \text{ C})}$ that at 25° C, and β a constant. β for salts is usually 0.022 to 0.025, for acids 0.016 to 0.019. Similar behavior is exhibited by the equivalent conductances of strong electrolytes in finite concentrations. However, with weak electrolytes the variation of Λ with temperature is not so regular, for in these not only do the velocities of the ions and the interionic forces change, but also the degree of dissociation.

The conductance behavior observed in nonaqueous solvents depends pretty much on the dielectric constant of the medium. The dielectric constant of water is high, 78.6 at 25° C, whereas that of most other solvents is considerably lower. Thus the dielectric constants D at 25° C for methyl alcohol, ethyl alcohol, and dioxane are, respectively, 31.5, 24.3, and 2.2. As the dielectric constant of a solvent is lowered, the conductance of an electrolyte in the medium also decreases. Beyond this conductance drop, and beyond the fact that some electrolytes that are strong in water may be weak in other solvents, the conductance behavior of these substances is not very different in nonaqueous solvents from that in water, provided the dielectric constant is above about 25. For example, the halides and nitrates of alkali metals, the thiocyanates of the alkali and alkaline earth metals, and the tetraalkyl ammonium salts are strong electrolytes in ethyl and methyl alcohols and behave pretty much as do strong electrolytes in water. Again, picric acid, various substituted acetic acids, and phenols are weak electrolytes in methyl alcohol, as are also hydrochloric, hydrobromic, and hydriodic acids in ethyl alcohol. The influence of the solvent on conductance can be judged from Table 8, where the

TABLE 8

Λ_0 FOR SOME ELECTROLYTES IN VARIOUS SOLVENTS

(25° C)

Electrolyte	Λ_0		
	$H_2O(D = 78.6)$	$CH_3OH(D = 31.5)$	$C_2H_5OH(D = 24.3)$
HCl	426.16	—	81.8
LiCl	115.03	90.9	39.2
NaCl	126.45	69.9	42.5
KCl	149.86	105.0	—
LiNO₃	110.13	100.2	42.7
KNO₃	144.96	114.5	—

Λ_0 values at 25° C for several electrolytes obtained in water and methyl and ethyl alcohol are compared.

In solvents of dielectric constant less than 25, the dependence of the equivalent conductance on the concentration becomes complex. Plots of log Λ vs. log C, instead of being linear or slightly curved as they are in solvents of higher dielectric constant, contain minima which appear at lower concentrations the lower the dielectric constant. To explain these minima and the curves in general it has been suggested[1] that in these solvents ions exhibit a tendency to associate into complexes such as A^+B^-, $A^+B^-A^+$, and $B^-A^+B^-$, which decrease the number of ions available to carry current, and hence the conductance. These theories seem to account, at least in part, for the observed phenomena.

THE INTERIONIC ATTRACTION THEORY OF CONDUCTANCE

The decrease in the equivalent conductance with increase in concentration for weak electrolytes can be explained as due essentially to a decrease in the degree of ionization. However, such an explanation cannot apply to strong electrolytes, for these, at least in the more dilute solutions, are completely dissociated. Consequently, to account for the variation of Λ with concentration in strong electrolytes some other explanation must be sought, and this is found in the Debye-Hückel-Onsager theory of conductance.

According to the Debye-Hückel theory of interionic attraction, as developed briefly in Chapter 6, each ion in solution is surrounded by an atmosphere of other ions whose net charge is on the average opposite to that of the central ion. When the ions have no external force applied upon them, this atmosphere is spherically and symmetrically distributed about the ion. However, when an external force is imposed, as when a potential is applied across two electrodes immersed in the solution during conductance, the ions are set in motion, and as a consequence certain effects and changes in the ionic atmosphere arise which result in a decrease in the speeds of the ions. Debye and Hückel[2] first pointed out that these effects are twofold, namely, (a) the *relaxation of the ionic atmosphere* due to an applied potential, and (b) the *electrophoretic effect*. The first of these arises from the fact that any central ion and its atmosphere are oppositely charged, i.e., when the central ion is positively charged the atmosphere is negative, and vice versa. Because of this difference in sign of the atmosphere and central ion, a potential applied across the combination will tend to move the central ion in one direction, the atmosphere in the other. Thus a central positive ion will tend to move toward the cathode while its ionic atmosphere will tend toward the anode. The symmetry of the atmosphere about an ion is destroyed by these opposing tendencies, and the atmosphere becomes distorted. In this state the force exerted by the atmosphere on the ion is no longer uniform in all directions, but is

---

[1] Kraus and Fuoss, *J. Am. Chem. Soc.*, **55**, 21 (1933); **55**, 476, 1019, 2387 (1933); **57**, 1 (1935).

[2] P. Debye and E. Hückel, *Physik. Zeit.*, **24**, 185, 305 (1923).

greater *behind* the ion than in front of it. Consequently the ion experiences a retarding force opposite to the direction of its motion, and the ion is slowed down by these interionic attractions.

The electrophoretic effect arises from the fact that an ion, in moving through the solution, does not travel through a stationary medium, but through one that moves in a direction opposite to that of the ion. Ions are generally solvated, and when these move, they carry with them solvent. Any positive ion migrating toward the cathode has, then, to thread its way through medium moving with the negative ions toward the anode. Similarly, negative ions have to migrate through molecules of solvent carried by positive ions in the opposite direction. These countercurrents make it more difficult for the ion to move through the solution, and thus slow it down in the same way as swimming against the current in a river would slow down a swimmer.

Debye and Hückel showed that both of these retarding effects on an ion produce a decrease in equivalent conductance dependent on the concentration. Their mathematical treatment was subsequently extended by Lars Onsager[1] to include not only the relaxation and electrophoretic effects, but also the natural Brownian movement of the ions. Onsager obtained the following equation for the dependence of the equivalent conductance of a binary strong electrolyte on the concentration,

$$\Lambda = \Lambda_0 - \left[\frac{0.9834 \times 10^6}{(DT)^{3/2}} w\Lambda_0 + \frac{28.94(z_+ + z_-)}{\eta(DT)^{1/2}} \right] \sqrt{(z_+ + z_-)C} \quad (30)$$

where

$$w = z_+ z_- \left(\frac{2q}{1 + \sqrt{q}} \right)$$

$$q = \frac{z_+ z_- \Lambda_0}{(z_+ + z_-)(z_+ l_-^0 + z_- l_+^0)}$$

In this equation Λ, Λ_0, C, l_+^0, and l_-^0 have the same significance as before, z_+ and z_- are the charges of the two ions, T is the absolute temperature, and D and η are the dielectric constant and viscosity of the solvent, respectively. Because of simplifications in derivation this equation is applicable only to very dilute solutions, and it must be considered as essentially a limiting equation for conductance. *For the special case of 1–1 electrolytes in water at 25° C, for which* $z_+ = z_- = 1$, $D = 78.55$, and $\eta = 0.008949$ poise, equation (30) reduces to

$$\Lambda = \Lambda_0 - [\theta\Lambda_0 + \sigma]\sqrt{C} \quad (31)$$

where θ and σ are constants with values $\theta = 0.2273$, and $\sigma = 59.78$. Since the quantity in brackets is a constant, equation (31) is identical in form with equation (25) proposed by Kohlrausch on empirical grounds.

[1] L. Onsager, *Physik. Zeit.*, **27**, 388 (1926); **28**, 277 (1927).

Equation (31) has the correct form for the dependence of Λ on $\sqrt{C}$. The question remaining is whether the experimental slope is in accord with that predicted by the Onsager equation, namely, slope $= [\theta\Lambda_0 + \sigma]$. Exhaustive tests by Shedlovsky, MacInnes, and others indicate that in very dilute solutions the Onsager equation is in agreement with observation not only for 1–1 strong electrolytes, but also for electrolytes of higher valence types, such as calcium chloride and lanthanum chloride. The concordance obtained may be judged from the fact that for potassium chloride Λ_0 found by graphical extrapolation is 149.86, while that calculated by equation (31) from the experimental data is 149.98.

The Onsager equation is applicable not only to aqueous solutions, but also to strong electrolytes in other solvents. However, the concordance usually is not so good as in water. In some instances the slopes predicted for the Λ vs. $\sqrt{C}$ plots deviate from the experimental quite appreciably and may be off as much as 100 per cent or over, as 126 per cent for silver nitrate in ethyl alcohol at 25° C.

ABSOLUTE VELOCITIES OF IONS

The absolute velocity with which any ion moves through a solution depends on the nature of the ion, the concentration of the solution, the temperature, and the applied potential drop per centimeter of conducting path. Such velocities can be measured directly by application of the moving boundary method. However, the velocities may also be calculated from conductance measurements, and to this end we turn now our attention.

For this purpose consider a pair of parallel electrodes d cm apart, such as those illustrated in Fig. 2, across which is applied a potential difference $\mathcal{E}$, and between which is contained a volume of solution containing 1 mole of an electrolyte A_xB_y. For the sake of generality, consider this electrolyte to be ionized to an extent α according to the equation

$$A_xB_y = xA^{z_+} + yB^{z_-}$$
$$1(1-\alpha) \quad x\alpha \quad y\alpha \tag{32}$$

where z_+ and z_- are the valences of the ions, while x and y are the numbers of these obtained from one molecule of A_xB_y. The quantities of the various species are, then, as indicated in equation (32), and the number of positive ions present between the two electrodes is $n_+ = x\alpha N$, where $N =$ Avogadro's number. Now, according to equation (10) of this chapter, the current I flowing between the plates is given by

$$I = \frac{n_+ z_+ e(v_+ + v_-)}{d}$$

Substituting for n_+ its equivalent $x\alpha N$, we have

$$I = \frac{x\alpha N z_+ e(v_+ + v_-)}{d}$$

$$= \frac{\alpha \mathfrak{F}(xz_+)(v_+ + v_-)}{d} \tag{33}$$

where $\mathfrak{F}$, the value of the faraday, was substituted for Ne.

One mole of $A_x B_y$ corresponds to xz_+ equivalents of substance, i.e., the the number of positive ions per molecule multiplied by the valence. Therefore, if the concentration of the solution is C equivalents per 1000 cc of solution, the volume per equivalent is $1000/C$, and per mole $(xz_+ 1000)/C$ cc. The latter volume is also equal to Ad, where A is the area of one of the parallel plates. Consequently,

$$Ad = \frac{1000 x z_+}{C}$$

and $$\frac{AC}{1000} = \frac{xz_+}{d} \tag{34}$$

Now, the conductance of the solution is given by equation (20), namely, $L = L_s A/d$. Again, by equation (21) $L_s = C\Lambda/1000$. Hence we may write for L,

$$L = \frac{L_s A}{d} = \left(\frac{AC}{1000}\right)\frac{\Lambda}{d}$$

$$= \frac{xz_+ \Lambda}{d^2} \tag{35}$$

in view of equation (34). Further, by Ohm's law $\mathcal{E}/R = \mathcal{E}L = I$, and so on substitution of equation (35) for L and equation (33) for I we get,

$$\frac{\mathcal{E}(xz_+)\Lambda}{d^2} = \frac{\alpha \mathfrak{F}(xz_+)(v_+ + v_-)}{d}$$

or $$\left(\frac{\mathcal{E}}{d}\right)\Lambda = \alpha \mathfrak{F}(v_+ + v_-) \tag{36}$$

If we set now $\mathcal{E}/d = \mathcal{E}'$, $\mu_+ = v_+/\mathcal{E}'$, and $\mu_- = v_-/\mathcal{E}'$, then equation (36) becomes

$$\Lambda = \alpha \mathfrak{F}(\mu_+ + \mu_-) \tag{37}$$

The quantity $\mathcal{E}'$ is the *voltage gradient*, i.e., the potential drop per centimeter of path between the electrodes. Again, the quantities μ_+ and μ_-, called the *ionic mobilities*, represent the velocities of the ions in centimeters per second when the potential gradient is 1 volt per centimeter.

At infinite dilution $\alpha = 1$, $\Lambda = \Lambda_0$, $\mu_+ = \mu_+^0$, and $\mu_- = \mu_-^0$. Equation (37) for infinite dilution becomes thus

$$\Lambda_0 = \mathfrak{F}\mu_+^0 + \mathfrak{F}\mu_-^0 \tag{38}$$

Again, for infinite dilution Kohlrausch's law of independent migration of ions yields,

$$\Lambda_0 = l_+^0 + l_-^0 \tag{26}$$

and hence we get on comparison of the two expressions

$$\mu_+^0 = \frac{l_+^0}{\mathfrak{F}} \tag{39}$$

and

$$\mu_-^0 = \frac{l_-^0}{\mathfrak{F}} \tag{40}$$

i.e., *at infinite dilution the velocity of any ion in centimeters per second, under a potential drop of 1 volt per centimeter, is given by the limiting equivalent conductance of the ion divided by the value of the faraday.*

The limiting mobilities of a number of ions calculated with the aid of equations (39) and (40) from the equivalent ionic conductances are given in Table 9. It will be observed that the velocities are unusually low. Further, with the exception of the hydrogen and hydroxyl ions, the speeds are not very different for the various ions. The hydrogen and hydroxyl ions are unique in their high mobility, and this fact is the basis of several applications of conductance measurements.

TABLE 9

ABSOLUTE VELOCITIES OF IONS AT 25° C
(cm² volt⁻¹ sec⁻¹)

Cation	μ_+^0	Anion	μ_-^0
K^+	0.000762	Cl^-	0.000791
Na^+	0.000520	Br^-	0.000812
Li^+	0.000388	I^-	0.000796
NH_4^+	0.000760	NO_3^-	0.000740
H^+	0.003620	HCO_3^-	0.000461
Ag^+	0.000642	OH^-	0.002050
Tl^+	0.000774	$C_2H_3O_2^-$	0.000424
Ca^{++}	0.000616	$C_3H_5O_2^-$	0.000411
Ba^{++}	0.000659	ClO_4^-	0.000705
Sr^{++}	0.000616	SO_4^{--}	0.000827
Mg^{++}	0.000550	$Fe(CN)_6^{---}$	0.001040
La^{+++}	0.000721	$Fe(CN)_6^{----}$	0.001140

If equation (37) is rewritten

$$\Lambda = \alpha\mathfrak{F}\mu_+ + \alpha\mathfrak{F}\mu_- \tag{37a}$$

the new form suggests that Λ at *finite* concentration can also be represented by

$$\Lambda = l_+ + l_- \tag{41}$$

where l_+ and l_- are now the equivalent ionic conductances for the concentration to which Λ corresponds. Analogously to equations (27) and (28) these equivalent conductances of the ions can be evaluated from Λ and the transport numbers by the relations

$$l_+ = t_+\Lambda \tag{42}$$
$$l_- = t_-\Lambda \tag{43}$$

By comparison of equations (37a) and (41), the mobilities of the ions at any given concentration follow as

$$\mu_+ = \frac{l_+}{\alpha \mathfrak{F}} \tag{44}$$

$$\mu_- = \frac{l_-}{\alpha \mathfrak{F}} \tag{45}$$

for weak electrolytes, and

$$\mu_+ = \frac{l_+}{\mathfrak{F}} \tag{46}$$

$$\mu_- = \frac{l_-}{\mathfrak{F}} \tag{47}$$

for strong electrolytes, since these are completely ionized.

DEGREE OF IONIZATION AND CONDUCTANCE

In developing his theory of electrolytic dissociation, Arrhenius ascribed the decrease in Λ with increase in concentration entirely to variation of the degree of dissociation of the electrolyte. If this is correct, it can readily be shown that the degree of dissociation α must be given by the ratio Λ/Λ_0. From equations (37) and (38), Λ/Λ_0 for any electrolyte follows as

$$\frac{\Lambda}{\Lambda_0} = \frac{\alpha(\mu_+ + \mu_-)}{(\mu_+^0 + \mu_-^0)} \tag{48}$$

Assuming, further, that the mobilities of the ions at any finite concentration are the same as at infinite dilution, then $(\mu_+ + \mu_-) = (\mu_+^0 + \mu_-^0)$, and, therefore,

$$\alpha = \frac{\Lambda}{\Lambda_0} \tag{49}$$

According to this equation the degree of dissociation of any electrolyte is unity at infinite dilution, i.e., the electrolyte is completely dissociated. On the other hand, as the concentration is increased Λ falls, and so does the value of α.

Arrhenius supposed equation (49) to be applicable to both strong and weak electrolytes. But, in view of the complete dissociation of strong electrolytes, Λ/Λ_0 cannot possibly have the significance given it by Arrhenius. Rather, this ratio must represent a measure of the effect of interionic forces upon the velocities of the ions. In line with this argument is the fact that the Debye-Hückel-Onsager theory of conductance of strong electrolytes can account for the variation of Λ with concentration in terms of interionic forces only, without the aid of partial dissociation. Again, careful measurements have revealed that transference numbers, and therefore ionic velocities, are not independent of concentration, and consequently the assumption introduced in passing from equation (48) to equation (49) cannot be valid for such electrolytes.

However, within a small correction, Λ/Λ_0 does give the degree of dissociation of weak electrolytes. In weak electrolytes the variation of Λ with concentration is due to two factors, namely, (a) the partial dissociation of the electrolyte and (b) the interionic attractions between ions present. Because of the relatively low degree of dissociation of these electrolytes, the concentrations of ions present in solution are quite low, and so are the interionic effects. Consequently most of the decrease in equivalent conductance is due to decrease in α, and within a fairly close approximation equation (49) holds true.

In a weak electrolyte such as acetic acid at a concentration C and degree of dissociation α, the concentration of dissociated acid is $C\alpha$. Because of this concentration of dissociated acid interionic forces are present that tend to decrease the value of Λ from Λ_0 to Λ_e, where Λ_e is the equivalent conductance of the completely dissociated acid at a concentration $C\alpha$. Consequently, in order to obtain the degree of dissociation of the electrolyte corrected for the interionic effects it would be more nearly correct to calculate α, not as Λ/Λ_0, but as

$$\alpha = \frac{\Lambda}{\Lambda_e} \tag{50}$$

i.e., as the ratio of the actual equivalent conductance to the equivalent conductance of the same electrolyte when completely dissociated at the same ionic concentration as is present in the solution. The evaluation of Λ_e for use in equation (50) may be illustrated with the following example. At $C = 0.1000$, Λ for acetic at 25° C is 5.201, while $\Lambda_0 = 390.71$. From these data we find provisionally that

$$\alpha = \frac{\Lambda}{\Lambda_0} = \frac{5.201}{390.71} = 0.0133 = 1.33\%$$

and hence $C\alpha = 0.00133$ equivalent per liter. Now, on the supposition that acetic acid is completely dissociated, and on the assumption that

Kohlrausch's law is applicable, it can be calculated from the Λ's of sodium acetate, sodium chloride, and hydrochloric acid, all at $C = 0.00133$, that for acetic acid Λ_e would be 385.40 rather than 390.71. Dividing now the observed Λ by the calculated Λ_e, we find for the true degree of dissociation

$$\alpha = \frac{\Lambda}{\Lambda_e} = \frac{5.201}{385.40} = 0.0135 = 1.35\%$$

Consequently, the true degree of dissociation is 1.35 per cent as against 1.33 per cent estimated from the ratio Λ/Λ_0.

Although such small corrections are found necessary in precise calculations, for our purposes the simpler approximate equation (49) will be sufficient and will be employed hereafter.

APPLICATION OF CONDUCTANCE MEASUREMENTS

Conductance measurements find extensive application in chemistry and chemical industry for obtaining important information concerning the behavior of electrolytes, for analysis, and for concentration control. A discussion of some of these applications follows.

Solubility of Difficultly Soluble Salts. Conductance offers a very simple and convenient means of determining the solubility of difficultly soluble salts such as barium sulfate, silver chloride, silver iodate, etc. The procedure involved is this. A saturated solution of the salt in water of known specific conductance, $L_{s_{(H_2O)}}$, is prepared. Next, the specific conductance of the saturated solution, L_s, is measured. This specific conductance is due to both the salt and the water, and hence the specific conductance of the salt alone, $L_{s_{(salt)}}$, is

$$L_{s_{(salt)}} = L_s - L_{s_{(H_2O)}} \tag{51}$$

From $L_{s_{(salt)}}$ the equivalent conductance follows as

$$\Lambda = \frac{1000 \, L_{s_{(salt)}}}{C}$$

where C is the concentration of the salt in equivalents per liter, and hence the solubility. Since the solution is at best very dilute, and since salts are strong electrolytes, Λ must be equal essentially to Λ_0. Making this substitution, C is obtained as

$$C = \frac{1000 \, L_{s_{(salt)}}}{\Lambda_0} \tag{52}$$

By looking up the value of Λ_0 in a table of limiting equivalent conductances, C can readily be calculated through equation (52) from the measured specific conductance of the saturated solution.

Determination of Degree of Ionization. The determination of the degree of ionization of weak electrolytes is a problem of great importance in physical and analytical chemistry, because from such information the ionization constants of such electrolytes are evaluated. More extensive reference to this subject will be made in the next chapter. Here attention will be directed only to the estimation of the degree of ionization of water.

TABLE 10

SPECIFIC CONDUCTANCE OF VERY PURE WATER

$t°$ C	L_s (mho cm^{-1})
0	0.14×10^{-7}
18	0.40
25	0.58
34	0.89
50	1.76

Although the specific conductance of water decreases as water is purified, Kohlrausch and Heydweiller[1] found that, no matter how long and how carefully the purification is continued, water still exhibits a definite though small conductance at each temperature, as may be seen from the data given in Table 10. From these results it must be concluded that water is a weak electrolyte and that it ionizes according to the equation

$$H_2O = H^+ + OH^- \tag{53}$$

To find the degree of ionization α at, say, 25° C, Λ is required. Since $\Lambda = L_s \times V_e$, where V_e is the volume in cubic centimeters containing one equivalent of water, V_e must be the molecular weight of water divided by the density of the water at 25° C. Therefore,

$$\Lambda = (0.58 \times 10^{-7}) \frac{18.016}{0.9971}$$
$$= 1.05 \times 10^{-6}$$

Again, Λ_0 for water is the sum of the equivalent ionic conductances of H^+ and OH^- ions, or $\Lambda_0 = 349.8 + 198 = 547.8$. Consequently,

$$\alpha = \frac{\Lambda}{\Lambda_0} = \frac{1.05 \times 10^{-6}}{547.8}$$
$$= 1.9 \times 10^{-9}$$

i.e., water is ionized to the extent of 1.9×10^{-7} per cent at 25° C. This degree of ionization, though extremely small, is sufficient to account for many phenomena encountered in aqueous solutions.

[1] Kohlrausch and Heydweiller, *Z. physik. Chem.*, **14**, 317 (1894).

Conductometric Titrations. Conductance measurements may be employed to determine the end points of various titrations. Consider first the titration of a strong acid like hydrochloric with a strong base like sodium hydroxide. Before base is added, the acid solution has a high content of the highly mobile hydrogen ions which give the solution a high conductance. As alkali is added the hydrogen ions are removed to form water, and their place is taken by the much slower cations of the base. Consequently the conductance of the solution decreases and keeps on falling with addition of base until the equivalent point is reached. Further addition of alkali introduces now an excess of the fast hydroxyl ions, and these cause the conductance to rise again. When this variation of the conductance of the solution is plotted against the volume of alkali added,

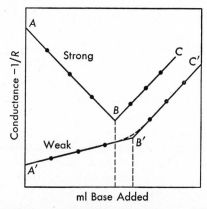

Fig. 10.   Conductometric Titration of Acids with a Strong Base.

the result is curve *ABC* in Fig. 10. The descending branch of this curve gives the conductances of mixtures of acid and salt, the ascending branch conductances of mixtures of the salt and excess base. At the minimum, point *B*, there is no excess present of either acid or base, and hence it is the end point.

Because the two branches of the curve are straight lines, it is not necessary to follow the titration carefully to the end point and past it. Instead, several measurements are made on each side of the curve, and straight lines are drawn through the points thus obtained. The volume of base required for neutralization is found then from the intersection of the two lines. In order to prevent curvature of the lines due to excessive dilution of the solution by added alkali, it is desirable to keep the titrating solution fairly strong, while the solution being titrated may be dilute.

Titration curves of the type just described are obtained only on neutralization of strong acids by strong bases. When the acid is weak, say acetic acid, and the base is strong, the titration curve has the general form of $A'B'C'$ in Fig. 10. Since the acid is weak, its conductance is correspondingly low. As base is added, the poorly conducting acid is converted to highly ionized salt, and consequently the conductance goes up along $A'B'$. Once the acid is neutralized, addition of excess base causes another sharp increase in conductance, and the curve rises along $B'C'$. The equivalence point is again the intersection of the two straight lines. Actually the intersection of $A'B'$ and $B'C'$ is not as sharp as shown but has the form indicated by the dotted lines. This rounding of the intersection is due to hydrolysis of the salt formed during the neutralization reaction. However, this rounding introduces no particular difficulty, for the straight-line portions of the curve may be extended, as in the figure, to give the correct end point.

The conductometric titration curves described apply only to the conditions specific above. When the relative strengths of acid and base are changed, so may be the titration curves. It is beyond our scope to go into a detailed discussion of the various possibilities that may be encountered. Suffice it to say that many titrations can be run conductometrically in water or mixed solvents which would be difficult or impossible with indicators, as in colored solutions, and that the method can be applied to mixtures of weak and strong acids, or weak and strong bases. Further, such titrations may be utilized also for precipitation, oxidation-reduction, and other types of reactions. Thus sodium acetate may be estimated by titration with hydrochloric acid, copper sulfate by titration with sodium hydroxide, magnesium sulfate with sodium or barium hydroxide, ferrous sulfate with dichromate, etc.

Other Applications. Besides the applications mentioned, conductance has been used to estimate the degree of hydrolysis of salts[1] and to follow the rates of a number of chemical reactions.[2] In industry, conductance measurements have been found useful in the control of certain processes where the concentration variation of a particular constituent or impurity affects the over-all conductance. Thus installation of conductance equipment has been found advantageous in mercerizing, sugar, and sulfuric acid plants, as well as in power plants for control of the purity of water.

REFERENCES FOR FURTHER READING

1. Creighton and Koehler, *Principles and Applications of Electrochemistry*, John Wiley & Sons, Inc., New York, 1943, Vol. I.
2. M. Dole, *Principles of Experimental and Theoretical Electrochemistry*, McGraw-Hill Book Company, Inc., New York, 1935.

[1] Bredig, *Z. physik. Chem.*, **13**, 289 (1894).
[2] Norris *et al.*, *J. Am. Chem. Soc.*, **50**, 1795 (1928); **57**, 1415 (1935). Nielson, *ibid.*, **58**, 206 (1936). Jander and Inning, *Berichte*, **69**, A, 1282 (1936). Maron and LaMer, *J. Am. Chem. Soc.*, **60**, 2588 (1938); **61**, 692 (1939).

3. H. Falkenhagen, *Electrolytes*, Oxford University Press, New York, 1934.
4. S. Glasstone, *Introduction to Electrochemistry*, D. Van Nostrand Company, Inc., New York, 1942.
5. Harned and Owen, *The Physical Chemistry of Electrolytic Solutions*, Reinhold Publishing Corporation, New York, 1950.
6. D. A. MacInnes, *The Principles of Electrochemistry*, Reinhold Publishing Corporation, New York, 1939.

PROBLEMS

1. When a potential of 110 volts d-c is applied to the terminals of an electric lamp, a current of 2 amp is found to flow. (a) What is the resistance of the lamp, and (b) how many calories of heat are dissipated per hour?
   Ans. (a) 55 ohms; (b) 189,300 cal.
2. A direct current of 0.5 int. amp flows through a circuit for 10 min. under an applied potential of 30 int. volts. Find the quantity of electricity transported by the current in (a) int. coulombs, (b) abs. coulombs, (c) emu, and (d) esu.
3. What is the rate of dissipation of energy by the current mentioned in the preceding problem in (a) int. watts, (b) abs. watts, (c) ergs sec^{-1}, (d) cal sec^{-1}?
4. The value of the faraday is 96,496 abs. coulombs per equivalent, while Avogadro's number is 6.0232×10^{23}. Find the value of the electronic charge in (a) abs. coulombs, (b) int. coulombs, (c) emu, and (d) esu.
5. A constant direct current flows through an iodine coulometer for a period of 2 hr. At the end of this time 25.2 cc of 0.08 molar $Na_2S_2O_3$ are required to react with the liberated I_2. What was the current passing through the coulometer?   *Ans.* 0.027 amp.
6. The platinum crucible used in a silver coulometer gains 0.500 g in a certain electrolysis. What would be the gain in weight of a copper cathode in a cell filled with potassium cuprocyanide [$KCu(CN)_2$] placed in the same circuit?
7. What volume of O_2 would be liberated from an aqueous solution of NaOH by a current of 2 amp flowing for $1\frac{1}{2}$ hr? The temperature is 27° C and the total pressure is 1 atm.   *Ans.* 688.8 cc.
8. (a) How long would it take a current of 1 amp to reduce completely 80 cc of 0.1 molar $Fe_2(SO_4)_3$ to $FeSO_4$? (b) How many cc of 0.1 molar $K_2Cr_2O_7$ could be reduced to chromic sulfate, $Cr_2(SO_4)_3$, by the same quantity of electricity?
9. What quantity of electricity would be required to reduce 10 g of nitrobenzene completely to aniline? If the potential drop across the cell is 2 volts, how much energy, in calories, is consumed in the process?
   Ans. 47,070 coulombs; 22,510 cal.
10. A 4 molal solution of $FeCl_3$ is electrolyzed between platinum electrodes. After the electrolysis the cathode portion, weighing 30 g, is 3.15 molal in $FeCl_3$ and 1.00 molal in $FeCl_2$. What are the transport numbers of Fe^{+++} and Cl^- ions?
    Ans. $t_+ = 0.45$.
11. A $AgNO_3$ solution containing 0.00739 g of $AgNO_3$ per gram of H_2O is electrolyzed between silver electrodes. During the experiment 0.078 g of Ag plate out at the cathode. At the end of the experiment the anode portion contains 23.14 g of H_2O and 0.236 g of $AgNO_3$. What are the transport numbers of Ag^+ and NO_3^- ions?
12. The transference numbers of the ions of 1.000 N KCl were determined by the moving boundary method using a solution 0.80 N $BaCl_2$ as the following solu-

tion. Using a current of 0.0142 amp, the time required for the boundary to sweep through a volume of 0.1205 cc was 1675 sec. What are the transport numbers of K^+ and Cl^- ions?   *Ans.* $t_+ = 0.49.$

13. The cathode, center, and anode chambers of an electrolytic cell contain each 10 milliequivalents of HCl in aqueous solution. What will be the number of milliequivalents of HCl in each compartment after the passage of 5 milliequivalents of electricity through the cell? Assume that t_+ is 0.8 and that H_2 is given off at the cathode and Cl_2 at the anode.

14. A conductivity cell filled with 0.01 demal KCl solution gives at $0°$ C a resistance of 11,210 ohms. The distance between the electrodes in the cell is 6 cm. Find (a) the cell constant and (b) the average cross-sectional area of the electrodes.   *Ans.* (a) 8.673; (b) 0.692.

15. A conductivity cell filled with 0.10 demal KCl solution gives at $25°$ C a resistance of 910 ohms. What will be the resistance when this cell is filled with a solution whose specific conductance at $25°$ C is 0.00532 mhos?

16. At $25°$ C a cell filled with 0.01 demal KCl solution gave a resistance of 484.0 ohms. The following data for NaCl solutions were then taken in the same cell at $25°$ C:

Normality	Resistance (ohms)
0.0005	10,910
0.0010	5,494
0.0020	2,772
0.0050	1,128.9

(a) Calculate Λ for NaCl at each concentration, and (b) evaluate Λ_0 by plotting Λ against $\sqrt{C}$ and extrapolating to infinite dilution.

17. At $25°$ C the equivalent conductances of dilute NaI solutions are as follows:

Molarity	Λ
0.0005	125.36
0.0010	124.25
0.0050	121.25

Find Λ_0 of NaI at $25°$ C.

18. From the following equivalent conductances at infinite dilution at $18°$ C, find Λ_0 for NH_4OH at $18°$ C:

$$Ba(OH)_2: \quad \Lambda_0 = 228.8$$
$$BaCl_2: \quad \Lambda_0 = 120.3$$
$$NH_4Cl: \quad \Lambda_0 = 129.8$$

19. At $25°$ C the equivalent conductance of a 0.02 molar $AgNO_3$ solution is 128.7, while the transport number of Ag^+ is 0.477. Calculate the equivalent ionic conductances and the ionic mobilities of Ag^+ and NO_3^- in a 0.02 molar solution of $AgNO_3$.

20. In measuring the mobility of H^+ ions by the moving boundary procedure, it is observed that the boundary moves a distance of 4.0 cm in 12.52 min. The voltage drop across the cell before the formation of the boundary is 16.0 volts. The distance between electrodes is 9.6 cm. Calculate from these data the mobility and ionic conductance of hydrogen ions.   *Ans.* $\mu_+ = 0.0032$ cm^2 volt^{-1} sec^{-1}.

21. At $18°$ C the mobility at infinite dilution of the ammonium ion is 0.00066 cm^2 volt^{-1} sec^{-1} while that of the chlorate ion is 0.00057 cm^2 volt^{-1} sec^{-1}.

Calculate Λ_0 of ammonium chlorate and the transport numbers of the two ions.

22. For $AgNO_3$ in aqueous solution $\Lambda_0 = 133.36$ at $25°$ C. Using the Onsager equation find Λ for a 0.0010 molar solution at the same temperature, and compare the result with the experimentally observed value of $\Lambda = 130.51$.

23. At $25°$ C the resistance of a cell filled with 0.01 demal KCl solution is 525 ohms. The resistance of the same cell filled with 0.1 N NH_4OH is 2030 ohms. What is the degree of dissociation of NH_4OH in this solution?

Ans. $\alpha = 0.0134$.

24. What will be the resistance of the cell used in the preceding problem when it is filled with H_2O having a specific conductance of 2×10^{-6} mho?

25. The specific conductance at $25°$ C of a saturated aqueous solution of $SrSO_4$ is 1.482×10^{-4} mho, while that of the H_2O used is 1.5×10^{-6} mho. Using the data in Table 7, determine at $25°$ C the solubility in grams per liter of $SrSO_4$ in water.

Ans. 0.0967 g/liter.

26. In the titration of 25.0 cc (diluted to 300 cc) of a $NaC_2H_3O_2$ solution with 0.0972 N HCl solution the following data were found:

Volume of HCl Used	Conductance $\times 10^4$
10.0	3.32
15.0	3.38
20.0	3.46
45.0	4.64
50.0	5.85
55.0	7.10

What is the strength of the $NaC_2H_3O_2$ solution in moles per liter?

27. Sketch the conductance against volume of reagent curves for the following titrations: (a) C_6H_5OH with NaOH; (b) $CuSO_4$ with NaOH; (c) K_2CrO_4 with $AgNO_3$.

16

Ionic Equilibria

Equilibrium constants for gaseous equilibria and for nonionic reactions in solution can be expressed in terms of concentrations to a fairly good approximation at relatively low pressures and concentrations. However, in dealing with ionic equilibria, with certain aspects of kinetics in solution, and with electromotive force studies, substitution of concentrations for activities is frequently not possible. For this reason it is essential to consider how ionic concentrations may be converted to activities, and how such activities can be evaluated.

ACTIVITIES AND ACTIVITY COEFFICIENTS OF STRONG ELECTROLYTES

In order to introduce some definitions commonly employed in dealing with the activities of strong electrolytes, consider an electrolyte $A_x B_y$ which ionizes in solution according to

$$A_x B_y = x A^{z+}, + y B^{z-} \qquad (1)$$

where z_+ and z_- are the charges of the two ions. The activity of the electrolyte as a whole, a_2, is defined in terms of the activities of the two ions a_+ and a_- as

$$a_2 = a_+^x a_-^y \qquad (2)$$

If we designate now by $\nu = x + y$ the total number of ions resulting from 1 molecule of the electrolyte, *the geometric mean activity of the electrolyte*, or more simply the *mean activity*, written $a_\pm$, is defined as

$$a_\pm = \sqrt[\nu]{a_2} = \sqrt[\nu]{a_+^x a_-^y} \qquad (3)$$

470

To relate the activities of the ions to their concentrations we write

$$a_+ = C_+ f_+ \qquad (4a)$$
$$a_- = C_- f_- \qquad (4b)$$

where C_+ and C_- are the gram ionic weights per liter of the two ions in solution, while f_+ and f_- are the *activity coefficients* of the two ions. These activity coefficients are appropriate factors which when multiplied by the concentrations of the respective ions yield their activities. Introducing equations (4a) and (4b) into equation (2), we obtain for a_2

$$
\begin{aligned}
a_2 &= (C_+ f_+)^x (C_- f_-)^y \\
&= (C_+^x C_-^y)(f_+^x f_-^y)
\end{aligned}
\qquad (5)
$$

and for the mean activity from equation (3),

$$
\begin{aligned}
a_\pm = \sqrt[\nu]{a_2} &= \sqrt[\nu]{(C_+^x C_-^y)(f_+^x f_-^y)} \\
&= (C_+^x C_-^y)^{1/\nu}(f_+^x f_-^y)^{1/\nu}
\end{aligned}
\qquad (6)
$$

The factor $(f_+^x f_-^y)^{1/\nu}$ is generally designated as the *mean activity coefficient* of the electrolyte, f; i.e.,

$$f = (f_+^x f_-^y)^{1/\nu} \qquad (7)$$

Similarly, the factor $(C_+^x C_-^y)^{1/\nu}$ is defined as the *mean molarity* of the electrolyte, $C_\pm$, or

$$C_\pm = (C_+^x C_-^y)^{1/\nu} \qquad (8)$$

In terms of the mean molarity and mean activity coefficient, equations (5) and (6) may be written simply as

$$a_\pm = a_2^{1/\nu} = C_\pm f \qquad (9)$$
$$a_2 = a_\pm^\nu = (C_\pm f)^\nu \qquad (10)$$

Finally, since for any electrolyte of molarity C we have $C_+ = xC$ and $C_- = yC$, equations (9) and (10) become also

$$
\begin{aligned}
a_\pm = a_2^{1/\nu} &= [(xC)^x (yC)^y]^{1/\nu} f \\
&= (x^x y^y)^{1/\nu} C f
\end{aligned}
\qquad (11)
$$
$$a_2 = a_\pm^\nu = (x^x y^y) C^\nu f^\nu \qquad (12)$$

Equations (11) and (12) are the expressions needed for converting activities to molarities, or vice versa. Although these expressions may appear complicated, they are actually not so when applied to specific cases. Thus for a 1–1 electrolyte, such as sodium chloride, of molarity C we have $x = 1$, $y = 1$, $\nu = 2$, and therefore

$$a_\pm = (1 \times 1)^{1/2} C f = C f$$
$$a_2 = a_\pm^2 = C^2 f^2$$

Again, for an electrolyte of the 2–1 type, such as barium chloride, we obtain $x = 1$, $y = 2$, $\nu = 3$, and hence

$$a_\pm = (1 \times 2^2)^{1/3} Cf$$
$$= \sqrt[3]{4}\, Cf$$
$$a_2 = a_\pm^3 = 4\, C^3 f^3$$

In Table 1 are summarized the relations connecting C, f, $a_\pm$, and a_2 for a number of different types of electrolytes. It will be observed that the expressions resulting from equations (11) and (12) depend on the electrolyte type and are identical for the 1–1, 2–2, 3–3 types; for the 1–2 and 2–1 types; for the 1–3 and 3–1 types; and for the 2–3 and 3–2 types.

TABLE 1

RELATION OF $a_\pm$ AND a_2 TO C AND f FOR VARIOUS ELECTROLYTES

Electrolyte Type	Example	x	y	ν	$C_\pm$	$a_\pm = C_\pm f$	$a_2 = a_\pm^\nu$
1–1	NaCl	1	1	2	C	Cf	$C^2 f^2$
2–2	CuSO$_4$	1	1	2	C	Cf	$C^2 f^2$
3–3	AlPO$_4$	1	1	2	C	Cf	$C^2 f^2$
1–2	Na$_2$SO$_4$	2	1	3	$\sqrt[3]{4}\ C$	$\sqrt[3]{4}\ Cf$	$4\ C^3 f^3$
2–1	BaCl$_2$	1	2	3	$\sqrt[3]{4}\ C$	$\sqrt[3]{4}\ Cf$	$4\ C^3 f^3$
1–3	Na$_3$PO$_4$	3	1	4	$\sqrt[4]{27}\ C$	$\sqrt[4]{27}\ Cf$	$27\ C^4 f^4$
3–1	La(NO$_3$)$_3$	1	3	4	$\sqrt[4]{27}\ C$	$\sqrt[4]{27}\ Cf$	$27\ C^4 f^4$
2–3	Ca$_3$(PO$_4$)$_2$	3	2	5	$\sqrt[5]{108}\ C$	$\sqrt[5]{108}\ Cf$	$108\ C^5 f^5$
3–2	La$_2$(SO$_4$)$_3$	2	3	5	$\sqrt[5]{108}\ C$	$\sqrt[5]{108}\ Cf$	$108\ C^5 f^5$

The definitions for the ionic and mean activity coefficients have been expressed in terms of concentration in moles per liter of solution. In electrochemical work quite frequently concentrations are expressed on a molality basis, i.e., moles per 1000 g of solvent, m. When this is the case the activities of the ions are defined analogously to equation (4) by

$$a_+ = m_+ \gamma_+ \qquad (13a)$$
$$a_- = m_- \gamma_- \qquad (13b)$$

By repeating the above argument with these new definitions, it can readily be shown that now

$$a_\pm = (x^x y^y)^{1/\nu} m\gamma \qquad (14)$$
$$a_2 = a_\pm^\nu = (x^x y^y) m^\nu \gamma^\nu \qquad (15)$$

where γ is the *mean activity coefficient of the electrolyte* for concentration in molalities, and is given by

$$\gamma = (\gamma_+^x \gamma_-^y)^{1/\nu} \qquad (16)$$

With equations (14) and (15) the expressions for the mean molality, $m_\pm$, i.e.,

$$m_\pm = (m_+^x m_-^y)^{1/\nu} \tag{17}$$

and a_2 in Table 1 have exactly the same form as for molarities, except that C and f are replaced by m and γ. Since C and m are not identical, neither will f as a rule be equal to γ. In fact, the two activity coefficients are related by the expression

$$f = \gamma \left(\frac{d_0 m}{C} \right) \tag{18}$$

where d_0 is the density of the pure solvent, and m/C is given by

$$\frac{m}{C} = \frac{1 + 0.001\ m M_2}{d} \tag{19}$$

Here M_2 is the molecular weight of the electrolyte, while d is the density of the solution. From equations (18) and (19) it can be shown that for dilute aqueous solutions f will be essentially equal to γ; however, in more concentrated solutions the two will have different values.

DETERMINATION OF ACTIVITY COEFFICIENTS

Equations (11) and (12) or (14) and (15) indicate that for conversion of molarities or molalities to activities the mean activity coefficients for various concentrations of an electrolyte must be known. Such mean activity coefficients can be determined from vapor pressure, freezing point lowering, boiling point elevation, osmotic pressure, distribution, solubility, and electromotive force measurements by well-known thermodynamic methods. Although in appropriate places in this book the solubility and electromotive force methods for evaluating activity coefficients will be explained, a discussion of the other methods is beyond our scope. For these, books on chemical thermodynamics should be consulted.

All evaluations of activity coefficients are made on the supposition that in the infinitely dilute solution $\gamma = 1$ or $f = 1$, depending on which concentration scale is employed; i.e., that

$$\frac{a_\pm}{m_\pm} = \gamma = 1 \text{ as } m \to 0 \tag{20}$$

or that

$$\frac{a_\pm}{C_\pm} = f = 1 \text{ as } C \to 0 \tag{21}$$

These definitions are equivalent to the statement that the activity of an ion is equal to its concentration in the infinitely dilute solution. On this basis the activity coefficients of all electrolytes are unity at zero concen-

TABLE 2

Mean Activity Coefficients, γ, of Electrolytes at 25° C

Molality m	HCl	LiCl	NaCl	KCl	HBr	NaOH	CaCl$_2$	H$_2$SO$_4$	Na$_2$SO$_4$	ZnSO$_4$	CuSO$_4$	La(NO$_3$)$_3$
0.000	1.000	1.000	1.000	1.000	1.000	1.000	1.000	1.000	1.000	1.000	1.000	1.000
0.001	0.966	0.965	0.966	0.965	0.966	—	0.888	0.830	—	0.734	0.762	—
0.005	0.929	—	0.928	0.927	0.930	—	0.789	0.639	—	0.477	—	—
0.01	0.905	0.901	0.903	0.902	0.906	0.899	0.732	0.544	0.721	0.387	0.404	0.571
0.02	0.876	—	0.872	0.869	0.879	0.860	0.669	0.453	—	0.298	0.320	0.491
0.05	0.830	0.819	0.821	0.817	0.838	0.818	0.584	0.340	0.514	0.202	0.216	0.391
0.10	0.796	0.792	0.778	0.769	0.805	0.766	0.531	0.265	0.435	0.148	0.150	0.326
0.20	0.767	0.761	0.732	0.719	0.782	0.719	0.482	0.209	—	0.104	0.110	0.271
0.50	0.757	0.742	0.679	0.651	0.790	0.693	0.457	0.154	0.267	0.063	0.067	—
1.00	0.809	0.781	0.655	0.606	0.871	0.679	0.509	0.131	0.206	0.044	—	—
1.50	0.896	0.841	0.657	0.585	—	0.683	0.628	0.124	0.172	0.037	—	—
2.00	1.009	0.931	0.670	0.576	1.169	0.698	0.807	0.124	0.152	0.035	—	—
3.00	1.316	1.174	0.719	0.571	1.671	0.774	—	0.141	—	0.041	—	—
4.00	1.762	1.554	0.791	0.579	—	0.888	—	0.171	—	—	—	—

tration. As the concentration is increased the activity coefficients decrease at first below unity, pass through a minimum, and then increase again to values which may rise considerably above one. In Table 2 are listed the γ's for a number of electrolytes at 25° C, while in Fig. 1 is shown a plot for some of these as function of $\sqrt{m}$. Although at the higher concentrations the behavior of the γ's is highly individualized, at the lower concentrations the curves converge in a manner dependent on the type of electrolyte. This fact is of great theoretical significance in explaining the thermodynamic behavior of dilute solutions of strong electrolytes.

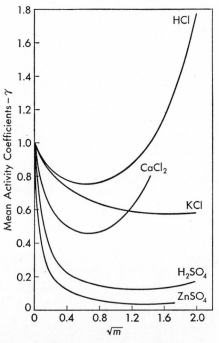

Fig. 1. Mean Activity Coefficients of Various Electrolytes at 25° C.

THE DEBYE-HÜCKEL THEORY OF ACTIVITY COEFFICIENTS

The deviation of activity coefficients from unity is an indication that solutions of strong electrolytes are nonideal in their thermodynamic properties. Arrhenius tried to account for this deviation by postulating that the cause is partial dissociation. However, in light of present information strong electrolytes must be considered to be completely dissociated, at least in the more dilute solutions, and interionic attraction rather than partial dissociation must be responsible for the observed behavior.

A theory which attempts to account for the activity coefficients of electrolytes in terms of electrostatic attractions operating between ions in a solution is that of Debye and Hückel. These authors start by assuming that electrically charged particles in solution, like other charges, are subject to the Coulomb law of force, namely, that the forces of attraction or repulsion between charges vary directly as the product of the charges, q_1 and q_2, and inversely as the square of the distance r between them,

$$\text{Force} = \frac{1}{D}\left(\frac{q_1 q_2}{r^2}\right) \tag{22}$$

The proportionality constant D, called the *dielectric constant*, is determined by the medium in which the charges are immersed, in our case the solvent. As a result of these forces the distribution of ions throughout a solution is not random but is such that any central positive ion is surrounded on an average by an atmosphere of other ions whose net charge is negative, while any central negative ion is surrounded by an atmosphere of net positive charge. Owing to the presence of an atmosphere about an ion there is a potential ε_i established at its surface whose magnitude Debye and Hückel showed to be

$$\varepsilon_i = \frac{-z_i e \kappa}{D(1 + \kappa a_i)} \tag{23}$$

In this equation z_i is the valence of the central ion, e the electronic charge, a_i the ionic diameter, and κ is

$$\kappa = \sqrt{\frac{4\,\pi e^2 \Sigma n_i z_i^2}{DkT}} \tag{24}$$

where k is the gas constant per *molecule*, i.e., R/N, T the absolute temperature, and n_i the number of any given kind of ions per *cubic centimeter* of solution. The summation Σ in equation (24) must be carried out over all the ions present in a given solution. κ has the dimensions of a reciprocal length and may be looked upon as the reciprocal of the average thickness of the ionic atmosphere about an ion.

The presence of a potential ε_i at the surface of an ion due to the ionic atmosphere can be shown to give the solution an electrical free energy F_e,

$$F_e = \frac{-z_i^2 e^2 \kappa}{2\,D(1 + \kappa a_i)} \tag{25}$$

in excess of what the solution would have if the ionic atmosphere resulting from electrostatic attraction were not present. This excess free energy F_e is thermodynamically related to the activity coefficient of the ion f_i by

$$F_e = kT \ln f_i \tag{26}$$

and hence from equations (25) and (26) we obtain

$$\ln f_i = \frac{-z_i^2 e^2 \kappa}{2\,kTD(1 + \kappa a_i)} \tag{27}$$

On introducing into equation (27) the value of κ from equation (24), and the concentration of the ions C_i in gram ionic weights per liter from the identity,

$$C_i = \frac{n_i}{N} \times 1000$$

equation (27) becomes

$$\log_{10} f_i = \frac{-A z_i^2 \sqrt{\mu}}{1 + B a_i \sqrt{\mu}} \tag{28}$$

For any given temperature and solvent, A and B in this equation are constants defined by

$$A = \frac{e^3}{2.303(DkT)^{3/2}} \sqrt{\frac{2\pi N}{1000}} \tag{29}$$

$$B = \sqrt{\frac{8\pi N e^2}{1000\, DkT}} \tag{30}$$

while μ is the ionic strength of the solution (see p. 208), i.e.,

$$\mu = \frac{1}{2} \Sigma C_i z_i^2 \tag{31}$$

Equation (28) gives the *activity coefficient of an ion* as a function of the ionic strength of the solution. Since experimentally we evaluate not the ionic activity coefficient but the mean activity coefficient of the electrolyte f, equation (28) must be transformed with the aid of equation (7) to the logarithm of the mean activity coefficient. The result is

$$\log_{10} f = \frac{-A z_+ z_- \sqrt{\mu}}{1 + B a_i' \sqrt{\mu}} \tag{32}$$

where a_i' is now an average ionic diameter. The constants A and B for this equation are given for *water as a solvent* at various temperatures in Table 3. The mean ionic diameter a_i' must be assumed to fit the data. However, *for very dilute solutions* $B a_i' \sqrt{\mu}$ is small compared to unity and may be

TABLE 3

DEBYE-HÜCKEL CONSTANTS A AND B FOR WATER AS SOLVENT*

t (°C)	A	B
0	0.4883	0.3241×10^8
15	0.5002	0.3267
25	0.5091	0.3286
40	0.5241	0.3318
55	0.5410	0.3353
70	0.5599	0.3392

* Harned and Owen, *Physical Chemistry of Electrolytic Solutions*, Reinhold Publishing Corporation, New York, 1950, p. 587.

neglected. We obtain, then,

$$\log_{10} f = -Az_+z_- \sqrt{\mu} \tag{33}$$

which is the *limiting equation of Debye and Hückel for the activity coefficients of strong electrolytes.*

TEST OF DEBYE-HÜCKEL THEORY

Because of certain simplifications necessitated by mathematical complexities of the derivation, the Debye-Hückel theory, as epitomized in equation (32), can be expected to be applicable only to *dilute solutions.*

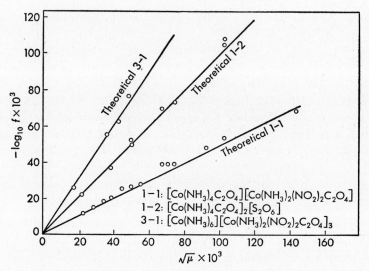

Fig. 2.   Test of Debye-Hückel Limiting Law at 15° C.

Further, equation (33) must be looked upon as a limiting law for the behavior of activity coefficients in *very dilute solutions.* According to equation (33) the activity coefficients of all strong electrolytes at high dilution should be determined, in a given solvent and at a given temperature, only by the ionic strength of the solution and the valence type (z_+z_-) of the electrolyte, and not at all by the nature of the electrolyte. Further, a plot of $-\log f$ vs. $\sqrt{\mu}$ for all electrolytes should yield straight lines through the origin, but the slope of the lines should depend on z_+z_-. For the 1–1 electrolytes this slope should be A, for 1–2 or 2–1 electrolytes $2A$, for 1–3 or 3–1 electrolytes $3A$, etc. That these requirements are met by experimented data in very dilute solutions may be seen from Fig. 2. In this figure are plotted $-\log f$ values of various complex cobalt ammines in aqueous solution as a function of the square root of the ionic strength.

The points are the experimentally observed − log f values as obtained by Brönsted and LaMer[1] from solubility measurements, while the solid lines give the plots predicted by theory. Considering the difficulties involved in the determination of solubilities in such dilute solutions, the agreement between theory and experiment must be considered satisfactory. Similar tests have been carried out for other substances with the same result. We may conclude, therefore, that for strong electrolytes in extremely dilute solutions the limiting law of Debye and Hückel does represent the behavior of activity coefficients to $\sqrt{\mu} = 0.1$ or less for electrolytes of z_+z_- up to three. With valence types higher than $z_+z_- = 3$ the agreement usually does not extend to $\sqrt{\mu} = 0.1$.

For reproducing the course of activity coefficients with $\sqrt{\mu}$ at ionic strengths higher than $\sqrt{\mu} = 0.1$, the more complete equation (32) must be used. By an appropriate choice of a'_i which must be of the order of atomic diameters, i.e., several angstroms, the activity coefficients of 1–1 electrolytes can be reproduced to $C = 0.1$, and of 2–1 electrolytes to $C = 0.05$ or so. Hückel and others had pointed out that equation (32) can be extended even further by the introduction of another term linear in μ, but for our purposes this modification is not necessary and will not be discussed.

Although the Debye-Hückel theory was originally proposed for strong electrolytes, nothing in the theory precludes its application to the *ionic portion of weak electrolytes*. This extension of the theory to weak electrolytes will be illustrated later in the chapter.

THE IONIZATION OF ELECTROLYTES

Arrhenius postulated that all electrolytes ionize in solution to a greater or lesser degree to yield ions in equilibrium with unionized molecules. If such equilibria do exist in all electrolytes, it should be possible to calculate from the values of α as obtained from conductance or colligative measurements the ionization equilibrium constants, K.

Table 4 shows values of ionization constants calculated from conductance data for several strong (potassium chloride, sodium sulfate) and weak (acetic acid, ammonium hydroxide) electrolytes at 25° C. The results immediately reveal that whereas the K's for the weak electrolytes show quite satisfactory constancy, the K's for the strong electrolytes do not. The reason for the inapplicability of the equilibrium constant principle to the strong electrolytes is, of course, that for such electrolytes $\alpha = \Lambda/\Lambda_0$ measures not degree of ionization but interionic attraction in completely dissociated electrolytes. Therefore, there can be no question of applying the principle to ionization of strong electrolytes,

[1] Brönsted and LaMer, *J. Am. Chem. Soc.*, **46**, 555 (1924).

TABLE 4

IONIZATION CONSTANTS OF STRONG AND WEAK ELECTROLYTES AT 25° C

C	KCl	Na$_2$SO$_4$	HC$_2$H$_3$O$_2$	NH$_4$OH
0 0001	—	—	1.82×10^{-5}	1.79×10^{-5}
0.0005	0.0355	0.283×10^{-4}	1.82	1.81
0.001	0.0496	0.788	1.81	1.80
0.005	0.109	7.46	1.82	1.85
0.01	0.155	19.3	1.82	1.81
0.02	0.222	49.9	1.82	1.79
0.05	0.360	172.	1.82	1.80

and we need concern ourselves only with the ionization equilibria of weak electrolytes, namely, the ionization of weak acids and bases.

IONIZATION CONSTANTS OF MONOBASIC ACIDS

The ionization equilibrium of any weak monobasic acid, such as acetic acid, can be represented by the equation

$$HA = H^+ + A^-$$

for which the *thermodynamic ionization constant K_a* is given by

$$K_a = \frac{a_{H^+}a_{A^-}}{a_{HA}} \tag{34}$$

Introducing the activity coefficients and concentrations for the activities, equation (34) becomes

$$K_a = \frac{(C_{H^+}f_{H^+})(C_{A^-}f_{A^-})}{(C_{HA}f_{HA})}$$
$$= \left(\frac{C_{H^+}C_{A^-}}{C_{HA}}\right)\left(\frac{f_{H^+}f_{A^-}}{f_{HA}}\right) \tag{35}$$

Now, for a total acid concentration C with degree of ionization α the concentration of HA will be $C_{HA} = C(1 - \alpha)$, while that of the ions will be $C_{H^+} = C_{A^-} = C\alpha$. On substitution of these into equation (35), we have

$$K_a = \frac{(C\alpha)(C\alpha)}{C(1 - \alpha)}\left(\frac{f_{H^+}f_{A^-}}{f_{HA}}\right)$$
$$= \left(\frac{C\alpha^2}{1 - \alpha}\right)\left(\frac{f_{H^+}f_{A^-}}{f_{HA}}\right)$$
$$= K_a'K_f \tag{36}$$

where $\qquad K_a' = \dfrac{C\alpha^2}{1 - \alpha} \tag{37}$

is the *ionization of the acid in terms of concentrations*, while

$$K_f = \frac{f_{H^+} f_{A^-}}{f_{HA}} \tag{38}$$

is the ratio of the activity coefficients. For dilute solutions K_f will be close to unity, and for such K_a will be essentially equal to K_a'. However, in more concentrated solutions a correction to K_a' for the deviation of the activity coefficients from unity will be in order.

Use of the above equations to calculate K_a' and K_a may be illustrated with data on the ionization of acetic acid obtained from conductance measurements by MacInnes and Shedlovsky.[1] The first column in Table 5 lists the concentrations of the acid, while the second column gives the

TABLE 5

THE IONIZATION CONSTANT OF ACETIC ACID AT 25° C

C	α	K_a'	K_a
0.00002801	0.5393	1.77×10^{-5}	1.75×10^{-5}
0.0001114	0.3277	1.78	1.75
0.0002184	0.2477	1.78	1.75
0.001028	0.1238	1.80	1.75
0.002414	0.08290	1.81	1.75
0.005912	0.05401	1.82	1.75
0.009842	0.04222	1.83	1.75
0.02000	0.02988	1.84	1.74
0.05000	0.01905	1.85	1.72
0.10000	0.01350	1.85	1.70

degree of ionization of the acid as estimated from equation (50) of the last chapter, i.e., $\alpha = \Lambda/\Lambda_e$. The concentration ionization constants K_a', calculated from C and α by means of equation (37), are given in the third column. It will be observed that although the K_a''s show a fairly satisfactory constancy, there is a consistent increase in K_a' with concentration. This drift is due to the neglect of K_f in equation (36). To take this factor into account we proceed as follows. On taking logarithms of this equation, we have

$$\log K_a = \log K_a' + \log K_f$$
$$= \log K_a' + \log \frac{f_{H^+} f_{A^-}}{f_{HA}} \tag{39}$$

Since f_{HA} is the activity coefficient of an unionized molecule, it cannot be far from unity. Again, since $f_{H^+} f_{A^-} = f^2$ according to equation (7), then

$$\log f_{H^+} f_{A^-} = 2 \log f$$

[1] MacInnes and Shedlovsky, *J. Am. Chem. Soc.*, **54**, 1429 (1932).

and on introduction of the limiting law of Debye and Hückel, equation (33), we find for $2 \log f$ at $25°$ C with $z_+ = z_- = 1$

$$2 \log f = -2\, A z_+ z_- \sqrt{\mu}$$
$$= -1.018 \sqrt{\mu} \qquad (40)$$

The ionic strength of the solution is in this instance one-half the total *ionic concentration*, namely, $\mu = C\alpha$. Inserting this value of μ into equation (40), and substituting equation (40) into equation (39), we obtain finally, for $\log K_a$,

$$\log K_a = \log K_a' - 1.018 \sqrt{C\alpha} \qquad (41)$$

The values of K_a calculated with equation (41) are shown in the last column of Table 5. It will be observed that within the range of validity of the limiting law of Debye and Hückel the values of K_a are now constant and do not exhibit the drift shown by K_a'. Consequently 1.75×10^{-5} is the thermodynamic ionization constant of acetic acid at $25°$ C.

Although strictly speaking the ionization constants should always be expressed in activities, for many purposes no appreciable error is introduced by using K_a for K_a' or vice versa. Hence, we shall hereafter follow the practice of expressing the ionization constants in concentrations rather than activities for calculation purposes.

IONIZATION OF POLYBASIC ACIDS

Acids possessing more than one ionizable hydrogen do not ionize in a single step, but in successive stages. Thus, sulfuric acid ionizes in two steps, namely,

$$H_2SO_4 = H^+ + HSO_4^-$$
$$HSO_4^- = H^+ + SO_4^{--}$$

while phosphoric acid dissociates in three steps

$$H_3PO_4 = H^+ + H_2PO_4^-$$
$$H_2PO_4^- = H^+ + HPO_4^{--}$$
$$HPO_4^{--} = H^+ + PO_4^{---}$$

In any dibasic acid the primary ionization is more complete than the second, while in any tribasic acid the primary dissociation is greater than the second, and the second greater than the third. Each of the dissociation stages constitutes a true equilibrium, and for each of these there is an ionization constant. In sulfuric acid the first ionization stage is complete, i.e., H_2SO_4 is a strong acid. However, the ionization of

HSO_4^- is incomplete, and hence for this ionization stage we have the constant

$$K_a = \frac{a_{H^+}a_{SO_4^{--}}}{a_{HSO_4^-}}$$

In phosphoric acid all three stages involve partial ionization, and we have thus for this acid three ionization constants. At 25° C the magnitudes of the three constants are $K_{a_1} = 7.5 \times 10^{-3}$, $K_{a_2} = 6.2 \times 10^{-8}$, and $K_{a_3} = 4.8 \times 10^{-13}$, indicating that at any given acid concentration the extent of dissociation of each stage decreases markedly from the primary to the tertiary. In fact, it can be calculated from the above ionization constants that in a 0.0233 molar solution of phosphoric acid, where the concentration of hydrogen ions is approximately 0.01, the concentrations of the various molecular and ionic species present are

$$C_{H_3PO_4} = 0.0133 \qquad C_{HPO_4^{--}} = 6 \times 10^{-8}$$
$$C_{H_2PO_4^-} = 0.01 \qquad C_{PO_4^{---}} = 2.9 \times 10^{-18}$$

These figures show that even dilute solutions of pure phosphoric acid consist primarily of undissociated H_3PO_4, H^+, and $H_2PO_4^-$ and that in such solutions practically no PO_4^{---} ions are present.

IONIZATION CONSTANTS OF WEAK BASES

Any weak base BOH, such as ammonium hydroxide, ionizes according to

$$BOH = B^+ + OH^- \tag{42}$$

For this process the *thermodynamic ionization constant of the base K_b* is

$$K_b = \frac{a_{B^+}a_{OH^-}}{a_{BOH}} \tag{43}$$

while the *concentration ionization constant K_b'* is

$$K_b' = \frac{C_{B^+}C_{OH^-}}{C_{BOH}} \tag{44}$$

As in weak acids, the two constants K_b and K_b' are identical only in dilute solutions. Otherwise,

$$K_b = K_b'K_f \tag{45}$$

where K_f is again the activity coefficient ratio for the various species. We shall employ K_b' expressed in concentration units as a sufficiently close approximation to K_b.

DETERMINATION OF IONIZATION CONSTANTS

Ionization constants of weak acids and bases can be determined from conductance data and measurements of the hydrogen ion concentration of a given solution of the acid or base in presence of its salt. The conductance method has already been discussed in connection with the ionization constant of acetic acid. We turn our attention, then, to the estimation of ionization constants from hydrogen ion concentration measurements.

TABLE 6

IONIZATION CONSTANTS OF WEAK ACIDS AT 25° C

Acid	Formula	K_{a_1}	K_{a_2}	K_{a_3}
Arsenic	H_3AsO_4	5.0×10^{-3}	8.3×10^{-8}	6×10^{-10}
Boric	H_3BO_3	5.80×10^{-10}		
Carbonic	H_2CO_3	4.52×10^{-7}	4.69×10^{-11}	
Hydrocyanic	HCN	7.2×10^{-10}		
Iodic	HIO_3	1.67×10^{-1}		
Phosphoric	H_3PO_4	7.52×10^{-3}	6.23×10^{-8}	4.8×10^{-13}
Phosphorus	H_3PO_3	1.6×10^{-2}	7×10^{-7}	
Sulfuric	H_2SO_4	strong	1.01×10^{-2}	
Sulfurous	H_2SO_3	1.72×10^{-2}	6.24×10^{-8}	
Formic	HCOOH	1.77×10^{-4}		
Acetic	CH_3COOH	1.75×10^{-5}		
Propionic	C_2H_5COOH	1.34×10^{-5}		
Chloracetic	$CH_2ClCOOH$	1.38×10^{-3}		
Dichloracetic	$CHCl_2COOH$	5×10^{-2}		
Benzoic	C_6H_5COOH	6.29×10^{-5}		
Oxalic	$(COOH)_2$	5.02×10^{-2}	5.18×10^{-5}	
Phenol	C_6H_5OH	1.20×10^{-10}		

For this purpose consider specifically a solution of acetic acid of concentration C containing also sodium acetate at concentration C'. If in this solution the concentration of hydrogen ions is C_{H^+}, then the concentration of unionized acid is $C_{HA} = C - C_{H^+}$, while the concentration of acetate ions is that due to ionization plus that contributed by the completely ionized salt. Since on ionization of the acid equivalent quantities of hydrogen and acetate ions result, the acetate ion concentration resulting from ionization is C_{H^+}; and this concentration plus C' from the salt gives $C_{A^-} = (C_{H^+} + C')$. In terms of these quantities, the ionization constant of the acid becomes

$$K_a' = \frac{C_{H^+}C_{A^-}}{C_{HA}}$$

$$= \frac{C_{H^+}(C_{H^+} + C')}{C - C_{H^+}} \qquad (46)$$

Therefore, as C and C' are known, measurement of C_{H^+} of the solution by some suitable means is all that is necessary to yield K_a'.

Similar considerations apply to the determination of the ionization constants of bases. For the base ammonium hydroxide at concentration C in the presence of ammonium chloride at concentration C', the ionization constant K_b' takes the form

$$K_b' = \frac{C_{OH^-}(C_{OH^-} + C')}{C - C_{OH^-}} \qquad (47)$$

As will be shown presently, the concentrations of hydrogen and hydroxyl ions in water solution are related in a definite manner, so that as soon as C_{H^+} is measured, C_{OH^-} is also known. Hence, by measuring the *hydrogen ion* concentration in the solution of the base and its salt, C_{OH^-} is also determined, and K_b' follows from equation (47).

In Table 6 are listed the ionization constants of a number of weak acids at 25° C, while in Table 7 are given the ionization constants of some weak bases at the same temperature.

TABLE 7

IONIZATION CONSTANTS OF WEAK BASES AT 25° C

Base	Formula	K_b
Ammonia	NH_4OH	1.81×10^{-5}
Silver hydroxide	$AgOH$	1.1×10^{-4}
Methyl amine	$(CH_3)NH_2$	4.38×10^{-4}
Dimethyl amine	$(CH_3)_2NH$	5.12×10^{-4}
Trimethyl amine	$(CH_3)_3N$	5.21×10^{-5}
Ethyl amine	$(C_2H_5)NH_2$	5.6×10^{-4}
Aniline	$(C_6H_5)NH_2$	3.83×10^{-10}
Hydrazine	$NH_2 \cdot NH_2$	3×10^{-6}
Pyridine	C_6H_5N	1.4×10^{-9}
Urea	$CO(NH_2)_2$	1.5×10^{-14}

CALCULATIONS INVOLVING IONIZATION CONSTANTS

When the ionization constant of an acid or base is known, it is readily possible to calculate the degree of ionization and the concentrations of the species present in solution under various given conditions. Two such calculations will be presented as examples of the procedure.

Calculation of the Degree of Ionization of Pure Acids or Bases. Suppose that it is desired to calculate the degree of ionization and the concentrations of the various species in a solution of a monobasic acid at concentration C. If α is the degree of ionization, then according to equation (37)

$$K'_a = \frac{C\alpha^2}{1 - \alpha} \tag{37}$$

from which α follows as

$$\alpha = \frac{-K'_a + \sqrt{(K'_a)^2 + 4\,K'_a C}}{2\,C} \tag{48}$$

When K'_a is small so will be α, and the denominator in equation (37) will be essentially unity. Under these conditions the equation for α reduces to

$$\alpha^2 = \frac{K'_a}{C}$$

$$\alpha = \sqrt{\frac{K'_a}{C}} \tag{49}$$

Once α is known, C_{HA}, C_{H^+}, and C_{A^-} are readily obtained.

For the specific case of 0.01 molar propionic acid at 25° C, where $K'_a = 1.34 \times 10^{-5}$, we find for α, from equation (48),

$$\alpha = \frac{-1.34 \times 10^{-5} + \sqrt{(1.34 \times 10^{-5})^2 + 4(1.34 \times 10^{-5})0.01}}{2(0.01)}$$

$$= 0.0364$$

If equation (49) had been used, α would be

$$\alpha = \sqrt{\frac{K'_a}{C}} = \sqrt{\frac{1.34 \times 10^{-5}}{0.01}}$$

$$= 0.0366$$

With this value of α we find that $C_{H^+} = C_{A^-} = C\alpha = 0.01(0.0364) = 0.00036$ and that $C_{HA} = C(1 - \alpha) = 0.00964$.

In an exactly analogous manner may be calculated α and the concentrations in the ionization of bases.

Degree of Ionization in Presence of a Common Ion. When the solution of a weak acid or base contains as well a substance possessing an ion in common with the weak electrolyte, the degree of ionization of the latter is invariably repressed. The generality of this statement may be illustrated with the following example. Suppose that we have a C molar solution of propionic acid, and suppose, further, that this solution contains also sodium propionate at concentration C'. If α is again the degree of ionization, then $C_{HA} = C(1 - \alpha)$, and $C_{H^+} = C\alpha$. But the concentration of propionate ions is now that due to ionization, $C\alpha$, plus that contributed by the salt, C', or, $C_{A^-} = (C\alpha + C')$. Inserting these concentrations into the expression for K'_a, we have

$$K'_a = \frac{C_{H^+} C_{A^-}}{C_{HA}}$$

$$= \frac{(C\alpha)(C\alpha + C')}{C(1 - \alpha)}$$

$$= \frac{\alpha(C\alpha + C')}{(1 - \alpha)} \tag{50}$$

and hence, $$\alpha = \frac{-(C' + K'_a) + \sqrt{(C' + K'_a)^2 + 4 K'_a C}}{2 C} \tag{51}$$

However, if we take $(1 - \alpha) = 1$, equation (51) becomes

$$\alpha = \frac{-C' + \sqrt{(C')^2 + 4 K'_a C}}{2 C} \tag{52}$$

For a mixture of propionic acid again at $C = 0.01$ molar and sodium propionate at $C' = 0.02$ molar, equation (52) yields for α

$$\alpha = \frac{-0.02 + \sqrt{(0.02)^2 + 4(1.34 \times 10^{-5})0.01}}{2(0.01)}$$

$$= 0.00070$$

Therefore, addition of 0.02 molar sodium propionate to 0.01 molar propionic acid reduces the ionization of the latter from 3.66 to 0.070 per cent.

With low values of K'_a no significant error is introduced when not only α is disregarded in the denominator of equation (50) but also $C\alpha$ compared to C' in the numerator. Equation (50) becomes then

$$K'_a = C'\alpha$$

and $$\alpha = \frac{K'_a}{C'} \tag{53}$$

For the case cited above, equation (53) would yield $\alpha = 0.00067$ as against 0.00070 by equation (52).

Another instance of common ion effect on the ionization of weak acids is the addition of a strong acid to the weak. In a solution containing 0.01 molar propionic acid and, say, 0.03 molar hydrochloric acid, we may take the hydrogen ion concentration as equal to that of the hydrochloric acid, namely, 0.03, and the concentrations of propionate ions and propionic acid as $(0.01 \, \alpha)$ and 0.01, respectively. Then,

$$K'_a = 1.34 \times 10^{-5} = \frac{(0.03)(0.01 \, \alpha)}{0.01}$$

$$\alpha = 0.00045$$

and we see that the hydrogen ions of the strong acid, like the propionate ions of the salt, depress the ionization of the weak acid.

THE ION PRODUCT OF WATER

Conductance measurements and other evidence definitely indicate that water ionizes according to the equation

$$H_2O(l) = H^+ + OH^- \qquad (54)$$

For this ionization, the equilibrium constant is

$$K = \frac{a_{H^+}a_{OH^-}}{a_{H_2O}} \qquad (55)$$

However, since the ionization is at best very slight, the activity of the water in any aqueous solution will be constant and may be included in K. Equation (55) becomes then

$$K_w = Ka_{H_2O} = a_{H^+}a_{OH^-} \qquad (56)$$

K_w is called the *ion product of water*. It indicates that in any aqueous solution both hydrogen and hydroxyl ions must be present and that at all times the product of the activities of the two ions must be a constant. In terms of concentrations this constant may be written as

$$K'_w = C_{H^+}C_{OH^-} \qquad (57)$$

where K'_w differs from K_w by the product of the activity coefficients of the ions. In solutions of low ionic strength K'_w is essentially equal to K_w.

The value of K'_w may be calculated from Kohlrausch and Heydweiller's data on the conductance of pure water given in the preceding chapter. These data yield for the degree of ionization of water at 25° C $\alpha = 1.9 \times 10^{-9}$. Now, as 1 liter of water at 25° C weighs 997.07 g, and as the molecular weight of water is 18.016, the molar concentration C of the water is $C = 997.07/18.016 = 55.34$ molar. From C and α the concentrations of the ions follow as

$$C_{H^+} = C_{OH^-} = C\alpha$$
$$= 55.34 \times 1.9 \times 10^{-9}$$
$$= 1.05 \times 10^{-7}$$

and therefore K'_w at 25° C is

$$K'_w = C_{H^+}C_{OH^-}$$
$$= (1.05 \times 10^{-7})^2$$
$$= 1.10 \times 10^{-14}$$

In Table 8 are given the present best values for the thermodynamic ion product of water, K_w, at a number of temperatures. One point of interest in this table is that the ion product of water is 1×10^{-14} only at 25° C. At other temperatures the constant has different values, and consequently the concentration of hydrogen and hydroxyl ions in pure water at these temperatures will *not* be the same as at 25° C, namely, 1×10^{-7} g ionic weights per liter.

TABLE 8

ION PRODUCT OF WATER, K_w, AT VARIOUS TEMPERATURES

Temperature ° C	K_w
0	0.114×10^{-14}
10	0.292
25	1.008
40	2.919
60	9.614

As the ion product principle must be valid in any solution in which water is present, this constant may be employed to calculate the concentrations of hydrogen and hydroxyl ions present in such solutions. For instance, in 0.001 molar aqueous sodium hydroxide at 25° C $C_{OH^-} = 0.001$, and therefore the concentration of hydrogen ions must be

$$C_{H^+} = \frac{K_w'}{C_{OH^-}}$$
$$= \frac{1.01 \times 10^{-14}}{1 \times 10^{-3}}$$
$$= 1.01 \times 10^{-11}$$

Similarly may be calculated the concentration of hydroxyl ions in any acid solution.

GENERALIZED CONCEPT OF ACIDS AND BASES

The term *acid* is ordinarily taken to mean any substance that yields hydrogen ions in solution, and *base* any substance that yields hydroxyl ions. Although these narrow definitions of acid and base may be satisfactory for some purposes in aqueous solutions, they are altogether insufficient to cover all observed phenomena either in water or in nonaqueous solvents.

A hydrogen ion has heretofore been considered to be a hydrogen atom with the electron removed, i.e., a *proton*. However, Brönsted[1] has shown that the free energy change of the reaction

$$H^+ + H_2O(l) = H_3O^+$$

[1] Brönsted, *Chem. Rev.*, **5**, 231 (1928).

is extremely large and negative, and hence the equilibrium constant of this reaction must also be very large. H^+ ions as such must be, then, practically nonexistent in aqueous media, and what we think of as the hydrogen ion is actually the hydrated proton, H_3O^+. The latter ion has variously been designated as the *hydronium, hydroxonium,* or *oxonium* ion. Likewise, certain studies of the glass electrode by Dole[1] and of the kinetics of reactions subject to acid catalysis have led to the conclusion that the proton is solvated.

These and other considerations have led Brönsted[2] and Lowry[3] to a redefinition of the concept of acid and base. These authors define an *acid* as *any substance that can give, or donate, a proton to any other substance.* Again, they define a *base* as *any substance that can receive, or accept, a proton from an acid.* In other words, an acid is any substance, whether charged or uncharged, that can act as a *proton donor*, while any substance, whether charged or uncharged, that can act as a *proton acceptor* is a base. Inherent in these new definitions of acid and base is the significant fact that when an acid gives off a proton there must be a base to receive it; and, vice versa, no base can act as such unless there is an acid present to donate protons to it.

The differences between the newer *generalized concept of acids and bases* and the older, more restricted concept can best be brought out with several examples. According to both points of view acetic acid is an acid. However, whereas the older concept represents the ionization of this acid by the process

$$CH_3COOH = H^+ + CH_3COO^- \qquad (58a)$$

the new concept represents the ionization as

$$CH_3COOH + H_2O(l) = H_3O^+ + CH_3COO^- \qquad (58b)$$

In the latter equation the acetic acid donates a proton to a water molecule, which acts as a *base*, to form a hydronium ion and an acetate ion. Furthermore, since H_3O^+ can donate a proton to the acetate ion to form acetic acid and water, H_3O^+ itself must be an acid, while *CH_3COO^- must be a base.* Consequently, any interaction of an acid and a base must always result in the formation of another acid and another base; i.e.,

$$Acid_1 + Base_1 = Acid_2 + Base_2 \qquad (59)$$

$Base_2$, which results from $Acid_1$, is said to be the base *conjugate* to $Acid_1$. Similarly, $Acid_2$, which results from $Base_1$, is said to be *conjugate* to $Base_1$.

[1] Dole, *J. Am. Chem. Soc.*, **54**, 2120, 3095 (1932).

[2] Brönsted, *loc. cit.; Rec. trav. chim.*, **42**, 718 (1923).

[3] Lowry, *J. Chem. Soc.*, **123**, 848 (1923).

By extending this argument, we obtain the following formulations for the ionization in water of a number of *generalized acids*:

Acid$_1$		Base$_1$		Acid$_2$		Base$_2$
HCl	+	H_2O	=	H_3O^+	+	Cl^-
HCOOH	+	H_2O	=	H_3O^+	+	$HCOO^-$
HSO_4^-	+	H_2O	=	H_3O^+	+	SO_4^{--}
NH_4^+	+	H_2O	=	H_3O^+	+	NH_3
$C_6H_5NH_3^+$	+	H_2O	=	H_3O^+	+	$C_6H_5NH_2$
H_3O^+	+	H_2O	=	H_3O^+	+	H_2O
H_2O	+	H_2O	=	H_3O^+	+	OH^-
H_2SO_3	+	H_2O	=	H_3O^+	+	HSO_3^-
HSO_3^-	+	H_2O	=	H_3O^+	+	SO_3^{--}

From these examples it may be seen that besides substances ordinarily considered to be acids, i.e., HCl, HSO_4^-, H_2SO_4, HCOOH, etc., H_3O^+, H_2O, NH_4^+, $C_6H_5NH_3^+$, and other proton donors are also acids. Again, bases are not only substances which possess hydroxyl ions, but also anions of acids, water, ammonia, aniline, HSO_3^-, and other proton acceptors. It will be observed that water may act as both acid or base, depending on the conditions and the reaction, i.e., water is *amphoteric*. Further, an ion like HSO_3^- is also amphoteric, for it may act as an acid or base, depending on circumstances of the reaction.

The strength of a given acid in the new theory is measured by its ability to donate protons to the solvent and is expressible by the ionization constant of the acid. On the other hand, the strength of a given base K_B is defined as

$$K_B = \frac{1}{K_a} \tag{60}$$

where K_a is the ionization constant of the acid conjugate to the base. For *aqueous* solutions it can also be shown that

$$K_B = \frac{K_b}{K_w} \tag{61}$$

K_b being the ionization constant of a base as defined by equation (43).

The generalized concept of acids and bases does not contradict the older views of these substances, but rather extends them. And, although the ideas involved may appear strange to one not accustomed to thinking in these terms, we shall see in a subsequent chapter that these ideas are very fruitful and permit the correlation and explanation of certain kinetic phenomena in aqueous solutions which would otherwise appear to be very puzzling.

A theory of acids and bases even broader in scope than the preceding has been proposed by G. N. Lewis. However, since this theory involves some ideas of molecular structure which have not as yet been presented, reference to this theory will be postponed until Chapter 22.

NEUTRALIZATION AND HYDROLYSIS

The reaction between an acid and a base in aqueous solution always results in the formation of water and a salt. If this reaction were complete, exact neutralization of an acid by a base, or vice versa, would always give an exactly neutral solution; i.e., one containing no excess of hydrogen or hydroxyl ions. This is very nearly the case when a strong acid like hydrochloric is neutralized by a strong base like sodium hydroxide. However, when a weak acid like acetic is neutralized by sodium hydroxide, it is found that the final solution is not neutral but basic. Again, when a weak base like ammonium hydroxide is neutralized by hydrochloric acid, the final solution is acid. The basicity of the final solution in one case and acidity in the other are due to the tendency of the salt formed by neutralization to react with water and thereby reverse the neutralization. This tendency of salts when dissolved in water to react with the solvent and thereby reverse the neutralization process is called *hydrolysis*.

In considering the hydrolytic behavior of various salts, four cases may be distinguished, namely, (a) salts of strong acids and strong bases, (b) salts of weak acids and strong bases, (c) salts of strong acids and weak bases, and (d) salts of weak acids and weak bases. Each of these categories will be discussed now in turn.

SALTS OF STRONG ACIDS AND STRONG BASES

Sodium chloride may be taken as an example of the hydrolytic behavior of a salt of a strong acid and a strong base. This salt exists in aqueous solution as sodium and chloride ions. If these two ions were to react with the water, the products would be hydrochloric acid and sodium hydroxide. However, since the latter two are also strong electrolytes, the products would again be sodium and chloride ions, and the hydrogen and hydroxyl ions would recombine to form water. In other words, the products of hydrolysis would be identical with the reactants, and there would be no change in the nature of the species in solution. We may say, therefore, that a salt of a strong acid and a strong base does not hydrolyze, and the solution of such a salt is essentially neutral.

SALTS OF WEAK ACIDS AND STRONG BASES

When a salt of a weak acid and a strong base, such as sodium acetate, is dissolved in water, the cation of the base, i.e., the sodium ion, will not undergo hydrolysis for the reason given above. However, the anion of the weak acid, i.e., the acetate ion, will react with water to form sufficient unionized acetic acid for the ionization constant of the acid to hold. The result is that the acetate ion undergoes the hydrolytic reaction

$$CH_3COO^- + H_2O = CH_3COOH + OH^-$$

which leads also to the formation of hydroxyl ions, and the solution becomes alkaline.

In general, the hydrolysis of any salt BA of a weak acid HA and a strong base BOH is due to the hydrolysis of the anion of the acid. This hydrolysis of the anion can be represented by the equation

$$A^- + H_2O = HA + OH^- \tag{62}$$

for which the equilibrium constant K_b, again including the activity of the water in the constant, is given by

$$K_h = \frac{a_{HA}a_{OH^-}}{a_{A^-}} \tag{63}$$

The constant K_h, called the *hydrolytic constant* of the ion A^-, determines the extent to which the ion A^- will react with water to form HA and OH^-. The magnitude of this constant, in turn, depends on the ionization constant of the acid HA, K_a, and the ion product of water K_w, as may be shown as follows. If the numerator and denominator of the right-hand side of equation (63) are multiplied by a_{H^+}, we obtain

$$K_h = \left(\frac{a_{HA}}{a_A \cdot a_{H^+}}\right)(a_{H^+}a_{OH^-})$$

But $\left(\dfrac{a_{HA}}{a_A-a_{H^+}}\right) = \dfrac{1}{K_a}$, and $K_w = a_{H^+}a_{OH^-}$. Therefore,

$$K_h = \frac{K_w}{K_a} \tag{64}$$

and the hydrolytic constant may be calculated from the ion product of water and the ionization constant of the weak acid.

SALTS OF STRONG ACIDS AND WEAK BASES

In salts of this class, of which ammonium chloride is an example, the anion of the strong acid will suffer no hydrolysis. But, the cation B^+ of the weak base BOH will undergo hydrolysis according to the reaction

$$B^+ + H_2O = BOH + H^+ \tag{65}$$

This time the hydrolysis yields molecules of the unionized base and hydrogen ions, and hence the solution of the salt in water is acid. The hydrolytic constant is now given by

$$K_h = \frac{a_{BOH}a_{H^+}}{a_{B^+}} \tag{66}$$

If the numerator and denominator of this expression are multiplied by a_{OH^-}, K_h becomes

$$K_h = \left(\frac{a_{BOH}}{a_{B^+}a_{OH^-}}\right)(a_{H^+}a_{OH^-})$$

But the first quantity in parentheses is $1/K_b$, where K_b is the ionization constant of the weak base BOH. Again, $K_w = a_{H^+}a_{OH^-}$. Therefore,

$$K_h = \frac{K_w}{K_b} \tag{67}$$

and the hydrolytic constant of a salt of a strong acid and a weak base can be calculated from the ion product of water and the ionization constant of the weak base BOH.

SALTS OF WEAK ACIDS AND WEAK BASES

When the salt BA is the product of the interaction of a weak acid HA and a weak base BOH, such as ammonium acetate, both the cation and anion of the salt undergo hydrolysis. The reaction is

$$B^+ + A^- + H_2O = BOH + HA \tag{68}$$

and whether the solution of the salt in water is acid or basic is determined by the relative strengths of the acid and base. In this instance the hydrolytic constant is defined by

$$K_h = \frac{a_{BOH}a_{HA}}{a_{B^+}a_{A^-}} \tag{69}$$

If now the numerator and denominator of equation (69) are multiplied by $a_{H^+}a_{OH^-}$, K_h becomes

$$K_h = \left(\frac{a_{BOH}}{a_{B^+}a_{OH^-}}\right)\left(\frac{a_{HA}}{a_{H^+}a_{A^-}}\right)(a_{H^+}a_{OH^-})$$

But, $\left(\dfrac{a_{BOH}}{a_{B^+}a_{OH^-}}\right) = \dfrac{1}{K_b}$, $\left(\dfrac{a_{HA}}{a_{H^+}a_{A^-}}\right) = \dfrac{1}{K_a}$, $(a_{H^+}a_{OH^-}) = K_w$. Therefore,

$$K_h = \frac{K_w}{K_b K_a} \tag{70}$$

This time the ionization constants of both the weak acid and the weak base are involved in the expression for the hydrolytic constant of the salt.

CALCULATIONS INVOLVING HYDROLYTIC CONSTANTS

Hydrolytic constants of salts may be calculated from known K_a, K_b, and K_w values by means of equations (64), (67), or (70), or they may be determined experimentally. In the latter instance the usual practice is to dissolve a given amount of the salt in water and measure the hydrogen ion concentration of the solution. Once this quantity and the original concentration of the salt are known, the hydrolytic constant may be calculated. In all the calculations which follow it will be assumed that concentrations may be substituted for activities. To illustrate the calculation of K_h from measurements of the hydrogen ion concentration of a salt in water, consider the following example.

Example: An 0.02 molar solution of sodium acetate in water at 25° C is found to have a hydrogen ion concentration of 3.0×10^{-9} gram ionic weights per liter. What is the hydrolytic constant of the salt? The hydrolytic reaction of this salt is given by

$$CH_3COO^- + H_2O = CH_3COOH + OH^-$$

Since $C_{H^+} = 3.0 \times 10^{-9}$, and since $K_w = 1.01 \times 10^{-14} = C_{H^+}C_{OH^-}$, the concentration of hydroxyl ions must be

$$C_{OH^-} = \frac{K_w}{C_{H^+}} = \frac{1.01 \times 10^{-14}}{3.0 \times 10^{-9}}$$
$$= 3.37 \times 10^{-6}$$

This must also be the concentration of the acetic acid, as the latter is formed in quantity equivalent to the hydroxyl ions during the hydrolysis. Finally, the concentration of acetate ions at hydrolytic equilibrium must be the original concentration of the salt minus the amount reacted. Or,

$$C_{Ac^-} = 0.02 - 3.37 \times 10^{-6}$$
$$= 0.02$$

to a very near approximation. Therefore

$$K_h = \frac{C_{HA}C_{OH^-}}{C_{Ac^-}}$$
$$= \frac{(3.37 \times 10^{-6})(3.37 \times 10^{-6})}{0.02}$$
$$= 5.68 \times 10^{-10}$$

Calculated from $K_w = 1.01 \times 10^{-14}$ and $K_a = 1.75 \times 10^{-5}$ for acetic acid at 25° C, K_h is

$$K_h = \frac{K_w}{K_a}$$
$$= \frac{1.01 \times 10^{-14}}{1.75 \times 10^{-5}}$$
$$= 5.77 \times 10^{-10}$$

Once K_h is known, it may be employed to estimate the degree of hydrolysis of the salt under other conditions. Thus, suppose it is desired to know the degree of hydrolysis of sodium acetate in 0.01 molar solution at 25° C. If we let α be the degree of hydrolysis of the acetate ion, then $C_{Ac^-} = 0.01(1 - \alpha)$, and $C_{HAc} = C_{OH^-} = 0.01\,\alpha$. Consequently,

$$5.77 \times 10^{-10} = \frac{(0.01\,\alpha)(0.01\,\alpha)}{0.01(1 - \alpha)}$$

As K_h is small, so will be α, and we may write $1 - \alpha = 1$. Then,

$$\frac{(0.01)^2\alpha^2}{0.01} = 5.77 \times 10^{-10}$$

$$\alpha = 2.40 \times 10^{-4}$$

i.e., the acetate ion is hydrolyzed to the extent of 0.024 per cent in 0.01 molar solution at 25° C.

pH AND pOH

In passing from acid to alkaline solutions the concentration of hydrogen ions can vary within very wide limits. To permit a convenient means of expressing the concentration of hydrogen ions without involving negative exponents, Sørensen suggested the use of the *pH* (puissance d'hydrogen) *scale*. On this scale the pH of any solution is defined as

$$\text{pH} = -\log_{10} a_{H^+} \tag{71}$$

i.e., the hydrogen ion activity of a solution is equal to 10^{-pH}. Thus, for a solution of $\text{pH} = 4$, $a_{H^+} = 10^{-4}$, while for a solution of $\text{pH} = 12$, $a_{H^+} = 10^{-12}$. Similarly, the activity of hydroxyl ions can be expressed on a *pOH scale* by the definition

$$\text{pOH} = -\log_{10} a_{OH^-} \tag{72}$$

Since in any aqueous solution $a_{H^+}a_{OH^-} = K_w$, we have

$$-\log_{10} a_{H^+} - \log_{10} a_{OH^-} = -\log_{10} K_w$$

and, therefore

$$\text{pH} + \text{pOH} = -\log_{10} K_w \tag{73}$$

From this equation it follows that the sum of pH and pOH for any aqueous solution must always be a constant equal to $-\log_{10} K_w$, and hence when the pH of a solution goes up the pOH must decrease, and vice versa. For neutrality the concentrations of hydrogen and hydroxyl ions must be equal, and so must pH and pOH. Then

$$\text{pH} = \text{pOH} = \frac{-\log_{10} K_w}{2} \tag{74}$$

Any solution having a pH lower than $-\frac{1}{2}\log_{10} K_w$ will thus be acid, while any solution having a pH higher than this value will be alkaline.

In the specific case of aqueous solutions *at 25° C*, $K_w = 1 \times 10^{-14}$, and $-\log_{10} K_w = 14$. For this temperature, then, pH + pOH = 14, and the neutral solution has a pH of seven. Any solution of pH lower than seven will be acid, while any solution of pH above seven will be alkaline.

BUFFER SOLUTIONS

Solutions composed of an acid and one of its salts, or of a base and one of its salts, possess the ability to resist to a greater or lesser degree changes in pH when some acid or base is added to them. Such solutions exhibiting the property of opposing a change in their pH are called *buffer solutions*, or simply *buffers*. Particularly effective in this respect are mixtures in which the acid or base involved is weak.

The buffering action of a solution of a weak acid HA in presence of one of its salts is explainable as follows. In any mixture of acid and salt the ionization equilibrium of the acid determines the hydrogen ion concentration of the solution. When hydrogen ions are added to this solution in the form of some acid, the equilibrium is disturbed by the presence of excess hydrogen ions. To remove this excess and to reestablish the ionization equilibrium, hydrogen ions combine with anions of the salt to form molecules of unionized acid HA, and thereby the pH of the solution reverts to a value not far different from what it was originally. Again, when base is added to the mixture of acid and salt, the excess of hydroxyl ions disturbs the ionization equilibrium of the water. To reestablish this equilibrium hydrogen and hydroxyl ions combine to form water. As this reaction removes hydrogen ions, the ionization equilibrium of the acid is also disturbed, and to reestablish the latter some of the acid HA ionizes to yield the requisite hydrogen ions. The result of these changes is that the excess hydroxyl ions are essentially neutralized, and the solution reverts to a pH close to its original value. These considerations apply only when the amount of acid or base added to a buffer solution is not so large as to change to any great extent the ratio of acid to salt.

In a like manner can be explained the buffering action of solutions of a weak base BOH and one of its salts. The particular pH at which a buffer solution is effective is determined by the ratio of acid or base to salt present and by the magnitude of the ionization constant of the acid or base. Thus, for a weak acid the hydrogen ion activity of the buffer is determined from the ionization constant by

$$a_{H^+} = K_a \frac{a_{HA}}{a_{A^-}} \qquad (75)$$

while for a weak base the hydroxyl ion activity is controlled by

$$a_{\mathrm{OH}^-} = K_b \frac{a_{\mathrm{BOH}}}{a_{\mathrm{B}^+}} \tag{76}$$

When the activity ratios of acid to salt or of base to salt are unity, these equations reduce to $a_{\mathrm{H}^+} = K_a$ and $a_{\mathrm{OH}^-} = K_b$. However, when these ratios are not unity, a_{H^+} and a_{OH^-} must be estimated from equations (75) and (76).

Buffers are used whenever solutions of known pH are required, or whenever it is necessary to keep the pH of a solution constant. MacIlvaine[1,2] has given instructions for preparing buffer solutions of definite pH ranging from pH = 3.4 to pH = 8.0 in 0.2 unit steps. These are based on the use of disodium acid phosphate and citric acid solutions in various proportions. Another system of buffer mixtures ranging from pH = 1 to pH = 10 in 0.2 unit steps has been proposed by Clark and Lubs. Details for preparing these buffers may be found in Lange's Handbook.[2]

OTHER HOMOGENEOUS IONIC EQUILIBRIA

Ionic equilibria in homogeneous systems are not limited to ionizations and hydrolyses. Many other types of equilibrium are possible, which may involve only ions, as in

$$2\,\mathrm{Fe}^{+++} + \mathrm{Sn}^{++} = 2\,\mathrm{Fe}^{++} + \mathrm{Sn}^{++++}$$
$$\mathrm{Ag}^+ + 2\,\mathrm{CN}^- = \mathrm{Ag(CN)_2^-}$$

or ions and unionized substances, as in

$$\mathrm{I}^- + \mathrm{I}_2 = \mathrm{I}_3^-$$
$$\mathrm{CH_3CH_2NO_2} + \mathrm{OH}^- = \mathrm{CH_3CH{=}NO_2^-} + \mathrm{H_2O}$$

All such equilibria are handled in exactly the same manner as the others discussed. Through appropriate means the equilibrium constants of such ionic reactions can be evaluated, and these in turn may be used for calculating the activities or concentrations of the substances involved under various specified conditions.

HETEROGENEOUS IONIC EQUILIBRIA

So far only ionic equilibria in homogeneous systems were mentioned. However, ions may also be involved in heterogeneous equilibria. As examples of such may be cited the reactions:

[1] MacIlvaine, *J. Biol. Chem.*, **49**, 183 (1921).
[2] N. A. Lange, *Handbook of Chemistry*, Handbook Publishers, Inc., Sandusky, Ohio, 1956.

$$NH_3(g) + H_2O(l) = NH_4^+ + OH^- \qquad (a)$$
$$Sn(s) + 2\,H^+ = Sn^{++} + H_2(g) \qquad (b)$$
$$AgBr(s) + I^- = AgI(s) + Br^- \qquad (c)$$
$$Sn(s) + Pb^{++} = Pb(s) + Sn^{++} \qquad (d)$$
$$BaSO_4(s) = Ba^{++} + SO_4^{--} \qquad (e)$$

The formulation of the equilibrium constants of heterogeneous reactions involving ions introduces nothing new. All that need be remembered is that the activity of pure solid and liquid phases is unity, while pressure will be approximately equal to the activity of gas phases. As an example for discussion may be taken the work of Noyes and Toabe[1] on the equilibrium between tin and lead ions given in (d). These authors studied this equilibrium by agitating solutions of lead perchlorate, tin perchlorate, or mixtures of the two, with solid lead and tin and then determined the concentrations of the stannous and plumbous ions at equilibrium. In Table 9 are given some of their results for 25° C.

TABLE 9

EQUILIBRIUM AT 25° C IN THE REACTION
$$Sn(s) + Pb^{++} = Pb(s) + Sn^{++}$$

Equilibrium Concentration (moles/liter)		$K = \dfrac{C_{Sn^{++}}}{C_{Pb^{++}}}$
$C_{Pb^{++}}$	$C_{Sn^{++}}$	
0.0132	0.0413	3.14
0.0148	0.0457	3.08
0.0233	0.0704	3.02
0.0235	0.0692	2.95
0.0275	0.0821	2.98

The fair constancy of the K's indicates that in this instance the use of concentrations gives a fairly close approximation to the thermodynamic constant expressed in activities. The reason is that both ions are divalent, and hence the ratio of their activity coefficients, as it appears in the equation, is not far from unity.

THE SOLUBILITY PRODUCT

A particularly important type of heterogeneous ionic equilibrium is involved in the solubility of difficultly soluble salts in water. When a difficultly soluble salt, such as barium sulfate, is agitated with water until the solution is *saturated*, the equilibrium established between the solid

[1] Noyes and Toabe, *J. Am. Chem. Soc.*, **39**, 1537 (1917).

phase and the completely ionized salt in solution is given by

$$BaSO_4(s) = Ba^{++} + SO_4^{--} \tag{77}$$

For this process the equilibrium constant is

$$K_s = a_{Ba^{++}}a_{SO_4^{--}} \tag{78}$$

i.e., *in any solution saturated with barium sulfate the product of the activities of barium and sulfate ions is a constant equal to K_s.* The constant K_s is called the *solubility product constant*, or simply the *solubility product*, of the salt.

Every difficultly soluble salt has a solubility product constant of its own. For salt yielding only two ions, such as barium sulfate or silver chloride, the solubility product is merely the product of the activities of the two ions. However, for salts yielding more than two ions the solubility product expression is a little more complicated. The solubility equilibrium of any salt A_xB_y yielding x positive ions of A and y negative ions of B is given by

$$A_xB_y(s) = xA + yB \tag{79}$$

and hence the most general expression for the solubility product is

$$K_s = a_A^x a_B^y \tag{80}$$

Thus, for a salt such as silver carbonate, for which $x = 2$ and $y = 1$, $K_s = a_{Ag^+}^2 a_{CO_3^{--}}$, while for calcium fluoride $x = 1$, $y = 2$, and $K_s = a_{Ca^{++}}a_{F^-}^2$.

The solubility products are readily evaluated from the saturation solubilities of salts in pure water. These solubilities may be obtained by direct analysis of the saturated solutions, by conductance measurements as described in the last chapter, or by electromotive force measurements. The calculations involved may be illustrated with the following example. At 25° C the solubility of silver carbonate in water is 1.16×10^{-4} mole per liter. Hence the concentration of carbonate ions in the saturated solution is $C_{CO_3^{--}} = 1.16 \times 10^{-4}$, while that of the silver ions is twice that of the carbonate, or $C_{Ag^+} = 2.32 \times 10^{-4}$ gram ionic weight per liter. For silver carbonate K_s is given by

$$
\begin{aligned}
K_s &= a_{Ag^+}^2 a_{CO_3^{--}} \\
&= (C_{Ag^+}^2 C_{CO_3^{--}})(f_{Ag^+}^2 f_{CO_3^{--}})
\end{aligned}
$$

If we assume now that the activity coefficients are unity in the very dilute solution involved, then K_s reduces to K_s', the stoichiometric solubility product. Therefore,

$$
\begin{aligned}
K_s = K_s' &= C_{Ag^+}^2 C_{CO_3^{--}} \\
&= (2.32 \times 10^{-4})^2(1.16 \times 10^{-4}) \\
&= 6.2 \times 10^{-12}
\end{aligned}
$$

TABLE 10

SOLUBILITY PRODUCTS FOR VARIOUS SUBSTANCES AT 25° C

Substance	K_s	Substance	K_s
$Al(OH)_3$	3.7×10^{-15}	HgI_2	3.2×10^{-29}
$BaSO_4$	1.08×10^{-10}	$AgBr$	7.7×10^{-13}
$CaCO_3$	8.7×10^{-9}	$AgCl$	1.56×10^{-10}
CuS (18°)	8.5×10^{-45}	AgI	1.5×10^{-16}
$Fe(OH)_3$ (18°)	1.1×10^{-36}	Ag_2CO_3	6.15×10^{-12}
$Fe(OH)_2$ (18°)	1.64×10^{-14}	Ag_2CrO_4	9×10^{-12}
PbI_2	1.39×10^{-8}	Ag_2S	1.6×10^{-49}
$Mg(OH)_2$ (18°)	1.2×10^{-11}	$SrCO_3$	1.6×10^{-9}
$HgBr_2$	8×10^{-20}	$TlCl$	2.0×10^{-4}

In Table 10 are listed the solubility products at 25° C for a number of salts as well as for several difficultly soluble hydroxides to which the solubility product principle is applicable. From these constants the solubility of these substances in water can readily be obtained by reversing the calculations for the solubility product given above.

EFFECT OF COMMON IONS ON SOLUBILITY

For any solution saturated with, say, thallous chloride, the solubility product principle demands that $a_{Tl^+}a_{Cl^-} = K_s$, or approximately $C_{Tl^+}C_{Cl^-} = K_s'$, *no matter what the source of the two ions may be.* Suppose now that to a saturated solution of this salt in water is added some potassium chloride. Addition of the potassium chloride increases the concentration of chloride ions, $C_{Tl^+}C_{Cl^-}$ becomes greater than K_s', and hence some thallous chloride must be precipitated from solution to reestablish the saturation equilibrium. The net result of the increase in the chloride ion concentration is, therefore, a decrease in the solubility of thallous chloride. Similarly, if a thallous salt, such as thallium nitrate, is added to a saturated solution of thallous chloride, the solubility of the latter must again decrease to preserve the constancy of the solubility product. This effect of common ions is operative in all solutions saturated with difficultly soluble salts. Consequently, we may state as a general rule that *addition of substances possessing ions in common with a dissolving salt causes a decrease in the solubility of the salt.* This rule is valid as long as the dissolving salt does not form a complex of some kind with the added substance. When complex formation does occur, the solubility of the salt may actually increase in presence of common ions. Thus, the solubility of $HgBr_2$ is greater in solutions containing bromides due to formation of $HgBr_3^-$. Since formation of the complex removes mercuric and bromide ions, more $HgBr_2$ must dissolve to satisfy the requirements of the solubility product principle.

The solubility of difficultly soluble salts in presence of common ions can be calculated from the solubility product. For this purpose we shall assume that $K_s = K_s'$. Taking again thallous chloride, Table 10 gives for this salt $K_s = 2.0 \times 10^{-4}$. To obtain from this constant the solubility of thallous chloride in presence of added chloride ions, we proceed as follows. If C is the concentration of added chloride ions, and S the solubility of

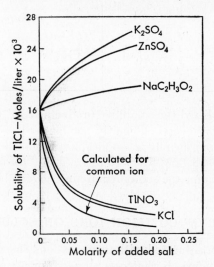

Fig. 3.   Effects of Salts on Solubility of TlCl at 25° C.

thallous chloride in presence of added substance, then the concentration of thallous ions at saturation will be S, that of choride $(C + S)$, and the expression for the solubility product becomes

$$K_s' = C_{Tl^+}C_{Cl^-}$$
$$= S(C + S) \tag{81}$$

With K_s' known, S may be calculated from equation (81) for any given value of C. Again, if the added salt contains thallous instead of chloride ions at a concentration C', the concentration of thallous ions will be $(C' + S)$, that of chloride ions S, and the expression for K_s' will become

$$K_s' = (C' + S)S \tag{82}$$

Equations (81) and (82) indicate that for the same value of C and C' the solubility of thallous chloride should be the same; i.e., the common ion effect for a given added concentration of chloride or thallous ions should be the same for both ions and should be dependent only on the concentration.

The lowest curve in Fig. 3 shows the solubility of thallous chloride predicted by equations (81) and (82) for various values of C or C'. The solubility of this salt actually observed in presence of added potassium chloride and thallium nitrate is shown in the next two curves. These data indicate that, although in general calculated and observed solubilities are parallel, the observed solubilities are higher than predicted by the approximate equations (81) and (82). Further, the common ion effect is not only dependent on the concentration, but also on the nature of the added substance. The reason for this behavior lies in what is known as the *salt effect*, to which we now turn.

SALT EFFECTS AND SOLUBILITY

From the formulation of the solubility product in terms of concentrations it is to be expected that only substances possessing an ion in common with the dissolving salt should affect the solubility. Actually it is found that electrolytes without common ions also exercise a very pronounced effect, causing an *increase in solubility* with increase in concentration of added substance. This may be seen from the upper three curves in Fig. 3, where the effect of various concentrations of added sodium acetate, zinc sulfate, and potassium sulfate on the solubility of thallous chloride is depicted.

Although inexplicable from the concentration approach, this marked increase in solubility with electrolyte concentration is just what is to be expected from the more exact activity formulation of the solubility product. The thermodynamic solubility product of thallous chloride is given by

$$K_s = a_{Tl^+}a_{Cl^-}$$
$$= (C_{Tl^+}C_{Cl^-})(f_{Tl^+}f_{Cl^-})$$
$$= K'_s f^2 \tag{83}$$

where f is the mean activity coefficient of the salt and K'_s the concentration solubility product. From equation (83) it follows that, since K_s must be a true constant, K'_s cannot be constant and equal to K_s unless $f = 1$. However, f is not unity except at zero ionic strength and varies with ionic strength as the latter is changed. Consequently, K'_s must also be a function of the ionic strength and must vary with it according to the dependence on μ of f^2 in the expression

$$K'_s = \frac{K_s}{f^2} \tag{84}$$

Now, at not too excessively high ionic strengths the activity coefficients are less than one, and consequently at these ionic strengths K'_s must be greater than K_s. Since the solubility is equal to $\sqrt{K'_s}$, the solubility in presence of added salt must also be greater. We see, therefore, that whereas the thermodynamic solubility product K_s remains constant, theory predicts that the concentration solubility product K'_s should increase with increase in ionic strength, and so should the solubility, as is the case. This argument accounts also for the fact that the observed solubilities in presence of common ions are greater than predicted when no allowance is made for activity coefficients. Since the common ion and salt effects operate against each other, the former to decrease and the latter to increase the solubility, and as the common ion effect is the more pronounced, the result of addition of common ions to a dissolving salt is to lower the solubility, but not quite to the extent which would be anticipated on the basis of no salt effect.

From these considerations it is evident that *exact* calculations can be made only when activity coefficients are included. When activity coefficients at various ionic strengths are available for a dissolving salt, such calculations introduce no difficulty. Thus, in presence of 0.1 molar potassium chloride the activity coefficient of thallous chloride is 0.715. Using $K_s = 2.0 \times 10^{-4}$ and this activity coefficient, K'_s follows from equation (84) as

$$K'_s = \frac{K_s}{f^2}$$
$$= \frac{2.0 \times 10^{-4}}{(0.715)^2}$$
$$= 3.9 \times 10^{-4}$$

Now, in presence of added chloride the solubility of thallous chloride is given by equation (81). For $C = 0.10$ and $K'_s = 3.9 \times 10^{-4}$, this equation gives $S = 0.0039$ mole per liter as against the observed 0.00396. Calculated without activity coefficients a solubility of 0.0020 would have been obtained.

ACTIVITY COEFFICIENTS FROM SOLUBILITY MEASUREMENTS

Solubility measurements in presence of added electrolytes may be employed to evaluate the activity coefficients of the *dissolving salt* at various ionic strengths. The procedure may again be illustrated with thallous chloride. If we represent the solubility of this salt in pure water by S_0, in presence of added electrolyte with no common ion by S, and let f_0 and f be the mean activity coefficients of the salt in the two solutions, then, in view of the constancy of K_s we have the relation

$$K_s = S_0^2 f_0^2 = S^2 f^2 \tag{85a}$$

and therefore,
$$S f = S_0 f_0 \tag{85b}$$

Taking logarithms, we have

$$\log S + \log f = \log S_0 f_0$$
$$\log S = \log S_0 f_0 - \log f \tag{86}$$

According to this expression f can be evaluated from the solubilities as soon as the product $S_0 f_0$ is available. To obtain this product $\log S$ is plotted against the square root of the total ionic strength of the solution, i.e., of dissolved salt and added electrolyte, and the plot extrapolated to $\sqrt{\mu} = 0$. As at zero ionic strength $f = 1$, the intercept on the $\log S$ axis gives immediately $\log S_0 f_0$. Once this quantity is known, subtraction of $\log S_0 f_0$ from $\log S$ yields $- \log f$, and hence f, at various ionic strengths. Or, on evaluating $S_0 f_0$, f follows from equation (85b) by dividing $S_0 f_0$ by S.

This procedure for evaluating f is illustrated with the data given in Table 11 for the solubility of thallous chloride at 25° C in water and in

TABLE 11

SOLUBILITY OF TlCl IN PRESENCE OF KNO$_3$ AT 25° C

Conc. KNO$_3$ Added C	Solubility TlCl S	$\mu = (C + S)$	Mean Activity Coefficient of TlCl f	$K_s = S^2 f^2$
0	0.01607	0.01607	0.885	2.02×10^{-4}
0.02	0.01716	0.03716	0.829	2.02×10^{-4}
0.05	0.01826	0.06826	0.779	2.02×10^{-4}
0.16	0.01961	0.11961	0.725	2.02×10^{-4}
0.30	0.02312	0.32313	0.615	2.02×10^{-4}
1.00	0.03072	1.03072	0.463	2.02×10^{-4}

presence of various concentrations of potassium nitrate. Column 1 gives the concentration C of added salt, column 2 the observed solubility S of thallous chloride in moles per liter, and column 3 $\mu = (C + S)$. From a plot of $\log S$ against $\sqrt{\mu}$ it is found that $S_0 f_0 = 0.01422$. Dividing now $S_0 f_0$ by S at the various ionic strengths, the activity coefficients in column 4 result. Finally, the last column gives the thermodynamic solubility product of thallous chloride as calculated from $K_s = S^2 f^2$. As it should be, K_s is constant throughout.

IONIC EQUILIBRIA AND TEMPERATURE

Equilibrium constants of ionic reactions, like all other equilibrium constants, vary with temperature. As before, the variation with temperature is given by

$$\frac{d \ln K}{dT} = \frac{\Delta H^0}{RT^2} \tag{87}$$

and this expression may be employed to evaluate the heats of various ionic reactions or to estimate K at one temperature from that at another when ΔH^0 is known.

REFERENCES FOR FURTHER READING

See references listed at end of Chapter 15 and also:

1. S. Glasstone, *Thermodynamics for Chemists*, D. Van Nostrand Company, Inc., New York, 1947.
2. K. Jellinek, *Lehrbuch der physikalischen Chemie*, Ferdinand Enke, Stuttgart, 1930, Vol. IV.
3. Kolthoff and Laitinen, *pH and Electrometric Titrations*, John Wiley & Sons, Inc., New York, 1941.

PROBLEMS

Note: In problems where insufficient data are given for ascertaining activities of ions of strong electrolytes, assume ionic activity equal to ionic concentration.

1. For each of the following solutions evaluate the mean molality, the mean ionic activity, and the activity of the salt:

	Molality	Mean Activity Coefficient
$K_3Fe(CN)_6$	0.010	0.571
$CdCl_2$	0.100	0.219
H_2SO_4	0.050	0.397

2. The density of a 1.19 molar solution of $CaCl_2$ in water is 1.10 g/cc at 20° C. What is the molality of the solution and the ratio of f to γ?
   Ans. 1.228 molal; $f/\gamma = 1.029$.

3. Using the Debye-Hückel limiting law, calculate the mean ionic activity coefficient at 25° C of a 0.001 molar solution of $K_3Fe(CN)_6$, and compare with the observed value of 0.808.

4. A solution is 0.002 molar in $CoCl_2$ and 0.002 molar in $ZnSO_4$. Calculate the activity coefficient of Zn^{++} ions in the solution using the Debye-Hückel limiting law.   *Ans.* 0.574.

5. The equivalent conductance of a 0.0140 N solution of chloracetic acid is 109.0 at 25° C. If Λ_0 is 389.5, what is the ionization constant of chloracetic acid?
   Ans. 1.52×10^{-3}.

6. From the following data calculate and compare the apparent ionization "constants" of HCl at the various concentrations:

Concentration	Λ	Concentration	Λ
0.000000	426.16	0.001877	419.76
0.000319	423.55	0.002994	418.10
0.000754	421.78		

7. Assuming that the conductance measurements give the true degree of dissociation in problem 5, use the Debye-Hückel limiting law to calculate the thermodynamic dissociation constant of chloracetic acid.

8. Find at 25° C the ratio of the degree of dissociation of a 0.1 molar aqueous solution of methylamine to that of a 0.001 molar solution.

9. Calculate the degree of dissociation and the hydrogen ion concentration in a 0.05 molar chloracetic acid solution at 25° C.

10. Calculate the H^+, H_3PO_4, $H_2PO_4^-$, HPO_4^{--}, and PO_4^{---} concentrations in a 0.1 molar H_3PO_4 solution at 25° C.   *Ans.* $C_{H^+} = 0.0239$; $C_{H_3PO_4} = 0.0761$.

11. Calculate at 25° C the degree of dissociation and hydrogen ion concentration (a) in a 0.05 molar solution of benzoic acid and (b) in a 0.05 molar solution of benzoic acid containing 0.1 molar sodium benzoate.

12. Calculate the sulfate ion concentration in (a) 0.04 molar H_2SO_4, (b) 0.10 molar $NaHSO_4$, (c) a solution 0.02 molar in H_2SO_4 and 0.02 molar in $NaHSO_4$.

13. Calculate the H^+ and OH^- concentrations at 25° C in each of the following solutions: (a) 0.001 molar H_2SO_4, (b) 0.001 molar $NaHSO_4$, (c) 0.01 molar NH_4OH.

14. Give the formulas of the acids conjugate to (a) methyl alcohol, (b) aniline, (c) dimethyl ether, and of the bases conjugate to (a) methyl alcohol, and (b) phenol.

15. Calculate the hydrolytic constants for each of the following salts at 25° C: (a) urea hydrochloride, (b) ammonium carbonate, (c) disodium acid phosphate, and (d) sodium bicarbonate.   *Ans.* (a) 0.672; (b) 11.9.

16. Calculate the degree of hydrolysis and the OH^- ion concentration in (a) a 0.01 molar Na_2CO_3 solution and (b) a 0.5 molar KCN solution.

17. To what extent will a 0.1 molar solution of aniline acetate ($C_6H_5NH_3C_2H_3O_2$) hydrolyze at 25° C? What will be the pH?   *Ans.* 55.1%; pH = 4.67.

18. Using the Debye-Hückel limiting law calculate at 25° C the hydrogen ion activity and pH of a 0.05 molar CH_3COOH solution. How do these values compare with those which would have been obtained on the assumption that ionic concentration is equal to ionic activity?

19. Calculate the pH of the following solutions at 25° C before and after the addition of 1 cc of 0.1 N HCl: (a) 100 cc pure H_2O, (b) 100 cc of 0.1 molar Na_2HPO_4.

20. If the final volume is to be 1 liter, how many moles of HCl will have to be added to 500 cc of 0.1 molar Na_2CO_3 in order to adjust the pH to 10.0?
                                                        Ans. 0.034.

21. Assuming no volume change during the titration, calculate the pH after the removal of the first hydrogen when 0.01 molar orthophosphoric acid (H_3PO_4) is titrated with a strong base. What is the pH after the removal of the second hydrogen?

22. Calculate the amounts of 0.1 normal NaOH and pure H_2O which would have to be used in order to make 1-liter portions of buffers having pH's: 6.0, 6.3, and 6.6, starting with 500 cc of 0.1 N NH_4Cl in each case.

23. What pH will result when the following solutions are mixed and made up to a total volume of 1 liter: (a) 500 cc of 0.1 molar KH_2PO_4 + 100 cc of 0.1 N NaOH, (b) 500 cc of 0.1 molar K_2HPO_4 + 50 cc of 0.1 N HCl, (c) 500 cc of 0.01 N benzoic acid + 100 cc of 0.02 N sodium benzoate?

24. The dissociation constant of the complex ion $Ag(CN)_2^-$ is 4×10^{-19}. Calculate the silver ion concentration in a solution which was originally 0.1 molar in KCN and 0.03 molar in $AgNO_3$.   *Ans.* 7.5×10^{-18} mole/liter.

25. Formulate equilibrium constants for each of the following equilibria:

  (a) $AgBr(s) + 2 NH_4OH = Ag(NH_3)_2^+ + Br^- + 2 H_2O(l)$
  (b) $IO_3^- + 5 I^- + 6 H^+ = 3 H_2O(l) + 3 I_2(s)$
  (c) $H^+ + HCO_3^- = H_2O(l) + CO_2(g)$

26. Calculate the solubility of PbI_2 in (a) pure H_2O, (b) 0.04 molar KI, and (c) 0.04 molar $Pb(NO_3)_2$ at 25° C.

27. The solubility of CaF_2 in water at 18° C is 2.04×10^{-4} mole/liter. Calculate (a) the solubility product and (b) the solubility in 0.01 molar NaF solution. *Ans.* (a) 3.4×10^{-11}; (b) 3.4×10^{-7} mole/liter.

28. At 25° C the solubility product of $AgBrO_3$ is 5.77×10^{-5}. Using the Debye-Hückel limiting law, calculate its solubility in (a) pure H_2O and (b) 0.01 molar $KBrO_3$. *Ans.* (a) 0.0084, (b) 0.0051 mole/liter.

29. At 25° C the solubility product of FeC_2O_4 is 2.1×10^{-7}. Using the Debye-Hückel limiting law, calculate the solubility of FeC_2O_4 in (a) a solution 0.002 molar in $MgSO_4$ and 0.005 molar in KNO_3, (b) pure H_2O.

30. The solubility product of CaF_2 at 18° C is 3.4×10^{-11} while that of $CaCO_3$ is 9.5×10^{-9}. What will be the nature of the first precipitate when a solution of $CaCl_2$ is added to a solution which is 0.05 molar in NaF and 0.02 molar in Na_2CO_3? In a 0.02 molar solution of Na_2CO_3 what is the minimum concentration of NaF at which CaF_2 and $CaCO_3$ will precipitate simultaneously?

31. Using data given in problem 24, predict whether or not AgCl would be precipitated from a solution which is 0.02 molar in NaCl and 0.05 molar in $KAg(CN)_2$.

32. The solubility product of PbI_2 is 7.47×10^{-9} at 15° C and 1.39×10^{-8} at 25° C. Calculate (a) the molar heat of solution of PbI_2 and (b) the solubility in moles per liter at 75° C. *Ans.* (a) 10,600 cal/mole; (b) 0.00357 mole/liter.

17

The Electromotive Force of Cells

Electrochemical cells may be used to perform two functions, namely, (a) *to convert chemical energy into electrical* and (b) *to convert electrical energy into chemical*. In the common dry cell and the lead storage battery we have converters of chemical into electrical energy, while in the charging of the storage battery and in the electrolytic purification of copper electrical energy is used to bring about chemical action. We shall divide our discussion of cells along these functional lines, and consider in this chapter cells as sources of electrical energy, while in the following chapter certain phenomena associated with the passage of electricity through cells will be elaborated on.

Before proceeding, a distinction should be made between the terms *cell* and *battery*, since they are not synonymous. A cell is a single arrangement of two electrodes and an electrolyte capable of yielding electricity due to chemical action within the cell, or of producing chemical action due to passage of electricity through the cell. A battery, on the other hand, is a combination of two or more cells arranged in series or parallel for the performance of either one or the other of these tasks. Thus, the ordinary 6-volt lead storage battery is a combination of three 2-volt cells connected in series.

REVERSIBLE AND IRREVERSIBLE CELLS

In dealing with the energy relations of cells thermodynamic principles find very extensive application. However, the use of these principles is subject to one very important restriction, namely, that the processes to which the principles are applied be *reversible*. It will be recalled that the conditions for the thermodynamic reversibility of processes are (a) that the driving and opposing forces be only infinitesimally different from each other and (b) that it should be possible to reverse any change taking place by applying a force infinitesimally greater than the one acting. When these requirements are satisfied by a cell, the cell is *reversible*, and its potential difference measured under appropriate conditions may be substituted into the relevant thermodynamic relations. When these conditions are not satisfied, the cell is said to be *irreversible*, and the thermodynamic equations do not apply.

The difference between reversible and irreversible cells may be illustrated with the following two examples. Consider first a cell composed of a zinc and a silver-silver chloride electrode, both dipping into a solution of zinc chloride. When the two electrodes are connected externally through a conductor, electrons flow through the outer circuit from the zinc to the silver-silver chloride. During this passage of current zinc dissolves at one electrode to form zinc ions, while at the other electrode the reaction

$$AgCl(s) = Ag(s) + Cl^- \tag{1}$$

takes place. The net reaction for the cell is, therefore,

$$\frac{1}{2} Zn(s) + AgCl(s) = Ag(s) + \frac{1}{2} Zn^{++} + Cl^- \tag{2}$$

and this process continues as long as the external opposing potential is infinitesimally smaller than that of the cell. However, as soon as the opposing potential becomes slightly larger than that of the cell, the direction of current flow is reversed, and so is the cell reaction. Now zinc ions go to form zinc at one electrode, silver chloride is formed from silver and chloride ions at the other, and the over-all cell reaction becomes

$$Ag(s) + \frac{1}{2} Zn^{++} + Cl^- = \frac{1}{2} Zn(s) + AgCl(s) \tag{3}$$

From this description it is obvious that the cell in question meets the second condition of reversibility. Again, the first condition can be satisfied by drawing from or passing through the cell a *very minute* current. Hence, this cell is reversible, and it may be treated by thermodynamic methods without any ambiguity.

Consider now instead a cell composed of zinc and silver electrodes immersed in a solution of sulfuric acid. When the two electrodes are short circuited, zinc dissolves with evolution of hydrogen to form zinc sulfate according to the scheme

$$Zn(s) + H_2SO_4 = ZnSO_4 + H_2(g) \tag{4}$$

However, when the cell is connected with an external source of potential slightly greater than its own, silver dissolves at one electrode, hydrogen is evolved at the other, and the cell reaction becomes

$$2 \, Ag(s) + H_2SO_4 = Ag_2SO_4 + H_2(g) \tag{5}$$

From equations (4) and (5) it is readily evident that, even though this cell may be made to satisfy the first condition of reversibility, the second does not hold, and consequently the cell cannot be reversible. The potential of such a cell does not have the definite thermodynamic significance which can be ascribed to the potentials of reversible cells.

There are a number of other types of irreversibility to which reference will be made later. For the present, suffice it to point out that in theoretical study of the potentials of cells it is the reversible ones which are of importance, and it is to these that we shall confine our prime attention.

ELECTROMOTIVE FORCE AND ITS MEASUREMENT

If a cell is connected in series with a galvanometer and the circuit is closed, the galvanometer is deflected, indicating that a current is flowing through the circuit. This current passage from one electrode to the other is evidence for the existence of a potential difference between them, for without the presence of a potential difference no electricity can flow from one point to another. *This difference of potential which causes a current to flow from the electrode of higher potential to the one of lower is called the electromotive force,* abbreviated emf, *of the cell* and is expressed in volts.

The most common method of determining the potential difference between any two points in an electric circuit is to connect a voltmeter *across* the two points. The potential difference or voltage is read then directly from the instrument. A serious objection to the use of the voltmeter for accurate measurement of cell potentials is that it draws some current from the cell, causing thereby a change in the emf due to formation of reaction products at the electrodes and changes in the concentration of the electrolyte around the electrodes. Again, with appreciable current flow part of the emf will have to be utilized to overcome the internal resistance of the cell, and hence the potential measured on the voltmeter will not be the total cell emf. For these reasons precise emf's of cells are never determined with voltmeters. Instead *potentiometers* are used which require extremely small currents at balance.

Potentiometers for emf measurements operate on the Poggendorff compensation principle. In this method the unknown emf is opposed by another known emf until the two are equal as shown by no deflection on a galvanometer present in the circuit. The setup and the conditions at balance may be understood from the diagram shown in Fig. 1. In this diagram A is a cell of known emf ε_A, whose potential is impressed across a uniform resistance ab. Connected with A in such a way that the two emf's oppose each other is the source X of unknown potential ε_X. To find ε_X the sliding contact C is moved along ab until a position S is found at which the galvanometer G gives no deflection. From ε_A, and the distances ab and aS, the unknown emf ε_X is found as follows. Since ε_A is impressed across the full length ab, for any given current passing through the resistance ε_A must be proportional to ab. Again, as ε_X is impressed only across the distance aS, it must be proportional to this length. Consequently, on dividing ε_X by ε_A we obtain

$$\frac{\varepsilon_X}{\varepsilon_A} = \frac{aS}{ab}$$

and therefore,

$$\varepsilon_X = \left(\frac{aS}{ab}\right)\varepsilon_A \qquad (6)$$

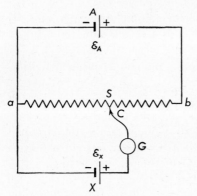

Fig. 1. Poggendorff Compensation Method for Measuring Emf.

The only requirements that need be met here are that ε_A be larger than ε_X, that the wire ab be uniform, and that the galvanometer be sufficiently sensitive to allow a balance of the potentials without appreciable current flow. Once these requirements are satisfied, the unknown emf can be obtained through equation (6) under conditions where the cell suffers no disturbance due to passage of current, and hence under conditions approximating very closely true reversibility.

To permit *direct reading* of voltage and to conserve the standard source of potential A, the setup shown in Fig. 1 is modified in practice to that given in Fig. 2. In this diagram W is the *working cell* whose emf can be impressed across ab, which is calibrated in volts, through the variable resistance R. Against this cell may be applied either the unknown emf X or the standard cell S.C. through the double-pole double-throw switch D. Before the emf of X can be measured, the slide wire must be standardized to read emf as follows. First pointer C is set at a point S' along ab corresponding to the value of the emf of the standard cell, say 1.0183 volts. Next, switch D is thrown to the S.C. side, the tapping key is closed gently, and F is moved along resistance R until the galvanometer G shows no deflection. When this balance is established, the current flowing through ab is of such a magnitude as to make the potential drop between a and S' exactly 1.0183 volts and the voltage drop anywhere along ab identical with the voltage markings on the slide wire. In other words, the potentiometer has been standardized to read voltage directly.

Now R is left undisturbed, the switch D is shifted to the unknown emf side, the key is closed, and this time C is moved along ab until a point S is found at which the galvanometer G again shows no deflection. The reading of the slide wire at S gives then the voltage of X directly.

In laboratory potentiometers the slide wire ab is usually not a single unit, but consists first of a series of coils of nominal 0.1 volt values, and an extended slide wire covering *in toto* a 0.1 volt range. By this means the Leeds and Northrup Student Type Potentiometer can be used to measure potentials up to 1.6 volts to 1×10^{-4} volt. In more precise

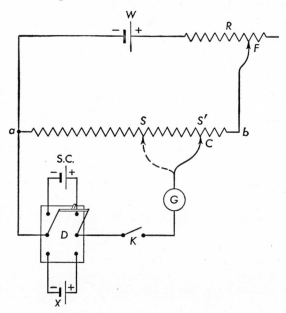

Fig. 2.   Principle of Direct Reading Potentiometer.

potentiometers, such as the Leeds and Northrup Type K-2, the precision can be extended to 1×10^{-5} volt, and for small values of emf down to 1×10^{-7} volt. With the latter instrument galvanometers of very high sensitivity are required.

STANDARD CELLS

The accuracy of emf measurements depends to a large degree on the accuracy with which the potentials of the cells used for reference are known. It is essential to have available as standards cells whose potentials are reproducible, constant with time, and well known. Also, such cells should be reversible, should not be subject to permanent damage due to passage of current through them, and should preferably have low temperature coefficients of emf. The cells that most closely approximate these properties are the *Weston unsaturated and saturated standard cells.*

The usual form of the Weston *saturated* standard cell is illustrated in Fig. 3. The cell consists of an H-shaped glass vessel containing in each arm one of the electrodes and filled throughout with the electrolyte. Contact with the active material is made through short platinum wires sealed into the bottoms of the arms. The positive electrode consists of

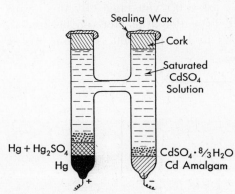

mercury covered with a paste of mercurous sulfate and mercury. The negative electrode, in turn, consists of a cadmium amalgam containing 12 to 14 per cent cadmium by weight. Over both electrodes are sprinkled some crystals of solid $CdSO_4 \cdot \frac{8}{3} H_2O$, the entire cell is filled with a saturated solution of cadmium sulfate, and the cell is closed with either corks and sealing wax, or the arms are drawn off. The pur-

Fig. 3.   Saturated Weston Standard Cell.

pose of the solid crystals of $CdSO_4 \cdot \frac{8}{3} H_2O$ is to keep the electrolyte saturated with this phase at all temperatures.

The operation of the Weston saturated standard cell depends on the reversible reaction

$$Cd(s) + Hg_2SO_4(s) + \frac{8}{3} H_2O(l) = CdSO_4 \cdot \frac{8}{3} H_2O(s) + 2 Hg(l) \quad (7)$$

The reaction as written occurs when the cell is acting as a source of current, while the reverse reaction takes place when current is passed through the cell.

The *unsaturated* Weston cell is similar to the saturated, except that the crystals of solid $CdSO_4 \cdot \frac{8}{3} H_2O$ are omitted, and the electrolyte is a solution of cadmium sulfate *saturated only at 4° C.* At all temperatures above 4° C the electrolyte in this cell is, therefore, unsaturated with respect to $CdSO_4 \cdot \frac{8}{3} H_2O$.

The Weston standard cells when carefully prepared and not subjected to abuse will preserve their potentials excellently for many years. The Weston *saturated cell*, or as it is frequently called the Weston normal cell, is generally used in laboratories as a standard of emf. Its potential at any temperature $t°$ C, in *international volts*,[1] is given by the equation

$$\mathcal{E}_t = 1.01830 - 4.06 \times 10^{-5}(t - 20) - 9.5 \times 10^{-7}(t - 20)^2 \quad (8)$$

---

[1] Since practically all emf data in the chemical literature are still expressed in international volts, no attempt will be made at present to convert the values given in this book to absolute volts.

The potential of the cell is thus 1.01830 volts at 20° C and 1.01807 volts at 25° C. The unsaturated cell is employed only as a secondary standard, possesses a lower temperature coefficient than the saturated, and has a potential close to 1.0186 volts at 20° C.

CELL REACTION AND EMF

In studying cells it is necessary to determine not only the emf of the cell but also the reaction responsible for it. The nature of the reaction proceeding in a cell can be deduced from the manner in which the electrodes must be connected to the standard cell in order to obtain a balance of the potentiometer. Since such a balance is possible only when the cells are connected so as to oppose each other, it must follow that the *electrode connected to the negative side of the standard cell is the negative electrode*, while the one connected to the positive side is the positive electrode. And, since a negative electrode contains electrons in excess of the number present on the positive electrode, *electrons will have to flow from the negative to the positive electrode in the external circuit.*

Once the direction of current flow is known, the processes responsible for emission of electrons at the negative electrode and the taking on of the electrons at the positive electrode can be ascertained from the nature of the electrode materials on the basis of our ordinary concepts of oxidation and reduction. The student is aware that any reaction that gives off electrons must be an oxidation, while any reaction that involves a taking on of electrons with consequent decrease in positive valence must be a reduction. Hence, *an oxidation must occur at the negative electrode* where electrons are given off, and *a reduction must take place at the positive electrode* where electrons enter. By *adding* the oxidation reaction at the negative electrode to the reduction at the positive electrode we obtain the cell reaction.

This manner of arriving at the cell reaction from the direction of electron flow may be illustrated with an example. Consider a cell composed of a zinc electrode dipping in a solution of zinc ions at unit activity and a cadmium electrode dipping into a solution of cadmium ions at the same activity; in other words, the cell

$$\ominus$$

$$\mathrm{Zn} \mid \mathrm{Zn}^{++}(a = 1) \parallel \mathrm{Cd}^{++}(a = 1) \mid \mathrm{Cd} \qquad (9)$$

At 25° C it is found with the aid of a potentiometer that this cell has an emf of $\varepsilon_{25°} = 0.3590$ volt and that the zinc electrode is negative. Hence the electron flow through the external circuit must be from the zinc to the cadmium electrodes, and consequently an oxidation occurs at the zinc electrode, a reduction at the cadmium electrode. The only oxidation process possible at the zinc electrode is, obviously,

$$Zn(s) = Zn^{++}(a = 1) + 2 \ominus$$

Again, the reduction at the cadmium electrode is

$$Cd^{++}(a = 1) + 2 \ominus = Cd(s)$$

The over-all cell reaction must be, then,

$$Zn(s) + Cd^{++}(a = 1) = Zn^{++}(a = 1) + Cd(s) \tag{10}$$

and this reaction yields an emf of $\varepsilon = 0.3590$ volt at 25° C.

It is important to realize that an emf without the reaction responsible for it is as meaningless as the age of an undesignated individual. For absolute clarity each emf must be accompanied by the reaction to which it refers, as well as by a complete statement of the nature of the phases, their concentrations, and the temperature.

CONVENTION REGARDING SIGN OF EMF

The net electrical work performed by a reaction yielding an emf ε and supplying a quantity of electricity Q is $Q\varepsilon$. For each equivalent reacting Q is equal to the faraday $\mathfrak{F}$, and hence for n equivalents reacting $Q = n\mathfrak{F}$. Therefore, the electrical work obtained from any reaction supplying $n\mathfrak{F}$ coulombs of electricity at a potential ε is

$$\text{Net electrical work} = n\mathfrak{F}\varepsilon$$

But any work performed by a cell can be accomplished only at the expense of a *decrease in free energy* occurring within the cell. Further, when the electrical work is a *maximum*, as when the cell operates *reversibly*, the decrease in free energy, $-\Delta F$, must equal the electrical work done. We obtain, therefore,

$$\Delta F = -n\mathfrak{F}\varepsilon \tag{11}$$

from which we see that the reversible emf of any cell is determined by the free energy change of the reaction going on in the cell. Equation (11) is the "bridge" between thermodynamics and electrochemistry. Through it the evaluation of various thermodynamic properties of reactions becomes possible from emf measurements.

It was shown in Chapter 11 that for any spontaneous reaction at constant temperature and pressure ΔF is negative, for any nonspontaneous one ΔF is positive, while for any reaction in equilibrium $\Delta F = 0$. In view of this, it may be deduced from equation (11) that for any spontaneous reaction ε will have to be positive, for any nonspontaneous reaction ε will be negative, while for any reaction in equilibrium ε will have to be zero. These relations between the spontaneity of a reaction and the signs of ΔF and ε are summarized in Table 1. They indicate that in order to have conformity between emf and ΔF it is necessary to prefix each and every emf with the appropriate sign depending on whether the reaction as written is the spontaneous one.

TABLE 1

RELATION BETWEEN SIGNS OF ΔF AND ε

Reaction	ΔF	ε
Spontaneous	−	+
Nonspontaneous	+	−
Equilibrium	0	0

The emf's of all cells under discussion here result from the spontaneous reactions occurring within the cells, and hence for all of them ε is positive. However, it is not always possible to tell *a priori* which of two processes possible, namely, the forward and reverse reactions, is the spontaneous one. Consequently it is necessary to have some means of ascertaining which reaction results in the measured positive emf. For this purpose we lay down the following rule: *If a cell is written on paper such that the negative electrode is on the left and the positive electrode on the right, in other words, so that electrons flow from left to right through the external circuit, the reaction deduced on the basis of oxidation-reduction described above is the spontaneous one, and the emf of the cell is positive.* By observing this rule the spontaneous reaction in any cell may be arrived at, and the correct sign ascribed to the emf corresponding to it.

We may illustrate the application of this rule with the cell given in equation (9). The cell is written with the negative electrode on the left, and hence the reaction deduced for it, equation (10), is the spontaneous one. For this reaction, then, $\varepsilon_{25°} = +0.3590$ volt. It follows, therefore, that the reverse of equation (10), namely,

$$Cd(s) + Zn^{++}(a = 1) = Zn(s) + Cd^{++}(a = 1) \qquad (12)$$

is not spontaneous, and for this reaction the emf at 25° C will be $\varepsilon_{25°} = -0.3590$. This means that in order to carry out the reaction in equation (12) at least 0.3590 volt will have to be applied to the cell; and, instead of obtaining electrical work from the cell, work will have to be done to get the reaction to go.

SINGLE ELECTRODE POTENTIALS

Any electrochemical reaction is the sum of the two electrode reactions, of which one is an oxidation, the other a reduction. Similarly, every cell emf may be thought of as being composed of two individual *single electrode potentials*, such that their *algebraic sum* is equal to the total emf of the cell. With these single electrode potentials the emf of any cell follows as the sum of the electrode potentials, just as the over-all cell reaction is the sum of the single electrode reactions.

Experimentally, only differences in potential between two electrodes can be measured. To determine directly single electrode potentials, it

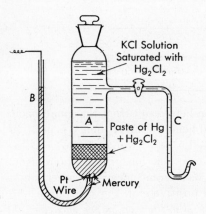

would be necessary to couple an electrode with another whose potential is zero. However, as no electrode of true zero potential is known, we must fall back upon an arbitrary standard electrode to which all other electrode potentials can be referred. For this reason *we define as the reference of emf the standard hydrogen electrode whose potential at all temperatures is taken as zero.* A standard hydrogen electrode consists of a piece of platinized platinum foil surrounded by hydrogen gas at 1 atm pressure and immersed in a solution containing hydrogen ions at unit activity. Details on the theory and operation of this electrode will be given later.

Fig. 4.   Calomel Electrode.

Because of experimental difficulties involved in the preparation and use of the standard hydrogen electrode, secondary reference electrodes have been compared with the former and are widely used. Among these are the three *calomel electrodes*, whose emf depends on the process spontaneous with respect to the hydrogen electrode reaction

$$Hg_2Cl_2(s) + 2 \ominus = 2\ Hg(l) + 2\ Cl^-(C = x) \qquad (13)$$

Here x is 0.1 N and 1 N potassium chloride for the 0.1 N and 1 N calomel electrodes, and a saturated potassium chloride solution for the saturated calomel electrode. A common form of these electrodes is shown in Fig. 4. The electrode consists of a glass vessel A to which are attached the sidearm B for making electrical contact and the arm C for insertion in any desired solution. Into the bottom of A is sealed a platinum wire over which are placed in turn a layer of specially purified mercury, a paste of mercury and calomel, and then the appropriate potassium chloride solution saturated with calomel so as to fill the cell and the arm C. In the 0.1 N calomel this solution is 0.1 N potassium chloride, in the 1 N calomel it is 1 N potassium chloride, and in the saturated calomel it is an aqueous solution saturated with both potassium chloride and mercurous chloride. In the latter electrode some crystals of potassium chloride are also placed over the mercury-mercurous chloride paste in order to keep the solution saturated at all temperatures.

The potentials of the various calomel electrodes depend at each temperature on the concentration of potassium chloride with which the

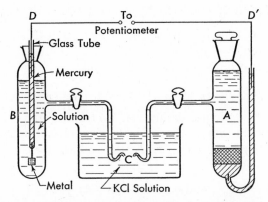

Fig. 5.   Determination of Single Electrode Potentials.

electrode vessels are filled. In Table 2 are given the potentials of these electrodes as a function of temperature, the emf at 25° C, and the corresponding electrode reactions. These emf's are highest for the 0.1 N calomel and decrease as the concentration is increased. Further, the 0.1 N calomel has the smallest temperature coefficient of emf, while the saturated calomel electrode has the highest.

TABLE 2

POTENTIALS OF CALOMEL ELECTRODES

Electrode	Symbol	Emf	$\varepsilon_{25°C}$	Reaction
0.1 N calomel	Hg $\mid$ Hg$_2$Cl$_2$(s), KCl(0.1 N)	$\varepsilon = 0.3338 - 7 \times 10^{-5}(t - 25)$	0.3338	Hg$_2$Cl$_2$(s) $+ 2 \ominus =$ 2 Hg(l) $+$ 2 Cl$^-$ (0.1 N)
1 N calomel	Hg $\mid$ Hg$_2$Cl$_2$(s), KCl(1 N)	$\varepsilon = 0.2800 - 2.4 \times 10^{-4}(t - 25)$	0.2800	Hg$_2$Cl$_2$(s) $+ 2 \ominus =$ 2 Hg(l) $+$ 2 Cl$^-$(1 N)
Saturated calomel	Hg $\mid$ Hg$_2$Cl$_2$(s), KCl (sat'd.)	$\varepsilon = 0.2415 - 7.6 \times 10^{-4}(t - 25)$	0.2415	Hg$_2$Cl$_2$(s) $+ 2 \ominus =$ 2 Hg(l) $+$ 2 Cl$^-$(sat'd.)

The manner in which these auxiliary reference electrodes are combined with other electrodes to form cells is shown in Fig. 5. Here A is the reference calomel electrode, B the other single electrode whose potential is to be determined, and C a *salt bridge* to permit electrical contact between A and B. The salt bridge consists usually of a beaker filled with $1 N$ or saturated potassium chloride solution into which the side-arms of the electrodes are immersed. Electrical contact with the potentiometer is made by means of the wires D and D'.

CALCULATION OF SINGLE ELECTRODE POTENTIALS

From emf's of cells involving various electrodes in combination with reference electrodes, single electrode potentials are readily calculated. To illustrate the procedure consider first the cell

$$\overline{\text{Cd}} \mid \text{Cd}^{++}(a = 1) \parallel \text{KCl}(1 \ N), \ \text{Hg}_2\text{Cl}_2(\text{s}) \mid \text{Hg} \qquad (14)$$

consisting of a cadmium-cadmium ion electrode and a $1 \ N$ calomel. For this cell it is found that at 25° C $\varepsilon = 0.6830$ volt and that the cadmium electrode is negative. Consequently the cadmium electrode undergoes the oxidation reaction

$$\text{Cd(s)} = \text{Cd}^{++}(a = 1) + 2 \ominus$$

while the calomel electrode undergoes the reduction,

$$\text{Hg}_2\text{Cl}_2(\text{s}) + 2 \ominus = 2 \ \text{Hg(l)} + 2 \ \text{Cl}^-(1 \ N)$$

For the latter process Table 2 shows that the emf at 25° C is $\varepsilon_C = +0.2800$ volt. Hence

$$\varepsilon = \varepsilon_{\text{Cd}} + \varepsilon_C$$
$$0.6830 = \varepsilon_{\text{Cd}} + 0.2800$$

and
$$\varepsilon_{\text{Cd}} = 0.4030 \text{ volt}$$

Therefore the reaction and the corresponding emf at 25° C for the $\text{Cd} \mid \text{Cd}^{++}(a = 1)$ electrode are

$$\text{Cd(s)} = \text{Cd}^{++}(a = 1) + 2 \ominus \qquad \varepsilon_{25°\text{C}} = 0.4030 \text{ volt}$$

As a second example let us take the cell

$$\overline{\text{Hg}} \mid \text{Hg}_2\text{Cl}_2(\text{s}), \ \text{KCl}(1 \ N) \parallel \text{Cu}^{++}(a = 1) \mid \text{Cu} \qquad (15)$$

consisting of a $1 \ N$ calomel and a copper electrode dipping in a solution of cupric ions at unit activity. At 25° C the emf of this cell is $\varepsilon = 0.0570$ volt, and *the calomel electrode is negative*. Since the latter electrode is negative, the reaction occurring in it must be an oxidation, or

$$2 \ \text{Hg(l)} + 2 \ \text{Cl}^-(1 \ N) = \text{Hg}_2\text{Cl}_2(\text{s}) + 2 \ominus$$

Further, as the reduction reaction yields an emf of $+0.2800$ volt, the emf on oxidation must be $\varepsilon_C = -0.2800$ volt. The corresponding reduction at the copper electrode involves the reaction

$$Cu^{++}(a = 1) + 2\ominus = Cu(s)$$

with a single electrode potential ε_{Cu}. We obtain, then,

$$\varepsilon = \varepsilon_C + \varepsilon_{Cu}$$
$$0.0570 = -0.2800 + \varepsilon_{Cu}$$
$$\varepsilon_{Cu} = 0.3370 \text{ volt}$$

and so for the $Cu \mid Cu^{++}(a = 1)$ electrode

$$Cu^{++}(a = 1) + 2\ominus = Cu(s) \qquad \varepsilon_{25°\,C} = 0.3370 \text{ volt}$$

CALCULATION OF CELL EMF'S FROM SINGLE ELECTRODE POTENTIALS

When the single electrode potentials and reactions are available, the calculations may be reversed to predict cell emf's and cell reactions. Suppose it is desired to know the reaction and the emf at $25°$ C for the cell

$$Cd \mid Cd^{++}(a = 1) \parallel Cu^{++}(a = 1) \mid Cu \qquad (16)$$

Assume that the cell as written is correct, i.e., that the cadmium electrode is negative. Then, for the oxidation at the cadmium electrode we have

$$Cd(s) = Cd^{++}(a = 1) + 2\ominus \qquad \varepsilon_{25°\,C} = 0.4030 \text{ volt}$$

Again, for the reduction at the copper electrode we get

$$Cu^{++}(a = 1) + 2\ominus = Cu(s) \qquad \varepsilon_{25°\,C} = 0.3370 \text{ volt}$$

Adding now the single electrode reactions and the single electrode potentials, we find for the cell reaction

$$Cd(s) + Cu^{++}(a = 1) = Cd^{++}(a = 1) + Cu(s) \qquad (17a)$$

and for the emf,

$$\varepsilon_{cell} = \varepsilon_{Cd} + \varepsilon_{Cu}$$
$$= 0.4030 + 0.3370$$
$$= +0.7400 \text{ volt at } 25° \text{ C} \qquad (17b)$$

Since the calculated emf is positive, the assumption made with respect to the polarity of the electrodes is correct, and the cell reaction as given is the spontaneous one.

On the other hand, had we assumed the copper electrode in equation (16) to be negative, the latter would have to undergo the oxidation

$$Cu(s) = Cu^{++}(a = 1) + 2\ominus$$

with emf equal to $\varepsilon_{Cu} = -0.3370$ volt; the cadmium electrode would have to suffer the reduction

$$Cd^{++}(a = 1) + 2 \ominus = Cd(s)$$

with emf $\varepsilon_{Cd} = -0.4030$ volt; and we would have found for the cell reaction and emf

$$Cu(s) + Cd^{++}(a = 1) = Cu^{++}(a = 1) + Cd(s)$$
$$\varepsilon_{cell} = -0.7400 \text{ volt at } 25° \text{ C} \qquad (18)$$

Equation (18) reveals that since ε_{cell} is negative the reaction as written is not spontaneous, and consequently the wrong assumption was made with respect to the polarity of the electrodes. All that need be done to rectify the situation is to *reverse the reaction* written in equation (18) and *to change the sign of* ε_{cell}. The result is then the spontaneous reaction and emf of the cell as given in equations (17a) and (17b).

SUMMARY OF RULES

Before proceeding it may not be out of place to summarize the various rules we have employed above with respect to cell reactions and emf's. These are:

1. Any cell reaction is the *sum* of the single electrode reactions *as they occur in the cell.*
   (a) At the *negative electrode* the reaction is an *oxidation.*
   (b) At the *positive electrode* the reaction is a *reduction.*
2. The total cell emf is the algebraic sum of the single electrode potentials provided each emf is affixed with the sign corresponding to the reaction as it actually takes place at the electrode.
3. If any cell is written down with the *negative electrode on the left,* so that electrons flow through the external circuit from left to right, the cell reaction deduced by rule (1) will be the *spontaneous* process, and the emf deduced by rule (2) for the cell will be *positive.*
4. If the wrong assumption be made with respect to the polarity of the electrodes, rule (3) will yield a *negative* emf corresponding to the *nonspontaneous* reaction. To obtain the spontaneous reaction and its emf, all that need be done is *to reverse the reaction and change the sign of the emf without changing its magnitude.*

By adhering *rigidly* to these rules the student can avoid confusion in regard to signs or reactions.

THERMODYNAMICS AND EMF: ΔH AND ΔS FROM EMF DATA

According to equation (18), Chapter 11, the change in free energy, ΔF, for *any* process is related to the change in heat content, ΔH, by the Gibbs-Helmholtz equation

$$\Delta F - \Delta H = T \left[\frac{\partial(\Delta F)}{\partial T} \right]_P \tag{19}$$

Again, the fundamental relation between emf and ΔF is

$$\Delta F = -n\mathfrak{F}\mathcal{E} \tag{11}$$

If equation (11) is differentiated with respect to temperature, then,

$$\left[\frac{\partial(\Delta F)}{\partial T} \right]_P = -n\mathfrak{F} \left(\frac{\partial \mathcal{E}}{\partial T} \right)_P \tag{20}$$

and on substitution of equations (20) and (11) into equation (19) we find for ΔH

$$-n\mathfrak{F}\mathcal{E} - \Delta H = -n\mathfrak{F}T \left(\frac{\partial \mathcal{E}}{\partial T} \right)_P$$

$$\Delta H = -n\mathfrak{F}\mathcal{E} + n\mathfrak{F}T \left(\frac{\partial \mathcal{E}}{\partial T} \right)_P$$

$$= n\mathfrak{F} \left[T \left(\frac{\partial \mathcal{E}}{\partial T} \right)_P - \mathcal{E} \right] \tag{21}$$

Equation (21) permits the calculation of the heat of a reaction from the measured emf and temperature coefficient of emf of the reaction, or $(\partial \mathcal{E}/\partial T)_P$ from ΔH and $\mathcal{E}$. In using this equation, ΔH follows in *joules* when $\mathcal{E}$ and $\mathfrak{F}$ are in volts and coulombs respectively, while ΔH must be substituted in *joules* to obtain $\mathcal{E}$ in volts, or $(\partial \mathcal{E}/\partial T)_P$ in volts per $°$ K.

To show the use of equation (21) for calculating ΔH, we may take the reaction

$$Zn(s) + 2 AgCl(s) = ZnCl_2(0.555 \ m) + 2 Ag(s) \tag{22}$$

for which $\mathcal{E}_{0°C} = 1.015$ volt while $(\partial \mathcal{E}/\partial T)_P = -4.02 \times 10^{-4}$ volt per degree. Since in equation (22) 2 faradays are necessary to accomplish the change, $n = 2$; and, with $\mathfrak{F} = 96,500$ and $T = 273.2°$ K,

$$\Delta H = n\mathfrak{F} \left[T \left(\frac{\partial \mathcal{E}}{\partial T} \right)_P - \mathcal{E} \right]$$
$$= 2 \times 96,500[273.2(-4.02 \times 10^{-4}) - 1.015]$$
$$= -217,100 \text{ joles}$$
$$= -\frac{217,100}{4.184} = -51,900 \text{ cal}$$

The heat of reaction found calorimetrically is $\Delta H = -52,050$ cal.

It should be noticed that $n = 2$ in equation (22) only for the reaction written. Had the reaction been given as

$$\frac{1}{2} \, Zn(s) + AgCl(s) = \frac{1}{2} \, ZnCl_2(0.555 \, m) + Ag(s) \tag{22a}$$

n would be one, but ε and $(\partial \varepsilon / \partial T)_P$ would remain the same. Then ΔH would follow as one-half the quantity given above, since only half the amounts of materials would be involved in reaction. For this reason it is essential to state the equation for which ΔH is calculated.

Equation (19) indicates that in general ΔF will differ from ΔH by

$T \left[\dfrac{\partial(\Delta F)}{\partial T} \right]_P$, or, in view of equation (20),

$$\Delta F - \Delta H = -n\mathfrak{F}T \left(\frac{\partial \varepsilon}{\partial T} \right)_P \tag{23}$$

Therefore, for any electrochemical reaction ΔF can equal ΔH only when $(\partial \varepsilon / \partial T)_P = 0$. Further, since

$$\Delta F - \Delta H = -T\Delta S \tag{24}$$

comparison of equations (23) and (24) yields

$$-T\Delta S = -n\mathfrak{F}T \left(\frac{\partial \varepsilon}{\partial T} \right)_P$$

and

$$\Delta S = n\mathfrak{F} \left(\frac{\partial \varepsilon}{\partial T} \right)_P \tag{25}$$

With the aid of equation (25) the entropy change of a reaction can readily be calculated from the temperature coefficient of emf. For the cell cited in equation (22a) $(\partial \varepsilon / \partial T)_P = -4.02 \times 10^{-4}$, $n = 2$, and so the entropy change of this reaction is

$$\Delta S = 2 \times 96,500(-4.02 \times 10^{-4})$$
$$= -77.59 \text{ joules degree}^{-1}$$
$$= -18.55 \text{ eu}$$

THERMODYNAMICS OF ELECTRODE POTENTIALS

Single electrode and cell potentials are determined not only by the nature of the constituents composing the electrodes, but also by the temperature and the activities of the solutions employed. The dependence of the emf's on the latter variables is deducible from thermodynamics. For any reaction such as

$$aA + bB + \cdots = cC + dD + \cdots \tag{26}$$

the change in free energy, ΔF, as a function of the *initial* activities of the reactants and the *final* activities of the products, is given by the *reaction isotherm* (Chapter 11, equation (47)) as

$$\Delta F = \Delta F^0 + RT \ln \frac{a_C^c a_D^d \; \cdots}{a_A^\alpha a_B^b \; \cdots} \tag{27}$$

Here the a's in the numerator are the activities of the products, those in the denominator the activities of the reactants, and ΔF^0, the standard free energy change, is the free energy change attending the reaction when the activities of products and reactants are all unity. If we substitute into equation (27) $\Delta F = -n\mathfrak{F}\mathcal{E}$, and define $\mathcal{E}^0$ by

$$\Delta F^0 = -n\mathfrak{F}\mathcal{E}^0 \tag{28}$$

where $\mathcal{E}^0$ is the value of $\mathcal{E}$ corresponding to ΔF^0, equation (27) becomes

$$-n\mathfrak{F}\mathcal{E} = -n\mathfrak{F}\mathcal{E}^0 + RT \ln \frac{a_C^c a_D^d \; \cdots}{a_A^\alpha a_B^b \; \cdots}$$

and hence $\mathcal{E}$ follows as

$$\begin{aligned} \mathcal{E} &= \mathcal{E}^0 - \frac{RT}{n\mathfrak{F}} \ln \frac{a_C^c a_D^d \; \cdots}{a_A^\alpha a_B^b \; \cdots} \\ &= \mathcal{E}^0 - \frac{2.3026 \, RT}{n\mathfrak{F}} \log_{10} \frac{a_C^c a_D^d \; \cdots}{a_A^\alpha a_B^b \; \cdots} \end{aligned} \tag{29}$$

Equation (29) gives the potential of any electrode or cell as a function of the initial and final activities. It shows that the emf is determined by the activities of the reacting species, the temperature, and by the quantity $\mathcal{E}^0$. Since ΔF^0 is a constant for any reaction at constant temperature, $\mathcal{E}^0$ *must also be a constant at constant temperature characteristic of the electrode or cell.* It is in fact the emf of the electrode or cell when all the activities are all unity. $\mathcal{E}^0$ is called the *standard potential* of the electrode or cell in question.

The *standard electrode potentials* at 25° C for a number of electrodes, evaluated by methods to which reference will be made later, are given in Table 3. The corresponding electrode reactions are also included. In every instance the sign of the emf refers to the *oxidation* reaction. Before using these $\mathcal{E}^0$ values in equation (29) it must first be ascertained whether the electrode reaction *as it actually occurs in the particular cell* is the oxidation or the reduction. For oxidation the $\mathcal{E}^0$'s tabulated are used directly. However, for reduction the sign of each and every $\mathcal{E}^0$ given must be reversed. Thus, for a process such as $K = K^+ + \ominus \; \mathcal{E}^0_{25°C} = +2.9241$, but for $K^+ + \ominus = K \; \mathcal{E}^0_{25°C} = -2.9241$ volts. Similarly, for $Cu = Cu^{++} + 2 \ominus \; \mathcal{E}^0_{25°C} = -0.337$ volt, while for $Cu^{++} + 2 \ominus = Cu \; \mathcal{E}^0_{25°C} = +0.337$ volt.

TABLE 3

STANDARD ELECTRODE POTENTIALS AT 25° C FOR OXIDATION REACTIONS

Electrode	Electrode Reaction	$\mathcal{E}^0$ (volts)
Li | Li$^+$	Li(s) = Li$^+$ + $\ominus$	+3.045
K | K$^+$	K(s) = K$^+$ + $\ominus$	+2.9241
Ca | Ca^{++}	Ca(s) = Ca^{++} + 2 $\ominus$	+2.87
Na | Na$^+$	Na(s) = Na$^+$ + $\ominus$	+2.7146
Zn | Zn^{++}	Zn(s) = Zn^{++} + 2 $\ominus$	+0.7618
Fe | Fe^{++}	Fe(s) = Fe^{++} + 2 $\ominus$	+0.441
Cd | Cd^{++}	Cd(s) = Cd^{++} + 2 $\ominus$	+0.403
Pb | PbSO$_4$(s), SO$_4^{--}$	Pb(s) + SO$_4^{--}$ = PbSO$_4$(s) + 2 $\ominus$	+0.3546
Tl | Tl$^+$	Tl(s) = Tl$^+$ + $\ominus$	+0.3363
Ni | Ni^{++}	Ni(s) = Ni^{++} + 2 $\ominus$	+0.236
Ag | AgI(s), I$^-$	Ag(s) + I$^-$ = AgI(s) + $\ominus$	+0.1522
Sn | Sn^{++}	Sn(s) = Sn^{++} + 2 $\ominus$	+0.140
Pb | Pb^{++}	Pb(s) = Pb^{++} + 2 $\ominus$	+0.1265
H$_2$ | H$^+$	H$_2$(g, 1 atm) = 2 H$^+$ + 2 $\ominus$	±0.0000
Ag | AgBr(s), Br$^-$	Ag(s) + Br$^-$ = AgBr(s) + $\ominus$	−0.0711
Hg | Hg$_2$Br$_2$(s), Br$^-$	2 Hg(l) + 2 Br$^-$ = Hg$_2$Br$_2$(s) + 2 $\ominus$	−0.1385
Pt | Sn^{++}, Sn^{++++}	Sn^{++} = Sn^{++++} + 2 $\ominus$	−0.14
Ag | AgCl(s), Cl$^-$	Ag(s) + Cl$^-$ = AgCl(s) + $\ominus$	−0.2225
Hg | Hg$_2$Cl$_2$(s), Cl$^-$	2 Hg(l) + 2 Cl$^-$ = Hg$_2$Cl$_2$ + 2 $\ominus$	−0.2680
Cu | Cu^{++}	Cu(s) = Cu^{++} + 2 $\ominus$	−0.337
I$_2$ | I$^-$	2 I$^-$ = I$_2$(s) + 2 $\ominus$	−0.5355
Hg | Hg$_2$SO$_4$(s), SO$_4^{--}$	2 Hg(l) + SO$_4^{--}$ = Hg$_2$SO$_4$(s) + 2 $\ominus$	−0.6141
Pt | Fe^{++}, Fe^{+++}	Fe^{++} = Fe^{+++} + $\ominus$	−0.771
Ag | Ag$^+$	Ag(s) = Ag$^+$ + $\ominus$	−0.7991
Br$_2$ | Br$^-$	2 Br$^-$ = Br$_2$(l) + 2 $\ominus$	−1.0652
Pt | Tl$^+$, Tl^{+++}	Tl$^+$ = Tl^{+++} + 2 $\ominus$	−1.250
Cl$_2$ | Cl$^-$	2 Cl$^-$ = Cl$_2$(g, 1 atm) + 2 $\ominus$	−1.3595
Pt | Ce^{+++}, Ce^{++++}	Ce^{+++} = Ce^{++++} + $\ominus$	−1.61
Pt | Co^{++}, Co^{+++}	Co^{++} = Co^{+++} + $\ominus$	−1.82

In equation (29) the factor $(2.3026\,RT)/\mathfrak{F}$ is a constant for any given temperature. To evaluate it R must be taken in joules, namely,

$$\frac{2.3026\,RT}{\mathfrak{F}} = \frac{2.3026 \times 8.3147\,T}{96,496}$$
$$= 1.9841 \times 10^{-4}\,T$$

Values of this quantity for a number of temperatures are given in Table 4.

Once the $\mathcal{E}^0$'s for various electrodes are available, they may be utilized to calculate the single electrode potentials. Specifically, suppose the emf of the zinc electrode

$$\text{Zn} \mid \text{Zn}^{++}(a = 0.1)$$

TABLE 4

VALUES OF $(2.3026\,RT)/\mathfrak{F}$ AT VARIOUS TEMPERATURES

$t°\ C$	$(2.3026\,RT)/\mathfrak{F}$
0	0.054195
10	0.056180
15	0.057172
20	0.058164
25	0.059156
30	0.060148

is sought at 25° C in a solution of zinc ions where the activity is 0.1. For *oxidation* the reaction at this electrode is

$$\text{Zn(s)} = \text{Zn}^{++}(a = 0.1) + 2\ominus$$

and hence on applying equation (29) we obtain for the single electrode potential, ε_{Zn},

$$\varepsilon_{Zn} = \varepsilon_{Zn}^0 - \frac{2.3026\,RT}{n\mathfrak{F}} \log_{10} \frac{a_{Zn^{++}}}{a_{Zn}}$$

For this reaction $n = 2$, $a_{Zn^{++}} = 0.1$, and $a_{Zn} = 1$, since zinc is a solid. Again, at 25° C, $(2.3026\,RT)/\mathfrak{F} = 0.05916$, while ε_{Zn}^0 for oxidation is $\varepsilon_{25°\,C}^0 = +0.7618$ volt. Substituting these quantities into the expression for ε_{Zn}, we find that

$$\varepsilon_{Zn} = +0.7618 - \frac{0.05916}{2} \log_{10} \frac{0.1}{1}$$
$$= 0.7618 + 0.0296$$
$$= 0.7914 \text{ volt}$$

However, when the reaction at the electrode is a *reduction*, namely,

$$\text{Zn}^{++}(a = 0.1) + 2\ominus = \text{Zn(s)}$$

the equation yields for ε_{Zn}:

$$\varepsilon_{Zn} = \varepsilon_{Zn}^0 - \frac{0.05916}{2} \log_{10} \frac{a_{Zn}}{a_{Zn^{++}}}$$
$$= \varepsilon_{Zn}^0 - \frac{0.05916}{2} \log_{10} \frac{1}{0.1}$$

Further, for reduction $\varepsilon_{Zn}^0 = -0.7618$, and therefore,

$$\varepsilon_{Zn} = -0.7618 - 0.0296$$
$$= -0.7914 \text{ volt}$$

i.e., the potential is the same as before but opposite in sign.

EQUATION (29) AND CELL EMF'S

Consider now a cell

$$\text{Zn} \mid \text{Zn}^{++}(a_{\text{Zn}^{++}}) \parallel \text{Cl}^-(a_{\text{Cl}^-}), \text{Hg}_2\text{Cl}_2(\text{s}) \mid \text{Hg} \tag{30}$$

In this cell the zinc electrode is negative, and undergoes the oxidation reaction

$$\text{Zn(s)} = \text{Zn}^{++}(a_{\text{Zn}^{++}}) + 2 \ominus \tag{31a}$$

for which the electrode emf is given by

$$\varepsilon_{\text{Zn}} = \varepsilon_{\text{Zn}}^0 - \frac{RT}{2\,\mathfrak{F}} \ln a_{\text{Zn}^{++}} \tag{31b}$$

Again, for the reduction at the calomel electrode the reaction is

$$\text{Hg}_2\text{Cl}_2(\text{s}) + 2 \ominus = 2\,\text{Hg(l)} + 2\,\text{Cl}^-(a_{\text{Cl}^-}) \tag{32a}$$

and the single electrode potential is

$$\varepsilon_{\text{C}} = \varepsilon_{\text{C}}^0 - \frac{RT}{2\,\mathfrak{F}} \ln a_{\text{Cl}^-}^2 \tag{32b}$$

On adding equations (31a) and (32a) we find the cell reaction to be

$$\text{Zn(s)} + \text{Hg}_2\text{Cl}_2(\text{s}) = 2\,\text{Hg(l)} + \text{Zn}^{++}(a_{\text{Zn}^{++}}) + 2\,\text{Cl}^-(a_{\text{Cl}^-}) \tag{33a}$$

and similarly on adding equations (31b) and (32b) the cell emf ε follows as

$$\begin{aligned}
\varepsilon &= \varepsilon_{\text{Zn}} + \varepsilon_{\text{C}} \\
&= \left(\varepsilon_{\text{Zn}}^0 - \frac{RT}{2\,\mathfrak{F}} \ln a_{\text{Zn}^{++}}\right) + \left(\varepsilon_{\text{C}}^0 - \frac{RT}{2\,\mathfrak{F}} \ln a_{\text{Cl}^-}^2\right) \\
&= (\varepsilon_{\text{Zn}}^0 + \varepsilon_{\text{C}}^0) - \frac{RT}{2\,\mathfrak{F}} \ln (a_{\text{Zn}^{++}} a_{\text{Cl}^-}^2)
\end{aligned} \tag{33b}$$

Instead of approaching the cell emf through the single electrode potentials, we may apply equation (29) directly to the cell reaction given in equation (33a). If this be done, we find that the cell emf is

$$\varepsilon = \varepsilon_{\text{cell}}^0 - \frac{RT}{2\,\mathfrak{F}} \ln (a_{\text{Zn}^{++}} a_{\text{Cl}^-}^2) \tag{34}$$

where $\varepsilon_{\text{cell}}^0$ is the *standard potential of the cell*. Comparison of equations (33b) and (34), which must be identical, shows that $\varepsilon_{\text{cell}}^0 = \varepsilon_{\text{Zn}}^0 + \varepsilon_{\text{C}}^0$, i.e., that the ε^0 *value of the cell is the sum of the* ε^0 *values of the electrodes composing* it. This relation between the standard electrode and cell potentials, namely,

$$\varepsilon_{\text{cell}}^0 = \varepsilon_1^0 + \varepsilon_2^0 \tag{35}$$

where ε_1^0 and ε_2^0 are the ε^0's for the two electrodes, applies to any cell. Consequently, as soon as the standard emf's of the electrodes are known, that of the cell composed of these is also available, and equation (29) may be applied directly to the over-all reaction of the cell.

In employing equation (35) each standard electrode potential must be prefixed by the *sign corresponding to the reaction as it occurs in the cell.* Thus the reaction at the zinc electrode in equation (30) is an oxidation, and therefore $\varepsilon_{Zn}^0 = +0.7618$ volt at 25° C. Again, the reaction at the calomel electrode is a reduction, and hence $\varepsilon_C^0 = +0.2680$ volt. Consequently ε_{cell}^0 is

$$\varepsilon_{cell}^0 = 0.7618 + 0.2680$$
$$= 1.0298 \text{ volts}$$

With this value of ε_{cell}^0 and $a_{Zn^{++}} = 0.1$, $a_{Cl^-} = 0.2$, the cell given in equation (30) would have, according to equation (34), the emf

$$\varepsilon = \varepsilon_{cell}^0 - \frac{RT}{2\,\mathfrak{F}} \ln a_{Zn^{++}} a_{Cl^-}^2$$

$$= 1.0298 - \frac{0.05916}{2} \log_{10} (0.1)(0.2)^2$$

$$= 1.0298 + 0.0708$$

$$= 1.1006 \text{ volts}$$

STANDARD POTENTIALS AND EQUILIBRIUM CONSTANTS

Standard electrode and cell emf's may also be utilized for obtaining equilibrium constants. According to equation (28), ΔF^0 for any electrochemical process is given by

$$\Delta F^0 = -n\mathfrak{F}\varepsilon^0$$

But, ΔF^0 is also related to the equilibrium constant K_a of the process by the equation

$$\Delta F^0 = -RT \ln K_a$$

If these two expressions for ΔF^0 are equated, we obtain

$$-n\mathfrak{F}\varepsilon^0 = -RT \ln K_a$$

and hence,
$$\varepsilon^0 = \frac{RT}{n\mathfrak{F}} \ln K_a \qquad (36)$$

With equation (36) K_a can be evaluated from ε^0, or, when K_a is available, ε^0 may be calculated. Thus, for the reduction of stannous ions by thallium, $\varepsilon^0 = 0.196$ volt at 25° C. For this process the equilibrium constant is, therefore,

$$0.196 = \frac{0.05916}{1} \log_{10} K_a$$

$$\log_{10} K_a = \frac{0.196}{0.05916} = 3.31$$

$$K_a = 2.0 \times 10^3$$

Since K_a for this reaction is

$$K_a = \frac{a_{Tl^+}}{a_{Sn^{++}}^{1/2}}$$

where the activities are those *at equilibrium*, this means that if thallium were added to a solution of stannous ions, the reaction would proceed and equilibrium would not be established until the activity of thallous ions became equal to

$$a_{Tl^+} = K_a \, a_{Sn^{++}}^{1/2}$$
$$= 2.0 \times 10^3 \, a_{Sn^{++}}^{1/2}$$

Once this condition is attained the system will be in equilibrium, and no further chemical action will take place.

In this manner may be calculated the equilibrium conditions for any electrode or cell reaction from the appropriate $\mathcal{E}^0$ values. Qualitatively the results to be anticipated may be arrived at as follows. Inspection of Table 3 shows that for the reactions listed above hydrogen $\mathcal{E}^0$ is positive, and hence for these the oxidation processes are spontaneous with respect to hydrogen. Further, the metals at the top of the table possess high values of $\mathcal{E}^0$, indicating that these substances are oxidized readily with a large decrease in free energy. Since any substance that is readily oxidized is a strong reducing agent, we may conclude that the metals high in the electromotive series of standard electrode potentials are powerful *reducing agents*, and that the reducing power of these decreases as we pass *down* the table. On the other hand, for the substances below hydrogen in the table the oxidation reactions are not spontaneous with respect to hydrogen, and hence such substances tend to undergo reduction reactions. Furthermore, the reduction proceeds the more readily the lower the reaction is in the electromotive series. As substances that are easily reduced are strong oxidizing agents, we find thus at the bottom of the table the *powerful oxidants*, such as Ce^{++++}, Tl^{+++}, chlorine, bromine; and, as we pass *up* the table the oxidizing power decreases. Consequently extent of reaction will be most complete for chemical interaction between substances at the top and bottom of the table and will decrease as the substances reacting lie closer and closer to each other. Thus, for reaction between lithium metal and ceric ions K_a at 25° C is 10^{78}, whereas for the reaction between iron metal and cadmium ions K_a is only 19.3.

Theoretically any substance should be reduced by any other above it in the series, and oxidized by any one below it, provided the activities of all reactants are unity. As the latter condition is hardly ever encountered in practice, this expectation does not always materialize. In fact, the position of various substances near each other in the series may actually be shifted about by changes in the concentrations of the reactants. However, for substances considerably removed from each other in the series such a shift is not possible.

CLASSIFICATION OF ELECTRODES

In electrochemical work the cells encountered involve various electrodes depending on the purpose at hand. These electrodes may be grouped into seven types, namely:

1. Metal-metal ion electrodes
2. Amalgam electrodes
3. Nonmetal nongas electrodes
4. Gas electrodes
5. Metal-insoluble salt electrodes
6. Metal-insoluble oxide electrodes
7. Oxidation-reduction electrodes

We proceed now to a discussion of each of these.

METAL-METAL ION ELECTRODES

Electrodes of this type involve a metal in equilibrium with a solution of its ions. They have already been described in some detail. Examples are the zinc, copper, cadmium, and sodium electrodes. All these electrodes operate on the general reaction

$$M = M^{+n} + n \ominus \tag{37}$$

for which the electrode potential equation is given by

$$\varepsilon_M = \varepsilon_M^0 - \frac{RT}{n\mathfrak{F}} \ln a_{M^{+n}} \tag{38}$$

Each of these electrodes is said to be *reversible* to its own ions; i.e., the potential of each of these electrodes is sensitive to and is determined by the activities of its own ions in the solution in which the metal is immersed. Thus, the zinc electrode is reversible to zinc ions, the iron electrode to ferrous ions, the tin electrode to stannous ions, etc.

AMALGAM ELECTRODES

It is quite common practice to substitute for the pure metals in metal-metal ion electrodes solutions of the metal in mercury, namely, *amalgams*. Amalgams of metals more active than mercury behave essentially as do the pure metals, the only difference being that the activity of the metal is lowered somewhat by dilution by the mercury. These amalgam electrodes are preferred frequently because equilibrium can as a rule be established much more rapidly with them than with the pure metals, and because they are more readily reversible. Again, with metals such as sodium, potassium, or calcium the activity in aqueous solutions is too great for direct use. However, by converting these metals to amalgams the activity can be moderated sufficiently to permit measurements in presence of water. Still another factor in favor of the amalgams is that small quantities of impurities, which may cause erratic behavior in pure metals, are often diluted enough by amalgamation to yield satisfactory and reproducible results.

As an example of electrodes in this class may be taken the lead amalgam electrode, consisting of the lead amalgam, written Pb(Hg), dipping into a solution of plumbous ions, namely, $\text{Pb(Hg)} \mid \text{Pb}^{++}(a_{\text{Pb}^{++}})$. For this electrode the reaction is

$$\text{Pb(Hg)} = \text{Pb}^{++}(a_{\text{Pb}^{++}}) + 2 \ominus \tag{39}$$

and hence the electrode potential ε_a is given by

$$\varepsilon_a = \varepsilon_{\text{Pb}}^0 - \frac{RT}{2\,\mathfrak{F}} \ln \frac{a_{\text{Pb}^{++}}}{a_{\text{Pb}}} \tag{40}$$

where $\varepsilon_{\text{Pb}}^0$ is the standard electrode potential of the pure lead electrode, $a_{\text{Pb}^{++}}$ is the activity of plumbous ions in solution, and a_{Pb} is the activity of *metallic lead in the amalgam*. In general a_{Pb} is not unity. The usual procedure is to write equation (40) as

$$\varepsilon_a = \left(\varepsilon_{\text{Pb}}^0 + \frac{RT}{2\,\mathfrak{F}} \ln a_{\text{Pb}} \right) - \frac{RT}{2\,\mathfrak{F}} \ln a_{\text{Pb}^{++}}$$

$$= \varepsilon_a^0 - \frac{RT}{2\,\mathfrak{F}} \ln a_{\text{Pb}^{++}} \tag{41}$$

where ε_a^0 is the standard potential of the given amalgam and to evaluate ε_a^0 first. Then, in order to transform ε_a^0 to $\varepsilon_{\text{Pb}}^0$, the emf of the amalgam is measured against pure lead when both are immersed in a solution of plumbous ions of the *same* concentration. Since for pure lead the single electrode potential equation is

$$\varepsilon_{\text{Pb}} = \varepsilon_{\text{Pb}}^0 - \frac{RT}{2\,\mathfrak{F}} \ln a_{\text{Pb}^{++}}$$

while for the amalgam it is equation (41), the difference in potential ε between the lead and amalgam electrodes follows as

$$\varepsilon = \varepsilon_{\text{Pb}} - \varepsilon_a$$

$$= \left(\varepsilon_{\text{Pb}}^0 - \frac{RT}{2\,\mathfrak{F}} \ln a_{\text{Pb}^{++}} \right) - \left(\varepsilon_a^0 - \frac{RT}{2\,\mathfrak{F}} \ln a_{\text{Pb}^{++}} \right)$$

$$= \varepsilon_{\text{Pb}}^0 - \varepsilon_a^0 \tag{42}$$

Consequently, with ε and ε_a^0 known ε_{Pb}^0 may be evaluated, and the emf data obtained with the amalgam may be reduced to the pure metal. Thus Carmody[1] found that for the particular lead amalgam he employed in his studies the standard electrode potential of Pb(Hg) | Pb^{++} was 0.1207 volt at 25° C, while the emf of a cell composed of this amalgam and pure lead in a solution of plumbous ions was 0.0058 volt. The standard potential of the Pb | Pb^{++} electrode at 25° C, ε_{Pb}^0, is then,

$$\begin{aligned} \varepsilon_{Pb}^0 &= \varepsilon + \varepsilon_a^0 \\ &= 0.0058 + 0.1207 \\ &= 0.1265 \text{ volt} \end{aligned}$$

NONMETAL NONGAS ELECTRODES

Electrodes may be constructed from nonmetals as well as from metals. For example, solid iodine in presence of iodide ions will serve as an electrode reversible to these ions. Similarly, liquid bromine in presence of bromide ions will act as an electrode reversible to bromide ions. In assembling such electrodes, the condensed nonmetal phase is placed in the bottom of a glass vessel, and over it is poured a solution containing the ions to which the substance is reversible. Electric contact is made by means of an inert metal, such as platinum, sealed into the bottom of the vessel or inserted through the top so as to touch the condensed phase.

The electrode reaction for the iodine electrode is

$$\frac{1}{2} I_2(s) + \ominus = I^-(a_I) \tag{43}$$

with the electrode emf given by

$$\varepsilon_{I_2} = \varepsilon_{I_2}^0 - \frac{RT}{\mathcal{F}} \ln a_{I^-} \tag{44}$$

In a like manner the single electrode process of the bromine electrode is

$$\frac{1}{2} Br_2(l) + \ominus = Br^-(a_{Br}) \tag{45}$$

with the emf given by

$$\varepsilon_{Br_2} = \varepsilon_{Br_2}^0 - \frac{RT}{\mathcal{F}} \ln a_{Br^-} \tag{46}$$

For both these electrodes ε^0 is positive for the reactions given in equations (43) and (45).

[1] Carmody, *J. Am. Chem. Soc.*, **51**, 2905 (1929).

GAS ELECTRODES

Gas electrodes consist of a gas bubbling about an inert metal wire or foil immersed in a solution containing ions to which the gas is reversible. The function of the metal wire or foil, which usually is platinized platinum, is to facilitate establishment of equilibrium between the gas and its ions and to serve as the electric contact for the electrode.

Among the gas electrodes are the hydrogen electrode, which is reversible to hydrogen ions, the chlorine electrode, reversible to chloride ions, and the oxygen electrode, whose emf depends on the activity of hydroxyl ions. However, though the first two electrodes can be made reversible, no suitable electrode material has so far been found which can catalyze satisfactorily the establishment of equilibrium between oxygen and hydroxyl ions. Whatever precise information is available on the latter electrode has been obtained not by direct emf measurements, but by calculation from suitable standard free energy data obtained from various other sources.

The fundamental electrode reaction for the hydrogen electrode is

$$\frac{1}{2} H_2(g, P_{H_2}) = H^+(a_{H^+}) + \ominus \tag{47}$$

Since the activity of hydrogen gas at relatively low pressures is equal to the pressure P_{H_2} of the gas in atmospheres, the single electrode potential of the hydrogen electrode must be determined both by the pressure of the hydrogen about the electrode, and the activity of hydrogen ions in solution. Namely,

$$\mathcal{E}_{H_2} = \mathcal{E}_{H_2}^0 - \frac{RT}{\mathcal{F}} \ln \frac{a_{H^+}}{P_{H_2}^{1/2}} \tag{48}$$

But $\mathcal{E}_{H_2}^0$, i.e., the *emf of the hydrogen electrode at 1 atm hydrogen pressure and at unit activity of hydrogen ions*, is the reference of all single electrode emf measurements and is taken by definition to be zero at all temperatures. Consequently equation (48) becomes

$$\mathcal{E}_{H_2} = - \frac{RT}{\mathcal{F}} \ln \frac{a_{H^+}}{P_{H_2}^{1/2}}$$

$$= - \frac{RT}{\mathcal{F}} \ln a_{H^+} + \frac{RT}{\mathcal{F}} \ln P_{H_2}^{1/2} \tag{49}$$

Further, when the pressure of hydrogen is 1 atm $P_{H_2}^{1/2} = 1$, and $\ln P_{H_2}^{1/2} = 0$. Then,

$$\mathcal{E}_{H_2} = - \frac{RT}{\mathcal{F}} \ln a_{H^+} \tag{50}$$

and the *hydrogen electrode becomes strictly dependent only on the activity of hydrogen ions in solution*, i.e., the pH. This use of the hydrogen electrode for pH measurements will be discussed later.

The chlorine electrode shows similar behavior. For this electrode the reduction reaction is

$$\frac{1}{2} Cl_2(g, P_{Cl_2}) + \ominus = Cl^-(a_{Cl^-}) \tag{51}$$

and hence the emf is given by

$$\varepsilon_{Cl_2} = \varepsilon^0_{Cl_2} - \frac{RT}{\mathfrak{F}} \ln \frac{a_{Cl^-}}{P^{1/2}_{Cl_2}} \tag{52}$$

However, $\varepsilon^0_{Cl_2}$ is not zero, but is in fact equal to 1.3595 volts at 25° C.

METAL-INSOLUBLE SALT ELECTRODES

Electrodes of this type are extremely important in electrochemistry and they are encountered very frequently. In this category fall the various calomel electrodes, the silver-silver chloride electrode, the lead-lead sulfate electrode, the silver-silver bromide electrode, and others.

The common characteristic of electrodes in this class is that they all consist of a metal in contact with one of its difficultly soluble salts and a solution containing the ion present in the salt *other than the metal.* For instance, a silver-silver chloride electrode is composed of a silver wire coated with silver chloride and immersed in a solution of chloride ions. Again, the lead-lead sulfate electrode may be either pure lead or a lead amalgam covered with crystals of lead sulfate and surrounded by solutions of sulfates. In all instances *these electrodes are reversible to the ions other than those of the metal present in the insoluble salt.* Thus the calomel and silver-silver chloride electrodes are reversible to chloride ions, the lead-lead sulfate electrode to sulfate ions, the silver-silver bromide electrode to bromide ions, etc. Why this is so may be seen from the following discussion of the silver-silver chloride electrode, a typical member of this class.

Consider a silver electrode dipping into a solution containing chloride ions and saturated with silver chloride. If we imagine this electrode to act as an ordinary metal-metal ion electrode, silver ions will pass from the electrode into the solution according to the reaction

$$Ag(s) = Ag^+ + \ominus \tag{a}$$

However, since the solution is saturated with silver chloride, the introduction of any silver ions will upset the requirements of the solubility product principle for this salt. Consequently, in order to reestablish the solubility equilibrium, silver ions will have to combine with chloride ions to precipitate solid silver chloride according to the relation

$$Ag^+ + Cl^- = AgCl(s) \tag{b}$$

Moreover, as the over-all electrode reaction is the sum of all the processes occurring at the electrode, the over-all electrode reaction will have to be the sum of (a) and (b), or

$$Ag(s) + Cl^- = AgCl(s) + \ominus \tag{53}$$

For this reaction the electrode potential equation is

$$\mathcal{E}_{Ag-AgCl} = \mathcal{E}^0_{Ag-AgCl} - \frac{RT}{\mathcal{F}} \ln \frac{1}{a_{Cl^-}} \tag{54}$$

and hence this electrode is reversible to *chloride ions*.

In an analogous manner may be deduced the reactions for other electrodes of this type. Thus we find for the calomel electrode

$$2\,Hg(l) + 2\,Cl^- = Hg_2Cl_2(s) + 2 \ominus \tag{55}$$

for the lead-lead sulfate electrode,

$$Pb(s) + SO_4^{--} = PbSO_4(s) + 2 \ominus \tag{56}$$

and for the silver-silver bromide electrode,

$$Ag(s) + Br^- = AgBr(s) + \ominus \tag{57}$$

METAL-INSOLUBLE OXIDE ELECTRODES

Metal-insoluble oxide electrodes are very similar to the metal-insoluble salt type, except that the difficultly soluble salt in the latter case is replaced by a difficultly soluble oxide. Such electrodes are reversible to *either hydrogen or hydroxyl ions*. The only important member of this category is the antimony-antimony trioxide electrode, consisting of a stick of antimony covered with a thin layer of the oxide resulting from oxidation of the surface by oxygen. The reaction for this electrode is

$$2\,Sb(s) + 6\,OH^- = Sb_2O_3(s) + 3\,H_2O(l) + 6 \ominus \tag{58}$$

from which the single electrode emf follows as

$$\begin{aligned} \mathcal{E}_{Sb} &= \mathcal{E}^0_{Sb} - \frac{RT}{6\,\mathcal{F}} \ln \frac{1}{a_{OH^-}^6} \\ &= \mathcal{E}^0_{Sb} - \frac{RT}{\mathcal{F}} \ln \frac{1}{a_{OH^-}} \end{aligned} \tag{59}$$

The antimony-antimony trioxide electrode is thus reversible to *hydroxyl ions*. To show that this electrode is reversible to *hydrogen ions* as well, we may introduce the equilibrium

$$6\,H_2O(l) = 6\,H^+ + 6\,OH^-$$

On combining the latter with equation (58) we obtain

$$2\,Sb(s) + 3\,H_2O(l) = Sb_2O_3(s) + 6\,H^+ + 6\,\ominus \tag{60}$$

and hence ε_{Sb} is also given by

$$\varepsilon_{Sb} = \varepsilon_{Sb}^{0\prime} - \frac{RT}{6\,\mathfrak{F}}\ln a_{H^+}^6$$

$$= \varepsilon_{Sb}^{0\prime} - \frac{RT}{\mathfrak{F}}\ln a_{H^+} \tag{61}$$

ε_{Sb}^0 and $\varepsilon_{Sb}^{0\prime}$ are related by the expression

$$\varepsilon_{Sb}^0 = \varepsilon_{Sb}^{0\prime} - \frac{RT}{\mathfrak{F}}\ln K_w \tag{62}$$

where K_w is the ion product of water. $\varepsilon_{Sb}^{0\prime}$ at 25° C has been found to be
-0.1445 volt. Consequently

$$\varepsilon_{Sb}^0 = -0.1445 - 0.05916\log_{10}(1.008 \times 10^{-14})$$
$$= +0.6835 \text{ volt}$$

OXIDATION-REDUCTION ELECTRODES

Although every electrode reaction involves an oxidation or a reduction,
the term *oxidation-reduction electrodes* is used to designate electrodes in
which the emf results from the presence of *ions* of a substance in two
different stages of oxidation. When a platinum wire is inserted into a
solution containing both ferrous and ferric ions it is found that the wire
acquires a potential. The same is true of solutions of cerous-ceric ions,
stannous-stannic ions, manganous-permanganate ions, etc. These electrode emf's arise from the tendency of ions in one state of oxidation to
pass over into a second more stable state. The function of the platinum
wire is merely to "pick up" the potential corresponding to this tendency
toward a free energy decrease, and to serve as the electrical contact of
the electrode.

The general reaction for all electrodes of the oxidation-reduction type
may be written as

$$A^{n_1}(a_1) + n\ominus = A^{n_2}(a_2) \tag{63}$$

where n_1 is the valence in the higher stage of oxidation, n_2 that in the
lower, while $n = n_1 - n_2$ is the *valence change* attending the electrode
process. From equation (63) the general emf equation follows as

$$\varepsilon = \varepsilon^0 - \frac{RT}{n\mathfrak{F}}\ln\frac{a_2}{a_1} \tag{64}$$

i.e., the emf of oxidation-reduction electrodes depends on the *ratio of the activities* of the two ions. Thus, for the ferric-ferrous electrode, designated symbolically as Pt | Fe^{+++}, Fe^{++}, the electrode reaction is

$$Fe^{+++}(a_{Fe^{+++}}) + \ominus = Fe^{++}(a_{Fe^{++}}) \tag{65}$$

and the electrode emf is given by

$$\varepsilon = \varepsilon^0 - \frac{RT}{\mathfrak{F}} \ln \frac{a_{Fe^{++}}}{a_{Fe^{+++}}} \tag{66}$$

In Table 3 are given ε^0 values for several electrodes of this type at 25° C.

ELECTROCHEMICAL CELLS

When various electrodes are combined, two general classes of cells may result, namely: (a) *chemical cells*, in which the emf is due to a *chemical reaction* occurring within the cell, and (b) *concentration cells*, in which the emf is due to the free energy decrease attending the *transfer of matter* from one part of the cell to another. Further, each of these types of cells may or may not involve a liquid junction; or, as it is usually said, the cell may or may not have *transference*. On this basis we arrive at the following classification of electrochemical cells:

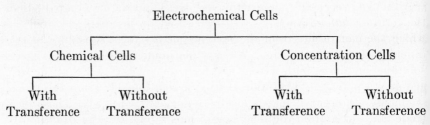

CHEMICAL CELLS WITHOUT TRANSFERENCE

To construct a chemical cell with no liquid junction or transference, two electrodes and an electrolyte must be selected such that *one of the electrodes is reversible to the cation, the other to the anion of the electrolyte*. For instance, if we desire a cell without transference employing hydrochloric acid as the electrolyte, we must use an electrode reversible to hydrogen ions, namely, the hydrogen electrode, and an electrode reversible to chloride ions. The latter may be either a silver-silver chloride, a mercury-mercurous chloride, or chlorine electrode, all of which are reversible to this ion. Again, for sulfuric acid as the electrolyte the electrodes will have to be hydrogen and either lead-lead sulfate or mercury-mercurous sulfate. Finally, for an electrolyte such as zinc bromide we shall have to employ zinc as one of the electrodes, and either bromine, mercury-mercurous bromide, or silver-silver bromide as the electrode for the bromide ions. Where a choice is possible, the electrode that can be handled most conveniently is selected. Although the particular electrode chosen determines the over-all cell reaction and the value of ε^0, it is characteristic of all such possibilities that they give the same dependence of the emf of the cell on the activity of the electrolyte.

As a typical example of chemical cells without transference we shall take the cell

$$\text{H}_2(\text{g}, P_{\text{H}_2}) \mid \text{HCl}(a_{\text{HCl}}), \text{AgCl(s)} \mid \text{Ag} \tag{67}$$

consisting of the hydrogen and silver-silver chloride electrodes in hydrochloric acid as the electrolyte. Since these electrodes are reversible to the ions of the electrolyte, they may be immersed directly in the acid to yield a cell with no liquid junction. The entire emf of the cell is composed then only of the emf's existing at the electrode-solution interfaces.

In cell (67) the hydrogen electrode is negative, and so we obtain for the oxidation at this electrode,

$$\frac{1}{2} \text{H}_2(\text{g}, P_{\text{H}_2}) = \text{H}^+(a_{\text{H}^+}) + \ominus \tag{68a}$$

and
$$\varepsilon_{\text{H}_2} = -\frac{RT}{\mathcal{F}} \ln \frac{a_{\text{H}^+}}{P_{\text{H}_2}^{1/2}} \tag{68b}$$

Again, for the reduction at the silver-silver chloride electrode we have

$$\text{AgCl(s)} + \ominus = \text{Ag(s)} + \text{Cl}^-(a_{\text{Cl}^-}) \tag{69a}$$

and
$$\varepsilon_{\text{Ag}-\text{AgCl}} = \varepsilon^0_{\text{Ag}-\text{AgCl}} - \frac{RT}{\mathcal{F}} \ln a_{\text{Cl}^-} \tag{69b}$$

Adding now equations (68a) and (69a), the cell reaction follows as

$$\frac{1}{2} \text{H}_2(\text{g}, P_{\text{H}_2}) + \text{AgCl(s)} = \text{Ag(s)} + \text{H}^+(a_{\text{H}^+}) + \text{Cl}^-(a_{\text{Cl}^-}) \tag{70a}$$

while the cell emf on combination of equations (68b) and (69b) is

$$\varepsilon_{\text{cell}} = \varepsilon^0_{\text{Ag}-\text{AgCl}} - \frac{RT}{\mathcal{F}} \ln \frac{(a_{\text{H}^+}a_{\text{Cl}^-})}{P_{\text{H}_2}^{1/2}}$$

$$= \varepsilon^0_{\text{Ag}-\text{AgCl}} - \frac{RT}{\mathcal{F}} \ln \frac{a_{\text{HCl}}}{P_{\text{H}_2}^{1/2}} \tag{70b}$$

In the last equation a_{HCl}, the activity of the electrolyte as a whole, has been substituted for its equivalent $a_{\text{H}^+}a_{\text{Cl}^-}$.

Equation (70a) indicates that the emf of this cell results from a chemical reaction, namely, the reduction of silver chloride by hydrogen gas to form solid silver and hydrochloric acid ($\text{H}^+ + \text{Cl}^-$) in *solution*. Since this cell possesses as well no liquid junction, it constitutes a chemical cell without transference. Further, equation (70b) shows that the emf of this cell depends on the activity of the acid in solution and on the pressure of hydrogen gas. When the latter is 1 atm, as it usually is under experimental conditions, equation (70b) reduces to

$$\mathcal{E}_{cell} = \mathcal{E}^0_{AgCl} - \frac{RT}{\mathcal{F}} \ln a_{HCl} \tag{71}$$

and the emf becomes dependent only on the activity of the hydrochloric acid in solution.

By following the above procedure the student can readily verify that

$$H_2(g,\ P_{H_2}) \mid H_2SO_4(a_{H_2SO_4}),\ Hg_2SO_4(s) \mid Hg \tag{72a}$$
$$Cd \mid CdSO_4(a_{CdSO_4}),\ Hg_2SO_4(s) \mid Hg \tag{73a}$$

are chemical cells without transference for which the reactions are

$$H_2(g,\ P_{H_2}) + Hg_2SO_4(s) = 2\ Hg(l) + H_2SO_4(a_{H_2SO_4}) \tag{72b}$$
$$Cd(s) + Hg_2SO_4(s) = 2\ Hg(l) + CdSO_4(a_{Cd_2SO_4}) \tag{73b}$$

Finally, the emf for (72b) at 1 atm hydrogen pressure is

$$\mathcal{E} = \mathcal{E}^0_{Hg-Hg_2SO_4} - \frac{RT}{2\ \mathcal{F}} \ln a_{H_2SO_4} \tag{72c}$$

while for (73b) $\mathcal{E}$ is

$$\mathcal{E} = \mathcal{E}^0_{cell} - \frac{RT}{2\ \mathcal{F}} \ln a_{CdSO_4} \tag{73c}$$

where $\mathcal{E}^0_{cell}$ is the sum of the standard electrode potentials of the cadmium and mercury-mercurous sulfate electrodes.

APPLICATION OF CHEMICAL CELLS WITHOUT TRANSFERENCE

Chemical cells without transference find extensive application for the evaluation of standard electrode potentials of cells and electrodes and for the determination from emf data of the activity coefficients of various electrolytes. To illustrate the method, let us take specifically the cell represented in equation (67), for which the cell emf at 1 atm hydrogen pressure is given by equation (71). The problem in this instance is: How can $\mathcal{E}^0_{Ag-AgCl}$ and the activity coefficients of hydrochloric acid solutions of various molalities be evaluated from a series of emf measurements made on cells such as equation (67) with different concentrations of the acid?

First, the activity of hydrochloric acid is related at any molality m to the mean activity coefficient γ by the expression $a_{HCl} = m^2\gamma^2$. Substituting this value of a_{HCl} into equation (71) and rearranging terms, we obtain

$$\mathcal{E}_{\text{cell}} = \mathcal{E}^0_{\text{Ag}-\text{AgCl}} - \frac{RT}{\mathcal{F}} \ln{(m^2 \gamma^2)}$$

$$= \mathcal{E}^0_{\text{Ag}-\text{AgCl}} - \frac{2\,RT}{\mathcal{F}} \ln m - \frac{2\,RT}{\mathcal{F}} \ln \gamma$$

$$\left(\mathcal{E}_{\text{cell}} + \frac{2\,RT}{\mathcal{F}} \ln m\right) = \mathcal{E}^0_{\text{Ag}-\text{AgCl}} - \frac{2\,RT}{\mathcal{F}} \ln \gamma \tag{74}$$

All the quantities on the left-hand side of equation (74) are experimentally available, and hence γ could be calculated if $\mathcal{E}^0_{\text{Ag}-\text{AgCl}}$ were known. To determine the latter quantity $[\mathcal{E}_{\text{cell}} + (2\,RT/\mathcal{F})\ln m]$ is plotted against $\sqrt{\mu}$, i.e., the square root of the ionic strength of the solution, which in this case is identical with $\sqrt{m}$, and the plot is extrapolated to $\sqrt{\mu} = 0$. To make this extrapolation with certainty, emf data for dilute solutions are necessary. As at $m = 0$, $\gamma = 1$, the last term on the right in equation (74) becomes thus zero, and the value of the extrapolated ordinate yields immediately $\mathcal{E}^0_{\text{Ag}-\text{AgCl}}$. Once this constant is known, the difference between $[\mathcal{E}_{\text{cell}} + (2\,RT/\mathcal{F})\ln m]$ and $\mathcal{E}^0_{\text{Ag}-\text{AgCl}}$ at each value of m gives immediately $(-2\,RT/\mathcal{F})\ln \gamma$, and hence γ.

In Table 5 column 1 gives the molalities of a number of dilute hydrochloric acid solutions and column 2 the emf's at 25° C obtained for these with cells of the type under discussion. By calculating from these data the quantity $[\mathcal{E}_{\text{cell}} + (2\,RT/\mathcal{F})\ln m] = (\mathcal{E}_{\text{cell}} + 0.11831 \log_{10} m)$, and plotting it against $\sqrt{m}$, it is found that on extrapolation to $\sqrt{m} = 0$ the ordinate is 0.2225 volt. Consequently, $\mathcal{E}^0_{\text{Ag}-\text{AgCl}}$ at 25° C is 0.2225 volt.

TABLE 5

Activity Coefficients of HCl from Emf's of the Cell
$H_2 \mid HCl,\ AgCl(s) \mid Ag$ at 25° C*

m_{HCl}	$\mathcal{E}_{\text{cell}}$ (volts)	Activity Coefficient γ
0.003215	0.52053	0.942
0.004488	0.50384	0.933
0.005619	0.49257	0.926
0.007311	0.47948	0.917
0.009138	0.46860	0.909
0.011195	0.45861	0.903
0.013407	0.44974	0.895
0.01710	0.43783	0.884
0.02563	0.41824	0.866
0.05391	0.38222	0.829
0.1238	0.34199	0.788

* From D. A. MacInnes, *Principles of Electrochemistry*, Reinhold Publishing Corporation, New York, 1939, p. 187.

Utilizing this value of $\varepsilon^0_{Ag-AgCl}$ and the various values of ε_{cell} and m in equation (74), the activity coefficients of hydrochloric acid are found to be those listed in column 3 of the table.

CHEMICAL CELLS WITH TRANSFERENCE

In chemical cells with transference the emf again results from a chemical reaction occurring within the cell, but this time assembly of the electrodes leads to a liquid junction between solutions of different electrolytes. Cells of this type are very common; in fact, of those described heretofore, such cells as

$$Zn \mid Zn^{++} \parallel Cd^{++} \mid Cd$$
$$Hg \mid Hg_2Cl_2(s), KCl(1\ N) \parallel Cu^{++} \mid Cu$$
$$Tl \mid Tl^+ \parallel Sn^{++} \mid Sn$$

belong to this category. In treating these we have assumed that the total measured emf is the sum of the two electrode potentials. Although this *may* be the case to a fairly close approximation, it is not exactly true, and consequently chemical cells where transference is present require further consideration.

Contact between two solutions of different concentrations, or different ions, or both, leads to a junction potential ε_j. This potential arises from *diffusion* of ions across the boundary between the two solutions. Because of a concentration gradient existing across the boundary, ions tend to diffuse from the side of higher to that of lower concentration. If the two ions of an electrolyte migrated with equal velocities, such diffusion would cause no complications. However, as in general this is not the case, the faster ion moves across the boundary ahead of the slower, and a separation of charges, analogous to a Helmholtz double layer, results. This separation of charges causes the establishment of a junction potential which is measured experimentally along with the two electrode potentials and appears in the total emf of the cell. In other words, whenever a junction potential ε_j is present, the emf of a cell is no longer $\varepsilon = \varepsilon_1 + \varepsilon_2$, where ε_1 and ε_2 are the two electrode potentials, but instead

$$\varepsilon = \varepsilon_1 + \varepsilon_2 + \varepsilon_j \tag{75}$$

In most instances junction potentials cannot be measured separately. Consequently various attempts have been made to calculate junction potentials,[1] and to arrive thereby through equation (75) at the sum of the electrode potentials corresponding to the cell reaction. However, the progress made in this direction is not sufficient to permit the calculation of $\varepsilon_1 + \varepsilon_2$ from ε without some ambiguity. For this reason chemical cells

[1] See D. A. MacInnes, *op. cit.*, Chapter XIII.

with transference are not considered suitable for *exact* evaluation of the thermodynamic properties of such cells. Nevertheless, under suitable experimental conditions these cells can be utilized to yield valuable even though not completely exact information, and they are employed a great deal for measurements of pH, electrometric titrations, etc.

METHODS OF FORMING LIQUID JUNCTIONS

The simplest means of forming a liquid junction between two solutions is to bring the two together in a tube without causing undue mixing. Although when carefully prepared such *static junctions* may remain sharp and give reproducible potentials, a more satisfactory arrangement is the *flowing junction*. In the latter the two solutions are brought together as two streams which merge in a common tube and flow out. By this artifice the boundary between the two solutions can be kept continually renewed and sharp.

However, the type of junction employed most frequently is the *salt bridge*. In this scheme a fairly concentrated solution of a salt, usually 1 N or saturated potassium chloride, is interposed between the two solutions in the manner indicated in Fig. 5. This salt bridge is supposed to minimize or reduce the junction potential. Exactly how this reduction is accomplished is not quite clear, but it is supposed to be associated with the fact that the two ions in potassium chloride possess about equal velocities, and these operate to yield junction potentials between the two solutions and the bridge which are opposite in sign, and hence cancel each other to a degree. Whether such a reduction in junction potentials with the aid of salt bridges actually occurs is problematical. Still more questionable is it whether such bridges can reduce the junction potentials to a point where they are negligible. Nevertheless, effective or not, the fact remains that salt bridges have come into extensive use and are encountered in various electrochemical assemblies.

CALCULATIONS INVOLVING CHEMICAL CELLS
WITH TRANSFERENCE

In calculations involving these cells it is assumed that a salt bridge eliminates completely the junction potential and that the measured cell emf is merely the sum of the two electrode potentials. When ε_j is disregarded in this manner, it is customary to write two vertical lines between the two solutions, namely,

$$Zn \mid Zn^{++} \parallel Cd^{++} \mid Cd$$

On the other hand, when the presence of the liquid junction is recognized and taken into account, only one line is interposed, as

$$\text{Zn} \mid \text{Zn}^{++} \mid \text{Cd}^{++} \mid \text{Cd}$$

It is characteristic of chemical cells with transference that they involve in their emf equations the *activities of ions* rather than mean activities of the electrolyte as a whole. This would suggest that such cells may be suitable for the evaluation of activities and activity coefficients of individual ions. However, this is not quite the case because of the junction potential uncertainty. In fact, it is generally agreed that there is no *exact* thermodynamic method known at present by which anything more than the geometric mean activity coefficient of an electrolyte can be determined. Therefore, when the emf's of chemical cells with transference are used to estimate activity coefficients of ions, this is done with the understanding that the quantities evaluated possess only quasi-thermodynamic significance. Again, in calculating the emf's of such cells from molalities and activity coefficients, the usual practice is to assume that the activity coefficient of any ion is essentially equal to the geometric mean activity coefficient of the electrolyte, and to use the latter. With these remarks in mind we are ready to consider a specific calculation.

Example: Suppose that it is desired to estimate at 25° C the emf of the cell

$$\text{Zn} \mid \text{ZnCl}_2(m = 0.5) \parallel \text{CdSO}_4(m = 0.1) \mid \text{Cd}$$

where the m's are the molalities of the two solutions. For this cell

$$\mathcal{E} = \mathcal{E}^0 - \frac{RT}{2\,\mathcal{F}} \ln \frac{a_{\text{Zn}^{++}}}{a_{\text{Cd}^{++}}}$$

Since $a_{\text{Zn}^{++}} = m_{\text{Zn}^{++}} \gamma_{\text{Zn}^{++}}$, and $a_{\text{Cd}^{++}} = m_{\text{Cd}^{++}} \gamma_{\text{Cd}^{++}}$, where γ's are the activity coefficients of the ions in their respective solutions, the above equation may be written as

$$\mathcal{E} = \mathcal{E}^0 - \frac{RT}{2\,\mathcal{F}} \ln \frac{m_{\text{Zn}^{++}} \gamma_{\text{Zn}^{++}}}{m_{\text{Cd}^{++}} \gamma_{\text{Cd}^{++}}}$$

Now, at 25° C $\mathcal{E}^0 = 0.359$ volt for this cell. Again, for 0.5 m ZnCl_2 $\gamma = 0.376$, while for 0.1 m CdSO_4 $\gamma = 0.137$. Assuming that these γ's are also the ionic activity coefficients, we find for $\mathcal{E}$

$$\mathcal{E} = 0.359 - \frac{0.05916}{2} \log_{10} \frac{(0.5)(0.376)}{(0.1)(0.137)}$$

$$= 0.359 - 0.034$$

$$= 0.325 \text{ volt at } 25° \text{ C}$$

CONCENTRATION CELLS

Unlike chemical cells, whose emf arises from a chemical reaction, *concentration cells depend for their emf on a transfer of material from one elec-*

trode to the other due to a concentration difference between the two. This difference in concentration may arise from the fact that two identical electrodes dipping in the same solution may be at different concentrations, as two hydrogen electrodes at unequal gas pressures immersed in the same solution of hydrogen ions, namely,

$$H_2(P_{H_2} = P_1) \mid H^+ \mid H_2(P_{H_2} = P_2)$$

or two amalgam electrodes of different concentration dipping in a solution of the metal ions, as

$$Cd(Hg)(C_{Cd} = C_1) \mid Cd^{++} \mid Cd(Hg)(C_{Cd} = C_2)$$

Again, the difference in concentration may not be in the electrodes, but in the solutions with which they are in contact, as in the cells

$$H_2(g, 1 \text{ atm}) \mid H^+(a_1) \mid H^+(a_2) \mid H_2(g, 1 \text{ atm})$$
$$Ag \mid Ag^+(a_1) \mid Ag^+(a_2) \mid Ag$$

In the first two cells mentioned there is no liquid junction present, and hence they are *concentration cells without transference.* On the other hand, the latter two cells involve a liquid junction between two solutions of the same kind but unlike concentration, and therefore these constitute *concentration cells with transference.*

ELECTRODE CONCENTRATION CELLS WITHOUT TRANSFERENCE

To see why an emf arises where two like electrodes are at different concentrations, but the electrolyte is the same for both, consider first the cell

$$H_2(P_{H_2} = P_1) \mid H^+(a_{H^+}) \mid H_2(P_{H_2} = P_2) \tag{76}$$

For the electrode on the left, the oxidation reaction yields

$$\frac{1}{2} H_2(P_1) = H^+(a_{H^+}) + \ominus \tag{77a}$$

and therefore, since $\mathcal{E}^0_{H_2} = 0$,

$$\mathcal{E}_1 = - \frac{RT}{\mathcal{F}} \ln \frac{a_{H^+}}{P_1^{1/2}} \tag{77b}$$

Similarly, for the reduction at the right-hand electrode the process is

$$H^+(a_{H^+}) + \ominus = \frac{1}{2} H_2(P_2) \tag{78a}$$

and

$$\mathcal{E}_2 = - \frac{RT}{\mathcal{F}} \ln \frac{P_2^{1/2}}{a_{H^+}} \tag{78b}$$

On adding equations (77a) and (78a), the cell reaction follows as

$$\frac{1}{2}\,H_2(P_1) = \frac{1}{2}\,H_2(P_2) \tag{79a}$$

while the cell emf, on adding equations (77b) and (78b), is

$$\varepsilon = -\frac{RT}{\mathcal{F}}\ln\frac{a_{H^+}}{P_1^{1/2}} - \frac{RT}{\mathcal{F}}\ln\frac{P_2^{1/2}}{a_{H^+}}$$

$$= -\frac{RT}{2\,\mathcal{F}}\ln\frac{P_2}{P_1} \tag{79b}$$

Equation (79a) shows that the cell reaction involves merely the *transfer of 0.5 mole of hydrogen gas from a pressure P_1 atm at one electrode to a pressure P_2 at the other;* i.e., that the cell reaction for the spontaneous process is an expansion of hydrogen gas from a pressure P_1 to a pressure P_2. Again, equation (79b) shows that the emf resulting from this expansion depends only on the two pressures and is *independent of the activity of the hydrogen ions* in which the electrodes are immersed.

Consider next another cell of this type, namely,

$$Zn(Hg)(a_{Zn} = a_1)\ |\ Zn^{++}(a_{Zn^{++}})\ |\ Zn(Hg)(a_{Zn} = a_2) \tag{80}$$

consisting of two zinc amalgams with activities of zinc equal to a_1 and a_2 immersed in a solution of zinc ions of activity $a_{Zn^{++}}$. Analogous to equations (39) and (40), the electrode reaction on the left is

$$Zn(Hg)(a_1) = Zn^{++}(a_{Zn^{++}}) + 2\ominus \tag{81a}$$

with ε_1 given by

$$\varepsilon_1 = \varepsilon_{Zn}^0 - \frac{RT}{2\,\mathcal{F}}\ln\frac{a_{Zn^{++}}}{a_1} \tag{81b}$$

Again, for the reduction on the right, we have

$$Zn^{++}(a_{Zn^{++}}) + 2\ominus = Zn(Hg)(a_2) \tag{82a}$$

and

$$\varepsilon_2 = \varepsilon_{Zn}^{0'} - \frac{RT}{2\,\mathcal{F}}\ln\frac{a_2}{a_{Zn^{++}}} \tag{82b}$$

where $\varepsilon_{Zn}^{0'} = -\varepsilon_{Zn}^0$. We obtain, therefore, for the cell reaction,

$$Zn(Hg)(a_1) = Zn(Hg)(a_2) \tag{83a}$$

and for the cell emf,

$$\varepsilon = \varepsilon_{Zn}^0 - \frac{RT}{2\,\mathcal{F}}\ln\frac{a_{Zn^{++}}}{a_1} + (-\varepsilon_{Zn}^0) - \frac{RT}{2\,\mathcal{F}}\ln\frac{a_2}{a_{Zn^{++}}}$$

$$= -\frac{RT}{2\,\mathcal{F}}\ln\frac{a_2}{a_1} \tag{83b}$$

From equation (83a) it is evident that the emf of this cell is due to a transfer of zinc from the amalgam where its activity is a_1 to the amalgam where its activity is a_2. Further, equation (83b) shows that this emf depends only on the ratio of the zinc activities in the two amalgams, and not at all on the activity of the zinc ions in the solution. In the final cell emf equation ε^0 does not appear. This is true of all concentration cells. We may conclude, therefore, *that for concentration cells ε^0 is zero*, and the emf equation takes on the simplified form

$$\varepsilon_{cell} = -\frac{RT}{n\mathfrak{F}} \ln \frac{a_2}{a_1} \qquad (84)$$

Since in cells of the type under discussion a_2 and a_1 refer to the activities of the metal in the amalgams, we may assume that for dilute amalgams these do not differ essentially from the concentrations C_1 and C_2. Hence equation (83b) may be written approximately as

$$\varepsilon = -\frac{RT}{2\,\mathfrak{F}} \ln \frac{C_2}{C_1} \qquad (85)$$

The applicability of the latter equation to zinc amalgams has been confirmed by Meyer.[1]

ELECTROLYTE CONCENTRATIONS CELLS WITHOUT TRANSFERENCE

Consider a chemical cell without transference, such as

$$H_2(g, 1\ atm)\ |\ HCl(a_1),\ AgCl(s)\ |\ Ag \qquad (86a)$$

For this cell the reaction is

$$\frac{1}{2} H_2(g, 1\ atm) + AgCl(s) = Ag(s) + HCl(a_1) \qquad (86b)$$

and the cell emf, equation (71),

$$\varepsilon_1 = \varepsilon^0 - \frac{RT}{\mathfrak{F}} \ln a_1 \qquad (86c)$$

Again, for the same cell but with a different activity of hydrochloric acid, namely,

$$H_2(g, 1\ atm)\ |\ HCl(a_2),\ AgCl(s)\ |\ Ag \qquad (87a)$$

the cell reaction will be

$$\frac{1}{2} H_2(g, 1\ atm) + AgCl(s) = Ag(s) + HCl(a_2) \qquad (87b)$$

and the cell emf

$$\varepsilon_2 = \varepsilon^0 - \frac{RT}{\mathfrak{F}} \ln a_2 \qquad (87c)$$

[1] G. Meyer, *Zeit physik. Chem.*, **7**, 477 (1891).

If these two cells are connected so as to *oppose* each other, i.e.,

$$H_2(g, 1 \text{ atm}) \mid HCl(a_1), AgCl(s) \mid Ag\text{-}Ag \mid AgCl(s),$$
$$HCl(a_2) \mid H_2(g, 1 \text{ atm}) \quad (88a)$$

the over-all reaction of the combination will be the *difference* between equations (86b) and (87b), namely,

$$\frac{1}{2} H_2(g, 1 \text{ atm}) + AgCl(s) - \frac{1}{2} H_2(g, 1 \text{ atm}) - AgCl(s) =$$

$$Ag(s) + HCl(a_1) - Ag(s) - HCl(a_2)$$

or $\qquad\qquad HCl(a_2) = HCl(a_1) \qquad\qquad (88b)$

Similarly the emf of (88a) will be the *difference* between equations (86c) and (87c). Hence,

$$\varepsilon = \varepsilon_1 - \varepsilon_2$$

$$= (\varepsilon^0 - \frac{RT}{\mathbf{F}} \ln a_1) - (\varepsilon^0 - \frac{RT}{\mathbf{F}} \ln a_2)$$

$$= -\frac{RT}{\mathbf{F}} \ln \frac{a_1}{a_2} \qquad\qquad (88c)$$

According to equation (88b) the over-all reaction resulting from the combination given in equation (88a) is a *transfer* for each faraday drawn from the cell of 1 mole of hydrochloric acid from the solution where the activity is a_2 to the solution where the activity is a_1. Consequently, whereas each of the individual cells constituting equation (88a) is a chemical cell, the combination of the two is a *concentration cell without transference in which the emf arises from different concentrations of the electrolyte.* For this emf to be positive, equation (88c) shows that a_2 must be greater than a_1; i.e., the transfer process is spontaneous for passage of electrolyte from the more concentrated to the more dilute solution.

Concentration cells of this type, may be assembled from any chemical cells without transference. For instance, a sodium chloride concentration cell results from the combination

$$Na(Hg) \mid NaCl(a_1), AgCl(s) \mid Ag\text{-}Ag \mid AgCl(s), NaCl(a_2) \mid Na(Hg)$$

and a zinc sulfate concentration cell from

$$Zn(Hg) \mid ZnSO_4(a_1), PbSO_4(s) \mid Pb(Hg)\text{-}Pb(Hg) \mid PbSO_4(s),$$
$$ZnSO_4(a_2) \mid Zn(Hg)$$

Such cells are suitable for the determination of the activity coefficients of the electrolytes involved. For this purpose the usual practice is to keep one of the electrolyte concentrations constant, and to measure the emf of the cells with varying concentrations of the second solution. If for a_1 and a_2 in equation (88c) we make the substitutions $a_1 = m_1^2 \gamma_1^2$ and

$a_2 = m_2^2\gamma_2^2$, the expression for ε becomes

$$
\begin{aligned}
\varepsilon &= -\frac{RT}{\mathfrak{F}} \ln \frac{m_1^2\gamma_1^2}{m_2^2\gamma_2^2} \\
&= \frac{2\,RT}{\mathfrak{F}} \ln \frac{m_2\gamma_2}{m_1\gamma_1} \\
&= \frac{2\,RT}{\mathfrak{F}} \ln \frac{m_2}{m_1} + \frac{2\,RT}{\mathfrak{F}} \ln \frac{\gamma_2}{\gamma_1}
\end{aligned}
\tag{89}
$$

As the molalities are known, equation (89) permits evaluation of the ratio of the activity coefficients of the electrolyte at any molality m_2 to that at the reference m_1. Hence when γ_1 corresponding to m_1 is available, the various activity coefficients follow from these ratios.

CONCENTRATION CELLS WITH TRANSFERENCE

A typical concentration cell with transference is

$$
\mathrm{H_2(g,\ 1\ atm)\ |\ HCl(}a_1)\ |\ \mathrm{HCl(}a_2)\ |\ \mathrm{H_2(g,\ 1\ atm)}
\tag{90}
$$

consisting of two identical hydrogen electrodes immersed in two hydrochloric acid solutions of different concentrations. For this cell the total emf is composed of the two single electrode potentials and the potential at the junction, ε_j. Further, the over-all cell reaction is the sum of the two electrode processes and any material transfer taking place across the junction. In a case such as this, where the electrolytes constituting the junction are identical except for their concentrations, these various processes can be analyzed, and an equation for the cell can be arrived at which takes into account the junction potential.

To understand how this is possible, assume that the electrode on the left in equation (90) is negative, which will be true when $a_2 > a_1$. For a faraday of electricity drawn from this cell, the reaction at the negative electrode will be

$$
\frac{1}{2}\mathrm{H_2(g,\ 1\ atm)} = \mathrm{H^+}(a_1) + \ominus
$$

that at the positive,

$$
\mathrm{H^+}(a_2) + \ominus = \frac{1}{2}\mathrm{H_2(g,\ 1\ atm)}
$$

and hence the sum of the two electrode reactions is

$$
\mathrm{H^+}(a_2) = \mathrm{H^+}(a_1)
\tag{91a}
$$

However, when electrons flow externally from left to right, they must complete the circuit by passing *through the cell from right to left;* i.e., electrons must pass across the liquid junction from right to left. This current in the cell is composed, of course, not of free electrons, but of negative ions, namely Cl^-, moving from *right to left*, and positive ions, or H^+, moving across the junction from *left to right*. If t_- is the transference number of the chloride ions, then for every faraday passing through the cell t_- equivalents of chloride ions will be transported from the solution of activity a_2 to the solution where the activity is a_1; i.e.,

$$t_-(Cl^-(a_2) = t_-Cl(a_1) \tag{91b}$$

Again, $t_+ = 1 - t_-$ equivalents of hydrogen ions will be transferred from the solution of activity a_1 to the solution of activity a_2, namely,

$$(1 - t_-)H^+(a_1) = (1 - t_-)H^+(a_2) \tag{91c}$$

Therefore, in order to obtain the *net transfer* of material we must add equations (91b) and (91c) to (91a). We get thus for the over-all process of the cell,

$$H^+(a_2) + t_-Cl^-(a_2) + (1 - t_-)H^+(a_1)$$
$$= H^+(a_1) + t_-Cl^-(a_1) + (1 - t_-)H^+(a_2)$$
$$t_-H^+(a_2) + t_-Cl^-(a_2) = t_-H^+(a_1) + t_-Cl^-(a_1)$$
$$t_-HCl(a_2) = t_-HCl(a_1) \tag{92}$$

Equation (92) shows that in the concentration cell with transference t_- equivalents of hydrochloric acid are transferred from the solution of activity a_2 to the solution of activity a_1 for every faraday of electricity. This may be contrasted with the same process in a concentration cell without transference, equation (88b), where for 1 faraday the transfer of a full equivalent of the electrolyte is accomplished.

Application of the emf equation to the process in (92) gives

$$\varepsilon = -\frac{RT}{\mathcal{F}} \ln \frac{a_1^{t_-}}{a_2^{t_-}}$$
$$= \frac{t_-RT}{\mathcal{F}} \ln \frac{a_2}{a_1} \tag{93a}$$

On insertion of the molalities and activity coefficients, ε becomes

$$\varepsilon = \frac{t_-RT}{\mathcal{F}} \ln \frac{m_2^2\gamma_2^2}{m_1^2\gamma_1^2}$$
$$= \frac{2\,t_-RT}{\mathcal{F}} \ln \frac{m_2\gamma_2}{m_1\gamma_1} \tag{93b}$$

and hence the emf of such a cell can be calculated from a knowledge of the molalities, activity coefficients, and the *transport number of the ion other than the one to which the electrodes are reversible.*

Equations analogous to equations (92), (93a), and (93b) are applicable to any concentration cell with transference in which the electrodes are reversible to the *cation*. However, when the electrodes are reversible to the *anion*, as in the cell

$$Ag \mid AgCl(s), HCl(a_1) \mid HCl(a_2), AgCl(s) \mid Ag \tag{94}$$

repetition of the above reasoning shows that the cell reaction is

$$t_+HCl(a_1) = t_+HCl(a_2) \tag{95}$$

and the emf

$$
\begin{aligned}
\varepsilon &= -\frac{RT}{\mathcal{F}} \ln \frac{a_2^{t_+}}{a_1^{t_+}} \\
&= \frac{t_+ RT}{\mathcal{F}} \ln \frac{m_1^2 \gamma_1^2}{m_2^2 \gamma_2^2} \\
&= \frac{2\, t_+ RT}{\mathcal{F}} \ln \frac{m_1 \gamma_1}{m_2 \gamma_2}
\end{aligned}
\tag{96}
$$

Now a_1 must be greater than a_2 for the reaction to be spontaneous.

THE JUNCTION POTENTIAL

The emf given by equation (93b) for cell (90) is the sum of the two electrode potentials and ε_j. It is of interest to ascertain how much of this total emf is due to the electrodes and how much to the liquid junction. According to equation (91a), the sum of the two electrode reactions in cell equation (91) is

$$H^+(a_2) = H^+(a_1)$$

and hence the sum of the two electrode potentials, $\varepsilon_1 + \varepsilon_2$, is

$$
\begin{aligned}
\varepsilon_1 + \varepsilon_2 &= -\frac{RT}{\mathcal{F}} \ln \frac{(a_{H^+})_1}{(a_{H^+})_2} \\
&= \frac{RT}{\mathcal{F}} \ln \frac{(m_{H^+}\gamma_{H^+})_2}{(m_{H^+}\gamma_{H^+})_1}
\end{aligned}
\tag{97}
$$

If equation (97) be subtracted from equation (94b), the result is ε_j, namely,

$$
\begin{aligned}
\varepsilon_j &= \varepsilon - (\varepsilon_1 + \varepsilon_2) \\
&= \frac{2\, t_- RT}{\mathcal{F}} \ln \frac{m_2 \gamma_2}{m_1 \gamma_1} - \frac{RT}{\mathcal{F}} \ln \frac{(m_{H^+}\gamma_{H^+})_2}{(m_{H^+}\gamma_{H^+})_1}
\end{aligned}
$$

But $(m_{H^+})_2 = m_2$ and $(m_{H^+})_1 = m_1$. Further, if we take the activity coefficient of an ion equal to the mean activity coefficient of the electrolyte, $(\gamma_{H^+})_2 = \gamma_2$ and $(\gamma_{H^+})_1 = \gamma_1$. ε_j follows thus as,

$$
\begin{aligned}
\varepsilon_j &= \frac{2\, t_- RT}{\mathcal{F}} \ln \frac{m_2 \gamma_2}{m_1 \gamma_1} - \frac{RT}{\mathcal{F}} \ln \frac{m_2 \gamma_2}{m_1 \gamma_1} \\
&= (2\, t_- - 1)\frac{RT}{\mathcal{F}} \ln \frac{m_2 \gamma_2}{m_1 \gamma_1}
\end{aligned}
\tag{98a}
$$

Again, since $(t_+ + t_-) = 1$, $(2 t_- - 1) = (2 t_- - t_+ - t_-) = (t_- - t_+)$, and equation (98a) may also be written as

$$\mathcal{E}_j = (t_- - t_+) \frac{RT}{\mathcal{F}} \ln \frac{m_2 \gamma_2}{m_1 \gamma_1} \qquad (98b)$$

We see, therefore, that besides the activities of the two solutions constituting the junction, $\mathcal{E}_j$ is determined also by the difference between the two transport numbers of the electrolyte. When these are equal, $(t_- - t_+) = 0$, and so is the junction potential. This fact is the basis for the use of potassium chloride as a bridge in cell measurements involving liquid junction, for in this electrolyte the two transference numbers are very nearly identical. In turn, when $t_- > t_+$, $\mathcal{E}_j$ is positive and adds to $\mathcal{E}_1 + \mathcal{E}_2$, while when $t_- < t_+$, $\mathcal{E}_j$ is negative and operates to yield for $\mathcal{E}$ of the cell a potential less than $\mathcal{E}_1 + \mathcal{E}_2$.

Similar considerations, applied to concentration cells with transference containing electrodes reversible to the *anion*, give for $\mathcal{E}_j$

$$\mathcal{E}_j = (2 t_+ - 1) \frac{RT}{\mathcal{F}} \ln \frac{m_1 \gamma_1}{m_2 \gamma_2} \qquad (99a)$$

or $\qquad\qquad \mathcal{E}_j = (t_+ - t_-) \frac{RT}{\mathcal{F}} \ln \frac{m_1 \gamma_1}{m_2 \gamma_2} \qquad (99b)$

Here m_1 is the more concentrated solution. From equation (99b) it is clear that again $\mathcal{E}_j = 0$ for $t_+ = t_-$, but this time $\mathcal{E}_j$ is positive for $t_+ > t_-$, and negative for $t_+ < t_-$.

TRANSFERENCE NUMBERS FROM EMF DATA

Since concentration cells with transference involve transport numbers in their emf equations, such cells may be utilized for obtaining these quantities from emf data. Equations (93b) and (96) suggest that we need for this purpose the emf's of the respective cells and the activity coefficients of the electrolytes used. However, it is possible to arrive at t_+ and t_- from emf's alone without a knowledge of the activity coefficients.

For any concentration cell *with* transference in which the electrodes are reversible to the *cation*, as

$$M \mid MX(a_1) \mid MX(a_2) \mid M \qquad (100)$$

equation (93a) gives for the emf

$$\mathcal{E}_M = \frac{t_- RT}{\mathcal{F}} \ln \frac{a_2}{a_1} \qquad (93a)$$

Again, for a concentration cell involving the same concentrations of the electrolyte but *without* transference, namely,

$$M \mid MX(a_1) \mid X - X \mid MX(a_2) \mid M \qquad (101)$$

the reaction would be, analogous to equation (88b),

$$MX(a_2) = MX(a_1)$$

and the emf ε, according to equation (88c),

$$\varepsilon = \frac{RT}{\mathcal{F}} \ln \frac{a_2}{a_1} \qquad (102)$$

On dividing equation (93a) by equation (102), we find that

$$\frac{\varepsilon_M}{\varepsilon} = \frac{(t_- RT/\mathcal{F}) \ln (a_2/a_1)}{(RT/\mathcal{F}) \ln (a_2/a_1)} = t_- \qquad (103)$$

and hence t_- follows as the *ratio of the emf's of the cell with transference and the same cell without transference.* Similarly, for a concentration cell with transference reversible to the *anion*, as

$$X \mid MX(a_1) \mid MX(a_2) \mid X \qquad (104)$$

equation (96) yields for the emf,

$$\varepsilon_X = \frac{t_+ RT}{\mathcal{F}} \ln \frac{a_1}{a_2} \qquad (96)$$

while with the same cell without transference, i.e.,

$$X \mid MX(a_1) \mid M - M \mid MX(a_2) \mid X \qquad (105)$$

the emf is

$$\varepsilon = \frac{RT}{\mathcal{F}} \ln \frac{a_1}{a_2} \qquad (106)$$

where $a_1 > a_2$. From the ratio of equation (96) to equation (106), t_+ follows then as

$$\frac{\varepsilon_X}{\varepsilon} = \frac{(t_+ RT/\mathcal{F}) \ln (a_1/a_2)}{(RT/\mathcal{F}) \ln (a_1/a_2)} = t_+ \qquad (107)$$

Consequently, by measuring ε_M of cell (100), ε_X of cell (104), and ε of cells (101) *or* (105), since these have the same emf, the transport numbers of the electrolyte MX can be obtained directly and independently through equations (103) and (107).

In precise determinations of transference numbers from emf measurements corrections have to be made for the variation of transport numbers with concentration. Means of making such corrections have been developed, and with these it is possible to obtain results in excellent accord with those given by other methods.

SOLUBILITY PRODUCTS AND EMF

The saturation solubility of any difficultly soluble salt such as silver bromide is given by the equation

$$AgBr(s) = Ag^+ + Br^- \tag{108}$$

where the product of the activities of the two ions is equal to the solubility product. Since this solubility product K_s is an equilibrium constant, it must be related to the ε^0 value of a cell in which the above reaction occurs. Hence, by finding two single electrodes whose reactions lead to the over-all process given in equation (108), and by appropriately combining their ε^0 values, it should be possible to calculate from the latter the solubility product.

Inspection of equation (108) suggests that the requisite combination in this case is the silver and silver-silver bromide electrodes. For the silver electrode, the reaction is

$$Ag(s) = Ag^+ + \ominus$$

for the silver-silver bromide electrode it is

$$AgBr(s) + \ominus = Ag(s) + Br^-$$

and therefore the sum of the two, namely,

$$AgBr(s) = Ag^+ + Br^- \tag{109}$$

is identical with equation (108). From Table 3 ε^0 for the silver electrode at 25° C is seen to be $\varepsilon^0_{Ag} = -0.7991$ volt, ε^0 of the silver-silver bromide electrode for reduction $\varepsilon^0_{Ag-AgBr} = +0.0711$ volt, and hence ε^0 for (108) follows as

$$\varepsilon^0 = \varepsilon^0_{Ag} + \varepsilon^0_{Ag-AgBr}$$
$$= -0.7991 + 0.0711$$
$$= -0.7280 \text{ volt at } 25° \text{ C}$$

Substituting this value of ε^0 into equation (36), we obtain for the solubility product of silver bromide

$$\varepsilon^0 = \frac{RT}{n\mathfrak{F}} \ln K_s$$
$$-0.7280 = 0.05916 \log_{10} K_s$$
$$K_s = 4.9 \times 10^{-13}$$

This value of K_s may be compared with $K_s = 7.7 \times 10^{-13}$ given in Table 10 of Chapter 16. In a like manner may be calculated the solubility products of other difficultly soluble salts.

A less exact method for estimating the solubility product of a difficultly soluble salt involves the measurement of the single electrode potential of an electrode reversible to one of the ions of the salt and immersed in a solution saturated with this salt. To explain this method let us consider specifically the determination of the solubility product of silver chloride. For this purpose a solution of a chloride is taken, say 0.1 m potassium chloride, and the solution saturated with silver chloride by addition of a few drops of silver nitrate. A silver wire is inserted then into this solution, and the silver electrode thus formed is combined with a reference calomel electrode to form the cell

$$Ag \mid KCl(0.1\ m, \text{sat'd. with AgCl}) \mid \text{Calomel electrode}$$

When the reference electrode is the 0.1 N calomel, the emf of this cell at 25° C is 0.0494 volt. Since ε_c of the 0.1 N calomel for reduction is 0.3338 volt at 25° C, we have that

$$\varepsilon = \varepsilon_{Ag} + \varepsilon_c$$
$$0.0494 = \varepsilon_{Ag} + 0.3338$$
$$\varepsilon_{Ag} = -0.2844 \text{ volt}$$

But, ε_{Ag} is also given by

$$\varepsilon_{Ag} = \varepsilon_{Ag}^0 - \frac{RT}{\mathcal{F}} \ln a_{Ag^+}$$

and hence the activity of silver ions in this solution follows as

$$-0.2844 = -0.7991 - 0.05916 \log_{10} a_{Ag^+}$$
$$\log_{10} a_{Ag^+} = -\frac{0.5147}{0.05916} = -8.700$$
$$a_{Ag^+} = 2.00 \times 10^{-9}$$

Now, for the activity of the chloride ions we may take the product of the molality, 0.1, and the mean activity coefficient of potassium chloride at this concentration, 0.769. We obtain thus for K_s of silver chloride at 25° C,

$$K_s = a_{Ag^+} a_{Cl^-}$$
$$= (2.00 \times 10^{-9})(0.1 \times 0.769)$$
$$= 1.54 \times 10^{-10}$$

The thermodynamic value of K_s for this salt at 25° C is 1.76×10^{-10}.

POTENTIOMETRIC DETERMINATION OF pH

One of the most extensive applications of emf measurements is in determining the pH of various solutions. In all potentiometric pH work the procedure followed is very much the same. First a cell is assembled in which one of the electrodes is reversible to hydrogen ions and dips into the solution whose pH is to be determined, while the other electrode is usually one of the calomels. Junction between the two is made either through a salt bridge or by immersing the reference electrode directly into the solution. Next the emf of the combination, ε, is measured with a potentiometer. From ε is subtracted the emf of the calomel to yield the single potential of the electrode reversible to hydrogen ions, and from the latter, in turn, the pH is calculated by means of the emf equation applicable to the particular electrode used.

Three electrodes are more or less suitable for potentiometric pH determinations. These are: (a) the hydrogen electrode, (b) the quinhydrone electrode, and (c) the glass electrode. A fourth possibility, the antimony-antimony trioxide electrode, is suitable for potentiometric acid-base titrations, but it is not reliable for pH measurements.

THE HYDROGEN ELECTRODE

This electrode is the standard of all pH measurements and is the electrode against which all the others are checked. According to equation (49), the emf of this electrode is given by

$$\varepsilon_{H_2} = -\frac{RT}{\mathfrak{F}} \ln a_{H^+} + \frac{RT}{\mathfrak{F}} \ln P_{H_2}^{1/2} \tag{49}$$

Since by definition pH $= -\log_{10} a_{H^+}$, equation (49) in terms of pH is

$$\varepsilon_{H_2} = -\frac{2.3026\,RT}{\mathfrak{F}} \log_{10} a_{H^+} + \frac{2.3026\,RT}{\mathfrak{F}} \log_{10} P_{H_2}^{1/2}$$

$$= \frac{2.3026\,RT}{\mathfrak{F}} \text{pH} + \frac{2.3026\,RT}{\mathfrak{F}} \log_{10} P_{H_2}^{1/2} \tag{110}$$

When P_{H_2} is exactly 1 atm, equation (110) reduces to

$$\varepsilon_{H_2} = \left(\frac{2.3026\,RT}{\mathfrak{F}}\right) \text{pH} \tag{111}$$

and hence under these conditions *the emf of the hydrogen electrode is linearly dependent only on the pH of the solution.*

It was mentioned already that the hydrogen electrode consists of a piece of platinized platinum foil immersed in the solution under test, and around which is bubbled hydrogen gas. For satisfactory operation the platinized coat must be freshly deposited from a solution of chloroplantinic acid, and the hydrogen gas must be carefully purified to remove impurities, particularly oxygen. With all details carefully controlled this electrode can give very accurate results over the entire pH range, provided the solution does not contain oxidizing agents that may react with the hydrogen or metals that may be thrown out of solution by the gas. However, because of the ease with which this electrode is poisoned even by oxygen of the air, and because of the rather elaborate setup required, its use is pretty much confined to the laboratory.

To illustrate the calculation of pH from data obtained with a hydrogen electrode, let us take the following example. Suppose it is found that the emf of the cell

$$\text{H}_2 \mid \text{solution (pH = } x) \mid 1 \ N \text{ calomel}$$

is $\varepsilon = 0.5164$ volt at 25° C when the corrected barometric pressure is 754.1 mm Hg. Subtracting from this emf the potential of the calomel electrode, we obtain for the emf of the hydrogen electrode

$$\varepsilon_{\text{H}_2} = \varepsilon - \varepsilon_C$$
$$= 0.5164 - 0.2800$$
$$= 0.2364 \text{ volt}$$

This emf is due to both the pH of the solution and the pressure of the hydrogen gas. The total barometric pressure at which the gas escapes from solution is composed of the pressure of the hydrogen and the pressure of water vapor with which this gas becomes saturated in bubbling through the solution; i.e.,

$$P_{\text{H}_2} + P_{\text{H}_2\text{O}} = P_{\text{barometer}}$$

For $P_{\text{H}_2\text{O}}$ we may take without any error the vapor pressure of water at 25° C, 23.8 mm. P_{H_2} is then

$$P_{\text{H}_2} = P_{\text{barometer}} - P_{\text{H}_2\text{O}}$$
$$= 754.1 - 23.8$$
$$= 730.3 \text{ mm Hg} = 0.961 \text{ atm}$$

Substituting now $\varepsilon_{\text{H}_2} = 0.2364$ and $P_{\text{H}_2} = 0.961$ atm into equation (110), the pH of the solution follows as

$$0.2364 = 0.05916 \text{ pH} + \frac{0.05916}{2} \log_{10} 0.961$$

$$\text{pH} = \frac{0.2364 + 0.0005}{0.05916}$$
$$= 4.00$$

It will be observed that the pressure correction to the emf is small and amounts in this case to only 0.01 of a pH unit.

THE QUINHYDRONE ELECTRODE

This interesting pH electrode consists of a platinum or gold wire immersed in the solution whose pH is to be determined, after the latter has been saturated with the difficulty soluble organic compound *quinhydrone*. Why such a system should be reversible to hydrogen ions may be gathered from the following argument.

When the organic compound hydroquinone, $C_6H_4(OH)_2$, is dissolved in water, it tends to undergo to a small extent oxidation to quinone, $C_6H_4O_2$, according to the reaction

$$C_6H_4(OH)_2 = C_6H_4O_2 + 2\,H^+ + 2\ominus \qquad (112)$$
$$\text{(HQ)} \qquad\qquad \text{(Q)}$$

If an inert wire is inserted into this solution, it will pick up the electrons thus liberated and will acquire the potential ε_Q,

$$\varepsilon_Q = \varepsilon_Q^0 - \frac{RT}{2\,\mathfrak{F}} \ln \frac{a_{H^+}^2 a_Q}{a_{HQ}}$$

$$= \varepsilon_Q^0 - \frac{RT}{\mathfrak{F}} \ln a_{H^+} - \frac{RT}{2\,\mathfrak{F}} \ln \frac{a_Q}{a_{HQ}} \qquad (113)$$

where ε_Q^0 is the standard potential of this organic oxidation-reduction electrode, a_{H^+} the activity of the hydrogen ions in solution, and a_Q and a_{HQ} the activities of the neutral quinone and hydroquinone. From equation (113) it is evident that ε_Q would be a function of pH alone if only the last term could be disposed of by making $a_Q = a_{HQ}$. For this purpose we take advantage of the fact that quinone and hydroquinone form a double compound, *quinhydrone*, composed of one molecule each of quinone and hydroquinone. In aqueous solutions this compound is only difficulty soluble; but, whatever amount does dissolve dissociates to yield *equal quantities* of the two constituents. Since quinone and hydroquinone are nonelectrolytes, we may take $a_Q = a_{HQ}$ in any solution *saturated with quinhydrone*, and equation (113) becomes

$$\varepsilon_Q = \varepsilon_Q^0 - \frac{RT}{\mathfrak{F}} \ln a_{H^+}$$

$$= \varepsilon_Q^0 + \left(\frac{2.3026\ RT}{\mathfrak{F}}\right) pH \qquad (114)$$

Equation (114) gives the single electrode potential of the *quinhydrone electrode* and indicates that ε_Q under the conditions outlined *depends only on the pH of the solution*. Comparison of the quinhydrone and hydrogen electrodes has established that between 0° and 40° C ε_Q^0 is given by

$$\varepsilon_Q^0 = -0.7176 + 0.000728\ t°\ C \qquad (115)$$

which leads to $\varepsilon_Q^0 = -0.6994$ volt at 25° C for the *oxidation* reaction shown in equation (112). For this temperature we have, therefore,

$$\varepsilon_Q = -0.6994 + 0.05916\ pH \qquad (116)$$

The quinhydrone electrode when combined with a normal calomel electrode yields a cell in which up to a pH = 7.1 at 25° C the *quinhydrone electrode is positive*, i.e.,

$$\overline{1\ N\ \text{Calomel}} \left\| \begin{array}{l} \text{Solution (pH}=x), \\ \text{Sat'd. quinhydrone} \end{array} \right| \text{Pt} \qquad \text{pH} < 7.1 \qquad (117a)$$

Consequently up to pH = 7.1 the calomel electrode undergoes an oxidation for which $\varepsilon_C = -0.2800$ at 25° C, while the quinhydrone electrode undergoes a *reduction* with ε_Q given by the reverse of equation (116). Adding ε_C and ε_Q, we obtain for the emf, ε, of the combination,

$$\begin{aligned} \varepsilon &= 0.6994 - 0.05916\ \text{pH} - 0.2800 \\ &= 0.4194 - 0.05916\ \text{pH} \end{aligned} \qquad (117b)$$

On the other hand, above pH = 7.1 the quinhydrone electrode becomes negative with respect to the normal calomel, i.e., the cell is now

$$\overline{\text{Pt}} \left| \begin{array}{l} \text{Solution (pH}=x'), \\ \text{Sat'd. quinhydrone} \end{array} \right\| 1\ N\ \text{Calomel} \qquad \text{pH} > 7.1 \qquad (118a)$$

and ε becomes the sum of equation (116) and $\varepsilon_C = 0.2800$, namely,

$$\begin{aligned} \varepsilon &= -0.6994 + 0.05916\ \text{pH} + 0.2800 \\ &= -0.4194 + 0.05916\ \text{pH} \end{aligned} \qquad (118b)$$

At pH = 7.1, $\varepsilon = 0$, and both equations apply. To facilitate the use of these equations we may combine them into the expression

$$\text{pH} = \frac{0.4194 - \varepsilon}{0.05916} \qquad (119)$$

where the experimentally observed value of ε is taken as *positive when the quinhydrone electrode is positive*, and *negative when the quinhydrone electrode is negative*. Similar equations can readily be derived for other reference electrodes used in connection with the quinhydrone electrode.

The quinhydrone electrode is very simple to use and reaches equilibrium quite rapidly. It is highly satisfactory for pH determinations in solutions below pH = 8.5 provided no strong oxidizing or reducing agents are present to attack the quinhydrone. In this range oxygen of the air does not affect the results. However, above pH = 8.5 oxygen reacts with the hydroquinone rather easily, and, further, in these alkaline solutions the ionization of the hydroquinone becomes sufficiently significant to affect the pH. Serious errors arise also in solutions containing appreciable quantities of salts and proteins.

THE GLASS ELECTRODE

Fritz Haber and Z. Klemensiewicz[1] first showed that, when two solutions of different pH are separated by a glass membrane, a potential is established across the membrane whose magnitude depends on the difference in pH of the two solutions. If the pH of one of these solutions is held constant while that of the second is varied, the emf of the *glass electrode* follows the equation

$$\varepsilon_G = \varepsilon_G^0 - \frac{RT}{\mathfrak{F}} \ln a_{H^+}$$

$$= \varepsilon_G^0 + \left(\frac{2.3026\ RT}{\mathfrak{F}}\right) pH \qquad (120)$$

where ε_G^0 is a constant determined by the magnitude of the fixed pH and the particular arrangement employed. Equation (120) is strikingly similar to equation (114) for the quinhydrone electrode and indicates that the glass electrode should be suitable for pH measurements.

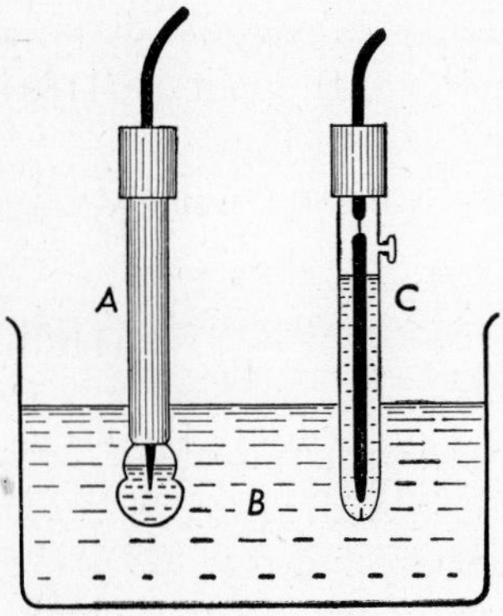

Fig. 6.   Glass Electrode Assembly for pH.

A glass electrode assembly frequently utilized for pH work is illustrated in Fig. 6. Here *A* is the glass electrode, *B* is the solution under test, and *C* is a calomel electrode used to complete the cell arrangement. The glass electrode, immersed directly in the solution whose pH is to be determined, consists of a bulb constructed of a special glass, on the inside of which is placed, say, 0.1 *N* hydrochloric acid and a silver-silver chloride electrode. This entire combination, namely,

$$Ag \mid AgCl(s),\ 0.1\ N\ HCl \mid Glass \mid$$

constitutes the glass electrode. When combined with the calomel the resulting cell is

$$Ag \mid AgCl(s),\ 0.1\ N\ HCl \mid Glass \mid Solution\ (pH = x) \mid Calomel \qquad (121)$$

from whose measured emf the single electrode potential of the glass electrode can be deduced, and therefrom the pH.

Because of the high internal resistance of the glass electrode, which may amount to as much as 100 million ohms, ordinary potentiometers cannot be used to measure the emf of cell (121). Either quadrant electrometers or vacuum tube voltmeters which require practically no current for their operation must be used. For this purpose vacuum tube cir-

[1] F. Haber and Z. Klemensiewicz, *Zeit. physik. Chem.*, **67**, 385 (1909).

cuits have been developed which not only are sensitive to 0.01 pH unit or better, but also are portable and very rugged.

Because of an "asymmetry potential," not all glass electrodes in a particular assembly have the same value of ε_G^0. For this reason it is best to determine ε_G^0 for each electrode before use. To do this a solution of definite pH is placed in B, the emf of the cell is measured, and ε_G^0 is evaluated. Then the first solution is discarded, the solution under test substituted, the measurement repeated, and the pH calculated with the ε_G^0 found above. In this manner any "asymmetry potential" is incorporated into ε_G^0 of the electrode, and errors are avoided.

A solution frequently used for calibration of glass electrode assemblies is 0.05 molar potassium acid phthalate. This solution has a pH of 4.00 between 10° C and about 30° C, and a pH of 4.02 at 38° C.

The glass electrode is the nearest approach to a universal pH electrode known at present. It is not poisoned easily, nor is it affected by oxidizing or reducing agents or by organic compounds. Further, it can be used on quantities of solution as small as a fraction of a cubic centimeter. Its only limitations arise in strongly alkaline solutions where the glass is attacked, and in solutions of pH = 9 and above where presence of various cations, particularly sodium, leads to appreciable errors. However, new glasses have been developed with which good results can be obtained up to pH = 13 or 14.

POTENTIOMETRIC ACID-BASE TITRATIONS

In Fig. 7(a) is shown a characteristic plot for the variation of pH with volume of added base during the titration of an acid such as hydrochloric acid with a base like sodium hydroxide. It will be observed that the pH of the solution rises gradually at first, then more rapidly, until at the equivalence point there is a very sharp increase in pH for a very small quantity of added base. Past the equivalence point the curve again tapers off, indicating that the pH increases only slightly on the addition of excess base.

These changes in pH during a titration may be followed potentiometrically by immersing in the solution being titrated an electrode reversible to hydrogen ions, and coupling it with a suitable reference electrode. Since the potential of the latter remains constant, the emf of such a cell will vary only with the pH of the solution. Further, since the emf of any electrode reversible to hydrogen ions is proportional to the pH, the cell emf will exhibit a course parallel to the curve shown in Fig. 7(a). Consequently, by measuring this emf at each stage of the titration and plotting it against the volume of base, we may deduce from the plot the equivalence point. This is the principle of all potentiometric acid-base titrations.

A more sensitive and satisfactory means of deducing the end point is to plot not ε of the cell against the volume, but the slope of the curve, i.e., $\Delta\varepsilon/\Delta cc$ vs. cc, Fig. 7(b). As the variation of the slope is greatest at the equivalence point, the latter plot exhibits a maximum at a volume corresponding to the end point of the titration. In practice a known volume of the acid is placed in a beaker, the electrodes are inserted, and the base is added with stirring in rather large increments at the start. After each addition the emf is read. When the latter begins to show a tendency to increase appreciably, the increments are made smaller and smaller until near the end point only 0.1 cc or less are added at a time. By such a procedure it is possible to obtain a sharp maximum and hence within narrow limits the volume of base equivalent to the acid taken.

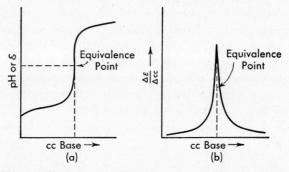

Fig. 7.   Potentiometric Titration of an Acid with a Base.

Potentiometric acid-base titrations possess a number of distinct advantages over the ordinary methods involving indicators. In the first place, indicators cannot be employed when solutions have a strong color of their own, whereas potentiometric titrations are not subject to this limitation. Second, indicators for any acid-base titration must be chosen so that the pH at which the indicator changes color corresponds more or less to the pH of the solution at the equivalence point. Hence some information is required *a priori* concerning the relative strengths of the acid and base involved. This is not true of potentiometric titrations. These always yield the equivalence point whether this point comes exactly at the neutral point, or on the acid or basic side.

Still a third advantage of the potentiometric method appears in the titration of polybasic acids or of mixtures of a strong and a weak acid with a base. With indicators it is as a rule impossible or difficult to titrate a polybasic acid in steps corresponding to different stages of neutralization. This is also the case with mixtures of strong and weak acids unless one indicator can be found whose color change corresponds to the neutralization of the strong acid, and another to that of the weak.

However, when the ionization constants of the different stages of a polybasic acid or of the different acids in a mixture differ by a factor of at least 1000, the potentiometric titration yields directly a number of distinct steps for the various neutralizations. This may be seen from Fig. 8, where the plot for the potentiometric titration of phosphoric acid with sodium hydroxide is shown. Point *A* indicates the neutralization of the first ionizable hydrogen, *B* of the second. The third cannot be thus obtained, because beyond *B* the solution is too alkaline for the sodium hydroxide to produce any significant difference in pH. To get around this difficulty calcium chloride is added to the solution at a point such as *C*. The calcium chloride reacts with the disodium phosphate present to precipitate calcium phosphate and to produce a quantity of hydrochloric

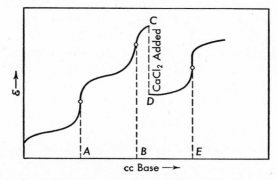

Fig. 8.   Stepwise Potentiometric Titration of H_3PO_4 with NaOH.

acid exactly equal to the acid content of the disodium phosphate. Because of the appearance of this strong acid the pH of the solution falls from *C* to a point *D*, thus making possible further titration from *D* until the third break *E*, corresponding to complete neutralization, results.

By such procedures it is possible to analyze mixtures of, say, phosphoric acid, sodium dihydrogen phosphate, and disodium phosphate. Likewise other combinations may be titrated in stages. But, such stepwise neutralization cannot be obtained with sulfuric acid. In this acid partial neutralization of the first hydrogen leads to appreciable ionization of the second, and the two titrate as if sulfuric acid were a monobasic acid.

OXIDATION-REDUCTION AND PRECIPITATION TITRATIONS

Oxidation-reduction titrations can be carried out potentiometrically in a manner identical to acid-base neutralizations by substituting for the electrode reversible to hydrogen ions an inert metal, such as a platinum wire. This metal acts as an oxidation-reduction electrode whose emf is determined by the activity ratio of the substance being oxidized or reduced.

The variation of the emf of the cell with volume of reagent added follows essentially a curve similar to Fig. 7(a). As the sharp change in emf occurs at the equivalence point, these plots may again be utilized to detect the end points. In this way may be titrated various reducing agents with oxidants, or vice versa, without dependence on color change or oxidation-reduction indicators. Further, in certain instances several substances may be estimated in the same solution by a single titration.

The same type of behavior is observed also in many precipitation reactions when an electrode reversible to one of the ions involved is used. Thus, in the titration of silver nitrate with sodium chloride a silver electrode will exhibit a sharp change in emf when all the silver is precipitated. Likewise a silver electrode will indicate the precipitation of all the chloride when the latter is titrated with silver nitrate. The power and speed of the potentiometric method is particularly well illustrated in the estimation of mixed halides. The analysis of solutions composed of chlorides, bromides, and iodides by ordinary methods is long, involved, and tedious. Potentiometrically, however, such mixtures can be analyzed under proper conditions by a single titration with silver nitrate in presence of a silver electrode. The three "breaks" obtained give first the precipitation of the least soluble silver iodide, next the intermediately soluble silver bromide, and finally the precipitation of the most soluble silver chloride. From the volumes of silver nitrate required to produce these "breaks," the amount of each halide present in the mixture can readily be calculated.

REFERENCES FOR FURTHER READING

See list at end of Chapter 15. Also:

1. R. G. Bates, *Electrometric pH Determinations*, John Wiley & Sons, Inc., New York, 1954.
2. Kortum and Bockris, *Textbook of Electrochemistry*, Elsevier Publishing Company, New York, 1951.
3. W. M. Latimer, *The Oxidation States of the Elements and Their Potentials in Aqueous Solutions*, Prentice-Hall, Inc., New York, 1952.
4. A. Weissberger, *Physical Methods of Organic Chemistry*, Interscience Publishers, Inc., New York, 1949, Chap. XXVII.

PROBLEMS

Note: In the following problems the temperature is to be taken as 25° C unless otherwise specified.

1. The resistance of a potentiometer for the full scale reading of 1.6 volts is 200 ohms. What steady current must be maintained through the potentiometer coils so that the instrument may read volts directly?   *Ans.* 0.008 amp.

2. Write the individual electrode reactions and the total cell reaction for each of the following cells. In each cell the negative electrode is at the left.

    (a) $Pb \mid PbSO_4(s), SO_4^{--} \parallel Cu^{++} \mid Cu$
    (b) $Cd \mid Cd^{++} \parallel H^+ \mid H_2(g)$
    (c) $Zn \mid Zn^{++} \parallel Fe^{+++}, Fe^{++} \mid Pt$

3. In each of the following cells write the cell reaction, and designate which reactions are spontaneous as written.

                                                      Sign of emf

    (a) $Ag \mid AgCl(s), Cl^- \parallel I^-, AgI(s) \mid Ag$ −
    (b) $K \mid K^+ \parallel Cl^-, Hg_2Cl_2(s) \mid Hg$ +
    (c) $Pt \mid Tl^+, Tl^{+++} \parallel Cu^{++} \mid Cu$ −
    (d) $Ni \mid Ni^{++} \parallel Pb^{++} \mid Pb$ +

4. A silver-silver ion electrode is measured against a normal calomel electrode at 25° C. The calomel electrode is negative, and the observed emf is 0.2360 volt. Write the cell reaction and calculate the potential of the silver-silver ion electrode.   *Ans.* $\varepsilon = 0.5160$ volt.

5. Assuming that the substances present in each of the cells of problem 2 are in their standard states, calculate the emf of each cell and the free energy change accompanying the cell reaction.

6. At 25° C the free energy of formation of $H_2O(l)$ is $-56,700$ cal/mole, while that of its ionization to hydrogen and hydroxyl ions is 19,050 cal/mole. (a) What will be the reversible emf at 25° C of the cell

$$H_2(g, 1 \text{ atm}) \mid H^+ \parallel OH^- \mid O_2(g, 1 \text{ atm})$$

    (b) What will be the single electrode potential of the oxygen electrode?
                                                 Ans. (a) 0.403 volt.

7. The heat of formation at 25° C of $H_2O(l)$ is $-68,320$ cal/mole, while its heat of ionization is 13,600 cal/mole. Calculate the temperature coefficient of emf at 25° C of the cell given in problem 6.

8. From the equation giving the emf of the Weston cell as a function of temperature, calculate ΔF, ΔH, and ΔS for the cell reaction at 25° C.

9. Calculate the oxidation potentials of each of the following single electrodes:

    (a) $Ag \mid AgCl(s), Cl^-(a = 0.0001)$
    (b) $Pt \mid I_2(s), I^-(a = 1.5)$
    (c) $Sn \mid Sn^{++}(a = 0.01)$
    (d) $H_2(g, 1 \text{ atm}) \mid H^+(a = 15)$

10. Calculate the potentials, and specify the electrode polarity for the spontaneous reaction, for the cells obtained by combining (a)–(d), (b)–(d), and (a)–(c) in problem 9.   *Ans.* 0.3897 volt for first cell.

11. Calculate the potential of the cell:

$$Fe \mid Fe^{++}(a = 0.6) \parallel Cd^{++}(a = 0.001) \mid Cd$$

What must be the polarity of the Cd electrode in order for the cell to serve as a source of energy?

12. Devise a cell in which the following reaction will take place:

$$\frac{1}{2} Br_2(l) + Fe^{++} = Br^- + Fe^{+++}$$

What will be the standard emf of the cell and the standard free energy change in calories accompanying the reaction? Is the reaction as written spontaneous?

13. For the cell

$$\text{Ag} \mid \text{AgBr(s)}, \text{Br}^-(a = 0.10) \parallel \text{Cl}^-(a = 0.01), \text{AgCl(s)} \mid \text{Ag}$$

write the cell reaction, and calculate the potential at 25° C. Is the reaction as written spontaneous?

14. Calculate the potential at 25° C of the cell:

$$\text{H}_2(P = 1 \text{ atm}) \mid \text{HBr}(a_\pm = 0.2), \text{Hg}_2\text{Br}_2(s) \mid \text{Hg}$$

Ans. 0.2212 volt.

15. The potential of the cell

$$\text{Cd} \mid \text{CdI}_2, \text{AgI(s)} \mid \text{Ag}$$

is 0.2860 volt at 25° C. Calculate the mean ionic activity of the ions in the solution, and the activity of the electrolyte.

Ans. $a_\pm = 0.403$; $a_{\text{CdI}_2} = 0.0656$.

16. Indicate the cell in which the equilibrium constant for the following reaction can be measured:

$$\frac{1}{2} \text{H}_2(g, 1 \text{ atm}) + \text{AgI(s)} = \text{H}^+ + \text{I}^- + \text{Ag(s)}$$

What is the equilibrium constant for this reaction at 25° C?

Ans. $K = 2.67 \times 10^{-3}$.

17. From the results of the preceding problem, calculate the activity of HI in equilibrium with AgI(s), Ag(s), and H_2(g, 1 atm) at 25° C.

18. Write the cell reaction and calculate the potential of the cell:

$$\text{H}_2(g, 0.4 \text{ atm}) \mid \text{HCl}(a_\pm = 3.0), \text{AgCl(s)} \mid \text{Ag}$$

19. Finely divided Ni is added to a solution in which the molality of Sn^{++} is 0.1. What will be the activities of Ni^{++} and Sn^{++} when equilibrium is established? Assume that the molality is equal to activity for this calculation.

Ans. $a_{\text{Ni}^{++}} = 0.10$; $a_{\text{Sn}^{++}} = 5.7 \times 10^{-5}$.

20. An excess of solid AgCl is added to a 0.1 normal solution of Br^- ions. Assuming activity equal to ionic concentration, calculate the concentration of Cl^- and Br^- ions at equilibrium.

21. Write the cell reaction and calculate the potential of the following cell:

$$\text{Zn} \mid \text{Zn}^{++}(a = 0.01) \parallel \text{Fe}^{++}(a = 0.001), \text{Fe}^{+++}(a = 0.1) \mid \text{Pt}$$

Ans. 1.710 volts.

22. It is desired to determine the $\mathcal{E}^0$ value of the $\text{Cu} \mid \text{Cu}^{++}$ electrode and the mean ionic coefficients of CuSO_4. Explain what cells may be assembled, what measurements made, and derive an expression for the emf of the cells chosen. Assume that the $\mathcal{E}^0$ value of the second electrode used is known.

23. Write the cell reaction and calculate the potential of the cell:

$$\text{H}_2(g, 1 \text{ atm}) \mid \text{H}_2\text{SO}_4(m = 0.05, \gamma = 0.340), \text{Hg}_2\text{SO}_4(s) \mid \text{Hg}$$

24. Explain what cell may be employed to measure the mean ionic activity coefficients of CdCl_2. Derive an expression for the emf of such a cell.

25. For the cells

$$Na(s) \left| \begin{array}{c} NaI \text{ in} \\ C_2H_5NH_2 \end{array} \right| Na(Hg)(0.206\%)$$

$$Na(Hg)(0.206\%) \mid NaCl(m = 1.022, \gamma = 0.650), Hg_2Cl_2(s) \mid Hg$$

the potentials are 0.8453 and 2.1582 volts respectively. Write the reaction for each cell, and find from the data the $\mathcal{E}^0$ value for the sodium electrode.

26. The potential of the cell

$$Zn(s) \mid ZnCl_2(m = 0.01021), AgCl(s) \mid Ag$$

was found to be 1.1566 volts. What is the mean ionic activity coefficient of $ZnCl_2$ in this solution?

Ans. 0.705.

27. Keston [*J. Am. Chem. Soc.*, **57**, 1671 (1935)] found that for cells of the type, $H_2(g, 1 \text{ atm}) \mid HBr(m), AgBr(s) \mid Ag(s)$ the emf's at various molalities of HBr are:

m	0.0003198	0.0004042	0.0008444	0.001355	0.001850	0.002396	0.003719
$\mathcal{E}$	0.48469	0.47381	0.43636	0.41243	0.39667	0.38383	0.36173

Obtain $\mathcal{E}^0$ for the cell by a graphical method, and then calculate the activity coefficients at each molality. Compare the activity coefficients thus obtained with those calculated from the Debye-Hückel limiting law.

28. The potential of the cell

$$Hg \mid Hg_2Cl_2(s), KCl \text{ (sat'd.)} \mid Cl_2(P = 0.283 \text{ atm})$$

was observed to be 1.0758 volts. Using the $\mathcal{E}^0$ value for the calomel electrode given in the text, calculate $\mathcal{E}^0$ for the chlorine electrode.

29. For the cell

$$Zn(Hg) \mid ZnSO_4, PbSO_4(s) \mid Pb(Hg)$$

having an $\mathcal{E}^0$ value of 0.4109 volt, the following data were obtained by Cowperthwaite and LaMer [*J. Am. Chem. Soc.*, **53**, 4333 (1931)]:

Molality of $ZnSO_4$	Emf
0.0005	0.61144
0.002	0.58319
0.01	0.55353
0.05	0.52867

Calculate the mean ionic activity coefficient of $ZnSO_4$ in each of these solutions.

30. Write the cell reaction and calculate the potential of the cell

$$Cl_2(P = 0.9 \text{ atm}) \mid NaCl \text{ (sol'n.)} \mid Cl_2(P = 0.1 \text{ atm})$$

Will the cell reaction be spontaneous as written?

31. Given the cells:

(a) $H_2(P = 1 \text{ atm}) \mid HBr(a_\pm = 0.001), AgBr(s) \mid Ag$
(b) same as (a) with $a_\pm = 2.5$
(c) same as (a) with $a_\pm = 0.01$

show how cell (a) may be combined with either (b) or (c) to give a positive emf, and calculate the emf in each case.

32. What will be the cell reaction and the potential of the cell

$$\text{Zn(s)} \mid \text{ZnCl}_2(m = 0.02, \gamma = 0.642), \text{AgCl(s)} \mid \text{Ag-Ag} \mid \text{AgCl(s)},$$
$$\text{ZnCl}_2(m = 1.50, \gamma = 0.290) \mid \text{Zn(s)}$$

Ans. 0.1359 volt.

33. Find the cell reaction and calculate the potential of the cell

$$\text{Cd(s)} \mid \text{CdSO}_4(m = 0.01, \gamma = 0.383), \text{PbSO}_4(s) \mid \text{Pb-Pb} \mid \text{PbSO}_4(s),$$
$$\text{CdSO}_4(m = 1.00, \gamma = 0.042) \mid \text{Cd(s)}$$

34. Find the cell reaction and calculate the potential of the following cell with transference:

$$\text{Pb(s)} \mid \text{PbSO}_4(s), \text{CuSO}_4(m = 0.2, \gamma = 0.110) \mid \text{CuSO}_4(m = 0.02,$$
$$\gamma = 0.320)\text{PbSO}_4(s) \mid \text{Pb}$$

The transport number of Cu^{++} is 0.370. Is the cell reaction spontaneous as written? *Ans.* 0.0117 volt; yes.

35. Given the cell with transference:

$$\text{H}_2(P = 1 \text{ atm}) \mid \text{H}_2\text{SO}_4(m = 0.005, \gamma = 0.643) \mid \text{H}_2\text{SO}_4(m = 2.00,$$
$$\gamma = 0.125) \mid \text{H}_2(P = 1 \text{ atm})$$

find the cell reaction and emf. The transport number of hydrogen ion is 0.821.

36. It is desired to determine the transport numbers of the ions in CdCl_2 by emf measurements. Show what cells would have to be assembled, and what measurements and calculations would have to be made.

37. The emf of the following cell

$$\text{Ag(s)} \mid \text{AgCl (sat'd.)}, \text{KCl}(m = 0.05, \gamma = 0.817 \mid \text{KNO}_3 \mid \text{AgNO}_3(m = 0.1,$$
$$\gamma = 0.723) \mid \text{Ag(s)}$$

is 0.4312 volt. Calculate from these data the solubility product of AgCl.
Ans. 1.52×10^{-10}.

38. Show how the proper $\mathcal{E}^0$ values from Table 3 may be used to calculate the thermodynamic solubility product of PbSO_4.

39. Using $\mathcal{E}^0$ values listed in Table 3, calculate $\mathcal{E}^0$ and ΔF^0 for the electrode process

$$\text{Fe} = \text{Fe}^{+++} + 3 \ominus$$

Ans. $\mathcal{E}^0 = 0.037$ volt; $\Delta F^0 = -2560$ cal.

40. The emf of the cell

$$\text{H}_2(g) \mid \text{Buffer} \parallel \text{Normal calomel electrode}$$

is 0.6885 volt at 40° C when the barometric pressure is 725 mm. What is the pH of the solution? *Ans.* 6.60.

41. The buffer in the cell of the preceding problem is replaced with a standard buffer of pH = 4.025, while all other conditions remain the same. What should then be the cell potential?

42. The potential of the cell

$$\text{Pt} \left| \begin{array}{c} \text{Buffer} \\ \text{Sat'd. quinhydrone} \end{array} \right\| \text{Normal calomel electrode}$$

is 0.0042 volt at 35° C. What is the pH of the buffer?

43. The buffer used in the preceding problem is replaced by another. The polarity of the cell is thereby reversed and a potential of 0.2175 volt observed. What is the pH of the second buffer?

44. Compare the emf's and the polarities which result when (a) a H_2 electrode ($P_{H_2} = 1$ atm) is placed in a buffer solution of pH = 6.55 using a normal calomel reference and (b) the H_2 electrode is replaced by a quinhydrone electrode.

45. The cell

$$Ag(s) \mid AgCl(s), HCl(0.1 \ N) \mid Glass \mid Buffer \parallel Sat'd. \ calomel \ electrode$$

gave an emf of 0.1120 volt when the pH of the buffer used was 4.00. When a buffer of unknown pH was used, the potential was 0.3865 volt. What is the pH of the unknown buffer?

46. What would be the potential of the cell used in the preceding problem if a buffer of pH = 2.50 were used?

47. A 100-cc solution of 0.01 N HCl is titrated with 0.1 N NaOH solution. Calculate the pH of the solution after the addition of 0, 9.0, 9.9, 9.99, 10.0, 10.1, 11.0, and 20.0 cc of base. Plot the pH obtained against the volume of base added. Assume that the volume does not change during the course of the titration and that the ionic concentration is equal to the ionic activity.

48. Repeat problem 47 using 100 cc of 0.01 N CH_3COOH in place of the HCl. The dissociation constant of CH_3COOH may be taken as 1.8×10^{-5}.

49. One hundred cc of 0.01 N KCl are titrated with 0.1 N $AgNO_3$. Calculate the potential of an Ag electrode in the solution after the addition of 9, 10, and 11 cc of the reagent. Assume no volume change, and that ionic activity is equal to ionic concentration. The solubility product of AgCl may be taken as 1.6×10^{-10}.

18

Electrolysis and Polarization

An electrochemical cell may be employed to convert chemical energy into electrical and to transform electrical energy into chemical. In performing the first of these functions the cell yields electrical energy as a result of a free energy decrease accompanying a spontaneous reaction within the cell. Under reversible conditions the electrical work obtained is exactly equal to the free energy decrease. When, on the other hand, the cell is operated irreversibly, the electrical energy available for doing work is less than the free energy decrease, and the difference becomes dissipated as heat.

Of necessity it must follow that reactions accompanied by a free energy increase cannot be utilized for doing work. Instead, to make such reactions possible energy must be supplied to raise the free energy content of the products above that of the reactants. Electrochemically this addition of energy is accomplished by passing electricity under a suitable applied potential through a cell in which the particular reaction can take place. By means of such *electrolysis* chemical changes are produced at the electrodes, and we obtain chemical action at the expense of the electrical energy.

From thermodynamic considerations it may be anticipated that the *minimum* electrical energy required to carry out a nonspontaneous reaction would be equal to the free energy increase accompanying the change; and this ΔF would in turn be equal, but be opposite in sign, to the free energy decrease attending the reverse spontaneous process. This would be true when the electrolysis is carried out reversibly, i.e., when the electrodes are completely reversible and when only a very minute current is passed through the cell. When these conditions of reversibility are not satisfied, the energy required will be the theoretical minimum plus the energy necessary to overcome the irreversibility. This means that in presence of any irreversibility the potential to be applied for electrolysis will have to be greater than the reversible emf of the cell. A cell requiring thus voltage in excess of the theoretical is said to be *polarized*. The excess voltage is called *polarization voltage*, while the phenomenon in general is referred to as *polarization*.

APPLIED POTENTIAL AND ELECTROLYSIS

To understand what happens when an external voltage is applied to a cell, consider the cell

$$Tl \mid Tl^+(a = 0.5) \parallel Sn^{++}(a = 0.01) \mid Sn$$

for which the spontaneous reaction is

$$Tl(s) + \frac{1}{2} Sn^{++}(a = 0.01) = \frac{1}{2} Sn(s) + Tl^+(a = 0.5) \tag{1}$$

and the potential 0.155 volt at 25° C. To reverse this reaction an outside potential must be applied to the cell of a magnitude sufficient to overcome the emf of the cell itself. For this purpose an external source of emf must be connected to the cell such that electrons enter the thallium electrode and leave through the tin electrode; i.e., the negative pole of the external source of emf must be connected to the negative electrode of the cell, the positive pole to the positive electrode. Electrons will then flow externally from the thallium to the tin as long as the applied potential is less than 0.155 volt. When the latter becomes equal to 0.155 volt, the two emf's are balanced, and no current flows in either direction. Finally, when the applied potential exceeds that of the cell, electrons from the external battery will enter the thallium electrode and exit through the tin electrode. Since now the direction of current flow is opposite to that of the spontaneous action of the cell, the reactions at the electrodes are also reversed, and we obtain thus the process opposite to that given in equation (1).

From this description it is evident that not all of the applied emf is effective in passing current through the cell. Part of it, in this case 0.155 volt at 25° C, has to be utilized in overcoming the spontaneous emf of the cell itself. In general, if we let ε be the applied potential and ε_b be the potential exerted by the cell itself, the net voltage operative in current passage is $\varepsilon - \varepsilon_b$. With this net voltage the current I resulting in a cell whose internal resistance is R follows from Ohm's law as

$$I = \frac{\mathcal{E} - \mathcal{E}_b}{R} \tag{2}$$

$\mathcal{E}_b$ is referred to as the *back emf* of the cell in question. Under reversible conditions $\mathcal{E}_b$ is nothing more than the reversible emf of the cell. However, under irreversible conditions, i.e., when polarization is present, $\mathcal{E}_b$ is greater than the reversible emf, and a higher potential is required to yield a given current.

Ordinarily the cells encountered in electrolysis are not of the type discussed above. Rather they involve a *single electrolyte* into which dip a pair of electrodes. For instance, for the electrolysis of water the cell may consist of a pair of platinum electrodes immersed in a solution of an acid or base. Such a cell possesses no initial back emf, since both the electrodes and the electrolyte are the same. It may appear, therefore, that in such a cell all of the applied emf will go toward passage of electricity, with none of it necessary for overcoming back emf. However, this is not the case, for it is found experimentally that a potential of about 1.7 volts must be applied to the cell before there sets in a continuous evolution of hydrogen and oxygen. When a potential of less than 1.7 volts is applied, there is observed a momentary surge of current which rapidly falls to practically zero and stays there. The reason for this behavior is that, owing to the initial surge of current, small amounts of hydrogen are generated at the negative electrode and oxygen at the positive electrode. These gases adhere to the electrode surfaces and convert these into hydrogen and oxygen electrodes with a back emf which operates to oppose the applied potential. At each potential below 1.7 volts the amounts of the two gases formed at the electrodes are just sufficient to make the back emf equal to the applied potential, and hence the first surge of current is rapidly reduced to practically zero. But, once the applied potential exceeds 1.7 volts, enough hydrogen and oxygen are formed to permit these gases to escape from the electrodes against the confining atmospheric pressure, and *continuous electrolysis* becomes possible. As the minimum voltage at which continuous evolution of hydrogen and oxygen sets in is about 1.7 volts, any voltage above this value is available for current passage. Therefore, by increasing the voltage above 1.7 volts higher and higher currents can be realized.

The significant fact in the above description is that *products of electrolysis convert even inert electrodes into active electrodes which can exercise a back emf*. This is true not only of gases but of other substances as well. Thus, as soon as some zinc is deposited on a piece of platinum, the latter is transformed into an active zinc electrode. Consequently, even where

there is no initial back emf present, one is generated on attempted electrolysis by formation of a cell involving the products of the electrolysis.

DECOMPOSITION POTENTIALS

Since even inert electrodes are converted on electrolysis into active
electrodes with back emf, it becomes necessary to ascertain the minimum
voltage required to produce continuous electrolysis of an electrolyte.
This minimum voltage, called the *decomposition potential* of an electrolyte,
can be determined by means of the setup illustrated in Fig. 1. In this

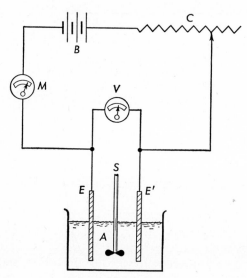

Fig. 1.   Determination of Decomposition Potentials.

diagram A is the electrolytic cell containing the electrolyte to be studied,
the two electrodes E and E', and the stirrer S. Connected to these electrodes through a variable resistance C is an external source of emf B
and a milliammeter M for measuring the current passing through the
circuit. By means of the variable resistance C it is possible to regulate the
voltage applied to the cell, and this voltage in turn can be measured by
means of the voltmeter V inserted across the two electrodes. By using a
high resistance voltmeter, all of the current indicated by the milliammeter
may be considered to pass through the cell. Otherwise the reading of the
milliammeter has to be corrected for the current passing through the
voltmeter. The latter is given by the reading of the voltmeter divided
by the internal resistance of the instrument.

To measure the decomposition voltage a series of current vs. applied
voltage readings are taken both below and above the decomposition

potential. At the start sufficient resistance is introduced at C to yield
only a very small potential. After reading both the milliammeter and
the voltmeter, some resistance is cut out at C, and another set of readings is taken. This procedure is continued until an appreciable current
is passing through the circuit and electrolysis proceeds freely. If the current readings are plotted against the corresponding voltages, the curve
resulting is of the type shown in Fig. 2. Along the branch AB, which is
below the decomposition voltage, the current is very small. Past B, however, the curve takes a sharp turn upward, and soon continuous electrolysis may be observed in the cell. Since the curve AB lies below the

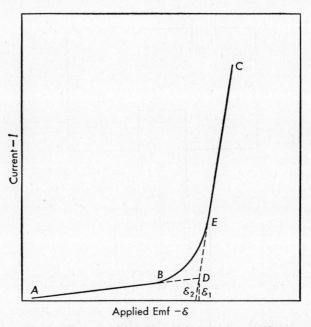

Fig. 2. Decomposition Potentials from I vs. ε Plots.

decomposition voltage while EC is above it, the voltage at which decomposition sets in must lie at the intersection of the two curves. To find
this point the usual practice is to extend lines AB and EC until they
intersect, as at D, and the voltage at this intersection, ε_1, is taken as the
decomposition voltage. An alternate procedure is to extend line BC until
it intersects the $I = 0$ axis, and the value of ε at the latter point, ε_2,
is chosen as the voltage at which continuous electrolysis becomes pos-
sible. The idea here is that, since Ohm's law is followed more or less
closely by the branch EC, extension of this law to $I = 0$ should yield
the decomposition voltage even though there is some current flow before
this voltage is attained. Despite the fact that the second method yields

somewhat lower results than the first, there is no way of deciding between them. Consequently either is chosen according to preference, with possibly the first more frequently chosen than the second.

The appearance of current below the decomposition potential arises from the fact that the products of electrolysis deposited on the electrodes tend to diffuse slowly back into the solution. To compensate for this loss by diffusion a small current must pass through the cell in order to regenerate the material lost. As the diffusion is continuous, the current must also be supplied continuously, and this accounts for the small but steady current observed below the decomposition potential.

TABLE 1

DECOMPOSITION POTENTIALS IN 1 N SOLUTIONS (Pt ELECTRODES)

Electrolyte	Dec. Potential $\mathcal{E}_d$ (volts)	Products of Electrolysis	Rev. Decomp. Potential $\mathcal{E}_r$	$\mathcal{E}_d - \mathcal{E}_r$
HNO_3	-1.69	$H_2 + O_2$	-1.23	-0.46
$CH_2ClCOOH$	-1.72	$H_2 + O_2$	-1.23	-0.49
$CHCl_2COOH$	-1.66	$H_2 + O_2$	-1.23	-0.43
$HClO_4$	-1.65	$H_2 + O_2$	-1.23	-0.42
H_2SO_4	-1.67	$H_2 + O_2$	-1.23	-0.44
H_3PO_4	-1.70	$H_2 + O_2$	-1.23	-0.47
$NaOH$	-1.69	$H_2 + O_2$	-1.23	-0.46
KOH	-1.67	$H_2 + O_2$	-1.23	-0.44
NH_4OH	-1.74	$H_2 + O_2$	-1.23	-0.51
$N(CH_3)_4OH$	-1.74	$H_2 + O_2$	-1.23	-0.51
HCl	-1.31	$H_2 + Cl_2$	-1.37	$+0.06$
HBr	-0.94	$H_2 + Br_2$	-1.08	$+0.14$
HI	-0.52	$H_2 + I_2$	-0.55	$+0.03$
$Cd(NO_3)_2$	-1.98	$Cd + O_2$	-1.25	-0.73
$CdSO_4$	-2.03	$Cd + O_2$	-1.26	-0.77
$CoCl_2$	-1.78	$Co + Cl_2$	-1.69	-0.09
$CoSO_4$	-1.92	$Co + O_2$	-1.14	-0.78
$CuSO_4$	-1.49	$Cu + O_2$	-0.51	-0.98
$Pb(NO_3)_2$	-1.52	$Pb + O_2$	-0.96	-0.56
$NiCl_2$	-1.85	$Ni + Cl_2$	-1.64	-0.21
$NiSO_4$	-2.09	$Ni + O_2$	-1.10	-0.99
$AgNO_3$	-0.70	$Ag + O_2$	-0.04	-0.66
$ZnBr_2$	-1.80	$Zn + Br_2$	-1.87	$+0.07$
$ZnSO_4$	-2.55	$Zn + O_2$	-1.60	-0.95

In column 2 of Table 1 are given the decomposition potentials obtained with platinum electrodes in 1 N solutions of various electrolytes at room temperature. In each instance the products of electrolysis are given, as well as the reversible decomposition potentials calculated for the various electrolytes. The manner of arriving at the latter and the significance of the observed results will now be explained.

CALCULATION OF REVERSIBLE DECOMPOSITION POTENTIALS

The reversible decomposition potential of an electrolyte is the sum of the reversible emf's established at the electrodes by the products of electrolysis. Consequently, as soon as the products of electrolysis, the concentration of the electrolyte, and the direction of the electrode reactions, i.e., oxidation or reduction, are known, the reversible decomposition potential can be calculated by the methods of the preceding chapter.

The direction of any electrode reaction in an electrolytic cell is readily ascertained from the polarity of the electrodes. In any electrolytic cell electrons enter through the electrode connected to the *negative* side of the external source of emf. At this electrode, therefore, called the *cathode*, the reaction must always be a *reduction*. On the other hand, electrons leave the cell through the electrode connected to the positive side of the external battery, and hence at this electrode, called the *anode*, the reaction must always be an *oxidation*. With this information we are ready to consider the calculation of the reversible decomposition potentials of various electrolytes.

For this purpose let us take first the electrolysis of 1 N hydrochloric acid between platinum electrodes. This electrolysis involves the reduction of hydrogen ions to hydrogen at the cathode and the oxidation of chloride ions to chlorine at the anode. Since at the decomposition potential the hydrogen and chlorine gases escape at the electrodes at 1 atm pressure, we have for the two electrode reactions

$$2 H^+(N = 1) + 2 \ominus = H_2(g, 1 \text{ atm})$$
$$2 Cl^-(N = 1) = Cl_2(g, 1 \text{ atm}) + 2 \ominus$$

For the first of these electrodes the reversible emf is given by

$$\varepsilon_{H_2} = \varepsilon_{H_2}^0 - \frac{0.059}{2} \log_{10} \left(\frac{1}{C_{H^+} f_{H^+}} \right)^2$$
$$= +0.059 \log_{10} (0.809)$$
$$= -0.005 \text{ volt}$$

Again, the emf of the chlorine electrode follows as

$$\varepsilon_{Cl_2} = \varepsilon_{Cl_2}^0 - \frac{0.059}{2} \log_{10} \left(\frac{1}{C_{Cl^-} f_{Cl^-}} \right)^2$$
$$= -1.360 + 0.059 \log_{10} (0.809)$$
$$= -1.365 \text{ volts}$$

Adding the two potentials, the reversible decomposition voltage of 1 N hydrochloric acid is at 25° C,

$$\varepsilon = \varepsilon_{H_2} + \varepsilon_{Cl_2}$$
$$= -0.005 - 1.365$$
$$= -1.37 \text{ volts}$$

As a second example may be taken the electrolysis of zinc bromide. In this electrolyte the deposition of zinc on the cathode produces a zinc electrode at which takes place the reaction

$$Zn^{++} + 2 \ominus = Zn(s)$$

while the oxidation of bromide ions to bromine at the anode converts the latter into a bromine-bromide electrode at which the process

$$2 \text{ Br}^- = Br_2(l) + 2 \ominus$$

occurs. At 25° C, and in 1 N solution, the mean activity coefficient is $f = 0.38$, while the concentrations of the two ions are $C_{Zn^{++}} = 0.5$ molar and $C_{Br^-} = 1.0$ molar. Therefore the emf's of the electrodes are

$$\varepsilon_{Zn} = \varepsilon^0_{Zn} - \frac{0.059}{2} \log_{10} \frac{1}{C_{Zn^{++}} f_{Zn^{++}}}$$
$$= -0.762 + \frac{0.059}{2} \log_{10} (0.5 \times 0.38)$$
$$= -0.783 \text{ volt}$$
$$\varepsilon_{Br_2} = \varepsilon^0_{Br_2} - \frac{0.059}{2} \log_{10} \frac{1}{(C_{Br^-} f_{Br^-})^2}$$
$$= -1.065 + 0.059 \log_{10} (1 \times 0.38)$$
$$= -1.090 \text{ volts}$$

and the reversible decomposition potential of zinc bromide,

$$\varepsilon = \varepsilon_{Zn} + \varepsilon_{Br_2}$$
$$= -0.783 - 1.090$$
$$= -1.87 \text{ volts}$$

In order to calculate the reversible decomposition potentials in electrolytes where oxygen is evolved, the ε^0 value of the oxygen-hydroxyl ion electrode is required. Since the oxygen electrode is highly irreversible, this quantity cannot be obtained directly from emf measurements, but must be calculated from free energy data from other sources. For this purpose we have the free energy change of the reaction

$$H_2(g) + \frac{1}{2} O_2(g) + H_2O(l) = 2 \text{ H}^+ + 2 \text{ OH}^- \qquad \Delta F^0_{25° C} = -18,600 \text{ cal} \qquad (3)$$

As 2 faradays are required to accomplish the reaction, the ε^0 corresponding to the ΔF^0 of this process is

$$\Delta F^0 = -n\mathbf{F}\boldsymbol{\varepsilon}^0$$
$$-18{,}600 \times 4.184 = -2 \times 96{,}500\ \boldsymbol{\varepsilon}^0$$
$$\boldsymbol{\varepsilon}^0 = 0.403\ \text{volt}$$

However, for the reaction $H_2(g) = 2\ H^+$, $\boldsymbol{\varepsilon}^0 = 0$. Subtracting this reaction from equation (3), we arrive then at the standard electrode potential for the solution of oxygen to form hydroxyl ions, namely,

$$\frac{1}{2}\ O_2(g) + H_2O(l) + 2\ominus = 2\ OH^- \qquad \boldsymbol{\varepsilon}^0_{25^\circ C} = 0.403\ \text{volt} \qquad (4)$$

For the converse process, i.e., the deposition of oxygen at 1 atm pressure from a solution containing hydroxyl ions at unit activity, the standard potential of the oxygen electrode follows, therefore, as

$$2\ OH^- = \frac{1}{2}\ O_2(g) + H_2O(l) + 2\ominus \qquad \boldsymbol{\varepsilon}^0_{25^\circ C} = -0.403\ \text{volt} \qquad (5)$$

With the $\boldsymbol{\varepsilon}^0$ of the oxygen electrode thus available, the reversible decomposition potentials for electrolytes involving evolution of oxygen on electrolysis may be calculated. As an initial example let us take the electrolysis of $1\ N$ silver nitrate, which yields silver at the cathode and oxygen at the anode. For the reduction at the silver electrode thus formed at the cathode, we have the reaction $Ag^+(N = 1) + \ominus = Ag(s)$. Hence the corresponding emf is

$$\boldsymbol{\varepsilon}_{Ag} = \boldsymbol{\varepsilon}^0_{Ag} - \frac{0.059}{1}\ \log_{10} \frac{1}{C_{Ag^+} f_{Ag^+}}$$
$$= 0.799 + 0.059\ \log_{10}\ (1 \times 0.396)$$
$$= 0.775\ \text{volt}$$

Again, for the oxidation at the oxygen electrode formed at the anode we have the process

$$2\ OH^- = \frac{1}{2}\ O_2(g) + H_2O(l) + 2\ominus$$

where, since the solution is essentially neutral, the concentration of hydroxyl ions may be taken as 10^{-7} gram ionic weights per liter. The potential of the oxygen electrode is, then,

$$\boldsymbol{\varepsilon}_{O_2} = \boldsymbol{\varepsilon}^0_{O_2} - \frac{0.059}{2}\ \log_{10} \frac{1}{a^2_{OH^-}}$$
$$= -0.403 + 0.059\ \log_{10}\ (10^{-7})$$
$$= -0.816\ \text{volt}$$

Adding the two, the reversible decomposition voltage of the silver nitrate follows as

$$\varepsilon = \varepsilon_{Ag} + \varepsilon_{O_2}$$
$$= 0.775 - 0.816$$
$$= -0.04 \text{ volt}$$

These examples show that the reversible decomposition potentials depend on the concentration of the electrolyte. However, this is not true when water is electrolyzed to yield hydrogen and oxygen. In the latter instance the over-all cell reaction is given by the converse of equation (3), for which the emf follows as

$$\varepsilon = \varepsilon^0 - \frac{0.059}{2} \log_{10} \frac{1}{a_{H^+}^2 a_{OH^-}^2}$$
$$= -0.403 + \frac{0.059}{1} \log_{10} (a_{H^+} a_{OH^-})$$

But, *in any aqueous solution* the product $a_{H^+} a_{OH^-}$ is a constant equal to 1×10^{-14} at 25° C. Hence,

$$\varepsilon = -0.403 + 0.059 \log_{10} (1 \times 10^{-14})$$
$$= -0.403 - 0.826$$
$$= -1.229 \text{ volts}$$

and this should be, therefore, the reversible decomposition potential of any cell in which the essential process is the electrolysis of water. Further, this potential should be independent of the concentration of the electrolyte or its nature. This deduction accounts for the fact that the reversible decomposition potentials in Table 1 for all the acids and bases yielding oxygen and hydrogen are the same.

SIGNIFICANCE OF OBSERVED DECOMPOSITION POTENTIALS

With this explanation of the calculation of reversible decomposition potentials, we are in a position to consider the significance of the experimental results given in Table 1. First, a comparison of the potentials given in columns 2 and 4 of the table for electrolytes that do not yield oxygen on electrolysis of 1 N solutions, namely, hydrochloric acid, hydrobromic acid, hydriodic acid, cobalt chloride, nickel chloride, and zinc bromide, reveals that for these the observed decomposition potentials are not far different from those calculated theoretically. From this it may be concluded that the ions in these substances, i.e., hydrogen, the metals, and the halogens, are deposited on platinum electrodes under conditions which approximate more or less to reversibility. On the other hand, in electrolytes in which oxygen is evolved, as in the acids and bases at the top of the table and in some of the salts, the potentials actually required for decomposition are considerably greater than those calculated on the assumption of reversibility. Moreover, since the metals and hydrogen are deposited essentially reversibly on platinum, this discrepancy indicates that the observed irreversibility must occur primarily in the evolution of oxygen at the platinum surfaces. In other words, oxygen electrodes, even at platinum surfaces, are appreciably polarized. In the case of the acids and bases the extent of this polarization, which for the moment may be ascribed totally to the oxygen, amounts to about 0.45 volt. However, in the deposition of oxygen from salt solutions the polarization is greater and may be as much as a volt.

Another interesting point in Table 1 is that acids and bases yielding oxygen and hydrogen have essentially the same decomposition potentials, namely, about -1.7 volts. This observation is in line with the conclusion reached in the preceding section for the decomposition potential of any electrolyte in which the essential process is the electrolysis of water. However, the decomposition potential is not 1.23 volts as predicted theoretically, but that plus the polarization voltage of about 0.45 volt for the oxygen evolution, which is very nearly the same for all the acids and bases. In this connection it may be pointed out that whereas the decomposition potential of $1 N$ hydrochloric is -1.31 volts, the potential increases as the acid is diluted, eventually reaching a value of -1.7 volts. From this it may be concluded that, whereas in the more concentrated solutions the products of electrolysis are hydrogen and chlorine, in dilute solutions they are hydrogen and oxygen. Between the two extremes both chlorine and oxygen are evolved at the anode in varying proportions, giving this electrode a potential intermediate between that of the oxygen and chlorine electrodes.

TYPES OF POLARIZATION

Measurements of decomposition potentials are not suitable for extended polarization studies. First, such data yield information on the sum of the polarization voltages at the two electrodes rather than on that at any one. Again, the results apply only to the conditions obtaining when continuous electrolysis sets in, and they tell us nothing about what happens at higher current densities. Consequently, in order to ascertain the extent of polarization at each electrode separately and at various current densities, more suitable methods are required.

However, before turning to these it is necessary to point out that any observed polarization can be of two types, namely, (a) *concentration polarization* and (b) *overvoltage*. The first arises from the fact that, with the changes in the concentration of the electrolyte about the electrodes during electrolysis, cells may arise which can develop an emf opposite to that applied. On the other hand, overvoltage is a polarization potential whose source lies in some process at the electrode which takes place irreversibly and is thus a phenomenon intimately associated with the nature of the electrode and the processes occurring at its surface. Under ordinary conditions the total polarization observed will be the sum of both effects. But since the overvoltage is of particular electrochemical interest, it becomes important to understand the nature of concentration polarization, and the methods by which it may be minimized or eliminated in order to arrive at the overvoltage.

CONCENTRATION POLARIZATION

The source of concentration polarization in an electrolytic cell may be illustrated with the following example. Suppose that a solution of 0.1 N silver nitrate is to be electrolyzed between *silver* electrodes. At the start the concentration of the electrolyte is uniform through the solution, the electrodes are identical, and so the cell has no initial back emf. However, as soon as current is sent through the cell, silver begins to dissolve at the anode while silver ions begin to deposit at the cathode. The solution in the immediate vicinity of the anode consequently becomes more concentrated in silver ions than 0.1 normal, that about the cathode less concentrated. As we have now two different concentrations about the electrodes, the combination must constitute a concentration cell whose emf is given by

$$\varepsilon = - \frac{RT}{n\mathfrak{F}} \ln \frac{C_2 f_2}{C_1 f_1}$$

A moment's reflection on the nature of the concentration cell thus formed will reveal that its emf operates against the applied potential. The result is thus a polarization requiring that part of the applied potential be utilized to overcome the emf developed due to the concentration changes about the electrodes.

Similarly it can be shown that current passage leads to concentration changes about the electrodes in all types of cells. Unless the concentration changes become very large, the polarizations developed are at best rather small and can hardly account for the large polarization potentials observed in many cells. Further, some forces operating in solution, such as electrolytic conduction by the current and thermal diffusion, tend to equalize the concentration differences. As increase in temperature favors electrolytic conduction and diffusion, this equalization can be promoted by raising the temperature. However, a much more effective method of overcoming concentration polarization is efficient stirring of the electrolyte. In electrolytic cells where the electrolyte is thoroughly agitated the concentration polarization can be practically eliminated, and hence any polarization voltage observed under such conditions must be essentially overvoltage due to irreversibility in the electrode processes.

MEASUREMENT OF OVERVOLTAGE

Direct measurements of overvoltage attending the deposition of electrolytic products at various electrodes are made by observing the potentials of the electrodes when current is passing, and under conditions where there is no concentration polarization, i.e., in stirred solutions. For this

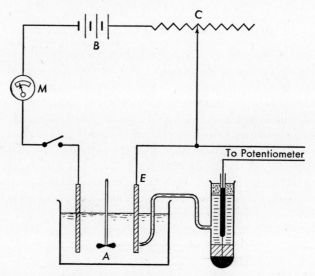

Fig. 3. Determination of Overvoltage.

purpose the setup generally employed is shown in Fig. 3. The electrolytic cell A, containing electrodes of known cross-sectional area, the electrolyte, and a stirrer, is connected in series with an external battery B through a variable resistance C, an ammeter M, and a switch. Any desired current strength can thus be sent through the electrolyzing circuit by varying the resistance at C. To obtain now the potential of, say, electrode E, the latter is made one-half of a new cell, the other half of which is a suitable reference electrode, such as a calomel, and the two are connected to a potentiometer. In order to avoid inclusion of any appreciable IR drop through the solution in measuring the potential of E against the reference electrode, the arm of the latter is usually drawn out to a fine tip and placed flush against the electrode.

To make a measurement the stirrer is started, the switch closed, and the current through the electrolyzing circuit, as indicated by M, is adjusted to any desired value by means of C. After the current has become steady, the emf of E against the reference electrode is read on the potentiometer, as well as the current given by M. The latter is then readjusted to some other value, and the whole operation is repeated. In this manner a series of emf readings can be obtained for various values of the current passing through the cell. On dividing the current strength at each point by the area of electrode E, the current density follows, while the emf of E at each stage is obtained by subtracting from the measured emf the potential of the reference electrode. Finally, in order to arrive at the overvoltage the reversible potential of E must be subtracted from the observed electrode potentials. These reversible emf's may be calculated, or they can be measured by taking the potential of E against a reference electrode when no current is flowing through the cell. In the latter instance an electrode material must be used at which the particular electrode reaction is reversible.

OVERVOLTAGE IN CATHODIC DEPOSITION OF METALS

Overvoltage studies on the cathodic deposition of metals indicate that the deposition of metals takes place with relatively small overvoltage. In line with theoretical requirements, metals do not begin to plate on the cathode until the potential of the given metal in the particular solution is exceeded. Thereafter the potential of the metal rises slowly with current density, indicating some polarization, but the overvoltage hardly ever exceeds several tenths of a volt at the higher current densities. Metals such as zinc, copper, and cadmium exhibit particularly low overvoltage, while metals of the iron group, namely, iron, cobalt, and nickel, show higher overvoltages. Just what is the cause of metal overvoltage is not yet clear. Various theories have been proposed, but at present too little information is available to make a choice among them.

The overvoltage of a particular metal is not the same for all salt solutions of the metal, but varies slightly with the nature of the co-ion. It is affected also by the presence of acids, colloids, and other addends. Finally, the overvoltage of metals is increased when these are deposited from solutions in which the particular metal can exist as a complex, as silver in cyanide solutions.

HYDROGEN OVERVOLTAGE

Of particular importance is the overvoltage exhibited by hydrogen in its deposition on various cathodic surfaces. *On platinized platinum and at zero current density the overvoltage of hydrogen is zero*, since these are the conditions under which the hydrogen electrode is reversible. However, as the current density is increased the overvoltage also goes up, but at no time does it become particularly large. In fact, at a current density of 1.5 amp per square centimeter it is only 0.05 volt at 25° C. On the other hand, at other cathodic surfaces the overvoltage is much higher, as may be seen from Fig. 4. These data, obtained in 2 N sulfuric acid at 25° C,[1] indicate that the overvoltage of hydrogen is low only on platinized platinum. On smooth platinum surfaces the overvoltage is low at very small current densities, but increases gradually with the latter to approach a limiting value at high current densities. This is true also of gold, graphite, tellurium, and palladium cathodes. However, on silver, mercury, bismuth, cadmium, tin, iron, zinc, nickel, and lead surfaces the hydrogen overvoltage is already quite large at zero current density. These electrodes, therefore, cannot function reversibly under any conditions, and it is not possible to deposit hydrogen on them at anywhere near the reversible potentials. Another characteristic of these metals with high hydrogen overvoltage is that they exhibit at low current densities a very rapid increase in overvoltage to values which remain essentially constant at the higher densities.

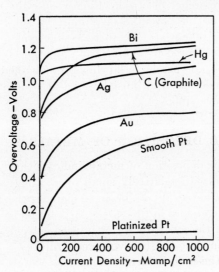

Fig. 4. Hydrogen Overvoltage on Various Metals (2 N H_2SO_4 at 25° C).

The variation of hydrogen overvoltage with current density at constant temperature can frequently be represented by the equation

$$\varepsilon_o = a + b \log_{10} I \qquad (6)$$

where ε_o is the overvoltage, I the current density, and a and b are constants. According to this equation a plot of ε_o against $\log_{10} I$ should be linear with slope equal to b and a y intercept of a. This expectation has been realized in a number of instances, and over a fairly wide range of current densities. Furthermore, many metals give approximately the same slope $b = 0.12$. This value of b corresponds very closely to $(2 \times 2.303 \, RT)/\mathfrak{F}$, which at 25° C is equal to 0.118. Again, study of the effect of temperature on overvoltage has shown that the slope of the ε_o-$\log_{10} I$ curve actually increases linearly with the absolute temperature in accord

[1] Knobel, Caplan, and Eiseman, *Trans. Am. Electrochem. Soc.*, **43**, 55 (1923).

with the relation

$$\mathcal{E}_o = a + \frac{(2 \times 2.303 \; RT)}{\mathfrak{F}} \log_{10} I \qquad (7)$$

Although in many cases equation (7) reproduces experimental data fairly closely, in certain others the discrepancy may be quite large. Thus slopes have been obtained as low as 0.025 on platinized platinum and as high as 0.3 on lead and graphite cathodes. Furthermore, equation (6) or equation (7) is insufficient frequently to represent the variation of over-voltage with current density over the full range of the latter. Another complicating factor encountered occasionally is a variation of overvoltage with time, due probably to changes taking place in the nature of the the electrode surface.

Increase of temperature has been found to decrease hydrogen over-voltage, although, as we have seen, the slope of the overvoltage-current density curve is steeper at higher temperatures. Thus, the overvoltage on copper at 0.4 amp per square centimeter decreases from 0.57 volt at 0° to 0.40 volt at 74° C. On mercury and several other electrodes the decrease in hydrogen overvoltage with temperature amounts to about 2 millivolts per degree temperature rise. Measurements of hydrogen overvoltage at various pressures, both above and below atmospheric, indicate that at higher pressures the overvoltage is changed only slightly, but at the lower pressures it rises sharply on copper, nickel, and mercury cathodes. Overvoltage is also influenced by the presence of various impurities in the cathode materials.

The available data show that the composition and pH of the solution exert little effect on the hydrogen overvoltage. On the other hand, the nature of the cathode surface is very important. On smooth, shiny, and polished surfaces the overvoltage is invariably greater than on rough, pitted, or etched surfaces. This difference is particularly well illustrated with the hydrogen overvoltage on smooth and platinized platinum. Analogous differences, though not so large, have been observed also on other metals.

OVERVOLTAGE IN ANODIC PROCESSES

The limited data on anodic deposition indicate that evolution of the halides at electrodes such as platinum and graphite takes place with relatively small overvoltages. Thus, at 1000 milliamperes per square centimeter the overvoltages of chlorine, bromine, and iodine at 25° C are about 0.07, 0.20, 0.20 volt on platinized platinum, 0.24, 0.4, 0.22 volt on smooth platinum, and 0.5, 0.33, 0.7 volt on graphite. At very small current densities the overvoltages are practically negligible, and, therefore, the deposition of the halogens takes place essentially reversibly.

However, this is not true of oxygen evolution. Although precise oxygen overvoltages are difficult to obtain because of attack of the electrodes by the oxygen, the data available indicate that they are invariably high even at low current densities. This may be seen from Table 2, where the oxygen overvoltages on various metals at several current densities are given. Another important fact revealed by this table is that oxygen overvoltages attain higher values on metals such as platinum and gold than on metals such as copper and nickel, which is just the opposite to the hydrogen overvoltages on these substances. Otherwise oxygen overvoltage behaves essentially analogously to that of hydrogen. In acid

TABLE 2

OXYGEN OVERVOLTAGES AT 25° C

Current Density (ma/cm²)	Overvoltage (volts)						
	Plat'd. Pt	Smooth Pt	Au	Graphite	Cu	Ag	Ni
1	0.40	0.72	0.67	0.53	0.42	0.58	0.35
10	0.52	0.85	0.96	0.90	0.58	0.73	0.52
50	0.61	1.16	1.06	—	0.64	0.91	0.67
100	0.64	1.28	1.24	1.09	0.66	0.98	0.73
500	0.71	1.43	1.53	1.19	0.74	1.08	0.82
1000	0.77	1.49	1.63	1.24	0.79	1.13	0.85
1500	0.79	1.38	1.68	1.28	0.84	1.14	0.87

solutions the overvoltage appears to be independent of pH, increase of temperature leads to a decrease in overvoltage, and the dependence of overvoltage on current density can again be represented by equation (7) with exactly the same expression for the slope of the curve. In alkaline solutions, however, the overvoltage appears to vary with the hydroxyl ion concentration.

THEORIES OF OVERVOLTAGE

When the various stages involved in any over-all electrode reaction proceed rapidly, equilibrium can readily be established between the ions in solution and the electrode, and the latter can thus behave reversibly and exhibit its equilibrium potential. On the other hand, if any of the intermediate processes for one reason or another are slow, or if any complicating reactions take place between the electrode and some of the substances appearing in the electrode reaction, equilibrium cannot be established, and hence the electrode cannot behave reversibly. Utilizing this idea, many theories have been proposed to account for overvoltage, especially that of hydrogen. However, no theory has as yet been proposed which can account satisfactorily for all the observed phenomena. A review of these theories has been given by Bockris.[1]

METAL DEPOSITION AND HYDROGEN OVERVOLTAGE

Deposition of most metals from aqueous solutions takes place with very little overvoltage and hence at essentially reversible potentials. Were the metal ions the only cations present, these potentials would alone determine the deposition. However, in any aqueous solution hydrogen ions are also present, and consequently two cathodic reactions are possible, the deposition of the metal and the evolution of hydrogen. The question arises, therefore: Under what conditions can a metal be deposited from aqueous solution before evolution of hydrogen sets in?

The answer to this question is simply this: If the potential required for metal deposition is less than that for the hydrogen, the product of electrolysis at the cathode will be the metal. If the reverse is true, cathodic liberation of hydrogen will occur. However, whereas the cathodic deposition of metals involves essentially only the reversible metal electrode potentials, the liberation of hydrogen involves not only the reversible potential of the hydrogen electrode in the particular solution, but also the overvoltage of hydrogen at the material composing the cathode. In fact, it is largely because of the latter factor that many metals can be deposited from aqueous solutions under conditions which in absence of overvoltage would invariably yield hydrogen.

To illustrate the above points, consider first the electrolysis of an aqueous solution of silver nitrate in which the activity of the salt is unity. In this solution the deposition potential of the silver will be the standard electrode potential of the metal, or $\varepsilon^0_{Ag} = +0.80$ volt at 25° C. Again, in this same solution the activity of hydrogen ions is 10^{-7}, and hence the potential for the reversible evolution of hydrogen would be

$$\varepsilon_{H_2} = -\frac{0.059}{1} \log_{10} \frac{1}{10^{-7}}$$
$$= -0.41 \text{ volt}$$

Since the deposition of silver requires a lesser expenditure of energy than the evolution of hydrogen, as the former process is spontaneous whereas the latter is not, silver will plate out in preference to hydrogen. In this case, therefore, silver will be the electrolytic product at the cathode whether hydrogen overvoltage is present or not. The same will be true

[1] J. Bockris, *Chem. Rev.*, **43**, 525 (1948).

also of copper deposition. Further, although the difference between the silver or copper potentials and that of hydrogen can be reduced by making the solutions acid, still the potential of the latter cannot be reduced below those of the metals mentioned, and these will plate out whether the solution is acid or neutral.

On the other hand, the deposition of most metals above hydrogen in the electromotive series would be impossible were it not for overvoltage. For a solution of cadmium ions at unit activity the potential of the cadmium electrode will be 0.40 volt, and hence the potential required for deposition will be -0.40 volt. This potential is so close to that of the hydrogen electrode in neutral solution, -0.41 volt, that both cadmium and hydrogen may be expected to deposit. Again, if the solution were acid, the potential of the hydrogen electrode would be less negative, and in such solutions it would appear to be impossible to plate cadmium at all. Still, this is not the case, for evolution of hydrogen does not take place reversibly on a cadmium cathode; in fact, at a current density as low as 1 milliampere per square centimeter the overvoltage of hydrogen on cadmium is already about a volt. Consequently, in order to plate hydrogen from neutral solutions of a cadmium salt a potential of about -1.4 volts will be necessary, while from strongly acid solutions, about -1.0 volt. As both of these potentials are considerably higher than that required for cadmium plating, -0.40 volt, the latter process takes place rather than hydrogen evolution.

In this manner may be explained the electrolytic separation of such metals as zinc, iron, nickel, tin, and lead from their aqueous solutions. Were it not for the presence of hydrogen overvoltage, the deposition of some of these metals would be complicated by appearance of hydrogen, while in other cases, as with zinc, hydrogen would be the exclusive product. Particularly illustrative in this connection is the fact that even sodium may be deposited on a mercury cathode in preference to hydrogen. With an overvoltage of about a volt on mercury, a potential near -1.4 volts is required to liberate hydrogen on this metal. On the other hand, deposition of sodium requires a potential of over 2 volts. However, when sodium is deposited on mercury, the former dissolves in the latter to form an amalgam in which the activity of the sodium is moderated. When the amalgam is dilute, the sodium potential is only about 1.2 volts, and hence the deposition of sodium on the amalgam can take place at -1.2 volts. As this potential is less than the -1.4 volts for hydrogen evolution on mercury, sodium can be recovered from aqueous solutions as an amalgam in preference to hydrogen. This fact is utilized commercially in the Castner cell for the electrolysis of sodium chloride, where the sodium is first deposited cathodically as an amalgam and is allowed then to react with water to yield hydrogen and sodium hydroxide.

ELECTROLYTIC SEPARATION OF METALS

Not only may metals be separated electrolytically from hydrogen ions in solution when sufficient differences in potential exist, but also various metals may be separated from each other. To accomplish clean-cut separation of one metal from another it is desirable that a difference of about 0.2 volt exist between the potential of one metal at near complete removal and the potential of the next metal at the inception of its deposition. When such conditions obtain, various metals can be removed from solution and separated from each other quantitatively with sufficient accuracy for analytical purposes. In this manner silver may be separated from copper, copper from cadmium, and cadmium from zinc. In a solution containing all of the metals mentioned the procedure is to adjust the electrolytic potential first at a point higher than that required to deposit silver, but not high enough to yield copper. At such a potential appreciable current will flow as long as any silver is present in solution, and deposition takes place. However, as soon as the silver is removed the potential is not sufficiently high to permit the next metal in the series to plate, and hence the current falls to a low value, indicating the end of the silver separation. At this stage the cathode is removed, a new one is inserted, the potential is adjusted to a value intermediate between the copper and cadmium, and electrolysis is again initiated. By repeating this sequence of potential adjustment and electrolysis, the copper can be removed next, then the cadmium, and finally the zinc.

Occasionally, in order to avoid gassing at the cathode due to hydrogen evolution, the acidity of the solution may require adjustment before separation of metals higher in the series. Again, frequently a greater difference in separation potentials can be obtained by converting some of the ions to complexes, or by changing the temperature. Various such artifices and other experimental details may be found described in books on quantitative electroanalysis.

SIMULTANEOUS DEPOSITION OF METALS

In order to deposit two metals simultaneously at a cathode it is necessary that the two have the same deposition potentials. This means that the concentrations of the two ions in solution must be so adjusted that the potentials of the two metals, which are ordinarily different, are brought together. Such adjustment is usually not possible with solutions of simple salts of the metals, but may be accomplished by converting the metal ions to complexes. The outstanding example of such behavior is the direct formation of brasses by simultaneous deposition of copper and zinc. In aqueous solutions of their simple salts these metals have deposition potentials that differ by over a volt. However, when the cations of these metals are converted to their cyanide complexes, the difference in potential between them is considerably reduced until at a given concentration of cyanide they become essentially the same. From such solutions, therefore, both metals can be plated simultaneously as a brass. Again, by varying the proportions of zinc, copper, and cyanide in the electrolyte, and by controlling the current density, deposits can be obtained varying in metal content from pure copper to pure zinc; i.e., brasses of any desired composition can be obtained. Further, various addition agents and the temperature alter the composition of the deposit. Increase in temperature invariably leads to an increase in copper content, so that at sufficiently high temperatures the product is exclusively this metal.

ANODIC SOLUTION OF METALS

When an inert anode, such as platinum, is used in the electrolysis of a solution which can yield only oxygen, the product at the anode is always this gas. On the other hand, when a more active metal is the anode material, the reaction at the anode may be either solution of the metal or evolution of oxygen, depending on which of these processes requires the lower potential. However, since the oxygen overvoltage is high on most metals, only platinum and gold will usually yield oxygen, while other metals will dissolve anodically to yield ions of the metals.

During anodic solution most metals exhibit their equilibrium potentials in the given solution, and hence the potential required for the process need be only slightly more positive than that of the metal itself. With iron, nickel, and cobalt, however, potentials exceeding the equilibrium value by 0.3 or 0.4 volt are required before solution commences. The solution of these metals is attended, therefore, by appreciable overvoltage. Nevertheless, as long as the requisite potential is applied and the current density is low, the metals continue to pass into solution. But if the current density is raised, a point is reached at which the potential of the metal rises rapidly, the current through the solution falls, and the metal stops dissolving. Any attempt to increase the current by raising the voltage does not rectify the situation. Finally, at a sufficiently high potential oxygen evolution sets in, and only then does the current begin to go up again.

This suspension of activity and solubility of the metals is called *passivity*. Of the three metals mentioned, nickel is rendered passive more readily than cobalt, and cobalt more readily than iron under identical conditions. Again, these metals become passive more readily in alkaline than in acid solutions; and the passivity is promoted by presence of oxidizing agents in the electrolyte but hindered by halide ions. On the other hand, molybdenum and tungsten are passivated more easily in acid than in alkaline solutions. In general a metal can be passivated more readily in a solution in which its ions are precipitated the more easily. Thus, iron, cobalt, and nickel cations are soluble in acid solutions but precipitate in alkaline solutions as the hydroxides, whereas molybdenum and tungsten are soluble in alkalies, but precipitate readily in acid solutions.

A metal once rendered passive will regain its activity slowly on standing after the current has been shut off. Reactivation can be accelerated appreciably by making the metal a cathode in an electrolytic cell, or by contacting it with a metal more active than itself. Scratching the surface also promotes the return of activity.

The passivity of metals has been traced to the formation of oxide films on the surfaces of the metals. These films are extremely thin, cannot ordinarily be seen, and are themselves not soluble. By covering the surface of the metal, the film of oxide can prevent the solution of the more active metal underneath and can thus make the metal behave as if it were much more noble than it actually is.

ELECTROLYTIC OXIDATION AND REDUCTION

Cathodic deposition of metallic ions or hydrogen, and anodic deposition of oxygen or solution of metals, are not the only processes which may take place at the electrodes. Any reduction reaction leading to a removal of electrons should be possible at the cathode, and any oxidation reaction leading to a giving up of electrons should be possible at the anode. This is actually the case. When such reductions and oxidations can take place at potentials lower than those required for evolution of oxygen or hydrogen, formation of these gases is avoided, and instead we get *reduction* of the substances in solution *at the cathode and oxidation at the anode*. Substances present in solution which can thus undergo oxidation or reduction, and at the same time prevent evolution of hydrogen or oxygen, are called *depolarizers*. Further, those substances which by their own reduction can prevent formation of hydrogen are called *cathodic depolarizers*, while those which by their own oxidation can prevent evolution of oxygen are referred to as *anodic depolarizers*.

The simplest depolarizers are inorganic ions capable of existence in two valence states. Thus ferric and stannic ions by reduction at the cathode to ferrous and stannous ions can depolarize the evolution of hydrogen, while the oxidation of ferrous or stannous ions at the anode can depolarize the formation of oxygen. In these instances there is evidently no deposition of gas, and the electrode processes involve apparently direct electron transfer between ions and electrode. Furthermore, such processes lead to the establishment of a definite potential at the electrode dependent on the ratio of the activities of the ions, although occasionally overvoltage is encountered.

On the other hand, the action of certain inorganic and organic depolarizers depends apparently on the deposition of hydrogen or oxygen and subsequent reaction with these gases. Thus the over-all processes in the reduction of nitrates and nitrobenzene at the cathode are

$$NaNO_3 + 2 H = NaNO_2 + H_2O$$
$$C_6H_5NO_2 + 6 H = C_6H_5NH_2 + 2 H_2O$$

while the anodic oxidation of alcohol to acetic acid is given by

$$C_2H_5OH + 2 O = CH_3COOH + H_2O$$

Such processes as a rule do not involve a definite potential for the system, and are usually irreversible. Their efficacy arises from the fact that by reaction with any oxygen or hydrogen deposited on an electrode they prevent accumulation and escape of these gases, and they thus allow the electrode processes to take place at lower potentials than would be required to form the gases.

Other examples of electrolytic reductions are the reduction of permanganate to manganate, chromate to chromic salts, quinone to hydroquinone, sugars to alcohols, and nitrobenzene to aniline and various other intermediate products. In the latter reduction high hydrogen overvoltage cathodes, such as lead, zinc, copper, tin, and mercury, invariably yield the product of most complete reduction, aniline. On the other hand, on nickel, carbon, silver, or platinum cathodes in neutral solution the product is mostly C_6H_5NHOH. Again, in acid solutions on these cathodes p-aminophenol ($H_2NC_6H_4OH$), benzidine ($NH_2C_6H_4$—$C_6H_4NO_2$), as well as aniline can be recovered, whereas in alkaline solutions azoxybenzene [$(C_6H_5N)_2O$] is the final reduction product. By varying the conditions of electrolysis, therefore, a multiplicity of reduction products can be obtained from a single depolarizer, nitrobenzene.

Many and varied types of anodic oxidations have been carried out electrolytically. Among these may be mentioned the oxidation of ferrous to ferric salts, stannous to stannic salts, of manganate to permanganate, of chromic salts to chromates, and of ferro- to ferricyanides. Interesting types of oxidations are the conversion of carbonates to percarbonates, $2 CO_3^{--} \longrightarrow C_2O_6^{--}$, of sulfates to persulfates, $2 SO_4^{--} \longrightarrow S_2O_8^{--}$, and of borax ($Na_2B_4O_7$) to sodium perborate ($NaBO_3 \cdot 4 H_2O$). The persulfates on heating with water yield hydrogen peroxide, and this is the electrolytic method for preparing this substance. Finally, electrolytic oxidations of organic compounds are exemplified by the oxidation of hydroquinone to quinone, of alcohol to acetic acid, and of salts of saturated organic acids to hydrocarbons and carbon dioxide (Kolbe's reaction)

$$2\,RCOO^- = R\!-\!R + 2\,CO_2$$

By this means hydrocarbons containing up to 34 carbon atoms have been prepared.

COMMERCIAL CELLS

We shall conclude this chapter with a description of several electrochemical cells commonly used as sources of electrical energy. Strictly speaking, the discussion of these cells belongs in the preceding chapter; however, certain features about them can be understood more readily at this junction.

The cells generally employed as sources of electric potential are of two types. In the *primary cells* electrical energy can be obtained at the expense of chemical reactivity only as long as the active materials are still present. Once these have been consumed, the cell cannot be profitably or readily rejuvenated and must be discarded. On the other hand, in *secondary* or *storage cells* the cell once used can be recharged by passage of current through it, and it may hence be used over and over again. Of cells of the first type, the only one of importance is the Leclanché or dry cell, while among the storage type the acid lead cell and the alkaline Edison cell are of common occurrence. These cells will now be described in turn.

The Leclanché or Dry Cell. The Leclanché primary cell consists of a negative zinc electrode, a positive carbon electrode surrounded by manganese dioxide, and a paste of ammonium chloride and zinc chloride as an electrolyte. The reaction at the negative electrode is solution of zinc to form zinc ions, while that at the positive electrode appears to be

$$2\,MnO_2(s) + H_2O(l) + 2\,\ominus = Mn_2O_3(s) + 2\,OH^-$$

From these the over-all process for the cell follows as

$$Zn(s) + 2\,MnO_2(s) + H_2O(l) = Zn^{++} + 2\,OH^- + Mn_2O_3(s) \quad (8)$$

The hydroxyl ions generated by the action of the cell liberate ammonia from the ammonium chloride, which in turn combines with the zinc ions to precipitate the difficulty soluble salt $Zn(NH_3)_2Cl_2$; i.e.,

$$2\,NH_4Cl + 2\,OH^- = 2\,NH_3 + 2\,Cl^- + 2\,H_2O \quad (9a)$$
$$Zn^{++} + 2\,NH_3 + 2\,Cl^- = Zn(NH_3)_2Cl_2 \quad (9b)$$

However, reactions (9a) and (9b) are secondary processes not involved directly in the electrode reactions, so they do not contribute to the potential of the cell.

The Leclanché cell develops a potential of about 1.5 volts on open circuit. With usage this voltage tends to fall until eventually the cell has to be discarded. At best these cells have a low capacity, and they are not intended for heavy duty.

The Lead Storage Cell. In this cell the negative electrode is lead, the positive electrode lead impregnated with lead dioxide, while the electrolyte is a solution of approximately 20 per cent sulfuric acid with a specific gravity of about 1.15 at room temperature. On drawing current from this cell lead dissolves at the negative electrode to form lead ions, which combine then with sulfate ions in solution to precipitate lead sulfate. The over-all electrode process is, therefore,

$$Pb(s) + SO_4^{--} = PbSO_4(s) + 2 \ominus \qquad (10)$$

which shows that actually this electrode is a lead-lead sulfate electrode reversible to sulfate ions. The action of the positive electrode, in turn, can be accounted for by postulating that the lead dioxide by hydration can yield plumbic ions,

$$PbO_2(s) + 2 H_2O(l) = Pb^{++++} + 4 OH^- \qquad (11a)$$

which are then reduced to plumbous ions by taking on two electrons from the electrode; i.e.,

$$Pb^{++++} + 2 \ominus = Pb^{++} \qquad (11b)$$

Since the plumbous ions are in solution, they react with sulfate ions to precipitate lead sulfate,

$$Pb^{++} + SO_4^{--} = PbSO_4(s) \qquad (11c)$$

while the hydroxyl ions formed in reaction (11a) are neutralized by the acid,

$$4 OH^- + 4 H^+ = 4 H_2O(l) \qquad (11d)$$

On adding the last four reactions, the over-all process at the lead dioxide electrode becomes

$$PbO_2(s) + 4 H^+ + SO_4^{--} + 2 \ominus = PbSO_4(s) + 2 H_2O(l) \qquad (11e)$$

from which we see that this is essentially an oxidation-reduction electrode dependent on both hydrogen and sulfate ions for its potential. From equations (10) and (11e) the over-all reaction in the lead storage cell on discharge follows as

$$Pb(s) + PbO_2(s) + 2 H_2SO_4 = 2 PbSO_4(s) + 2 H_2O(l) \qquad (12)$$

According to equation (12) the potential of the lead storage cell should depend at any given temperature only on the activity of sulfuric acid in solution. This is actually the case. Thus, at 25° C and at a concentration of 7.4 per cent sulfuric acid the potential is 1.90 volts, at 21.4 per cent 2.00 volts, and at 39.2 per cent 2.14 volts. Further, since sulfuric acid is consumed in the operation of the cell, the specific gravity of the electrolyte should fall on discharge, as it does. Finally, the heats of reaction (12) for different concentrations of sulfuric acid obtained electrochemically are in excellent accord with thermally obtained results, confirming thus, if not the mechanism of the electrode processes, at least the validity of the over-all cell reaction.

To recharge a lead storage cell, reaction (12) taking place on discharge must be reversed. For this purpose a potential higher than that of the cell must be applied externally. During this electrolysis lead is deposited on the cathode, lead dioxide is formed at the anode, and sulfuric acid is regenerated in the cell. Owing to this increase in acid concentration the potential of the cell rises, and so does the specific gravity. As long as lead ions are present in solution, no gassing will occur on charging. However, if the electrolysis is permitted to proceed until all the lead is removed, evolution of hydrogen at the lead surface and oxygen at the lead dioxide surface will take place, and there is danger of injury to the electrode plates. For this reason lead cells should be charged only until the specific gravity is up to the desired point and no further.

The voltage of a lead cell does not depend on the size of the cell or of the electrodes. Small or large, a lead cell always has the same potential for a given acid concentration. The only advantage of large electrodes is that they give a cell a higher capacity to deliver electrical energy. Finally, the lead cell is quite efficient in its operation, yielding on discharge 90 to 95 per cent of the electrical energy put into it on charge.

The Edison Cell. The Edison storage cell consists of a negative iron electrode and a positive electrode of nickel in contact with the sesquioxide Ni_2O_3. The electrolyte is a 21 per cent by weight solution of potassium hydroxide to which is added some lithium hydroxide. Just exactly what is the function of the latter is not well understood, but it seems to improve the capacity of the cell. On discharge the net electrode reaction at the iron surface is

$$Fe(s) + 2\ OH^- = FeO(s) + H_2O(l) + 2 \ominus$$

while that at the positive electrode is

$$Ni_2O_3(s) + H_2O(l) + 2 \ominus = 2\ NiO(s) + 2\ OH^-$$

From these the over-all cell reaction on discharge follows as

$$Fe(s) + Ni_2O_3(s) = FeO(s) + 2\ NiO(s) \tag{13}$$

while on charge it is the reverse of this. Equation (13) indicates that the voltage of the cell should be independent of the concentration of the electrolyte. This, however, is not quite the case, for the potential does depend slightly on the concentration of the base. This dependence may be accounted for by postulating that the various oxides involved in equation (13) are hydrated, in which instance water would appear in the cell reaction. As the activity of the water changes with the concentration of potassium hydroxide, so would the emf of the cell.

The potential of the Edison cell is lower than that of the lead cell, being only about 1.3 volts. Its efficiency is also lower. On the other hand, its lighter weight compared to the lead cell and the absence of acid recommend it for certain purposes.

REFERENCES FOR FURTHER READING

1. Creighton and Koehler, *Principles and Applications of Electrochemistry*, Vol. II, John Wiley & Sons, Inc., New York, 1944.
2. S. Glasstone, *Introduction to Electrochemistry*, D. Van Nostrand Company, Inc., New York, 1942.
3. Kortum and Bockris, *Textbook of Electrochemistry*, Elsevier Publishing Company, New York, 1951.
4. C. L. Mantell, *Industrial Electrochemistry*, McGraw-Hill Book Company, Inc., New York, 1950.
5. G. W. Vinal, *Storage Batteries*, John Wiley & Sons, Inc., New York, 1940, 3rd ed.

PROBLEMS

1. Which of the following cells, as *written*, are electrolytic and which are primary cells:

     (a) $Cd(s) \mid CdSO_4(a = 1), PbSO_4(s) \mid Pb(s)$
     (b) $Au(s) \mid H_2SO_4$ (dilute solution) $\mid Pt(s)$
     (c) $Pt(s) \mid Na_2SO_4$ solution $\mid Pt(s)$
     (d) $Ag(s) \mid AgNO_3(m = 0.5) \parallel AgNO_3(m = 0.005) \mid Ag(s)$
     (e) $Pb(s) \mid Pb^{++}(a = 1) \parallel Ag^{+}(a = 1) \mid Ag(s)$

2. Write the electrode and cell reactions which will occur in the above cells when a current is passed through them.
3. A 2.00-volt storage battery is used in an electrolysis in which a back emf of 1.45 volts is developed. If the resistance of the entire circuit is 10 ohms, (a) what is the magnitude of the current, and (b) what quantity of heat is generated by the current flow per faraday of electricity?

                                 Ans. (a) 0.055 amp; (b) 12,690 cal.

4. Under reversible conditions what applied potential will be necessary to initiate steady electrolysis in each of the following cells:

     (a) $Pb(s) \mid PbSO_4(s), H_2SO_4, PbSO_4(s) \mid Pb(s)$
     (b) $Pt(s) \mid Fe^{++}(a = 1), Fe^{+++}(a = 1) \parallel Br^-(a = 1), AgBr(s) \mid Ag(s)$
     (c) $Ni(s) \mid NiSO_4(a = 1), PbSO_4(s) \mid Pb(Hg)$
     (d) $Ag(s) \mid AgCl(s), ZnCl_2(a = 1) \mid Zn(s)$

The ε^0 value for the $Pb(Hg) \mid PbSO_4(s), SO_4^{--}(a = 1)$ electrode is 0.3505 volt.

5. Repeat the preceding problem for each of the following cells:

   (a) $Pt(s) \mid HI(a = 1) \mid Pt(s)$
   (b) $Pt(s) \mid CdCl_2(a = 1) \mid Pt(s)$
   (c) $Pt(s) \mid NiSO_4(a = 1) \mid Pt(s)$

6. Calculate the reversible decomposition potentials of the following cells:

   (a) $Pt(s) \mid HBr(m = 0.05, \gamma = 0.860) \mid Pt(s)$
   (b) $Ag(s) \mid AgNO_3(m = 0.5, \gamma = 0.526) \parallel AgNO_3(m = 0.01,$
   $$\gamma = 0.902) \mid Ag(s)$$

   Ans. (a) -1.2269 volts; (b) -0.0867 volt.

7. In the cell

   $$Pt(s) \begin{vmatrix} CdCl_2(m\gamma = 1) \\ NiSO_4(m\gamma = 1) \end{vmatrix} Pt(s)$$

   what will be the cell reaction and the reversible decomposition potential when electrolysis is initiated?

8. The overvoltage of H_2 on Pb was determined in a 0.1 molal H_2SO_4 solution ($\gamma = 0.265$) by measuring during electrolysis the potential of the lead cathode against a normal calomel celectrode. The potential thus observed was 1.0685 volts. What is the overvoltage of H_2 on Pb?   *Ans.* 0.713 volt.

9. The overvoltages of H_2 and O_2 on Ag at a current density of 0.1 amp/cm^2 are, respectively, 0.87 and 0.98 volt. What will be the decomposition potential of a dilute NaOH solution between Ag electrodes at this current density?

10. (a) Using the data of Table 2, plot overvoltage against the log of the current density for Ag, and evaluate the constants a and b in equation (6). (b) At what current density will the overvoltage be 0.80 volt?
    Ans. (a) $a = 0.58$, $b = 0.19$; (b) 15.5 ma/cm^2.

11. The overvoltage of H_2 on polished Pt is 0.24 volt when the current density is 1 ma/cm^2. What will be the deposition potential of H_2 on this electrode from a solution of pH = 3?

12. The overvoltage of H_2 on Fe is 0.40 volt at a current density of 1 ma/cm^2. In a solution containing Fe^{++} ions at unit activity, what is the lowest pH at which deposition of Fe is possible under these conditions? *Ans.* 0.69.

13. The overvoltage of H_2 on Zn is 0.72 volt. If it is desired to deposit Zn^{++} down to a concentration of 10^{-4} mole/liter without deposition of H_2 occurring, what must be the lowest permissible pH of the solution?

14. A solution contains Fe^{++} and Zn^{++} ions at unit activity. If the overvoltage of H_2 on Fe is 0.40 volt, what must be the maximum pH of the solution in order to plate Fe but obtain "gassing" at the cathode prior to Zn deposition? What will be the activity of Fe^{++} ions when "gassing" begins?
    Ans. pH = 6.11; $a_{Fe^{++}} = 1.41 \times 10^{-11}$.

15. A solution contains Fe^{++} ions at unit activity. (a) Under reversible conditions what must be the activity of Cd^{++} ions in the same solution in order to obtain simultaneous deposition of Fe and Cd? (b) What would have to be the activity of Ni^{++} ions to obtain Ni and Fe simultaneously?

16. A solution contains $Ag^+(a = 0.05)$, $Fe^{++}(a = 0.01)$, $Cd^{++}(a = 0.001)$, Ni^{++} $(a = 0.1)$, and $H^+(a = 0.001)$. The overvoltage of H_2 on Ag is 0.20 volt, on Ni 0.24 volt, on Fe 0.18 volt, on Cd 0.30 volt. Predict what will happen at a cathode immersed in this solution as the potential applied is gradually increased from zero.

17. A solution containing Zn^{++}, Na^+, and H^+ ions at unit activity is electrolyzed with a Hg cathode. Explain what will occur at the cathode as the potential is gradually increased.

18. The overvoltage of O_2 on a Pt anode is 0.72 volt. Which ion will be deposited first from a solution of pH = 7 containing Cl^- at 0.1 activity?

19. A solution is made originally 0.1 molar in Ag^+ ions and 0.25 molar in KCN. If the dissociation constant of $Ag(CN)_2^-$, $K = [Ag^+][CN^-]^2/[Ag(CN)_2^-]$, is 3.8×10^{-19}, what will be the concentration of Ag ions in this solution, and what will be the deposition potential of Ag? For this calculation assume activities equal to concentrations.   *Ans.* 1.52×10^{-17}; -0.196 volt.

20. A solution is 0.1 molar in Au^+ and 0.1 molar in Ag^+ ions. The standard reduction potential of Au^+ is 1.68 volts, while the dissociation constant of $Au(CN)_2^-$, $K = [Au^+][CN^-]^2/[Au(CN)_2^-]$, is 5×10^{-39}. What concentration of NaCN will have to be added to the given solution in order to deposit Au and Ag simultaneously?   *Ans.* 0.2 molar.

19

Kinetics of Homogeneous Reactions

Chemical kinetics is the branch of physical chemistry which concerns itself with the study of the velocity of chemical reactions and with the elucidation of the mechanisms by which they proceed.

A question of importance which thermodynamics does not touch upon is: *How rapidly and by what mechanism does a reaction take place?* Thermodynamics considers only the energy relations between reactants and the products of a reaction. It makes no attempt to indicate the stages through which the reactants may have to pass to reach the final products, nor is it concerned with the rate at which equilibrium is attained. Chemical kinetics complements thermodynamics by supplying information about the rate of approach to equilibrium and also, whenever possible, about the mechanism responsible for the conversion of reactants to products.

Not all reactions lend themselves readily to kinetic study. Many ionic reactions are so rapid that to all appearances they are instantaneous. Explosions and certain other reactions, of which $N_2O_4 \longrightarrow 2\,NO_2$ is an example, also proceed so quickly that either it is impossible to determine their rate, or special methods have to be devised to do so. On the other hand, some reactions are so slow that months and even years are necessary to observe any perceptible transformation at ordinary temperatures. Between these extremes lie the reactions whose velocities are measurable. In this category fall many gaseous reactions, as well as many reactions in solution involving both organic and inorganic substances.

The rates of reactions depend on the nature of the reacting substances, the temperature, and the concentrations of the reactants. An increase in temperature leads to an increase in velocity; in fact, for many reactions an increase of 10° C in temperature may increase the rate of reaction twofold or more. Again, with the exception of certain (zero order) reactions, upon which concentration is without effect, an increase in the initial concentration of reactants also results in an acceleration of the rate. However, the rate for any given initial concentration does not remain constant during the course of the reaction but is highest at the beginning and decreases with time as the reactants are consumed. In general the variation of the rate of a reaction with time is represented by a curve such as that shown in Fig. 1. This curve indicates that the rate decreases rapidly in the initial stages of the reaction, then much more slowly, and approaches zero asymptotically to the time axis. Theoretically infinite time would be required for the rate to fall to zero. Practically, however, the rate becomes so low after a time that to all intents and purposes the reaction may be considered completed within a finite time interval.

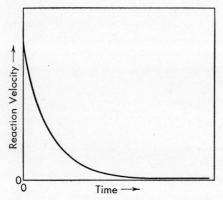

Fig. 1. Variation of Reaction Rate with Time.

Further, many reactions are influenced by the presence of substances which possess the ability of accelerating or decelerating the rates of such reactions. Substances possessing this property of affecting the rates of chemical reactions are called *catalysts*, while the reactions thus affected are designated as *catalyzed reactions*. Again, certain reactions are uninfluenced by light, while others, called *photochemical reactions*, are greatly stimulated when light of appropriate frequency is permitted to pass through the reacting mixture.

Kinetic studies of reactions are generally carried out at constant temperature. A reacting mixture of known composition is prepared, thermostated, and the decrease in concentration of reacting substances with time is observed by some suitable means. From the time-concentration data thus obtained the kinetic behavior of the reaction can be deduced with the aid of certain principles which will be developed shortly. By repeating this procedure at a number of temperatures, the temperature coefficient of the reaction can be obtained, and from this the dependence of the rate of a reaction on the temperature.

Reactions may be classified kinetically as being either *homogeneous* or *heterogeneous*. A reaction is said to be kinetically *homogeneous* if it takes place in one phase only. If two or more phases are involved in the process, as in a gaseous reaction proceeding on the surface of a solid catalyst or on the walls of the container, the reaction is said to be *heterogeneous*. The principles governing the kinetics of some heterogeneous reactions will be discussed in the next chapter. Here attention will be devoted to three types of homogeneous reactions, namely, (a) uncatalyzed reactions, (b) catalyzed reactions, and (c) chain reactions. Photochemical reactions will be discussed in Chapter 23.

ORDER AND MOLECULARITY OF REACTIONS

The rate of a chemical reaction is the rate at which the concentrations of reacting substances vary with time, i.e., $-dC/dt$, where C is the concentration of reactant and t the time. The minus sign is used to denote that the concentration decreases with time. The dependence of this rate on the concentrations of reacting substances is given by the *law of mass action*. This law states that *the rate of any reaction is at each instant proportional to the concentrations of the reactants, with each concentration raised to a power equal to the number of molecules of each species participating in the process.* Thus, for the reaction

$$A \longrightarrow \text{Products} \tag{a}$$

the rate should be proportional to C_A, for

$$2\,A \longrightarrow \text{Products} \tag{b}$$
and
$$A + B \longrightarrow \text{Products} \tag{c}$$

to C_A^2 and $C_A C_B$, respectively, while for

$$A + 2\,B \longrightarrow \text{Products} \tag{d}$$
or
$$2\,A + B \longrightarrow \text{Products} \tag{e}$$

to $C_A C_B^2$ and $C_A^2 C_B$. These proportionalities indicate that different rate dependencies on concentration are obtained at constant temperature for various reactions, and to distinguish these the term *order of reaction* is employed. By the order of a chemical reaction is meant *the sum of all the exponents to which the concentrations in the rate equation are raised.* Thus when the rate of a reaction is given by

$$\frac{-dC}{dt} = kC_1^{n_1} C_2^{n_2} C_3^{n_3} \cdots \tag{1}$$

where k is a constant, the reaction orders of the individual constituents are n_1, n_2, n_3, etc., and the order of the reaction as a whole, n, is

$$n = n_1 + n_2 + n_3 + \cdots \tag{2}$$

In examples (a) to (e) the order of reaction is identical with the number of molecules of reactants participating in the reaction. Thus, the first order reaction (a) is also *unimolecular*, the second order reactions (b) and (c) are *bimolecular*, while the third order reactions (d) and (e) are *termolecular*. Although this identity of reaction order and the number of molecules reacting as given by the stoichiometric equation of the process is observed in many reactions, it does not hold in all cases. For the reactions

$$CH_3CHO \longrightarrow CH_4 + CO$$
$$3\ KClO \longrightarrow KClO_3 + 2\ KCl$$

we would anticipate *a priori* that the first of these would be first order, the second, third order. Actually both reactions are found to be second order. Since the reaction order *may* differ from the number of molecules participating in the reaction, a distinction must be made between the *molecularity*, i.e., the number of molecules involved in the step leading to reaction, and the order of a reaction. According to the former, reactions are unimolecular, bimolecular, etc., depending on whether one, two, or more molecules are involved in the rate determining step. On the other hand, the term reaction order is confined to the dependence of the observed rate on the concentrations of the reactants.

It is evident that the order, or for that matter the molecularity, of a reaction cannot always be predicted from the stoichiometric equations of a reaction but that each and every reaction must be investigated kinetically to ascertain both order and molecularity. Further, care must be exercised in interpreting an observed reaction order and in inferring from it the molecularity and the mechanism of the process. When the order of a reaction agrees with the rate equation obtained by applying the law of mass action to the stoichiometric equation of the reaction, it is fairly safe to assume that the reaction proceeds as given by the chemical equation. When the two are not the same, however, a mechanism has to be devised which is in accord both with the observed reaction order and with the over-all equation of the process.

In developing the rate equations for reactions of various orders we shall proceed on the supposition that molecularity and order are identical. Whenever necessary attention will be directed to any discrepancy between the two.

FIRST ORDER REACTIONS

According to the law of mass action the rate of any unimolecular reaction

$$A \longrightarrow \text{Products} \tag{3}$$

should at any time t be directly proportional to the concentration of A,

C_A, present in the system at that instant, i.e.,

$$\frac{-dC_A}{dt} = k_1 C_A \tag{4}$$

The proportionality factor k_1 is called the *specific rate* or the *specific velocity constant* of the first order reaction. On setting $C_A = 1$ in equation (4), the significance of this constant may be seen to be the speed of the reaction when the concentration of A is constant and equal to unity. Again, the units of k_1 follow from $k_1 = (-1/C_A)(dC_A/dt)$ as a reciprocal time or frequency. For any first order reaction k_1 should be a constant characteristic of the reaction, independent of the concentration, and a function of the temperature only.

Before integrating this differential equation, it is desirable to transform it into an alternate form. To do this let a be the initial concentration of A, and x the decrease in concentration of A due to reaction up to time t. Then $C_A = a - x$ at time t,

$$\frac{-dC_A}{dt} = \frac{-d(a - x)}{dt} = \frac{dx}{dt}$$

and equation (4) becomes

$$\frac{dx}{dt} = k_1(a - x) \tag{5}$$

This equation gives the rate for a first order reaction in terms of the initial concentration and the amount of substance reacted. Integrating equation (5) and remembering that at the start of the reaction $t = 0$ and $x = 0$, and at time t $x = x$, we obtain

$$\int_{x=0}^{x=x} \frac{dx}{a - x} = \int_{t=0}^{t=t} k_1 dt$$

$$\left[-\ln(a - x) \right]_{x=0}^{x=x} = \left[k_1 t \right]_{t=0}^{t=t}$$

$$\ln \frac{a}{a - x} = k_1 t \tag{6}$$

Any first order reaction must satisfy equation (6). To ascertain whether a particular reaction obeys this equation, several methods are available. First, knowing the initial concentration and the concentrations of reactant at various elapsed times, a, $(a - x)$, and t corresponding to the latter may be substituted into the equation and k_1 solved for. If the reaction is first order, a series of k_1's are thus obtained which are constant within the accuracy of the experiment. However, if the k_1 values exhibit an appreciable drift the reaction is not first order, and higher order equations must then be tried to find one that will satisfy the observed data.

Equation (6) may also be tested graphically. On rearrangement this equation becomes

$$\ln (a - x) = -k_1 t + \ln a$$

or
$$\log_{10} (a - x) = \left(\frac{-k_1}{2.303}\right) t + \log_{10} a \tag{7}$$

Since for any one experiment a is constant, a plot of $\log (a - x)$ vs. t should yield a straight line in which the y intercept will be $\log_{10} a$ and the slope $(-k_1/2.303)$. Consequently, when such a plot constructed from the experimental data is found to be linear, the reaction is first order; and, by taking the slope of the line, k_1 follows as

$$k_1 = -2.303 \text{ (slope)} \tag{8}$$

A third means of testing first order reactions is known as the *fractional life method*. In this method the time necessary to decompose a definite fraction of the reactant, usually one-half, is determined for a number of different values of a. When one-half of the reactant has undergone decomposition, $a - x = a/2$, and the time, $t_{1/2}$, necessary for this to occur follows from equation (6) as

$$t_{1/2} = \frac{1}{k_1} \ln \frac{a}{a/2}$$

$$= \frac{\ln 2}{k_1} \tag{9}$$

$t_{1/2}$ is known as the *half-life period* of the reaction. According to equation (9) *the half-life period of any first order reaction is independent of the initial concentration.* In other words, it takes a first order reaction just as much time to go halfway to completion when the initial concentration is high as when it is low. That this requirement is met by first order reactions is shown by the data given in Table 1 for the thermal decomposition of gaseous acetone at 601° C. Although the initial pressure of the acetone is seen to vary about fourfold, the half-life period nevertheless remains constant within the experimental accuracy. Taking as an average $t_{1/2} = 81$ sec, we find for the rate constant of this reaction

$$k_1 = \frac{\ln 2}{t_{1/2}} = \frac{0.693}{81}$$
$$= 0.0086 \text{ sec}^{-1}$$

In calculating rate constants the common practice is to express the time in minutes or seconds. Occasionally, with very slow reactions time may be expressed in hours or even days. Concentrations, on the other hand, should invariably be expressed in moles per liter for reactions in

TABLE 1

HALF-LIFE PERIODS FOR THERMAL DECOMPOSITION
OF ACETONE AT 601° C*

a (mm Hg)	$t_{1/2}$ (sec)
98	86
192	78
230	85
296	80
362	77

* Hinshelwood and Hutchison, *Proc. Roy. Soc.*, **111A**, 245 (1926).

solution, and in these or some suitable pressure units for gaseous reactions. In any case, for complete clarity the units of time and concentration for which k is given should be stated, as well as the temperature. However, for first order reactions, *and only for these*, the units in which the concentrations are expressed do not matter, since k_1 depends on the ratio of two concentrations. Consequently, as long as a and $a - x$ are expressed in the same units the value of the ratio is unaffected, and any convenient units may be employed.

FIRST ORDER REACTIONS IN GASES

Examples of homogeneous gaseous first order reactions are the thermal dissociations of nitrous oxide, nitrogen pentoxide, acetone, propionic aldehyde, various aliphatic ethers, azo compounds, amines, and ethyl bromide, and the isomerization of d-pinene to dipentene. As typical of these may be taken the thermal decomposition of azoisopropane to hexand and nitrogen,

$$(CH_3)_2CHN{=\!=}NCH(CH_3)_2 \longrightarrow N_2 + C_6H_{14}$$

which was investigated by Ramsperger[1] over the pressure range 0.0025 to 46 mm Hg and between 250 and 290° C. The rate of reaction was followed by pressure measurements with a McLeod gage. The only data necessary were the initial pressure of the reactant and the total pressures of the system at various stages of decomposition. From these pressures the rate constant of the process may be calculated as follows. If we let P_i be the initial pressure of azoisopropane, P the total pressure, P_A the pressure of azoisopropane, and x the decrease in pressure of azoisopropane, all at time t, then at each stage of the reaction $P_A = P_i - x$,

[1] Ramsperger, *J. Am. Chem. Soc.*, **50**, 714 (1928).

$P_{N_2} = P_{C_6H_{14}} = x$, and the total pressure of the system is given by

$$
\begin{aligned}
P &= P_A + P_{N_2} + P_{C_6H_{14}} \\
&= (P_i - x) + x + x \\
&= P_i + x
\end{aligned}
$$

From this equation we find $x = P - P_i$, and on substitution of this value for x into $P_A = P_i - x$, we get

$$
\begin{aligned}
P_A &= P_i - x \\
&= P_i - (P - P_i) \\
&= 2 P_i - P
\end{aligned}
$$

Since a in equation (6) is proportional to P_i, and $(a - x)$ to P_A, the expression for k_1 is

$$
\begin{aligned}
k_1 &= \frac{2.303}{t} \log_{10} \frac{P_i}{P_A} \\
&= \frac{2.303}{t} \log_{10} \frac{P_i}{2 P_i - P}
\end{aligned}
$$

The constants thus calculated from experimental data for a typical run at 270° C are shown in Table 2. Column 1 gives the time in seconds, column 2 the total pressure P, and column 3 the values of k_1. P_i is the pressure of the system at $t = 0$, which for the experiment in question was 35.15 mm Hg. Since k_1 exhibits satisfactory constancy, the decomposition of azoisopropane must be a first order reaction.

TABLE 2

DECOMPOSITION OF AZOISOPROPANE AT 270° C

t (sec)	P (mm Hg)	k_1 (sec^{-1})
0	35.15	—
180	46.30	2.12×10^{-3}
360	53.90	2.11
540	58.85	2.07
720	62.20	2.03
1020	65.55	1.96
	Mean =	2.06×10^{-3}

FIRST ORDER REACTIONS IN SOLUTION

An example of a first order reaction in solution is the decomposition of benzene diazonium chloride, $C_6H_5N{=}NCl$, in water. This compound, known only in solution, dissociates readily on heating to liberate nitrogen. As the nitrogen all comes from the compound, the volume of it liberated may be used as a measure of the decrease in concentration of the diazo salt. Cain and Nicoll[1] utilized this fact in their kinetic study of this reaction. A freshly prepared solution of the salt was quickly heated to the desired temperature, and the reaction was then permitted to proceed in a thermostat. The course of the reaction was followed by measuring in a gas burette the volumes V of nitrogen evolved at various time intervals. To complete the required data, the initial concentration, expressed as cubic centimeters of nitrogen V_0, was calculated from the amount of diazo compound originally present. In terms of V_0 and V, the velocity constant of the reaction follows as

$$k_1 = \frac{2.303}{t} \log_{10}\left(\frac{a}{a - x}\right) = \frac{2.303}{t} \log_{10}\left(\frac{V_0}{V_0 - V}\right)$$

The results obtained in an experiment at 50° C with an amount of benzene diazonium chloride equivalent to 58.3 cc nitrogen are shown in Fig. 2, where a plot of $\log_{10}$ $(a - x) = \log_{10} (58.3 - V)$ vs. t is given. The plot is linear with slope $= -0.0308$. Consequently k_1, according to equation (8), is

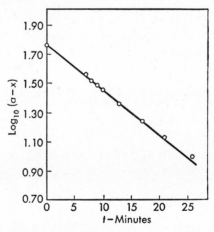

$$k_1 = -2.303 \text{ (slope)}$$
$$= -2.303 \text{ } (-0.0308)$$
$$= 0.0709 \text{ min}^{-1}$$

Fig. 2.   Plot of $\log_{10}$ $(a - x)$ vs. t for First Order Reactions.

Other first order reactions in solution are the decomposition of nitrogen pentoxide and the isomerization of d-pinene in various organic solvents, the decomposition of malonic, trichloracetic, and acetonedicarboxylic acids in water, and the dissociation of various diazonium salts in the same solvent.

SECOND ORDER REACTIONS

Any bimolecular reaction can in general be represented by the equation

$$A + B \longrightarrow \text{Products} \tag{10}$$

If we let a and b be the initial concentrations of A and B respectively, and x the decrease in concentration of each at time t, then the concen-

[1] Cain and Nicoll, *J. Chem. Soc.*, **81**, 1412 (1902).

trations of A and B will be $(a - x)$ and $(b - x)$, and the rate equation for the *second order* reaction becomes

$$\frac{dx}{dt} = k_2(a - x)(b - x) \tag{11}$$

Here k_2 is the specific rate constant for such a reaction and is equal to the rate when both A and B are unity. Its units are $t^{-1}C^{-1}$, and its magnitude depends on the nature of the reaction, the temperature, and the units in which t and C are expressed. Integration of this equation, again remembering that $x = 0$ when $t = 0$, yields

$$k_2 = \frac{1}{t(a - b)} \ln \frac{b(a - x)}{a(b - x)}$$

or
$$k_2 = \frac{2.303}{t(a - b)} \log_{10} \frac{b(a - x)}{a(b - x)} \tag{12}$$

This is the equation which any second order reaction must obey.

Equation (12) is considerably simplified when A and B are present in equal initial concentrations, or when A and B are the same, as in the reaction

$$2\, A \longrightarrow \text{Products} \tag{13}$$

For these conditions equation (11) reduces to

$$\frac{dx}{dt} = k_2(a - x)^2 \tag{14}$$

and on integration becomes either

$$\left(\frac{1}{a - x}\right) = k_2 t + \frac{1}{a} \tag{15}$$

or
$$k_2 = \frac{1}{at}\left(\frac{x}{a - x}\right) \tag{16}$$

These expressions for second order reactions may be tested by the methods described for first order reactions. Values of a, b, and x, or a and x may be substituted along with t and k_2 solved for, or k_2 may be evaluated graphically. For the latter procedure equation (12) is best written in the form

$$t = \frac{2.303}{k_2(a - b)} \log_{10} \frac{(a - x)}{(b - x)} + \frac{2.303}{k_2(a - b)} \log_{10} \left(\frac{b}{a}\right) \tag{17}$$

from which we see that, since k_2, a, and b are constant for any experiment, a plot of t against $\log_{10}(a - x)/(b - x)$ should yield a straight line with

$$\text{Slope} = \frac{2.303}{k_2(a - b)} \tag{18}$$

and y intercept equal to the second term on the right of equation (17). By taking the slope of such a plot and substituting into equation (18), k_2 can be obtained. On the other hand, to test the rate law when the concentrations are the same, equation (15) is used. According to this equation a plot of $1/(a - x)$ vs. t should be linear, with slope equal to k_2 and the y intercept equal to $1/a$. By taking the slope k_2 is obtained directly.

The half-life method cannot be used with reactions where the concentrations of A and B are different, since A and B will have different times for half reaction. However, it may be used where the concentrations are the same, or where the two reacting molecules are identical. In these instances $x = a/2$ at the half-life point, and the period of half-life, $t_{1/2}$, follows from equation (16) as

$$t_{1/2} = \frac{1}{k_2} \cdot \frac{(a/2)}{a(a/2)}$$

$$= \frac{1}{k_2 a} \tag{19}$$

i.e., *for a second order reaction the period of half-life is inversely proportional to the first power of the initial concentration.* Knowing $t_{1/2}$ and a, k_2 is readily evaluated from equation (19).

It may be stated as a general rule that the period of half-life for any n order reaction is inversely proportional to the $(n - 1)$ power of the initial concentration, i.e.,

$$t_{1/2} \propto \frac{1}{a^{n-1}} \tag{20}$$

The proportionality constant for equation (20) depends on the reaction order and is $(\ln 2)/k_1$ for first order, $1/k_2$ for second order, and $\frac{3}{2} k_3$ for third order reactions.

SECOND ORDER GAS REACTIONS

Homogeneous gas reactions of second order are very common. In this category are included various thermal dissociations, such as those of hydrogen iodide, nitrogen dioxide, ozone, chlorine monoxide, nitrosyl chloride, formaldehyde, and acetaldehyde; the combination of hydrogen and iodine to form hydrogen iodide; the polymerization of ethylene; the hydrogenation of ethylene; and others. The behavior of all such reactions is exemplified by the thermal decomposition of acetaldehyde. This reaction, investigated by Hinshelwood and Hutchison,[1] was found to be almost totally homogeneous and to proceed according to the equation

$$2 \text{ CH}_3\text{CHO} \longrightarrow 2 \text{ CH}_4 + 2 \text{ CO}$$

[1] Hinshelwood and Hutchison, *Proc. Roy. Soc.*, **111A**, 380 (1926).

Since in this reaction there is an increase in pressure at constant volume on dissociation, the change in pressure observed on a manometer attached to the system may be employed to follow the reaction course. From these pressure measurements k_2 is calculated as follows.

If we let P_i be the initial pressure of acetaldehyde and x the decrease in pressure after time t, then the pressure of the reactant at time t is $(P_i - x)$. Again, when the pressure of acetaldehyde drops by x, the pressures of methane and carbon monoxide must each increase by x. We obtain thus for the total pressure of the system, P,

$$P = P_{CH_3CHO} + P_{CH_4} + P_{CO}$$
$$= (P_i - x) + x + x$$
$$= P_i + x$$

from which x follows as $x = P - P_i$. Further, since $P_i - x$ is proportional to $(a - x)$ and P_i to a, substitution of these into equation (16) yields for k_2

$$k_2 = \frac{1}{at}\left(\frac{x}{a-x}\right)$$
$$= \frac{1}{P_i t}\left(\frac{x}{P_i - x}\right)$$

In Table 3 are given data obtained by Hinshelwood and Hutchison for this reaction during an experiment at 518° C with an initial pressure of acetaldehyde equal to 363 mm Hg. The good constancy of k_2 confirms both the reaction order and the correctness of the formulation.

TABLE 3

THERMAL DECOMPOSITION OF ACETALDEHYDE AT 518° C
(P_i = 363 mm Hg)

t (sec)	$x = P - P_i$ (mm Hg)	$k_2 = \dfrac{1}{P_i t}\left(\dfrac{x}{P_i - x}\right)$
42	34	6.79×10^{-6}
73	54	6.59
105	74	6.71
190	114	6.64
242	134	6.66
310	154	6.55
384	174	6.61
480	194	6.59
665	224	6.68
840	244	6.72
1070	264	6.86
1440	284	6.88

Average = 6.69×10^{-6} mm^{-1} sec^{-1}

SECOND ORDER REACTIONS IN SOLUTION

Among the many reactions in solution which are of second order may be mentioned the saponifications of various esters by bases, the conversion of nitroparaffins to aci-nitroparaffins by bases, the reactions of alkyl halides with amines, the hydrolyses of esters, amides, and acetals, esterifications of organic acids, the combination of NH_4^+ and CNO^- ions to form urea, and the reactions of bromacetates with thiosulfates and thiocyanates.

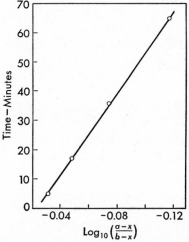

Fig. 3. Graphical Test of Second Order Reactions.

As a prototype of these reactions may be taken the saponification of ethyl butyrate by hydroxyl ions in water solution, namely,

$$CH_3CH_2CH_2COOC_2H_5 + OH^- \longrightarrow$$
$$CH_3CH_2CH_2COO^- + C_2H_5OH$$

which was studied by Williams and Sudborough[1] at 20° C. The reaction mixture was prepared by bringing together solutions of ethyl butyrate and barium hydroxide so as to yield an initial concentration a of the ester and b of the base. The course of the reaction was followed by removing periodically samples of solution and titrating these with standard acid to ascertain the concentration of unreacted barium hydroxide. The concentrations of base thus determined give directly $(b - x)$, while a minus the amount of reacted base yields $(a - x)$. Table 4 shows some of the data

TABLE 4

SAPONIFICATION OF ETHYL BUTYRATE BY BARIUM HYDROXIDE AT 20° C

t (min)	$a - x$	$b - x$	k_2 [equation (12)]
	(arbitrary units)		
0	19.75	20.85	—
5	14.75	15.85	0.0032
17	9.40	10.50	0.0030
36	5.93	7.03	0.0029
65	3.57	4.67	0.0030

[1] Williams and Sudborough, *J. Chem. Soc.*, **101**, 415 (1912).

obtained in this manner, and the value of k_2 calculated from these by equation (12). As an alternate test, t may be plotted against $\log_{10}[(a - x)/(b - x)]$ to see whether a straight line results in accordance with equation (17). Such a plot, given in Fig. 3, is linear.

THIRD ORDER REACTIONS

The most general type of termolecular reaction is one where three different molecules react, namely,

$$A + B + C \longrightarrow \text{Products} \qquad (21)$$

If the reactants are all present at different initial concentrations a, b, c, and x is the decrease in the concentration of each at time t, then the *third order* rate equation is

$$\frac{dx}{dt} = k_3(a - x)(b - x)(c - x) \qquad (22)$$

The integrated form of equation (22) is rather complex. For a simpler case where two of the initial concentrations are equal, say $a = b$, equation (22) reduces to

$$\frac{dx}{dt} = k_3(a - x)^2(c - x) \qquad (23)$$

which on integration yields for k_3,

$$k_3 = \frac{1}{t(c - a)^2}\left[\frac{x(c - a)}{a(a - x)} + \ln\frac{c(a - x)}{a(c - x)}\right] \qquad (24)$$

On the other hand, when two of the molecules are identical, as in

$$2\,A + B \longrightarrow \text{Products} \qquad (25)$$

the concentrations at any time are $(a - 2\,x)$ and $(b - x)$. Then the rate equation becomes

$$\frac{dx}{dt} = k_3(a - 2\,x)^2(b - x) \qquad (26)$$

and k_3 is given by

$$k_3 = \frac{1}{t(2\,b - a)^2}\left[\frac{2\,x(2\,b - a)}{a(a - 2\,x)} + \ln\frac{b(a - 2\,x)}{a(b - x)}\right] \qquad (27)$$

The simplest case is a reaction of the type

$$3\,A \longrightarrow \text{Products} \qquad (28)$$

or reaction (21) with $a = b = c$. Then the rate equation is

$$\frac{dx}{dt} = k_3(a - x)^3 \qquad (29)$$

and on integration

$$k_3 = \frac{1}{2\,t}\left[\frac{1}{(a-x)^2} - \frac{1}{a^2}\right] \tag{30}$$

$$= \frac{1}{2\,ta^2}\left[\frac{x(2\,a-x)}{(a-x)^2}\right] \tag{31}$$

From (31) the period of half-life of a third order reaction follows as

$$t_{1/2} = \frac{3}{2\,k_3 a^2} \tag{32}$$

and hence for such a reaction $t_{1/2}$ is inversely proportional to a^2.

Only five homogeneous gas reactions are definitely known to be third order, and every one of these involves the interaction of nitric oxide with either chlorine, bromine, oxygen, hydrogen, or heavy hydrogen. As an example of one of these may be taken the work of Hinshelwood and Green[1] on the reaction

$$2\ NO + H_2 \longrightarrow N_2O + H_2O$$

For hydrogen present in excess, k_3 for this reaction should be given by equation (27). Now, at a time t' when the nitric oxide is half consumed $2\,x = a/2$, and this equation becomes

$$k_3 = \frac{1}{t'(2\,b-a)^2}\left[\frac{2\,b-a}{a} + \ln\frac{2\,b}{4\,b-a}\right] \tag{33}$$

This is the relation Hinshelwood and Green used to evaluate k_3 from various initial pressures of nitric oxide ($a = P_{NO}$) and hydrogen ($b = P_{H_2}$), and the observed times, t', of half decomposition of nitric oxide. Their results, given in Table 5, yield fairly satisfactory constants, and indicate that the reduction of nitric oxide by hydrogen is a third order reaction.

TABLE 5

KINETICS OF THE REACTION

$2\ NO + H_2 \longrightarrow N_2O + H_2O$ at $826°$ C

P_{NO} (mm Hg)	P_{H_2} (mm Hg)	t' (sec)	k_3
110	316	270	1.19×10^{-7}
152	404	204	0.91
359	400	89	1.12
144	323.5	227	1.10
181	209.5	264	1.39
370	376	92	1.17
300	404	100	1.09
232	313	152	1.19

[1] Hinshelwood and Green, *J. Chem. Soc.*, **128**, 730 (1926).

Reactions in solution which appear to be third order are the oxidation of ferrous sulfate in water, the reaction between iodide and ferric ions in aqueous solution, and the action between benzoyl chloride and alcohols in ether solution. The decomposition of hypobromous acid at constant pH in the pH range of 6.4 to 7.8 has also been found to be third order with respect to the acid.[1]

PSEUDO-MOLECULAR REACTIONS

There are many reactions which obey a first order rate equation although in reality they are bi- or ter-molecular. As an example of these may be taken the decomposition of carbonyl sulfide in water, namely,

$$COS + H_2O \longrightarrow CO_2 + H_2S$$

According to the law of mass action this reaction should be second order, with the rate dependent on the concentration of both the carbonyl sulfide and the water. Actually, however, the rate is found to be first order with respect to the carbonyl sulfide and independent of the water. Reactions exhibiting such behavior are said to be *pseudo-molecular*.

The pseudo-unimolecular nature of this reaction is explainable by the fact that water is present in such excess that its concentration remains practically constant during the course of the reaction. Under these conditions $b - x = b$, and the rate equation becomes

$$\frac{dx}{dt} = k_2(a - x)b \tag{34}$$

On integration this leads to

$$k = bk_2 = \frac{2.303}{t} \log_{10} \frac{a}{a - x} \tag{35}$$

which is the equation for a first order reaction. It is evident, however, that the new constant k is not independent of the concentration, as is the case with true first order constants, but may vary with b if the latter is changed appreciably. When such is the case, the true constant k_2 can be obtained from k by dividing the latter by b.

Pseudo-molecular reactions are encountered whenever one or more of the reactants remain constant during the course of an experiment. This is the case with reactions conducted in solvents which are themselves one of the reactants, as in the decomposition of carbonyl sulfide in water, or in the esterification of acetic anhydride in alcohol,

$$(CH_3CO)_2O + 2\ C_2H_5OH \longrightarrow 2\ CH_3COOC_2H_5 + H_2O$$

[1] Prutton and Maron, *J. Am. Chem. Soc.*, **57**, 1652 (1935).

Again, this is also true of reactions subject to catalysis, in which case the concentration of the catalyst does not change. The decomposition of diacetone alcohol to acetone in aqueous solution is catalyzed by hydroxyl ions, with the rate proportional to the concentration of the alcohol and that of the base. Since the concentration of the base does not change within any one experiment, however, the rate equation reduces to one of first order with respect to the alcohol. But, the rate constants k obtained for various concentrations of base are not identical, as may be seen from Table 6. To obtain from these the true second order velocity constant, the k's must be divided by the hydroxyl ion concentration. When this is done excellent k_2 values result, as column 3 indicates.

TABLE 6

Decomposition of Diacetone Alcohol in Water at 25° C*
(Catalyst: NaOH)

C Conc. of NaOH	k (min^{-1})	$k_2 = k/C$
0.0205	0.0455	2.22
0.0292	0.0651	2.23
0.0518	0.1160	2.24
0.0710	0.1576	2.22
0.1045	0.2309	2.21

* LaMer and Miller, *J.Am. Chem. Soc.*, **57**, 2674 (1935).

REVERSIBLE OR OPPOSING REACTIONS

The above formulation of the rate equations involves the tacit assumption that the processes proceed in the direction indicated without any tendency for the reactions to reverse themselves. Such an assumption is justifiable only with reactions whose point of equilibrium lies way over on the side of the products. When this is not the case, the products formed initiate a reaction counter to the forward process whose rate increases as the products accumulate, and eventually becomes equal to that of the forward reaction. At this point the over-all rate becomes zero, and the system is in equilibrium.

Reactions exhibiting this tendency to reverse themselves are called *reversible* or *opposing reactions*. As an illustration of one of these and of the method of dealing with them kinetically may be taken the oxidation of nitric oxide to nitrogen dioxide,

$$2 \text{ NO} + \text{O}_2 \underset{k_2}{\overset{k_3}{\rightleftharpoons}} 2 \text{ NO}_2$$

investigated by Bodenstein and Lindner.[1] These authors found that below 290° C the rate of the forward reaction is third order and proceeds as written without complications. However, above this temperature the rate of dissociation becomes noticeable and leads to a decrease in the rate of disappearance of nitric oxide and oxygen. To correct for this back reaction we proceed as follows. If we let a and b be the initial concentrations of nitric oxide and oxygen respectively, and x the amount of oxygen reacted in time t, then at t the concentration of oxygen is $(b - x)$, of nitric oxide $(a - 2x)$, while that of nitrogen dioxide formed $2x$. The rate of the forward reaction is hence given by

$$\left(\frac{dx}{dt}\right)_f = k_3(a - 2x)^2(b - x) \tag{36}$$

and that of the reverse reaction by

$$\left(\frac{dx}{dt}\right)_r = k_2(2x)^2 \tag{37}$$

Since these two rates oppose each other, the net rate of the forward reaction, dx/dt, must be the difference between them, or

$$\frac{dx}{dt} = \left(\frac{dx}{dt}\right)_f - \left(\frac{dx}{dt}\right)_r$$
$$= k_3(a - 2x)^2(b - x) - k_2(2x)^2 \tag{38}$$

This equation involves two constants, and hence another relation between k_3 and k_2 is required before the constants can be evaluated. For obtaining this relation we utilize the fact that when the reaction reaches equilibrium $dx/dt = 0$, and therefore

$$k_2 = \frac{k_3(a - 2x_e)^2(b - x_e)}{(2x_e)^2} \tag{39}$$

where x_e is the value of x at equilibrium. On substitution of this value of k_2 into the integrated form of equation (38), an expression is obtained involving only k_3 which may be used to test the kinetics of the reaction. It will be observed that here not only the initial concentrations and x at various times are required, but also the value of x at equilibrium, x_e. To find the latter the reaction is permitted to proceed until equilibrium is attained, and x_e is measured.

In Table 7 are shown some results obtained by Bodenstein and Lindner during an experiment at 339° C. Column 2 gives the values of k_3 calculated by using only equation (36), while column 3 gives the values of k_3 obtained after correction for the back reaction. Whereas the constants in

[1] Bodenstein and Lindner, Z. *physik. Chem.*, **100**, 87 (1922).

TABLE 7

KINETICS OF THE REACTION

2 NO + O_2 ⟶ 2 NO_2 at 339° C

t (min)	k_3 [equation (36)]	k_3 [equation (38)]
4	0.58×10^{-5}	0.58×10^{-5}
5	0.58	0.59
6	0.57	0.59
8	0.54	0.58
10	0.53	0.59
12	0.50	0.59
17	0.46	0.61
22	0.37	0.63

column 2 diminish regularly with time, those in column 3 are constant and confirm the applicability of equation (38) to this reaction.

Other reactions which are reversible, and which can be treated in a manner analogous to the one described, are the mutarotation of glucose, the combination of hydrogen and iodine to form hydrogen iodide, the hydrogenation of ethylene, and the hydrolyses of various esters.

CONSECUTIVE REACTIONS

Chemical reactions such as

$$A \xrightarrow{k_1} B \xrightarrow{k_2} C \tag{40}$$

which proceed from reactants to products through one or more intermediate stages are called *consecutive reactions*. In these reactions each stage has its own rate and its own velocity constant. Further, whether one or another of these particular rates, or some combination of all, is measured experimentally depends on the relative magnitudes of the velocity constants of the various stages. It is a well-established fact that in any sequence of reactions of varying speed the one that is *slowest* will determine the rate of the over-all reaction. This follows of necessity because any succeeding stage has to wait for any preceding before it can take place. Consequently, if, in a reaction such as that represented by equation (40), $k_1 \gg k_2$, the conversion of B to C will determine the rate of formation of the product. On the other hand, if $k_2 \gg k_1$, the formation of B from A will control the rate, and C will result from B as soon as the latter appears. However, when k_1 and k_2 are comparable in magnitude, the rate of the over-all reaction depends on both constants, and the situation becomes more complex.

An instance of a consecutive reaction proceeding in two stages with appreciably different velocity constants is the decomposition of sodium hypochlorite in alkaline solutions. Although the stoichiometric equation of the process,

$$3 \text{ NaClO} \longrightarrow 2 \text{ NaCl} + \text{NaClO}_3 \tag{41}$$

suggests a third order reaction, the process is actually second order. To explain this result the suggestion has been advanced that the reaction proceeds in two steps, the first of which is

$$2 \text{ NaClO} \longrightarrow \text{NaCl} + \text{NaClO}_2 \tag{41a}$$

and the second

$$\text{NaClO}_2 + \text{NaClO} \longrightarrow \text{NaCl} + \text{NaClO}_3 \tag{41b}$$

The sum of equations (41a) and (41b) is equation (41). To decide which of these two reactions is rate determining, Förster and Dolch[1] investigated not only the decomposition of sodium hypochlorite but also the reaction between sodium chlorite and hypochlorite to form the chlorate. They found that the rate of the latter reaction is about 25 times that of the former, and consequently the rate of equation (41a) must control the rate of the over-all reaction given by equation (41).

The exact mathematical analysis of consecutive reactions with comparable velocity constants is as a rule very difficult unless the reactions are of the simplest kind, such as the one given in equation (40). To show the method of attack, let a be the initial concentration of A, x the amount of it decomposed in time t, and y the concentration of C formed at the same instant. Then at time t we have $C_A = (a - x)$, $C_C = y$, and $C_B = x - y$, since the total amount of B formed is x, and y of it has decomposed to form C. From these the rate of disappearance of A follows as

$$\frac{dx}{dt} = k_1(a - x) \tag{42}$$

while the rate of decomposition of B, which is the same as the rate of formation of C, is

$$\frac{dy}{dt} = k_2(x - y) \tag{43}$$

To find the dependence of the concentrations of A, B, and C on time these rate equations must be solved. This is accomplished by integrating equation (42) first, finding x, substituting it into equation (43), and then integrating the latter. As a result we obtain the following expressions for the concentrations:

[1] Förster and Dolch, *Z. Elektrochem.*, **23**, 137 (1917).

$$C_A = (a - x) = ae^{-k_1 t} \tag{44a}$$

$$C_B = (x - y) = \frac{k_1 a}{k_2 - k_1} \left(e^{-k_1 t} - e^{-k_2 t} \right) \tag{44b}$$

$$C_C = \frac{a}{k_2 - k_1} \left[(k_2 - k_2 e^{-k_1 t}) - (k_1 - k_1 e^{-k_2 t}) \right] \tag{44c}$$

Figure 4 shows C_A, C_B, and C_C as a function of time for $a = 1$, $k_1 = 0.01$, and $k_2 = 0.02$. It will be observed that, whereas the concentration of A falls and that of C increases continuously, the concentration of B rises to a maximum and then decreases with time. This behavior of the concentration of the intermediate product is characteristic of consecutive reactions with comparable values of velocity constants and may be used to identify such reactions.

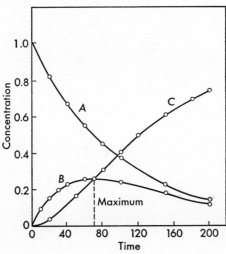

Fig. 4. Dependence of Concentration on Time in Consecutive Reactions.

In practice the picture is not quite so simple, because usually the overall reaction is known and the intermediate steps have to be deduced from it. Under these conditions it may be necessary to follow not only the rate of disappearance of A, but also the rates of formation of B and C before analysis of the reaction becomes possible. Further, with reactions of higher order the mathematics become more formidable, and various artifices have to be relied upon to arrive at a solution of the kinetic processes. Nevertheless, a number of consecutive reactions have been unraveled, and these substantiate the general validity of the attack outlined above.

SIDE REACTIONS

In *side reactions* the reacting substances, instead of proceeding along one path to yield a given set of products, follow also one or more other paths to give different products. Thus, in the nitration of phenol, p- and o-nitrophenols are formed simultaneously from phenol and nitric acid by the parallel reactions:

$$\text{phenol} + HNO_2 \xrightarrow{k_1} o\text{-nitrophenol} + H_2O \tag{45a}$$

o-nitrophenol

$$\text{phenol} + HNO_3 \xrightarrow{k_2} p\text{-nitrophenol} + H_2O \tag{45b}$$

p-nitrophenol

If we let a and b be the initial concentration of phenol and nitric acid, and x the amount of these which react, then at any instant the rate of formation of o-nitrophenol would be given by

$$\frac{d(o\text{-nitrophenol})}{dt} = k_1(a - x)(b - x) \tag{46}$$

and that of p-nitrophenol by

$$\frac{d(p\text{-nitrophenol})}{dt} = k_2(a - x)(b - x) \tag{47}$$

From these the rate of disappearance of the reactants, dx/dt, follows as the *sum* of equations (46) and (47), or

$$\frac{dx}{dt} = (k_1 + k_2)(a - x)(b - x) \tag{48}$$

Again, the ratio of equation (46) to equation (47) yields

$$\frac{d(o\text{-nitrophenol})}{d(p\text{-nitrophenol})} = \frac{k_1(a - x)(b - x)}{k_2(a - x)(b - x)}$$
$$= \frac{k_1}{k_2} \tag{49}$$

Consequently, by following the disappearance of the reactants the sum of the rate constants can be found, while from the rates of formation of the individual products the ratio k_1/k_2 can be obtained. From this sum and ratio are evaluated then the individual constants.

Side reactions are very common, particularly in organic chemistry. The reaction yielding the largest amount of a product is generally referred to as the *main reaction*, while the others, yielding smaller amounts of products, are called the *side reactions*.

EFFECT OF TEMPERATURE ON REACTION VELOCITY

Increase in temperature leads to a tremendous increase in reaction velocity and hence in rate constants. The only known exception to the generality of this statement is the reaction $2 NO + O_2 \longrightarrow 2 NO_2$, which exhibits a small negative temperature coefficient. This rapid acceleration of reaction rate is observed both in gaseous and liquid phase reactions, as may be seen from the typical data cited in Table 8. In the

TABLE 8

VARIATION OF REACTION RATE CONSTANTS WITH TEMPERATURE

Decomposition of CH_3CHO in Gas Phase*		Decomposition of $CO(CH_2COOH)_2$ in Aqueous Solution†		
$T°$ K	k_2 [sec^{-1} (moles/liter)$^{-1}$]	$T°$ K	k_1 (sec^{-1})	$t_{1/2}$ (sec)
703	0.011	273	2.46×10^{-5}	28,200.
733	0.035	283	10.8	6,410.
759	0.105	293	47.5	1,460.
791	0.343	303	163.	425.
811	0.79	313	576.	120.
836	2.14	323	1850.	37.4
865	4.95	333	5480.	12.6

* Hinshelwood and Hutchison, *Proc. Roy. Soc.*, **111A**, 380 (1926).
† Wiig, *J. Phys. Chem.*, **34**, 596 (1930).

second order decomposition of gaseous acetaldehyde an increase of 162° C in temperature results in a 450-fold increase in the velocity constant. On the other hand, in the first order decomposition of acetone-dicarboxylic acid,

$$CO(CH_2COOH)_2 \longrightarrow CO(CH_3)_2 + 2 CO_2$$

in aqueous solution the constants increase 2200-fold for only a 60° C change in temperature. For the latter reaction are tabulated also the half-life periods at various temperatures. These exhibit the tremendous range of 28,200 to 12 sec on passing from 0° to 60° C.

Arrhenius first pointed out that the variation of rate constants with temperature can be represented by an equation similar to that used for equilibrium constants, namely,

$$\frac{d \ln k}{dT} = \frac{E^*}{RT^2} \qquad (50)$$

In this *Arrhenius equation* k is the reaction rate constant, T the absolute temperature, R the gas constant in calories, and E^* a quantity characteristic of the reaction with the dimensions of an energy. E^* is known as the *energy of activation* and plays a very important role in chemical kinetics. Its significance will be discussed presently.

If equation (50) is integrated on the supposition that E^* is a constant, we obtain

$$\ln k = -\frac{E^*}{RT} + C'$$

or
$$\log_{10} k = \left(\frac{-E^*}{2.303\ R}\right)\frac{1}{T} + C \qquad (51)$$

where C' and C are constants of integration. However, if we integrate between the limits $k = k_1$ at $T = T_1$ and $k = k_2$ at $T = T_2$, then,

$$\log_{10} \frac{k_2}{k_1} = \frac{E^*}{2.303\ R}\left(\frac{T_2 - T_1}{T_1 T_2}\right) \qquad (52)$$

From equation (52) it is evident that as soon as two values of k are available at two different temperatures E^* may be evaluated; or, when E^* and a value of k at some one temperature are known, k at another temperature may be calculated. Thus, for the decomposition of acetonedicarboxylic acid, $k = 2.46 \times 10^{-5}$ at $273°$ K and 163×10^{-5} at $303°$ K. Substituting these into equation (52) we find for E^*,

$$\begin{aligned}
E^* &= \frac{2.303\ RT_1 T_2}{T_2 - T_1} \log_{10} \frac{k_2}{k_1} \\
&= \frac{2.303 \times 1.987 \times 273 \times 303}{303 - 273} \log_{10} \frac{163 \times 10^{-5}}{2.46 \times 10^{-5}} \\
&= 23{,}000 \text{ cal}
\end{aligned}$$

This value of E^* may now be employed to estimate the values of k's at other temperatures.

To test the validity of the Arrhenius equation we resort to equation (51). According to this equation a plot of $\log_{10} k$ against $1/T$ should be a straight line with

$$\text{slope} = \frac{-E^*}{2.303\ R} = \frac{-E^*}{4.576} \qquad (53)$$

and y intercept equal to C. Consequently, if such a plot is found to be linear the equation is confirmed. Further, by taking the slope of the line, E^* may be calculated readily through equation (53).

In Fig. 5 are shown plots of $\log_{10} k$ vs. $1/T$ for the data given in Table 8. As predicted by the Arrhenius equation, both reactions yield satisfactory straight lines. From these we find the slope for the acetaldehyde decomposition curve to be -9920, while that for the acetonedicarboxylic acid

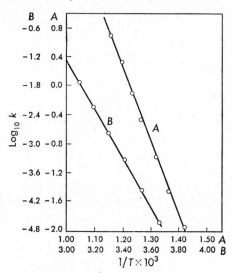

Fig. 5.   Variation of Reaction Rate with Temperature. *A*, Decomposition of Acetaldehyde in Gas Phase; *B*, Decomposition of Acetonedicarboxylic Acid in Aqueous Solution.

decomposition -5070. Hence the energy of activation for the first of these reactions is

$$E^* = -4.58(-9920)$$
$$= 45,500 \text{ cal}$$

and for the second,

$$E^* = -4.58(-5070)$$
$$= 23,200 \text{ cal}$$

THE ENERGY OF ACTIVATION

In reactions involving two or more molecules it is logical to presuppose that before reaction can take place the molecules must come into contact with each other; in other words, they must collide. If collision is a sufficient cause for reaction, the rate of reaction should equal the rate of collision. However, when the number of molecules actually reacting in a gaseous reaction, as obtained from the observed velocity constants, is compared with the total number of molecules colliding, calculated from kinetic theory, the latter is found to exceed the number undergoing transformation by many powers of ten. This discrepancy can be explained only by the assumption that molecules in order to react must be in some special configuration at collision, or that they must be in some exceptionally high energy state, or both. Although configuration does play a part in certain reactions, the appearance of the E^* term in the Arrhenius equation and other considerations definitely favor an exceptional energy state as a prime requisite for reaction; i.e., *molecules must be activated before they can react on collision.*

According to the concept of activation, reactants do not pass directly to products but must first acquire sufficient energy to pass over an activation energy barrier. The ideas involved can be made clear with the aid of Fig. 6. In this figure A represents the average energy of the reactants, C that of the products, and B the minimum energy which the reactants must possess in order to react. Molecules in state B are said to be *activated* or to be in an *activated state.* Since molecules must be activated before reaction, the reaction must proceed from A to C not directly, but along the path ABC. In other words, molecules must first climb the energy barrier before they can roll down the hill to form products.

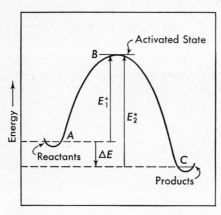

Fig. 6.   Energy of Activation.

The energy that the reactants at A must absorb in order to become activated and react is the energy of activation E_1^* of the process $A \longrightarrow C$. This energy is obviously $E_1^* = E_B - E_A$, i.e., the difference in energy between the activated state and that corresponding to the average energy of the reactants. By the same argument the energy of activation E_2^* of the reverse process $C \longrightarrow A$ must be $E_2^* = E_B - E_C$. Consequently the difference, ΔE, between E_1^* and E_2^* follows as

$$\begin{aligned}
\Delta E &= E_1^* - E_2^* \\
&= (E_B - E_A) - (E_B - E_C) \\
&= E_C - E_A
\end{aligned} \tag{54}$$

But ΔE is the difference in energy between products and reactants, or the *heat of reaction at constant volume.* This must mean that in going from the activated state to the products the molecules give up, not only the energy absorbed on activation from A to B, but also the energy ΔE corresponding to the difference in the energy levels of C and A. Hence it may be concluded that the concept of an activation energy in no way violates the thermodynamic relations between the energies of products and reactants.

All it does is to introduce two thermal quantities whose difference always leads to the heat of reaction.

THE COLLISION THEORY OF BIMOLECULAR REACTIONS

The collision theory of reaction velocity attempts to account for the observed kinetics of reactions in terms of the molecular behavior of the reacting systems. We shall consider this theory first for bimolecular and then for unimolecular reactions. The theory of termolecular reactions is not sufficiently developed for discussion here.

According to the collision theory of bimolecular reactions two molecules in order to react must (a) collide and (b) possess on collision sufficient energy for them to be activated. This means that out of all the collisions occurring only those will be fruitful which involve active molecules. Consequently, if Z is the number of molecules colliding per cubic centimeter per second in a reacting system containing 1 mole of reactant per liter, and q the fraction of these that are activated, then the specific rate of the bimolecular reaction in molecules per cubic centimeter per second, k, should be given by

$$k = Zq \qquad (55)$$

For bimolecular *gaseous* reactions Z and q can be calculated with the aid of the kinetic theory of gases. We have seen in Chapter 1 equation (39), that for a gas containing only *one kind* of molecule the number of colliding molecules per cubic centimeter per second is

$$Z_1 = \sqrt{2}\,\pi\sigma^2 v (n^*)^2 \qquad (56)$$

where σ is the molecular diameter, v the average molecular velocity in centimeters per second, and n^* the number of molecules per cubic centimeter. Substituting $v = 0.921\sqrt{(3\,RT/M)}$ from equation (37) of the same chapter, and collecting constants, Z_1 becomes

$$Z_1 = 0.921\,\sqrt{2}\,\pi\sigma^2 (n^*)^2 \sqrt{\frac{3\,RT}{M}}$$

$$= 6.51 \times 10^4\, \sigma^2 (n^*)^2 \sqrt{\frac{T}{M}} \qquad (57)$$

However, when two *different* molecules are involved, $Z = Z_{1,2}$ and is given by

$$Z_{1,2} = n_1^* n_2^* \left(\frac{\sigma_1 + \sigma_2}{2}\right)^2 \sqrt{\frac{8\,\pi RT(M_2 + M_1)}{M_1 M_2}}$$

$$= 1.14 \times 10^4 (\sigma_1 + \sigma_2)^2 n_1^* n_2^* \sqrt{\frac{T(M_2 + M_1)}{M_1 M_2}} \qquad (58)$$

Here σ_1 and σ_2 are the molecular diameters of the respective molecules, M_1 and M_2 their molecular weights, n_1^* and n_2^* the numbers of molecules of each type per cubic centimeter at temperature T. $Z = Z_1$ is used when all the reacting molecules are the same, as in $2\ HI \longrightarrow H_2 + I_2$; on the other hand, $Z = Z_{1,2}$ is utilized when the two molecules are unlike, as in the reaction $H_2 + I_2 \longrightarrow 2\ HI$.

The fraction of activated molecules q can also be ascertained from kinetic theory. The molecules in a gas are in constant motion during which they enter into repeated collisions with each other. These collisions cause a redistribution of translational energy, resulting in a small fraction of the molecules acquiring an energy considerably above the average translational energy of all the molecules. From the Maxwell distribution law for molecular velocities it can be shown that, in any gas containing n^* molecules per cubic centimeter at a temperature T, the number of these, n', which will possess an energy E or higher is

$$n' = n^* e^{-E/RT} \tag{59}$$

If E is identified with E^*, the energy of activation, the *fraction* of molecules activated follows from equation (59) as

$$\frac{n'}{n^*} = e^{-E^*/RT} = \frac{\text{number of activated molecules}}{\text{total number of molecules}} \tag{60}$$

and this is also q. The expression for k becomes, therefore,

$$k = Z e^{-E^*/RT} \tag{61}$$

where Z is given by equation (57) for like molecules or by equation (58) for unlike molecules.

We are in a position now to test this theory with an actual calculation. For this purpose we shall take the reaction $2\ HI \longrightarrow H_2 + I_2$ at $556°$ K, for which the observed value of k is 3.5×10^{-7} sec^{-1} (moles/liter)$^{-1}$, and $E^* = 44{,}000$ cal. For hydrogen iodide $\sigma = 3.5 \times 10^{-8}$ cm, $M = 127.9$, and since 1 mole of gas per liter contains 6.0×10^{23} molecules, the number per cubic centimeter is $n^* = 6.0 \times 10^{20}$. Inserting these values of σ, n^*, T, and M into equation (57), Z_1 follows as

$$Z_1 = 6.51 \times 10^4 (3.5 \times 10^{-8})^2 (6.0 \times 10^{20})^2 \sqrt{\frac{556}{127.9}}$$

$$= 6.0 \times 10^{31} \text{ molecules}$$

Again,

$$q = e^{-E^*/RT}$$
$$= e^{-44.000/1.99 \times 556}$$
$$= 5.2 \times 10^{-18}$$

Therefore,

$$k = Zq = 6.0 \times 10^{31} \times 5.2 \times 10^{-18}$$
$$= 3.1 \times 10^{14} \text{ molecules reacting per cubic centimeter per second}$$

Multiplying this number by 1000 and dividing by Avogadro's number to obtain the number of moles reacting per liter, we find

$$k = \frac{3.1 \times 10^{14} \times 1000}{6.0 \times 10^{23}} = 5.2 \times 10^{-7} \text{ mole per liter per sec}$$

as against the experimentally observed value of $k = 3.5 \times 10^{-7}$. Keeping in mind the absolute nature of the calculation and the uncertainties involved, the agreement between theory and experiment must be considered very good.

Similar concordance between the collision theory and experiment has been obtained with several other bimolecular gas reactions, and also with a number of bimolecular reactions in solution by extending to the latter the ideas outlined above. However, there are many reactions, both in the gas phase and in solution, for which the theory yields results that are too high by factors ranging up to 10^9. For such reactions it is customary to write equation (61) in the form

$$k = PZe^{-E^*/RT} \tag{62}$$

where P, called the *probability factor*, is inserted to allow for the disparity between calculated and observed rate constants. P may have values ranging from unity for reactions obeying the collision theory to about 10^{-9}. It has been suggested that such "slow" reactions require not only collision between molecules which are active, but also a preferred critical orientation of the reacting molecules. If this is the case, not all collisions between activated molecules will result in reaction, and thus the calculated rate will be higher than the observed. On this basis it may be possible to account for probability factors as low as $10^{-3} - 10^{-4}$, but it is very questionable whether such an explanation can account for P's lower than these. In fact, it will be shown that the collision theory omits from consideration an *entropy of activation* which cannot be disregarded.

THE COLLISION THEORY OF UNIMOLECULAR REACTIONS

Offhand it is difficult to see how the collision theory could possibly be employed to explain the mechanism of unimolecular reactions. In unimolecular processes only one molecule participates in the reaction, and consequently the question arises: How do molecules in unimolecular reactions attain their energy of activation? The answer to this question was first suggested by Lindemann[1] in 1922. Lindemann pointed out that the behavior of unimolecular reactions can be explained on the basis of bimolecular collisions provided we postulate that a *time lag exists between activation and reaction* during which activated molecules may either react or be deactivated to ordinary molecules. Worded differently, the Lindemann hypothesis states that in any unimolecular reaction an equilibrium exists between activated and unactivated molecules; and, out of this equilibrium activated molecules are removed by reaction. The process may be indicated by the equation

$$A + A \rightleftharpoons A + A^* \tag{63}$$

$$\searrow$$
$$\text{Products}$$

where A represents inactive and A^* activated molecules. Since the rate of reaction will have to be proportional to the concentration of active molecules, we may write for it

$$\frac{dx}{dt} = k_1' C_{A*}$$

Again, for the equilibrium between active and inactive molecules

$$K = \frac{C_A C_{A^*}}{C_A^2} = \frac{C_{A^*}}{C_A}$$

and therefore $C_{A*} = KC_A$. Substituting this value of C_{A*} into the rate expression, we obtain

$$\frac{dx}{dt} = k_1' K C_A$$
$$= k_1 C_A \tag{64}$$

which is the equation for a unimolecular reaction.

The time lag postulated for unimolecular reactions becomes plausible when the complexity of the gaseous molecules undergoing unimolecular and bimolecular reaction is compared. Many of the molecules reacting bimolecularly are found to contain several atoms only and to be thus structurally simple. On the other hand, most of the molecules decomposing unimolecularly contain many atoms. In simple molecules it may be expected that any energy acquired on activation will flow rapidly into the bond to be ruptured and cause immediate reaction. However, in a structurally complex molecule some time may be required for the energy to become localized in the bond where fission occurs, occasioning thereby a time lag between activation and dissociation.

When equation (61) is applied to estimate for unimolecular reactions

[1] Lindemann, *Trans. Faraday Soc.*, **17**, 598 (1922).

the number of molecules becoming activated due to bimolecular collisions, it is found that the number of molecules calculated is considerably
smaller than the number actually entering reaction. To allow for this
fact, the suggestion has been advanced that in unimolecular reactions
not only are translational energies involved in activation but also vibrational. With the latter included, the fraction of the molecules becoming
activated is much larger, and the number of molecules activated can be
reconciled with the number observed to react in many unimolecular
reactions both in the gas phase and in solution.

According to Kassel,[1] the energy of activation of a unimolecular reaction may be defined as the minimum energy per mole, translational,
vibrational, and rotational, which a molecule must possess in order to
react. Furthermore, an appreciable part of this energy must be localized
in the weakest bond in the molecule. When such a bond receives the
requisite energy it is loosened or broken, and decomposition results.

One of the interesting consequences of the Lindemann hypothesis is
that gaseous reactions proceeding by a unimolecular mechanism should
at low pressures become bimolecular. The reason for the transformation is
that at low pressures the time between collisions may become long enough
to be comparable to, or greater than, the time lag between activation and
reaction. Under these circumstances the rate of activation will be the
governing factor, and the rate should follow the bimolecular law. Such
changes in molecularity have been observed in a number of unimolecular
reactions.

THE THEORY OF ABSOLUTE REACTION RATES

The *theory of absolute reaction rates*,[2] based on statistical mechanics, is
an alternate approach to the problem of reaction kinetics. This theory
postulates that molecules before undergoing reaction must form an *activated complex* in equilibrium with the reactants and that the rate of any
reaction is controlled by the concentration of the complex present at any
instant. The state of affairs in any reaction $A + B$ can be represented by
the scheme

$$A + B \underset{\text{reactants}}{\rightleftharpoons} \underset{\substack{\text{activated} \\ \text{complex}}}{[A \cdot B]^*} \overset{k}{\longrightarrow} \text{Products} \qquad (65)$$

The activated complex is assumed to be endowed with certain properties
of an ordinary molecule and to possess some, although temporary, stability. On the basis of these ideas Eyring was able to show that the rate con-

[1] Kassel, *J. Phys. Chem.*, **32**, 225 (1928).
[2] Eyring, *J. Chem. Physics*, **3**, 107 (1935); Wynne-Jones and Eyring, *ibid.*, **3**, 492 (1935).

stant k of *any* reaction, no matter what the molecularity or order may be, should be given by

$$k = \frac{RT}{Nh} e^{-\Delta F^*/RT} \tag{66}$$

In this equation R is the gas constant in ergs mole^{-1} degree^{-1}, N Avogadro's number, h Planck's constant, equal to 6.625×10^{-27} erg-sec, T the absolute temperature, and ΔF^* is the *free energy of activation*, i.e., the difference in free energy between the activated complex and the reactants. We may resort to thermodynamics and write for ΔF^*,

$$\Delta F^* = \Delta H^* - T\Delta S^* \tag{67}$$

where ΔH^* is the *heat of activation* and ΔS^* is the *entropy of activation*. Inserting equation (67) into equation (66) we obtain for k

$$k = \frac{RT}{Nh} e^{\Delta S^*/R} e^{-\Delta H^*/RT} \tag{68}$$

Equation (68) is the fundamental relation of this theory. For reactions in solution, for gaseous reactions where the rate constants are expressed in pressure units, and for unimolecular gas reactions with k in concentration units, ΔH^* is related to the experimentally observed activation energy E^* by the relation

$$\Delta H^* = E^* - RT \tag{69}$$

However, for bimolecular gas reactions with k in concentration units

$$\Delta H^* = E^* - 2\,RT \tag{70}$$

while for termolecular gas reactions with k in such units

$$\Delta H^* = E^* - 3\,RT \tag{71}$$

By means of these relations it is possible to convert observed E^* values into the corresponding ΔH^*'s.

Comparison of equation (68) with equation (62) of the collision theory shows that essentially

$$PZ = \frac{RT}{Nh} e^{\Delta S^*/R} \tag{72}$$

and consequently the difficulty occasioned in the latter theory by the appearance of the probability factor P can be reconciled by the introduction of the entropy of activation. Although at present it is not possible to estimate theoretically ΔS^* for any but the simplest reactions, the theory of absolute reaction rates does represent a step forward in elucidating chemical kinetics. Further, its use has also proved fruitful in a number of other directions.[1]

PRIMARY SALT EFFECT IN IONIC REACTIONS

The velocity constants of reactions in solution involving either non-electrolytes or nonelectrolytes and ions are essentially unaffected by the presence of electrolytes. On the other hand, the velocity constants of reactions between ions are sensitive to variation of the ionic strength of the solution and change with the latter in a manner dependent on the charges of the reacting ions.

To explain the existence of this *primary salt effect*, Brönsted[2] in 1922 suggested a theory of ionic reactions which is in essence a special case of the theory of absolute reaction rates. We shall follow here a treatment due to Bjerrum because it is simpler than Brönsted's. Bjerrum postulated that reacting ions go to form an activated complex in equilibrium with the reactants and that the rate of reaction is proportional to the *concentration* of the complex. Thus, any ionic reaction between A^{z_A} and B^{z_B} can be represented by the scheme

$$A^{z_A} + B^{z_B} \underset{\text{reactants}}{\rightleftharpoons} \underset{\text{activated complex}}{[(A \cdot B)^{(z_A + z_B)}]^*} \xrightarrow{\ k'\ } \text{Products} \qquad (73)$$

where z_A and z_B are the charges of the two ions, while $(z_A + z_B)$ is the charge on the activated complex. If we let C_X be the concentration of the complex at any instant, then the rate at any time t is given by

$$\frac{dx}{dt} = k'C_X \qquad (74)$$

But, since the complex is in equilibrium with the reactants, the thermo-dynamic equilibrium constant K must be

$$K = \frac{a_X}{a_A a_B}$$

$$= \frac{C_X f_X}{(C_A f_A)(C_B f_B)} \qquad (75)$$

The a's, C's and f's represent, respectively, the activites, concentrations, and activity coefficients of the respective species. From equation (75) C_X follows as

$$C_X = (K C_A C_B) \frac{f_A f_B}{f_X}$$

---

[1] See Glasstone, Laidler, and Eyring, *The Theory of Rate Processes*, McGraw-Hill Book Company, Inc., New York, 1941.

[2] See Brönsted, *Chem. Rev.*, **5**, 231 (1928), for a very exhaustive treatment of this subject.

which on substitution into equation (74) yields for the rate

$$\frac{dx}{dt} = k'KC_AC_B \cdot \frac{f_Af_B}{f_X}$$

$$= \left(k_0 \frac{f_Af_B}{f_X}\right) C_AC_B \tag{76}$$

where $k_0 = k'K$.

Equation (76) indicates that the experimentally evaluated constant k, as obtained from the ordinary rate equation for the process depicted in equation (73), namely,

$$\frac{dx}{dt} = kC_AC_B$$

is not the true reaction constant k_0 but involves also the activity coefficients of the reactants and the complex.   In fact,

$$k = k_0 \frac{f_Af_B}{f_X} \tag{77}$$

Since the activity coefficients of the charged reactants and complex depend on the ionic strength of the solution, the velocity constant k will also be a function of the ionic strength. By applying the Debye-Hückel theory of activity coefficients, it can be shown that for *dilute* solutions k should vary with ionic strength μ according to the equation

$$\log_{10} \frac{k}{k_0} = 2\,Az_Az_B\,\sqrt{\mu} \tag{78}$$

where A is the Debye-Hückel constant.[1] According to equation (78), a plot of $\log_{10} k$ or of $\log_{10} k/k_0$ against $\sqrt{\mu}$ should be linear with a slope equal to $(2\,Az_Az_B)$, i.e., *dependent only on the product z_Az_B of the charges of the reacting ions*. That this requirement is in line with observation is indicated by Fig. 7, where a plot of $\log_{10} k/k_0$ vs. $\sqrt{\mu}$ is given for reactions of various z_Az_B values. The solid lines are those predicted by equation (78), while the points are experimental results.

It should be noticed that when $z_Az_B = 0$, as for a reaction between a nonelectrolyte and an ion, the primary salt effect is essentially zero. This will be true for a reaction of the type

$$CH_2ICOOH + CNS^- \longrightarrow CH_2(CNS)COOH + I^-$$

Again, when z_Az_B is positive, as for the reaction

$$CH_2BrCOO^- + S_2O_3^{--} \longrightarrow CH_2(S_2O_3)COO^- + Br^- \quad (z_Az_B = +2)$$

the salt effect will be positive, and k will increase with ionic strength.

[1] See Table 3, Chapter 16.

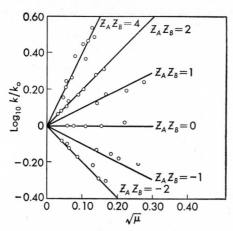

Fig. 7.   Primary Salt Effect in Ionic Reactions.

Lastly, when $z_A z_B$ is negative, as for

$$[Co(NH_3)_5Br]^{++} + OH^- \longrightarrow [Co(NH_3)_5OH]^{++} + Br^- \quad (z_A z_B = -2)$$

the salt effect is negative, and k will fall with increasing ionic strength.

CATALYSIS

It is a well-established fact that the velocity of many reactions can be changed by introducing certain substances other than the reactants appearing in the stoichiometric equation of the process. Thus, a pinch of manganese dioxide promotes the evolution of oxygen from potassium chlorate, unsaturated hydrocarbons can be hydrogenated in presence of nickel, sulfur dioxide can be oxidized to sulfur trioxide in the presence of platinum, and iodine accelerates the decomposition of nitrous oxide. In all these processes the foreign substances added remain unchanged at the end of the reaction and may be used over again. *Any substance which influences the rate of a chemical reaction but itself remains unchanged chemically at the end is called a catalyst.* And, the phenomenon of rate acceleration, both negative and positive, is designated as *catalysis*.

The power of a suitable catalyst lies in its ability to change the rate at which a reaction determined by the free energy relations can take place. For any reaction to be thermodynamically feasible the change in free energy must be negative. Nevertheless, even with a negative ΔF the rate of transformation may be so slow as to make the reactants appear to be inert. In such cases the purpose of a catalyst is to speed the reaction and to permit a more rapid approach to equilibrium. From a thermodynamic standpoint, therefore, catalysis introduces no complications into the energy relations of the system. Free energy, heat of reaction, and entropy calculations for a reaction remain the same whether the process takes place *per se* or is "coaxed along" by a catalyst.

Since a catalyst cannot change the ΔF^0 of a reaction, neither can it modify the equilibrium constant. Consequently if the forward rate is affected so must also be the reverse rate. In other words, a catalyst must accelerate equally both the forward and reverse reactions. This is found to be the case. Occasionally a catalyst may appear to shift the point of equilibrium, but in such instances study will reveal that either the catalyst participates actively as a reactant, or some other complications exist which have not been allowed for.

The activity of a catalyst increases generally with its concentration, although this is not invariably true. Further, the concentration of the catalyst appears in the rate equation. This suggests that the catalyst participates as a reactant but that it is regenerated on completion of the sequence of reaction steps. However, this function of a catalyst as modifier of the mechanism of a reaction is not its only effect. Use of a catalyst also leads usually to a decrease of activation energy; and this lowering of the energy barrier between reactants and products results in a higher rate of reaction.

Catalysis may be homogeneous or heterogeneous, depending on whether the catalyst forms a single phase with the reactants or constitutes a separate phase. Here we shall consider homogeneous catalysis in gases and in solution, while heterogeneous catalysis will be discussed in the next chapter.

HOMOGENEOUS CATALYSIS IN GASES

A familiar example of catalysis of a gas reaction by another gas is the oxidation of sulfur dioxide to sulfur trioxide in presence of nitric oxide in the chamber sulfuric acid process. Nitric oxide catalyzes also the oxidation of carbon monoxide to carbon dioxide and the decomposition of nitrous oxide to nitrogen and oxygen. The latter reaction is catalyzed as well by iodine, chlorine, and bromine vapors. Iodine vapor is also effective in accelerating the decomposition of ethers such as methyl ethyl, di-ethyl, and di-isopropyl ether. Without the catalyst these decompositions proceed unimolecularly with activation energies of 54,500, 53,000, and 61,000 cal for the ethers in the order mentioned. However, in presence of iodine vapor the decompositions take place by a bimolecular mechanism involving a molecule of the ether and of iodine, and with activation energies of 38,000, 34,300, and 28,500 cal respectively.

For more extended discussion we may choose the decomposition of acetaldehyde. This decomposition, we have seen, proceeds of itself as a second order reaction with an energy of activation of 45,500 cal. But, when iodine vapors are introduced into the system, it is found that the rate is given by $dx/dt = kC_{\text{acetaldehyde}}C_{I_2}$, where k is about 10,000 times *larger* at 518° C than the constant for the reaction in absence of iodine. Further, the energy of activation is reduced to 32,500 cal. To account for these observations it has been suggested that, instead of decomposing directly to methane and carbon monoxide, the reaction in presence of iodine vapor takes place in the two steps:

$$CH_3CHO + I_2 \longrightarrow CH_3I + HI + CO$$
$$CH_3I + HI \longrightarrow CH_4 + I_2$$

The first of these is considered to be the slower and therefore rate determining. As this alternate mechanism involves a lower energy of activation, the reaction can occur at a faster rate.

HOMOGENEOUS CATALYSIS IN SOLUTION

Homogeneously catalyzed reactions in solution are very common, as may be judged from Table 9. Of particular interest are the reactions catalyzed by hydrogen or hydroxyl ions, and by acids and bases in the generalized sense. Reactions catalyzed by hydrogen ions only are said to be subject to *specific hydrogen ion catalysis*. For such reactions the rate is proportional to the concentration of the substrate, i.e., the reacting molecule or ion, and to the concentration of the catalyzing hydrogen ions. Again, in *specific hydroxyl ion catalysis* the rate is proportional to the concentrations of substrate and hydroxyl ions. The latter type of catalysis is illustrated by the data given in Table 6 for the hydroxyl ion catalyzed decomposition of diacetone alcohol in water.

In distinction to specific hydrogen ion and hydroxyl ion catalaysis, we have *generalized acid or generalized base catalysis*. In generalized acid catalysis every species present in solution which is an acid in the Brönsted sense acts as a catalyst for the reaction. Thus, if a substrate S, subject to generalized acid catalysis, is allowed to react in a solution of acetic acid and sodium acetate in water, we have in this solution the acids H_2O, H_3O^+, and $CH_3COOH(HA)$, and hence in such a solution the rate of reaction of the substrate will be given by

$$\frac{dx}{dt} = k_{H_2O}C_{H_2O}C_S + k_{H_3O^+}C_{H_3O^+}C_S + k_{HA}C_{HA}C_S$$
$$= C_S(k_{H_2O}C_{H_2O} + k_{H_3O^+}C_{H_3O^+} + k_{HA}C_{HA}) \qquad (79)$$

From a knowledge of the sundry concentrations, and by choosing suitable experimental conditions, the various k's, called *catalytic coefficients*, can be evaluated, and the over-all reaction rate can thus be ascertained.

TABLE 9

Reaction	Catalyst	Solvent
Decomposition of H_2O_2	HBr, HCl, HI	H_2O
Oxidation of persulfates	Ag^+	H_2O
$Ce^{++++} + S_2O_3^{--}$	I^-	H_2O
Inversion of menthone	$C_2H_5O^-$	C_2H_5OH
Inversion of sucrose	H^+	H_2O
Hydrolysis of esters, amides, acetals	H^+	H_2O
Decomposition of diazoacetic acid	H^+	H_2O
Hydrolysis of sulfamic acid	H^+	H_2O
Hydrolysis of pyrophosphates	H^+	H_2O
Decomposition of nitroso-triacetone-amine	OH^-	H_2O
Decomposition of triacetone alcohol	OH^-	H_2O
Conversion of acetone to triacetone alcohol	OH^-	H_2O
Hydrolysis of ethyl orthocarbonate, ortho-acetate and orthopropionate	Generalized acid	H_2O
Oxidation of phosphorous and hyphosphorous acids by iodine	Generalized acid	H_2O
Rearrangement of N-bromacetanilide	Generalized acid	C_6H_6, C_6H_5Cl
Decomposition of nitramide	Generalized base	H_2O, isoamyl alcohol, m-cresol
Isomerization of nitromethane	Generalized base	H_2O
Mutarotation of glucose	Generalized acid-base	H_2O
Enolization of acetone	Generalized acid-base	H_2O
Acetylation of β-naphthol	Generalized acid-base	CH_3COOH

On the other hand, in generalized basic catalysis the substrate is catalyzed by bases in the generalized sense. If a substrate S, subject to this type of catalysis, is permitted to react in the acetate-acetic acid mixture mentioned above, the bases present are H_2O, OH^-, and acetate ions (A^-), and the rate equation becomes now

$$\frac{dx}{dt} = k_{H_2O}C_{H_2O}C_S + k_{OH^-}C_{OH^-}C_S + k_A{}_-C_A{}_-C_S$$
$$= C_S(k_{H_2O}C_{H_2O} + k_{OH^-}C_{OH^-} + k_A{}_-C_A{}_-) \quad (80)$$

By utilizing again suitable methods the catalytic coefficients of various bases may be found, and from these the total rate of the reaction.

Finally, there are some reactions, such as the enolization of acetone or the mutarotation of glucose, which are subject to *generalized acid-base catalysis*. In such reactions the over-all rate is the sum of the products of the catalytic coefficient, the concentration of substrate, and the concentration of all acid or basic species present; i.e., the total rate equation is the sum of expressions of the type given in equations (79) and (80).

In generalized acid, base, or acid-base catalysis the catalytic coefficients of various acids and bases vary greatly in magnitude. For generalized acid catalysis the coefficients increase as the acid strength of the catalyzing acid goes up, while in basic catalysis the same parallelism is found with the basic strength of the catalyzing base.

CHAIN REACTIONS

In 1906 Bodenstein and Lind, in studying the kinetics of combination of hydrogen and bromine to form hydrogen bromide, found that the rate of the process could not be represented by any equation deduced on a simple basis, but had to be expressed by the relation

$$\frac{dC_{HBr}}{dt} = \frac{kC_{H_2}\sqrt{C_{Br_2}}}{1 + k'(C_{HBr}/C_{Br_2})} \tag{81}$$

A satisfactory explanation of equation (81) was finally proposed by Christiansen, Herzfeld, and Polanyi in 1919–1920. These men postulated that the first stage in the reaction is a dissociation of bromine molecules to bromine atoms,

$$Br_2 \longrightarrow 2\,Br \tag{a}$$

followed next by the slow reaction,

$$Br + H_2 \longrightarrow HBr + H \tag{b}$$

and then by the rapid changes,

$$H + Br_2 \longrightarrow HBr + Br \tag{c}$$
$$H + HBr \longrightarrow H_2 + Br \tag{d}$$
$$Br + Br \longrightarrow Br_2 \tag{e}$$

With this mechanism they were able to show that a rate equation of the form of (81) can be deduced and that consequently the combination of bromine and hydrogen proceeds through a series of consecutive reactions initiated by the appearance of bromine atoms in the system.

A reaction like the above, proceeding in a series of successive stages initiated by a suitable primary process, is called a *chain reaction*. In the hydrogen-bromine and also in the hydrogen-chlorine reaction, which is similar in behavior, the initial step is the appearance of bromine or chlorine atoms. These atoms may result from thermal or photochemical dissociation of the molecules, or they may be produced by the introduction of metallic vapors, such as sodium, which yield atoms through a reaction of the type

$$Na + Cl_2 \longrightarrow NaCl + Cl$$

In other reactions the chain may be initiated by the appearance of *free radicals*, such as CH_3, C_2H_5, or CH_3CO, which then react with molecules but are eventually regenerated to propagate the chain. Finally, a chain may start at the wall of the reacting vessel. This appears to be the case in the reactions $H_2 + O_2$, $CS_2 + O_2$, and $CO + O_2$, which have been shown to be chain processes.

Chains initiated in the manner indicated and propagated by atoms or free radicals are called *material chains*. An alternate method of initiation of chain reactions is through "hot molecules." Suppose an atom A reacts with another atom B to yield AB with a large evolution of heat. This liberated energy cannot be removed except by collision with another atom or molecule, which then acquires sufficient energy to become activated. Through a continuation of this process a chain may be started and continued. Chains initiated and propagated through transfer of excess energy are called *energy chains*.

Inspection of equations (a) to (e) for the hydrogen-bromine reaction will reveal that not all the stages of a chain reaction operate to continue a chain once started, but that some of them lead to a termination or "breaking" of chains. Thus, reactions (a) to (d) favor the propagation of the chain by formation of hydrogen or bromine atoms, while reaction (e) results in removal of bromine atoms, and hence in chain stoppage. The same would be true of combination of two hydrogen atoms to form a hydrogen molecule. Another important factor in terminating chains is collision of chain propagators with the walls of the reacting vessel. These collisions may result in either deactivation or reaction of the active agent with the walls. The consequence in either case is a broken chain.

Chain reactions are encountered in the oxidations of various gaseous hydrocarbons, phosphine, and methyl alcohol; in the decomposition of ozone; and in photochemical reactions. Again, indications are that some reactions in solution, such as oxidation of sodium sulfite by oxygen and the decomposition of certain acids by sulfuric acid, also proceed by a chain mechanism.

NEGATIVE CATALYSIS

The rates of some reactions are readily inhibited by the presence of small quantities of various substances. As examples of this *negative catalysis* may be mentioned the inhibiting action of bromine on the methane-chlorine reaction, and the action of a number of alcohols and aldehydes on the oxidation of sodium sulfite in solution. The readiness with which such substances inhibit the reaction when present in even small quantities suggests that we are dealing here with chain reactions and that the action of the negative catalysts results from their ability to react with chain propagators to bring about termination of chains. This idea has actually been confirmed by Bäckström for inhibition of the sodium sulfite oxidation, and it is quite probable that a similar explanation may be valid in other cases as well.

REFERENCES FOR FURTHER READING

1. E. S. Amis, *Kinetics of Chemical Change in Solution*, The Macmillan Company, New York, 1949.
2. R. P. Bell, *Acid-Base Catalysis*, Oxford University Press, Oxford, 1941.
3. F. Daniels, *Chemical Kinetics*, Cornell University Press, Ithaca, N.Y., 1938.
4. Friess and Weissberger, *Investigation of Rates and Mechanisms of Reactions*, Interscience Publishers, Inc., New York, 1953.
5. Frost and Pearson, *Kinetics and Mechanism*, John Wiley & Sons, Inc., New York, 1953.
6. Glasstone, Laidler, and Eyring, *The Theory of Rate Processes*, McGraw-Hill Book Company, Inc., New York, 1941.
7. C. N. Hinshelwood, *Kinetics of Chemical Change*, Oxford University Press, New York, 1940.
8. K. J. Laidler, *Chemical Kinetics*, McGraw-Hill Book Company, Inc., New York, 1950.
9. E. A. Moelwyn-Hughes, *Kinetics of Reactions in Solution*, Oxford University Press, New York, 1947.

PROBLEMS

1. Heppert and Mack [*J. Am. Chem. Soc.*, **51**, 2706 (1929)] give the following data for the vapor phase decomposition of ethylene oxide into methane and carbon monoxide at 414.5° C:

Time (min)	0	5	7	9	12	18
Pressure (mm)	116.51	122.56	125.72	128.74	133.23	141.37

Show that the decomposition follows a first order reaction, and calculate the mean specific rate constant.   *Ans.* $k_1 = 0.0123$ min^{-1}.

2. From the mean rate constant for the decomposition of azoisopropane at 270° C given in Table 2 calculate (a) the percentage of the original sample decomposed after 25 sec, and (b) the time required for the reaction to go 95% to completion.

3. An artificially produced radioactive isotope decomposes according to the first order law with the emission of α particles. The half-life period is 15 min. In what time will 80% of the sample be decomposed?

4. At 25° C the half-life period for the decomposition of N_2O_5 is 5.7 hr and is independent of the initial pressure of N_2O_5. Calculate (a) the specific rate constant and (b) the time required for the reaction to go 90% to completion.
                    Ans. (a) 0.122 hr^{-1}; (b) 18.9 hr.

5. The first order catalyzed decomposition of H_2O_2 in aqueous solution is followed by titrating the undecomposed H_2O_2 with $KMnO_4$ solution. By plotting the proper function, ascertain from the following data the value of the rate constant:

Time (min)	0	5	10	20	30	50
Ml of $KMnO_4$ for given amount of H_2O_2 solution		46.1	37.1	29.8	19.6	12.3	5.0

Ans. $k_1 = 0.0437$ min^{-1}.

6. Show the steps in the integration of the rate expression:

$$\frac{dx}{dt} = k_2(a - x)(b - x)$$

7. The following table gives kinetic data [Slator, *J. Chem. Soc.*, **85**, 1286 (1904)] for the reaction between $Na_2S_2O_3$ and CH_3I at 25° C, the concentrations being expressed in arbitrary units:

Time (min)	0	4.75	10	20	35	55	∞
$Na_2S_2O_3$	35.35	30.5	27.0	23.2	20.3	18.6	17.1
CH_3I	18.25	13.4	9.9	6.1	3.2	1.5	0

Show that the reaction is second order, and calculate the mean specific rate constant.

8. The rate of saponification of methyl acetate at 25° C was studied by making up a solution 0.01 molar in both base and ester, and titrating the mixture at various times with standard acid. The following data were thus obtained:

Time (min.)	3	5	7	10	15	21	25
Concentration of base found	0.00740	0.00634	0.00550	0.00464	0.00363	0.00288	0.00254

Show by a graphical method that the reaction is second order, and determine the specific rate constant.

9. From the data of the preceding problem, calculate the time required for the reaction to proceed 95% to completion when the initial concentrations of base and ester are both 0.004 mole/liter. What would be the half-life period in this case?   *Ans.* 408 min; 21.5 min.

10. The following reaction [Maron and LaMer, *J. Am. Chem. Soc.*, **60**, 2588 (1938)]

$$CH_3CH_2NO_2 + OH^- \longrightarrow H_2O + CH_3CH{=}NO_2^-$$

is second order, with the rate proportional to the concentrations of nitroethane and OH^- ions. The specific rate constant at 0° C is 39.1 (moles/liter)$^{-1}$ min^{-1}. After what time will the base be 99% neutralized in a solution containing 0.005 mole/liter of nitroethane and 0.003 mole/liter of NaOH at 0° C?

11. At 25° C the specific rate constant for the hydrolysis of ethyl acetate by NaOH is 6.36 (moles/liter)$^{-1}$ min^{-1}. Starting with concentrations of base and ester of 0.02 mole/liter, what proportion of ester will be hydrolyzed in 10 min?   *Ans.* 56%.

12. For the reduction $2\,FeCl_3 + SnCl_2 \longrightarrow 2\,FeCl_2 + SnCl_4$ the following data were obtained at 25° C

t (min)	1	3	7	11	40
y	0.01434	0.02664	0.03612	0.04102	0.05058

where y is the amount of $FeCl_3$ reacted in moles per liter. The initial concentrations of $SnCl_2$ and $FeCl_3$ were respectively 0.03125 and 0.0625 mole/liter. What is the order of the reaction, and the average specific rate constant?

13. The conversion of hydroxyvaleric acid into valerolactone at 25° C in 0.025 N HCl solution was followed by titration with standard base. The data obtained were:

Time (min)	0	48	124	289	∞
Cc of base	19.04	17.60	15.80	13.37	10.71

What is the reaction order and mean specific rate constant?

14. A substance decomposes according to a zero order reaction with a rate constant k. (a) What will be the expression for the period of half-life when the initial concentration is a? (b) How long will it take the reaction to go to completion?

15. Consider the reversible reaction $H_2(g) + I_2(g) \underset{k_2}{\overset{k_1}{\rightleftharpoons}} 2 HI(g)$. Assuming that we start with equal initial concentrations of the two reacting gases, (a) set up the rate expression for the reaction, (b) integrate it, and (c) show how the two rate constants can be evaluated when the equilibrium constant K is known.

16. In the following table are listed specific rate constants k for the decomposition N_2O_5 at various temperatures:

$t°$ C	k (sec^{-1})
0	7.87×10^{-7}
25	3.46×10^{-5}
35	1.35×10^{-4}
45	4.98×10^{-4}
55	1.50×10^{-3}
65	4.87×10^{-3}

Determine graphically the energy of activation, and find the specific rate constant at 50° C.

17. At 378.5° C the half-life period for the first order thermal decomposition of ethylene oxide is 363 min, and the energy of activation of the reaction is 52,000 cal/mole. From these data estimate the time required for ethylene oxide to be 75% decomposed at 450° C.   *Ans. 13.5 min.*

18. The racemization of pinene is a first order reaction. In the gas phase the specific rate constant was found to be 2.2×10^{-5} min^{-1} at 457.6° K and 3.07×10^{-3} at 510.1° K. From these data estimate the energy of activation, and the specific rate constant at 480° K.

19. The specific rate constants for the second order neutralization of 2-nitropropane by base in aqueous solution are given by the expression [Maron and LaMer, *J. Am. Chem. Soc.*, **60**, 2588 (1938)]:

$$\log_{10} k = \frac{-3163.0}{T} + 11.899$$

The time is in minutes, while the concentrations are in moles per liter. Calculate the energy of activation, and the half-life period at 10° C when the initial concentrations of base and acid are each 0.008 mole/liter.

20. The molecular diameters of O_2 and H_2 respectively are 3.39×10^{-8} cm and 2.47×10^{-8} cm. When 1 g of O_2 and 0.1 g of H_2 are mixed in a 1-liter flask at 27° C, what will be the number of collisions per cubic centimeters per second?   *Ans. 2.76×10^{29}.*

21. The energy of activation for a bimolecular gaseous decomposition is 20,000 cal/mole. Calculate the fraction of the molecules having sufficient energy to decompose at 27° C and at 227° C.

22. The gas phase reaction $2A \longrightarrow B + C$ is bimolecular with an activation energy of 24,000 cal/mole. The molecular weight and diameter of A are, respectively, 60 and 3.5 Å. Calculate from kinetic theory the specific rate constant for the decomposition at 27° C.

   Ans. 3.8×10^{-7} (mole/liter)$^{-1}$ sec^{-1}.

23. For the hydrolysis of sulfamic acid [Maron and Berens, *J. Am. Chem. Soc.*, **72**, 3571(1950)] $k = 1.16 \times 10^{-3}$ (mole/liter)$^{-1}$ sec^{-1} at 90° C, while $E^* = 30,500$ cal mole^{-1}. From these data find (a) ΔF^*, (b) ΔH^*, and (c) ΔS^* of the reaction.

   Ans. (a) 26,400 cal mole^{-1}; (b) 29,800 cal mole^{-1}; (c) 9.4 eu mole^{-1}.

24. Using the results obtained in the preceding problem, calculate the rate constant to be expected for the hydrolysis of sulfamic acid at 98° C.

25. According to the Brönsted theory, will the specific rate constants of the following reactions remain unchanged, increase, or diminish as the ionic strength is increased:

   (a) $NH_4^+ + CNO^- \longrightarrow CO(NH_2)_2$
   (b) The saponification of an ester.
   (c) $S_2O_8^{--} + I^- \longrightarrow$ products.

26. For a certain reaction catalyzed by hydrogen ions, the following specific rate constants were observed at 25° C in solutions containing formic acid (HA) and sodium formate (NaA):

HA (mole/liter)	NaA (mole/liter)	k (min^{-1})
0.250	0	2.55
0.250	0.025	0.682
0.250	0.100	0.172
0.250	0.250	0.0679

At this temperature the ionization constant of formic acid is 1.77×10^{-4}. Find the catalytic coefficient of the H$^+$ ions.

27. For the reaction

$$NH_2SO_2OH + H_2O = NH_4HSO_4$$

in aqueous solution at 80.35° C, the following constants were observed at the indicated ionic strengths:

$\mu \times 10^3$	k (mole/liter)$^{-1}$ hr^{-1}
5.06	1.07
11.21	1.02
15.85	0.976
22.94	0.886

From these data ascertain (a) the valencies of the reacting ions, and (b) the rate constant corrected for primary salt effects. At this temperature the Debye-Hückel constant $A = 0.574$.

20

Kinetics of Heterogeneous Gas Reactions

Although many types of heterogeneous reactions are possible through various combinations of solid, liquid, and gas phases, we shall limit ourselves to a discussion of the kinetics of gaseous reactions which proceed at the surfaces of solid catalysts. Because such reactions are of great practical importance, they have been investigated more extensively than others, and the principles governing their kinetics are better understood.

Of the importance of heterogeneously catalyzed gas reactions little need be said. Mention of the contact process for manufacture of sulfuric acid, the Haber ammonia process, the oxidation of ammonia to nitric acid, and the catalytic synthesis of methanol from carbon monoxide and hydrogen, among many others, should suffice to make one appreciate the great changes such reactions have wrought in the chemical industry as well as in our national economy.

The feature characterizing all gas reactions catalyzed by solids is the fact that the reactions proceed not in the gas phase but at the surface of the solid catalyst. For this reason this type of process is frequently referred to as *contact catalysis*. The catalytic reaction is believed[1] to involve at least four distinct steps, namely: (a) adsorption of the reacting gases on the surface of the catalyst; (b) activation of the adsorbed reactants; (c) reaction of the activated gas in the adsorbed phase; and (d) diffusion of the products of the reaction from the surface into the gas phase. Although any one of these processes may be slowest and therefore rate determining, it has been found possible to approach the kinetics of

[1] Schwab, Taylor, and Spence, *Catalysis*, D. Van Nostrand Company, Inc., New York, 1937, p. 219.

such reactions from the standpoint of adsorption and to formulate rate equations in terms of principles based on the Langmuir adsorption isotherm.

THE LANGMUIR ADSORPTION ISOTHERM

The theory of contact catalysis starts with the Langmuir concept of *unimolecular* adsorbed films as developed in Chapter 7. According to the Langmuir theory a gas is adsorbed on the surface of a solid in a layer *one molecule deep.* Further, the entire surface need not be covered with adsorbed gas. In fact, parts may be covered and parts may be bare, but it is only the covered portions which will lead to reaction and hence will determine the rate. If, then, we are to employ the law of mass action to set up the rate equations of such reactions, we must consider not the concentration or pressure of the reactants in the gas phase, but their concentration in the adsorbed film. The function of the gas phase is merely to control the concentration of molecules in the adsorbed layer. Since the latter concentration is at any instant proportional to the *fraction of surface covered*, the rate of reaction must also be proportional to this fraction, and hence

$$\frac{dx}{dt} = k'\theta \tag{1}$$

where θ is the fraction of surface covered by reactant, while k' is a proportionality constant.

We have seen in Chapter 7, equation (3), that for any adsorbed gas θ is given by

$$\theta = \frac{bP}{1 + bP} \tag{2}$$

where b is a constant and P is the pressure of the gas in contact with the adsorbent. This is the expression for θ to be inserted into equation (1). However, in two limiting cases equation (2) can be simplified as follows. When a gas is only weakly adsorbed b is small, and bP may be disregarded compared to unity. Under these conditions θ becomes

$$\theta = bP \tag{3}$$

i.e., *the fraction of the surface covered when a gas is only slightly adsorbed is directly proportional to the pressure.* Again, when a gas is strongly adsorbed, as when either b or P or both are large, then $bP \gg 1$, and equation (2) reduces to

$$\theta = \frac{bP}{bP} = 1 \tag{4}$$

Therefore, *when a gas is strongly adsorbed the surface is practically completely covered with a film of gas at all times, and $\theta = 1$.*

Another deduction which can be made from equation (2) is also of importance for our purposes. Since θ is the fraction of surface covered, $(1 - \theta)$, the fraction of surface bare, is

$$(1 - \theta) = 1 - \left(\frac{bP}{1 + bP}\right)$$

$$= \frac{1}{1 + bP} \tag{5}$$

For strong adsorption $bP \gg 1$, and hence,

$$(1 - \theta) = \frac{1}{bP} = \frac{'b'}{P} \tag{6}$$

From equation (6) we see that, when a gas is strongly adsorbed on a surface, *the fraction* of the latter still *free and available for adsorption of other gases is inversely proportional to the pressure of the adsorbed gas.*

With the aid of these equations we are prepared now to illustrate the kinetics of heterogeneous reactions in a number of simple cases. The examples will be confined to reactions in which only a single gas participates as a reactant. For more complex situations the student may refer to the book by Schwab, Taylor, and Spence.[1]

ONE REACTANT GAS SLIGHTLY ADSORBED

Consider a gas A decomposing on the surface of a solid catalyst according to

$$A \longrightarrow \text{Products} \tag{7}$$

Let θ_A be the fraction of the surface covered by A at time t and pressure P. Then according to equation (1) the rate of the reaction should be

$$\frac{dx}{dt} = k'\theta_A$$

When A is only slightly adsorbed, θ_A is given by equation (3). Hence,

$$\frac{dx}{dt} = k'bP = kP = k(P_i - x) \tag{8}$$

where $k = k'b$ is the *velocity constant* of the reaction, P_i the initial pressure, and x the decrease in it at any time t. On integration equation (8) becomes

$$k = \frac{2.303}{t} \log_{10}\left(\frac{P_i}{P_i - x}\right) \tag{9}$$

[1] See reference on p. 643.

which is identical in form with the equation for a first order homogeneous reaction. For this reason equations (8) or (9) are said to represent *first order* heterogeneous reactions.

Quite a number of reactions have been found to follow equation (9). Among these may be mentioned the decomposition of phosphine on glass, porcelain, and silica; the decomposition of formic acid vapors on glass, platinum, and rhodium; the decomposition of nitrous oxide on gold; and the dissociation of hydrogen iodide on platinum. In Table 1 are shown some data for the dissociation of nitrous oxide on gold[1] which may be considered typical of all such reactions.

TABLE 1

DECOMPOSITION OF N_2O ON GOLD AT 900° C

t (sec)	$P_i - x$ (mm)	$k = \dfrac{2.303}{t} \log_{10} \dfrac{P_i}{P_i - x}$
0	200	—
900	167	2.01×10^{-4}
1800	136	2.15
3180	100	2.18
3900	86	2.17
4800	70	2.19
6000	54	2.18
7200	44	2.10

ONE REACTANT GAS STRONGLY ADSORBED

Since for a strongly adsorbed reactant $\theta \equiv 1$, the rate of the reaction is given by

$$\frac{dx}{dt} = k \tag{10}$$

i.e., the rate of the reaction is *constant and independent of pressure*. A reaction obeying equation (10) is said to be of *zero order*. On integration equation (10) becomes

$$k = \frac{x}{t} \tag{11}$$

Hinshelwood and Burk[2] found the decomposition of ammonia on tungsten to be practically independent of the initial pressure and to proceed in accordance with equation (10). This may be seen from the

[1] Hinshelwood and Pritchard, *Proc. Roy. Soc.*, **108A**, 211 (1925).
[2] Hinshelwood and Burk, *J. Chem. Soc.*, **127**, 1116 (1925).

TABLE 2

Decomposition of NH_3 on Tungsten at 856° C

(P_i = 200 mm)

t (sec)	x (mm Hg)	$k = \dfrac{x}{t}$
100	14	0.14
200	27	0.14
300	38	0.13
400	48	0.12
500	59	0.12
1000	112	0.11

results quoted in Table 2. The same behavior has been observed in the decomposition of ammonia on the surfaces of molybdenum and osmium, and in the dissociation of hydrogen iodide on gold.

ONE REACTANT GAS MODERATELY ADSORBED

When the reactant is moderately adsorbed, the rate of reaction is proportional to the fraction of surface covered as given by equation (2), namely,

$$\frac{-dP}{dt} = k' \left(\frac{bP}{1 + bP} \right) = \frac{kP}{1 + bP} \tag{12}$$

This equation can frequently be approximated by the expression

$$\frac{-dP}{dt} = kP^n \tag{13}$$

which makes the rate proportional to the amount adsorbed as given by the Freundlich isotherm. Stock and Bodenstein[1] used equation (13) to represent the decomposition of stibine on antimony at 25° C, while equation (12) was found to hold in the decomposition of nitrous oxide on indium oxide.[2]

RETARDED REACTIONS

In some reactions the catalytic surface adsorbs not only the reactant but also a product of the reaction. In fact, the product may be adsorbed more strongly than the reactant. Since a strongly adsorbed product diminishes the surface available for condensation of reactant, the fraction

[1] Stock and Bodenstein, *Berichte*, **40**, 570 (1907).
[2] Schwab, Staeger, and v. Baumbach, *Z. physik. Chem.*, **21B**, 65 (1933).

of the surface covered by the latter must decrease, and thereby also the rate of reaction. Hence *the effect of a strongly adsorbed product is to retard the reaction producing it.*

Consider specifically the reaction

$$A \longrightarrow B + C + \cdots \qquad (14)$$

where the reactant A is weakly adsorbed, while the product B is strongly adsorbed. Let P_A and P_B be the pressures of A and B respectively at time t, and let $(1 - \theta_B)$ be the fraction of the surface not covered by B. The rate of reaction of A will then be proportional to the rate at which molecules of A can become attached to the surface, namely, to the fraction of surface exposed and the pressure of A

$$\frac{dx}{dt} = k'(1 - \theta_B)P_A \qquad (15)$$

But when a gas is strongly adsorbed, $(1 - \theta)$ is given by equation (6), which in this case takes the form $(1 - \theta_B) = b'/P_B$. Substituting this value of $(1 - \theta_B)$ into equation (15), we obtain for the rate of reaction

$$\frac{dx}{dt} = \frac{k'b'P_A}{P_B}$$
$$= \frac{kP_A}{P_B} \qquad (16)$$

i.e., the rate is directly proportional to the pressure of the reactant and *inversely* to the pressure of the product responsible for the retardation.

The decomposition of ammonia on platinum at 1138° C was found by Hinshelwood and Burk[1] to conform essentially to equation (16). Nitrogen appears to have no effect on the reaction, but the hydrogen formed exhibits a strong retardation, as may be seen from Table 3. In

TABLE 3

RETARDATION OF NH_3 DECOMPOSITION ON Pt AT 1138° C BY H_2
$(P_i = 100 \text{ mm})$

ΔP_{NH_3} in 120 sec (mm)	P_{H_2} initially added (mm)
33	50
27	75
16	100
10	150

[1] Hinshelwood and Burk, *J. Chem. Soc.*, **127**, 1114 (1925).

this table column 1 gives the decrease in the pressure of ammonia observed in 120 sec on starting in each case with 100 mm, while column 2 gives the pressures of added hydrogen present initially. For a threefold increase in the pressure of the retarding gas the decomposition is decreased in an equal period from 33 to 10 per cent of the total.

When the product responsible for the retardation is moderately rather than strongly adsorbed, equation (15) is still applicable, but $(1 - \theta_B)$ is given by equation (5). For this case we obtain, therefore,

$$\frac{dx}{dt} = \frac{kP_A}{1 + bP_B} \tag{17}$$

This equation has been applied to the decomposition of nitrous oxide on platinum, cadmium oxide, cupric oxide, and nickel oxide. The retarding gas is oxygen.

THE ORDER OF HETEROGENEOUS REACTIONS

The order of a heterogeneous reaction is defined as the total power to which the pressures appear in the rate equation. A more suitable criterion of the order n of a heterogeneous reaction is the period of half-life, which is inversely proportional to the $(n - 1)$ power of the initial pressure. By studying the period of half-life of a reaction as a function of the initial pressure, it is possible to evalute $n - 1$, and hence the reaction order.

The value of n so obtained is not necessarily the true order of the reaction as it takes place on the surface. Rather, it is the apparent order ascertained by following the surface reaction indirectly through its influence on the pressure of the gas phase. As we have seen in the examples cited, n may or may not be a whole number. When a single reacting gas is weakly adsorbed, the reaction is first order and $n = 1$. Again, when a single reactant is strongly adsorbed, $n = 0$, and the reaction proceeds independently of the pressure. On the other hand, for the intermediate adsorption involved in the decomposition of stibine on antimony, $n = 0.6$. The last two results would be hard to understand unless it is remembered that in heterogeneous reactions only apparent orders are obtained and that changes may proceed on the surface with orders which may be quite different.

For a single reacting gas only slightly adsorbed, and where products exhibit no retardation, the apparent and true orders may be inferred to be identical. For fractional and zero order reactions the true and apparent orders cannot possibly be the same. In such cases the true order must be deduced from the nature of the reaction and from any other data available. This correlation of reaction orders is further complicated by adsorption of and retardation due to products. In general, the effect of a strongly adsorbed product, i.e., to the extent that the free surface is inversely proportional to its pressure, is to yield an apparent order *one less than the true order*. This can readily be shown by integrating the rate equation of such a process and solving for the time of half-life. Consequently, when an apparent zero order reaction is found to be retarded by a strongly adsorbed product, it may be assumed that the reaction has a true first order.

EFFECT OF TEMPERATURE ON HETEROGENEOUS REACTIONS

As for homogeneous reactions, the influence of temperature on the rate constant k of heterogeneous reactions is given by the Arrhenius equation,

$$\frac{d \ln k}{dT} = \frac{E_a^*}{RT^2} \tag{18}$$

E_a^* is called here the *apparent energy of activation*. The apparent energy of activation, evaluated from the observed velocity constants, is not necessarily the energy required to activate the reactants on the *surface*, which is the true activation energy. The latter may be modified by the heats of adsorption of reactants, or reactants and products, to yield an apparent activation energy which may be quite different from the true. A discussion of the relation between these two activation energies is given by Hinshelwood.[1]

TABLE 4

ACTIVATION ENERGIES FOR HOMOGENEOUS AND
HETEROGENOUS REACTIONS*

Decomp. of Gas	E^* Homog.	E_a^* Heterog.
HI	44,000	25,000 (gold)
N_2O	58,500	29,000 (gold)
N_2O	58,500	32,500 (platinum)
NH_3	80,000 (est.)	39,000 (tungsten)

* C. N. Hinshelwood, *Kinetics of Chemical Change*, The Clarendon Press, Oxford, 1940, p. 224.

The energy of activation appears to be intimately connected with the function of the catalyst in heterogeneous reactions. Comparison of the energies of activation of gaseous reactions at some surface with those of the same reactions proceeding homogeneously almost invariably indicates

[1] C. N. Hinshelwood, *Kinetics of Chemical Change*, The Clarendon Press, Oxford, 1940, p. 214.

that the energy of activation of the heterogeneous reaction is considerably lower than that of the homogeneous. This may be seen from the figures quoted in Table 4. These results point to the fact that the action of the catalyst leads to a lowering of the activation energy. With a lower energy barrier more molecules may become active and enter into reaction than is possible with a high energy threshold.

CATALYTIC POISONS

Small quantities of foreign substances added to a reacting system are frequently sufficient to impair seriously the catalytic activity of a surface. Such substances are termed *catalytic poisons*. Poisons may be of two kinds, temporary and permanent. In temporary poisoning the surface decreases in activity, or loses it entirely, only for the period that the poison is in contact with it. As soon as the poison is removed from the presence of the catalyst, the activity is restored. The diminution in activity is due in most instances to a strong preferential adsorption of the poison on the catalyst surface. With sufficiently strong adsorption the reactant may be displaced completely, and the entire surface may be covered with an inactive blanket of the poison.

An illustration of temporary poisoning is the retarding effect exercised by carbon monoxide on the hydrogenation of ethylene in presence of copper.[1] Into this class fall also the reactions in which retardation by products takes place. In expressing the rate of such reactions the pressure of the poison appears in the denominator of the rate equation whether the poison takes part in the reaction or not.

Permanent poisoning, on the other hand, involves a chemical interaction between the surface and the poison to form a new surface which is catalytically inert. Activity can be reestablished only by chemical rejuvenation. Among the permanent poisons volatile silicon and sulfur compounds are particularly fatal to the life of many catalysts. So are arsenic compounds, especially to platinum.

The very small quantities sufficient to poison a catalytic surface have led H. S. Taylor to suggest that only a fraction of the total exposed surface is catalytically active. He, as well as others, showed that the quantity of poison effective in stopping activity is sometimes too small to cover the whole surface with a film one molecule deep. In his theory of *active centers* Taylor accounts for this by considering the surface as irregular, with high catalytic activity localized in certain spots that are more elevated than others. As soon as those spots become covered with poison, the activity of the surface diminishes to practically zero. Further-

---

[1] Pease, *J. Am. Chem. Soc.*, **45**, 1196, 2235 (1923); Pease and Stewart, *ibid.*, **47**, 1235 (1925).

more, since those spots are only a small part of the total surface, the amount of substance necessary to poison a catalyst is correspondingly small.

Catalytic poisoning is occasionally very specific and may be taken advantage of to control the products of a reaction. For instance, the decomposition of alcohol in presence of copper proceeds in two stages,

$$CH_3CH_2OH \longrightarrow CH_3CHO + H_2$$
$$CH_3CHO \longrightarrow CH_4 + CO$$

the first of which is uninfluenced by water vapor, while the second is considerably retarded. Therefore, by using alcohol with some water in it, Armstrong and Hilditch[1] were able to increase the yield of acetaldehyde and to prevent materially the formation of undesired methane. This type of selective poisoning is of great industrial importance.

PROMOTERS

Whereas some substances decrease the catalytic activity of a surface, others, known as *promoters*, increase it. The promoter itself usually is noncatalytic and consists in most instances of a metal or highly fusible metallic oxide incorporated into the body of the catalyst. The amount of promoter required is small; and the increase in velocity produced is considerably greater than would correspond to any increase in total surface area. Thus, Russell and Taylor found that for a 20 per cent increase in surface due to promoters the rate of reaction increased tenfold. This observation and others point to an actual improvement in the quality of a surface by promoters, rather than to a mere evolution of surface. No satisfactory and generally acceptable explanation of promoter action has yet been advanced.

NATURE OF CATALYSTS

Technical catalysts vary greatly both in their chemical nature and in the form in which they are used. Chemically catalysts may be pure metals, metallic oxides, or salts. They may further be individual substances, like nickel in hydrogenation processes, or a mixture of several substances, as Fe_2O_3–Bi_2O_3 in the oxidation of ammonia to nitric acid. The mixed catalysts, because of promoter action exerted by small quantities of a second or third substance, are as a rule more active than the individual components. Again, catalysts may be supported or unsupported. An unsupported catalyst is one used by itself without any mounting. Supported catalysts, in turn, are those which, either because of added strength or

---

[1] Armstrong and Hilditch, *Proc. Roy. Soc.*, **97A**, 262 (1920).

increased surface, are mounted on some base. The latter is usually an inert porous substance with large exposed surface upon which the catalyst is deposited. Supports used frequently are asbestos, kieselguhr, silica and other gels, and various salts. A familiar supported catalyst is platinized asbestos.

The activity of catalysts depends also on the method and care of their preparation. Generally only the purest chemicals can be employed, and the temperature must be carefully controlled to avoid sintering of the fine mass with attendant reduction in surface area.

REFERENCES FOR FURTHER READING

1. K. C. Bailey, *The Retardation of Chemical Reactions*, Edward Arnold & Co., London, 1937.
2. Berkman, Morrell, and Egloff, *Catalysis*, Reinhold Publishing Corporation, New York, 1940.
3. R. H. Griffith, *The Mechanism of Contact Catalysis*, Oxford University Press, New York, 1946.
4. C. N. Hinshelwood, *Kinetics of Chemical Change*, Oxford University Press, New York, 1940.
5. Komarewsky and Riesz, in *Catalytic, Photochemical and Electrolytic Reactions*, Interscience Publishers, Inc., New York, 1948.
6. Schwab, Taylor, and Spence, *Catalysis*, D. Van Nostrand Company, Inc., New York, 1937.

PROBLEMS

1. The diameter of an O_2 molecule is 3.39×10^{-8} cm. Assuming a unimolecular layer and that the effective area occupied by the molecules is the square of the diameter, how much O_2 could be adsorbed by a W filament whose diameter is 0.02 cm and whose effective length is 10 cm? What pressure would be exerted by this amount of O_2 when contained in a 100-cc flask at 27° C?
   Ans. 9.07×10^{-10} mole; 1.69×10^{-4} mm Hg.
2. I. Langmuir [*J. Am. Chem. Soc.*, **40**, 1361 (1918)] measured the volume, reduced to 1 atm pressure, of various gases adsorbed at 20° C by cover glasses having a total surface area of 1966.0 cm^2 with the following results:

	Volume (mm^3)	Molecular Diameter (Å)
H_2O	354	2.20
CO_2	64 0	4.18
N_2	49.0	3.75

Assuming that each molecule occupies an area equal to the square of its diameter, calculate in each case the molecular thickness of the surface layer.
3. Calculate the pressure of N_2O in contact with a gold surface at 900° C after $2\frac{1}{2}$ hr if the initial pressure is 350 mm. After what time will the decomposition be 95% complete? Use the data given in Table 1. *Ans.* 51 mm; 233 min.
4. Integrate equation (13) to obtain k in terms of P, t, n, and the initial pressure P_i.

5. Using the result obtained in problem 4, deduce the expression for the period of half-life in terms of n, k, and P_i.

6. Stock and Bodenstein give the following data for the decomposition of SbH_3 on Sb at 25° C.

Time (min)	0	5	10	15	20	25
$P_{Stibine}$	1.000	0.731	0.509	0.327	0.189	0.093

Show that the decomposition may be represented satisfactorily by the rate expression $-dP/dt = kP^n$, where $n = 0.6$, and determine the rate constant.

7. Using the data in problem 6 determine graphically the half-life period of the reaction, and compare your result with that given by the equation derived in problem 5.

8. Kunsman [*J. Am. Chem. Soc.*, **50**, 2100 (1928)] reports the following data for the decomposition of NH_3 on W at 1100° K:

Initial pressure of NH_3 (mm)	265	130	58	16
Half-life period (min)	7.6	3.7	1.7	1.0

Show that the reaction is approximately zero order, and calculate the mean specific rate constant.

9. From the data given in Table 2 estimate the percentage of NH_3 decomposed after 1 hr, and the time required for the decomposition of 75% of the original sample. *Ans.* 100%; 1154 sec.

10. According to Hinshelwood the decomposition of N_2O on Pt follows the rate equation

$$\frac{-d(a - x)}{dt} = \frac{k(a - x)}{1 + bx}$$

where a is the initial pressure of N_2O in mm, x is the decrease in pressure of N_2O in time t, while k and b are constants. On integration this rate equation yields

$$k = \frac{1 + ab}{t} \ln \frac{a}{a - x} - \frac{bx}{t}$$

From the following data obtained at 741° C with $a = 95$ mm:

t (sec)	315	750	1400	2250	3450
x (mm)	10	20	30	40	50

determine the constants k and b by a graphical method.
Ans. $k = 3.36 \times 10^{-4}$; $b = 0.0254$.

11. Using the constants obtained in problem 10 calculate the half-life period for the decomposition of N_2O on Pt at 741° C when the initial pressure of the gas is 200 mm.

12. Derive the rate expression for the kinetics of a heterogeneous reaction in which two reactants are moderately adsorbed and the products do not retard the reaction.

13. Formic acid decomposes into CO_2 and H_2 on a gold surface, following a first order law. Hinshelwood and Topley [*J. Chem. Soc.*, **123**, 1014 (1923)] observed a rate constant of 5.5×10^{-4} at 140.0° C and 9.2×10^{-3} at 185.0° C. Calculate the apparent energy of activation. *Ans.* 23,450 cal.

14. The decomposition of phosphine on fused silica follows the first order law. At 828° K the half-life period is 580 sec, while at 956° K it is 22 sec. Determine (a) the apparent energy of activation of the reaction and (b) the half-life period of the reaction at 800° K.

21

Atomic Structure and
Nuclear Chemistry

The first modern attempt at an explanation of the reactivity of chemical elements is Dalton's atomic theory formulated in 1808. Dalton postulated that every element consists of indivisible particles called atoms, each of which has the same mass for a given element and that these atoms react with each other to form compounds. In terms of such atoms he was able to interpret the law of definite and multiple proportions, and also Lavoisier's law of conservation of mass. However, attempts to apply Dalton's theory to Gay-Lussac's law of volumes, namely, that gases combine with each other in simple proportions by volume, met with failure because no distinction was made between atoms and molecules. This misconception was first clarified by Avogadro in 1811, when he enunciated his famous hypothesis that at constant pressure and temperature equal volumes of all gases contain the same number of molecules — and not necessarily atoms. With the aid of this principle Cannizzaro in 1858 was able to show how molecular weights may be estimated, and that the law of combining volumes is explicable when it is realized that molecules of an element may consist of more than one atom. This principle permits also a differentiation between atomic and molecular weight of an element and removes thereby a great deal of the uncertainty involved in early atomic weight assignments.

Dalton, in setting up the atom as the unit of elementary chemical combination, made no effort to establish any relation between the atoms of various elements. This was first done in 1815 by Prout who, reasoning from the proximity of the atomic weights of elements to whole numbers on the basis of hydrogen as unity, suggested that all elements were composed of multiples of hydrogen atoms. However, further atomic weight determinations, particularly of such elements as chlorine and copper, showed marked differences from whole numbers, so this principle fell into disrepute. Only when the existence of isotopes was established at a much later date, and the true significance of deviations from close proximity to whole numbers was appreciated, did Prout's hypothesis become reestablished as an important principle in considerations of atomic constitution.

Another important principle which indicated the existence of a regular relationship among the elements was the periodic law discovered independently by Mendeléeff (1869) in Russia and Lothar Meyer (1870) in Germany. This law, that the chemical and physical properties of the elements are periodic functions of their atomic weights, pointed to regularities in the structure of atoms and to the fact that certain structures repeated themselves periodically to yield similarity of chemical and physical properties. Nevertheless, it was not until much later that the reason for this behavior was found, and it was observed that the regularity does not follow atomic weight but *atomic number*, i.e., the numerical sequence of an element in the periodic table.

Finally, the electrical researches of Nicholson and Carlisle, Davy, Berzelius, and Faraday showed that matter and electricity are intimately associated and that electricity itself is corpuscular in nature. These findings, followed by studies of electric discharges through rarefied gases and the discovery of radioactivity, eventually established that atoms are divisible and that on subdivision all atoms consist of the same structural units. These are: (a) the electron, (b) the proton, (c) the neutron, and (d) the positron. A description of these units, their properties, and the manner in which they enter into the makeup of atoms, as far as is known, will be the concern of this chapter.

THE ELECTRON

Gases are as a rule poor conductors of electricity. However, when a tube filled with gas is evacuated to pressures of 0.01 mm or lower, and an electric potential is applied across a pair of electrodes sealed into the tube, a discharge takes place between the electrodes during which a stream of rays, called *cathode rays*, is found to be emitted *from the cathode*. These rays travel in straight lines perpendicular to the cathode surface, they produce a temperature rise in any object they strike, they pass through thin films of metals interposed in their path but are stopped by thicker foils, and they can make any opaque object placed in their path cast a sharp shadow. When they strike the wall of the tube, a fluorescence is produced. The fact that these rays can cast a sharp shadow suggests that they consist of material particles and not electromagnetic radiation. Again, these particles can be deflected by electric and magnetic fields, indicating that they are electrically charged; and, further, the direction of deflection is always such as to indicate that these particles always bear a *negative charge*. Finally, no matter what the nature of the cathode or the gas in the tube may be, the particles are always the same.

These particles constituting the cathode rays have been named *electrons*. The fact that electrons are independent of the nature of the source from which they come suggests that they are constituents of all matter. To study more precisely the properties of electrons, Thomson utilized a combination of electric and magnetic fields placed across the path of these through the discharge tube. His apparatus, shown in Fig. 1, consisted of a tube T, into which were sealed the cathode C, the anode A, a slit system S for defining the electron beam, and a pair of electrodes D and D' for applying an electric field. The electromagnet for supplying the magnetic field (not shown) was placed outside the tube. A beam of electrons emanating from C passes through a hole in the anode A, is collimated as

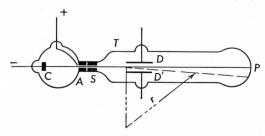

Fig. 1.   J. J. Thomson's Apparatus for Determination of e/m of Electron.

a fine pencil by the slit S, and in absence of any applied electric or magnetic fields strikes the phosphorescent tube wall at point P. However, when a magnetic field is applied across the electron path, the beam is deflected upward or downward from P according to the direction and strength of the field. If now an electric field of correct direction is superimposed over the magnetic field, it is possible to adjust the electric field strength until the displaced beam is returned to its original position at P. From the relations of the forces involved, the ratio of the electron charge e to its mass m may then be evaluated, and Thomson found thus e/m to be 1.79×10^7 electromagnetic units per gram. More refined measurements have modified this value to

$$e/m = 1.75890 \times 10^7 \text{ emu g}^{-1}$$
$$= 1.75890 \times 10^8 \text{ abs. coulombs g}^{-1} \qquad (1)$$

CHARGE ON ELECTRON

In order to resolve this ratio, the charge on the electron must be ascertained independently. This determination was first carried out with a high degree of precision in 1913 by R. A. Millikan through his famous oil-drop experiments.

A schematic diagram of Millikan's apparatus is shown in Fig. 2. It consisted of a chamber B, immersed in a thermostat (not shown) and filled with air whose pressure could be controlled by a vacuum pump and read on a manometer M. At the lower end of the chamber were installed two condenser plates C and C', across which could be applied a potential from the battery S. The space between the plates was illuminated by a light source located in front of a window in the chamber, W_1, and could be observed through a low-power telescope mounted in front of the apparatus and fitted with cross hairs a definite distance apart.

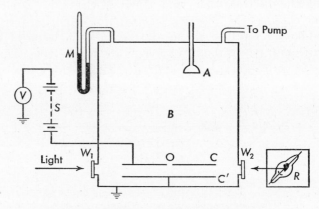

Fig. 2.   Millikan's Oil-Drop Apparatus.

By means of an atomizer A, a spray of fine droplets of oil was introduced into B. In due course one of these droplets worked its way down toward C and passed through an opening O in this plate into the space between C and C'. As soon as this happened the opening O was closed, and the rate of fall of the droplet through the air under gravity was determined by measuring the time necessary for it to pass between the cross hairs of the telescope. At this stage a beam of x rays from the source R was passed into the space between the plates through the window W_2. This beam caused the air molecules to become ionized, forming ions which would from time to time be captured by the oil droplet and impart to it a charge. When the electrostatic field was now applied from S across the condenser plates, an oil droplet with a charge upon it could be made to fall faster or actually rise against gravity with a velocity dependent on the direction of the field, its magnitude, and the charge on the drop. The rate of rise or fall could again be observed by timing the passage between the cross hairs. In fact, once a particle was trapped between the plates, it could be made to fall or rise at will by either shutting off or turning on the electrostatic field, and hence the measurements on any particle could be repeated a number of times.

If we let v_1 be the rate of fall of the particle under gravity g, v_2 the rate of rise of the particle against gravity when an electrostatic field strength X is applied, and m' and e' the mass of and charge on the oil droplet, then in the oil drop experiments these quantities are connected by the relation

$$\frac{v_1}{v_2} = \frac{m'g}{Xe' - m'g} \tag{2}$$

The values of m' required in equation (2) in order to find e' were obtained by use of a modified form of Stokes's law. From his many experiments with all types of drops and various field strengths Millikan found that e' was not constant. However, he did find that there was a *common factor* for all the values of e' which made the various charges observed *whole number multiples of the common factor*. This is an excellent confirmation of the atomicity of electricity and indicates that the various oil droplets had captured and retained one, two, or more gaseous ions on their surfaces. The value of this least common factor deduced by Millikan was $(4.774 \pm 0.005) \times 10^{-10}$ electrostatic unit, and this must be, therefore, the charge of the unit of electricity, or the electron.

Since this work a redetermination of the viscosity of air and other corrections have shown that a better value of the electronic charge, e, is

$$\begin{aligned} e &= 4.80286 \times 10^{-10} \text{ esu/electron} \\ &= 1.60206 \times 10^{-20} \text{ emu/electron} \\ &= 1.60206 \times 10^{-19} \text{ abs. coulomb/electron} \end{aligned} \tag{3}$$

The validity of this value of the electronic charge can readily be tested by using it to calculate Avogadro's number from the value of the faraday. Since a faraday represents the quantity of electricity associated with Avogadro's number of unit electric charges, and since the quantity of electricity in unit charge is presumably e, N should be given by

$$\begin{aligned} N &= \frac{\mathfrak{F}}{e} = \frac{96,496 \text{ abs. coulombs}}{1.60206 \times 10^{-19} \text{ abs. coulomb}} \\ &= 6.0232 \times 10^{23} \end{aligned}$$

MASS OF THE ELECTRON

From e/m and e the mass of the electron follows as

$$\begin{aligned} m &= \frac{e}{(e/m)} \\ &= \frac{1.60206 \times 10^{-19}}{1.75890 \times 10^{8}} \\ &= 9.1083 \times 10^{-28} \text{ g/electron} \end{aligned} \tag{4}$$

This mass of the electron may be compared with the mass of a hydrogen atom, which is, of course, the atomic weight of hydrogen divided by Avogadro's number, namely,

$$m_H = \frac{1.0080}{6.0232 \times 10^{23}} = 1.6735 \times 10^{-24}\,g$$

From m_H and m it is seen that the mass of the hydrogen atom is 1837 times greater than the mass of the electron.

The mass of the electron given in equation (4) is the *rest mass*, i.e., the mass when the electron is either at rest or moving with velocities that are low compared to that of light. However, when the electron is moving at very high speeds, according to the theory of relativity the mass of the electron is increased in line with the equation

$$m = \frac{m_0}{\sqrt{1 - (v/c)^2}} \tag{5}$$

where m_0 is the mass of the electron at rest, m the mass when the electron is moving with a velocity v, and c the velocity of light. Equation (5) shows that m increases with v, until at $v = c$ the mass of the electron becomes infinite. This equation is applicable also to any other body of rest mass m_0 moving with extremely high velocities.

WAVE NATURE OF THE ELECTRON

Heretofore the electron has been treated as a particle. However, it was pointed out in Chapter 4 that electrons possess also wave properties. From this it must be concluded that, depending on the manner of observation, electrons have the faculty of behaving both as particles and waves. Thus in a discharge tube the electrons exhibit their attributes as particles, whereas in electron diffraction experiments they act as electromagnetic waves and yield diffraction patterns on reflection from crystalline surfaces.

This duality of behavior, exhibited also by light and even atoms, is an illustration of the *Heisenberg uncertainty principle* enunciated in 1927, which states that *it is impossible to define simultaneously the exact momentum and position of a body.* Precisely, Heisenberg showed that the product of the uncertainty in the position of a body Δx, and the uncertainty in the momentum Δp, and hence the velocity, is even in the perfect experiment related to Planck's constant h by the expression

$$(\Delta x)(\Delta p) \geq \frac{h}{4\pi} \tag{6}$$

Consequently, as soon as any attempt is made to define exactly the position of a body, i.e., make Δx very small, Δp becomes large. Similarly, any attempt to define Δp exactly leads to large uncertainties in x. Now, in studying the electron in discharge experiments we concentrate on the exact definition of its velocity and momentum, and arrive thus at the conclusion that the electron is a particle. On the other hand, when electron diffraction experiments are performed, the emphasis is on the position of the electron. Hence its momentum becomes an ambiguous quantity, and the electron behaves like a wave. From these considerations it may be deduced that the corpuscular nature of the electron becomes manifest when the particular experiment performed involves definition of its velocity, momentum, or energy, whereas the wave properties come to the fore when its position is being fixed.

THE PROTON

The researches described establish that all matter contains negative electricity whose unit is the electron particle of relatively low mass. Since the atoms composing matter are generally electrically neutral, and since the mass of even the lightest atom, hydrogen, is very much greater than that of the electron, there must evidently be present in atoms positive electricity with which, in all probability, most of the mass is associated. The problem is, therefore, to find the unit of this positive charge and to ascertain its mass.

As a preliminary indication of the answer to this problem, let us consider the simplest and lightest of atoms, hydrogen. Under ordinary conditions, this atom is electrically neutral and has a mass of 1.67×10^{-24} g, which is 1837 times as great as that of the electron. When this atom is converted into an ion, it is found that its charge is exactly equal to that of the electron but is opposite in sign. Further, the mass of the positively charged hydrogen ion, or *proton*, is very nearly the same as that of the hydrogen atom. These facts suggest that the unit of positive electricity is the proton with a mass 1836 times that of the electron and that the hydrogen atom is composed of one proton and one electron.

It is not necessary to rely completely on this type of conjectural reasoning, for there are direct ways of producing positive rays and measuring their e/m ratio. In 1886 Goldstein discovered that there are present in a discharge tube not only cathode rays composed of electrons moving toward the anode, but also positive rays moving in the opposite direction. By perforating the cathode these *positive* or *canal rays* can be made to pass through the holes to the rear, and there be studied by the effect of electric and magnetic fields upon them. By such methods it was established that these rays consist of *positively charged particles* which, unlike the electrons, have associated with them practically all of the mass of the atoms from which they come. Further, these particles are not emitted by the anode, but originate between the electrodes from ionization of the gas atoms through electron bombardment. By appropriate means these rays can be generated also by emission of positive ions from anodes, in which instance the rays consist of ions of the metal used. The significant fact revealed by all such studies is that, although unit positive charge may be associated with ions of various masses, no particle found is of a mass lower than that of the proton. Of added importance is the observation that the masses of all ions heavier than that of hydrogen are within close limits whole number multiples of the mass of the proton. These facts indicate that the proton is the unit of positive electricity and that like electrons the protons enter into the constitution of all atoms. This conclusion is essentially a revival of Prout's hypothesis in more modern terms.

POSITIVE RAY ANALYSIS AND ISOTOPES

A method of investigating positive rays is the Aston *mass spectrograph,* with which masses of positively charged particles can be determined

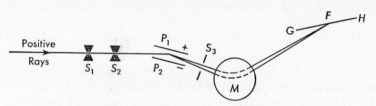

Fig. 3.   Schematic Diagram of Aston's Mass Spectrograph.

with an accuracy greater than one part in a million. The principle of the mass spectrograph can be understood with the aid of the schematic diagram in Fig. 3. A beam of positive rays, narrowed by means of the slits S_1 and S_2, is passed between two charged plates P_1 and P_2. Under the influence of the electrostatic field between the plates the beam spreads out by downward deflection of the particles, the extent of deflection being determined by the charge and velocity of each particle. From the spread-out beam only those ions are selected which can pass through the narrow slit S_3, and these are sent into an electromagnetic field M directed to deflect the ions in a direction opposite to that of the electric field. From the relations obtaining for the apparatus it can be shown that, for any given electric and magnetic field strength, all particles of a given charge to mass ratio will be brought to a focus at a point such as F. Furthermore, the focus of all particles of various charge to mass ratios will lie on a straight line situated along GH. Consequently, a photographic plate placed along GH will record by a narrow exposed band the point of focus of all the ions of a fixed charge to mass ratio, while a series of these dark bands will give the loci of all ions of various charge to mass ratios in the beam. The striking similarity of such an exposed plate to an ordinary spectrum plate accounts for the name given to this apparatus.

From a study of the mass spectrograms of various elements Aston was able to deduce the charge to mass ratios and from these very precise values of the atomic weights. The mass spectrograph also revealed that many elements, which from ordinary atomic weight determinations were considered to consist of atoms of the same mass, are in reality mixtures of atoms of different masses although of the same atomic number. Such atoms of different mass but same atomic number are called *isotopes*. Thus chlorine, with a chemical atomic weight of 35.457, was shown to consist of two isotopes of atomic weights 35 and 37 on the O = 16.000 scale mixed in such proportion as to yield an over-all atomic weight of 35.457. Again, magnesium, atomic weight 24.32, was shown to consist of isotopes of relative masses 24, 25, and 26. In every instance the abundance of the isotopes in the mixture is such as to yield the chemically observed atomic weight.

In Table 1 are given the atomic masses of a number of the lighter elements as deduced from the mass spectrograph. Inspection of this table reveals that the masses of the various elements are very nearly whole numbers and multiples of the atomic weight of the hydrogen atom of mass 1.00814. This fact lends credence to the Prout hypothesis. Again, the existence of isotopes accounts for fractional atomic weights deduced

TABLE 1

ATOMIC MASSES DEDUCED FROM MASS SPECTROGRAPH

Atomic No.	Atom	Rounded Mass	Mass
1	H	1	1.00814
		2	2.01474
2	He	3	3.01698
		4	4.00387
3	Li	6	6.01702
		7	7.01822
4	Be	9	9.01504
5	B	10	10.01631
		11	11.01292
6	C	12	12.00380
		13	13.00747
7	N	14	14.00752
		15	15.00486
8	O	16	16.00000
		17	17.00453
		18	18.00487

by chemical methods and shows why no satisfactory regularity could be observed in these to substantiate Prout's suggestion.

The atomic weights listed in Table 1 are on the *physical scale*, i.e., on the basis that oxygen of atomic weight 16 is 16.0000. On the other hand, chemical atomic weights are based on ordinary oxygen being 16.0000. Since the latter has been shown to be composed of three isotopes, the two scales are not quite the same. To obtain the chemical atomic weight from the physical it is necessary to multiply the latter by 0.999728.

RELATION OF MASS TO ENERGY

For strict applicability of Prout's hypothesis the masses of various atoms should be exact whole number multiples of the mass of the hydrogen atom, 1.00814. Actually, however, this is not the case. Thus helium of atomic weight four should have a mass of $4 \times 1.00814 = 4.03256$, but the actually observed mass is 4.00387. The mass loss of 0.02869 g in the formation of a helium atom from four hydrogen atoms can be accounted for in terms of an equation derived by Einstein, in which he shows that mass may be converted to energy, or vice versa, according to the relation

$$E = mc^2 \tag{7}$$

In this equation E is the energy in ergs, m the mass in grams, and c the velocity of light, 3×10^{10} cm sec^{-1}. If it is postulated now that the formation of the helium atom from four hydrogen atoms takes place with an evolution of energy equivalent to the loss in mass, then the process in question involves a liberation of

$$
\begin{aligned}
E &= 0.0287 \times (3 \times 10^{10})^2 \\
&= 2.58 \times 10^{19} \text{ ergs} \\
&= 6.17 \times 10^{11} \text{ cal}
\end{aligned}
$$

per gram atom of helium formed. In a like manner may be explained the mass defects observed in other atomic nuclei.

It is customary to define the mass defect of an isotope, ΔM, as the difference between the atomic weight of the isotope on the physical scale, M, and its rounded atomic mass, M', called the *mass number*. In terms of this mass defect the *packing fraction*, f, is given by the relation

$$f = \frac{\Delta M}{M'} = \frac{M - M'}{M'} \tag{8}$$

This fraction gives the deviation of the atomic weight of an isotope from its integral mass number and is also a measure of the energy which would be evolved or absorbed in the formation of the given isotope from hydrogen atoms. Thus for beryllium $M = 9.01504$, $M' = 9$, and hence

$$f = \frac{9.01504 - 9}{9} = 16.7 \times 10^{-4}$$

Starting with hydrogen of $M' = 1$, for which the packing fraction is 81.4×10^{-4}, the values of f decrease with increase in mass number, pass through a minimum between $M' = 50 - 60$, and then they increase gradually. Further, the packing fractions are positive only for elements lighter than $M' = 16$ and heavier than about $M' = 170$. Between $M' = 16$ and $M' = 170$ the packing fractions are negative, and hence the formation of these elements from hydrogen would involve an absorption rather than an evolution of energy.

HYDROGEN AND DEUTERIUM

Among the methods which have been employed to separate or enrich isotopes are the mass spectrograph, diffusion, centrifuging, thermal diffusion, electrolysis, fractional distillation, and chemical exchange. It is not possible to describe here either these methods or the results obtained. Nevertheless, it is of interest to point out the differences found between ordinary hydrogen and its heavier isotope *deuterium*, symbol D. Deuterium was discovered spectroscopically in 1932 by Urey and his co-workers at Columbia University. In ordinary hydrogen gas deuterium is present as about one part in 6400 parts of light hydrogen. The heavier isotope is usually concentrated by electrolysis of aqueous alkali solutions, in which instance the lighter hydrogen atoms escape more readily than the heavier deuterium, and the solution becomes more concentrated in D_2O, *heavy water*. By repeating the electrolysis a number of times, pure D_2O can be prepared and studied.

In Table 2 are contrasted some physical properties of hydrogen and deuterium, while in Table 3 are compared the properties of ordinary and heavy water. These data show appreciable differences in the properties of

TABLE 2

COMPARISON OF PROPERTIES OF HYDROGEN ISOTOPES

Property	H_2	D_2
Molar volume of solid	26.15 cc	23.17 cc
Triple point	13.92° K	18.58° K
Heat of fusion	28 cal/mole	47 cal/mole
Boiling point	20.38° K	23.50° K
Heat of vaporization at triple point	217.7 cal/mole	303.1 cal/mole

H_2 and D_2, and of H_2O and D_2O. The differences in the two forms of water affect significantly the solubility, conductance, equilibrium relations, and the rates of various reactions conducted in these media as solvents. However, the differences between hydrogen and deuterium are much more pronounced than are those between isotopes of other elements where the relative difference in mass is much less than it is here.

TABLE 3

COMPARISON OF PROPERTIES H_2O AND D_2O

Property	H_2O	D_2O
Relative density, 25°/25° C	1.000	1.1079
Melting point	0.00° C	3.82° C
Boiling point	100.00° C	101.42° C
Surface tension, 20° C	72.75 dynes/cm	67.8 dynes/cm
Temperature of maximum density	4.0° C	11.6° C
Dielectric constant, 25° C	78.54	78.25
Viscosity, 20° C	10.09 millipoises	12.6 millipoises
Heat of fusion	1436 cal/mole	1510 cal/mole
Heat of vaporization	10,480 cal/mole	10,740 cal/mole

THE NEUTRON

In 1920 Rutherford suggested that there may also be present in atoms a particle of essentially *the same mass as the proton but with no charge*. The existence of such uncharged particles, called *neutrons*, was actually established in 1932 by Chadwick. These particles have been found to be independent of their source in their properties, to be unaffected by electric and magnetic fields, indicating thus absence of charge, and to have a mass of 1.00898 atomic weight units, which is almost identical with that of the proton, 1.00759. Methods of producing neutrons will be mentioned later in the chapter.

EARLIER THEORIES OF ATOMIC STRUCTURE

Although the preceding evidence points to protons, neutrons, and electrons as the constituents of all matter, it does not indicate how these are arranged to yield the various atoms. An early attempt to solve this problem was Rutherford's proposal of a nuclear atom. Rutherford's theory is based on some observations made by Geiger, Marsden, and himself on the scattering of α particles by metallic foils. α particles are emission products of certain radioactive disintegrations. They have a mass approximately four times that of the proton and bear two positive charges. These particles are in fact helium nuclei, i.e., helium atoms from which two electrons have been removed. When Geiger and Marsden bombarded thin metallic foils with these α particles, they found that whereas most of these went through the foils unaffected, about one particle in 20,000 suffered a violent deflection through angles of 90° or greater. In seeking an explanation of these results it must be realized that electrons, because of their low mass, would not be able to deflect α particles. Again, to cause the sharp deflection of the particles through the large observed angles would require strong forces which can arise only from interaction of particles of the same charge as those used in the bombardment. Finally, since most of the α particles go through unaffected, these sources of deflection cannot be continuous throughout the foil, but must be localized in spaces that are relatively small compared to the space occupied by the foil as a whole. Basing his argument on these points, Rutherford suggested that atoms consist of miniature solar systems in which all of the positive

charge is located in a nucleus at the center of the atom, while the electrons required for electrical balance revolve about the nucleus at some distance from it, much as the planets revolve about the sun. As in terms of this picture the atom consists mostly of empty space, α particles directed against a thin metallic foil should be able to pass through it without deflection as long as they do not approach too near to a positive nucleus.

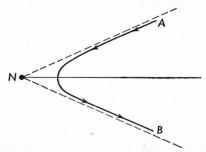

Fig. 4.   Scattering of α Particles by Nuclei.

However, when an α particle is so directed as to come near the nucleus, the strong repulsive force developed between the nucleus and the positive α particle causes the latter to be deflected in the manner indicated in Fig. 4. Here N is the nucleus of an atom, while AB is the path of the α particle on approach and deflection.

From a mathematical analysis of the scattering Rutherford was able to deduce that the charge on the nucleus responsible for the observed deflections was equal approximately to one-half the atomic weight of the metal constituting the foil. Further, he was able to estimate that the dimensions of the nuclei were of the order of 10^{-12}–10^{-13} cm, dimensions which along with the volume of the electrons involved are only 10^{-12}–10^{-15} of the volumes actually occupied by the atoms. From these figures it follows that only $1/10^{12}$ to $1/10^{15}$ of the volume of an atom is occupied by protons, electrons, and neutrons, with the rest being nothing but empty space.

THE CHARGE ON THE NUCLEUS

Rutherford's earlier researches on α-particle scattering did not lead him to an exact definition of the nuclear charge. The first precise statement that the *nuclear charge of an atom is identical with its atomic number* was made by van der Broeck in 1913. Nevertheless, the first direct evidence on this point is due to Moseley's investigations (1913, 1914) of the x radiations emitted by various elements. These will now be described.

X rays are emitted when a metallic target is bombarded with rapidly moving electrons. No x radiation from a given target is observed until the electrons acquire a certain threshold speed which is characteristic for each metal. Once the required speed of bombarding electrons is attained or exceeded, each metal emits x radiation which is not continuous but consists of series of lines possessing fixed frequencies characteristic of the target substance. The various sets of lines thus obtained can be divided into series designated in turn as the *K, L, M*, etc., series, while the lines within each series are referred to in sequence as the α, β, γ, etc., lines. Thus, the K_α line is the first line in the *K* series, the L_β is the second line in the second series, etc.

Moseley undertook the task of studying the x-ray spectra of elements lying between aluminum and gold in the periodic table to ascertain whether any regularities exist among them. As a result of this exhaustive investigation he found that the spectra observed followed the same sequence as do the elements in the periodic table. And, what is more important, he also found that if we take the frequencies of any particular line in all the elements, such as the K_α or K_β lines, then the frequencies are related to each other by the equation

$$\sqrt{\nu} = a(Z - k) \tag{9}$$

where ν is the frequency of any particular K_α or K_β, etc., line, Z is the *atomic number* of the element in the periodic table, and a and k are constants for any particular type of line. The regularity thus observed can be obtained only when the *atomic number* is used, but not with the atomic weight. This suggests that the fundamental quantity involved in x radiation is not the atomic weight but the atomic number. Furthermore, since x radiation arises from energy shifts taking place in extranuclear electrons, and since x radiation of the various elements exhibits regularity with atomic number, Moseley concluded that the change in atomic number from element to element represents the regular variation in the number of extranuclear electrons in the neutral atom; i.e., *the number of extranuclear electrons is identical with the atomic number of an element*. Moreover, since the number of extranuclear electrons in an atom must be equal to the charge of the nucleus for over-all electroneutrality, it must follow also that *the atomic number gives the number of units of positive charge on the nucleus.* The correctness of this conclusion has subsequently been verified by Chadwick's work on scattering of α particles, and by certain observations on radioactive disintegrations.

DISTRIBUTION OF ELECTRONS, PROTONS, AND NEUTRONS IN AN ATOM

We are prepared now to consider the number of electrons, protons, and neutrons in an atom and their distribution. On the oxygen scale of atomic weights the mass of the proton or neutron is essentially unity. Further, because of the relatively low mass of electrons compared to that of protons or neutrons, the mass of atoms will be due primarily to the latter two. Therefore, if we let A be the atomic weight of any atom, this will also be the sum of the protons and neutrons in it. Now, Moseley showed that the number of extranuclear electrons is Z, where Z is the atomic number, and that the nuclear charge is also Z. Since only the protons carry a charge, this must mean that there are present in the nucleus Z protons and $(A - Z)$ neutrons.

The following then is the picture of an atom. Each atom consists of a nucleus composed of Z protons and $(A - Z)$ neutrons. To balance the nuclear charge Z electrons are distributed outside the nucleus and revolve about it as a center. Thus, in the hydrogen atom with $A = 1$ and $Z = 1$ there must be only one proton in the nucleus and one electron revolving about it. Again, in beryllium with $A = 9$ and $Z = 4$ there must be a nucleus composed of four protons and five neutrons, and four external electrons. Finally, in an atom such as uranium, with $A = 238$ and $Z = 92$, there must be present 92 protons and 146 neutrons in the nucleus, and 92 external satellite electrons.

Rutherford believed that the external electrons may occupy any and all positions outside the nucleus and possess thereby energies which can vary continuously. However, this concept of continuous variation in energy is contradicted by atomic spectra, which are not continuous but discontinuous. Again, since a revolving electron is a charged body in motion, then according to classical electrodynamics such a body should radiate energy continuously. As a result of this loss of energy by radiation the orbit of revolution of an electron should get smaller and smaller, until eventually the electron should fall into the nucleus and be retained there. Such behavior on the part of electrons has never been observed. To overcome these difficulties inherent in the Rutherford atom, Niels Bohr advanced in 1913 his now famous theory of atomic structure. Before this theory can be presented, however, two other subjects must be introduced first, namely, Planck's quantum theory of radiation and the emission of line spectra by excited atoms.

THE QUANTUM THEORY OF RADIATION

When radiation strikes any surface of a body, part of the radiant energy is generally reflected, part is absorbed, and part is transmitted. The reason for the incomplete absorption is that ordinary bodies are as a rule imperfect absorbers of radiation. In contrast to these we have the *black body*, which by definition is the perfect absorber of energy and retains any radiant energy that strikes it. Although a blackened metallic surface or carbon black approximates fairly closely a black body, a hollow sphere, blackened on the inside and with a small opening, meets the defined condition much more satisfactorily. Any radiation that enters through the small opening is reflected repeatedly from the walls of the enclosure until all of the energy eventually becomes absorbed.

A black body is not only a perfect absorber of radiant energy, but also a perfect radiator. In fact, of all bodies heated to a given temperature, it is the black body which will radiate the maximum amount of energy possible for the given temperature. Furthermore, a black body is in thermal equilibrium with its surroundings and radiates in any given time per unit area the same amount of energy as it absorbs.

The total amount of energy E radiated by a black body per unit area and time is given by the *Stefan-Boltzmann fourth power law*, namely,

$$E = \sigma T^4 \tag{10}$$

where T is the absolute temperature, while σ is a universal constant equal to 5.6687×10^{-5} for energy in ergs, time in seconds, and area in square centimeters. This energy is not emitted with a single frequency, nor is it uniformly distributed along the spectrum. Lummer and Pringsheim showed that the energy emitted depends on the temperature and wave length in the manner indicated in Fig. 5. For each temperature there is a wave length at which the energy radiated is a maximum. Again, the position of this maximum shifts with increase in temperature toward lower wave lengths, and the maximum itself is the more pronounced the higher the temperature.

Wien in 1896 and Lord Rayleigh in 1900 made attempts to account for this distribution of black body radiation on the basis of classical concepts of *continuous emission* of radiation. Although Wien's equation proved fairly satisfactory at low wave lengths and Rayleigh's at high ones, neither theory could account completely for the observed phenomena. This failure of classical theories of radiation led Max Planck in 1900 to discard these and to come forward with the bold hypothesis that *black bodies radiate energy not continuously, but discontinuously in energy packets called quanta,* given by the relation

$$E = h\nu \tag{11}$$

E is the quantum of energy radiated, ν is the frequency, and h, called *Planck's constant*, is a universal constant equal to 6.62517×10^{-27} erg-sec. Equation (11) is the fundamental relation of the *quantum theory of radiation*. Planck considered the black body to consist of oscillators of molecular dimensions, each with a fundamental vibration frequency ν, and that each oscillator could emit energy either in the unit quantum

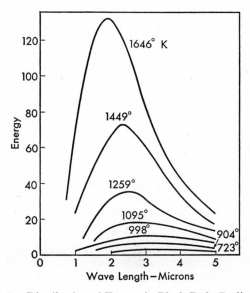

Fig. 5.   Distribution of Energy in Black Body Radiation.

$E_1 = h\nu$, or in *whole number multiples* n thereof, $E_n = nh\nu$. On this basis he was able to deduce for the energy E_ν radiated by a black body at any frequency ν the relation

$$E_\nu = \frac{2\pi\nu^2}{c^2} \cdot \frac{h\nu}{e^{h\nu/kT} - 1} \tag{12}$$

where c is the velocity of light, T the absolute temperature, and k the gas constant per molecule, i.e., R/N. This equation not only reproduced in excellent fashion the spectral distribution of energy, but reduced as well for low wave lengths to Wien's equation and for high wave lengths to the Rayleigh equation.

Planck's success with the quantization of black body radiation led Albert Einstein in 1905 to a generalization of the quantum theory.

Einstein postulated that *all radiant energy must be absorbed or emitted by a body in quanta whose magnitude depends on the frequency according to equation (11), or multiples thereof.* Furthermore, Einstein argued that radiation is not only emitted or absorbed in quanta, but it is also propagated through space in these units, called *photons* of light. This theory ascribes to light a corpuscular character similar to that established for electricity and matter.

Einstein's theory of the corpuscular nature of all light has been amply substantiated by observations on electron emission produced by light, by the inverse photoelectric effect, i.e., the emission of radiation by electron bombardment, as in the generation of x rays, by the Compton effect arising from collisions between photons and electrons, and other phenomena. Details may be found in books on the quantum theory.

THE LINE SPECTRA OF ATOMS

Bodies on being heated to high temperatures emit radiation which can be passed through a spectrograph, resolved there into its component wave lengths, and recorded photographically. When such spectograms are analyzed, it is found that solids generally give spectra that are continuous. On the other hand, gases and vapors yield a series of lines, called *line spectra*, or bands, called *band spectra*, which consist of many lines close together. The *band spectra* are radiations emitted by *molecules*, whereas the *line spectra* are due to *atoms*. At present we are interested only in the latter, and so we shall turn to a discussion of these.

Of all the elements the simplest line spectrum is that exhibited by atomic hydrogen. The spectrum of this element consists of a number of lines which can be classified into groups or series. Each series of lines is related by a formula, which for the *Balmer* series, appearing in the visible spectral range, takes the form

$$\frac{1}{\lambda} = \bar{\nu} = R_H \left(\frac{1}{2^2} - \frac{1}{n^2} \right) \tag{13}$$

Here λ is the wave length of the line, whose reciprocal, $\bar{\nu}$, is called the *wave number*, i.e., the number of waves per centimeter, R_H is a constant, called the *Rydberg constant* and equal to 109,677.58 cm^{-1}, and n is a running number taking on for the various lines of this series values of 3, 4, 5, etc. Similarly, the lines in the various other series found in hydrogen can be expressed by formulas analogous to equation (13). In fact, the lines of all series can be represented by the general expression

$$\bar{\nu} = R_H \left(\frac{1}{n_1^2} - \frac{1}{n_2^2} \right) \tag{14}$$

where the values of n_1 and n_2 for the various series are summarized in Table 4. The significant fact to be observed here is that every line in any given series can be represented as a difference of two terms, one R_H/n_1^2, where n_1 has a fixed value for a given series, and a second R_H/n_2^2, where n_2 can take on a series of integral consecutive values beginning with $n_2 = n_1 + 1$. The significance of this important regularity will appear as soon as the Bohr theory is presented.

TABLE 4

SPECTRAL SERIES OBSERVED IN ATOMIC HYDROGEN

Series	n_1	n_2	Spectral Region
Lyman	1	2, 3, 4, $\cdots$	Ultraviolet
Balmer	2	3, 4, 5, $\cdots$	Visible
Paschen	3	4, 5, 6, $\cdots$	Infrared
Brackett	4	5, 6, 7, $\cdots$	Infrared
Pfund	5	6, 7, $\cdots$	Infrared

The spectra of other elements are more complicated. The spectra of ionized gaseous atoms such as singly ionized helium, He^+, doubly ionized lithium, Li^{++}, or trebly ionized beryllium, Be^{+++}, bear a striking resemblance to that of hydrogen, and these are said to be hydrogenic in character. With heavier atoms, however, and with unionized atoms of the elements mentioned, the situation is more complex, and a different method of classification is necessary. Nevertheless, the spectra of all these elements can be arranged into series; and every series can again be represented as a difference of two terms, one fixed and characteristic of the series, another integrally variable with each line.

BOHR'S THEORY OF THE HYDROGEN ATOM

To account for the line spectra of elements and to circumvent the objections leveled against the Rutherford atom, Niels Bohr advanced in 1913 a theory of atomic structure radically different from any that preceded it. Along with Rutherford, Bohr considered the atom to consist of a nucleus with electrons revolving about it. However, whereas Rutherford placed no restrictions on the electron orbits, Bohr postulated that the only possible orbits for electron revolution are those for which the angular momentum is a *whole number* multiple n of the quantity $(h/2\,\pi)$, h being Planck's constant. This assumption constitutes a *quantization of the angular momentum* of the electron. Bohr further postulated that as long as any electron stays in a given orbit it does not radiate energy, despite the demands of classical electrodynamics, and hence the energy of an electron remains constant as long as it does not change orbits. This second postulate introduces the concept that there are definite *energy levels* or *stationary states* within the atom in which an electron possesses a definite and invariable energy content. Finally, Bohr assumed as his third postulate that each line observed in the spectrum of an element results from the passage of an electron from an orbit in which the energy is E_2 to one of lower energy E_1 and that that this difference in energy is emitted as a quantum of radiation of frequency ν in line with the equation

$$\Delta E = E_2 - E_1 = h\nu \qquad (15)$$

Bohr proceeded immediately to apply these ideas to the hydrogen atom. If the single electron in hydrogen revolves about the proton nucleus in a circular orbit, the situation in the hydrogen atom can be represented essentially by the diagram shown in Fig. 6. In this diagram point A represents the proton of positive charge $+e$, where e is the electronic charge. About this nucleus in an orbit of radius r revolves an electron B, with a tangential velocity v, charge e equal but opposite to that of the proton, and a mass m. This electron is attracted on the one hand by electrostatic forces to the nucleus, while at the same time it experiences a centrifugal force which tends to make it escape from its orbit. For the electron to remain in its orbit these two forces must be equal. Equating them, and introducing his postulate of quantization of angular momentum, Bohr was able to show that the velocity of the electron in its orbit should be given by

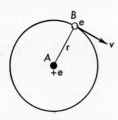

Fig. 6.   Bohr's Model of Hydrogen Atom.

$$v = \frac{2\pi e^2}{nh} \qquad (16)$$

and its energy E by

$$E = \frac{-2\pi^2 m e^4}{n^2 h^2} \qquad (17)$$

Equation (17) gives the total energy of an electron in a hydrogen atom. This equation involves known constants and the integer n which may have only integral values 1, 2, 3, etc. For any given value of n, which is called the *principal quantum number*, the energy of the electron will be fixed, and this will be the constant energy of the particular energy level or stationary state. The energies of the various levels, since they are proportional to $1/n^2$, will decrease according to the square of the quantum number, so that the level for which $n = 2$ will have only ¼ the energy of the level for which $n = 1$, the one with $n = 3$, ⅑ the energy, etc. In other words, the energy levels which an electron in a hydrogen atom can occupy do not change continuously, but involve abrupt changes in energy on passage from one level to another.

This same abruptness in change is exhibited also by the radii of the paths in
which the electron revolves, which are
given by

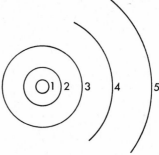

$$r = \frac{n^2 h^2}{4\,\pi^2 m e^2} = (0.53 \times 10^{-8}) n^2 \ \text{cm} \quad (18)$$

We see, therefore, that the orbit closest to
the nucleus, i.e., for $n = 1$, has a radius
of 0.53 Å, the one for $n = 2$ a radius of
4×0.53 Å, the one for $n = 3$, 9×0.53
Å, etc. The relative locations of these

Fig. 7.   Bohr Orbits for Electron in Hydrogen Atom.

orbits for several values of n are illustrated in Fig. 7.

BOHR'S THEORY OF THE HYDROGEN SPECTRA

According to Bohr's third postulate, spectral lines are supposed to result when an electron jumps from one energy level to another, and thereby the atom emits a quantum of energy whose frequency is given by equation (15). This point can be tested very readily. Suppose the electron is originally in an orbit for which $n = n_2$ and that it changes into an orbit with $n = n_1$. In its initial state the electron will have, according to equation (17), the energy

$$E_{n_2} = -\frac{2\,\pi^2 m e^4}{h^2 n_2^2}$$

while in the final state

$$E_{n_1} = -\frac{2\,\pi^2 m e^4}{h^2 n_1^2}$$

The difference in energy, $\Delta E = E_{n_2} - E_{n_1}$ should be emitted then as a quantum of energy $h\nu$. Hence the wave number $\bar{\nu}$ of the emitted line should be given by

$$h\nu = \Delta E = E_{n_2} - E_{n_1}$$
$$= -\frac{2\,\pi^2 m e^4}{h^2 n_2^2} + \frac{2\,\pi^2 m e^4}{h^2 n_1^2}$$
$$\nu = \frac{2\,\pi^2 m e^4}{h^3}\left(\frac{1}{n_1^2} - \frac{1}{n_2^2}\right)$$
$$\bar{\nu} = \frac{\nu}{c} = \frac{2\,\pi^2 m e^4}{h^3 c}\left(\frac{1}{n_1^2} - \frac{1}{n_2^2}\right) \quad (19)$$

The striking similarity of equation (19) to equation (14) for the spectral lines of hydrogen is immediately evident; and, if Bohr's theory is correct, the Rydberg constant R_H should be equal to

$$R_H = \frac{2\,\pi^2 m e^4}{h^3 c} \tag{20}$$

Substitution into equation (20) of the values of m, e, h, and c yields for R_H 109,737 cm^{-1}, as against the experimental $R_H = 109,678$ cm^{-1}. This remarkably close agreement constitutes a strong confirmation of Bohr's postulates and his explanation of the origin of hydrogen spectra.

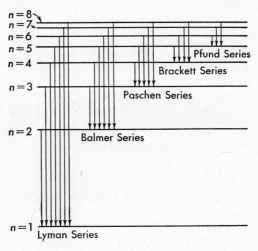

Fig. 8.   Origin of Spectral Series in Hydrogen.

Further comparison of equations (19) and (14) supplies the significance of the various series observed in the spectral lines emitted by the hydrogen atom. In the Lyman series $n_1 = 1$, and hence the lines observed result from passage of electrons from the second, third, fourth, etc., orbits into the first. Similarly, the Balmer series, for which $n_1 = 2$, arise from passage of electrons from the third, fourth, etc., orbits into the second orbit. Likewise the Paschen, Brackett, and Pfund series arise from electron transitions from higher orbits into the third, fourth, and fifth orbits respectively. These various transitions for the sundry series are illustrated schematically in the energy level diagram for the hydrogen atom shown in Fig. 8. Each horizontal line in this figure shows the energy content of a particular level corresponding to the indicated quantum number, while the vertical lines represent the various electron transitions from which arise the spectral lines observed in each series.

The Bohr theory of hydrogen spectra can be extended to account also for the *hydrogen-like* spectra of singly ionized helium, He^+, doubly ionized lithium, Li^{++}, and trebly ionized beryllium, Be^{+++}. By a hydrogen-like spectrum is meant one that results from a system consisting of a nucleus and a single external electron. In the instances mentioned the wave numbers of the respective lines are given by

$$\bar{\nu} = \left(\frac{M}{m + M}\right) RZ^2 \left(\frac{1}{n_1^2} - \frac{1}{n_2^2}\right) \tag{21}$$

where M is the mass of the nucleus, Z its charge, m the mass of the electron, and R a constant.

SOMMERFELD EXTENSION OF BOHR THEORY

In describing the spectra of atoms it was assumed that each emitted line is a single unit. Actually, however, it is found on strong resolution that many lines consist of two or more lines spaced so closely together as to constitute apparently a single line. This appearance of multiple fine lines in place of a single line is referred to as *multiplet* or *fine structure* of spectral lines.

Now, although the Bohr theory does account for the various lines in hydrogen or hydrogenic spectra, it does not explain their fine structure. To meet this deficiency Arnold Sommerfeld advanced in 1915 the suggestion that electrons may revolve in elliptical as well as circular orbits. Assuming, in line with all elliptical motions, that the nucleus is situated at one of the foci of the ellipse, and resolving the angular momentum along a radius vector and a direction perpendicular to it, Sommerfeld showed that, on the basis of quantization of both resolved momenta, the energy of the hydrogen atom should be given by

$$E = -\frac{2\pi^2 e^4 m}{h^2(n_r + k)^2} \tag{22}$$

In this equation n_r is an integer called the *radial quantum number*, while k is an integer called the *azimuthal quantum number*. Comparison of this equation with the Bohr equation (17) shows that the two are identical on setting the principal quantum number n equal to

$$n = n_r + k \tag{23}$$

Further, it can be shown that the principal and azimuthal quantum numbers are related to the lengths of the major and minor axes of the ellipse by the equation

$$\frac{n}{k} = \frac{\text{Length of major axis}}{\text{Length of minor axis}} \tag{24}$$

From equation (24) it may be seen that when $n = k$, i.e., when $n_r = 0$, the two axes are the same and the path is therefore a circle. When k is less than n, however, various elliptical paths are possible depending on the values of k. These values of k may be $(n - 1)$, $(n - 2)$, etc., down to $k = 1$, since when $k = 0$ the ellipse would degenerate into a straight line through the nucleus, an impossible situation. A series of the possible paths for $n = 4$ and the values of k resulting therefrom is given in Fig. 9.

With his theory Sommerfeld was able to account not only for the fine structure of hydrogen spectra, but also for those of the hydrogenic type. However, although this theory does give the correct number of values

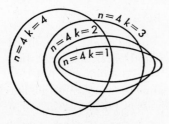

Fig. 9. Electron Orbits in Hydrogen (Sommerfeld).

that k may adopt, the actual values of the k's are wrong. Thus spectroscopic studies show that k values should not vary from $k = n$ down to $k = 1$, but from $k = n - 1$ down to $k = 0$. Yet the Bohr theory, as modified by Sommerfeld, is believed to be essentially correct in its pictorial aspects of the electron behavior in atoms, and is still the simplest working model of atomic architecture.

Before leaving the Bohr-Sommerfeld theory of atomic structure, it may be well to summarize its physical significance. According to this theory each atom is a miniature "solar system" in which the role of the sun is taken by the positive nucleus, while the role of the planets is taken by the external electrons. These electrons revolve about the nucleus in orbits which may be circular or elliptical. The orbits of revolution possible are not any and all imaginable, but only those permitted by the quantization of the angular momenta of the electrons. In these various orbits the electrons possess definite energies, and this fact leads us to the concept of stationary or energy levels. However, whereas Bohr considered each energy level to be constituted of only one definite energy, the Sommerfeld extension points to the fact that any energy level corresponding to a given value of the principal quantum number n may in fact be composed of a series of *sublevels*, each with a different value of the azimuthal quantum number, and each only slightly different from the other in total energy. Finally, the spectral lines emitted by atoms result from the passage of electrons from one energy level to a lower one. Were there no sublevels present, each line thus emitted would be a singlet with no fine structure. But, since sublevels may be present, transitions from those in any one major level to others at lower levels lead to a number of closely spaced lines instead of only one line, and this, therefore, is the cause of the appearance of fine structure.

QUANTUM NUMBERS

The Borh-Sommerfeld theory indicates that two quantum numbers, the principal quantum number n and the azimuthal quantum number k, are necessary to express the energy of an electron in an atom. Spectroscopic study of atoms shows, however, that in actuality *four* quantum numbers are required: (a) the *principal quantum number n*, (b) the *azimuthal quantum number*, which in its correct form is represented by l, (c) the *magnetic quantum number m*, and (d) the *spin quantum number s*.

The principal quantum number n of any electron in an atom represents the *major energy level* to which an electron belongs. This number may take on the integer values 1, 2, 3, etc., depending on whether the electron is in the first, second, third, etc., major level. Corresponding to every major energy level n, there are n *sublevels* possible whose designation is given by the azimuthal quantum number l. This quantum number may have values ranging from $l = 0$ up to $l = (n - 1)$. For instance, when $n = 1$ there is only one value of l possible, $l = 0$. Again, for a level $n = 2$ we may have $l = 0$ and $l = 1$, whereas for a value of $n = 4$ we may have $l = 0, 1, 2$, and 3.

The magnetic quantum number arises from the fact that in a strong magnetic field *each* spectral line can be split into a number of component lines. This phenomenon, called the *Zeeman effect*, can be explained on the supposition that each sublevel exists in fact as a number of closely related levels whose presence is brought out in a magnetic field. For description of these extra levels the *magnetic quantum number m* is required. The values which this quantum number can have are determined by the values of l of the sublevels, and range from $-l \longrightarrow 0 \longrightarrow + l$, i.e., a total of $(2l + 1)$ values for each value of l. For example, for $l = 0$ there is only one value of m, namely, $m = 0$. Again, for $l = 1$ we may have $m = -1$, 0, and $+1$, a total of three values. On the other hand, if $l = 3$, we have seven values of m, these being $m = -3, -2, -1, 0, +1, +2, +3$.

Finally the *spin quantum number s* arises from a suggestion made by Uhlenbeck and Goudsmit in 1925 that an electron in its motion in an orbit may rotate or spin about its own axis. Such a spin would contribute to the angular momentum of the electron and would modify thus the energy relations. Assuming that this spin is also quantized, there are only two possible values which s may have, $s = +\frac{1}{2}$ or $s = -\frac{1}{2}$, depending on whether the electron spins in one direction or in another.

The four quantum numbers and the values they may take on may be summarized as follows:

1. *Principal quantum number, n.* This number can only have the integral values $n = 1, 2, 3$, etc.

2. *Azimuthal quantum number, l.* For each value of n there may be n values of l, namely, $l = 0, 1, 2 \cdots (n - 1)$

3. *Magnetic quantum number, m.* For each value of l there may be $(2l + 1)$ values of m. These range from $m = -l$ through $m = 0$ to $m = +l$ in integral values; i.e., $m = 0, \pm 1, \pm 2 \cdots \pm l$.

4. *Spin quantum number, s.* There are only two possible values of s, $s = \frac{1}{2}$ and $s = -\frac{1}{2}$ for each value of l.

By specifying its four quantum numbers, the "address" of any electron in a given atom is completely defined; i.e., the four quantum numbers locate each electron in the major energy level (n), the particular sublevel (l), the sub-sublevel (m), and the direction of its spin (s).

WAVE MECHANICAL THEORY OF ATOMIC STRUCTURE

According to De Broglie every moving particle can be considered to have associated with it a wave of frequency determined by its velocity. Starting with this idea, Schrödinger in 1926 developed the theory of *wave mechanics* and showed that any moving particle must obey the fundamental equation

$$\left(\frac{\partial^2 \psi}{\partial x^2} + \frac{\partial^2 \psi}{\partial y^2} + \frac{\partial^2 \psi}{\partial z^2} \right) + \frac{8 \pi^2 m}{h^2} (E - V)\psi = 0 \qquad (25)$$

In this Schrödinger wave equation m, E, and V are, respectively, the mass, total energy, and potential energy of the moving body, h is again Planck's constant, ψ is a quantity called the *wave function* of the moving body, and x, y, and z are the three perpendicular coordinates along which the motion of the body may be resolved. The wave function is a quantity rather difficult to describe here. Suffice it to say that for an electron the value of ψ^2 at any point may be interpreted as the density of the electric charge at the given point. Further, the wave function ψ has the mathematical attributes of being finite, single valued, and continuous for any physical situation.

Equation (25) has been applied to the hydrogen atom. Solution of the equation shows that the total energy of the electron in this atom must be given by

$$E = - \frac{2 \pi^2 m e^4}{n^2 h^2} \qquad (26)$$

where n is an integer. This expression is identical with equation (17) for the hydrogen atom deduced by Bohr. However, whereas derivation of equation (17) required on Bohr's part the arbitrary assumption of the quantization of the angular momentum, equation (26) follows directly from the mathematical requirements of the wave equation. Furthermore, the solution also indicates that for any given value of n there must be several values of the azimuthal quantum number such that $l = 0$, $1, 2 \cdots (n - 1)$, and that there is also a magnetic quantum number such that, for every value of l, $m = 0, \pm 1, \pm 2, \cdots \pm l$. Finally, the spin requirements can also be deduced from this theory. We have here, therefore, a theory that ties together all the various factors introduced on postulate and experiment and yields these as essential and integral requirements of the mathematical relations involved.

THE PAULI EXCLUSION PRINCIPLE

Nothing said thus far would preclude several electrons in an atom from occupying the same energy level, and having, therefore, four identical quantum numbers. However, study of spectra reveals that this is not possible, and this fact led Pauli to enunciate in 1923 his *exclusion principle*. According to this principle *no two electrons in an atom may have all four quantum numbers the same*. To exist in the same atom electrons may have three quantum numbers identical, but the fourth must be different. We shall see presently that this simple principle is of fundamental value and aids greatly in deducing the possible distribution of electrons in the atoms of various elements.

ELECTRON SHELLS AND SUBSHELLS

Before turning to the question of electron distribution in atoms, it is necessary to develop the concept of *shells and subshells*. Just as the energy levels of electrons in atoms may be considered to be divided into levels and sublevels, so may the electrons be considered to exist in groups and subgroups, referred to respectively as shells and subshells. All electrons possessing the same principal quantum number n are said to be present in the same shell. Again, all the electrons in a given shell which occupy the sublevels with the same l value are said to be present in the same subshell. Thus all the electrons for which $n = 1$ and $l = 0$ occupy not only the same shell, but the same subshell. Likewise all electrons for which $n = 2$ and $l = 1$ are present in the second shell and in the $l = 1$ subshell.

This concept finds its justification in the explanation of the origin of x-ray spectra. The ordinary line spectra of elements are due to electrons present in the outermost shell, i.e., the *optical electrons*. Because the optical electrons are most weakly bound to the nucleus, they are exicted more readily than electrons embedded deeper in the atom, and they yield, therefore, the more easily obtainable line spectra. On the other hand, the x-ray spectra are much more difficult to excite, as they involve much higher emitted energies, and hence x-rays must arise from electrons closer to the nucleus than the optical electrons. For these reasons the generally accepted theory of the origin of x-ray spectra is this. On bombardment of an atom by high-speed electrons, collisions occur between bombarding electrons and those in the atom. When the energy of the missile particles is great enough, these may dislodge electrons deep within the atom, leaving vacant spaces. To reoccupy the vacancies, electrons from higher levels will then pass into these, causing the emission of a spectrum. When this passage is from levels of $n = 2$ or higher into the $n = 1$ level, the result is the K-series of x-ray spectra. Again, when the jumps are from $n = 3$ levels or above into the $n = 2$ level, the emission is the L-series. Similarly, all transitions into the $n = 3$ level yield the M-series, those into the $n = 4$ level the N-series, etc., provided the atom contains enough electrons to yield all these series. When this is not the case, as with the lighter atoms, only the K-series, or the K- and part of the L-series are observed. It will be seen that this theory of the origin of x-ray spectra ascribes their appearance not to electron jumps from sublevel to sublevel, but to electron passage from one major level to another, i.e., from shell to shell. The particular sublevel in a shell from which an electron comes determines only the fine structure of the line, not its position. The latter is determined primarily by the change in the principal quantum number n.

With the aid of this theory the x-ray spectra of elements can readily be accounted for, and this constitutes, therefore, a confirmation of the concept of electron shells. By association with the series of spectra resulting from vacancies in various shells, it is customary to refer to the shell for which $n = 1$ as the K-shell, the one for which $n = 2$ as the L-shell, the one with $n = 3$ as the M-shell, etc.

THE PERIODIC TABLE AND ATOMIC STRUCTURE

If theories of atomic structure are to be of any value, they must be able to explain the differences in the chemical reactivity of various elements, and why the chemical and physical properties of elements repeat themselves in the manner represented by the periodic table. The periodicity of the elements definitely rules out mass as the determining factor in chemical reactivity, and hence the nuclei of atoms cannot possibly be responsible for chemical behavior. We must seek our explanation, therefore, in the configurational architecture of the external electrons in order to ascertain why elements act as they do. It is one of the crowning achievements of modern theories of atomic structure that they have been able to shed a great deal of light on this point and to account for the observed periodic repetition of chemical properties.

In passing from one element to another in the periodic table, the atomic number increases by one and so does the nuclear charge. To preserve the electroneutrality of the atoms, this progressive increase in nuclear charge must be accompanied by a simultaneous increase in the number of orbital electrons. Consequently, in passing from hydrogen with $Z = 1$ to fermium with $Z = 100$, the number of electrons about the nucleus must increase progressively by one from a single electron for hydrogen to 100 for fermium. As these electrons enter the outer structure of the atom, they must become arranged in shells and subshells, each containing the number of electrons commensurate with the number present and the number that may be crowded into each. This much about the electronic arrangement appears to be clear. But the problems which still remain are (a) how many electrons may be located in each shell and subshell, and (b) where does each successive electron go?

The first satisfactory suggestion about the number of electrons in various shells and their possible arrangement was advanced in 1921 independently by Bury and Bohr. These men proposed that the maximum number of electrons in each shell should be given by $2 n^2$, where n is the principal quantum number. This would give for the maximum number of electrons in successive shells 2, 8, 18, 32, and 50. Further, Bury and Bohr suggested that *there can be present no more than eight electrons in the outermost shell of an atom before the next shell is started*. In other words, in shells where more than eight electrons can be present, only eight of these enter, then a new shell is started, and the incompleted shell is left to be filled in later.

That the Bury-Bohr assignment of electrons to the various shells is correct can be proved with the aid of the Pauli exclusion principle and the rules given for the possible values of quantum numbers. For the K-shell $n = 1$, and hence the values which l, m, and s may have are $l = 0, m = 0,$ and $s = +\frac{1}{2}$ or $s = -\frac{1}{2}$. Since no two electrons may have the same four quantum numbers, the following are the only possibilities for four different quantum numbers in the K-shell:

$$n = 1 \qquad l = 0 \qquad m = 0 \qquad s = +\frac{1}{2}$$

$$n = 1 \qquad l = 0 \qquad m = 0 \qquad s = -\frac{1}{2}$$

This means that in the K-shell there is only one subshell, $l = 0$, in which only two electrons can be accommodated. On the other hand, for $n = 2$ we may have $l = 0$ and $l = 1, m = 0, m = -1,$ and $m = +1,$ and $s = \frac{1}{2}$ or $s = -\frac{1}{2}$. These possibilities lead to the following combinations of four different quantum numbers:

$$n = 2 \qquad l = 0 \qquad m = 0 \qquad s = +\frac{1}{2}$$

$$n = 2 \qquad l = 0 \qquad m = 0 \qquad s = -\frac{1}{2}$$

$$n = 2 \qquad l = 1 \qquad m = 0 \qquad s = +\frac{1}{2}$$

$$n = 2 \qquad l = 1 \qquad m = 0 \qquad s = -\frac{1}{2}$$

$$n = 2 \qquad l = 1 \qquad m = -1 \qquad s = +\frac{1}{2}$$

$$n = 2 \qquad l = 1 \qquad m = -1 \qquad s = -\frac{1}{2}$$

$$n = 2 \qquad l = 1 \qquad m = 1 \qquad s = +\frac{1}{2}$$

$$n = 2 \qquad l = 1 \qquad m = 1 \qquad s = -\frac{1}{2}$$

On this basis the L-shell should consist of eight electrons, with two of these in the $l = 0$ subshell, and six in the $l = 1$ subshell. In a like manner it can be shown that the M-shell can contain 18 electrons, with 2 of these in the $l = 0$ subshell, 6 in the $l = 1$ subshell, and 10 in the $l = 2$ subshell; the N-shell 32 electrons with the subshell distribution 2, 6, 10, and 14; while the O-shell has a possible maximum of 50 electrons. These numbers are exactly those predicted by Bohr and Bury.

ARRANGEMENT OF ELECTRONS IN ATOMS

The arrangement of electrons in atoms has been deduced from a combined use of the Pauli exclusion principle, the Bohr-Bury postulates, and spectroscopic study. In order to appreciate the significance of the results, reference must first be made to the periodic classification of the elements shown in Table 5. Here the elements are ordered according to chemical similarity in vertical *groups*, and horizontally into repetitive *periods*. The first period consists of only 2 elements, hydrogen and helium. The second and third, again, contain 8 elements each, with each period terminating with a rare gas, i.e., neon and argon. On the other hand, before the next rare gas, krypton, is reached in the fourth period 18 elements are traversed. Of these the 8 elements potassium, calcium, gallium, germanium, arsenic, selenium, bromine, and krypton behave more or less normally and exhibit fairly close similarity to preceding members of their own group, while the 10 elements starting with scandium and ending with zinc are somewhat more unusual in their behavior. The latter are generally referred to as the *transition elements*. In the fifth period the situation

TABLE 5

Periodic Arrangement of the Elements

Period	Group I	Group II	Group III	Group IV	Group V	Group VI	Group VII	Group VIII	Group O
1	1 H								2 He
2	3 Li	4 Be	5 B	6 C	7 N	8 O	9 F		10 Ne
3	11 Na	12 Mg	13 Al	14 Si	15 P	16 S	17 Cl		18 A
4	19 K	20 Ca	21 Sc	22 Ti	23 V	24 Cr	25 Mn	26 Fe 27 Co 28 Ni	
4	29 Cu	30 Zn	31 Ga	32 Ge	33 As	34 Se	35 Br		36 Kr
5	37 Rb	38 Sr	39 Y	40 Zr	41 Nb	42 Mo	43 Tc	44 Ru 45 Rh 46 Pd	
5	47 Ag	48 Cd	49 In	50 Sn	51 Sb	52 Te	53 I		54 Xe
6	55 Cs	56 Ba	57–71*	72 Hf	73 Ta	74 W	75 Re	76 Os 77 Ir 78 Pt	
6	79 Au	80 Hg	81 Tl	82 Pb	83 Bi	84 Po	85 At		86 Rn
7	87 Fr	88 Ra	89–†						

* Rare Earths: 57 La, 58 Ce, 59 Pr, 60 Nd, 61 Pm, 62 Sm, 63 Eu, 64 Gd, 65 Tb, 66 Dy, 67 Ho, 68 Er, 79 Tm, 70 Yb, 71 Lu.

† Actinide Series: 89 Ac, 90 Th, 91 Pa, 92 U, 93 Np, 94 Pu, 95 Am, 96 Cm, 97 Bk (berkelium), 98 Cf (californium), 99 E (einstein-ium), 100 Fm (fermium).

is exactly the same as in the fourth, the period consisting again of 18 elements, 8 of which are more or less "normal," while 10 elements, beginning with yttrium and ending with cadmium, are transition elements. However, when we come to the sixth period, we find that 32 elements are involved here. A study of these shows that they may be divided into three groups: (a) 8 more or less " normal" elements, cesium, barium, thallium, lead, bismuth, polonium, astatine, and radon; (b) 9 transition elements, lanthanum, hafnium, tantalum, tungsten, rhenium, osmium, iridium, platinum, and gold; and (c) the rare earths listed at the bottom of the table. The latter elements exhibit such striking similarity in chemical properties that the only way to accommodate them in the table is to list all of them as a group in the space between barium and hafnium. Finally, the seventh period contains francium, radium, and the elements of the actinide series, among which are included all the transuranium elements discovered thus far.

The explanation of the above-described behavior lies in the arrangement of the electrons shown in Table 6. In this table the common practice is followed of designating the major shells by the letters K, L, M, etc., corresponding to $n = 1$, 2, 3, and so on, and the subshells by symbols such as $1s$, $2p$, $3d$, $4f$, etc. In the latter the numerals represent the number of the major shell, while the letters, s, p, d, and f stand for $l = 0$, 1, 2, and 3 respectively. Starting with hydrogen, we see that there is only one electron present in the K-shell. In helium a second electron is added to this shell; and since only two electrons can be present in any energy level with $n = 1$, this shell becomes completely occupied and closed with this element. The next element, lithium, must start, therefore, a new shell, which is the L-level, and electrons in the succeeding elements continue to occupy this shell until it also becomes completely filled when neon is reached. The only thing the added electron in sodium can do now is to start the M-shell, and the following elements up to argon continue the filling-in process in normal sequence until the first two subshells of the M-level are occupied.

But, when we come to potassium, the electron instead of filling in the $3d$ level starts a new shell. This behavior is in line with the Bohr-Bury theory that no external shell can contain more than eight electrons. Calcium follows potassium, but scandium, instead of continuing the process, starts to fill in the $3d$ subshell. This entrance of electrons into an inner shell continues through gallium until this subshell becomes completely occupied. Once this happens the tendency initiated by potassium is continued, and electrons again enter the outer shell in sequence until eight are present.

In the electron behavior just described lies the difference between the "normal" and the transition elements. Whereas in the "normal" ele-

TABLE 6

ARRANGEMENT OF ELECTRONS IN VARIOUS ELEMENTS

Shell		K	L		M			N				O				P				Q	
Subshell		1s	2s	2p	3s	3p	3d	4s	4p	4d	4f	5s	5p	5d	5f	6s	6p	6d	6f	7s	7p
At. No.	Elem.																				
1	H	1																			
2	He	2																			
3	Li	2	1																		
4	Be	2	2																		
5	B	2	2	1																	
6	C	2	2	2																	
7	N	2	2	3																	
8	O	2	2	4																	
9	F	2	2	5																	
10	Ne	2	2	6																	
11	Na	2	2	6	1																
12	Mg	2	2	6	2																
13	Al	2	2	6	2	1															
14	Si	2	2	6	2	2															
15	P	2	2	6	2	3															
16	S	2	2	6	2	4															
17	Cl	2	2	6	2	5															
18	A	2	2	6	2	6															
19	K	2	2	6	2	6		1													
20	Ca	2	2	6	2	6		2													
21	Sc	2	2	6	2	6	1	2													
22	Ti	2	2	6	2	6	2	2													
23	V	2	2	6	2	6	3	2													
24	Cr	2	2	6	2	6	5	1													
25	Mn	2	2	6	2	6	5	2													
26	Fe	2	2	6	2	6	6	2													
27	Co	2	2	6	2	6	7	2													
28	Ni	2	2	6	2	6	8	2													
29	Cu	2	2	6	2	6	10	1													
30	Zn	2	2	6	2	6	10	2													
31	Ga	2	2	6	2	6	10	2	1												
32	Ge	2	2	6	2	6	10	2	2												
33	As	2	2	6	2	6	10	2	3												
34	Se	2	2	6	2	6	10	2	4												
35	Br	2	2	6	2	6	10	2	5												
36	Kr	2	2	6	2	6	10	2	6												

TABLE 6 (*Continued*)

Shell		K	L		M			N				O				P				Q	
Subshell		1s	2s	2p	3s	3p	3d	4s	4p	4d	4f	5s	5p	5d	5f	6s	6p	6d	6f	7s	7p
At. No.	Elem.																				
37	Rb	2	2	6	2	6	10	2	6			1									
38	Sr	2	2	6	2	6	10	2	6			2									
39	Y	2	2	6	2	6	10	2	6	1		2									
40	Zr	2	2	6	2	6	10	2	6	2		2									
41	Cb	2	2	6	2	6	10	2	6	4		1									
42	Mo	2	2	6	2	6	10	2	6	5		1									
43	Tc	2	2	6	2	6	10	2	6	6		1									
44	Ru	2	2	6	2	6	10	2	6	7		1									
45	Rh	2	2	6	2	6	10	2	6	8		1									
46	Pd	2	2	6	2	6	10	2	6	10											
47	Ag	2	2	6	2	6	10	2	6	10		1									
48	Cd	2	2	6	2	6	10	2	6	10		2									
49	In	2	2	6	2	6	10	2	6	10		2	1								
50	Sn	2	2	6	2	6	10	2	6	10		2	2								
51	Sb	2	2	6	2	6	10	2	6	10		2	3								
52	Te	2	2	6	2	6	10	2	6	10		2	4								
53	I	2	2	6	2	6	10	2	6	10		2	5								
54	Xe	2	2	6	2	6	10	2	6	10		2	6								
55	Cs	2	2	6	2	6	10	2	6	10		2	6			1					
56	Ba	2	2	6	2	6	10	2	6	10		2	6			2					
57	La	2	2	6	2	6	10	2	6	10		2	6	1		2					
58	Ce	2	2	6	2	6	10	2	6	10	2	2	6			2					
59	Pr	2	2	6	2	6	10	2	6	10	3	2	6			2					
60	Nd	2	2	6	2	6	10	2	6	10	4	2	6			2					
61	Il	2	2	6	2	6	10	2	6	10	5	2	6			2					
62	Sm	2	2	6	2	6	10	2	6	10	6	2	6			2					
63	Eu	2	2	6	2	6	10	2	6	10	7	2	6			2					
64	Gd	2	2	6	2	6	10	2	6	10	7	2	6	1		2					
65	Tb	2	2	6	2	6	10	2	6	10	8	2	6	1		2					
66	Dy	2	2	6	2	6	10	2	6	10	9	2	6	1		2					
67	Ho	2	2	6	2	6	10	2	6	10	10	2	6	1		2					
68	Er	2	2	6	2	6	10	2	6	10	11	2	6	1		2					
69	Tm	2	2	6	2	6	10	2	6	10	12	2	6	1		2					
70	Yb	2	2	6	2	6	10	2	6	10	13	2	6	1		2					
71	Lu	2	2	6	2	6	10	2	6	10	14	2	6	1		2					
72	Hf	2	2	6	2	6	10	2	6	10	14	2	6	2		2					
73	Ta	2	2	6	2	6	10	2	6	10	14	2	6	3		2					
74	W	2	2	6	2	6	10	2	6	10	14	2	6	4		2					
75	Re	2	2	6	2	6	10	2	6	10	14	2	6	5		2					
76	Os	2	2	6	2	6	10	2	6	10	14	2	6	6		2					
77	Ir	2	2	6	2	6	10	2	6	10	14	2	6	9							

TABLE 6 (*Continued*)

Shell	K	L		M			N				O				P				Q	
Subshell	1s	2s	2p	3s	3p	3d	4s	4p	4d	4f	5s	5p	5d	5f	6s	6p	6d	6f	7s	7p
At. No. / Elem.																				
78 Pt	2	2	6	2	6	10	2	6	10	14	2	6	9		1					
79 Au	2	2	6	2	6	10	2	6	10	14	2	6	10		1					
80 Hg	2	2	6	2	6	10	2	6	10	14	2	6	10		2					
81 Tl	2	2	6	2	6	10	2	6	10	14	2	6	10		2	1				
82 Pb	2	2	6	2	6	10	2	6	10	14	2	6	10		2	2				
83 Bi	2	2	6	2	6	10	2	6	10	14	2	6	10		2	3				
84 Po	2	2	6	2	6	10	2	6	10	14	2	6	10		2	4				
85 At	2	2	6	2	6	10	2	6	10	14	2	6	10		2	5				
86 Rn	2	2	6	2	6	10	2	6	10	14	2	6	10		2	6				
87 Fr	2	2	6	2	6	10	2	6	10	14	2	6	10		2	6			1	
88 Ra	2	2	6	2	6	10	2	6	10	14	2	6	10		2	6			2	
89 Ac	2	2	6	2	6	10	2	6	10	14	2	6	10		2	6	1		2	
90 Th	2	2	6	2	6	10	2	6	10	14	2	6	10		2	6	2		2	
91 Pa	2	2	6	2	6	10	2	6	10	14	2	6	10		2	6	3		2	
92 U	2	2	6	2	6	10	2	6	10	14	2	6	10		2	6	4		2	
93 Np	2	2	6	2	6	10	2	6	10	14	2	6	10	5	2	6			2	
94 Pu	2	2	6	2	6	10	2	6	10	14	2	6	10	5	2	6	1		2	
95 Am	2	2	6	2	6	10	2	6	10	14	2	6	10	6	2	6	1		2	
96 Cm	2	2	6	2	6	10	2	6	10	14	2	6	10	7	2	6	1		2	
97 Bk	2	2	6	2	6	10	2	6	10	14	2	6	10	8	2	6	1		2	
98 Cf	2	2	6	2	6	10	2	6	10	14	2	6	10	9	2	6	1		2	
99 E	2	2	6	2	6	10	2	6	10	14	2	6	10	10	2	6	1		2	
100 Fm	2	2	6	2	6	10	2	6	10	14	2	6	10	11	2	6	1		2	

ments electrons are added in sequence to the outermost electronic shell, in the transition elements the outermost shell remains essentially stationary, while succeeding electrons enter the shell immediately below the surface. Because of the filling-in process the length of the period is extended. Again, since the distribution of electrons in the outer shell is primarily responsible for the chemical properties of elements, we may anticipate that "normal" elements will act differently from the transition elements, and such is in fact the case.

The situation in the fourth period starting with rubidium and ending with xenon is essentially the same as in the third period. Like potassium, rubidium initiates a new shell, and strontium follows suit. But, starting with yttrium and continuing through cadmium, succeeding electrons enter the 4d level until it is filled, then the building up of the 5p subshell is continued to xenon. Here again the transition elements arise from entrance of electrons into the shell below the surface.

The sixth period starts just like the preceding two, with cesium and barium entering the 6s subshell and lanthanum the 5d sublevel. However, the electrons in cerium, instead of following lanthanum, begin to fill in the unoccupied 4f sublevel. Once initiated, this filling in of the second shell from the surface persists until it is terminated with lutecium. Hafnium continues then the process started by lanthanum, and when this is ended with mercury, thallium and the succeeding elements proceed to build up the P-shell. Reference to Table 5 will show that the elements which so solicitously fill the gap in the N-shell are exactly the ones for which no room could be found in the periodic classification, namely, the rare earths. Since in these elements the external electronic configuration remains unchanged from element to element, they all exhibit great similarity of chemical properties and act as if they were a single element in the periodic sequence.

Finally, in the seventh period a new shell is started into which enter the electrons for francium and radium. With actinium begins a new group of elements, the actinide series, where the succeeding electrons start first to fill the 6d level, and then change their mind and enter the open 5f shell.

Thus far the emphasis has been on the reason for the periods and their length. However, the similarity of chemical properties within groups also follows from the table. Inspection of the *outermost* electronic configurations of hydrogen, lithium, sodium, potassium, rubidium, cesium, and francium shows that they are the same, and consist of a single electron in a new shell. Again, the outer electronic configurations of the elements in group II involve two electrons, group III three electrons, etc. The electronic configuration of the rare gases is always such as to necessitate the inception of a new shell by a succeeding element. This fact indicates that a rare gas configuration must be a highly stable arrangement of electrons and accounts for the reluctance these elements exhibit to enter combination with other atoms.

THE ATOMIC NUCLEUS

This description of the arrangement of orbital electrons in the various atoms concludes the discussion of the external part of the atom. The question which requires attention now is the nature of the nucleus. The information presented thus far indicates that the nucleus consists of protons in number equal to the atomic number of the element, and of neutrons in number equal to the difference between the atomic mass A and the nuclear charge Z, i.e., $(A - Z)$. No further insight can be obtained from pursuing mass spectrographic or spectroscopic studies, since these leave the nuclei unaffected. Neither can ordinary chemical investigation be of help, for chemical reactivity is associated only with the external electrons. As a matter of fact, the only phenomenon which does involve changes in the atomic nucleus is *radioactivity*, both natural and artificial, so we shall turn to a brief exposition of this subject.

NATURAL RADIOACTIVITY

In 1895 Henri Becquerel discovered that uranium salts emit radiation which can cause fogging of photographic plates. Subsequently it was shown that this radiation can ionize air, is emitted from the element as well as its salts, and is not at all affected by temperature or the source of the uranium. This spontaneous emission of radiation by an element is called *radioactivity*, while the elements which exhibit this behavior are said to be *radioactive*.

In 1898 Marie and Pierre Curie found that the mineral pitchblende (mainly U_3O_8) exhibited radioactivity more promounced than uranium itself. This suggested the presence of elements more active than uranium, and Madame Curie actually succeeded in isolating from this mineral two new radioactive elements, polonium and radium. At about the same time thorium and actinium were also shown to be radioactive. Since that time over 30 elements have been proved to be naturally radioactive, and many others have been induced to become radioactive by artificial means to be described later.

The rays emitted by radioactive elements can be detected and measured by their ability to ionize gases. Another means is to employ a Wilson cloud chamber. C. T. R. Wilson found that, when any ionizing particle passes through supersaturated water vapor, droplets of water tend to condense along the path of motion. To take advantage of this fact Wilson designed the apparatus that bears his name. This apparatus consists of a chamber filled with dust-free air saturated with water vapor, and fitted with a piston. As the particles enter through a window the air is made to expand, the temperature drops, and the vapor becomes supersaturated. As a result a fog track deposits along the path of the particles which can be photographed. From such fog tracks the velocity and energy of the particles can be ascertained.

NATURE OF RADIOACTIVE EMISSION

The rays emitted by radioactive elements and their salts have been shown to consist of three types of radiation, α, β, and γ rays. Study of the α rays in a magnetic field has revealed that these consist of material particles possessing a mass four times and a positive charge twice that of the proton. This would make the charge and mass of the α particles identical with that of the helium nucleus, and this identity has actually been established. These particles have the ability to ionize gases and penetrate matter, as Rutherford showed in his scattering experiments. The initial velocity of the α particles on emisson is very high, ranging from 1–2 $\times$ 10^9 cm sec^{-1} as against 3 $\times$ 10^{10} cm sec^{-1} for the velocity of light.

β rays have also been shown to consist of particles, but with a much lower mass and a negative charge. Their e/m ratio is the same as that of the electron, and this, in fact, is what they are, electrons. These rays again can ionize gases, affect a photographic plate, and penetrate matter. But whereas their penetrating power is about 100 times that of α particles, their ionizing power is only about $\frac{1}{100}$ as great because of their much lower mass. Finally, the velocity of the emitted electrons depends on their source and is very large, approaching in some instances very close to the velocity of light.

γ rays are quite different from either the α or β rays. They are totally unaffected by electric and magnetic fields and behave in every respect as electromagnetic radiation of the same nature as x rays. Measurements of their wave length indicate that they are of the order of 10^{-8}–10^{-11} cm in length and hence are shorter than x radiation. Like the other rays they affect photographic plates, ionize gases, and penetrate matter. In penetrating power they are about 10 to 100 times as effective as β rays, but in ionizing power they are proportionately weaker.

THEORY OF RADIOACTIVE DISINTEGRATION

The fact that radioactive elements emit α particles indicates that the portion of the atom involved in the emission must be the *nucleus*. To account for this nuclear radiation Rutherford and Soddy advanced in 1903 their theory of *radioactive disintegration*. Rutherford and Soddy proposed that the nuclei of radioactive elements are unstable, and decompose spontaneously by emission of an α or β particle to form a *new element* of different chemical and physical properties. Thus, when uranium-I with $A = 238$ and $Z = 92$ emits an α particle to yield uranium-X_1, the mass should decrease by four units to $A = 234$, and the nuclear charge by two units to $Z = 90$. Since the nuclear charge has decreased, two external electrons which are no longer necessary will also be lost, and we obtain a new element of $Z = 90$ and $A = 234$, which is an isotope of thorium. Again, when uranium-X_1 emits a β particle the nuclear mass remains unchanged, but the nuclear charge is increased to $Z = 91$. The new product, uranium-X_2, has now a mass of 234 and an atomic number of 91 and hence is an isotope of protactinium. This idea, that as a result of radioactive spontaneous disintegration new elements are formed, has been amply verified, and is a well-established principle in the field of radioactivity.

From the examples cited it may be observed that the product of a radioactive decay may itself be radioactive and undergo further decomposition. This is generally the case. For example, uranium-I yields a whole series of consecutive disintegration products until eventually radium-G, a stable isotope of lead, is reached. Analogously thorium goes through a sequence of disintegrations until the stable thorium-D, again an isotope of lead, is attained. Each of the intermediate steps involves the emission of either an α or a β particle, and only rarely both. The γ radiation arises from energy rearrangements within the nucleus after an α or β particle ejection. When the rearrangement leads to a lower potential energy, the excess is evolved as a quantum of energy of the frequency of the γ ray. Not all nuclear transformations are accompanied by emission of γ rays.

The transformation brought about by the emission of an α or β particle from the nucleus is summarized in the Fajans-Soddy-Russell *displacement law*. This law states that whenever a parent nucleus emits an α particle its atomic number is decreased by *two units*, and the new element is shifted two positions *to the left* in the periodic table from that of the parent. On the other hand, when the parent nucleus emits a β particle, the atomic number is increased by *one*, and hence the product is shifted one place *to the right* in the periodic table. This law is merely an epitome of the changes described in the above examples.

RATE OF RADIOACTIVE DECAY

Radioactive disintegrations proceed at rates which cannot be modified by any known chemical or physical means. For a given element this rate at any instant of time is proportional only to the number N of the nuclei present, namely,

$$-\frac{dN}{dt} = kN \tag{27}$$

where k is a rate constant characteristic of the element. Integration of equation (27) between the limits $N = N_0$ at $t = 0$, and $N = N$ at $t = t$, yields

$$t = \frac{1}{k} \ln \frac{N_0}{N} \tag{28}$$

from which the half-life period, $t_{1/2}$, of the radioactive element follows as

$$t_{1/2} = \frac{1}{k} \ln \frac{N_0}{(N_0/2)}$$

$$= \frac{\ln 2}{k} \tag{29}$$

Equation (29) shows that the time necessary for one-half of a quantity of radioactive substance to be disintegrated is a constant independent of the initial amount present and is characteristic only of the element in question. For the naturally radioactive elements $t_{1/2}$ may range from 10^{-11} sec to 1.3×10^{10} years.

RADIOACTIVE SERIES

Naturally radioactive elements belong to one of three radioactive series in which the parent elements are either uranium, thorium, or protactinium, and in which the end products of final disintegration are all isotopes of lead. These series bear in each instance the name of the parent element. Many of the radioactive elements in any given series are isotopes of each other, as well as of members of other series.

THE POSITRON

The occurrence of the electron suggests that there may be present in matter also a corresponding positive particle of low mass, namely, a *positron*. However, even though Dirac showed theoretically in 1928 that positrons should exist, all attempts to find such a particle proved fruitless until 1932. In that year, while studying cosmic rays, Carl Anderson detected in the Wilson cloud chamber a fog track which could only be produced by a positively charged particle of very low mass. Anderson ascribed this track to the passage of a positron. This conclusion was confirmed quickly by other workers, and the existence of positrons was thus definitely established.

The positron has been shown to have a mass identical with that of the electron, and a charge equal in magnitude but opposite in sign. However, whereas the electron is stable, the positron is very short-lived. On release from a nucleus a positron loses its kinetic energy very rapidly, in 10^{-10} sec or so, and combines then with an electron to cause the annihilation of both particles. To compensate for the destroyed mass 2 quanta of x radiation are formed whose total energy is equal to the mass destroyed in accordance with the Einstein relation $E = mc^2$.

Various methods are available at present for the production of positrons. When beryllium, magnesium, or aluminum are bombarded by α particles, these elements become *artificially radioactive* and emit positrons. In each instance the process involves two consecutive *nuclear* reactions, the first of which is the formation of an artificially radioactive element, the second the emission of the positron. For aluminum these reactions are:

$$_{13}Al^{27} + {}_2\alpha^4 \longrightarrow {}_{15}P^{30} + {}_0n^1 \qquad (30a)$$
$$_{15}P^{30} \longrightarrow {}_{14}Si^{30} + e^+ \qquad (30b)$$

In these equations the superscripts give the nuclear masses, the subscripts the nuclear charges. e^+ is the symbol for the positron while n is the symbol for the neutron. Thus equation (30a) states that aluminum, with mass 27 and nuclear charge 13, reacts with an α particle, mass 4 and atomic number 2, to form phosphorus, of mass 30 and charge 15, and a neutron of unit mass and zero charge. Again, equation (30b) states that the phosphorus is radioactive and decomposes to yield a positron and silicon of mass 30 and atomic number 14.

Similar reactions result also from bombardment of nitrogen, fluorine, sodium, phosphorus, and potassium with α particles, from the bombardment of various elements with protons or deuterons, and from the interaction of lead with γ rays.

GENERATION OF NEUTRONS

Equation (30a) shows a means of producing neutrons, namely, by bombardment of a suitable metal with α particles. The reaction given involves the capture of an α particle by the aluminum nucleus with the resultant formation of phosphorus and the emission of a neutron. Other important methods of neutron generation are the bombardment of deuterium and lithium atoms with deuterons (d),

$$_1D^2 + {}_1d^2 \longrightarrow {}_2He^3 + {}_0n^1 \qquad (31)$$
$$_3Li^7 + {}_1d^2 \longrightarrow {}_4Be^8 + {}_0n^1 \qquad (32)$$

and the interaction of deuterium with γ radiation,

$$_1D^2 + \gamma \text{ rays} \longrightarrow {}_1H^1 + {}_0n^1 \qquad (33)$$

OTHER NUCLEAR PARTICLES

When a mass-energy balance is made for a radioactive disintegration, and the masses of all the particles as well as energies involved are considered, it is found that the law of conservation of mass-energy is frequently violated. To account for this fact, Pauli suggested in 1927 the existence of a particle, called the *neutrino*, whose charge is zero and whose mass is variable and less than that of the electron. Although considerable circumstantial evidence has been accumulated on the existence of such particles, they could not be detected directly because of their very low mass and no charge. However, Allen and Rodeback obtained some results in 1952 which point directly to the existence of free neutrino particles.

In 1935, H. Yukawa predicted the existence of nuclear particles with a mass intermediate between that of the electron and the proton. Since then two kinds of such particles, called *mesons*, have been found in both cosmic rays and in the laboratory. One variety, the π meson, has been shown to have a mass 273 times that of the electron and a charge which may be positive, negative, or zero. The second kind, called the μ meson, carries a positive or negative charge and has a mass 206 times that of the electron.

Finally, in 1955 Segre' and co-workers at the University of California announced the discovery of the *anti-proton*, a particle with the mass of the proton but with a negative charge.

The discovery of these particles complicates further an already complex situation. We have seen that the nucleus can be considered to be composed of protons and neutrons. At the same time the nucleus can yield also α particles, electrons, positrons, neutrinos, mesons, and anti-protons. How all these nuclear particles arise is unknown, as no theory has as yet been developed which can account satisfactorily for the structure of the atomic nucleus and the forces which bind together its constituents.

TRANSMUTATION OF ELEMENTS

In the preceding discussion various examples were given of the transmutation of one element into another. Until about 1919 the only instances of such transformations were the natural radioactive disintegrations in which a more complex element changed into simpler elements by emission of either α or β particles. All these processes were spontaneous and could not be controlled in any known manner. However, since 1919 various means have been developed by which hundreds of transmutations of elements have been brought about *artificially*. These all entail the bombardment of elements with relatively high-speed atomic particles such as α rays, neutrons, protons, deuterons, and electrons as the transmuting projectiles. For certain processes high-energy γ rays are also suitable. Until relatively recently the only sources of such high-speed, and therefore high-energy, missiles were the α and β particles emitted by naturally radioactive elements. This is no longer true. At present apparatus is available, such as powerful transformers, electrostatic generators, high voltage discharge tubes, betatrons, and the cyclotron developed by Lawrence at the University of California, by means of which charged particles can be formed and accelerated to terrific velocities. Another powerful source of missiles is the nuclear reactor or pile. The neutrons and other particles generated in such piles are very effective in accomplishing the transmutations of various elements.

ARTIFICIAL RADIOACTIVITY

In 1934 I. and F. Joliot discovered that some products of nuclear reactions are unstable and tend to change to more stable nuclei by *spontaneous* positron emission. Since that time many such elements have been observed, and it has been found that the emissions may involve not only positrons, but also electrons and γ radiation. Since this type of radioactivity does not arise spontaneously but must be brought about by preliminary appropriate bombardment, the phenomenon is referred to as *artificial or induced radioactivity*. In each instance the elements exhibiting induced radioactivity are unstable isotopes of the known elements. They do not appear among the stable isotopes because their life period is usually short, and hence it is hardly to be expected that they will be found in nature.

TABLE 7

SOME ARTIFICIALLY RADIOACTIVE ELEMENTS

Element	Method of Production*	Half-Life Period	Emitted Radiation†
$_1H^3$	$_1D^2 + _1d^2$	12 years	e
$_2He^6$	$_4Be^9 + _0n^1$	0.87 sec	e
$_5B^{12}$	$_5B^{11} + _1d^2$	0.022 sec	e
$_6C^{11}$	$_5B^{10} + _1d^2$	20.5 min	e^+
$_6C^{14}$	$_6C^{13} + _1d^2$	6000 years	e
$_7N^{13}$	$_6C^{12} + _1p^1$	10.1 min	e^+
$_8O^{15}$	$_7N^{14} + _1d^2$	2.1 min	e^+
$_{11}Na^{24}$	$_{11}Na^{23} + _1d^2$	14.8 hours	e
$_{15}P^{30}$	$_{13}Al^{27} + _2\alpha^4$	2.55 min	e^+
$_{18}A^{41}$	$_{18}A^{40} + _0n^1$	110 min	e
$_{19}K^{38}$	$_{19}K^{39} + _0n^1$	7.5 min	e^+
$_{35}Br^{80}$	$_{35}Br^{79} + _0n^1$	18 min	e
$_{53}I^{124}$	$_{51}Sb^{121} + _2\alpha^4$	4.0 days	e^+
$_{79}Au^{198}$	$_{79}Au^{197} + _0n^1$	2.7 days	e

* p = proton; d = deuteron; α = α particle.
† e = electron; e^+ = positron.

Artificially radioactive elements behave very much like those which are naturally radioactive. They disintegrate in each instance according to the same rate law, equation (27), and exhibit thus constant half-life periods characteristic of the element in question. Further, although some artificially radioactive elements may be produced by several different methods, once formed each element decomposes at the same rate and has thus the same life period. There is, however, one respect in which the two do differ. Whereas natural radioactivity is confined only to the very massive nuclei, artificial radioactivity can be induced in light nuclei as well. Thus not only Bi^{210}, Pb^{209}, Pb^{205}, Tl^{206}, and Au^{198} are artificially radioactive, but also such light nuclei as H^3, He^6, Be^7, and C^{10}.

In Table 7 are given some examples of artificially radioactive elements, the methods by which they are produced, their half-life periods, and the nature of the emitted radiation.

NUCLEAR FISSION

For the nuclear reactions described above the change in mass produced by bombardment of a nucleus is always small. In each case the nucleus either increases in mass by capture of a particle or loses some mass by emission of a particle, but never does it rupture to yield fragments of appreciably smaller masses. However, in 1934 Enrico Fermi discovered that uranium when bombarded with neutrons yielded electrons and some strange products of decay. In 1939 Hahn and Strassmann showed that what happens here is a *rupture* of the uranium nucleus to form fragments which have a mass and atomic number considerably lower than that of uranium. Thus they showed that two of the major fragments resulting from uranium ($Z = 92$) fission were barium ($Z = 56$) and lanthanum ($Z = 57$). This process is, therefore, not a relatively minor nuclear transformation, but a drastic neutron bombardment initiated smashing of a nucleus into considerably smaller fragments.

Further research has established that of the various uranium isotopes the one primarily responsible for the fission is U^{235}. Accompanying the breakup of this nucleus is the emission of a tremendous amount of energy which is associated with the various fragments. Measurements indicate that the total energy thus released is as high as 4×10^{12} cal per gram atom ruptured. The liberation of such high energies immediately raised the prospect of the utilization of atomic energy as a source of power, a long and cherished hope. But the realization of this hope was faced with a difficulty. Ordinary uranium consists of 99.28 per cent U^{238}, 0.71 per cent U^{235}, and about 0.01 per cent U^{234}. To obtain from this isotopic mixture the desired U^{235}, methods of separation were required which could yield appreciable quantities of this isotope. Such methods have been developed, and they are at present under the control of the United States Atomic Energy Commission.

In the meantime it was found that U^{238} could also be converted into fissionable materials. When U^{238} is bombarded with neutrons, the following series of reactions sets in

$$_{92}U^{238} + _{0}n^{1} \longrightarrow _{92}U^{239} \longrightarrow _{93}Np^{239} + e$$
$$_{93}Np^{239} \longrightarrow _{94}Pu^{239} + e$$

i.e., the U^{238} on capture of a neutron is transformed into U^{239}, which is radioactive, and passes over with emission of an electron into the transuranic element neptunium. The latter, in turn, is also radioactive, and emits an electron to form plutonium of atomic number 94. Plutonium like U^{235} undergoes fission and is apparently the substance employed in the atomic bomb.

It is of interest to point out that to date eight transuranium elements have been prepared by such means as indicated above. These are neptunium (93), plutonium (94), americium (95), curium (96), berkelium (97), californium (98), einsteinium (99), and fermium (100).

NUCLEAR FUSION

The converse of nuclear fission is *nuclear fusion*. From the calculation given on p. 664 it is evident that tremendous quantities of energy can be obtained by formation of heavier nuclei from those of light elements such as hydrogen, deuterium, and helium, i.e., by the fusion of lighter nuclei into heavier ones. Such fusion processes are responsible for the radiant energy of the sun and for the energy released by the hydrogen bomb.

APPLICATIONS

Many of the isotopes and nuclear particles described in this chapter find extensive application in the fields of physics, chemistry, biology, and medicine. We have already seen how α particles, protons, neutrons, and deutrons can serve as projectiles for the transmutation of elements, for the production of artificial radioactivity, and for nuclear fission. γ rays are employed in medicine for the treatment of cancer as well as in nuclear studies. In the former application radon resulting from radium decomposition is collected, compressed, and sealed into tiny ampoules which are then used to treat the infected areas.

Radioactive elements, both natural and artificial, have been employed to determine the solubility of difficultly soluble salts and to estimate the surface area of adsorbents. Both of these applications depend on the fact that a radioactive element added to the same stable element will persist in a definite ratio irrespective of the state the element may be in. Consequently, when, say, a trace of radioactive lead is added to a solution of ordinary lead, and the lead is precipitated as either the sulfate or chromate, a determination of the radioactivity of the filtrate readily yields the concentration of lead still dissolved. Similarly, from the activity of a material adsorbed from a mixture of stable and radioactive isotopes it is possible to estimate the extent of adsorption, the number of adsorbed molecules, and the area covered by these.

Isotopes, stable and radioactive, have been used to trace the course of chemical and physiological reactions. Used in this manner these substances are called *isotopic tracers*. Deuterium, and the isotopes of carbon, oxygen, and nitrogen, have been used to elucidate the mechanism of reactions and to follow the course these elements take in passing through an animal body. In the first instance the rates of reactions with the ordinary isotopic species are measured, then the heavier or lighter isotopes are incorporated, and the rates are measured again. From such data it is frequently possible to infer the path followed by the reaction, and hence the mechanism. In physiologic work the uncommon isotopes are incorporated in various foods, as D and O in water or the carbohydrates, N in proteins, C in carbohydrates or fats, fed to animals, and the concentration of these in various organs estimated. From the accumulation of any of these tracers in an organ it is possible to decide just where each food goes. For these purposes radioactive isotopes are also of value, for they permit the tracing of a food by the emission intensity. In this manner have been used radioactive phosphorus and iodine.

Another interesting application of isotopes is in *exchange reactions*. When a compound containing hydroxyl or carboxyl groups is placed in heavy water, it is found that dueterium exchanges itself for ordinary hydrogen atoms in these compounds. This fact indicates that the hydrogen atoms in these compounds are not static, but ionize to be replaced by the more plentiful deuterium atoms. Similar exchange has been found in the hydrogens of acetylene, acetone, and chloroform, but not in some of the paraffin hydrocarbons. In like manner various halogens have been found to exchange with their ions in solution, indicating a mobile equilibrium in action, but not with alkyl halides. A particularly interesting fact revealed by exchange studies is that sulfur atoms in sulfates do not exchange while those in thiosulfates do, and that, whereas no exchange can take place between manganous and permanganate ions, interchange does occur rapidly between manganous and manganic ions.

REFERENCES FOR FURTHER READING

1. F. W. Aston, *Mass Spectra and Isotopes*, Edward Arnold & Co., London, 1942.
2. Calvin *et al.*, *Isotopic Carbon*, John Wiley & Sons, Inc., New York, 1949.
3. Friedlander and Kennedy, *Introduction to Radiochemistry*, John Wiley & Sons, Inc., New York, 1949.
4. G. Herzberg, *Atomic Spectra and Atomic Structure*, Dover Publications, New York, 1944.
5. Pollard and Davidson, *Applied Nuclear Physics*, John Wiley & Sons, Inc., New York, 1951.

6. Schweitzer and Whitney, *Radioactive Tracer Techniques*, D. Van Nostrand Company, Inc., New York, 1949.
7. R. S. Shankland, *Atomic and Nuclear Physics*, The Macmillan Company, New York, 1955.
8. Wahl and Bonner, *Radioactivity Applied to Chemistry*, John Wiley & Sons, Inc., New York, 1951.
9. Whitehouse and Putnam, *Radioactive Isotopes*, Oxford University Press, London, 1953.
10. R. R. Williams, *Principles of Nuclear Chemistry*, D. Van Nostrand Company, Inc., New York, 1950.

PROBLEMS

1. One volume of hydrogen gas combines with one volume of chlorine gas to give two volumes of hydrogen chloride gas. Show that the assumption that hydrogen and chlorine are diatomic is in accord with the observed facts, while the assumption that these gases are monatomic or triatomic would be contradictory.

2. A water droplet of unit density and radius 10^{-4} cm captures three unit charges of electricity. What electric field in volts cm^{-1} will be required to keep the drop at rest? One electrostatic unit of potential is equal to 300 volts. If the distance between the parallel charged plates is 2.40 cm, what must be the potential difference across the plates?   *Ans.* 855 volts cm^{-1}; 2052 volts.

3. Using Stokes's law, find the radius and mass of a water droplet which falls freely in air with a velocity of 0.5 cm sec^{-1}. The viscosity coefficient of air is 0.00018 cgs. unit.   *Ans.* 6.43×10^{-4} cm; 1.11×10^{-9} g.

4. Calculate the mass in grams of an NH_3 molecule.

5. What will be the mass of an electron moving with (a) a velocity of 5×10^9 cm sec^{-1} and (b) 2.9×10^{10} cm sec^{-1}?

6. (a) What is the mass in grams of the proton at rest? (b) What will be its mass when it is moving with a velocity of 2.0×10^{10} cm sec^{-1}.

7. Silver possesses two stable isotopes whose atomic weights on the physical scale are 106.945 and 108.944. Determine the abundance of each of these isotopes in ordinary silver.   *Ans.* 51.78 and 48.22%.

8. Magnesium possesses three stable isotopes. For one of these the atomic weight is 23.9925 while the abundance is 78.60%. For the second the atomic weight is 24.9938 while the abundance is 10.11%. The abundance of the third is 11.29%. Find the atomic weight of the third isotope.

9. Calculate the energy change accompanying the transformation of two atoms of H to an atom of D.   *Ans.* 3.29×10^{10} cal/g atom.

10. The atomic weight on the physical scale of one of the isotopes of Sn is 121.945. (a) Calculate its packing fraction. (b) Find how much energy in calories per gram atom would be evolved or absorbed in the formation of this isotope from hydrogen atoms.

11. Calculate and compare the molar volumes in cc of H_2O and D_2O at 25° C.

12. What is the number of neutrons and protons in an atom of gold of atomic mass 197?

13. The gram atomic mass of one of the isotopes of Pt is 194.039. Calculate the masses of the electrons and of the nuclei in one gram atomic weight of this isotope.

14. Calculate the amount of energy in calories which would be emitted per second at $2000°$ K from a perfect black body 1 sq mm in area.   *Ans.* 0.217 cal.

15. The wave length of a certain line in the Balmer series is observed to be 4341 Å. To what value of n_2 does this correspond?   *Ans.* 5.

16. Calculate the frequency in wave numbers and the wave length in angstrom units of (a) the first two lines of the Lyman series, (b) the third and fourth lines of the Paschen series.

17. (a) What total amount of energy in calories would be required to shift all the electrons from the first Bohr orbit to the sixth Bohr orbit in a gram atom of hydrogen atoms? (b) Through what distance would each electron have to move? (c) What frequency of radiation would be emitted if the electrons returned to their initial state?   *Ans.* (a) 304,800 cal.

18. Calculate the velocities, in centimeters per second, of the electron in a hydrogen atom in the first and tenth orbits.

19. What is the frequency and wave length of radiation emitted by the transition of the electron from the second to the first Bohr orbit in singly ionized helium? Assume that R is the same as the Rydberg constant R_H for hydrogen.

20. What possible values may the other quantum numbers assume when the principal quantum number is 5?

21. According to the Pauli principle, what maximum number of electrons may be found in each of the l subshells in problem 20?

22. Explain the fundamental difference between the electronic configurations of the group IA elements (Li, Na, K, etc.) and those of the group IB elements (Cu, Ag, Au).

23. Uranium of mass number 235 undergoes natural radioactive disintegration with the emission of an α particle. (a) What are the mass and atomic numbers of the product? (b) What is the element formed?

24. Ac^{222} has a half-life period of 6.13 hr. What fraction of a sample of this substance will remain undecomposed at the end of 5 hr?   *Ans.* 0.568.

25. In what period of time will a sample of Na^{24} lose 90% of its intensity?

26. One gram of Ra is placed in an evacuated tube whose volume is 5.0 cc. Assuming that each Ra nucleus yields 4 He atoms which are retained in the tube, what will be the partial pressure at $27°$ C of the He produced at the end of a year? For Ra the period of half-life is 1590 years.   *Ans.* 28.5 mm Hg.

27. Assuming that the nucleus is composed of α particles and neutrons, what would be the number of each of these in Pb^{206}?

28. Li^6 when bombarded with neutrons emits α particles. Write a balanced equation for the nuclear reaction involved.

29. On bombardment of Kr^{82} with deutrons, protons are emitted. Write the equation for the nuclear reaction.

30. $_{79}Au^{197}$ on bombardment with neutrons yields $_{79}Au^{198}$. The latter substance is radioactive and emits electrons. Write the equations for the process.

31. $_{13}Al^{27}$ on bombardment with α particles yields $_{15}P^{30}$, which is radioactive and emits a positron. Write the equations for the nuclear reactions involved.

32. $_{94}Pu^{239}$ captures a neutron to form $_{94}Pu^{240}$. The latter captures another neutron to form the radioactive $_{94}Pu^{241}$, which decomposes then with emission of an electron. Write the equations for the nuclear changes.

22

Molecular Structure

The *periodic* recurrence of chemical properties of the elements on increase of atomic number, and hence mass, rules out the nucleus and points to the extranuclear electrons as the seat of chemical reactivity. Again, we have seen that, independently of the total number of electrons present, the electronic configuration in the external shells of all atoms belonging to a given group is essentially identical. The latter fact strongly suggests that chemical reactivity is associated primarily with the outermost electrons in an atom, and does not depend to any degree on electrons in shells much below the surface. Therefore, any explanation for the laws of chemical combination and valency must be sought in the behavior of the outermost electrons and in the interaction of these with the similar electrons of other atoms.

THE IONIC BOND

The first attempt to explain valence in terms of electrons was made by W. Kossel in 1916. The starting point of Kossel's theory was the observation that the great stability of the inert gases is attained when the external shell of the atom contains two electrons in helium and eight electrons in every other case. Kossel suggested, therefore, that all atoms tend to reach rare gas configurations either by taking on or losing electrons. For example, an atom of sodium contains two closed shells with one electron outside of these. Disregarding the closed shells and writing a dot to represent an electron, the neutral sodium atom may be designated by Na. Again, chlorine contains two closed shells of electrons with seven electrons outside of these, namely, $: \overset{..}{\underset{..}{Cl}} \cdot$. Now, to attain a rare gas configuration sodium can either divest itself of the one external electron it possesses and become the positive ion Na^+, or it may acquire seven electrons and become Na^{-7}. Obviously the first of these processes should be easier to accomplish, and so the tendency of sodium will be to lose an electron and become Na^+. On the other hand the chlorine atom may acquire a rare gas configuration either by gaining one electron or by losing all seven. Here evidently the first process is the more probable, and hence chlorine would tend to form the ion Cl^-. These natural tendencies come into play when sodium and chlorine are brought together. We obtain thus the reaction

$$Na + \cdot \overset{..}{\underset{..}{Cl}} : = Na^+ + [: \overset{..}{\underset{..}{Cl}} :]^-$$

in which an electron is transferred from the sodium to the chlorine to yield a sodium and a chloride ion, each with a rare gas configuration. Similarly, the reaction of barium and sulfur can be represented by the electron transfers

$$\overset{.}{\underset{.}{Ba}} + \overset{..}{S} : = Ba^{++} + [: \overset{..}{\underset{..}{S}} :]^{--}$$

This type of atomic interaction, involving the *outright transfer* of one or more electrons from one atom to another, leads to the formation of ions which are held together by electrostatic attraction. Because of the electrostatic nature of the binding force, the bond between the atoms is said to be *electrovalent*, and the valence exhibited is said to be an *electrovalence*. This is the type of binding found in simple salts such as sodium chloride, potassium iodide, and barium nitrate.

THE COVALENT BOND

Although the above explanation is satisfactory for ionic substances, it can hardly account for the formation of molecules such as CH_4, NO, H_2, N_2, and others of this category. In these no ions can be detected, and no reason is immediately apparent why, for instance, two atoms of hydrogen should combine into a molecule. To get around this difficulty, G. N. Lewis proposed in 1916 that union between atoms can be attained also from *sharing of electrons in pairs*. For example, if one hydrogen atom with a single external electron were to share this electron with another hydrogen atom, the result wold be a hydrogen molecule, H : H, in which each hydrogen atom could claim the pair and possess thereby the helium structure.

Again, the formation of a molecule such as CH_4 would arise from the sharing of electrons between hydrogen and carbon as follows

$$4\,H \cdot + \cdot \overset{\displaystyle \cdot}{\underset{\displaystyle \cdot}{C}} \cdot = H : \overset{\displaystyle \cdot\cdot}{\underset{\displaystyle \cdot\cdot}{C}} : H$$

Here again each hydrogen attains by sharing electrons the rare gas configuration of helium, while the carbon, by being able to share its own as well as the four acquired electrons, has the rare gas configuration of neon. In all such sharings *every electron pair corresponds to a single valence bond*. To differentiate the sharing type of atomic combination from electrovalent union, the terms *covalence* and *covalent bond* are employed.

Covalent binding can be used also to account for the formation of double and triple bonds in molecules. Thus the formation of an oxygen molecule can be represented by

$$\overset{\cdot\cdot}{\underset{\cdot\cdot}{O}} : + : \overset{\cdot\cdot}{\underset{\cdot\cdot}{O}} = \overset{\cdot\cdot}{\underset{\cdot\cdot}{O}} :: \overset{\cdot\cdot}{\underset{\cdot\cdot}{O}}$$

in which instance four electrons, corresponding to two valence bonds, are shared by the two atoms. Similarly, the electronic structure of ethylene can be written as

$$H : \overset{}{\underset{\cdot\cdot}{C}} :: \overset{}{\underset{\cdot\cdot}{C}} : H$$
$$H \qquad H$$

where the four electrons between the two carbons indicate the double bond. Finally, in triple bonds three electron pairs are shared as in N_2, $: N ::: N :$, or C_2H_2, $H : C ::: C : H$. In the one instance each nitrogen contributes three electrons to the formation of the covalent triple bond, whereas in the other each carbon supplies three electrons.

A covalent bond can arise also from the sharing of electrons *supplied by one atom only*. The bond then is said to be *coordinate covalent* or it is said that we have *coordinate covalence*. The atom contributing the electron pair to form the bond is called the *donor atom*, and the one to which the pair is donated the *acceptor atom*. An example of this is found in the formation of the NH_4^+ ion from ammonia and the hydrogen ion, namely,

$$H : \overset{H}{\overset{\cdot\cdot}{\underset{\cdot\cdot}{N}}} : + H^+ = \left[H : \overset{H}{\overset{\cdot\cdot}{\underset{\cdot\cdot}{N}}} : H \right]^+$$

In the ammonia molecule four electron pairs are present, of which only three are shared. When a hydrogen ion comes near this molecule the nitrogen allows the proton to share with it the free pair of electrons, and the result is thus the formation of the ammonium ion. Once established, the bond between the acceptor hydrogen and the donor nitrogen is indistinguishable from the other N—H bonds, and the positive charge becomes the property of the whole group rather than of any one hydrogen. As other examples of coordinate covalent binding may be cited the formation of $BF_3 \cdot NH_3$ from BF_3 and NH_3, and of BF_4^- from BF_3 and F^-. In both these instances the acceptor atom, boron, possesses only six electrons about it. In order to reach the stable octet of electrons, it accepts an electron pair from the donors NH_3 and F^- to form the respective complexes. By this means both the donor and acceptor atoms attain rare gas configurations.

NATURE OF BOND AND PHYSICAL PROPERTIES

The manner in which a chemical bond arises reflects significantly in the properties of the resulting compounds. Because electrovalency leads to the formation of ions held together by electrostatic attraction, compounds possessing this type of binding are ionized in the solid as well as in the molten states. In the latter state they are good conductors of electricity; and, on solution in such solvents as water, they yield strong electrolytes which also conduct a current. Further, because of the strong electrostatic forces between the electrically charged ions the compounds exhibit relatively high melting and boiling points. In contrast to the electrovalent compounds those resulting from covalency are unionized and hence nonconducting, and they exhibit much lower melting and

TABLE 1

COMPARISON OF PROPERTIES OF ELECTROVALENT AND COVALENT COMPOUNDS

Property	Electrovalent		Covalent	
	NaCl	BaCl$_2$	CCl$_4$	CH$_4$
Melting point	800° C	962° C	−22.6° C	−182.6° C
Boiling point	1413° C	1560° C	76.8° C	−161.4° C
Equiv. conductance at m.p.	133	64.6	0	0
Solubility in H$_2$O at 20° C (g/100 g H$_2$O)	36.0	35.7	Insoluble	Insoluble
Solubility in ether	Insoluble	Insoluble	∞	104 cc at 10° C

...nitials   Last Name (Please Print)

Articles	
Shirt (Tux)	
Shirt	**Check Type of Service**
Collars	Personal
Undershirts	
Drawers (Shorts)	Fluff Dry
Socks	
Handkerchiefs	Family
Pajama Suits	
Face Towels	
Bath Towels	All claims should be ac-
Face Cloths	companied by both this slip
Coveralls	and the package slip with-
Pants	in five days.
Sheets	
Pillow Slips	
Bed Spreads	If this slip is submitted with
Blankets	your laundry, it will be
Table Cloths	promptly returned unalter-
Napkins	ed.
Laundry Bag	
	Sorry—We can not be re-
	sponsible for goods left
	over 30 days.
	NO STARCH

MOORE BUSINESS FORMS, INC., ELMIRA, N. Y.

$$\frac{.0420 - .0065}{2} = \frac{.0355}{2}$$

$$= \frac{.0178}{2}$$

$$R = \frac{2.303}{(.091)(.008)} \; \log \; \frac{(.017)(.0420 - .0355)}{.0172 \,(.0172 - .0355)}$$

boiling points. Again, whereas electrovalent compounds are generally more soluble in polar solvents such as water or ethyl alcohol, covalent compounds are much more readily soluble in typical organic solvents such as benzene, ether, or carbon tetrachloride. These differences in the two types of binding are reflected by the data given in Table 1 for several electrovalent and covalent compounds.

The products resulting from coordinate covalent binding may, as we have seen, be both uncharged molecules, as $BF_3 \cdot NH_3$, or ions, as NH_4^+ or BF_4^-. In this category belong also such compounds as the hydrates, ammoniates, alcoholates, etherates, etc. For this variety of compounds it is very difficult to state with clarity any property differentiations. As a matter of fact, all gradations of behavior ranging from pure covalency on the one hand to almost electrovalency on the other may be found. In general the evidence seems to indicate that coordinate covalent binding tends to increase the melting and boiling points of compounds containing only covalent bonds.

THE ELECTRONIC THEORY OF ACIDS AND BASES

In Chapter 16 was mentioned a general theory of acids and bases proposed by G. N. Lewis. This theory is based on the concept of coordinate covalence. According to Lewis, *a base is any substance which donates a pair of electrons* to the formation of a coordinate bond. In turn, *an acid is any substance which accepts a pair of electrons* to form such a bond. This theory embraces not only the acids and bases in the Brönsted-Lowry theory, but many other substances which are usually not classified in this category. For details the student must be referred to the literature.[1]

EXCEPTIONS TO THE OCTET RULE

The Lewis-Kossel theory can account for the formation of many compounds by electron transfer and sharing. In doing this the theory relies on the concept that for stability there can be present no more than eight electrons about an atom. However, many compounds are known for which this electron octet rule is apparently exceeded, namely, PCl_5, SF_6, OsF_8, etc. In terms of an electron pair per bond, the phosphorus atom in PCl_5 would have to be surrounded by 10 electrons, the sulfur in SF_6 by 12, and the osmium in OsF_8 by 16. Again, in a molecule such as B_2H_6 there are present insufficient electrons to bind by sharing both the two borons and the six hydrogens. Since each boron possesses three electrons, the total of six for the two would be just sufficient to bind the hydrogens

[1] See Luder and Zuffanti, *The Electronic Theory of Acids and Bases*, John Wiley & Sons, Inc., New York, 1946.

without leaving any for the bond between the borons. Still, although not very stable, B_2H_6 exists.

To account for the existence, and in some instances high stability, of compounds apparently violating the octet rule, the suggestion has been made that more than eight electrons may be coordinated about an atom. However, Sugden pointed out that the octet rule can be preserved provided it is granted that in some cases a bond can be formed by the *sharing of a single electron* rather than a pair. Thus for phosphorus pentachloride the structure may be written as a combination of three electron pairs and two singlet electron bonds, namely,

$$
\begin{array}{c}
\text{Cl} \\
\quad\;\; \overset{\cdot\cdot}{}\;\; \text{Cl} \\
\text{Cl} : \text{P} : \\
\quad\;\; \overset{\cdot\cdot}{}\;\; \text{Cl} \\
\text{Cl}
\end{array}
$$

for SF_6 as a combination of two pairs and four singlets, and for OsF_8 as a combination of eight singlet bonds. Likewise the formation of B_2H_6 may be accounted for by the structure

$$
\begin{array}{c}
\text{H} \quad\; \text{H} \\
\overset{\cdot\cdot}{} \quad \overset{\cdot\cdot}{} \\
\text{H} : \text{B} : \text{B} : \text{H} \\
\overset{\cdot}{} \quad\;\; \overset{\cdot}{} \\
\text{H} \quad\; \text{H}
\end{array}
$$

Although single electron bonds are possible under certain conditions, as in the hydrogen-molecule ion $[\text{H} \cdot \text{H}]^+$, it is questionable whether they exist in the form postulated. Where they do exist the stability results apparently from a quantum-mechanical phenomenon called *resonance*, in which the singlet electron, instead of being fixed, oscillates between bonds involving the singlets. For example, in B_2H_6 each singlet electron would oscillate between one hydrogen and another, with the result that each singlet bond would possess an electron doublet for part of the time of an oscillation. As quantum mechanics has shown that whenever resonance appears it leads to increased stability, the formation of stable bonds with supposedly singlet electrons may well be the consequence of resonance.

WAVE-MECHANICAL THEORIES OF VALENCE

Two theories of valence based on wave mechanics have been advanced which express the concept of valence and chemical combination in quantitative terms. Although both the *Heitler-London* theory and the *Hund-Mulliken* theory employ the same principles, they differ in mode of treatment. The Heitler-London theory ascribes particular electrons to the atoms from which they come and considers the manner of interaction of these with other electrons during chemical reaction. On the other hand, the Hund-Mulliken theory does not treat the electrons as belonging to a particular atom, but considers rather the molecule as a whole and the manner in which all the electrons present interact with each other and with the positive atomic nuclei. Despite this difference of approach, both theories lead to conclusions which in all essential details are the same. In this connection it may be emphasized that, because of mathematical difficulties, exact solutions of the wave equations involved have been obtained only in such simple systems as the hydrogen molecule and the hydrogen-molecule ion, H_2^+. In more complicated cases various approximate methods of solution must be resorted to. Nevertheless, even these approximate treatments yield considerable information on valence and bonding, and they are, therefore, of great interest and importance to the chemist.

According to the Heitler-London theory, the valence of an element results from presence in the external shell of the atom of electrons with *unpaired spins*. By an electron with unpaired spin is meant an electron with spin quantum number $+\frac{1}{2}$ or $-\frac{1}{2}$ for which no complementary electron with *opposite* spin is present in the atom. As long as electrons with opposite spins are paired off, they are not available for chemical combination. When they are not paired off, they may satisfy their tendencies for spin coupling by combining with the electrons of opposite spin in other atoms to form a valence bond and thereby a molecule. *Valence and chemical combination are the result, therefore, of the tendency of unpaired electrons with opposite spins to pair off and balance thereby the electronic spins.* It will be observed that the electron pair covalent bond concept of Lewis finds thus its explanation in this theory as a coupling of two electrons with opposite spins.

The Heitler-London theory emphasizes the electron pair type of bonding, i.e., covalency, and so it is frequently referred to as the *homopolar method*. On the other hand, the Hund-Mulliken or *molecular orbital* treatment results not only in homopolar terms in the wave equation of the molecule, but also in certain terms corresponding to possible ionic binding. When the values of the homopolar terms are considerably greater than those of the ionic, the binding is essentially of the covalent type. On the other hand, when the ionic terms are much more significant than the homopolar, we encounter electrovalence. Between these two extremes the binding is of mixed type and leads to the appearance of molecules with permanent dipole moments to which reference will be made later.

Another difference between the two theories lies in the fact that, whereas the homopolar theory emphasizes the pairing of electrons of opposite spins, the molecular-orbital method divides all the electrons in a molecule into *bonding, antibonding,* and *nonbonding* electrons. Any electron whose presence contributes to molecular stability is a bonding electron, while one whose presence leads to instability is an antibonding electron. A nonbonding electron, in turn, is one which contributes neither to stability nor instability. Of necessity any stable molecule will have to contain an excess of bonding over antibonding electrons. When the reverse is true the molecule cannot be stable, and chemical combination of the atoms involves is not possible.

RESONANCE

A fundamental contribution of wave mechanics to the theory of molecular structure is the concept of *resonance* or *exchange energy*. This idea of resonance has no counterpart in any classical theory of atomic combination. In order to explain it, let us consider specifically the formation of a hydrogen molecule from two hydrogen atoms. Each of these hydrogen atoms contains one electron. When the molecule is formed it may be thought off-hand that each electron remains essentially attached to its own atom. But it is quite possible that the two electrons may exchange orbits, namely, electron$_1$ from atom$_1$ may exchange places with electron$_2$ from atom$_2$. When this happens the molecule may consist not only of the configuration atom$_1$ electron$_1$—atom$_2$ electron$_2$, but also of atom$_1$ electron$_2$—atom$_2$ electron$_1$. These two configurations are not static, but involve *continuous oscillation* of the molecule from one of these to the other. Wave mechanics shows that, when such electron exchange is possible and does occur, the energy of the resonating structure is *less* than that of the molecule without exchange; i.e., that *exchange or resonance leads to an increase in stability*. The increase in binding energy thus resulting is called *resonance* or *exchange energy*.

Resonance may arise also from oscillation of electrons from one position in the molecule to another. As a consequence of this oscillation the molecule may take on a number of resonance structures, each of which is essentially equivalent in total energy to another. Thus the carbon dioxide molecule may have the possible equivalent structures

$$O : C ::: O \qquad O :: C :: O \qquad O ::: C : O$$
$$\text{I} \qquad\qquad\qquad \text{II} \qquad\qquad\qquad \text{III}$$

At one time structure II was thought to be predominant, with I and III practically nonexistent. However, at present it is believed that carbon dioxide is a *resonance hybrid* of all three forms; and, as a consequence, its stability is greater than it would be if only one structure persisted. Similarly, it has been shown that the stability of the benzene molecule is due in large degree to resonance between at least five equivalent structures. In fact, whenever the possibility of resonance exists, greater stability in a molecule or ion can be anticipated.

THE HYDROGEN MOLECULE IN WAVE MECHANICS

Since the formation of a hydrogen molecule from two hydrogen atoms has been treated exactly by wave mechanics, it is of some interest to recapitulate briefly the results obtained. A solution of the appropriate wave equations indicates that the total energy of the hydrogen molecule consists of three parts: (a) the energy of the original atoms; (b) coulombic energy resulting from electrostatic attractions between the electrons and nuclei; and (c) exchange energy. Further, the treatment leads to two expressions for the total energy as a function of the distance of separation of the two nuclei. In one of these the total energy is always such as to lead to continual *repulsion* of the two atoms at all possible distances of separation, and hence this solution cannot possibly correspond to the formation of a stable molecule. This case is illustrated by curve A in Fig. 1. Here the ordinate is the total energy of the molecule taken on the basis that the energy of the atoms is zero at infinite distance of separation, while the abscissa is

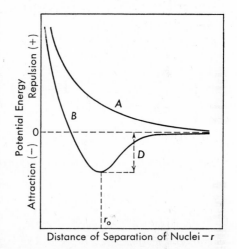

Fig. 1.   Potential Energy Diagram of H_2 Molecule.

the distance of separation of the two nuclei, r. In turn, the second solution gives curve B for the total energy as a function of the distance of separation. This curve shows that as the two nuclei are brought closer together an attraction results which increases as r decreases, until at $r = r_0$ the attraction is a maximum. r_0 must correspond, therefore, to the distance of separation of the two nuclei in the stable molecule. If this distance is decreased the attraction is also diminished, until at very small distances of separation the two nuclei actually repel each other.

A plot such as Fig. 1 of energy vs. distance of separation of the nuclei is called a *potential energy diagram*. The potential energy curve for the hydrogen molecule indicates that to disrupt the molecule into its constitutent atoms it is necessary to increase the distance of separation r theoretically to infinity. For this purpose an amount of energy is required corresponding to the difference between the energy of the molecule, D, and the energy of the two atoms, which is zero by definition. Consequently D must be the *energy of dissociation* of a hydrogen molecule into its constituent atoms. Spectroscopy yields for this energy $D = 102,900$ cal per gram mole, corresponding to $r_0 = 0.74 \times 10^{-8}$ cm. The values of these two quantities for the hydrogen molecule deduced by James and Coolidge from wave mechanics are exactly the same, and hence theory and experiment are here in accord.

THE HYDROGEN BOND

In certain compounds a hydrogen already bound by two electrons to an atom may further coordinate two more electrons to form another bond. Examples of such *hydrogen bonding* may be found in water,

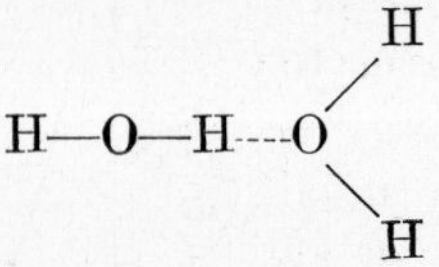

alcohols,

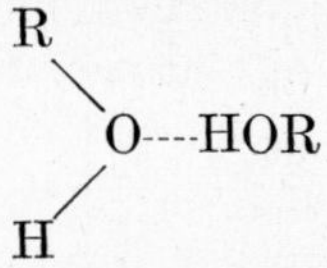

carboxylic acids,

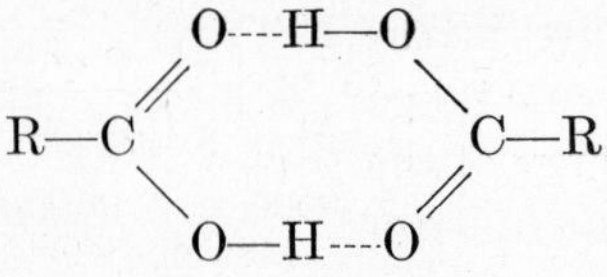

nitrophenols,

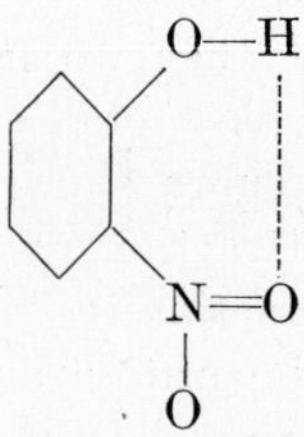

and in amides,

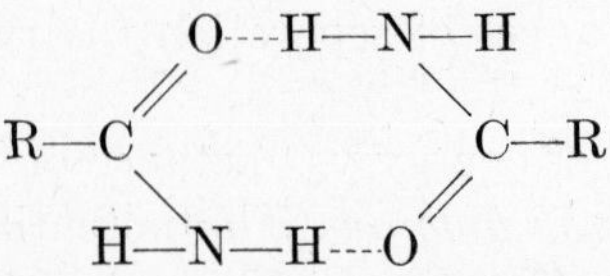

In each of these instances the hydrogen bond arises from the donation of a pair of electrons by a nitrogen or oxygen atom to a hydrogen already bound to a nitrogen or oxygen. In the nitrophenols hydrogen bonding results in the formation of a second ring in which the properties of both the nitro and hydroxyl groups are modified. However, with carboxylic acids and amides hydrogen bonding leads to an association of two molecules, while in water and the alcohols the bonding may well extend throughout the entire mass. In terms of hydrogen bonding it is understandable why water, acids, alcohols, and amides are associated liquids, whereas hydrocarbons, carbon tetrachloride, and chloroform are not. The same explanation applies to liquid hydrogen fluoride, where as a result of hydrogen bond formation between the fluorine of one molecule and the hydrogen of another the dimer H_2F_2 is formed.

Hydrogen bonding is not confined to the liquid state. X-ray studies of ice and solid carboxylic acids, and vapor density measurements on the latter, reveal that hydrogen bonding extends also into the solid and vapor phases. The presence of hydrogen bonds in the liquid state is indicated by higher boiling points, heats of vaporization, and viscosities than shown by corresponding normal liquids. Hydrogen bonding can be detected also by infrared studies. Thus the spectrum of aceto-acetic acid ester gives no bands associated with the hydroxyl group, while in other molecules the hydroxyl bands are displaced from their normal positions.

The relatively high stability of hydrogen bonds is ascribed to the existence of resonance in compounds where the bond occurs. Thus in water, the alcohols, and carboxylic acids the hydrogen bond between the two oxygens is believed to resonate between these two atoms. The same applies to the hydrogen in the nitrophenols. In the amides, on the other hand, the resonance involves alternate attachment of the hydrogen to the oxygen or nitrogen atom, and as a consequence the net resulting structure is stable.

MOLECULAR OR BAND SPECTRA

Just as study of atomic spectra has proved helpful in elucidating the structure of atoms, so the spectra emitted by gaseous molecules have yielded valuable information on the structure of molecules. Unlike the *line* spectra emitted by atoms, molecules of a gas when excited emit a *band* spectrum which strong resolution reveals to be composed of many lines very closely spaced. In general the sorting and classification of lines in a band spectrum is a difficult and tedious task. Nevertheless, the spectra of most diatomic and many polyatomic molecules have been unraveled, and from these a deep insight has been obtained into what occurs within the molecule.

Three types of molecular spectra are recognized, namely, (a) *rotation spectra*, (b) *vibration-rotation spectra*, and (c) *electronic band spectra*. To appreciate the origin of these, an understanding is required of the energy levels in a molecule. For this purpose consider a diatomic molecule AB. This molecule consists of two nuclei corresponding to the atoms A and B and their accompanying electrons. As in the constituent atoms, the various electrons in the molecule may exist in a number of energy levels such that on excitation an electron may shift from one to another. Once thus excited the electron on return will emit a spectral line of frequency determined by the energy difference of the two levels and the quantized Bohr relation. Were this the only manner in which the molecule could absorb energy, the electronic spectrum of a molecule would be a line spectrum akin to that of atoms. But a molecule may also absorb energy to cause a *vibration* of the nuclei with respect to each other, and to set the molecule as a whole *rotating*. These vibrational and rotational motions are quantized and are superimposed upon the kinetic motion of the molecule. From the standpoint of band spectra the latter motion may be disregarded, but the other two cannot be. The incidence of quantized vibration and rotation coupled with the electronic levels leads to the diagrammatic picture of the energy levels of a molecule shown in Fig. 2. The group of levels represented by $n = 1$ corresponds to the lowest electronic energy level of the molecule. Similarly, the group given by $n = 2$ is the energy structure of the next higher, excited, electronic level. Each of these electronic levels is subdivided into the *vibrational* sublevels designated by the

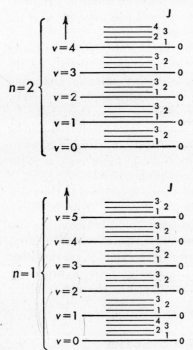

Fig. 2. Molecular Energy Levels (Schematic).

vibrational quantum numbers v on the left. In turn, each of the vibrational sublevels has associated with it a number of *rotational* quantum levels, the energy of which is determined by the rotational quantum numbers J shown on the right. In a like manner every higher electronic level of a molecule will consist of vibrational and rotational levels of the form shown in Fig. 2 and will lie in sequence above those for $n = 2$.

From this description it is evident that the energy required for excitation of various emissions will be least for rotation and will be increasingly greater for vibration and then electron transfer. If the exciting energies are kept suitably small, it is possible to produce only transitions from one rotational quantum level to another within a given vibrational level, and the result is then the appearance of the *rotational spectrum alone*. Since the energies involved are small these spectra are found in the far infrared, i.e., at wave lengths above 50 μ.[1] On the other hand, when the exciting energies are sufficiently large to cause vibration level transitions within a given electronic level, emissions are observed corresponding to the changes in the vibration quantum numbers. Further, since a change in vibrational levels involves also changes in rotational levels, the over-all result is a vibrational spectrum where in each line is accompanied by a rotational fine-structure. We obtain thus the *vibration-rotation spectrum* of a molecule which is generally located in the near infrared, i.e., at wave lengths of 1 to 50 μ. Finally, with still higher exciting energies electron transitions may take place which are accompanied by vibrational level changes, and each of these in turn by rotational fine-structure. The spectrum is then a complex *electronic band* consisting of lines due to electronic, vibrational, and rotational transitions. As more than a single electronic excitation may occur, the complete spectrum may consist of a *band system* composed of individual electronic bands, each accompanied by its own vibrational and rotational lines. Electronic bands are found in the visible and ultraviolet spectral ranges.

ROTATIONAL SPECTRA

The rotational spectrum of a *diatomic* molecule can be accounted for by considering the molecule to a first approximation as a rigid rotator, i.e., as a rigid dumbbell joined along its line of centers by a bond equal in length to the distance r_0 between the two nuclei. With the energy of rotation quantized, wave mechanics shows that the energy E_J of such a rigid rotator in any given rotational quantum level J is given by

$$E_J = \left(\frac{h^2}{8\,\pi^2 I} \right) J(J+1) \tag{1}$$

In this equation h is Planck's constant, while I is the *moment of inertia* of the molecule given in terms of the two atomic masses, m_1 and m_2, and the internuclear distance r_0 by the relation

$$I = \left(\frac{m_1 m_2}{m_1 + m_2} \right) r_0^2 \tag{2}$$

J may have integral values of 0, 1, 2, 3, etc. For a transition from a rotational level of quantum number J to one of lower quantum number

[1] $1\,\mu = 10^{-4}\,\text{cm} = 10{,}000\,\text{Å}$.

J', the energy difference would correspond to

$$\Delta E_r = E_J - E_{J'} = \left(\frac{h^2}{8\,\pi^2 I}\right)[J(J+1) - J'(J'+1)] \qquad (3)$$

As a rule rotational transitions are restricted to changes in J corresponding to $\Delta J = J - J' = 1$. Inserting this condition into equation (3), we obtain

$$\Delta E_r = h\nu = \left(\frac{2\,h^2}{8\,\pi^2 I}\right) J \qquad (4)$$

and hence

$$\nu = \left(\frac{h}{4\,\pi^2 I}\right) J \qquad (5)$$

Here the values of J start with $J = 1$. Since the quantity in parentheses is a constant for a given molecule, equation (5) shows that the rotational spectrum should consist of a number of equally spaced lines the frequencies of which are determined by J. Hence, by determining the frequencies of lines corresponding to various J values in the pure rotation spectrum of a molecule, the moment of inertia of the molecule may be obtained through equation (5) and from it the internuclear distance of the atoms r_0 by means of equation (2).

Although pure rotation spectra offer the simplest means of deducing moments of inertia of molecules, technical difficulties in far infrared studies impair high accuracy. For this reason this quantity is deduced more frequently from the other types of spectra which can be measured more conveniently and precisely, or by microwave spectorscopy.

MICROWAVE SPECTROSCOPY

In infrared work the energy source is a heated bar or filament which supplies nonmonochromatic radiation. The latter is passed through a suitable prism which disperses the light and allows selection of a narrow band of desired wave length to be transmitted through the substance under test. The intensity of the transmitted light is measured then by means of a thermopile and compared with that of the incident beam. On the other hand, in microwave spectroscopy an electronically controlled oscillator is used to generate monochromatic electromagnetic energy of frequency corresponding to a wave length range of 0.1 to several centimeters. Since the energies at such wave lengths are of the same order of magnitude as those involved in rotational transitions in molecules, the microwaves may be used to measure these. The procedure employed is to pass the monochromatic energy through a gaseous sample of the substance under investigation, and to measure the intensity of the transmitted radiation by means of an electronic receiver and cathode-ray oscillograph.

By varying the frequency of the oscillator and observing the intensity of the transmitted beams, it is possible to obtain data from which moments of inertia and internuclear distances of the molecules involved can be calculated.

The microwave method is applicable only to molecules which possess permanent dipole moments. Compared to infrared measurements its accuracy is very high and corresponds to about ± 0.001 Å in r_0. The method may also be used for identification and analysis of substances which can be obtained in gaseous form for observation. For details see the book by Gordy, Smith, and Trambarulo.[1]

VIBRATION-ROTATION SPECTRA

To a first approximation the vibratory motion of the nuclei of a diatomic molecule can be represented as the vibration of a *simple harmonic oscillator;* i.e., an oscillator in which the restoring force is proportional to the displacement in accordance with Hooke's law. For such an oscillator with quantized energy, wave mechanics shows that the vibrational energy E_v is related to the fundamental vibrational frequency ν_0 by the relation

$$E_v = \left(v + \frac{1}{2}\right) h\nu_0 \tag{6}$$

Here v is the *vibrational quantum number*, which may take on the values $v = 0, 1, 2$, etc. Equation (6) reveals that such an oscillator retains in its lowest vibrational level $v = 0$ the energy $E_0 = \frac{1}{2}h\nu_0$. This residual energy, called the *zero-point energy* of the oscillator, cannot be removed from the molecule even by cooling it to 0° K.

For a vibrational transition from any level of quantum number v to another of quantum number v', the emitted energy is given by

$$\Delta E_v = E_v - E_{v'} = \left(v + \frac{1}{2}\right)h\nu_0 - \left(v' + \frac{1}{2}\right)h\nu_0 = (v - v')h\nu_0 \tag{7}$$

Upon these vibrational transitions are superposed accompanying rotational changes which may *add* or *subtract* from equation (7) the energy change given by equation (4). The energy change resulting is, therefore, the *sum* or the *difference* of equations (7) and (4), or

$$\Delta E = \Delta E_v \pm \Delta E_r$$
$$= (v - v')h\nu_0 \pm \left(\frac{h^2}{4\pi^2 I}\right)J \tag{8}$$

[1] Gordy, Smith, and Trambarulo, *Microwave Spectroscopy*, John Wiley & Sons, Inc., New York, 1953.

The frequencies of the emitted spectral lines due to the energy changes given by equation (8) follow from $\Delta E = h\nu$. Hence

$$\nu = (v - v')\nu_0 \pm \left(\frac{h}{4\,\pi^2 I}\right) J \qquad (9)$$

From equation (9) it can be deduced that the appearance of a vibration-rotation spectrum will be as follows: Instead of obtaining a single line corresponding to the vibrational transition from a given value of v to v', the line will be missing, and instead a pair of lines on either side of the expected position will be found for each value of J, one corresponding to the plus sign in equation (9), the second to the minus sign. Since a pair of such lines will be obtained for each of the possible values of J, the spectrum for the particular difference in v will have a blank space flanked on either side by the rotational fine-structure lines, Fig. 3. Here the spacings of the lines are shown to be constant in accord with equation

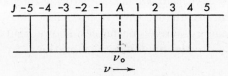

Fig. 3.   Diagram of Vibration-Rotation Spectrum (Schematic).

(9), but actually they are variable because of complications to be mentioned later. As one unit such as Fig. 3 is obtained for each possible change in vibrational quantum number from v to v', the complete vibration-rotation spectrum will be composed of a number of such units.

The bands corresponding to $v' = 0$ and $v = 1, 2$, etc., are called respectively the *fundamental* band, the *first harmonic* band, the *second harmonic* band, etc. By ascertaining in the fundamental band the frequency corresponding to the missing vibration line, i.e., position A in Fig. 3, ν_0 is obtained directly. Similarly, the frequencies at the positions corresponding A in the first and second harmonics gives $2\,\nu_0$ and $3\,\nu_0$. These may be used, then, to check the value of ν_0, the fundamental vibration frequency of the molecule. With ν_0 known, measurement of the line frequencies for various values of J permits calculation of the moment of inertia through equation (9), and from it, in turn, the internuclear distance r_0. In this manner it is possible to ascertain from vibration-rotation spectra the fundamental frequency of the molecule, the moment of inertia, and the distance of separation of the nuclei.

ELECTRONIC SPECTRA

Electronic spectra arise from excitation of electrons in a molecule from one energy level to a higher one. As a result of this excitation the electron on return will emit radiation corresponding to the energy difference between the two electronic levels involved. Since during the excitation a change takes place also in vibrational and rotational levels, the electronic emission is always accompanied by vibrational and rotational transitions. Thus, if we let E'_e, E'_v, and E'_r be, respectively, the electronic, vibrational, and rotational energies of the molecule after the transition, and E_e, E_v, and E_r the corresponding quantities before the change, then the total energy of the molecule in the initial state is

$$E = E_e + E_v + E_r \tag{10}$$

and, in the final state,

$$E' = E'_e + E'_v + E'_r \tag{11}$$

The energy change involved in the electronic transition is, consequently,

$$\Delta E = (E_e - E'_e) + (E_v - E'_v) + (E_r - E'_r)$$
$$= \Delta E_e + \Delta E_v + \Delta E_r \tag{12}$$

and the resulting frequency of radiation follows as

$$\nu = \frac{\Delta E}{h} = \frac{\Delta E_e + \Delta E_v + \Delta E_r}{h} \tag{13}$$

As ΔE_v and ΔE_r may have different values depending on the rotational and vibrational quantum numbers involved, the number of lines possible for a given change in E_e is large and leads to a complex electronic band. Further, with different values of ΔE_e possible as well, the complete band spectrum will consist of a band system composed of a series of individual bands.

Despite their complexity electronic band spectra are frequently studied in preference to the other types. This is because these spectra occur in the visible or ultraviolet ranges and hence may be photographed and inspected easily. In general the information deduced from electronic bands is the same as that obtained from vibration-rotation spectra. Besides, it is possible to ascertain from electronic band spectra information about the excited states of the molecule as well as the energy of dissociation of the molecule into its component atoms.

When the electronic band spectrum of a molecule is inspected, it is found that at one end of the spectrum the distance of separation of the lines becomes smaller and smaller, until at a given position the line spectrum terminates, and a space of continuous emission starts. The position of the limit where the lines end gives the frequency of radiation necessary for *dissociation* of the molecule. When the dissociation is into normal atoms the spectroscopic dissociation energy D_s can be calculated directly from the observed frequency. However, when the dissociation results in one or more excited atoms, a correction has to be applied for the energy of excitation. From the value of D_s thus obtained the thermochemical dissociation energy of the molecule follows as

$$D = D_s + \frac{1}{2} h\nu_0 \tag{14}$$

where $\frac{1}{2} h\nu_0$ is the zero-point energy of the molecule.

The above discussion of the molecular spectra of diatomic molecules is a simplification of the actual situation. The molecule as a whole is not quite a rigid rotator nor a simple harmonic oscillator. Because of these defects in ideal behavior corrections have to be introduced which tend to complicate equations (5), (7), and (9). For the purpose at hand, however, the treatment given should suffice.

TABLE 2

MOLECULAR CONSTANTS OF DIATOMIC MOLECULES

Molecule	$m^* \times 10^{24}$ (g)	$I \times 10^{40}$ (g-cm^2)	$r_0 \times 10^8$ (cm)	$\nu_0 \times 10^{-12}$ (sec^{-1})	D Kcal/mole	D Thermal Kcal/mole
H_2	0.832	0.46	0.75	132.4	102.9	103.2
N_2	11.54	13.8	1.09	70.76	170.	
O_2	13.19	19.15	1.20	47.42	116.7	
Cl_2	28.86	113.5	1.98	16.03	56.8	57.6
Br_2	65.89	445.	2.28	9.71	45.2	46.2
I_2	104.65	740.	2.66	6.42	35.4	35.1
HCl	1.62	2.65	1.28	87.70	102.	107.0
CO	11.31	15.0	1.13	65.07	223.	
NO	12.31	16.4	1.15	57.18	123.	

In Table 2 are summarized the molecular constants of some diatomic molecules deduced from band spectra in the manner described. In this table column 2 gives the reduced mass of the molecule, i.e., $m^* = (m_1 m_2)/(m_1 + m_2)$, columns 3, 4, and 5 the moments of inertia, the interatomic distances, and the fundamental frequencies of vibration, respectively, while column 6 gives the spectroscopically deduced dissociation energies. For comparison there are included in column 7 some values of the dissociation energy obtained by thermochemical methods. The agreement between the two sets of D values is satisfactory.[1]

---

[1] In terms of ordinary thermodynamic quantities, D is the internal energy change on dissociation of a diatomic molecule into atoms at the *absolute* zero of temperature, i.e., $D = \Delta E_0$. To obtain the value of ΔH from D at any temperature T the thermal energy entering between $T = 0$ and $T = T$ must be added to ΔE_0. In other words, $\Delta H_T = \Delta E_0 + \int_0^T \Delta C_p dT$. The thermal values of D given in column 7 are corrected to $T = 0$.

POTENTIAL ENERGY DIAGRAMS OF DIATOMIC MOLECULES

Curve B of Fig. 1 shows the potential energy diagram for the stable hydrogen molecule. Similar diagrams can be constructed for other diatomic molecules with the aid of the molecular constants deduced from spectroscopy. For the *lowest* or *ground electronic state* of a molecule the potential energy diagram will have the general form given in Fig. 4.

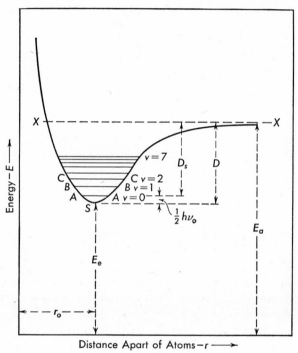

Fig. 4.   Potential Energy Diagram of Diatomic Molecule.

To any excited state an analogous potential energy curve will correspond, except that because of the higher energy content it will lie above the one for the ground state.

The total energy E of any molecule consists of the electronic energy E_e, the vibrational energy E_v, the rotational energy E_r, and the energy of thermal motion E_t; i.e.,

$$E = E_e + E_v + E_r + E_t \qquad (15)$$

At the absolute zero of temperature E_t and E_r are both zero, and E_v reduces to the zero-point energy of the molecule, namely, $E_0 = \frac{1}{2} h\nu_0$. At the absolute zero, therefore, the energy is given by

$$E_{T=0} = E_e + \frac{1}{2} h\nu_0 \qquad (16)$$

For such a stable molecule in its ground state point S in Fig. 4, corresponding to the normal distance of separation r_0, gives the electronic energy content E_e. When the zero-point energy is added to this quantity, the energy level is raised to the line A–A, and we arrive thus at the energy of the molecule at the absolute zero. As the vibrational frequencies of the molecule are excited, the total energy levels are raised to the lines B–B, C–C, etc., in accordance with the increase in the vibrational quantum number v. The spacings of the lines within the potential energy diagram depend on the differences in energy between vibrational quantum levels. For an ideal harmonic oscillator the spacings between the lines would be constant, but actually they get smaller as v increases. When eventually line X–X is reached, the molecule dissociates into the two neutral atoms. The difference in energy between X–X and $E = 0$, namely E_a, is the energy content of the two resulting atoms. If from this energy we subtract the electronic energy E_e of the original molecule, the result is the energy of dissociation D of the molecule. However, if instead of subtracting E_e we deduct $E_e + \frac{1}{2} h\nu_0$, we obtain the spectroscopic energy of dissociation D_s.

A diagram such as Fig. 4 indicates, therefore, the energy of a molecule in its ground electronic state and in various vibrational states as a function of the distance of separation. To obtain the total energy of the molecule at any given temperature it would be necessary to add to $(E_e + E_v)$ the rotational and thermal energy contributions.

In dealing with specific heats and other thermodynamic properties of molecules, the consideration is always with energy differences, and hence in absence of electronic excitation E_e cancels out. Under such conditions the energy reference point may be transposed to point S; i.e., the energy at S may be taken as zero. On this basis the potential energy E_P of any diatomic molecule can be derived from an empirical equation due to Morse, namely,

$$E_P = D[1 - e^{-a(r-r_0)}]^2 \tag{17}$$

Here again D is the energy of dissociation, r_0 the equilibrium separation distance of the molecule, r the distance of separation at any other point, and a is a constant characteristic of a particular molecule. The constant a may be evaluated from the relation

$$a = \pi\nu_0 \sqrt{\left(\frac{2\,m_1 m_2}{m_1 + m_2}\right)\frac{1}{D}} \tag{18}$$

where ν_0 is the fundamental vibration frequency of the molecule, while m_1 and m_2 are the masses of the two atoms involved. In using equation (18) D must be expressed in *ergs*, but in equation (17) it may have any desired units, as kilogram calories. Finally, to establish the vibrational levels, i.e., the lines $A-A$, $B-B$, etc., in Fig. 4, recourse is had to equation (6). By substituting into this relation $v = 0$ the zero-point energy follows, $v = 1$ the level $B-B$, $v = 2$ the level $C-C$, etc. The lines thus obtained will be idealized and equidistant. For their true positions information on the anharmonicity of the oscillator is required.

POLYATOMIC MOLECULES

In describing band spectra and their origin attention was confined to diatomic molecules. With molecules containing more than two atoms the situation is more involved. Any diatomic molecule must of necessity be linear, and hence it can have only one moment of inertia. This is true also of linear polyatomic molecules. However, when the polyatomic molecules are nonlinear, i.e., when the valence bond directions are oriented at angles other than 180° to each other, then *three* moments of inertia are present. These three moments correspond to the respective rotations of the molecule as a whole about a set of x, y, and z axes passed through the center of gravity of the molecule. Again, whereas a diatomic molecule can have only one fundamental frequency of vibration, the number of such frequencies increases with the number of atoms. For a linear polyatomic molecule the number of possible modes of vibration the molecule *may* have is $(3\ n - 5)$, where n is the number of atoms in the molecule, while for a nonlinear molecule it is $(3\ n - 6)$. Thus, in passing from a diatomic to a triatomic linear molecule the possible vibration frequencies increase from one to four and for a nonlinear molecule, from one to three. Not all the possible vibrations are necessarily active, nor are all of the frequencies necessarily different. Nevertheless, the added modes of motion complicate the situation, and consequently the resulting spectra are much more complex and difficult to interpret.

OTHER APPLICATIONS OF BAND SPECTROSCOPY

Band spectroscopy finds extensive application at present in the identification and analysis of organic compounds. Band spectroscopic data have also been used extensively in the calculation of thermodynamic properties of gases, and, in a limited number of simple cases, for the calculation of the energies of activation of reactions.

RAMAN SPECTRA

An alternate and simpler method than band spectroscopy of obtaining vibrational and rotational frequencies of molecules is through observations of the *Raman effect*. In 1928 Raman found that when light of a definite frequency ν was passed through a gas, liquid, or solid, and the scattered radiation was observed at right angles to the direction of the incident beam, the scattered radiation contained lines not only of the original light, but also some of lower, and occasionally higher frequency. The lines shifted toward the lower frequencies are called *Stokes lines*, those toward the higher frequencies *anti-Stokes lines*. Raman further found that the difference $\Delta\nu$ between the incident and any given scattered line was *constant and characteristic of the substance irradiated*, and *completely independent of the frequency ν of the incident radiation*. Such differences $\Delta\nu$ between incident and scattered lines are called *characteristic Raman frequencies*.

The Raman effect arises from absorption by a molecule from the incident radiation of sufficient quanta of energy to cause transitions from lower to higher vibrational levels, or from lower to higher rotational levels. In vibrational excitation a *single* quantum of energy is removed in magnitude equal to the energy necessary for passage from one vibrational quantum level to the next. In rotations, however, *two* quanta are extracted to cause a change in rotational level from a value J to $(J + 2)$. As a result of such removal of energy from the original beam the energy of the latter must decrease, and so must the frequency. We obtain thus the Stokes lines. On the other hand, the molecule, instead of absorbing energy, may emit some by rotational or vibrational transitions from higher levels to lower. When this happens the emitted energy is added to that of the incident light, the frequency of the latter becomes larger and anti-Stokes lines are obtained.

The Raman frequencies observed for various rotational and vibrational transitions are identical with the same transitions observed in band spectra. Since this is true, vibrational and rotational frequencies may be ascertained more conveniently from the Raman effect, which may be studied in the visible spectral range rather than in the more difficult infrared, where the rotational and vibrational bands are found. Utilizing this advantage, investigators have identified and measured the frequencies corresponding to various types of bonds in organic and inorganic molecules. Raman spectroscopy has proved thus a great aid in the study of molecular structure and has supplied a check on the interpretation of the band spectra of molecules.

ELECTRON DIFFRACTION OF GASES

Electron diffraction of gases offers still another powerful tool for arriving at the geometric configuration of molecules and the distance between atoms in these. The experimental arrangement involves generation of electrons by a hot filament, acceleration of these by a constant electric field of about 40,000 volts cm^{-1}, passage of the electrons through a sample of gas or vaporized liquid or solid kept at a low pressure, and, finally, impingement of the electrons upon a photographic plate placed in their path. The image formed on the latter consists of a series of concentric rings similar to those obtained in the powder method of x-ray analysis.

The principle of the procedure is also similar to that of the powder method. The electrons, acting as waves of length ca. 0.05 Å, are diffracted by the atoms in the gas molecules. Since these molecules are randomly oriented with respect to the electron beam, some of the diffracted rays experience interference, while others are reinforced. The result is a series of rings whose positions and intensities depend on the geometry of the apparatus, the configurational structure of the molecules, and the atomic radii. From such rings and their intensities can be ascertained whether the molecules are linear or nonlinear, whether they are planar or non-planar, the bond distances, and also the angles between bonds in the case of nonlinear molecules.

ORTHO- AND PARA-HYDROGEN

A detailed analysis of atomic spectra reveals that nuclei of atoms may possess spin similar to that shown by electrons. The units of quantized nuclear spin may be zero for no spin, or a whole number multiple of $\frac{1}{2}$, namely, $\frac{1}{2}$, 1, $\frac{3}{2}$, etc. For any given atomic nucleus the spin is fixed. Thus the nuclei of atomic oxygen, carbon, or helium have no spin. On the other hand, the spins for nuclei of hydrogen and fluorine are $\frac{1}{2}$, for deuterium and nitrogen 1, for sodium $\frac{3}{2}$, and for chlorine $\frac{5}{2}$.

Now, when *two identical atoms with spin* are combined into a molecule, as two hydrogen atoms into H$_2$, two possible combinations arise: (a) one in which the two atoms involved have nuclei spinning in the same direction, i.e., *parallel* spins or (b) another in which the two nuclei have opposite or *antiparallel* spins. From hydrogen nuclei with parallel spins we get *ortho-hydrogen*. This molecule yields a rotational band spectrum with fairly intense lines corresponding to levels of *odd rotational quantum numbers J* in the ground state of the molecule. On the other hand, when the spins are antiparallel, the molecule obtained is called *para-hydrogen*, and its rotational band spectrum shows less intense lines corresponding to *even* rotational quantum levels in the ground state. Electronic band spectra of ordinary hydrogen gas show alternate intense and less intense rotational lines. This must mean that ordinary hydrogen is a mixture of ortho- and para-hydrogen. From a comparison of the intensities of the rotational lines in ordinary hydrogen it has been established that in this gas the ratio of ortho- to para-hydrogen is fixed and is equal to three parts ortho to one part para in equilibrium with each other.

Para-hydrogen has been prepared and studied. Some of its properties, such as vapor pressure, boiling point, triple point, specific heat, and electrical conductivity, have been found to be different from those of ordinary hydrogen. It has been established, in fact, that the above properties of ordinary hydrogen are the averages of the properties of the ortho- and para-hydrogen composing the mixture.

Ortho and para states are observed only when the two atoms composing the molecule are identical and when they possess nuclear spin. When the nuclei of the atoms do not possess spin, or when the two atoms are different, no ortho-para states can exist. Thus D_2 exists in ortho and para states, but O_2 and HCl do not. In O_2 the nuclei do not have spin. Again, although nuclear spin is present in both H and Cl, the two atoms are different in hydrogen chloride and hence no ortho-para states are possible.

THE PARACHOR

One of the more reliable relations for the variation of the surface tension of a liquid with temperature is the McLeod equation,

$$\gamma = C(d_l - d_v)^4 \tag{19}$$

where γ is the surface tension of a liquid, d_l and d_v are, respectively, the density of the liquid and vapor at a given temperature, and C is a constant characteristic of the substance in question. If the fourth root of both sides of equation (19) is taken, we obtain

$$\gamma^{1/4} = C^{1/4}(d_l - d_v)$$

and hence on solution for $C^{1/4}$ and multiplication of both sides by the molecular weight of the liquid, M, there follows

$$C^{1/4} = \frac{\gamma^{1/4}}{(d_l - d_v)}$$
$$P = MC^{1/4} = \frac{M\gamma^{1/4}}{(d_l - d_v)} \tag{20}$$

The quantity P is called the *parachor*. Since both M and C are constants, the parachor for any substance should be a constant independent of temperature and determined only by the nature of the liquid. Of necessity d_l, d_v, and γ must all be determined at the same temperature for use in equation (20). When the temperature at which these are measured is considerably below the critical, d_v may be neglected in comparison to d_l, and we may write

$$P = \frac{M\gamma^{1/4}}{d_l} = \gamma^{1/4}V_m \tag{21}$$

where $V_m = M/d_l$ is the molar volume of the liquid.

The physical significance of the parachor may be obtained by comparing the parachors of two substances, A and B, namely,

$$\frac{P_A}{P_B} = \frac{\gamma_A^{1/4} V_{m(A)}}{\gamma_B^{1/4} V_{m(B)}}$$

At a temperature where the two liquids have equal surface tensions $\gamma_A = \gamma_B$, and therefore, the ratio of the two parachors will be the ratio of the two molar volumes. Consequently, comparison of the parachors of various substances is essentially equivalent to a comparison of their molar volumes under conditions of equal surface tension.

By studying the measured parachors of various related substances, Sugden was able to show that the parachor is an additive property of a liquid. The contributions to the parachor of a compound made by various atoms, bonds, and structures as thus found are summarized in Table 3. From this table it is evident that not only the kind and number of atoms involved in a molecule determine the parachor, but also in certain instances their manner of arrangement and binding. Thus the presence of a double bond contributes 23.2 units, of a triple bond 46.6 units, while the difference between cyclic and noncyclic arrangements appears in the ring contributions.

TABLE 3

ATOMIC AND STRUCTURAL PARACHOR CONTRIBUTIONS

Carbon	4.8	Double bond	23.2
Hydrogen	17.1	Triple bond	46.6
Nitrogen	12.5	3-membered ring	16.7
Oxygen	20.0	4-membered ring	11.6
Chlorine	54.3	5-membered ring	8.5
Bromine	68.0	6-membered ring	6.1
Iodine	91.0	Naphthalene ring	12.2
Fluorine	25.7	Semipolar bond	−1.6
Sulfur	48.2	Esters	−3.2
Phosphorus	37.7		

The use of Table 3 in calculating parachors may be illustrated with the following examples. Suppose it is desired to verify the structure of benzene, C_6H_6. The generally accepted structure of this compound is form I below,

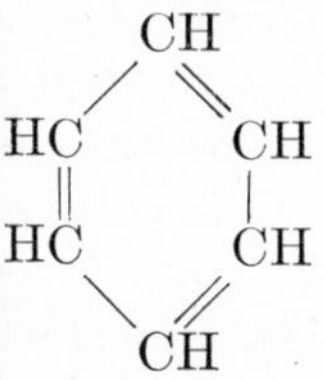

I

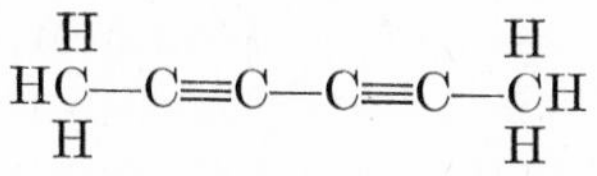

II

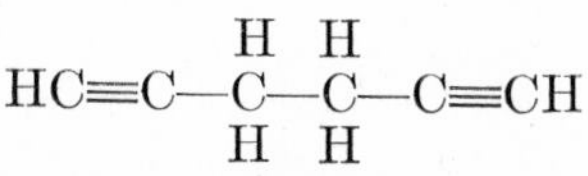

III

but forms II and III are also possibilities. Calculating the parachors for these three forms we have:

I

$$6 \text{ C} = 6 \times 4.8 = 28.8$$
$$6 \text{ H} = 6 \times 17.1 = 102.6$$
$$3(=\!=) = 3 \times 23.2 = 69.6$$

$$1 \bigcirc = 1 \times 6.1 = \underline{\quad 6.1}$$
$$207.1$$

II

$$6 \text{ C} = 6 \times 4.8 = 28.8$$
$$6 \text{ H} = 6 \times 17.1 = 102.6$$
$$2(\equiv) = 2 \times 46.6 = \underline{93.2}$$
$$224.6$$

III

$$6 \text{ C} = 6 \times 4.8 = 28.8$$
$$6 \text{ H} = 6 \times 17.1 = 102.6$$
$$2(\equiv) = 2 \times 46.6 = \underline{93.2}$$
$$224.6$$

The measured parachor of benzene is 206.3. This result is evidently in good accord with the calculated value for form I.

Although the above example may suggest the use of the parachor for determination of the structure of molecules, there is some question at present whether such a use is valid. Further, even when applied for differentiation of structure, the parachor is not capable of distinguishing structural isomers which do not differ from each other by a multiple bond or ring. For example, the measured parachors of *o*-, *m*-, and *p*-toluonitriles are, respectively, 290.6, 295.6, and 294.4, whereas calculation yields the same value for all, 292.9. Again, for a pair of isomers such as methyl valerate, $CH_3CH_2CH_2CH_2COOCH_3$, and propyl propionate, $CH_3CH_2COOCH_2CH_2CH_3$, both of which have the formula $C_6H_{12}O_2$, there is only one calculated parachor, 294.0, while two different values are observed, 292.5 for the first and 295.3 for the second.

THE MOLAR REFRACTION

Another quantity which is also an additive property is the *molar refraction*. Lorenz and Lorentz showed in 1880 that the expression

$$R_s = \left(\frac{n^2 - 1}{n^2 + 2} \right) \frac{1}{d} \tag{22}$$

should be a constant independent of temperature for any given substance. In this equation R_s is the *specific refraction* of the substance, n the index of refraction, and d is the density measured at the same temperature as n. From equation (22) the molar refraction R_m is obtained on multiplying R_s by the molecular weight of the substance M, namely,

$$R_m = R_s M = \left(\frac{n^2 - 1}{n^2 + 2}\right) \frac{M}{d} \qquad (23)$$

The index of refraction of any medium is the ratio of the velocity of light in a vacuum to that in the given medium. It is measured by means of such optical instruments as the Pulfrich, Abbé, or immersion refractometers. Measured in this manner the index of refraction is not constant but increases as the wave length of light is decreased. To obtain comparable results it is necessary, therefore, to use light of a fixed frequency. For this purpose the common practice is to employ the yellow light of the sodium D-line from, say, a sodium vapor lamp. However, white light may be employed in the Abbé or immersion refractometers through the use of an incorporated prism which eliminates color fringes and reduces the results to sodium light.

The molar refraction R_m defined by equation (23) has been demonstrated to be an additive property for any given substance provided all measurements are referred to a given wave length of light. The atomic and various bond contributions evaluated for sodium D-light are given in Table 4. The molar refraction, like the parachor, may be seen to depend

TABLE 4

MOLAR REFRACTION CONTRIBUTIONS
(For Sodium D-Light)

Carbon	2.418	Oxygen (in OH group, O—)	1.525
Hydrogen	1.100	Oxygen (in CO group, O=)	2.211
Chlorine	5.967	Oxygen (in ethers, O—)	1.643
Bromine	8.865	3-membered ring	0.71
Iodine	13.900	4-membered ring	0.48
Double bond	1.733		
Triple bond	2.398		

both on the number and nature of the atoms present, and also on the character of the binding. These values may be used to compare calculated with observed molar refractions in the same manner as explained for the parachor.

To illustrate the calculation of molar refractions we may take acetic acid, CH_3COOH. For this substance at 22.9° C the density is 1.046, the index of refraction for sodium light 1.3715, while the molecular weight is 60.05. The observed value of the molar refraction is, therefore,

$$R_m = \left(\frac{n^2 - 1}{n^2 + 2}\right) \frac{M}{d}$$

$$= \left[\frac{(1.3715)^2 - 1}{(1.3715)^2 + 2}\right] \frac{60.05}{1.046}$$

$$= 13.303$$

To compare with this value we find from Table 4 for acetic acid

$$
\begin{aligned}
2\,\mathrm{C} &= 2 \times 2.418 = 4.836 \\
4\,\mathrm{H} &= 4 \times 1.100 = 4.400 \\
1\,\mathrm{O}\!\!- &= 1 \times 1.525 = 1.525 \\
1\,\mathrm{O}\!\!= &= 1 \times 2.211 = \underline{2.211} \\
& 12.972
\end{aligned}
$$

The two values are seen to agree within 0.06 unit. Since the index of refraction is dimensionless, the units of the molar refraction are the units of M/d, i.e., volume. R_m is expressed thereby in cubic centimeters.

Calculated and observed molar refractions as a rule agree very closely. Exceptions arise only in open chain molecules with conjugated double bonds and in certain ring systems, where the phenomenon of *optical exaltation* is observed; i.e., the observed value is generally higher than the calculated. Further, the molar refraction principle can be applied to gases, liquids, as well as solids. The molar refraction of gases is usually found to be identical with that of the corresponding liquids. Solids are studied best by dissolving them first in a solvent and measuring the refractive index n and density d of the solution. The molar refraction of the solution, $R_{1,2}$, follows then as

$$
R_{1,2} = \left(\frac{n^2 - 1}{n^2 + 2}\right)\left(\frac{N_1 M_1 + N_2 M_2}{d}\right) \tag{24}
$$

where M_1 and M_2 are the molecular weights of the solvent and solute, while N_1 and N_2 are their mol fractions in solution. $R_{1,2}$ is in turn related to the individual molar refractions R_1 and R_2 by the equation

$$
R_{1,2} = N_1 R_1 + N_2 R_2 \tag{25}
$$

and hence when R_1 of the solvent is known, R_2 may be found from equation (25). This value of R_2 may then be compared with values calculated from the molar refraction contributions given in Table 4. Such application of molar refraction to mixtures works out very satisfactorily.

ELECTRICAL POLARIZATION OF MOLECULES

Any molecule is composed of positively charged nuclei and negatively charged electrons. When such a molecule is introduced into an electric field between two charged plates, the field will act to attract the positive nuclei toward the negative plate and the electrons toward the positive plate, as shown in Fig. 5(a). The result is thus an electrical distortion or *polarization* of the molecule to form an *electric dipole*, Fig. 5(b), with the positive charge at one end and the negative charge at the other. This polarization lasts only as long as the field is applied. When the field is removed the distortion disappears, and the molecule reverts to its original condition. For this reason this type of electrical distortion of a molecule is called *induced polarization,* and the electric dipole formed is called an *induced dipole.*

Unlike the original molecule, where the centers of positive and negative electricity were coincident, in the induced dipole these charges are separated by a distance l. Again, since the molecule as a whole is neutral, the positive charge at one end, z_+, must be equal but be opposite in sign to the negative charge, z_-, at the other end. To such an induced dipole

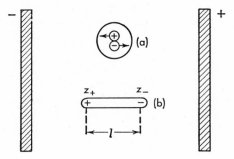

Fig. 5. Polarization of a Molecule in an Electric Field: (a) Original State; (b) Polarized.

may be ascribed an electric moment μ_i, which by definition is the value of the charge at *one* end of the dipole multiplied by the distance between the charges, namely,

$$\mu_i = zl \qquad (26)$$

The subscript i is used to denote that the dipole moment is induced only in an electric field.

The magnitude of μ_i is determined by the electric field strength X acting on the molecule in accordance with the relation

$$\mu_i = \alpha X \qquad (27)$$

Here α is a constant called the *polarizability* of the given molecule. Clausius and Mosotti have shown from electromagnetic theory that the constant α is in turn related to the *dielectric constant* D of the medium between the plates, i.e., of the molecules, by the equation

$$\left(\frac{D-1}{D+2}\right)\frac{M}{d} = \frac{4}{3}\pi N\alpha = P_i \qquad (28)$$

In this equation M and d are the molecular weight and density of the molecules, while N is Avogadro's number. Since both N and α are constants independent of temperature, the quantity P_i should also be a constant independent of the temperature and should be determined only by the nature of the molecules. P_i is called the *induced molar polarization* of the given substance, and it gives the electrical distortion produced in 1 mole of a substance when the electric field strength is unity. As D is unitless, the units of P_i are those of M/d, namely volume, and are expressed in cubic centimeters.

The dielectric constant is a property of any given medium. For a vacuum $D = 1$, but for any other medium D is greater than unity. The dielectric constant of a substance can be determined by measuring first the capacity of a condenser with a vacuum between the plates, C_0, and next the capacity of the same condenser when filled with the given substance, C. Then the dielectric constant follows from electrical theory as

$$D = \frac{C}{C_0} \tag{29}$$

To measure the capacity, various electronic circuits are available which use alternating currents with frequencies of 10^6 to 10^7 cycles per second.

With the dielectric constant and density of a substance measured at a given temperature, the molar polarization can be calculated by equation (28). When this is done, it is found that the molar polarizations of such substances as oxygen, carbon dioxide, nitrogen, and methane are constant and independent of the temperature. On the other hand, for substances such as hydrogen chloride, chloroform, nitrobenzene, and methyl chloride the molar polarization is not constant but decreases as the temperature is raised. The explanation of this anomalous behavior has proved of great import to studies of molecular structure.

PERMANENT DIPOLE MOMENTS

To account for the variation of the molar polarization of certain substances with temperature, Peter Debye made in 1912 the significant suggestion that such molecules possess a *permanent* dipole moment of their own. The permanent dipole moment would arise from the fact that in some molecules the centers of positive and negative electricity may not coincide. As a result there would be present in the molecule even outside of an electric field positive and negative centers of electrical gravity a distance l apart; and, consequently, such a molecule will be a permanent dipole and possess a permanent dipole moment μ of magnitude zl. Outside of an electric field the permanent dipoles of various molecules in an aggregation would, because of thermal agitation, be oriented more or less randomly in space. However, when placed in an electric field two disturbing effects will arise. First, the electric field will tend to rotate and orient the permanent dipoles in the direction of the field; and second, the field will tend to polarize the molecules. Were the molecules perfectly stationary, the orienting effect

of the electric field would result in an alignment of the dipoles at an angle
of 180° to the direction of the field and 90° to the condenser plates.
But the perfect alignment of the dipoles is disturbed by thermal agitation of the molecules, and hence the resulting orientation will be some
point intermediate between the original position of the dipole in space
and the final completely oriented position. This situation in an electric
field is illustrated in Fig. 6, where (a) gives the initial orientation of the
molecule with the permanent dipole and (b) the orientation resulting from
the effect of the applied field.

In the absence of a permanent dipole moment in a molecule the molar
polarization, as calculated from the measured dielectric constant by
means of equation (28), gives only the induced molar polarization P_i.

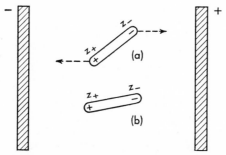

Fig. 6.   Polarization of a Molecule with Permanent Dipole: (a) Original State; (b)
Polarized and Oriented Position.

On the other hand, when a dipole moment is present, this quantity
measures not only the induced polarization, but also the *molar orientation polarization P_o*. The *total molar polarization P_t* is, therefore,

$$P_t = \left(\frac{D-1}{D+2}\right)\frac{M}{d} = P_i + P_o \tag{30}$$

As before, the induced molar polarization is given by the Clausius-
Mosotti equation, namely, $P_i = \frac{4}{3}\pi N\alpha$. Again, Debye showed that the
orientation polarization P_o should be equal to

$$P_o = \frac{4}{3}\pi N\left(\frac{\mu^2}{3\,kT}\right) \tag{31}$$

where μ is the *permanent dipole moment* of the molecule, k is the gas
constant per molecule, i.e., R/N, and T is the temperature. Substituting
these values of P_i and P_o into equation (30), the total molar polarization,
as given by the measured dielectric constant, becomes

$$P_t = \left(\frac{D-1}{D+2}\right)\frac{M}{d} = \frac{4}{3}\pi N\alpha + \frac{4}{3}\pi N\left(\frac{\mu^2}{3\,kT}\right) \tag{32}$$

In equation (32) the first term on the right is a constant which may be represented by A. In the second term, again, all quantities are constant except T, and hence this term may be written as B/T. With these substitutions equation (32) takes the form

$$P_t = \left(\frac{D-1}{D+2}\right)\frac{M}{d} = A + \frac{B}{T} \tag{33}$$

which shows that *for molecules with permanent dipoles the total molar polarization P_t should vary linearly with $1/T$*. Further, the slope of a plot of P_t vs. $1/T$ should be equal to

$$B = \frac{4\pi N\mu^2}{9\,k} \tag{34a}$$

from which, on insertion of the values of N and k, μ should follows as

$$\mu = 0.0128\,\sqrt{B}\times 10^{-18} \tag{34b}$$

Therefore, by plotting P_t against $1/T$ and taking the slope B of the linear plot, μ may be calculated from equation (34b), and thereby the permanent dipole moment of the molecule in question may be found.

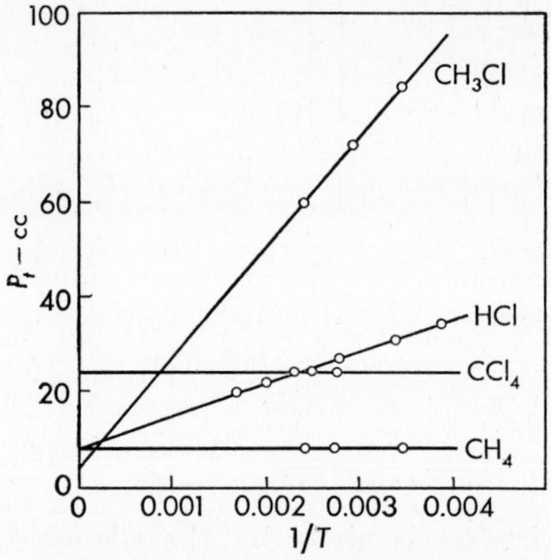

Fig. 7. Variation of Total Polarization with Temperature for Polar and Nonpolar Compounds.

Debye's theory of permanent dipole moments is confirmed by experimental data in every respect. In Fig. 7 are given plots of P_t vs. $1/T$ for hydrogen chloride and methyl chloride which show that for these substances P_t varies linearly with $1/T$, and hence these substances must possess permanent dipole moments. However, since the molar polarizations of methane and carbon tetrachloride are independent of temperature, no permanent dipole moments are present in these substances, and all electrical polarization is due, therefore, to induction.

Molecules possessing permanent dipole moments are said to be *polar* and those without permanent dipoles *nonpolar*. The units of the dipole moment are those of the electronic charge multiplied by a distance. As the electronic charge is of the order of 10^{-10} electrostatic unit and molecular distances are of the order of 10^{-8} cm, the dipole moments of molecules will always have a magnitude of $10^{-10} \times 10^{-8} = 10^{-18}$. The quantity

10^{-18} is called a *Debye unit*, symbol D. A dipole moment may be given thus as 1.6×10^{-18} or 1.6 D.

DETERMINATION OF DIPOLE MOMENTS

Equation (32) should be applicable primarily to gases and vapors. For such substances all that need be done is to measure the dielectric constants and densities at several temperatures, calculate from these P_t, and plot the latter against $1/T$. If the plot is independent of temperature, the substance possesses no permanent dipole moment. If, however, P_t varies with $1/T$, a permanent dipole is present and μ is evaluated from the slope by equation (34b).

TABLE 5

DIPOLE MOMENTS OF VARIOUS MOLECULES*

(In Debye Units)

Inorganic Molecules	μ	Organic Molecules	μ
H_2, Cl_2, Br_2, I_2, N_2	0	CH_4, C_2H_6, C_2H_4, C_2H_2	0
CO_2, CS_2, $SnCl_4$, SnI_4	0	CCl_4, CBr_4	0
HCl	1.03	C_6H_6, naphthalene, diphenyl	0
HBr	0.78	CH_3Cl	1.86
HI	0.38	RCl	2.04
H_2O	1.84	CH_3Br	1.78
H_2S	1.10	RBr	2.0
HCN	2.93	RCN	3.57
NH_3	1.46	ROH	1.65
SO_2	1.6	RNH_2	1.3
N_2O	0.14	CH_3COOH	1.4
CO	0.12	*p*-dichlorbenzene	0
PH_3	0.55	*m*-dichlorbenzene	1.48
PCl_3	0.9	*o*-dichlorbenzene	2.25
$SbCl_3$	3.75	*p*-chlornitrobenzene	2.55
$AsCl_3$	2.15	*m*-chlornitrobenzene	3.38
$AgClO_4$	4.7	*o*-chlornitrobenzene	4.25

* R in this table is C_2H_5 or any higher straight-chain paraffinic group.

With substances which are not gaseous, or which cannot be converted readily to a gas, an alternate procedure is employed. First several *dilute* solutions of the substance to be investigated are prepared in a *nonpolar* solvent, such as benzene, carbon tetrachloride, or carbon disulfide, and the dielectric constants and densities of these are measured at several temperatures. Next at each temperature are calculated the molar polarizations of the solutions, $P_{1,2}$, from the relation

$$P_{1,2} = \left(\frac{D-1}{D+2}\right)\left(\frac{N_1M_1 + N_2M_2}{d}\right) \tag{35}$$

where N_1 and N_2 are the mol fractions of solvent and solute in the solution, M_1 and M_2 the respective molecular weights, and d the density of the solution. Third, from $P_{1,2}$, defined also as

$$P_{1,2} = N_1 P_1 + N_2 P_2 \qquad (36)$$

where P_1 and P_2 are the molar polarizations of the solvent and solute, P_2 of the solute is calculated from the known values of N_1, N_2, and P_1. If the values of P_2 thus determined are constant at each temperature for a number of concentrations, P_2 is the molar polarization of the pure solute. However, if P_2 is found to vary with concentration due to effect of the solvent, then P_2 is plotted against N_2, and the curve is extrapolated to $N_2 = 0$ to yield P_2 freed of solvent influence. Finally, the values of P_2 thus obtained at each temperature are plotted against $1/T$, and μ is found from the slope in the same manner as for gases.

Other procedures are also available, but these need not be described here. Some results for the permanent dipole moments of various substances obtained either in the gas phase or in solution are shown in Table 5.

MOLECULAR STRUCTURE AND DIPOLE MOMENTS

The absence of a dipole moment in molecules such as hydrogen, chlorine, and nitrogen indicates that the electron pairs binding the atoms are situated equidistant between the constituents of the molecule. Were this not true a dipole moment would be present. Again, in linear molecules such as carbon dioxide and carbon disulfide, even if the electron pairs are not equidistant between the atoms, the electric moment on one side of the molecule balances the moment on the other side, and the net dipole moment is therefore zero. The same considerations apply also to such molecules as stannic chloride, carbon tetrachloride, and the paraffin hydrocarbons, both saturated and unsaturated. In aromatic molecules such as benzene, naphthalene, and diphenyl the absence of a net dipole moment can be accounted most readily on the basis of a planar structure for these. On the other hand, the presence of a dipole moment in the hydrogen halides and carbon monoxide definitely points to a nonequidistant distribution of the electron pairs between the two atoms. In all probability this pair lies closer to the halogens and oxygen than to the hydrogen or carbon, and this leads to the formation of a dipole. In a similar manner may be explained the dipole moments appearing in the alkyl halides, nitriles, amines, and alcohols.

The fact that water, hydrogen sulfide, and sulfur dioxide have appreciable dipole moments rules out linear structures for these molecules. If we postulate that the two hydrogens in water and hydrogen sulfide, and the two oxygens in sulfur dioxide, line on the same side of the central atom, there will be no tendency for the moments to cancel each other, and an appreciable net moment will result. Quantitative calculations indicate that this is the only way in which the dipole moments of these molecules can be accounted for. In a like manner the dipole moment of ammonia can be explained on the basis of a triangular pyramidal structure in which the nitrogen is situated at the apex of the pyramid, and the hydrogens lie at the other three corners.

It is of interest to observe that in *p*-dichlorbenzene, where the chlorines are at opposite ends of the benzene ring, the dipole moment is zero, and hence electrical symmetry is present. However, when substitution of the second chlorine takes place in a meta or ortho position, the symmetry is destroyed and a dipole appears. Furthermore, the dipole is larger the greater the asymmetry, as may be seen from a comparison of the μ values of *m*- and *o*-dichlorbenzenes. On the other hand, when the two substituents in the benzene ring are different, as in chlornitrobenzene, dipole moments are present in all three forms. Nevertheless the dipole moment of the para form is least and increases successively with meta and ortho substitution.

ABSORPTION OF LIGHT BY LIQUIDS AND SOLUTIONS

A gaseous molecule on being irradiated with light of suitable wave length will first be excited and on return to its original state will emit a band spectrum. Investigation of molecules in this manner is called study in *emission*. However, a molecule may also be studied in *absorption*, in which case the energies required for excitation of various transitions are ascertained. For this purpose a gaseous substance is exposed to continuous radiation from which the molecule removes light of frequencies which correspond to those necessary to cause rotational, vibrational, or electronic transitions. The frequencies thus absorbed by a molecule can readily be determined by inspecting the transmitted light in a spectrograph. There in place of a continuous spectrum will be found light portions interspersed with dark spaces which correspond to the frequencies of the removed light. Of necessity the positions of the dark spaces will be the same as those of emitted light for the same internal transitions.

On the other hand, liquids and solutions yield absorption bands which are continuous. This continuity may be due either to overlapping of vibrational bands or to destruction of quantized absorption by interaction of intermolecular with intramolecular energies. Whatever the cause, the absorption appears usually as a continuous band extending over part of the spectrum. The spectral range where the maximum absorption takes place depends on the energy involved in the electronic transition responsible for the absorption. If the energy of the latter is large, the absorption will occur primarily in the ultraviolet. With smaller energies, however, the absorption band will appear in the near ultraviolet or in the visible light regions.

The color exhibited by a substance is determined by the light the substance transmits in the visible range, and this, in turn, is related to the spectral range in which the substance absorbs light. Any substance that absorbs only in the ultraviolet will transmit all white light, and as a consequence the substance will appear colorless. If, however, the substance shows a color in white light, the color indicates the light which was *not* absorbed. For instance, carbon black has the particular color because it absorbs nonselectively the white light that reaches it. Again, sodium chloride solutions are colorless because they do not absorb selectively any light in the visible region. On the other hand, a copper sulfate solution is blue because it absorbs out of the white light the yellow and red, leaving the blue to be transmitted to the eye. It is evident that the characteristic of the absorbing substance is not the light it transmits but rather the light it absorbs. Consequently it is by studying the latter that information about the absorbing substance can be obtained. Further, it also follows that only colored substances can be studied in the visible region. Substances which are colorless do not absorb white light appreciably, and hence these must be investigated in the ultraviolet.

SPECTROPHOTOMETRY

In the spectral range where absorption is appreciable the intensity of the initial light is reduced greatly on passing through the absorbing medium. On the contrary, to either side of the absorption band the intensity is reduced considerably less or not at all. The position of an absorption band can be ascertained, therefore, by measuring the decrease in intensity of the original light after passage through an absorbing medium as a function of the wave length. Then, on plotting the fraction of the original light absorbed against the wave length, the position of the absorption band will be given by a maximum in the curve. Conversely, if we plot instead the fraction of light transmitted vs. the wave length, a minimum in the plot will indicate the position of maximum absorption.

The decrease in intensity of incident light of *any given wave length* on passage through an absorbing substance is given by *Lambert's law*. This law states that the rate of decrease of intensity with thickness of absorbing material, $-dI_t/dl$, where I_t is the intensity at thickness l, is proportional to the intensity of the light at point l; namely, that

$$-\frac{dI_t}{dl} = kI_t \qquad (37)$$

In equation (37) the proportionality constant k is called the *absorption coefficient* and is characteristic of the absorbing medium. Since at $l = 0$ we have the original intensity I_0, the intensity I_t at any point l can be found from equation (37) by integration between these limits. We obtain thus

$$\int_{I_0}^{I_t} \frac{dI_t}{I_t} = \int_{l=0}^{l=l} - kdl$$

$$\ln \frac{I_t}{I_0} = -kl \tag{38a}$$

$$\frac{I_t}{I_0} = e^{-kl} \tag{38b}$$

The last equation may be written also as

$$\frac{I_t}{I_0} = 10^{-k'l} \tag{39}$$

in which case $k' = k/2.303$ is the *extinction coefficient* of the substance. Consequently, $\ln I_t$ falls off linearly, and I_t exponentially, with the distance l the light travels through the absorbing medium.

For absorbing solutes the decrease in intensity with l is proportional not only to I_t, but also to the concentration of the solution C. For solutions, therefore,

$$\frac{-dI_t}{dl} = \varepsilon I_t C \tag{40}$$

where ε, called the *molar absorption coefficient*, is a proportionality constant determined by the nature of the absorbing solute and the wave length of light used. Integration of equation (40) between the same limits as before, and at constant C, yields

$$\int_{I_0}^{I_t} \frac{dI_t}{I_t} = - \int_{l=0}^{l=l} \varepsilon C dl$$

$$\ln \frac{I_t}{I_0} = -\varepsilon C l \tag{41a}$$

and $$\frac{I_t}{I_0} = e^{-\varepsilon C l} \tag{41b}$$

Equations (40) and (41) are expressions of *Beer's law* for absorption of light by solutions. These show that the intensity of the transmitted light falls off exponentially with both C and l, or that the logarithm of the transmitted intensity I_t is proportional to both the concentration and the length of the absorbing path.

As before the natural logarithm can be changed in equation (41b) to base 10, in which case

$$\frac{I_t}{I_0} = 10^{-\varepsilon' Cl} \tag{42}$$

The constant $\varepsilon' = \varepsilon/2.303$ is called the *molar extinction coefficient* of the absorbing solution.

The ratio I_t/I_0 is determined with some form of spectrophotometer. At present spectrophotometers utilizing photoelectric cells are available which give I_t/I_0 directly. Once I_t/I_0 for a pure liquid is determined and the thickness of the cell used is known, the absorption or extinction coefficient of the substance for the given wave length can readily be calculated. Similarly, from the measured I_t/I_0 and the known values of l and C may be found the molar absorption or extinction coefficients. Next, to ascertain the wave length at which maximum absorption takes place, we may plot (a) these coefficients or their logarithms against the wave length λ or (b) the ratios I_t/I_0 or $\log I_t/I_0$ vs. λ. On any one of these plots the wave length at which appreciable absorption occurs will be indicated by a minimum. Each of these minima corresponds to a separate electronic excitation of the molecule.

Absorption spectrophotometry finds application in the definition of the spectral colors of indicators, in the exact definition of color of solutions, liquids, and solids, in analysis, and in the solution of various structural problems.

INTERMOLECULAR FORCES

Throughout the book frequent reference has been made to intermolecular or van der Waals forces and the important role these play in deviation of gases from ideal behavior, liquefaction, and the stability of nonionic crystals. However, very little has been said about the nature of these forces or their cause.

Intermolecular forces leading to attraction are due to three actions called, respectively, (a) the orientation, (b) the induction, and (c) the dispersion effects. There is also a repulsion which comes into play between the molecules on close approach. The orientation effect, present only in molecules with permanent dipoles, arises from the attractions and orientations such dipoles exercise upon each other. For molecules with dipole moment μ, this force of attraction between a pair of molecules has been shown to be

$$f_o = \left(\frac{4\,\mu^4}{kT}\right)\frac{1}{r^7} \tag{43}$$

where k is the Boltzmann constant, T the absolute temperature, and r the distance of separation of the molecules. Again, the presence of permanent dipoles causes polarization in neighboring molecules, and thereby induced dipoles. Interaction of the induced and permanent dipoles leads to an attractive force, f_i, between a pair of molecules given by

$$f_i = (12\ \alpha\mu^2)\ \frac{1}{r^7} \tag{44}$$

In this expression for the force resulting from the induction effect r and μ have the same significance as before, while α is the polarizability of the molecules.

The existence of the dispersion effect was first pointed out by F. London, and for this reason the forces involved here are frequently referred to as London as well as dispersion forces. London showed that, due to vibrations of electron clouds with respect to the nuclei of atoms in a molecule, tiny instantaneous dipoles of a specific orientation are formed. These dipoles induce dipole moments in neighboring atoms, and the latter interact with the original dipoles to produce an attraction between the molecules. For a pair of molecules the attractive force, f_d, due to this dispersion effect is given by

$$f_d = \left(\frac{9\ h\nu_0\alpha^2}{2}\right) \frac{1}{r^7} \tag{45}$$

where h is Planck's constant and ν_0 is a characteristic frequency for the oscillation of the charge distribution.

Finally, the repulsion between molecules arises from the interaction on close approach of the electron atmospheres and nuclei of the atoms in one molecule with those in another. As a result a repulsive force, f_r, is developed, whose magnitude can be represented by

$$f_r = -\frac{B}{r^n} \tag{46}$$

where B is a constant for a given substance and n may range from 10 to 13. On adding equations (43)–(46), we obtain for the total force f acting between a pair of molecules

$$\begin{aligned}
f &= f_0 + f_i + f_d + f_r \\
&= \left(\frac{4\ \mu^4}{kT}\right)\frac{1}{r^7} + (12\ \alpha\mu^2)\ \frac{1}{r^7} + \left(\frac{9\ h\nu_0\alpha^2}{2}\right)\frac{1}{r^7} - \frac{B}{r^n} \\
&= \frac{A}{r^7} - \frac{B}{r^n}
\end{aligned} \tag{47}$$

where
$$A = \left(\frac{4\ \mu^4}{kT}\right) + (12\ \alpha\mu^2) + \left(\frac{9}{2}\ h\nu_0\alpha^2\right) \tag{48}$$

From equation (47) it may be seen that the attractive forces between molecules are inversely proportional to the seventh power of the distance between them, while the force of repulsion is proportional to a higher inverse power of the distance. Further, equation (48) shows that in molecules possessing no permanent dipole moments, i.e., $\mu = 0$, only the dispersion forces are operative, and hence these are responsible for the van der Waals forces in such substances as the rare gases, H_2, Cl_2, and the straight chain hydrocarbons. On the other hand, for molecules which have a permanent dipole moment all the effects contribute to the observed van der Waals interactions.

TABLE 6

COMPARISON OF ENERGIES AND DISTANCES INVOLVED
IN VARIOUS INTERACTIONS

Interaction	Bond Energy (Kcal mole^{-1})	Bond Distance (Å)
Primary valence	50–200+	1–2
Hydrogen bonding	4–10	2–3
Intermolecular attraction	0.5–5	3–5

Finally, Table 6 gives a comparison of the energies per mole and distances involved in primary valence, hydrogen bonding, and van der Waals attractions. From this table it may be seen that primary valence involves the highest energies, van der Waals interactions the smallest, with the hydrogen bonds being intermediate between the two.

REFERENCES FOR FURTHER READING

1. W. R. Brode, *Chemical Spectroscopy*, John Wiley & Sons, Inc., New York, 1947.
2. A. G. Gaydon, *Dissociation Energies and Spectra of Diatomic Molecules*, Chapman and Hall, Ltd., London, 1947.
3. Gordy, Smith, and Trambarulo, *Microwave Spectroscopy*, John Wiley & Sons, Inc., New York, 1953.
4. G. Herzberg, *Infrared and Raman Spectra of Polyatomic Molecules*, D. Van Nostrand Company, Inc., New York, 1945.
5. G. Herzberg, *Spectra of Diatomic Molecules*, D. Van Nostrand Company, Inc., New York, 1950.
6. R. J. W. LeFévre, *Dipole Moments*, Methuen & Co. Ltd., London, 1948.
7. M. G. Mellon, *Analytical Absorption Spectroscopy*, John Wiley & Sons, Inc., New York, 1950.
8. L. Pauling, *Nature of the Chemical Bond*, Cornell University Press, Ithaca, N. Y., 1940.
9. Rice and Teller, *The Structure of Matter*, John Wiley & Sons, Inc., New York, 1949.
10. Sirkin and Dyatkina, *The Structure of Molecules and the Chemical Bond*, Interscience Publishers, Inc., New York, 1950.

11. C. S. Smyth, *Dielectric Behavior and Structure*, McGraw-Hill Book Company, Inc., New York, 1955.
12. A. Weissberger, *Physical Methods of Organic Chemistry*, Interscience Publishers, Inc., New York, 1949, Vol. I, Chaps. XX, XXI, XXII, XXIII, and XXIV.

PROBLEMS

1. Show the external electronic configuration of the following substances: (a) H_2O_2, (b) CH_3COOH, (c) H_2SO_4, (d) butadiene (C_4H_6), and (e) $HClO_4$.
2. Show the electronic configurations of the following complex ions: (a) $[Cu(NH_3)_4]^{++}$, (b) $[(CH_3)_4N]^+$, and (c) $[Ag(CN)_2]^-$. Which of the bonds are covalent and which are coordinate covalent?
3. If N can have no more than eight electrons in its valence shell, what is the most reasonable electronic formula for R_3NO, where R is an alkyl group?
4. In the CO molecule the binding energy appears to be greater than may be expected for a C–O double bond. Explain what resonating structures of CO might account for this fact.
5. Experimental evidence indicates that liquid HCN and liquid NH_3 are associated through hydrogen. Write electronic formulas to show how these associations may take place.
6. From the internuclear distance of 1.15 Å for NO, calculate the moment of inertia for the molecule. What spectral frequency in wave numbers will be emitted when NO falls from the first excited rotational state to the ground rotational state? Assume that no changes take place in vibrational or electronic energy.   *Ans.* $I = 1.64 \times 10^{-30}$ g-cm^2.
7. Using the data of problem 6, calculate the rotational frequencies for $J = 2, 3$, and 4.
8. From Table 2 calculate the wave length in angstroms of the fundamental, and the first and second harmonic vibration frequencies of the I_2 molecule. What will be the wave length of the fundamental for $J = \pm 1$?
                              Ans. For fundamental $\lambda = 467{,}300$ Å.
9. Repeat problem 8 for $J = \pm 2, \pm 3, \pm 4$. What are the corresponding frequencies in wave numbers?
10. What is the energy difference in calories per mole between I_2 in its lowest energy level and I_2 in its first vibrational and rotational state?
                              Ans. 612.2 cal/mole.
11. What is the energy difference in calories per mole between I_2 in its lowest energy level and I_2 in its first excited rotational state, the vibrational level being the same?   *Ans.* 0.22 cal/mole.
12. How many principal moments of inertia and fundamental modes of vibration should methyl fluoride have?
13. The heat of dissociation of Cl_2 gas is 56,800 cal/mole. Calculate the work in calories required to separate the two Cl atoms a distance of 0.1 Å from their equilibrium position in the molecule. Repeat the calculation for a distance of 0.03 Å. Use any necessary data given in Table 2.
14. Calculate the zero point energy of HCl in cal/mole.
15. The band spectrum of Br_2 terminates at a wave length of 5107 Å. The energy of the excited atoms formed in the dissociation is 10,400 cal in excess of that possessed by the normal atoms. What is the energy of dissociation of Br_2 in cal/mole?   *Ans.* 45,500 cal/mole.

16. Using the molecular constants for I_2 given in Table 2, calculate the potential energy as a function of the internuclear distance of separation, and construct a Morse potential energy curve for I_2.

17. Given the following bond distances

$$
\begin{array}{ll}
\text{C—C} & 1.54 \text{ Å} \\
\text{C—H} & 1.06 \\
\text{C—Cl} & 1.78
\end{array}
$$

calculate the atomic radii of H, C, and Cl on the supposition that the atoms are spheres which contact each other.

18. At 20° C the surface tension of $C_2H_5OH(l)$ is 22.27 dyne cm^{-1}, while the density is 0.7893 g cc^{-1}. Assuming the density of the vapor to be negligible, calculate the parachor for this substance.　　　*Ans.* 126.8.

19. At 20° C the vapor pressure of $C_2H_5OH(l)$ is 44.5 mm Hg. Using the data given in the preceding problem, and assuming the vapor to behave as an ideal gas, calculate the parachor for the alcohol.

20. The surface tension of allyl alcohol is 25.8 dyne cm^{-1} and the density 0.854 g cc^{-1} at 20° C. From parachor evidence which of the following two structures should be the correct one

$$
\text{CH}_2\!\!=\!\!\text{CH—CH}_2\text{OH} \quad \text{or} \quad
\begin{array}{c}
\text{CH}_2 \\
| \quad\backslash \\
\quad\quad \text{CHOH} \\
| \quad/ \\
\text{CH}_2
\end{array}
$$

21. Predict from calculated parachor values the surface tensions at 20° C of cyclohexane and brombenzene, and compare with observed values. The densities of the two substances are, respectively, 0.779 and 1.495 g cc^{-1}.
　　　Ans. Calc. 24.5 and 36.4; obs. 25.3 and 36.5 dynes/cm.

22. Calculate the parachor of ethyl lactate, $CH_3CHOHCOOC_2H_5$, and compare your result with the experimental value of 268.5.

23. Calculate the molar refractions of the following compounds

Compounds	Density	Refractive Index
(a) Methyl chloroformate	1.223	1.3868
(b) Tertiary butyl chloride	0.843	1.3869
(c) Secondary butyl alcohol	0.806	1.3924

and compare your results with those obtained from the additivity rule.
　　　Ans. (a) Obs. 18.18, calc. 17.84.

24. The density of allyl chloride ($CH_2\!\!=\!\!CH—CH_2Cl$) is 0.938 g cc^{-1} at 20° C. Calculate the index of refraction, and compare your answer with the observed value of 1.4154.

25. The refractive index of naphthalene decahydride ($C_{10}H_{18}$) is 1.4804 at 18° C. Calculate the density and compare with the observed value of 0.895 g cc^{-1}.

26. The density of ethyl alcohol at 20° C is 0.789 g cc^{-1} while that of methyl alcohol is 0.792 g cc^{-1}. Assuming that these substances form an ideal solution, calculate by using Table 4 the refractive index of a solution containing 50% by weight of each constituent.　　　*Ans.* 1.348.

27. The dielectric constant of $CH_4(g)$ at 0° C and 1 atm pressure is 1.00094. Assuming that methane behaves as an ideal gas, calculate (a) the induced molar polarization and (b) the polarizability of this substance.
　　　Ans. (a) 7.02 cc; (b) 2.79×10^{-24} cc.

28. For $SO_2(g)$ at 0° C and 1 atm pressure the dielectric constant is 1.00993. This gas has a permanent dipole moment of 1.6 D. Assuming that SO_2 behaves as an ideal gas, calculate per mole (a) the total, (b) the orientation, and (c) the induced polarizations.

29. From the following data giving the dielectric constant D at various temperatures, determine the dipole moment of gaseous HCl by a graphical method:

D	$t°$ C
1.0076	−75
1.0046	0
1.0026	100
1.0016	200

The pressure is 1 atm in every case. Assume the ideal gas law in calculating the density of HCl.   *Ans.* 1.18 *D.*

30. From the dipole moment calculate the mean distance between the centers of positive and negative electricity in the HBr molecule.

31. The dielectric constant of cyclohexane at 20° C is 2.033 while its density is 0.7784 g cc^{-1}. In turn, for a solution of ethyl ether in cyclohexane, for which the mole fraction of solute is 0.04720 and density is 0.7751 g cc^{-1}, the dielectric constant is 2.109. Assuming the solution to be ideal, find the total molar polarization of the ethyl ether.

32. A certain glass filter, 0.35 cm in thickness, transmits 45.3% of light of $\lambda = 6000$ Å. What are the absorption and extinction coefficients of the glass?
                       Ans. $k = 2.26$ cm^{-1}; $k' = 0.982$ cm^{-1}.

33. Suppose it is desired to use the filter mentioned in the preceding problem to reduce the transmission of light of $\lambda = 6000$ Å to 0.1%. What thickness of filter will be required?

34. Using a cell 1 cm in thickness, the following data for K_2CrO_4 solutions were obtained at $\lambda = 3660$ Å in a photoelectric colorimeter:

I_t/I_0	Concentration (moles/liter × 10⁴)
0.420	0.8
0.275	1.2
0.175	1.6
0.110	2.0

Plot these data to test Beer's law, and from the plot determine the molar absorption and extinction coefficients of K_2CrO_4 at this wave length.

35. Using the results of the preceding problem, calculate what will be the per cent of light of $\lambda = 3660$ Å transmitted by a 1.0×10^{-4} molar solution of K_2CrO_4 when placed in a cell 5 cm in thickness.

36. For argon $\mu = 0$ and $h\nu_0 = 2.47 \times 10^{-11}$ erg. Calculate the total attractive force between two argon molecules separated by a distance of 4Å.
                       Ans. 1.80×10^{-6} dyne.

37. For water $\mu = 1.84 \times 10^{-18}$ esu cm, $\alpha = 1.48 \times 10^{-24}$ cc, and $h\nu_0 = 2.88 \times 10^{-11}$ erg. Calculate (a) the total force of attraction at 300° K between a pair of water molecules 5 Å apart, and (b) the percentages of the total force contributed by the orientation, induction, and dispersion effects.

38. Assuming that for a certain substance $A = B = 15.0 \times 10^{-2}$ for force in dynes and distance in Å, construct a plot of the total force operating between two molecules of the substance as a function of distance from $r = 0$ to $r = 5$ Å. Take $n = 10$.

23

Photochemistry

Photochemistry concerns itself with the study of the effect of radiant energy on chemical reactions and with the rates and mechanisms by which reactions initiated by light proceed.

Ordinary or *thermal* reactions are initiated by activation brought about through molecular collisions. It is characteristic of all such reactions that they can occur only when the reactions are accompanied by a free energy decrease. If a free energy increase is involved, no reaction is possible. However, thermal activation is not the only means by which the energy of atoms and molecules can be raised sufficiently to cause reaction. We have seen that atoms and molecules can absorb radiation. In fact, with absorption of a sufficiently large quantum of radiant energy a molecule may be ruptured. Such absorption of light by an atom or molecule leads to its excitation; and if the activation is sufficiently great, chemical reaction may result. It is in this manner that absorbed light can affect the rate of a chemical reaction and frequently bring about chemical changes under conditions where thermal activation alone would not be effective.

The rate of thermal uncatalyzed reactions at any fixed concentration can be varied only by change of temperature. With photochemical reactions, however, the rate can be controlled also by varying the intensity of the light used for irradiation. In the latter reactions the number of molecules activated depends on the intensity of the light, and hence the concentration of activated molecules will be proportional to the light intensity to which the reactant is exposed. With sufficiently intense light sources it is thus possible to attain reaction rates at ordinary temperatures which would not result thermally except at considerably elevated temperatures. Again, since photochemical activation does not depend to any degree on temperature, the rate of activation is usually temperature independent. Any increase in the rate of a photochemical reaction with temperature is due primarily to thermal reactions which follow the activation process.

Further, not only spontaneous reactions can be made to proceed photochemically, but also many reactions attended by a free energy increase. In the spontaneous reactions the light acts to speed up the thermal reactions, i.e., it acts essentially as a catalyst. In the nonspontaneous reactions, on the other hand, the radiant energy supplied to the system may increase the free energy of the reactants sufficiently to make the ΔF negative. An outstanding example of such a process is *photosynthesis*. Under the action of sunlight and promoted by chlorophyll (the green coloring matter of vegetation), carbon dioxide and water are combined in plants into complex carbohydrate materials and oxygen. On removal of the light the products oxidize slowly back to carbon dioxide and water, releasing at the same time the energy accumulated from the sun's radiation. Other examples of such reversals of thermodynamically spontaneous processes are the photochemical conversion of oxygen to ozone and the decomposition of HCl to hydrogen and chlorine.

THE GROTTHUS-DRAPER LAW

The Grotthus-Draper law, referred to also as the first law of photochemistry, states that *only light which is absorbed can be effective in producing chemical change*. However, it does not necessarily follow that absorbed light will always cause reaction. Atoms and molecules can absorb radiation only to reemit it either as a line or band spectrum. Under such conditions the absorption does not result in reaction. The circumstances under which absorption of light does lead to reaction will be described later.

For application of the Grotthus-Draper law to processes where absorption of light does lead to chemical change it is necessary to know the amount of light absorbed. In general light directed toward a given absorbing medium will be partially reflected, partially absorbed by the medium, and partially transmitted. If we let I_0 be the intensity of the light that *does enter* the medium and I_t the intensity of the transmitted light, then the intensity of the light absorbed I_a must be

$$I_a = I_0 - I_t \tag{1}$$

Now, for substances other than solutions or gases the intensity of the transmitted light is given by Lambert's law, equation (38b) of Chapter

22, namely,

$$I_t = I_0 e^{-kl}$$

Again, for solutions or gases I_t is given by Beer's law, equation (41b) of the same chapter,

$$I_t = I_0 e^{-\epsilon Cl}$$

From these relations the light absorbed by media other than solutions or gases follows then as

$$\begin{aligned} I_a &= I_0 - I_0 e^{-kl} \\ &= I_0(1 - e^{-kl}) \end{aligned} \tag{2}$$

while that absorbed by solutions or gases is

$$\begin{aligned} I_a &= I_0 - I_0 e^{-\epsilon Cl} \\ &= I_0(1 - e^{-\epsilon Cl}) \end{aligned} \tag{3}$$

THE EINSTEIN LAW OF PHOTOCHEMICAL EQUIVALENCE

Another principle of importance is the *law of photochemical equivalence* proposed by Einstein. This law, sometimes called the second law of photochemistry, states that *any molecule or atom activated by light absorbs only 1 quantum of the light which causes the activation.* The energy acquired by a single atom or molecule in absorbing the 1 quantum depends on the frequency of the irradiating light and is given by the Planck relation $E = h\nu$, where h is Planck's constant and ν is the frequency. Per mole or gram atomic weight the energy absorbed will be Avogadro's number times $h\nu$, or

$$E = Nh\nu \quad \text{per mole} \tag{4}$$

The quantity of energy defined by equation (4) is called an *einstein*, and its magnitude for wave length λ in Å is given by

$$\begin{aligned} E &= \frac{1.196 \times 10^{16}}{\lambda} \quad \text{ergs mole}^{-1} \\ &= \frac{2.859 \times 10^{8}}{\lambda} \quad \text{cal mole}^{-1} \end{aligned} \tag{5}$$

The energies contained in an einstein for various wave lengths of light are shown in Table 1. From this table it is evident that the energy absorbed per mole by a system varies widely with the wave length of the light used. Ordinarily activating radiation is confined to wave lengths of 2000–10,000 A, and hence activating energies may range from 28,000 to 143,000 cal per mole.

The photochemical equivalence law applies only to the absorption or primary photochemical process. When as a result of the primary absorp-

TABLE 1

ENERGIES PER EINSTEIN AT VARIOUS WAVE LENGTHS OF LIGHT

Wave Length (Å)	Spectral Range	Energy per Einstein (cal)
1	X rays	2.86×10^8
1000	Ultraviolet	285,900
2000	Ultraviolet	142,950
3000	Ultraviolet	95,300
4000–4500	Visible (violet)	71,470–63,530
4500–5000	Visible (blue)	63,530–57,180
5000–5750	Visible (green)	57,180–49,720
5750–5900	Visible (yellow)	49,720–48,460
5900–6500	Visible (orange)	48,460–43,980
6500–7500	Visible (red)	43,980–38,120
8000	Infrared	35,740
9000	Infrared	31,770
10000	Infrared	28,590

tion only one molecule decomposes, and the products enter no further reaction, the number of molecules reacting will be equal to the number of energy quanta absorbed. More frequently, however, a molecule activated photochemically initiates a sequence of thermal reactions as a result of which several or many reactant molecules may undergo chemical change. Under such conditions there will be no 1:1 relation between reacting molecules and the number of energy quanta absorbed. Again, in certain processes where deactivation is active, less than one molecule may react per quantum. To express the relation between the number of molecules entering reaction and the number of quanta absorbed, the *quantum yield* or efficiency of a process ϕ is introduced. This quantity is defined as

$$\phi = \frac{\text{Number of molecules reacting in a given time}}{\text{Number of quanta of light absorbed in the same time}}$$
$$= \frac{\text{Number of moles reacting in a given time}}{\text{Number of einsteins of light absorbed in the same time}} \qquad (6)$$

and gives the number of molecules observed to undergo chemical transformation per quantum of absorbed energy. The quantum efficiency of a reaction may vary from almost zero to about 10^6 observed for the combination of hydrogen and chlorine. Nevertheless, no matter how large or small ϕ may be, it is generally accepted that the Einstein equivalence law is valid and that the primary step initiating a photochemical change is the absorption of a single quantum of energy by a molecule or atom. Whatever happens thereafter is beyond the concern of this law.

CONSEQUENCES OF LIGHT ABSORPTION BY ATOMS

Before proceeding to a discussion of the kinetics of photochemical reactions and the estimation of quantum yields, it is essential to consider the possible effects of absorption of light by atoms and molecules.

When an *atom* absorbs radiant energy, the energy, depending on its amount, may cause the atom to ionize, or it may go to produce electronic excitation. Here we are primarily interested in the latter possibility. An electronically excited atom has a life period of about 10^{-7} to 10^{-8} sec. If during this brief period the atom suffers no collision with another particle to which some or all of the excess energy can be passed on, the atom will reemit part or all of this energy as radiation. Such an emission of radiation by an excited atom or molecule is called *fluorescence*. When the excited electron returns to its initial state and emits thereby radiation of exactly the same frequency as that absorbed, we obtain *resonance fluorescence*. However, the excited electron may pass also to an energy level intermediate between the excited and ground states. The frequency of the emitted fluorescence ν' will then be less than that of the absorbed light ν. In rare instances ν' may actually be greater than ν, i.e., more radiant energy is emitted than has been absorbed. When this happens it is usually an indication that some kinetic energy has been converted into energy of internal motion and has been radiated along with the excitation energy of the atom.

Ordinarily fluorescent emission ceases as soon as the incident radiation is removed. However, in some instances the fluorescence may persist for some time after the light has been shut off, and we have then *phosphorescence*. Phosphorescence and fluorescence are believed to arise in the same way, except that in the former the emission of the radiation takes place much more slowly.

When a photochemically excited atom undergoes collision with another atom or molecule before it has a chance to fluoresce, the fluorescence may be *quenched*, i.e., the intensity of the fluorescent emission may be diminished or stopped. The quenching of fluorescence is due to transfer of energy from the excited atom to the particle with which it collides. As a result of this energy transfer the following changes may occur:

1. An excited atom may activate another atom with which it collides. An example is the activation of thallium atoms by excited mercury vapor

$$\text{Hg}^* + \text{Tl} = \text{Hg} + \text{Tl}^* \tag{7}$$

The asterisk denotes the activated or excited particle.

2. The excited atom may collide with a molecule and activate it. An instance is the activation of hydrogen by excited cadmium atoms

$$Cd^* + H_2 = Cd + H_2^* \tag{8}$$

3. An excited atom may react with the colliding molecule. Such a process is the reaction

$$Hg^* + O_2 = HgO + O \tag{9}$$

4. Finally, an excited atom may collide with a molecule and by energy exchange cause the molecule to dissociate. A dissociation thus brought about by an excited atom is called *photosensitization*. It is exemplified by the photosensitized dissociation of hydrogen gas by excited mercury vapor, namely,

$$Hg^* + H_2 = Hg + 2 H \tag{10}$$

Whether or not fluorescence will be quenched depends greatly on the concentration of the fluorescent atoms and of the quenching substance. In a gas at low pressure the time interval between collisions is usually greater than the life of the excited atoms, and hence very little quenching will occur. At higher pressures the time interval between collisions is shorter, and consequently appreciable quenching will take place. Since in a liquid medium collisions are very frequent, the fluorescence emitted by liquid media will generally be appreciably quenched. Further, the quenching of fluorescence is to a large degree specific. Thus in the quenching of mercury fluorescence oxygen gas is most effective, followed by hydrogen and carbon monoxide, while helium and argon are very inefficient quenchers at the same pressure.

The photochemical importance of the quenching of fluorescence lies in the fact that excited atoms or molecules resulting from the quenching process may react further to continue the photochemically initiated change. Thus in reactions such as (7) and (8) the activated products may combine with other reactants to yield new products. Similarly, the atoms formed in reactions (9) and (10) may enter further reaction. Nevertheless, the absorbed light is involved only in the initial activation of some atom. Any succeeding reactions are generally thermal in character.

CONSEQUENCES OF LIGHT ABSORPTION BY MOLECULES

When a molecule absorbs incident radiation the latter may go either to activate the molecule or to dissociate it. Whether one or the other of these possibilities occurs depends on the amount of energy absorbed, and this, in turn, depends on the frequency of the light. A molecule activated photochemically will emit the energy as fluorescence unless it manages to collide with another molecule or atom to which the excitation energy may be passed on. In the latter eventuality the product of the collision may be again an activated particle, a new molecule, or a photo-sensitized reaction in which the quenching molecule is dissociated. The products of the quenching process may then continue the sequence of changes by further combination with atoms or molecules. As in atomic fluorescence, the extent of quenching varies with the pressure or concentration and depends also on the nature of the substances involved.

Absorption of radiant energy may lead also to dissociation of the absorbing molecule. In fact, in most photochemical reactions involving molecules the primary step is usually dissociation of some molecule into atoms, simpler molecules, or free radicals, which by further interaction either with each other or with different molecules continue the reaction sequence. As in atomic systems, the primary photochemical stage is the dissociation. The secondary reactions proceed by thermal means.

PHOTOCHEMICAL KINETICS

The rate laws which photochemical reactions follow are generally more complex than those for thermal reactions. In the first place, the rate of the primary activating process is controlled by the intensity of the activating radiation used and is proportional to it. The primary process is then followed by one or more reactions whose nature must be known before a rate law for the over-all process can be deduced. Further, in many instances even the nature of the activating step is unknown. To obtain information about all the possible changes that may occur it is necessary to measure the rates at which various reactants disappear, the rates at which products are formed, and also the effect of the intensity of light as well as its frequency on these. From the data thus collected it is frequently possible to postulate a mechanism to account for the observed facts. Of considerable help in this connection are atomic and molecular spectra of the reactants involved. For some reactions these spectra allow the definite establishment of the nature of the primary step. In others the processes that cannot occur are eliminated, and thereby the number of mechanisms to be considered is reduced.

It is neither expedient nor necessary to formulate here the various rate expressions which photochemical reactions follow. We shall confine ourselves instead to an illustration of the procedure by setting up the relations for several relatively simple cases.

Consider first a hypothetical reaction

$$A_2 \longrightarrow 2A$$

which proceeds by photochemical activation. Assume further that the reaction follows the mechanism:

(a)　$A_2 + h\nu \longrightarrow A_2^*$ (Activation)　　　k_1
(b)　$A_2^* \longrightarrow 2\,A$ (Dissociation)　　　k_2
(c)　$A_2^* + A_2 \longrightarrow 2\,A_2$ (Deactivation)　　　k_3

The first stage in this sequence is the absorption of a quantum of light by A_2 with the formation of an activated molecule. This activated molecule may undergo now dissociation according to reaction (b), or it may be deactivated by collision with an inactive molecule of A_2 according to reaction (c). The rate constants with which these reactions occur are indicated to the right of each step.

The final product A is formed only in reaction (b). Consequently the rate of formation of A must be given by

$$\frac{dC_A}{dt} = k_2 C_{A_2^*} \tag{11}$$

To eliminate from this rate expression the unavailable concentration of active molecules, we resort to the concept of the *stationary state*. This concept postulates that when a *short-lived* intermediate is formed in a reaction, such as A_2^* above, a state is attained in a brief time interval in which *the rate of formation of the intermediate becomes exactly equal to its rate of disappearance*. Once such a condition is attained, the concentration of the intermediate is said to be the *stationary concentration*, and the state resulting in this rate equality is called the *stationary state*.

If we apply this concept of the stationary state to the intermediate A_2^*, we observe that A_2^* is formed by reaction (a) and that it disappears by reactions (b) and (c). For reaction (a) the rate is determined only by the rate at which the light is absorbed, i.e., the rate is directly proportioned to the intensity of the absorbed light I_a. We obtain thus

$$\frac{dC_{A_2^*}}{dt} = k_1 I_a \tag{12}$$

The rate of disappearance of A_2^* is given in turn by the sum of the rates of reactions (b) and (c), namely,

$$-\frac{dC_{A_2^*}}{dt} = k_2 C_{A_2^*} + k_3 C_{A_2^*} C_{A_2} \tag{13}$$

Equating (12) and (13) to obtain the condition for the stationary state, we find that

$$k_1 I_a = k_2 C_{A_2^*} + k_3 C_{A_2^*} C_{A_2}$$
$$C_{A_2^*} = \frac{k_1 I_a}{k_2 + k_3 C_{A_2}} \tag{14}$$

Inserting $C_{A_2^*}$ from equation (14) into equation (11), the rate of formation of A is seen to be

$$\frac{dC_A}{dt} = k_2 C_{A_1^*} = \frac{k_2 k_1 I_a}{k_2 + k_3 C_{A_2}} \tag{15}$$

Finally, since for every two molecules of A formed one molecule of A_2 reacts, the photochemical efficiency of the process ϕ will be

$$\phi = \frac{1}{2 I_a} \cdot \frac{dC_A}{dt} = \frac{1}{2} \left[\frac{k_2 k_1}{k_2 + k_3 C_{A_2}} \right] \tag{16}$$

As a second example may be taken the photochemical chlorination of chloroform in the gas phase,

$$Cl_2 + CHCl_3 + h\nu = CCl_4 + HCl \tag{17}$$

For this reaction Schumacher and Wolff[1] found that the rate of formation of carbon tetrachloride is given by the expression

$$\frac{dC_{CCl_4}}{dt} = k C_{Cl_2}^{1/2} I_a^{1/2} \tag{18}$$

To account for this rate, the following mechanism has been proposed:

(a) $\quad Cl_2 + h\nu \longrightarrow 2\,Cl \qquad\qquad k_1 I_a$

(b) $\quad Cl + CHCl_3 \longrightarrow CCl_3 + HCl \qquad k_2 C_{Cl} C_{CHCl_3}$

(c) $\quad CCl_3 + Cl_2 \longrightarrow CCl_4 + Cl \qquad k_3 C_{CCl_3} C_{Cl_2}$

(d) $\quad 2\,CCl_3 + Cl_2 \longrightarrow 2\,CCl_4 \qquad k_4 C_{CCl_3}^2 C_{Cl_2}$

To the right of each reaction is given the rate at which it proceeds. In these reactions carbon tetrachloride is formed only in steps (c) and (d), and hence the rate of formation of this substance must be

$$\frac{dC_{CCl_4}}{dt} = k_3 C_{CCl_3} C_{Cl_2} + k_4 C_{CCl_3}^2 C_{Cl_2} \tag{19}$$

To eliminate from this expression C_{CCl_3} we assume first a stationary state for this species. Since CCl_3 is formed only in step (b) and it is removed in steps (c) and (d), the rate of the former must be equal to the sum of the rates of the latter two, namely,

$$k_2 C_{Cl} C_{CHCl_3} = k_3 C_{CCl_3} C_{Cl_2} + k_4 C_{CCl_3}^2 C_{Cl_2} \tag{20}$$

Further, since Cl is also a short-lived intermediate, a stationary state may be assumed for it as well. This means that the rate of steps (a) and (c) equals the rate of step (b), or

$$k_1 I_a + k_3 C_{CCl_3} C_{Cl_2} = k_2 C_{Cl} C_{CHCl_3} \tag{21}$$

[1] Schumacher and Wolff, *Z. physik. Chem.*, **25B**, 161 (1934).

Adding equations (20) and (21), we obtain

$$k_1 I_a = k_4 C^2_{CCl_3} C_{Cl_2}$$

and

$$C_{CCl_3} = \left[\frac{k_1 I_a}{k_4 C_{Cl_2}} \right]^{1/2} \tag{22}$$

Substituting C_{CCl_3} from equation (22) into equation (19), the rate of formation of CCl_4 follows as

$$\frac{dC_{CCl_4}}{dt} = k_3 \left[\frac{k_1 I_a}{k_4 C_{Cl_2}} \right]^{1/2} C_{Cl_2} + k_4 \left[\frac{k_1 I_a}{k_4 C_{Cl_2}} \right] C_{Cl_2}$$

$$= k I_a^{1/2} C_{Cl_2}^{1/2} + k_1 I_a \tag{23}$$

where the substitution $k = k_3 (k_1/k_4)^{1/2}$ has been made. If it is assumed now that the second term on the right in equation (23) is negligible compared to the first term, equation (23) reduces to

$$\frac{dC_{CCl_4}}{dt} = k I_a^{1/2} C_{Cl_2}^{1/2} \tag{24}$$

which is identical with the observed rate equation (18).

In photochemical rate equations time is generally expressed in seconds, concentrations either in molecules or moles per cubic centimeter. For the first of these concentration units I_a must be expressed in quanta of light absorbed per cubic centimeter, i.e., the total number of quanta absorbed in 1 second divided by the volume of the absorbing medium. For the second concentration unit, on the other hand, I_a must be taken in einsteins absorbed per cubic centimeter per second, namely, the total number of einsteins absorbed in 1 sec divided by the volume in cubic centimeters.

EXPERIMENTAL STUDY OF PHOTOCHEMICAL REACTIONS

To measure the rate of a photochemical reaction it is necessary to irradiate a reaction mixture with light of a selected wave length and to observe the manner in which the concentration of reactants or products varies with time. For this purpose some arrangement such as that shown in Fig. 1 is required. In this diagram A is a light source emitting radiation of suitable intensity in the desired spectral range. To select radiation of only a single wave length or to confine the radiation to a narrow band, the light is passed through the lens B into a monochromator or filter at C. From C the light enters the cell D immersed in a thermostat and containing the reaction mixture. Finally, the light transmitted through D falls on some suitable recorder E, where its intensity is determined.

The light sources used depend on the spectral range in which radiation is desired and include filament lamps, carbon and metal arcs, and various gas discharge tubes. The reaction cells may be glass or quartz vessels, usually with optically plane windows for entrance and exit of light. In some instances metal cells have been used with windows cemented to the ends. Glass can be used only in the visible spectral range. Below 3500 Å not only the cells but also any other optical parts through which the light passes must be of quartz. With gases no provision need be made for stirring; solutions, however, must be agitated.

The radiant energy is measured with some form of thermopile or actinometer. The thermopile is essentially a multijunction thermocouple consisting usually of silver and bismuth soldered to metal strips blackened with lamp, platinum, or bismuth black. The radiation falling on the blackened strips is absorbed almost completely and nonselectively and is converted into heat. The heat thus generated raises the temperature of the hot junctions above the cold, and the current generated thereby is

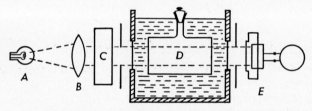

Fig. 1. Apparatus for Study of Photochemical Reactions (Schematic).

measured. The current produced is proportional to the energy absorbed, and this, in turn, depends on the intensity of the incident light and the area exposed to it. Thermopiles are calibrated with standard light sources.

Photocells may be used in place of thermopiles. Still other devices are chemical actinometers, which are merely gas mixtures or solutions sensitive to light. When radiation impinges upon these, a chemical reaction ensues whose extent is determined by the amount of energy absorbed. The most common of these is the uranyl oxalate actinometer, consisting of 0.05 molar oxalic acid and 0.01 molar uranyl sulfate (UO_2SO_4) in water. Under the action of light the reaction

$$H_2C_2O_4 \longrightarrow H_2O(l) + CO_2(g) + CO(g)$$

takes place, whose extent can be ascertained by titrating the remaining oxalic acid with permanganate solution. For best results this actinometer should be calibrated against a thermopile in the spectral range in which it is to be employed. When this is not possible, the quantum yields recorded in the literature may be utilized.[1] This actinometer is applicable to radiations lying between 2000 and 5000 Å.

[1] See Noyes and Leighton, *The Photochemistry of Gases*, Reinhold Publishing Corporation, New York, 1941, Table 13, p. 82.

To obtain the total radiant energy absorbed in unit time the procedure is as follows. First the empty cell, or the cell filled with solvent alone in the case of solutions, is interposed in the light beam, and a reading is taken on the thermopile or actinometer. This gives the total energy incident in a given time upon the system. Next the cell with the reactants is substituted, and the reading is again taken, which gives now the total energy transmitted. The difference between these readings is the total energy absorbed by the reacting mixture in the given time. If this time is 1 sec, the total energy absorbed divided by the volume of the reacting mixture is I_a, the intensity of the radiation absorbed.

The rate of the chemical reaction taking place in the system is ascertained in the usual manner. For this purpose the change in some physical property can be followed, or samples can be removed periodically from the cell and analyzed. It is thus possible to collect data on the rate of the chemical reaction and the light intensity, from which the rate law and the quantum yield may be deduced.

PHOTOCHEMICAL GAS REACTIONS

In Table 2 are listed some photochemical gas reactions and their quantum yields. From this table it may be seen that quantum yields vary within very wide limits, as from 0.25 for ammonia decomposition to 10^6 for the combination of chlorine and hydrogen. Several of these reactions will be discussed now to illustrate some of the mechanisms by which they proceed.

THE PHOTOLYSIS OF AMMONIA

The *photolysis*, or photochemical decomposition, of ammonia was studied by Wiig,[1] who found that the reaction proceeds quantitatively according to

$$2 \text{ NH}_3(g) \longrightarrow \text{N}_2(g) + 3 \text{ H}_2(g)$$

with an average quantum yield of 0.25 up to 500 mm pressure of NH_3. The following mechanism has been proposed to explain these results:

$$
\begin{array}{lll}
\text{(a)} & \text{NH}_3 + h\nu \longrightarrow \text{NH}_2 + \text{H} \\
\text{(b)} & \text{NH}_2 + \text{H} \longrightarrow \text{NH}_3 \\
\text{(c)} & \text{H} + \text{H} \longrightarrow \text{H}_2 \\
\text{(d)} & \text{NH}_2 + \text{NH}_2 \longrightarrow \text{N}_2\text{H}_4 \\
\text{(e)} & \text{N}_2\text{H}_4 + \text{H} \longrightarrow \text{NH}_3 + \text{NH}_2 \\
\text{(f)} & \text{NH}_2 + \text{NH}_2 \longrightarrow \text{N}_2 + 2 \text{ H}_2
\end{array}
$$

[1] Wiig, *J. Am. Chem. Soc.*, **57**, 1559 (1935); **59**, 827 (1937).

TABLE 2

SOME NONSENSITIZED PHOTOCHEMICAL GAS REACTIONS

Reaction	Wave Length (Å)	Quantum Yield	Remarks
$2\,NH_3 = N_2 + 3\,H_2$	2100	0.25	Depends on pressure
$SO_2 + Cl_2 = SO_2Cl_2$	4200	1	
$HCHO = H_2 + CO$	2500–3100	1–100	At 100–400° C
$CH_3CHO = CH_4 + CO$	2500–3100	1–138	At 100–400° C
$2\,HI = H_2 + I_2$	2070–2820	2	Constant over wide range of pressures and temperatures
$2\,HBr = H_2 + Br_2$	2070–2530	2	
$H_2 + Br_2 = 2\,HBr$	Below 6000	2	Near 200° C. Very small at 25° C
$CH_3N:NCH_3 = C_2H_6 + N_2$	3660	2	Up to 300° C
$3\,O_2 = 2\,O_3$	1700–2530	1–3	
$nC_2H_2 = (C_2H_2)_n$	2150	9	Near room temperature
$CO + Cl_2 = COCl_2$	4000–4360	ca. 10^3	Falls with temperature. Depends also on pressure of reactants
$H_2 + Cl_2 = 2\,HCl$	4000–4360	Up to 10^6	Varies with P_{H_2} and impurities

From this mechanism it can be shown that the quantum yield should be small and that it should vary with pressure. These conclusions are in accord with the observed results.

THE COMBINATION OF HYDROGEN AND BROMINE

The photochemical combination of hydrogen and bromine was studied by Bodenstein and Lütkemeyer[1] between 160 and 218° C. They found that at any given temperature the rate of formation of hydrogen bromide is given by

$$\frac{dC_{HBr}}{dt} = \frac{kC_{H_2}I_a^{1/2}}{1 + k'\left[C_{HBr}/C_{Br_2}\right]} \qquad (25)$$

and that the quantum yield ϕ, as given by

$$\phi = \frac{1}{I_a} \cdot \frac{dC_{HBr}}{dt} = \frac{kC_{H_2}I_a^{-1/2}}{1 + k'\left[C_{HBr}/C_{Br_2}\right]} \qquad (26)$$

increased with temperature up to 2 near 200° C, and was greater above it. These results are explainable by a series of reaction steps identical with those given on p. 637 for the thermal chain reaction between these

[1] Bodenstein and Lütkemeyer, *Z. physik. Chem.*, **114**, 208 (1925).

two substances, except that the dissociation indicated by step (a) takes place photochemically. The variation of the quantum yield with temperature is accountable by changes in the magnitudes of k and k' as the temperature is raised.

THE HYDROGEN-CHLORINE REACTION

In the photolysis of ammonia the sequence of reactions leading to the final products is initiated by formation of NH_2 and H. Once formed, these particles are removed in every subsequent reaction, and neither of these intermediates is regenerated except in the secondary step (e). Consequently a reaction cycle is started primarily by the first step, while practically every subsequent one operates to remove the active intermediates. On the other hand, in the hydrogen-bromine reaction the cycle initiated by the appearance of bromine atoms in reaction (a) is kept going by regeneration of these atoms in reactions (c) and (d), and by formation of hydrogen atoms in (b). Every bromine or hydrogen atom thus formed is just as capable of starting a reaction as step (a), and hence each is able to start a new chain. Such reactions are called, therefore, *photochemical chain reactions*. Nevertheless the chains here do not acquire great length because of their rapid termination, and the quantum yield is thus low.

The situation is different, however, in the hydrogen-chlorine reaction. Here the chains acquire great length, and as many as 10^6 molecules of hydrogen chloride have been observed to be formed per absorbed quantum of light. As a rule the yield, although still high, is less than the figure quoted, particularly when impurities are present in the reaction mixture. By reacting with atoms of hydrogen and chlorine, these operate to terminate chains, thus reducing the quantum efficiency of the process. The chains are terminated also by the walls of the reaction vessel.

At moderate gas pressures, and with comparable proportions of chlorine to hydrogen, Bodenstein and Unger,[1] and others, found that the rate of formation of HCl is given by

$$\frac{dC_{HCl}}{dt} = kI_aC_{H_2} \tag{27}$$

This rate equation can be accounted by the following mechanism:

(a)	$Cl_2 + h\nu \longrightarrow 2\ Cl$	k_1
(b)	$Cl + H_2 \longrightarrow HCl + H$	k_2
(c)	$H + Cl_2 \longrightarrow HCl + Cl$	k_3
(d)	$Cl\ (\text{at walls}) \longrightarrow \frac{1}{2}\ Cl_2$	k_4

Here every reaction continues the chain except the last one.

[1] Bodenstein and Unger, *Z. physik. Chem.*, **11B**, 253 (1930).

In all combinations of atoms, free radicals, or atoms and free radicals to form stable molecules, considerable energy is evolved. Unless this energy is removed, the resulting molecule cannot be stable. Consequently in all such reactions it is necessary to assume either that a third body is involved in the collision which carries off the energy, or that the reaction occurs at the walls. The third body may be a molecule of the reactants, the products, or some other neutral impurity present in the system.

PHOTOSENSITIZED GAS REACTIONS

When a reaction mixture is exposed to light to which the reactants are insensitive, no reaction will take place. However, it is possible to introduce into the reaction mixture molecules or atoms which will absorb the light, become excited, and then pass on this energy to one of the reactants and thereby activate it for reaction. A substance acting in this manner is called a *photosensitizer*, while the reaction resulting is said to be *photosensitized*.

An example of such a reaction is the combination of carbon monoxide and hydrogen sensitized by mercury vapor. The products are primarily formaldehyde and some glyoxal. The steps involves may be written as:

$$
\begin{aligned}
&\text{(a)} \qquad \text{Hg} + h\nu \longrightarrow \text{Hg}^* \\
&\text{(b)} \quad \text{Hg}^* + \text{H}_2 \longrightarrow 2\,\text{H} + \text{Hg} \\
&\text{(c)} \qquad \text{H} + \text{CO} \longrightarrow \text{HCO} \\
&\text{(d)} \quad \text{HCO} + \text{H}_2 \longrightarrow \text{HCHO} + \text{H} \\
&\text{(e)} \qquad 2\,\text{HCO} \longrightarrow \text{HCHO} + \text{CO} \\
&\text{(f)} \qquad 2\,\text{HCO} \longrightarrow \text{CHO}\!-\!\text{CHO (glyoxal)}
\end{aligned}
$$

Step (a) indicates the activation of the mercury vapor by light absorption, step (b) a transfer of the activation energy to a hydrogen molecule. The energy absorbed by the latter causes it to dissociate into atoms which initiate then the remainder of the reaction cycle.

Many merucry-photosensitized reactions have been investigated. These include decompositions of H_2, NH_3, H_2O, PH_3, AsH_3, various hydrocarbons, alcohols, ethers, acids, and amines; hydrogenations such as that of ethylene, propylene, and butylene; combinations, such as that of oxygen and hydrogen to water, oxygen to ozone, and hydrogen and nitrogen to ammonia; and polymerizations, such as that of ethylene. The dissociation of hydrogen is sensitized also by xenon, the polymerization of ethylene by cadmium vapor. The latter is effective as well in the decomposition of ethane and propane into hydrogen, methane, and higher hydrocarbons. The halogens have also been employed frequently as sensitizers. Thus chlorine, bromine, and iodine sensitize the decomposition of ozone; bromine that of Cl_2O; while chlorine promotes the combination of oxygen and hydrogen to water and of carbon monoxide and oxygen to carbon dioxide.

In Table 3 are given several photosensitized gas reactions along with their quantum yields and the wave lengths at which these were obtained.

TABLE 3

SOME PHOTOSENSITIZED GAS REACTIONS

Reaction	Sensitizer	Wave Length (Å)	Quantum Yield	Remarks
$2 O_3 = 3 O_2$	Cl_2	4300	2–30	Increases with O_3 concentration
$2 H_2 + O_2 = 2 H_2O$	Cl_2	4300	2	
$H_2 + CO = HCHO$	Hg	2537	2	
$2 CO + O_2 = 2 CO_2$	Cl_2	4050–4360	1000	Depends on temperature and concentration

PHOTOCHEMICAL REACTIONS IN THE LIQUID PHASE

Many substances undergo photochemical reaction when liquefied or dissolved in a solvent. Again such reactions may be initiated by direct light absorption on the part of a reactant, or they may be photosensitized. *A priori* it may be anticipated that the quantum efficiency of a photochemical process will be less in the liquid phase than for the same reaction in the gas phase. The reason for this is that in the liquid phase an active molecule or atom may readily be deactivated by frequent collisions with other molecules, or by reaction with the solvent. Furthermore, because of the very short mean free path in the liquid phase, free radicals or atoms when formed photochemically will tend to recombine before they have a chance to get very far from each other. The net effect of these processes will be to keep the quantum yield relatively low. In fact, only those reactions may be expected to proceed to any extent for which the primary products of the photochemical act are relatively stable particles. Otherwise the active intermediates will tend to recombine or react with the solvent and thereby keep the yield low.

That these considerations apply in many instances is shown by the data in Table 4. In every case except the last the yield is lower in the liquid phase than in the gas for the same wave length of irradiating light. However, in a number of reactions, of which the photolysis of $Ni(CO)_4$ is an example, just the reverse is true. This reversal may be due to formation of intermediates of kinetic energy sufficiently high to separate them rapidly, thereby preventing their combination, or to the specific effect of solvent which makes it inefficient as a deactivator. That solvents may exert specific effects is borne out by the observation that the same reaction conducted in different media may have different quantum efficiencies under the same conditions. Thus for the photolysis of ClO_2 at 4358 Å $\phi = 1.0$ in CCl_4 and only 0.20 in water. Similarly the photolysis of $N_2CH_2COOC_2H_5$ at 2600 Å gives $\phi = 1.1$ in heptane, 1.42 in methyl alcohol, and 2.8 in water.

TABLE 4

Comparison of Quantum Yields in the Gas and Liquid Phases

Reaction	Wave Length (Å)	Quantum Yield	
		Gas	Liquid Phase
$2\,NH_3 = N_2 + 3\,H_2$	2100	0.14–0.32	0 (In liquid NH_3)
$CH_3COOH = CH_4 + CO_2$	<2300	1	0.45 (In H_2O)
$Cl_2O = Cl_2 + \frac{1}{2}\,O_2$	4358	3.2	1.8 (In CCl_4)
$NO_2 = NO + \frac{1}{2}\,O_2$	4050	0.50	0.03 (In CCl_4)
$Pb(CH_3)_4 = Pb + 2\,C_2H_6$	2357	1.1	0.4 (In hexane)
$Ni(CO)_4 = Ni + 4\,CO$	3010–3135	0	2.8 (In CCl_4)

In Table 5 are given results for several other sensitized and nonsensitized reactions in solution. The mechanisms for some of these may be indicated. The quantum efficiency of unity for the chloracetic acid reaction may be accounted by the simple sequence

$$ClCH_2COOH + h\nu \longrightarrow ClCH_2COOH^*$$
$$ClCH_2COOH^* + H_2O \longrightarrow HOCH_2COOH + HCl$$

For the cis-butene iodination Forbes and Nelson[1] found the rate to be

$$\frac{dC_{C_4H_8I_2}}{dt} = kC_{C_4H_8}C_{I_2}I_a \qquad (28)$$

To deduce this rate law it is necessary to assume that the mechanism involved is:

(a) $\qquad I_2 + h\nu \longrightarrow 2\,I$

(b) $\qquad I + C_4H_8 \rightleftharpoons C_4H_8I$

(c) $\qquad C_4H_8I + I_2 \longrightarrow C_4H_8I_2 + I$

(d) $\qquad C_4H_8I_2 + I \longrightarrow C_4H_8I + I_2$

(e) $\qquad I \longrightarrow \frac{1}{2}\,I_2$

The reaction is initiated by formation of iodine atoms which subsequently become involved in reactions (b), (d), and (e). Step (c), however, oper-

[1] Forbes and Nelson, *J. Am. Chem. Soc.*, **59**, 693 (1937).

ates to regenerate these. Further, it is necessary to postulate that step (b) proceeds in both directions. From these equations an expression equivalent to the observed relation (28) may be derived.

The exact mechanism by which the UO_2^{++}-sensitized dissociation of oxalic acid occurs is uncertain. Indications are that a complex is formed between the acid and UO_2^{++}. In the reactions involving bromine the sensitization is probably caused by dissociation of the molecule into bromine atoms, which continue then the reaction.

TABLE 5

FURTHER EXAMPLES OF PHOTOCHEMICAL REACTIONS IN SOLUTION

Reaction	Solvent	Wave Length (Å)	Quantum Yield	Remarks
Nonsensitized				
$2\,HI = H_2 + I_2$	H_2O	2070	0.34	Depends on concentration and wave length
cis-$C_4H_8 + I_2 = C_4H_8I_2$	$CHCl_3$	4360	2.48	Each reactant 0.01 molar at $-55°C$
$2\,Fe^{+++} + I_2 = 2\,Fe^{++} + 2\,I^-$	H_2O	5790	1	
$ClCH_2COOH + H_2O =$				
$\quad HOCH_2COOH + HCl$	H_2O	2537	1	0.3–0.5 molar
$H_2C_2O_4 = H_2O + CO + CO_2$	H_2O	2650	0.01	
$2\,H_2O_2 = 2\,H_2O + O_2$	H_2O	3100	7–80	
Sensitized				
$H_2C_2O_4 = H_2O + CO + CO_2$	H_2O	2540–4350	0.49–0.60	0.05 molar acid 0.01 molar UO_2^{++} as sensitizer
$2\,CCl_3Br + O_2 = 2\,COCl_2 +$ Br$_2$	CCl_3Br	4070–4360	0.9	Br_2 as sensitizer
Maleic ester = Fumaric ester	CCl_4	4360	295	Br_2 as sensitizer

PHOTOCHEMICAL EFFECTS IN SOLIDS

Solid substances may also be affected by light. Thus silver salts exposed to light tend to darken, sodium chloride crystals in ultraviolet light develop a yellowish tinge which can be removed by heating, and dyes tend to fade in sunlight. Again, zinc oxide and titanium dioxide accelerate the reduction of prussian blue and the decolorization of other dyes, and hence these act apparently as photosensitizers in paints films containing such dyes.

The outstanding application of photolysis in the solid state is in photography. A photographic emulsion is a dispersion of finely divided silver chloride or bromide in a gelatin base. When such an emulsion is exposed to light, the halides are acted upon to form an invisible latent image of density proportional to the light intensity. To make the image visible, it must be developed by treatment with a reducing agent which acts primarily on the exposed portions of the emulsion to yield a finely divided deposit of silver. A photographic plate thus developed is treated with a fixing agent, such as sodium thiosulfate, to dissolve the undeveloped silver halide, but not the part exposed. On the resulting negative the portions that were lightest on the object photographed appear darkest, and vice versa. To obtain from the negative a print in which the light densities are rectified, the above process is repeated by photographing the negative. The exposure thus obtained will have, when developed, the light and dark portions of the negative reversed, and these will correspond, therefore, to the relative light and dark shadings of the original object.

Photographic emulsions consisting of silver halides alone are sensitive only to light near the ultraviolet. To extend the range of sensitivity to longer wave lengths, various dyes which absorb in the yellow and red are incorporated into the emulsion. Photographic emulsions have also been developed which are sensitive to near infrared radiation and thus make possible night photography.

EFFECT OF TEMPERATURE ON PHOTOCHEMICAL REACTIONS

The effect of temperature on photochemical reactions is quite different from that on thermal ones. For the latter an increase of 10° C in temperature generally leads to a two- or threefold increase in the rate. In photochemical reactions, however, the same increase in temperature results as a rule in only a very small increase in rate, as may be seen from Table 6. For most such reactions the temperature coefficient is not far from unity. Occasionally it does approach a value close to that for a thermal reaction, as in the potassium oxalate-iodine reaction, but such behavior is exceptional. Further, in some photochemical reactions, of which the chlorination of benzene is an example, the unusual phenomenon of decrease in rate with temperature is encountered.

To explain the observed temperature coefficients of photochemical reactions it is necessary to consider separately the effect of this variable on the primary and secondary reactions in the complete process. The primary light absorption process should be practically temperature independent. Again, since secondary reactions in photochemical processes are thermal in character, these should have temperature coefficients akin to those of ordinary reactions. However, most secondary reactions in photochemical processes involve interaction between atoms or free radicals, or of these with molecules. For such reactions the energy of activation is usually small or even zero. As the temperature coefficient of a reaction is determined by the magnitude of the activation energy, we may conclude that even for the secondary reactions the temperature coefficient should be smaller than for thermal ones involving only molecules. The net result should be, therefore, a small temperature coefficient for the over-all process. This is generally the case.

TABLE 6

TEMPERATURE COEFFICIENTS OF PHOTOCHEMICAL REACTIONS
(Per 10° C temperature increase)

Reactants	Medium	Temp. Coefficient	Temp. Range
$CO + O_2$	Gas	0.94	20–40°
$H_2 + Cl_2$	Gas	1.1–1.2	−170–200°
$H_2 + Br_2$	Gas	1.48	160–220°
$COCl_2$	Gas	1.0	20–165°
$Cl_2 + Cl_2C\!\!=\!\!CHCl$	Gas	1.2	80–115°
$Cl_2 + C_6H_6$	Gas	0.67	25–35°
1,2-diiodobutane	$CHCl_3$	1.07	−55–25°
$H_2C_2O_4 + UO_2^{++}$	H_2O	1.03	5–80°
CH_3COOH	CCl_4	1.4	
$H_2C_2O_4 + H_2CrO_4$	H_2O	1.7	20–40°
$K_2C_2O_4 + I_2$	H_2O	3.2	25–40°

When a large temperature coefficient is observed in a photochemical reaction it is usually an indication that one or more of the intermediate steps have a high activation energy. Another possibility is that some step in the reaction sequence is an equilibrium whose variation with temperature involves an appreciable positive heat of reaction. Thus suppose that an observed velocity constant k is composed of the product of a rate constant k_1 and an equilibrium constant K; i.e.,

$$k = k_1 K \qquad (29)$$

Taking logarithms and differentiating with respect to temperature, equation (29) yields

$$\frac{d \ln k}{dT} = \frac{d \ln k_1}{dT} + \frac{d \ln K}{dT} \qquad (30)$$

The first term on the right is E^*/RT^2, where E^* is the energy of activation of the step involving k_1. Again, the second term is $\Delta H / RT^2$, where ΔH is the heat of the reaction for which K is the equilibrium constant. Substitution of these into equation (30) gives

$$\begin{aligned} \frac{d \ln k}{dT} &= \frac{E^*}{RT^2} + \frac{\Delta H}{RT^2} \\ &= \frac{E^* + \Delta H}{RT^2} \end{aligned} \tag{31}$$

Even if E^* is small, a large positive ΔH will give a large value for the quantity on the right in equation (31), and hence the temperature coefficient will be large. On the other hand, if ΔH is negative and numerically greater than E^*, then $(E^* + \Delta H)$ will be negative, and so will $d \ln k/dT$. Under these conditions the reaction will have a negative temperature coefficient. This may well be the explanation for the decrease in rate with temperature observed in the photochemical chlorination of benzene and some other reactions of this type.

PHOTOCHEMICAL EQUILIBRIUM

Consider a reaction

$$A + B \xrightarrow{\text{light}} C + D \tag{32}$$

proceeding as indicated under the influence of absorbed radiation. Suppose, further, that the products are not photosensitive, but that they combine in a thermal reaction to reform the reactants, namely,

$$C + D \xrightarrow{\text{thermal}} A + B \tag{33}$$

As these reactions proceed, a state will eventually be reached in which the rates of the two become equal, and the equilibrium

$$A + B \underset{\text{thermal}}{\overset{\text{light}}{\rightleftharpoons}} C + D \tag{34}$$

is established. Similarly, both forward and reverse reactions may be light sensitive, in which case an equilibrium of the type

$$A + B \underset{\text{light}}{\overset{\text{light}}{\rightleftharpoons}} C + D \tag{35}$$

is attained. Equilibria such as (34) or (35), resulting from opposing processes in which one or both reactions are photosensitive, are called *photochemical equilibria*. An example of the first of these is the dimerization of anthracene,

$$2\ C_{14}H_{10} \underset{\text{thermal}}{\overset{\text{light}}{\rightleftharpoons}} C_{28}H_{20} \tag{36}$$

and of the second the decomposition of sulfur trioxide,

$$2\,SO_3 \underset{\text{light}}{\overset{\text{light}}{\rightleftharpoons}} 2\,SO_2 + O_2 \tag{37}$$

The equilibrium constants for photochemical equilibria are *constant only for a given light intensity*, and vary as the latter is changed. Further, they do *not* correspond to the equilibrium constants obtained for the reactions under purely thermal conditions. For instance, thermal equilibrium calculations show that to obtain 30 per cent dissociation of SO_3 at 1 atm pressure this substance must be heated to 630° C. On the other hand, Coehn and Becker[1] found that photochemically SO_3 may be dissociated to the extent of about 35 per cent at 45° C. Again, whereas the thermal equilibrium constant varies very markedly with temperature, the photochemical equilibrium constant was found at constant light intensity to be temperature independent between 50 and 800° C. From these observations, and others, it is evident that the usual equilibrium considerations do not apply to photochemical reactions. A moment's reflection will indicate the reason. In thermal equilibrium we are concerned only with the normal free energy relations of products and reactants as they apply to the conditions of these at the temperature and pressure in question. In photochemical equilibria, on the other hand, these free energy relations are modified by the free energy supplied by the light. Addition of the latter changes the $\Delta F°$ of the reaction, and thereby also the equilibrium constant. In other words, by supplying free energy in the form of light it is possible to make a reaction go in a direction which from ordinary thermodynamic considerations alone would appear to be impossible.

CHEMILUMINESCENCE

In photochemical reactions chemical change results from absorption of light. The converse of this process is the emission of light by a system at ordinary temperatures as a result of a chemical reaction. Such emission of "cold light," called *chemiluminescence*, is a well-known phenomenon.

When yellow phosphorus is oxidized in oxygen or air at low pressures and at temperatures between −10 and 40° C, the phosphorus is converted to P_2O_5 with emission of a visible greenish-white luminescence. Similarly, the oxidation of certain Grignard reagents, silicon compounds, and 3-amino-phthalic acid hydrazine in alkaline solution is accompanied by light emission. In all these instances part or all of the energy change of the reaction, instead of appearing as heat, goes to activate electronically

[1] Coehn and Becker, *Z. Elektrochem.*, **13,** 545 (1907); Z. physik. Chem., **70,** 88 (1909).

some molecule. This activated molecule emits then the excitation energy as radiation and reverts to a normal state.

The chemiluminescence which is possibly best understood is that emitted in the reaction of alkali metal vapors with halogens. When streams of alkali metal vapors and halogens at pressures of 10^{-2} to 10^{-3} mm Hg are mixed, alkali halides are formed with the emission of luminescence. Polanyi and his co-workers showed that in such reactions a chain sets in as a result of which an activated alkali atom is obtained. This atom on return to its ground state emits the observed radiation. In the sodium-chlorine reaction the amount of light obtained is only about 1 quantum per 1000 sodium chloride molecules formed, while in the sodium-iodine reaction it is only 1 quantum per 2000 sodium iodide molecules. The significant fact established in all these reactions is that at no time is radiation obtained whose energy exceeds the heat of the respective reaction. Usually the light emitted is lower in energy than the latter, with the balance being dissipated as translational kinetic energy of the atom.

Chemiluminescence phenomena are not confined to the laboratory. Every student is familiar with the cold light emitted by fireflies. This light arises from the oxidation of a protein substance called luciferin. Certain marine species are also luminescent. Finally, chemiluminescent glow, due to oxidation, may be observed above marshes where wood and vegetation undergo decay. In all these instances part of the energy change accompanying a given process is emitted as radiation instead of heat.

RADIATION CHEMISTRY

Chemical activation can be obtained not only by the use of ultraviolet, visible, and near infrared light, but also by α, β, and γ rays, protons, neutrons, deuterons, and high voltage electric discharges. The energies involved in these initiators are very high and may amount to 50 or more million electron volts (mev).[1] The primary effect of the passage of such high energy radiation through matter is the production of extensive *ionization*, both by direct impact and by the secondary radiation resulting from the initial ionization. The heavier particles, i.e., α particles, protons, neutrons, and deuterons, are more effective in producing ionization than are the lighter and faster electrons and γ rays. The reason for this is that the heavier particles, by moving slower, have a greater opportunity to collide with molecules and cause thereby more extensive ionization.

The ions produced in this manner may be discharged by interaction with electrons, or, more importantly, they may initiate reactions which

[1]   1 ev = 1.60206 × 10^{-12} erg/particle = 23,063 cal mole^{-1}.
   1 mev = 1 × 10^6 ev.

may lead to the formation of new products. The latter are frequently substances of lower molecular weight than the initial molecules, but such is not always the case. Thus irradiation of water yields not only hydrogen but also hydrogen peroxide. Again, irradiation of a monomer mixture can produce polymerization. Further, a polymer exposed to a high energy source is found to exhibit properties quite different from those of the original substance, and more in line with what is to be expected of a product of higher molecular weight. Such modification of polymer properties by high energy radiation is of great interest at present, and considerable research is being conducted in this direction.

The effect of high energy radiation appears to be proportional to the number of ion pairs formed in the exposed substance. However, the efficiency of the processes initiated is generally low, with the changes resulting being far from commensurate with the energy input.

REFERENCES FOR FURTHER READING

1. E. J. Bowen, *The Chemical Aspects of Light*, Oxford University Press, New York, 1946.
2. G. F. J. Garlick, *Luminescent Materials*, Oxford University Press, New York, 1949.
3. Noyes and Boekelheide in *Catalytic, Photochemical, and Electrolytic Reactions*, Interscience Publishers, Inc., New York, 1948.
4. Noyes and Leighton, *The Photochemistry of Gases*, Reinhold Publishing Corporation, New York, 1941.
5. P. Pringsheim, *Fluorescence and Phosphorescence*, Interscience Publishers, Inc., New York, 1949.
6. Pringsheim and Vogel, *Luminescence of Liquids and Solids*, Interscience Publishers, Inc., New York, 1946.
7. E. I. Rabinowitch, *Photosynthesis and Related Processes*, Interscience Publishers, Inc., New York, 2 vols., 1945–1954.
8. Rollefson and Burton, *Photochemistry and the Mechanism of Chemical Reactions*, Prentice-Hall, Inc., New York, 1939.
9. W. A. Waters, *The Chemistry of Free Radicals*, Oxford University Press, New York, 1948.

PROBLEMS

1. A 2-mm layer of Pyrex glass will transmit 10% of incident radiation of 3000 Å. What percentage of light of the same wave length will be absorbed by a 1-mm layer of the glass?
2. A certain substance in a cell of length l absorbs 10% of the incident light. What fraction of the incident light will be absorbed in a cell five times as long?
3. In a cell of a certain length and at a pressure of 100 mm Hg gaseous acetone transmits 25.1% of the incident light of wave length 2650 Å. Assuming Beer's law to apply, calculate the pressure at which 98% of the incident light will be absorbed by acetone in the same cell and at the same temperature.

Ans. 283 mm Hg.

4. From the data given in the preceding problem find what percentage of the incident radiation will be absorbed by acetone at a pressure of 200 mm Hg in a cell one-third as long as used before.

5. Calculate the energy per mole of spectral lines having wave lengths of (a) 850 Å, (b) 2500 Å, and (c) 5 μ. In what spectral region does each line fall?
   Ans. (a) 3.36×10^5 cal., ultraviolet.

6. The energy of activation for the thermal decomposition of $N_2O(g)$ is 53,000 cal mole^{-1}. Calculate the frequency and wave length of the radiation corresponding to this energy, and tell in what region of the spectrum it is to be found.

7. From the energy of activation given in the preceding problem calculate (a) the fraction of the total number of molecules and (b) the actual number of molecules which can be activated thermally in 1 liter of N_2O at a pressure of 50 mm Hg and 27° C.

8. In the photochemical combination of $H_2(g)$ and $Cl_2(g)$ a quantum efficiency of about 1×10^6 is obtained with a wave length of 4800 Å. How many moles of $HCl(g)$ would be produced under these conditions per calorie of radiant energy absorbed?
   Ans. 33.6 moles.

9. A certain system absorbs 2.0×10^{16} quanta of light per second. At the end of 10 min it is observed that 0.001 mole of the irradiated substance has reacted. What is the quantum efficiency of the process?

10. The incident radiation from a monochromatic source of 2537 Å on a slit is 80 ergs/sec/sq mm. The radiation is passed through a slit whose area is 5 sq mm and onto a cell whose face transmits 30% of the incident radiation. If the solution in the cell transmits 10% of the radiation, how much energy in cal is absorbed by the solution per hour?
    Ans. 9.3×10^{-3} cal.

11. If the quantum efficiency in the preceding problem is unity for the substance decomposing and if all the radiation absorbed by the solution is used in the photochemical decomposition, how many moles of substance would be decomposed per hour?

12. The dissociation energy of H_2 is 102,900 cal mole^{-1}. If H_2 is illuminated with radiation whose wave length is 2537 Å and is thereby dissociated, how much of the original radiant energy per mole will be converted into kinetic energy?
    Ans. 9800 cal.

13. When gaseous HI is illuminated with radiation of 2530 Å, it is observed that 1.85×10^{-2} mole decomposes per 1000 cal of radiant energy absorbed. Calculate the quantum efficiency of the reaction.

14. An uranyl oxalate actinometer is irradiated for 15 min with light of 4350 Å. At the end of this time it is found that oxalic acid equivalent to 12.0 cc of 0.001 molar $KMnO_4$ has been decomposed by the light. At this wave length the quantum efficiency of the actinometer is 0.58. Find the average intensity of the light used in (a) ergs per sec and (b) in quanta per sec.

15. Assuming stationary states for Cl and H atoms, show that the mechanism proposed for the photochemical combination of $H_2(g)$ and $Cl_2(g)$ leads to the observed rate equation (27). What is the expression for k in this equation in terms of the rate constants for reactions (a) to (d)?

16. Assuming stationary states for Br and H atoms, show that the mechanism given on p. 637 for the *thermal* combination of $H_2(g)$ and $Br_2(g)$ is in accord with equation (81) given on the same page. What are the expressions for k and k' in terms of the individual reaction rate constants?

17. Making the same assumptions as before, deduce the expression for the rate of

the *photochemical* combination of $H_2(g)$ and $Br_2(g)$, and show that it is in accord with equation (25) of this chapter. What are the expressions in this instance for k and k' in terms of the individual reaction rate constants?

18. Suppose that in a certain over-all reaction the observed velocity constant k, in terms of the velocity constants of the individual reactions involved, k_1, k_2, and k_3, is given by

$$k = \frac{k_1 k_2}{k_3^{1/2}}$$

What will be the relation between the observed activation energy and the activation energies of the individual reaction steps?

19. In a certain reaction

$$A + B = 2\,D$$

the forward reaction proceeds photochemically with a rate given by

$$\frac{dD_f}{dt} = kI_a C_A C_B$$

while the reverse reaction proceeds thermally and bimolecularly with a velocity constant k'. Deduce the expression for the concentration of D at photochemical equilibrium.

$$Ans.\ C_D = \left(\frac{kI_a C_A C_B}{k'}\right)^{1/2}.$$

20. Assuming that the rate of thermal dissociation of $HBr(g)$ molecules is negligible compared to the rate of the photochemical combination of $H_2(g)$ and $Br_2(g)$, derive the expression for the concentration of $HBr(g)$ at photochemical equilibrium.

21. For the photochemical dimerization of anthracene

$$2\,C_{14}H_{10} \longrightarrow C_{28}H_{20}$$

the following mechanism has been proposed:

(a) $C_{14}H_{10} + h\nu \longrightarrow (C_{14}H_{10})^*$ k_1
(b) $(C_{14}H_{10})^* + C_{14}H_{10} \longrightarrow C_{28}H_{20}$ k_2
(c) $C_{28}H_{20} \longrightarrow 2\,C_{14}H_{10}$ k_3
(d) $(C_{14}H_{10})^* \longrightarrow C_{14}H_{10} + h\nu'$ k_4

(a) Derive the expression for the rate of formation of the dimer.
(b) Deduce from the latter the expression for the concentration of dimer at photochemical equilibrium.
(c) How does this concentration depend upon the intensity of absorbed light?

22. What will be the wave length of γ rays possessing energies of (a) 1 mev and (b) 10 mev?

23. Calculate the velocities of 100 ev electrons and protons.

24. Calculate the velocities of 100 ev neutrons, deuterons, and α particles.

Index

LOGARITHMS

Natural Numbers	0	1	2	3	4	5	6	7	8	9	PROPORTIONAL PARTS								
											1	2	3	4	5	6	7	8	9
10	0000	0043	0086	0128	0170	0212	0253	0294	0334	0374	4	8	12	17	21	25	29	33	37
11	0414	0453	0492	0531	0569	0607	0645	0682	0719	0755	4	8	11	15	19	23	26	30	34
12	0792	0828	0864	0899	0934	0969	1004	1038	1072	1106	3	7	10	14	17	21	24	28	31
13	1139	1173	1206	1239	1271	1303	1335	1367	1399	1430	3	6	10	13	16	19	23	26	29
14	1461	1492	1523	1553	1584	1614	1644	1673	1703	1732	3	6	9	12	15	18	21	24	27
15	1761	1790	1818	1847	1875	1903	1931	1959	1987	2014	3	6	8	11	14	17	20	22	25
16	2041	2068	2095	2122	2148	2175	2201	2227	2253	2279	3	5	8	11	13	16	18	21	24
17	2304	2330	2355	2380	2405	2430	2455	2480	2504	2529	2	5	7	10	12	15	17	20	22
18	2553	2577	2601	2625	2648	2672	2695	2718	2742	2765	2	5	7	9	12	14	16	19	21
19	2788	2810	2833	2856	2878	2900	2923	2945	2967	2989	2	4	7	9	11	13	16	18	20
20	3010	3032	3054	3075	3096	3118	3139	3160	3181	3201	2	4	6	8	11	13	15	17	19
21	3222	3243	3263	3284	3304	3324	3345	3365	3385	3404	2	4	6	8	10	12	14	16	18
22	3424	3444	3464	3483	3502	3522	3541	3560	3579	3598	2	4	6	8	10	12	14	15	17
23	3617	3636	3655	3674	3692	3711	3729	3747	3766	3784	2	4	6	7	9	11	13	15	17
24	3802	3820	3838	3856	3874	3892	3909	3927	3945	3962	2	4	5	7	9	11	12	14	16
25	3979	3997	4014	4031	4048	4065	4082	4099	4116	4133	2	3	5	7	9	10	12	14	15
26	4150	4166	4183	4200	4216	4232	4249	4265	4281	4298	2	3	5	7	8	10	11	13	15
27	4314	4330	4346	4362	4378	4393	4409	4425	4440	4456	2	3	5	6	8	9	11	13	14
28	4472	4487	4502	4518	4533	4548	4564	4579	4594	4609	2	3	5	6	8	9	11	12	14
29	4624	4639	4654	4669	4683	4698	4713	4728	4742	4757	1	3	4	6	7	9	10	12	13
30	4771	4786	4800	4814	4829	4843	4857	4871	4886	4900	1	3	4	6	7	9	10	11	13
31	4914	4928	4942	4955	4969	4983	4997	5011	5024	5038	1	3	4	6	7	8	10	11	12
32	5051	5065	5079	5092	5105	5119	5132	5145	5159	5172	1	3	4	5	7	8	9	11	12
33	5185	5198	5211	5224	5237	5250	5263	5276	5289	5302	1	3	4	5	6	8	9	10	12
34	5315	5328	5340	5353	5366	5378	5391	5403	5416	5428	1	3	4	5	6	8	9	10	11
35	5441	5453	5465	5478	5490	5502	5514	5527	5539	5551	1	2	4	5	6	7	9	10	11
36	5563	5575	5587	5599	5611	5623	5635	5647	5658	5670	1	2	4	5	6	7	8	10	11
37	5682	5694	5705	5717	5729	5740	5752	5763	5775	5786	1	2	3	5	6	7	8	9	10
38	5798	5809	5821	5832	5843	5855	5866	5877	5888	5899	1	2	3	5	6	7	8	9	10
39	5911	5922	5933	5944	5955	5966	5977	5988	5999	6010	1	2	3	4	5	7	8	9	10
40	6021	6031	6042	6053	6064	6075	6085	6096	6107	6117	1	2	3	4	5	6	8	9	10
41	6128	6138	6149	6160	6170	6180	6191	6201	6212	6222	1	2	3	4	5	6	7	8	9
42	6232	6243	6253	6263	6274	6284	6294	6304	6314	6325	1	2	3	4	5	6	7	8	9
43	6335	6345	6355	6365	6375	6385	6395	6405	6415	6425	1	2	3	4	5	6	7	8	9
44	6435	6444	6454	6464	6474	6484	6493	6503	6513	6522	1	2	3	4	5	6	7	8	9
45	6532	6542	6551	6561	6571	6580	6590	6599	6609	6618	1	2	3	4	5	6	7	8	9
46	6628	6637	6646	6656	6665	6675	6684	6693	6702	6712	1	2	3	4	5	6	7	7	8
47	6721	6730	6739	6749	6758	6767	6776	6785	6794	6803	1	2	3	4	5	5	6	7	8
48	6812	6821	6830	6839	6848	6857	6866	6875	6884	6893	1	2	3	4	4	5	6	7	8
49	6902	6911	6920	6928	6937	6946	6955	6964	6972	6981	1	2	3	4	4	5	6	7	8
50	6990	6998	7007	7016	7024	7033	7042	7050	7059	7067	1	2	3	3	4	5	6	7	8
51	7076	7084	7093	7101	7110	7118	7126	7135	7143	7152	1	2	3	3	4	5	6	7	8
52	7160	7168	7177	7185	7193	7202	7210	7218	7226	7235	1	2	2	3	4	5	6	7	7
53	7243	7251	7259	7267	7275	7284	7292	7300	7308	7316	1	2	2	3	4	5	6	6	7
54	7324	7332	7340	7348	7356	7364	7372	7380	7388	7396	1	2	2	3	4	5	6	6	7